NEUROCHEMISTRY

SECOND EDITION

NEUROCHEMISTRY

—— The Chemistry of ——
Brain and Nerve

Edited by

K. A. C. ELLIOTT

IRVINE H. PAGE

J. H. QUASTEL

CHARLES C THOMAS · PUBLISHER

Springfield · Illinois · U.S.A.

Published and Distributed Throughout the World by

CHARLES C THOMAS • PUBLISHER
BANNERSTONE HOUSE
301-327 East Lawrence Avenue, Springfield, Illinois, U.S.A.

*With THOMAS BOOKS careful attention is given to all details of
manufacturing and design. It is the Publisher's desire to present books
that are satisfactory as to their physical qualities and artistic possibilities
and appropriate for their particular use. THOMAS BOOKS will be true
to those laws of quality that assure a good name and good will.*

Printed in the United States of America

CONTRIBUTORS

C. W. M. Adams, M.A., M.D.
  Lecturer in Pathology, Guy's Hospital Medical School, London, S.E.1. England.

I. Aravindakshan, M.Sc., Ph.D.
  Senior Research Fellow (C.S.I.R. India), Indian Cancer Research Centre, Parel, Bombay 12, India.

Beatriz M. Braganca, M.Sc., Ph.D.
  Senior Research Officer, Head of Enzyme Chemistry Department, Indian Cancer Research Centre, Parel, Bombay 12, India.

James Crossland, M.A., Ph.D.
  Reader in Pharmacology, University of Nottingham, Nottingham, England.

J. E. Desmedt, M.D.
  Chargé de Cours, Faculté de Médicine, University of Brussels, Belgium.

Frank Dickens, M.A., D.Sc., F.R.S.
  Phil Hill Professor of Experimental Biochemistry, Middlesex Hospital Medical School, London, W.1. England.

K. A. C. Elliott, M.Sc., Ph.D., Sc.D.
  Professor and Chairman of the Department of Biochemistry, McGill University, and Director of the Neurochemistry Laboratories, Montreal Neurological Institute, Montreal, Quebec, Canada.

U. S. von Euler, M.D., F.A.C.P. (Hon.)
  Professor of Physiology, Karolinska Institute (Faculty of Medicine), Stockholm, Sweden.

Ernst Florey, Ph.D.
  Associate Professor of Zoology, University of Washington, Seattle, Washington, U.S.A. Honorary Member, Faculty of Medicine and Biology, Universidad Catolica de Chile, Santiago, Chile.

Alexander Geiger, M.D.
  Professor of Neurophysiology, Department of Psychiatry, University of Illinois College of Medicine, Chicago 12, Illinois, U.S.A.

G. D. Greville, M.A., Ph.D., F.R.I.C.
  Head of the Biochemistry Department, Agricultural Research Council Institute of Animal Physiology, Babraham, Cambridge, England.

v

CATHERINE O. HEBB, M.A., PH.D.
Head, Subdepartment of Chemical Physiology, Agricultural Research Council, Institute of Animal Physiology, Babraham, Cambridge, England.

HAROLD E. HIMWICH, B.S., M.D.
Director, Research Division, Galesburg State Research Hospital, Galesburg, Illinois, and Professorial Lecturer, Department of Physiology, University of Illinois, Medical School, Chicago, Illinois, U.S.A.

HUDSON HOAGLAND, PH.D., SC.D.
Executive Director, Worcester Foundation for Experimental Biology, Shrewsbury, Massachusetts.

HOLGER HYDEN, M.D.
Professor and Head at the Institute of Histology and Neurobiology, Faculty of Medicine, University of Göteborg, Sweden.

ROSE M. JOHNSTONE, PH.D.
Research Fellow, McGill-Montreal General Hospital Research Institute, Assistant Professor of Biochemistry, McGill University, Montreal, Quebec, Canada.

SEYMOUR S. KETY, M.D.
Henry Phipps Professor of Psychiatry and Director, Department of Psychiatry, The Johns Hopkins University; Psychiatrist-in-Chief, The Johns Hopkins Hospital, Baltimore 5, Maryland.

JACK KLINGMAN, PH.D.
Research Associate, Department of Biophysics, Johns Hopkins University, Baltimore, Maryland; now at Department of Biochemistry, University of Buffalo School of Medicine, Buffalo, New York, U.S.A.

KREŠIMIR KRNJEVIĆ, M.B., CH.B., B.SC., PH.D.
Principal Scientific Officer, Agricultural Research Council, Institute of Animal Physiology, Babraham, Cambridge, England.

ABEL LAJTHA, PH.D.
Associate Research Scientist, New York State Research Institute for Neurochemistry and Drug Addiction. Assistant Professor of Biochemistry, College of Physicians and Surgeons, Columbia University, New York, New York, U.S.A.

MARTIN LARRABEE, PH.D.
Associate Professor of Biophysics, Thomas C. Jenkins Department of Biophysics, Johns Hopkins University, Baltimore, Maryland, U.S.A.

H. McIlwain, Ph.D., D.Sc.

Professor of Biochemistry in the University of London at the In-
stitute of Psychiatry (British Postgraduate Medical Federation);
Honorary Biochemist, the Bethlem Royal Hospital and the
Maudsley Hospital, London, England.

William M. McIsaac, M.B., B.S., Ph.D., M.R.C.S.

Staff Member, Research Division, Cleveland Clinic Foundation,
Cleveland, Ohio, U.S.A.

David Nachmansohn, M.D.

Professor of Biochemistry, College of Physicians and Surgeons,
Columbia University, New York, New York, U.S.A.

Irvine H. Page, M.D.

Director of Research, Cleveland Clinic Foundation, Cleveland,
Ohio, U.S.A.

L. S. Penrose, M.A., M.D., D.Sc., F.R.S.

Galton Professor of Eugenics, Galton Laboratory, University College, London, England.

Sir Rudolph A. Peters, M.C., M.D., D.Sc., F.R.C.P., F.R.S., F.R.S.E.

Emeritus Professor of Biochemistry, Oxford University. Presently
at the Department of Biochemistry, Cambridge University, England.

J. H. Quastel, D.Sc., Ph.D., F.R.S., F.R.S.C.

Professor of Biochemistry, McGill University and Director,
McGill-Montreal General Hospital Research Institute, Montreal,
Quebec, Canada.

Derek Richter, M.A., Ph.D., M.R.C.S.

Director, Medical Research Council Neuropsychiatric Research
Unit, Carshalton, Surrey, England.

Eugene Roberts, Ph.D.

Chairman, Department of Biochemistry, City of Hope Medical
Center, Duarte, California, U.S.A.

R. J. Rossiter, M.A., D.Phil., B.M., B.Ch., F.R.S.C.

Professor and Head, Department of Biochemistry, University of
Western Ontario, London, Ontario, Canada.

P. G. Scholefield, Ph.D., D.Sc.

Assistant Director, McGill-Montreal General Hospital Research
Institute; National Cancer Institute of Canada Associate Professor
of Biochemistry, McGill University, Montreal, Quebec, Canada.

ABRAHAM M. SHANES, M.S., PH.D.
Professor of Pharmacology, University of Pennsylvania Medical School and Graduate School of Medicine, Philadelphia 4, Pennsylvania, U.S.A.

T. L. SOURKES, M.SC., PH.D.
Associate Professor of Biochemistry, Department of Psychiatry, McGill University and Senior Research Biochemist, Allan Memorial Institute of Psychiatry, Montreal, Quebec, Canada.

WARREN M. SPERRY, PH.D.
Professor of Biochemistry, Columbia University; Chief of Psychiatric Research (Biochemistry), New York Psychiatric Institute, New York, New York, U.S.A.

JOHN D. SPILLANE, M.D., B.SC., F.R.C.P.
Neurologist, United Cardiff Hospitals; Lecturer in Neurology at the Welsh National School of Medicine. Department of Neurology, Cardiff Royal Infirmary, Cardiff, Wales.

J. W. STEVENSON, M.D., C.M.
Associate Professor of Bacteriology and Immunology, McGill University, Montreal, Quebec, Canada.

JAMES E. P. TOMAN, PH.D.
Professor and Chairman of Department of Pharmacology, Chicago Medical School, 710 South Wolcott Avenue, Chicago 12, Illinois, U.S.A.

HEINRICH WAELSCH, M.D., SC.D.
Professor of Biochemistry, Columbia University, College of Physicians and Surgeons; Chief, Psychiatric Research (Pharmacology), New York State Psychiatric Institute, New York, New York, U.S.A.

H. WEIL-MALHERBE, M.D., D.SC.
Chief, Section of Neurochemistry, Clinical Neuropharmacology Research Center, National Institute of Mental Health, National Institutes of Health, Department of Health, Education and Welfare, U.S. Public Healh Service, Saint Elizabeth Hospital, Washington 20, District of Columbia, U.S.A.

C. E. C. WELLS, M.B., M.R.C.P.
Neurologist, Welsh Regional Hospital Board. Department of Neurology, St. David's Hospital, Cardiff, Wales.

L. S. WOLFE, M.SC., PH.D., M.D.
Assistant Professor of Experimental Neurology and Associate Neurochemist, Montreal Neurological Institute, McGill University, Montreal, Quebec, Canada.

PREFACE

STUDY OF THE comparatively new discipline of neurochemistry is advancing rapidly. Although only seven years have passed
since the first edition of *Neurochemistry* was published, a new edition
seems desirable and necessary. During this period a *Journal of Neurochemistry* has appeared and become well established but neurochemical
papers continue to appear in many scientific journals, for the subject
matter of neurochemistry merges with many disciplines—neuropharmacology, neuropathology, neurology, psychiatry, histochemistry,
enzymology. It is, therefore, important at reasonable periods of time,
to take fresh stock of the neurochemical field and to have experts in
the relevent fields of inquiry present summaries of recent advances.

Relatively short monographs on general neurochemistry have recently appeared, e.g., *Biochemistry and the Central Nervous System*
(second edition) by H. McIlwain (Churchill) and *Chemistry of Brain
Metabolism in Health and Disease* by J. H. Quastel and D. M. J.
Quastel, American Lecture Series (Charles C Thomas) and books em-
bracing articles written for various neurochemical symposia have been
published. In *Neurochemistry* we have attempted to produce a more
detailed and comprehensive coverage of the subject than was possible
in the other types of book.

The present edition of *Neurochemistry*, whilst bringing up-to-date
the various subjects handled in the first edition, contains new chapters devoted to topics that were not then discussed or were mentioned
only briefly. As a result the present edition is considerably larger than
the first, in spite of efforts by the Editors to keep the size of the volume
within reasonable limits

As with the first edition the editors have not attempted to interfere
with the presentation of opinions expressed by the authors. We have
tried to avoid excessive overlap between chapters and duplication of
material, but have not demanded rigorous cutting of articles since it
seemed desirable that authors should be allowed to express individual
opinions or conclusions on similar data, to stimulate thinking. We
hope that the new edition of *Neurochemistry* will be found to be a
fairly complete guide to the present situation in the neurochemical
field.

The editors are again most grateful to the contributors, publishers and the indexer, Dr. P. G. Scholefield, for their valuable cooperation.

K.A.C.E.
I.H.P.
J.H.Q.

CONTENTS

NEUROCHEMISTRY

I

THUDICHUM AND THE CHEMISTRY OF THE BRAIN

Irvine H. Page

The central problem of philosophy, from its beginning in the cloudy realm of the most ancient past, concerns the nature of man. The necessary preface to this problem is to consider the validity and nature of thought. In all recorded time, men have divided themselves according to whether they consider the process primarily physical or primarily spiritual. But none has ever denied the necessity of a physical substrate for the thought of man. In the subsiding swirl of deterministic materialism, it seemed likely that a full explanation of the nature of man's mind would emerge from a study of the chemical mechanisms which subserve its activity. It is now again apparent to most that the nature of the soul of man is not a matter for chemical analysis.

Unfortunately, and, it must be added, surprisingly, in view of the inherent importance of the subject, the chemistry of the brain has failed to receive wholehearted investigation. Possibly the philosophical strife which preceded chemical study tended to detract from it. In any case, anatomy, physiology and cytological pathology have been turned to the brain of man almost unaccompanied by the sister science of chemistry. True, certain fragments were investigated, just as cholesterol was isolated from the brain. But there was little consideration given the possibility of integrating these scraps into an organized body of knowledge.

The first formal effort with the aim of understanding its metabolism, normal and abnormal, was made by Thudichum in about 1862. He worked until 1901 without reward and almost without regard. The investigation was not again undertaken until 25 years after his death.

But why this blind spot in the eye of the medical strategists? The reasons are many. Chief among them, however, is the view expounded seriously but a few years ago that the passage of nerve impulses required no chemical metabolic change and no expenditure of energy. Then too, physiologists had no demonstrable phenomena which lent

3

themselves readily to chemical analysis. This was not strictly true. For example, Elliott in 1905 demonstrated the identity of the action of adrenaline with that of stimulation of sympathetic nerves. This brilliant observation with its imaginative possibilities remained undeveloped by chemists.

About the time of this discovery, great activity was stirring in anatomical circles. Institutes for the study of anatomy and pathology of the brain were springing up at a great rate. By 1907, six such institutes were accredited by the Central Brain Commission. Associated with them were such distinguished men as Cajal, Fleschsig, Monakow, Edinger, Vogt and Donaldson. But no chemists were among them. The field lay fallow. Neurology, and later, psychiatry, developed phenomenally but without aid from chemistry. A few scientists outside the field viewed with growing alarm the lack of the sound chemical understanding which already underlay knowledge of the functioning of other organs, but most of those within the field of neurology and psychiatry were oblivious of the lack. I well recall the contempt with which a distinguished neurologist in London dismissed brain chemistry with the remark that nothing would ever be learned by the analysis of cerebral hash.

Again in 1921 appeared a revelation foreshadowing the vital importance of chemical investigation of nerve tissue. This time it was in the description of a substance, the *Vagusstoff*, which acted as a transmitter of vagus nerve impulses. This discovery of Otto Loewi's set up another sign post which went unheeded by neuro-psychiatrists. Thanks in part to Dale and Dudley's isolation and identification in 1929 of acetylcholine, notice was taken of it by neurophysiologists. This perhaps marked the turning point in the long endeavor to stimulate investigation into the chemical nature of nervous activity.

Although the concept is by no means universally accepted, still, it has acted as a nidus for much illuminating work. The interpretation of the original work of Loewi may be changed, but this does not detract from its fundamental significance.

Now to turn back and look more closely at that remarkable man, Dr. J. L. W. Thudichum, the father of brain chemistry. Thudichum was born August 27, 1828, in Büdingen (Grand Duchy of Hesse) of a family characterized by scholarly attainment. His youth was uneventful in a period of relative peace and security in Germany. The degree of Doctor of Medicine was granted him by the University of Giessen in 1851, and at this time it would have appeared that his future lay in an indistinguished career as a practicing physician. But times became more unsettled politically, and emotionally as well, for him. He left Germany to settle in London and marry Charlotte Dupré, sister of Dr. Augustus Dupré, lecturer in chemistry at Westminister Hospital Medical School.

Then began a period, not to end until his death, of extraordinary curiosity, adventurousness and scientific productivity. Probably the

Fig. 1. Dr. J. L. W. Thudichum—father of the chemistry of the brain.

first serious attempt to understand the nature and method of formation of gallstones was undertaken by Thudichum, the results being published in book form in 1863. In a letter written to Thudichum, the distinguished Justus von Liebig complimented him on the discovery that in the center of gallstones, cells may be found which presumably initiate stone formation. He marveled that Thudichum was able to accomplish so much in a big city and wondered how he did it (to this day an unanswered question). A treatise on nasal polyps appeared in 1869, and went through several editions; a nasal speculum was described, as well as the use of electrocautery in nasal surgery.

In 1858, he was appointed lecturer in chemistry at Grosvenor Place School of Medicine and this date roughly marks the beginning of a period of productivity in his chemical studies. To say the least, it is extraordinary that a man who had a busy practice of medicine, from which he derived most of his income, managed not only to contribute work of a high investigative level to medicine but completed a wide variety of other researches, many of which are classic.

These began with his isolation and characterization of urochrome in 1864. The studies were extended to include a variety of other pigments, a group which he called the "luteins." Today their importance is recognized under the names, lipochromes, or better, the carotinoids. One of them, carotene, is the precursor of vitamin A.

It is curious and interesting that the beginnings of the chemistry of the brain were initiated by the interest of a government agency in the effects of typhus on the brain. Sir John Simon, then Medical Officer to the Privy Council, suggested financial support of a study of the chemistry of the nervous system. The progress he was able to report in 1874, ". . .was sufficiently great to ensure acquiescence in the continuance of any efforts on the part of the former authority and subsequently to the Local Government Board, to whom the functions with regard to the administration of the Parliamentary grant for researches in aid of pathology and medicine, previously exercised by the Privy Council, were transferred." One cannot help reflect that 65 years ago public support of science was starting. After support of Thudichum's work on neurochemistry by the government, no similar endeavor has been undertaken either by private or government initiative until the last few years.

Thudichum's monumental treatise, *Physiological Chemistry of the Brain,* appeared in 1884 in London and a revised edition in Germany in 1901. In it are described the first systematic attempts to understand the chemical mechanisms of nervous tissue. Very rightly, he set about to isolate and characterize the substances which compose the brain, a work which today has only been carried a bit further. Thanks to Dr. Otto Rosenheim, I had the privilege of visiting Thudichum's laboratory in his house and seeing the vast array of bottles containing both the pure and impure substances he had separated from the brain. His four daughters and son had, until the war, kept his beautiful gardens intact. Dr. Rosenheim has undertaken the task of preserving the price-less chemical mementoes of this great investigator.

Thudichum and his assistants, Drs. Kingzett and Page, isolated and characterized a number of new compounds from the brain. As was to be expected from his education, euphoneous names of Greek deriva-

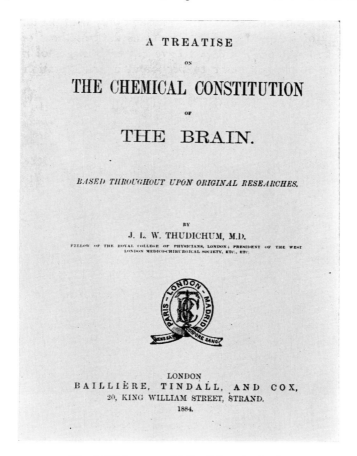

A TREATISE

ON

THE CHEMICAL CONSTITUTION

OF

THE BRAIN.

BASED THROUGHOUT UPON ORIGINAL RESEARCHES.

BY

J. L. W. THUDICHUM, M.D.

FELLOW OF THE ROYAL COLLEGE OF PHYSICIANS, LONDON; PRESIDENT OF THE WEST LONDON MEDICO-CHIRURGICAL SOCIETY, ETC., ETC.

LONDON
BAILLIÈRE, TINDALL, AND COX,
20, KING WILLIAM STREET, STRAND.
1884.

Fig. 2. Title page of Thudichum's classic.

tion were given them: cephalin, phrenosin, sphingomyelin, sphingo-sine, cerebronic acid, etc. Analyses of a very painstaking sort covering a wide range of constituents were made. Compared with more modern methods they are still surprisingly good.

It may seem unnecessary to point out that the difficulties of breaking the brain down into its chemical constituents have not yet been trans-cended. It is for lack of this elementary knowledge that so little can be understood of its chemical metabolism. The necessity to put first things first led Thudichum to undertake this philosophically simple but technically difficult approach. In discussion of the application of neurochemistry to medicine, Thudichum says, for example, "I could go further and unfold, e.g., a chemical connection between the function of the liver and that of the brain, opening views into the pathology of the future and illuminating, though only with the disappointing brevity of an electric spark, regions as dark as those of general paralysis and melancholly. But I have (in early stages of my work) formed the resolution never to propound a generalisation on any

Fig. 3. Some of Thudichum's contributions to scientific literature.

subject before having proved the validity of all data obtainable by observation or experiment. And I must say that I have not yet found any subject in chemical biology on which, governed by that resolution, I should have liked to proceed to generalisation." This bit of self restraint might well constitute the closing sentence to most current applications for grants-in-aid.

But Thudichum was by no means a paragon of scientific virtue. He managed to antagonize somewhat more than his share of his contemporaries. He certainly did not underrate his achievements, and, as was the custom of his day, he spoke well of them. It is with a chuckle that we read, "In order, however, that the reader may not, from this avowal, come to any erroneous conclusions regarding my own estimate of the value of my researches communicated in this treatise, I undertake to assure him that they are of fundamental importance, and that all further developments in chemical neurology must start from them as a basis. I say this in view of the records of the work of all those who have grappled with the problem before me, and in kindness to all who may like to deal with it hereafter."

As Thudichum grew older, his work on the brain slowed and finally stopped. His own active brain undertook the task of providing firm scientific underpinnings for hedonism. *The Spirit of Cookery* appeared in 1895, prized today by epicureans and those whose interest in food is of a more scientific nature. This work was followed closely by *A Treatise on Wines,* in 1896. How differently we round out our lives today!

After Thudichum's death by cerebral hemorrhage in 1901, work in the field all but stopped. But in about 1928 interest in the development of a separate discipline of neurochemistry again began to take root. The formation of a department of brain chemistry at the Kaiser Wilhelm Institute in Munich, Germany, and work at Cardiff in England testified at least to local reawakening of interest. In the next decade, it had become clear that the field was becoming firmly established and 30 years later it has been populated by a highly competent group of able young investigators. These beginnings I have described elsewhere.[1,2]

Since the appearance of the first edition of this book, a full length biography of Thudichum written by Drabkin[3] has appeared. This is a fascinating story, ably told by a man who knows more about Thudichum than anyone alive. It was highly desirable that the background material be gathered and this book written before it was too late. Dr. Drabkin and I have both given our collections of Thudichumiana to the National Institute of Neurological Diseases and Blindness at the National Institutes of Health in Bethesda, Maryland. It is good that this "father of brain chemistry" should receive full, if belated, recognition.

REFERENCES

1. PAGE, I. H.: Neurochemistry and Serotonin: A Chemical Fugue. *Ann. New York Acad. Sc., 66:*592 (1957)
2. PAGE, I. H. Chemistry of the Brain—Past Imperfect, Present Indicative, and—Future Perfect? *Science, 125:*721 (1957).
3. DRABKIN, D. L.: *Thudichum, Chemist of the Brain.* Philadelphia Univ. Pennsylvania Press (1958).

II

CHEMICAL CONSTITUENTS OF BRAIN AND NERVE

R. J. ROSSITER

In 1884 Thudichum[1,2] first published his classic, *A Treatise on the Chemical Constitution of the Brain*. Since that time chemists have been concerned with the isolation and the quantitative determination of the various chemical constituents of the nervous system. In 1937, Page[3] summarized much of the then available work on the chemistry of the brain. Previously the chemistry of peripheral nerve had been reviewed by Gerard.[4] More recent studies on the constituents of the nervous system have been summarized by Folch and LeBaron,[5] McIlwain[6] and LeBaron.[7] The chemistry of the lipids has been reviewed by Bloor,[8] LeBaron and Folch[9] and Hanahan.[10] The phosphatides were reviewed by Wittcoff[11] and Rossiter and Strickland,[12] the inositol phosphatides by Folch and LeBaron[13,14] and the sphingolipids by Carter *et al.*[15,16]

This review is an attempt to present in outline some of the more significant findings concerning the nature of the constituents of brain and nerve. Of necessity, reference can be made to only a limited number of the relevant publications. The review will be restricted further to a consideration of four groups of substances only: (1) lipids, (2) mucopolysaccharides and mucoids, (3) proteins and (4) minerals. Other important constituents of the nervous system, such as enzymes, coenzymes, metabolites, vitamins, pharmacologically-active amines and phosphate esters are discussed elsewhere in this volume.

LIPIDS (LIPOIDS)

Bloor[8] accepted the term *lipid* for the "group of naturally-occurring substances consisting of the higher fatty acids, their naturally-occurring compounds, and substances found naturally in chemical association with them."

In the past, lipids were classified partly by their solubility in different organic solvents, partly by their chemical structure and partly by the fact that certain lipids contain characteristic chemical groupings, e.g., phosphate, or a reducing sugar, by which they can be readily recognized. As the structure of more of the brain lipids becomes understood, a classification based upon chemical constitution rather than upon solubility, or upon the more or less coincidental presence of easily-detected groupings, becomes important. From the practical point of view, however, it is still convenient to classify the lipids of the nervous system according to the chemical groupings by which they are usually recognized.

Such a classification is presented in Table I. The lipids are divided into: (a) phosphatides, containing phosphorus; (b) glycolipids, con-

TABLE I

CLASSIFICATION OF LIPIDS FOUND IN THE NERVOUS SYSTEM

(a) *Phosphatides* (Phospholipids)
    (1) *Glycerophosphatides* (Phosphoglycerides)
        Phosphatidyl cholines (Lecithins)
        Phosphatidyl ethanolamines
        Phosphatidyl serines
        Plasmalogens (Phosphatidal ethanolamines)
        Cephalin B
    (2) *Inositol phosphatides* (Phosphoinositides)
    (3) *Sphingomyelins* (Phosphosphingosides)

(b) *Glycolipids*
    (1) *Cerebrosides* (Glycosphingosides)
    (2) *Cerebroside sulfate esters* (Sulfatides) } Sphingolipids
    (3) *Mucolipids*
        Gangliosides
        Strandin

(c) *Non-saponifiable lipids*
    (1) *Sterols*
    (2) *Hydrocarbons*

(d) *Neutral Fat* (Triglycerides)

(e) *Protein-bound Lipids*
    (1) *Proteolipids*
    (2) *Phosphatidopeptides*
    (3) *Lipoproteins*

taining a carbohydrate; (c) non-saponifiable lipids; (d) neutral fat; and (e) protein-bound lipids. The sphingomyelins of group (a) and all the lipids of group (b) contain the base sphingosine and hence are sometimes grouped together as sphingolipids. In many instances the assigning of a particular lipid to a particular place in a classification such as that shown in Table I is quite arbitrary. For instance, it is probable that in the future the classification of the plasmalogens will have to be expanded. Other modifications are likely, as more is learned concerning the structure of lipids, particularly of the inositol phosphatides and the mucolipids.

(a) Phosphatides (Phospholipids)

The phosphatides of the nervous system have been classified in many ways. Classically, they were divided, according to their solubilities, into lecithin, cephalin and sphingomyelin. They have also been classified into monoaminophospholipids (lecithins, cephalins, and plasmalogens) and diaminophospholipids (sphingomyelins) and into choline-containing phospholipids (lecithins and sphingomyelins) and non-choline-containing phospholipids (cephalins and plasmalogens). In the past some of these terms have been used rather indiscriminately to refer either to a characterized chemical compound or to a crude fraction, defined by solubility alone. The important discovery of Folch[17,18] that the original "cephalin" of brain was a mixture of at least three phospholipids, made necessary a new classification of phospholipids.

(1) Glycerophosphatides (Phosphoglycerides)

The first three glycerophosphatides listed in Table I, the phosphatidyl cholines, the phosphatidyl serines and the phosphatidyl ethanolamines, may be considered as esters of a phosphatidic acid and the appropriate nitrogen-containing compound. Phosphatidic acids were discovered by Chibnall and Channon[19] in vegetable sources. They are esters of glycerophosphate and long-chain fatty acids (I). Hokin and Hokin[20] demonstrated that phosphatidic acids are present in brain.

$$
\begin{array}{ll}
\mathrm{CH_2OCOR'} & \mathrm{CH_2OCOR'} \\
| & | \\
\mathrm{RCOOCH} & \mathrm{RCOOCH} \\
| \quad \mathrm{O^-} & | \quad \mathrm{O^-} \quad + \\
\mathrm{CH_2OPO^-} & \mathrm{CH_2OPOCH_2CH_2N(CH_3)_3} \\
\quad \;\; \| & \quad \;\; \| \\
\quad \;\; \mathrm{O} & \quad \;\; \mathrm{O} \\
\end{array}
$$

L-α-Lecithin
(L-α-Phosphatidyl choline)

L-α-Phosphatidic acid

(I)   (II)

Baer and his associates have synthesized a number of phosphatidic acids,[21] phosphatidyl cholines,[22-24] phosphatidyl ethanolamines[25] and phosphatidyl serines.[26] These syntheses, taken in conjunction with parallel hydrolysis studies,[27,28] have made it clear that all naturally-occurring glycerophosphatides so far examined have a configuration related to that of L-α-glycerophosphate. Tattrie and McArthur[29] synthesized an L-α-lecithin by esterifying L-α-glycerophosphorylcholine.

Phosphatidyl Cholines (Lecithins).—Phosphatidyl choline was obtained in pure form by Levene and Rolf[30] and subsequently an improved method of preparation was described by Pangborn.[31] Lecithins are esters of choline and phosphatidic acids (II). The principal fatty acid components would appear to be palmitic, stearic, oleic and arachidonic acids. Although a fully saturated lecithin has been obtained from brain[32] and a fully unsaturated lecithin has been obtained from yeast,[33] it is probable that most brain lecithins, like liver lecithins, are mixed.[34] The recent work of Tattrie[35] and Hanahan, Brockerhoff and Barron[36] indicates that in naturally-occurring lecithins the fatty acids esterified at the β-position of the glycerol molecule are mainly unsaturated, whereas those at the α'-position are mainly saturated.

It is generally considered that lysolecithin is not a component of brain lipids. The recent reports of Thompson *et al.*[36a] and Papadopoulos *et al.*,[36b] however, indicate that a lysolecithin may be present in brain tissue.

Phosphatidyl Ethanolamines.—Thudichum[1,2] gave the name cephalin to the brain phospholipid fraction that was soluble in ether but insoluble in ethanol. For many years cephalin was thought to be a single substance with a formula corresponding to diacylglycerolphosphoryl ethanolamine (III). Folch[17] showed that this traditional "ceph-

$$CH_2OCOR'$$
$$|$$
$$RCOOCH$$
$$|\quad\quad O^-$$
$$|\quad\quad |\quad\quad +$$
$$CH_2OPOCH_2CH_2NH_3$$
$$\quad\quad ||$$
$$\quad\quad O$$

L-α-Phosphatidyl
ethanolamine

(III)

$$CH_2OCOR'$$
$$|$$
$$RCOOCH$$
$$|\quad\quad O^-\quad NH_3^+$$
$$|\quad\quad |\quad\quad |$$
$$CH_2OPOCH_2CHCOO$$
$$\quad\quad ||$$
$$\quad\quad O$$

L-α-Phosphatidyl
L-serine

(IV)

alin" is a mixture of at least three phosphatides, each individual phosphatide exhibiting differences in solubility in mixtures of chloroform and ethanol. Subsequently, Folch[18] published evidence to show that these three constituents are: (a) phosphatidyl ethanolamine (III), a phosphatide with the structure classically attributed to cephalin; (b) phosphatidyl serine (IV); and (c) an inositol-containing compound, for which he proposed the name *diphosphoinositide*. It is now known that the traditional "cephalin" fraction also contains ethanolamine plasmalogen.[37]

Recently Debuch[38] obtained a phosphatidyl ethanolamine preparation from brain using the method of counter-current distribution. The fatty acids, a mixture of almost equal proportions of saturated and unsaturated acids, were chiefly of the C_{18} series. The lipid as isolated contained little ash.

Phosphatidyl Serines.—Folch[39] obtained from brain a preparation of phosphatidyl serine (IV) of at least 92% purity. On hydrolysis it gave glycerophosphoric acid, L-serine, and fatty acids in the ratio of 1:1:2. The serine is attached to the phosphoric acid through its hydroxyl group, leaving both the carboxyl and the amino groups free. The fatty acids were found to be mainly stearic and oleic acids, in approximately equimolecular proportions. The molecule has one free basic group, the amino group of the serine, and two free acidic groups, the carboxyl group of the serine and one acid group from the phosphoric acid. The substance is thus acidic and, when isolated from neutral solvents, it is obtained as the potassium and sodium salt with one equivalent of base per atom of phosphorus. Recently, using the technique of silicic acid chromatography, Marinetti *et al.*[40] were able to separate brain phosphatidyl serines into two ionic forms, a free acid and a sodium salt.

The phosphatidyl serine isolated by Folch accounts for about 60% of the lipid amino acid nitrogen in brain, as determined by the Van Slyke volumetric ninhydrin method. It is thus possible that small amounts of unidentified phosphatides containing acids other than serine may be present in brain (see Westley *et al.*[41] and Wren[42] for references). In addition, it is probable that brain contains small amounts of phosphatidyl serines with fatty acids other than stearic and oleic acid.

Plasmalogens (Phosphatidal ethanolamines).—The presence of plasmalogens in tissues was first suggested by Feulgen and Rossenbeck[43] in 1924. Subsequently, Feulgen *et al.*[44] demonstrated the presence of long-chain aldehydes in lipids of animal tissues, including brain, an observation confirmed by Anchel and Waelsch.[45] Klenk and Schumann[46] prepared an acetalphosphatide from brain. They considered this lipid to be similar to phosphatidyl ethanolamine, with the exception that the fatty acids were replaced by fatty aldehydes.

Thannhauser, Boncoddo and Schmidt[47] isolated from calf brain

a crystalline acetalphosphatide from which they obtained on hydrolysis glycerolphosphorylethanolamine, palmitaldehyde and stearalde-
hyde. It was suggested that this substance could be represented by
formula V. However, Schmidt et al.[48] showed that the phosphorus of
the isolated lipid became acid-soluble on mild acid hydrolysis, in contrast to the findings for native plasmalogen. Baer and Stancer[49] and
Klenk and Dubuch[50,51] suggested a hemiacetal form (VI) for native

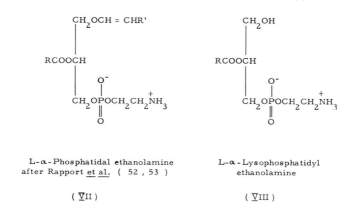

Acetalphosphatide

($\underline{V}$)

Ethanolamine plasmalogen
after Klenk and Debuch (50, 51)

($\underline{V}$I)

plasmalogen. On mild alkaline hydrolysis this would give V, and on
further acid treatment would give glycerolphosphorylethanolamine.

Recently, Rapport and colleagues[52,53] have provided evidence for
an 1:2-unsaturated ether structure (VII). They suggest that eth-

L-α-Phosphatidal ethanolamine
after Rapport et al. (52 , 53)

($\underline{V}$II)

L-α-Lysophosphatidyl
ethanolamine

($\underline{V}$III)

anolamine-containing plasmalogen be called phosphatidal ethanolamine. Subsequent findings have tended to substantiate formula
VII.[54-57] From the work of Marinetti and colleagues it seems probable

that the unsaturated ether side-chain is attached at the α'–rather than at the β-position on the glycerol.[58-60] Further evidence for this is to be found in a recent publication of Debuch.[61] Rapport and colleagues[52,53] originally suggested that the aldehydogenic side-chain is attached at the β-position. As a result of the re-evaluation of the specificity of phospholipase A reported by Tattrie[35] and Hannahan et al.,[36] it now seems likely that the unsaturated ether side-chain is attached at the α'-position, in confirmation of the suggestions of Marinetti[58-60] and Debuch.[61] Acid hydrolysis removes the unsaturated ether side-chain from the α'-position to leave a lysophosphatidyl ethanolamine (VIII), whereas alkaline hydrolysis removes the fatty acid from the β-position to form a lysoplasmalogen (IX), rather than the

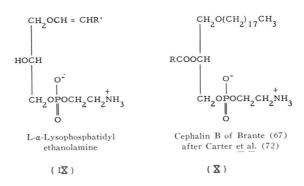

L-α-Lysophosphatidyl
ethanolamine

(IX)

Cephalin B of Brante (67)
after Carter et al. (72)

(X)

structure depicted by formula V. In addition to ethanolamine plasmalogen, it is now known that brain contains a small amount of serine plasmalogen.[37,62,63] It is doubtful whether significant quantities of choline plasmalogen are present in brain,[63a,b] although choline plasmalogens are known to occur in many other tissues.[63] The ether linkage in plasmalogens is quite unstable. The breakdown of plasmalogens has been studied by Bergman and Liebrecht[64] and Thiele.[65,66]

Cephalin B.—Brante[67] showed that brain contained an alkali-stable lipid which did not contain choline and so was distinct from sphingomyelin. This finding has been confirmed in many laboratories.[63,68-71] Recently Carter, Smith and Jones[72] demonstrated the presence of a phosphorylethanolamine derivative of batyl alcohol in egg yolk. On hydrolysis this compound behaved as the cephalin B of Brante.[67] Svennerholm and Thorin[73] reported the isolation of a similar compound from both calf and human brain. They provided evidence to support the suggestion that the naturally-occurring compound is esterified, so

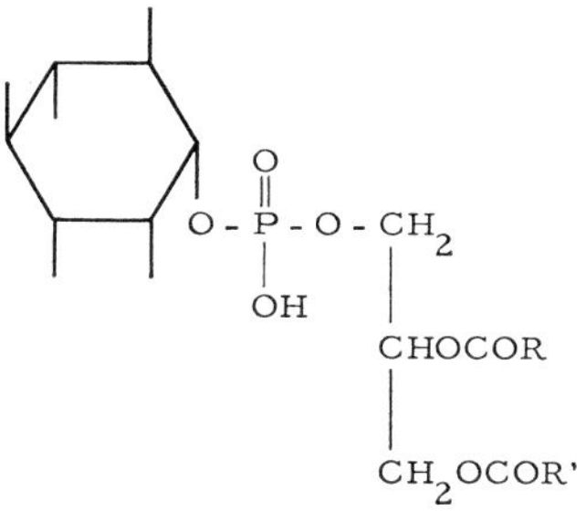

1 - phosphatidyl - L - myo - inositol

(XI)

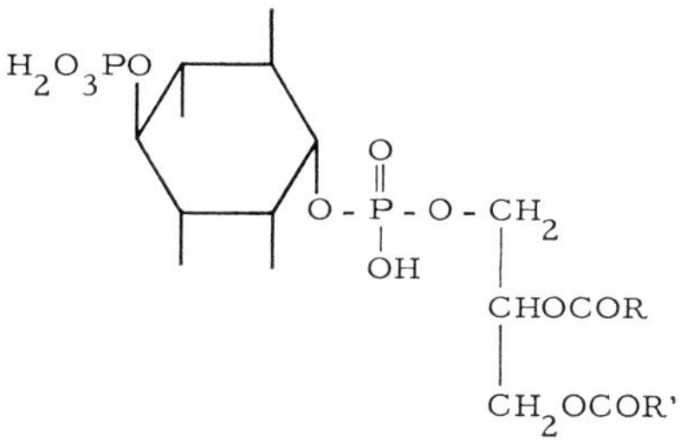

1 - phosphatidyl - L - myo - inositol 4 - phosphate

(XIa)

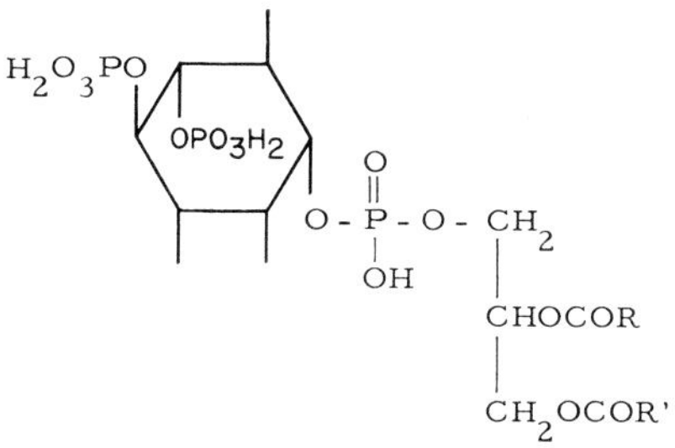

1 - phosphatidyl - L - myo - inositol 4,5 - diphosphate

(XIb)

that it may be represented by formula X. It will be noted that such a lipid can be regarded as a saturated plasmalogen.

(2) Inositol Phosphatides (Phosphoinositides)

Folch and Woolley[74] showed that an inositol-containing compound is present in the classical "cephalin" of brain. Subsequently Folch[75] isolated a substance from brain which he called brain diphosphoinositide. The compound is less soluble in methanol than either phosphatidyl serine or phosphatidyl ethanolamine and on hydrolysis it was reported to yield fatty acid, glycerol and inositol *meta*diphosphate in equimolecular proportions. The diphosphoinositide is acidic and, when prepared from brain with the use of neutral solvents, it was obtained as the magnesium calcium salt, with one equivalent of base per atom of phosphorus.

The structure of brain diphosphoinositide cannot be given at present. Indeed the situation has become somewhat confused, first by the report of Hörhammer and colleagues[76,77] that brain diphosphoinositide preparations may be resolved chromatographically into three fractions, and secondly by the reports of Grado and Ballou[78] and Ellis, Kemp and Hawthorne[79] that brain diphosphoinositide preparations yielded a complex mixture of inositol mono-, di- and triphosphates on mild alkaline hydrolysis. Also Dittmer and Dawson[80] have described the preparation of a triphosphoinositide from brain (see below).

In addition to diphosphoinositides and triphosphoinositides, there is now considerable evidence that brain also contains a monophosphoinositide. Using the method of countercurrent distribution, Hörhammer and colleagues[81] have isolated a monophosphoinositide from brain which behaves chromatographically in a fashion similar to the monophosphoinositide of liver.[76,77] Evidence for the presence in brain of a monophosphoinositide, presumably phosphatidyl inositol (XI), has also been presented by Dittmer and Dawson[80] and Ellis *et al.*[79] It is

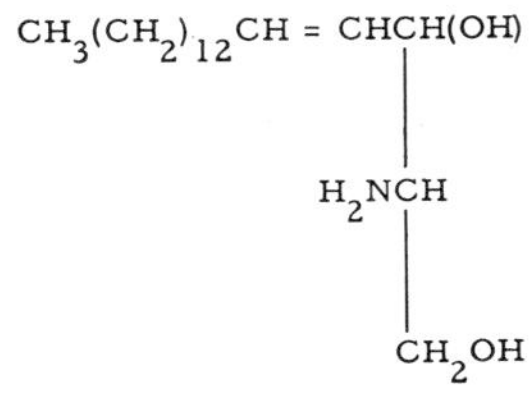

$$CH_3(CH_2)_{12}CH = CHCH(OH)$$

$$H_2NCH$$

$$CH_2OH$$

Sphingosine

($\underline{X}$II)

of interest to note that this substance is quite active metabolically. Hokin and Hokin[82] reported that this is the inositol lipid that is most readily labelled when brain slices are incubated in the presence of inorganic P[32]. Strickland *et al.*[83,84] showed that the same lipid was labelled when rat brain homogenates were incubated in the presence of inositol-H[3] or L-α-glycerophosphate-P[32].

Recently the problem of brain phosphoinositides has been clarified greatly by the excellent work of Ballou and his colleagues.[84a,b] A preparation of beef brain phosphoinositide was found to yield on alkaline hydrolysis a mixture of inositol phosphates. This mixture contained myo-inositol 4-phosphate, small quantities of myo-inositol 1-phosphate,[78] L-myo-inositol 4,5-diphosphate, myo-inositol 1,4-diphosphate, L-myo-inositol 1,4,5-triphosphate and myo-inositol 2,4,5-triphosphate.[84a] Deacylation of the brain phosphoinositide with hydroxylamine gave three glycerol myo-inositol phosphates. Identification of these suggested that beef brain phosphoinositide is a complex of substances which contain 1-phosphatidyl-L-myo-inositol (XI), 1-phosphatidyl-L-myo-inositol 4-phosphate (XIa) and 1-phosphatidyl-L-myo-inositol 4,5-diphosphate (XIb).[84b]

(3) Sphingomyelins (Phosphosphingosides)

Sphingomyelins, together with the glycolipids, were referred to by Carter *et al.*[85] as *sphingolipids,* because they contain the long-chain amino-alcohol, sphingosine (XII). More recently it has been shown that other long-chain amino-alcohols, including dihydrosphingosine, are present in brain lipids.

Much of the early work on the chemistry of sphingolipids was summarized by Thierfelder and Klenk.[86] Sphingosine was discovered in brain by Thudichum.[1,2] A useful method for its preparation was described by Brady and Burton,[87] who outlined the properties of the purified compound. Carter and his associates showed that sphingosine is D-erythro-1,3-dihydroxy-2-amino-4-*trans*-octadecene,[15,16] a finding in agreement with studies of Kiss, Fodor and Bánfi.[88] Carter and Norris[89] isolated dihydrosphingosine from brain and spinal cord. This substance is identical with that formed by the catalytic reduction of naturally-occurring sphingosine. The relative distribution of sphingosine and dihydrosphingosine in brain phosphatides was determined by Sweeley and Moscatelli.[90]

Thudichum[1,2] first isolated sphingomyelin from brain. He recognized it as a diaminophospholipid with a nitrogen to phosphorus ratio of 2:1. The first reasonably pure preparations were obtained by Thannhauser *et al.* from lung,[91] brain and spleen.[32] Subsequently Rapport and Lerner[92] described a simpler method of preparation of sphingomyelin from ox heart. Thannhauser and Boncoddo[32] reported the presence of stearic, lignoceric and nervonic acids in brain sphingomyelin and Fujino and Negishi[93] reported the presence of behenic acid in sphingomyelin from spinal cord.

The findings of Rouser *et al.*[94] indicate that the phosphorylcholine is esterified to the hydroxyl group of sphingosine at the 1-position. The fatty acid is attached to the sphingosine by an amide linkage. The structure of sphingomyelin thus may be represented by formula XIII. Two dihydrosphingomyelins were synthesized by Shapiro *et al.*[95]

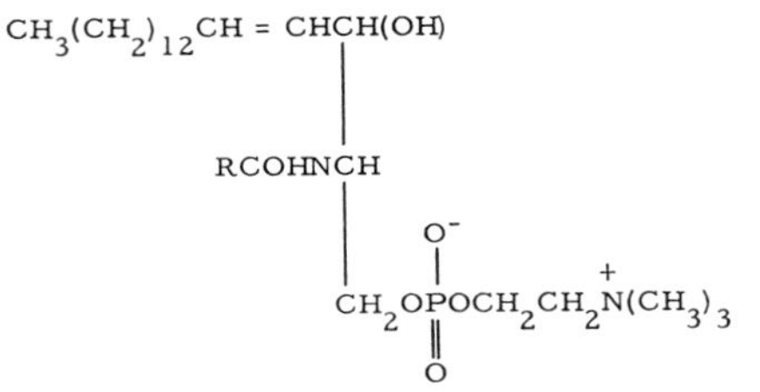

$$CH_3(CH_2)_{12}CH = CHCH(OH)$$

$$RCOHNCH$$

$$CH_2OPOCH_2CH_2\overset{+}{N}(CH_3)_3$$

Sphingomyelin

(XIII)

$$CH_3(CH_2)_{12}CH = CHCH(OH)$$

$$RCONHCH$$

$$CH_2 - O - CH$$
$$HCOH$$
$$HOCH$$
$$HOCH$$
$$HC$$
$$CH_2OH$$

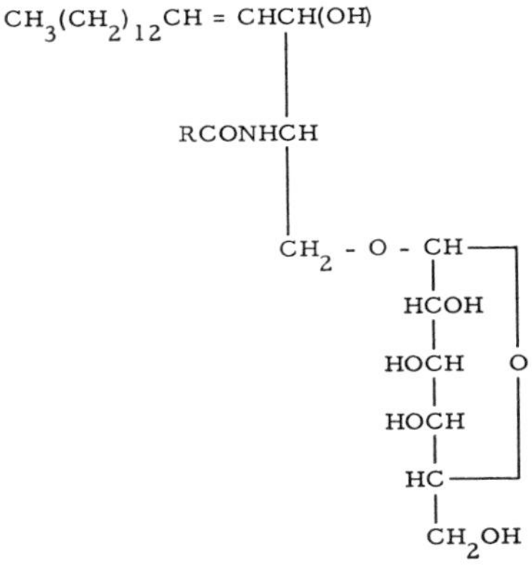

Cerebroside

(XIV)

Although Klenk[96] reported that the concentration of sphingomyelin is increased in many of the organs of patients suffering from Niemann-Pick's disease, the concentration in brain is usually normal (see Thannhauser and Schmidt[97] and Cumings[98] for further references).

(b) Glycolipids

(1) Cerebrosides (Glycosphingosides)

Cerebrosides contain the base sphingosine or dihydrosphingosine, a long-chain fatty acid, and a sugar. Thudichum[1,2] isolated two carbohydrate-containing lipids from brain, to which he gave the names *kerasin* and *phrenosin,* also called *cerebron* by Thierfelder.[99] Subsequently, Klenk and co-workers[100,101] reported the presence of two further cerebrosides, *nervon* and *oxynervon.* The cerebrosides were called *glycosphingosides* by Folch and Sperry.[102] Inasmuch as the carbohydrate of the cerebrosides of brain is galactose,[103,104] these lipids may be called *galactosphingosides*. However, glucose rather than galactose is present in the spleen of patients with Gaucher's disease.[105-108]

A new procedure for the large-scale purification of cerebrosides was developed by Radin *et al.*[109] The cerebroside was purified by the successive use of columns containing Florisil and mixed ion exchange resins. Also Weiss[69] was able to separate kerasin and phrenosin from other sphingolipids by means of chromatography with silicic acid and Long and Staples[110] separated a cerebroside plus sulfatide fraction from brain with alumina columns.

Classically cerebrosides were thought to yield chiefly C_{24} fatty acids on hydrolysis, e.g., lignoceric acid (n-tetracosanoic acid) from kerasin, cerebronic or phrenosinic acid (α-hydroxy-n-tetracosanoic acid) from phrenosin, nervonic acid (9,10-dehydrolignoceric acid) from nervon and oxynervonic acid (α-hydroxynervonic acid) from oxynervon. However, Chibnall *et al.*[111] reported that lignoceric acid from brain kerasin was a mixture of n-docosanoic acid C_{22}, n-tetracosanoic acid C_{24} and n-hexacosanoic acid C_{26}, and that phrenosinic acid from brain phrenosin was a mixture of the corresponding α-hydroxyacids. Using the technique of gas chromatography, Kishimoto and Radin[112] studied the fatty acids of brain cerebrosides. Cerebronic acid was present in greatest concentrations, although there were appreciable quantities of α-hydroxy C_{23} and C_{22} and other lower saturated fatty acids. Unsaturated acids and hydroxy unsaturated acids were present in lesser amounts. Recently Skipski *et al.*[113] reported the presence of hydroxystearic acid in beef spinal cord.

The molecular structure of cerebroside (XIV) resembles that of sphingomyelin. The fatty acid is attached to the sphingosine by an amide linkage and Carter and Greenwood[114] showed that the galactose is attached to the sphingosine in the 1-position. The synthesis of dihydrocerebrosides was recently reported by Shapiro and Flowers.[115]

(2) Cerebroside Sulfate Esters (Sulfatides)

A sulfur-containing lipid (sulfatide) was obtained from brain by Thudichum.[1,2] Since that time many reports have appeared in the literature on the presence of sulfur in lipid extracts of brain. Folch and Lees[116] showed that much of this sulfur may be attributed to the sulfur-containing amino acids of the proteolipids (see below). It is now clear, however, that sulfatides as such occur in the nervous system. In 1933 Blix[117] isolated from ox brain the potassium salt of a lipid that contained fatty acid (chiefly cerebronic acid), galactose, sphingosine and sulfate in equimolecular proportions. Thannhauser *et al.*[118] confirmed that the principal fatty acid of this lipid was cerebronic acid and they showed that the sulfate group was esterified with the hydroxyl group of carbon-6 of the galactose, so that the structure can be represented by formula XV. Radin *et al.*[119] and Lees *et al.*[120] described improved methods for the preparation of brain sulfatides. Lees *et al.*[120] obtained two main fractions: one (sulfatide A) that is similar to XV and another that contains both sulfur and phosphorus. This latter fraction could be separated into a phosphorus-free sulfatide fraction and a phosphatide mixture by passage through a Florisil column. Jatzkewitz[121] also reported the presence of a phosphorus-containing sulfatide in the sphingolipid fraction of human brain.

Both Jatzkewitz[121] and Austin[121a] have shown that the concentration of sulfatides was increased in brains from patients with the metachromatic form of diffuse cerebral sclerosis, an observation recently confirmed by Norman, Urich and Tingey.[121b]

(3) Mucolipids

The term *mucolipid* was introduced by Rosenberg, Howe and Chargaff[122] to designate the group of complex lipid polymers that contain the constituents considered characteristic of cerebrosides (long-chain fatty acid, carbohydrate, sphingosine, or similar base) together with those characteristic of mucoids (amino sugar and sialic acid or related substance). They are soluble in water, but also in organic solvents. They are relatively unstable in the presence of acid and have a high molecular weight.

Blix[123] obtained a crystalline substance from submaxillary gland mucin and a brain lipid fraction, which he called *sialic acid*. Klenk[124] isolated a substance which he called *neuraminic acid* from a similar brain fraction. These two substances were shown to have comparable color reactions and for some time the relation between the two was somewhat obscure. The nomenclature of Blix, Gottschalk and Klenk[125] is now generally accepted. The name neuraminic acid is reserved for the unsubstituted compound and sialic acid is a group name for a series of acylated neuraminic acids. Thus the chief sialic acid in brain lipids is N-acetyl neuraminic acid (XVI). A number of other sialic acids occur in nature (see Gottschalk[126,127] for references). N-acetyl neuraminic acid was synthesized by Cornforth, Firth and Gottschalk,[128] who proposed a structure similar to that represented by formula XVI. More recent studies,[129] including an enzymic synthesis by Comb and Roseman,[130] have shown, however, that neuraminic acid is related stereochemically to D-mannosamine and not to D-glucosamine, as was originally thought.

Many workers have reported the presence of sialic acids in lipid extracts of brain. There is considerably more in gray matter than in white matter,[131,132] a finding that suggests that the mucolipids are located chiefly in gray matter, possibly in relation to neurones.

Gangliosides.—Early reports of the occurrence of mucolipids in brain are those of Landsteiner and Levine,[133,134] Walz[135] and Blix.[136] Subsequently, Klenk[137,138] obtained in crystalline form a lipid from gray matter of brain, to which he gave the name *ganglioside*. On hydrolysis it yielded neuraminic acid, sphingosine, fatty acids (mainly stearic

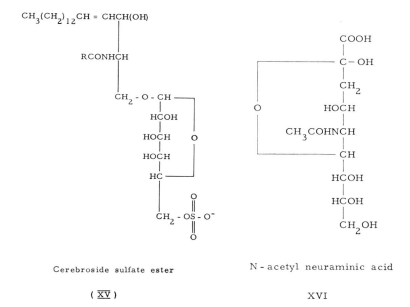

Cerebroside sulfate ester   N - acetyl neuraminic acid

($\overline{XV}$)   XVI

and nervonic acids), hexoses, chiefly galactose but some glucose, and galactosamine. A similar substance was studied by Blix, Svennerholm and Werner[139] and extensive studies of gangliosides have been reported by Svennerholm.[140-143]

Klenk and Schumann[144] showed that in brains from patients with Tay-Sach's disease the cerebrosides are largely replaced by gangliosides. Previously Klenk[96] had reported that considerable quantities of ganglioside are present in the sphingomyelin fraction of brains from patients with Niemann-Pick's disease. These findings are supported by the reports of Cumings[145] and Tingey[146] that there is an increase in the concentration of lipid neuraminic acid and hexosamine in brains from patients with these conditions.

Strandin.—Folch, Arsove and Meath[147] in 1951 isolated from gray matter of brain an electrophoretically homogeneous lipid, the main component of which was reported to have a minimum molecular weight of 250,000. The name *strandin* was proposed for this substance because, when dried from aqueous solution, it had the property of forming long strands that show good orientation in polarized light. The material contained sialic acid, sphingosine, fatty acids, galactose, glucose and galactosamine.[122,148,149]

Using a procedure similar to that described by Folch *et al.*,[147] Rosenberg and Chargaff[150] prepared a highly polymerized complex mucolipid from the gray matter of ox brain. This substance, which was homogeneous electrophoretically and ultracentrifugally, was reported to have a molecular weight of 180,000. The constituents were sialic acid (N-acetyl neuraminic acid), sphingosine, fatty acids (chiefly lignoceric acid), galactose, glucose, N-acetylgalactosamine. In addition the substance contained small amounts of amino acids.

Gangliosides and strandin resemble each other in many ways. They have similar constituents, similar color reactions and similar solubility properties. However, they differ in their crystalline form and probably in the relative distribution of their constituents. It is possible that both are derived from the same more complex structure and that the differences may be due to differences in the method of isolation. Strandin was obtained by the use of mild procedures, whereas in the isolation of ganglioside hot glacial acetic acid was used. If strandin is treated with hot acetic acid, it loses some sialic acid and its crystalline form changes from strands to spherules.[9] Thus gangliosides may be products of the partial breakdown of strandin. Svennerholm,[140,143] using an isolation procedure more mild than that of Klenk, obtained several mucolipid fractions. Meltzer,[151] employing a three-phase distribution system, separated the strandin of Folch into a number of components, as did Weicker *et al.*,[151a] using silica-gel chromatography. It is possible that these components represent different degrees of polymerization of the same monomeric unit.

Bogoch[152] reported studies on a homogeneous high-molecular weight mucolipid from brain, which he referred to as ganglioside rather than strandin. He examined both the diffusible and non-diffusible products obtained during a quantitative stepwise hydrolysis. As one of the products of hydrolysis, he obtained a glucostearocerebroside different from the known brain cerebrosides, for which he suggested the name *gangliocerebroside*. In addition, Bogoch reported the isolation of a hexodicerebroside.

On the basis of (a) the constant order of release of certain of the constituents of hydrolysis and (b) the structure of the isolated fragments, Bogoch[152] proposed a structure for the repeating unit of the mucolipid molecule. Although the formula was not inconsistent with the data presented, it should be understood that the validity of such a structure has not been established. More conservatively, Rosenberg and Chargaff[150] have warned that "a detailed discussion of the arrangement of the constituents is not yet advisable." More recently, however, Klenk and Gielen[153] have provided evidence that brain gangliosides may be represented by the structures shown as formulae XVII and XVIII.

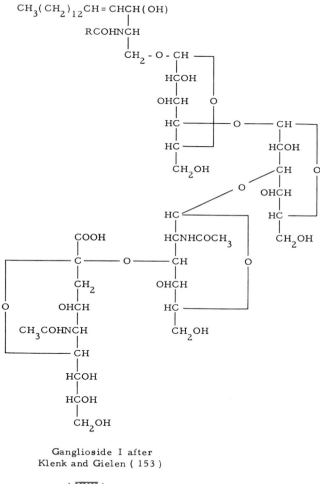

Ganglioside I after
Klenk and Gielen (153)

(XVII)

The physical properties of brain mucolipid, e.g., lack of significant flow birefringence in aqueous solution and low viscosity, indicate that the repeating units are not arranged linearly. For suggestions as to possibilities of how such a repeating structure may be arranged, the reader is referred to the papers of Bogoch[152] and Rosenberg and Chargaff.[150]

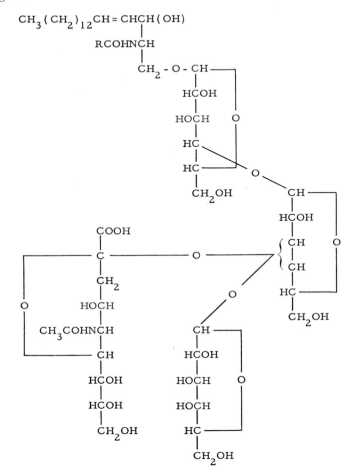

Ganglioside II after
Klenk and Gielen (153)

($\overline{\text{XVIII}}$)

(c) Non-Saponifiable Lipids

(1) Sterols

Cholesterol was recognized as a constitutent of brain by Gmelin.[154] The high concentration of cholesterol in both white matter of brain and in myelinated peripheral nerve has been noted by many workers. Other tissues contain cholesterol esters as well as non-esterified cholesterol, but in normal adult brain and nerve almost all of the cholesterol is in the non-esterified form. Adams and Davison[155] have reported that large amounts of cholesterol ester (up to 40% of the total) are present in human foetal spinal cord and in the spinal cord of chick embryos. It is possible that the cholesterol ester is associated with the process of myelination. Ester cholesterol is present in the brains of patients suffering from certain degenerative diseases[156,157] and in peripheral nerve during experimental Wallerian degeneration.[158,159] Konnikova[160] reported that much of the cholesterol of brain, especially that in the gray matter, is attached to protein. Le-Baron and Folch[161] confirmed that in brain much cholesterol is attached to the water-soluble proteins. The total synthesis of cholesterol recently was achieved by Woodward *et al.*[162]

It is clear that brain contains small amounts of other sterols related to cholesterol. Thus cholestanol (dihydrocholesterol),[163] 7-dehydrocholesterol,[164] cerebrosterol (24-hydroxycholesterol),[165-167] lanthosterol, cholestane-3β,5α,6α-triol and a substance called "ketone 104 precursor" by Fieser *et al.*[166,167] have been identified in brain extracts. Whether all of these substances are naturally-occurring, or whether some of them may be formed from cholesterol during the isolation procedure, is of course difficult to establish. Russian workers have reported the presence of a 7-hydroxycholesterol in brain, particularly in gray matter.[168,169] In addition, Silberman and Silberman-Martyncewa[170] reported the presence of dicholesteryl ether in ox spinal cord.

(2) Hydrocarbons

Nicholas, Hiltibran and Wadkins[171] reported the results of a study on the hydrocarbons of the non-saponifiable fraction of brain lipids. From the crude fraction two hydrocarbons were isolated. Other substances also were present, but little is known concerning their chemical nature.

(d) Neutral Fat (Triglycerides)

Most tissues of the body contain triglycerides. Brain is an exception. It contains neither cholesterol esters nor triglycerides. Peripheral nerve, however, which contains no cholesterol ester, contains considerable amounts of triglyceride.[158] Probably most of this neutral fat is not in the nerve fiber proper (axon, myelin sheath, Schwann cell), but in the surrounding epineural and perineural connective tissue.

(e) Protein-bound Lipids

(1) Proteolipids

The concept of a proteolipid was introduced into brain chemistry by Folch and Lees.[116] Proteolipids are substances having both a protein and lipid moiety, the complex being insoluble in water, but freely soluble in chloroform-methanol-water mixtures. Lipoproteins, which are usually soluble in water or dilute salt solutions, have the properties of a protein with an attached lipid. Proteolipids, on the other hand, have the properties of a lipid with an attached protein.

Folch and Lees[116] isolated three proteolipids from the white matter of brain. Proteolipid A is a mixture. Proteolipid B has been obtained in crystalline form. It contains 50% protein and 50% lipid material, the lipids being a mixture, in equal proportions, of phospholipids and cerebrosides. About 50% of the phospholipids appear to be phospho-sphingosides. Proteolipid C contains 75% protein and 25% lipid material. The lipids are chiefly phospholipids of the phosphoglyceride type. All three proteolipids are birefringent white powders, insoluble in water, but soluble in mixtures of chloroform and methanol almost saturated with water.

Chatagnon *et al.*[172] reported on the amino acid composition of the proteolipids of both bovine and human brain. Recently Folch, Webster and Lees[173] described an improved method for isolating proteolipids. The finding that proteolipid preparations can produce experimental allergic encephalomyelitis is discussed elsewhere in this volume and the possibility that proteolipids may be components of myelin is discussed later in this chapter.

(2) Phosphatidopeptides

A second type of lipid-peptide complex was isolated from brain by LeBaron and Folch[174,175]. These substances were extracted with 200:100:1 chloroform:methanol:concentrated HCl (v/v/v) from the insoluble protein residue remaining after brain tissue had been extracted with chloroform-methanol and then digested with trypsin. They are reported to be comprised of phosphatides, chiefly phosphoinositides, combined with amino acids, probably as relatively short-chain peptides. Subsequently, LeBaron and Rothleder[176] developed a new method, which employed milder procedures, for the preparation of phosphatidopeptides. The peptides in the phosphatidopeptides obtained by this method were apparently of somewhat longer chain length than those in the material obtained by the original method.

In relation to phosphatidopeptides in general, it is of interest to note that Huggins and Cohn[177] presented data for the analysis of a phosphatidopeptide fraction derived from pig kidney and that Baer *et al.*[178] described the chemical synthesis of the phosphatidyl tripeptide O- (distearoyl-L-*a*-glycerolphosphoryl)-L-serylglycylglycine.

It was mentioned previously that Dittmer and Dawson[80] described the preparation of two phosphoinositides from ox brain. The first of these is a monophosphoinositide, which probably does not differ from the phosphatidyl inositol (XI) of other tissues. The other is firmly attached to the protein residue remaining after the usual extraction of the brain with chloroform-methanol to remove lipids. The simplest composition of this compound was reported to be glycerol:inositol: phosphate:acyl ester, in molar ratios of 1:1:3:2. The lipid is thus similar to the triphosphoinositide described by Ballou and associates.[84a,b]

Both Dawson and Dittmer[179] and Ballou *et al.*[84a,b] have reported extensive studies on the brain "diphosphoinositide" fraction of Folch.[75] An analysis of the products of acid and alkaline hydrolysis, together with an investigation of the products of deacylation, indicate that the "diphosphoinositide" is a mixture comprised of phosphatidyl inositol (XI), phosphatidyl inositol monophosphate (XIa) and phosphatidyl inositol diphosphate (XIb).

The monophosphoinositide is readily extracted from brain with lipid solvents, but the di- and triphosphoinositides resemble the phosphatidopeptides in that they are firmly bound to protein. They can be extracted either by pre-treating the tissues with acetone or by acidifying the solvents used for extraction. It thus seems likely that these compounds form part of the lipid moiety of the phosphatidopeptides. As discussed in a subsequent section, it is probable that they are also present in the trypsin resistant protein residue (TRPR) of LeBaron and Folch[175] and in the classical neurokeratin, both of which are constituents of brain residue protein.

(3) Lipoproteins

Whereas proteolipids are lipophilic, i.e., they may be considered as lipids with an attached protein, lipoproteins are hydrophilic, i.e., they may be considered as protein with an attached lipid. A number of such lipid-protein complexes behave as homogeneous substances on electrophoresis or on ultracentrifugation. Although there is much evidence that lipoproteins are substances of great biological importance, it is still an open question as to what extent many of them may be regarded as definite chemical entities. In some of the lipoproteins that have been investigated, the lipid moiety was found to consist of a mixture of two or more known lipids.

It is probable that lipoproteins are present in most animal tissues, but it is those of the blood plasma that have received the most study. Some of the brain lipoproteins are discussed under the heading of water-soluble brain proteins.

(f) Miscellaneous

Fatty Acids.—Because of their wide distribution in brain lipids, fatty acids are the most abundant lipid constituent per unit weight of brain tissue. Knowledge of the fatty acids of brain lipids is far from complete, but it may be said that they are characterized by a long chain length (C_{18} to C_{26}). Brain lipids also contain a high proportion of unsaturated fatty acids. The distribution of fatty acids in brain has been summarized in tabular form by LeBaron and Folch[9]. More recent data on the nature of brain fatty acids may be found in publications by Klenk and Montag,[180,181] Klenk[182] and Johnston and Kummerow.[183]

Whenever possible in the preceding sections, the nature of the fatty acids in the major brain lipids has been given. With the rapid development of improved methods of isolating lipids and improved methods of detecting fatty acids in small lipid samples, more complete data should be available in the near future.

Other Lipids.—It is, of course, possible that many other lipids may be present in small quantities in the nervous system. The following reports refer to lipids that as yet have not been fully described and characterized:-

(1) Brante[67] suggested that ceramides (N-acyl sphingosines) might occur in brain. Klenk[184] isolated from brain a ceramide containing cerebronic acid.

(2) From the hydrolysis products of ether-insoluble lipids of brain Niemann[185] isolated a substance which appears to be an ether of sphingosine and tetradecyl alcohol.

(3) By submitting the N-2,4-dinitrophenyl and methyl derivatives of sheep brain phospholipids to countercurrent distribution procedures, Collins[186] separated two complex phosphatides. One of these has a molecular weight of 2030 and contains glycerophosphate, ethanolamine, choline, sugar, fatty alcohol and fatty acids in the molecular ratio of 2:1:1:1:1:2, as well as two nitrogen-containing compounds.[187] It is reported that this complex lipid constitutes 28% of the total phospholipid of sheep brain.

State of Lipids in Situ

It was pointed out above that many of the lipids of brain are attached to protein, either in the form of proteolipid or lipoprotein. In addition, it is probable that *in situ* many of the brain lipids are present as complexes amongst themselves. The changing behaviour of a lipid as it is purified from a crude extract suggests that there must be considerable interaction between the various lipid components of the extract.

Examples of lipid-lipid complexes have been referred to already. It is possible that gangliosides are components of a more complex strandin and there is evidence that a cerebroside unit recurs throughout the whole of the larger molecule. The recent work of Collins[186,187] also suggests that some of the ethanolamine- and choline-containing lipids of brain may be considerably more complex than had been expected hitherto.

In general, it might be concluded that, as milder preparative techniques are employed in an attempt to preserve tissue constitutents in their "native" or *in situ* condition, more evidence is obtained for interaction between the various constitutents. Thus lipids, polysaccharides, proteins and nucleic acids may be associated with each other and with themselves to form what is possibly a wide variety of much more complex structures. At the present time the chemical nature of a few of the simpler tissue components has been elucidated, but almost nothing is known of how the simpler, smaller units are arranged together to form what are probably quite complex highly organized structures.

Quantitative Determination of Lipids

The range for the concentration of a number of lipids in gray matter and white matter of vertebrate brain and in spinal cord and peripheral nerve is shown in Table II. For brain, the figures have been presented only if the authors attempted to separate white matter from gray matter. In comparing the concentration of any constitutent in white matter of brain with that of the same substance in gray matter, the standard of reference must be considered. Because of the high content of lipid in white matter, the dry weight of a given weight of fresh white matter is considerably greater than that of the same weight of fresh gray matter. In Tables II to V the values are given in terms of wet weight rather than in terms of dry weight, because this more closely represents the amount of the constitutent in a given volume of brain substance and, in the case of water-soluble substances such as electrolytes (Table V), it more nearly represents the amount of the substance in a given volume of tissue water.

The figures represented in Table II are taken from the publications of a number of different workers, who employed an almost equal variety of technical methods. They are presented uncritically, with the only apology that in the opinion of the author they are the best

TABLE II

CONCENTRATION OF LIPIDS IN BRAIN, SPINAL CORD AND PERIPHERAL NERVE OF VERTEBRATES

(g. per 100 g. fresh tissue)

Constituent	Gray Matter	White Matter	Reference	Spinal Cord	Reference	Peripheral Nerve	Reference
Total lipids	4.0-7.9	13.9-23.1	67, 294, 295	15.5-22.7	67, 188	4.4-23	67, 158, 247, 296, 297
Total phospholipids	3.1-4.6	6.2-9.3	67, 250, 294, 295, 298, 299, 300, 302	7.8-10.6	67, 188, 301	2.2-13.9	67, 158, 159, 247, 250, 296, 297, 298
Lecithins	0.6-1.5	0.9-1.9	67, 294, 295, 302	1.5-2.2	67, 188	0.3-2.0	67, 158, 159, 296
Phosphatidyl serines	0.6	1.4	5			0.7	247
'Cephalins'*	1.1-2.5	2.6-5.4	67, 294, 295, 302	4.1-5.4	67, 188	0.4-7.6	67, 158, 159, 296
Plasmalogens	0.6-0.9	2.1-3.1	303, 63b	2.0-4.7	63b	1.0-1.3	63b
Sphingomyelins†	0.3-0.9	1.8-4.3	67, 294, 295, 302	2.1-3.4	67, 188	1.3-4.7	67, 158, 159, 247, 296
Cerebrosides**	0.3-1.9	4.1-7.4	67, 294, 295, 302	3.8-6.2	67, 188	1.1-4.7	67, 158, 159, 247, 296, 297
Mucolipids‡	0.6-0.7	0.06-0.07	5			0.01	247
Cholesterol	0.6-1.4	3.6-5.4	67, 294, 295, 302	3.9-5.9	67, 188	1.1-4.8	67, 158, 159, 296, 297

*Total monoaminophosphatide minus lecithin. Includes phosphatidyl serine plus phosphatidyl ethanolamine plus plasmalogens (cephalin A of Brante[7]).
†Total phosphatide minus monoaminophosphatide (sphingomyelin + cephalin B of Brante[7]). See Ansell and Spanner[71].
**Includes all glycolipids, i.e., includes sulfatides and mucolipids.
‡Includes gangliosides and strandin.

available at the present time. In many instances the concentration of a certain lipid was calculated from the quantitative determination of some degradation product. It was assumed, often incorrectly, that all of the chosen degradation product was derived from the designated lipid. With the added warning that many of the techniques employed now must be considered out of date, the reader is referred to the original papers for further information.

In reviewing the literature from a number of different sources on the quantitative determination of brain lipids, one is surprised at how similar some of the reported values are, despite many differences in the technical methods employed. There is no great or consistent difference in the concentration of the lipids in brain relative to species, age, sex and various dietary conditions, including extreme starvation.

In general, the composition of peripheral nerve, which contains much myelin, resembles that of spinal cord and white matter rather than that of gray matter, which is poor in myelin. Notable exceptions are mucolipids and proteolipids (Table III), which are reported to be present only in very low concentrations in peripheral nerve.

For the most part the figures of Table II refer to mammalian tissue, although for peripheral nerve some figures for frog nerve are given. The distribution of lipids in the nervous system of some of the lower vertebrates, and some invertebrates, has been found to differ from that in the mammalian nervous system (see McColl and Rossiter[188] for references). In cephalopods and insects the nervous system would appear to contain no cerebroside,[189-191] although some cerebroside, or at least some glycolipid, has been detected in the nervous system of a a number of invertebrate species.[67,192,193]

MUCOPOLYSACCHARIDES AND MUCOIDS

Present knowledge concerning the mucopolysaccharides and mucoids of brain is summarized in three reviews by Brante.[194-196] The presence of glucosamine, galactosamine,[195] hexuronic acid,[195,197] sulfur[195] and sialic acid[142,196] in the non-lipid fraction of the nervous system has been established. These findings, taken in conjunction with the results of chromatographic studies, indicate that brain contains most of the known mucoids and mucopolysaccarides, both sulfur-containing and sulfur-free. Chondroitin sulfate is possibly the chief acid mucopolysaccharide, whereas at best heparin is present only as a minimal component.

On the basis of hexosamine determinations, fresh brain contains 0.15-0.25% mucopolysaccharide and mucoid, with a concentration in white matter similar to that in gray matter. This is in contrast to con-

TABLE III

CONCENTRATION OF PROTEINS IN BRAIN, SPINAL CORD AND PERIPHERAL NERVE OF VERTEBRATES

(g. per 100 g. fresh tissue)

Constituent	Gray Matter	White Matter	Reference	Spinal Cord	Reference	Peripheral Nerve	Reference
Water	81–87	67–74	67, 295, 304, 305	66–75	67, 188, 266, 304	56–71	67, 266, 297, 304
Total protein	5.6–12.5	6.0–12.7	299, 300, 306	8.8–10.0	210, 307	11–15	159, 308, 309, 310
Proteolipid	0.5–0.6	2.0–2.5	116			0.06	246, 247
Globulin*	2.4	1.0	5				
Albumin*	0.3	0.3	5				
Collagen	0.1	0.08	311			3–6.5	247, 308, 311
Total ash	1.0–2.6	0.7–2.7	1, 2, 299, 306	1.2–1.9	307, 309	1.0–1.1	309

*Extractable with 20% NaCl.

clusions made from histochemical studies,[198-200] where mucoids and mucopolysaccharides were reported to be more abundant in gray matter.

From histochemical evidence it has been claimed that the amount of acid mucopolysaccharide is increased in brains of rats with experimental hypothyroidism[201] and in brains from patients with gargoylism.[202] Such histochemical findings must be interpreted with care, but it is noteworthy that both Uzman[203] and Brante[204] demonstrated the presence of polysaccharides and glycolipids in the liver and other organs from patients with gargoylism.

Abood and Abul-Haj[193] presented histochemical evidence for the presence of hyaluronic acid in the axoplasm and neurilemma of frog and bovine peripheral nerve. They separated and partially purified a substance from frog nerve, which was identified as hyaluronic acid by chemical means.

Wolman[205] reported the presence of a weakly acidic mucopolysaccaride in rat nerve undergoing Wallerian degeneration. It was present from the first day after section, whereas later in the degenerative process a non-acidic polysaccharide appeared. It was suggested that this non-acidic polysaccharide might be responsible for the Marchi staining reaction, since its appearance coincides in time with the appearance of positive Marchi staining.

PROTEINS

Compared to the great amount of work that has been done on the lipids of the nervous system, surprisingly little attention has been paid to proteins. This is possibly due to the fact that brain and nerve are unfavourable tissues for the study of proteins, first because of their high lipid content, and secondly, because many of the proteins exist as complexes with lipids. Proteins account for some 40% of the dry weight of whole brain compared to 50% for lipids. Many of the essential features of the proteins of brain are summarized in recent reviews by LeBaron[7] and Richter.[206]

Proteins Extracted into Aqueous Media.—The extraction of brain proteins into various aqueous media was described by Palladin and Goryukhina.[207] Subsequently Nakamura, Hayashi and Tanaka[208] and Polyakova and Gotovtseva[209] reported on the rate of extraction of proteins by physiological saline and the effect of pH on the process. More recently, LeBaron and Folch[161] published a systematic study of the effect of ionic strength and pH on the completeness of the extraction. Maximum amounts of protein were obtained at an ionic strength of about 3.0 and a pH in the range 6-9. Dialysis of extracts of gray and white matter against $3M$-NaCl gave a lipid-free albumin fraction and a globulin fraction containing 25% lipid, about 25% of which was cholesterol.

There have been a number of attempts to fractionate the water-soluble brain proteins. One of the earliest was that of Halliburton[210] in 1894, who obtained three fractions by the method of fractional heat coagulation. Subsequently McGregor[211] in 1917 studied fractional precipitation of brain proteins, using ammonium sulfate, acid and heat. A more recent attempt at a chemical fractionation of the proteins of brain is that of Dingman, Sporn and Davies.[212]

Many workers have described attempts to separate the water-soluble brain proteins using the technique of electrophoresis. Russian workers have been particularly active in this field. Two reviews of this work have been published, one by Palladin[213] in English and one by Palladin and Polyakova[214] in German. English, German, Italian and Japanese workers also have published numerous papers on the electrophoresis of brain proteins. The presence of up to eight or ten fractions has been reported. Because of the differences in extraction procedures and the techniques used for the electrophoresis, it is not profitable to attempt to correlate these findings at the present time. References to this work are given in the publications of LeBaron[7] and Robertson.[215]

Reports also have appeared on the electrophoretic patterns of soluble brain proteins in different areas of the brain[216,217] and on the effect of certain pathological conditions on the electrophoretic pattern[218,219]

Similar electrophoretic techniques have been applied to peripheral nerve. Polyakova[220] and Missere, Tonini and DeRisio[221] independently reported that in peripheral nerve the relative amount of a fraction having a similar electrophoretic mobility to serum albumin was greater than that of a comparable fraction in extracts of brain. In addition, Polyakova and Kabak[222] reported that peripheral nerve contains a fraction that migrates towards the cathode under the same conditions. The albumin fraction was isolated from peripheral nerve by Deuticke *et al.*[223] and Li and Sheng.[224] The latter workers published evidence to the effect that the nerve albumin was identical with serum albumin. However, Palladin and Polyakova[214] concluded that nerve albumin, although it has the same electrophoretic mobility as serum albumin, is not derived from blood or lymph.

Many of the water-soluble proteins of brain and nerve are combined with lipids. They thus fall into the catagory of lipoproteins. Nedzvetskii and Ratnitskaya[225] published data on the cholesterol and phospholipid content of brain lipoproteins.

Several apparently quite distinct water-soluble proteins have been studied:

(1) Porter and Folch[226] described the separation from brain tissue under copper-free conditions of three different copper-containing fractions. From one of these fractions of bovine brain they isolated a homogeneous protein containing 0.3% copper, for which they suggested the name *cerebrocuprein 1*.[227] Porter and Ainsworth[228] isolated a similar protein from human brain.

Much of the excess copper in brains from patients with hepatolenticular degeneration is in the fraction from which cerebrocuprein 1 was isolated.[226] This copper was found to react more readily with sodium diethyldithiocarbamate than does the copper of cerebrocuprein 1.[229] This reacting copper in diseased brain may represent copper bound to proteins that in normal brain are copper-free.

(2) Roboz, Henderson and Kies[230] reported the isolation of a fibrous protein from spinal cord. Because its properties and amino acid composition resembled collagen, the protein was referred to as collagen-like. The relation of this protein to the factor producing experimental allergic encephalomyelitis[231] is discussed in a subsequent chapter.

(3) A fibrous protein was isolated from the axoplasm of the giant axon of the common squid, *Loligo pealii,* by Maxfield[232] and Maxfield and Hartley.[233] These authors described the physicochemical properties of this protein, which is believed to be derived from the axon filaments of the nerve. A similar study was made of a protein from the axoplasm of the larger squid, *Dosdicus gigas* by Davison and Taylor.[234]

(4) Maxfield[235] purified and determined the physicochemical properties of a protein from lobster nerve. Subsequently the amino acid composition of this protein was determined by Koechlin and Parish.[236]

(5) A liponucleoprotein was isolated from brain by Folch and Uzman.[237] The lipid component of this lipoprotein was shown to be a mixture of phospholipid and carbohydrate-containing lipid, whereas the lipid-free material had the characteristics of a nucleoprotein. The lipoprotein is birefringent and the x-ray pattern shows a degree of order consistent with a crystalline structure.

The concentration of water-soluble protein and total protein in gray matter and white matter of brain and in spinal cord and peripheral nerve is shown in Table III. The effect of age on the protein content of the brain and the protein content of different areas of the brain were discussed by Clouet and Gaitonde.[238]

Proteins Extracted into Non-polar Solvents.—The proteolipids of Folch and Lees[116] and the phosphatidopeptides of LeBaron and Folch[175] have been referred to already.

Uzman[239] described the occurrence of a number of lipophilic peptides in mouse brain. One of these, to which he gave the name *neuro-*

sclerin, had a constant composition. The amount increased steadily with age during the first 24 days after birth. In a second publication the amino acid composition of neurosclerin was given.[240]

Residue Protein.—This is a convenient name for the protein remaining after successive thorough extractions of brain tissue with aqueous and lipid solvents. The residue protein is of interest in relation to the protein classically called *neurokeratin.* Ewald and Kühne[241] and Kühne and Chittenden[242] studied the insoluble protein remaining in brain after successive extractions with fat solvents, dilute acid and alkali, and treatment with pepsin and trypsin. Block[243] showed that the amino acid composition of this protein was quite different from that of true keratin, a protein with similar solubility properties. There have been many chemical studies of neurokeratin (see LeBaron and Folch[175] for references), the most recent of which is that of Stary and Arat.[244]

LeBaron and Folch[175] considered the nature of the residue protein, particularly in relation to the components of classical neurokeratin. They prepared from brain a trypsin-resistant protein residue (TRPR). This differed from neurokeratin in that it was free from proteolipid and contained phosphorus, chiefly in the form of inositides. This phosphorus could be extracted in the form of phosphatidopeptides by acidified solvents. The possible relation of these phosphatidopeptides to the triphosphoinositide of Dittmer and Dawson[80] has been discussed already.

In addition, LeBaron and Folch[175] found that the original extraction procedures used for the preparation of neurokeratin causes a chemical hydrolysis of the phosphatidopeptides and splits the proteolipids into a lipid moiety, which is extracted, and a protein moiety, which would remain with the residue since it is resistant to proteolytic enzymes.[116] It would thus appear that classical neurokeratin is an artifact comprised of a mixture of the protein moiety of proteolipids and possibly the degradation products of other lipid-protein complexes.

Histologically, neurokeratin forms part of the myelin sheath of a mammalian nerve. Kühne and Chittenden[242] reported that white matter of brain contains more neurokeratin than gray matter. The same is true for the proteolipids of Folch and Lees,[116] a finding consistent with the suggestion that neurokeratin contains the protein moiety of proteolipids. The histochemical studies of Koenig[245] further support this view. It should be pointed out, however, that both Finean *et al.*[246] and Folch *et al.*[247] have reported that proteolipids may be obtained from white matter of brain, but not from peripheral nerve, by the present methods of preparation. Thus the attractive hypothesis that proteolipids are components of histological neurokeratin and hence components of the myelin sheath must await further study.

Residue Phosphorus.—It is generally assumed that, when animal tissues are extracted to remove both water-soluble substances and lipids, the protein-bound phosphorus remaining is chiefly derived from nucleic acid and phosphoprotein. The phosphorus of the phosphoprotein may be released as inorganic phosphate by mild alkaline hydrolysis. These assumptions form the basis of the useful procedure developed by Schmidt and Thannhauser[248] for the estimation of nucleic acids in tissues. However, when the method is applied to brain and nerve difficulties arise.[249,250] Logan, Mannell and Rossiter[250] found that, if the nucleic acids are extracted from brain tissue by some method such as that of Schneider[251] or that of Hammarsten,[252] the residue phosphorus remaining, called "phosphoprotein" phosphorus by Schneider,[251] was far in excess of the phosphoprotein of Schmidt and Thannhauser.[248] The amount of this residue is such as to render the method of Schmidt and Thannhauser[248] unsuitable for the determination of nucleic acids in tissue from the nervous system. The nature of this residue phosphorus is far from perfectly understood. It contains small amounts of classical phosphoprotein that yields inorganic phosphate on mild alkaline hydrolysis. This phosphoprotein was studied by Heald[253,254] and the Russian workers.[255,256] In addition, there is a complex fraction referred to as ROP (residue organic phosphorus) by Findlay, Strickland and Rossiter[257] and Magee and Rossiter[258] and previously referred to as "inositide P" by Logan, Mannell and Rossiter.[250] It is now known that this fraction contains the phosphatidopeptide of LeBaron and Folch[175] and the triphosphoinositides of Dittmer and Dawson.[80]

The concentrations of total protein-bound phosphorus, phosphoprotein and residue organic phosphorus in white matter and gray matter of brain and in spinal cord and peripheral nerve are shown in Table IV. The table also lists the concentrations of the other major phosphorus-containing fractions in these tissues.

Collagen.—Histochemical methods have failed to show the presence of collagen in the central nervous system, other than in blood vessels, whereas large amounts of collagen are present in the connective tissue elements of peripheral nerve. This finding is confirmed by chemical analysis (Table III). It can be seen from the table that the concentration of collagen in peripheral nerve is much greater than that in brain and that collagen accounts for a considerable proportion of the nerve protein. It will be recalled that Roboz, Henderson and Kies[230] reported the isolation of a collagen-like protein from spinal cord.

TABLE IV

CONCENTRATION OF PHOSPHORUS-CONTAINING FRACTIONS IN BRAIN, SPINAL CORD AND PERIPHERAL NERVE OF VERTEBRATES

(mg.P per 100 g. fresh tissue)

Constituent	Gray Matter	White Matter	Reference	Spinal Cord	Reference	Peripheral Nerve	Reference
Total P	190–290	330–490	250, 299, 304, 307	520–550	304, 307	200–480	250, 304
Inorganic P	29–64	11–60	298, 300			11–32	250, 298
Acid-Soluble P	71–190	60–190	250, 298, 300, 304	60–70	304	28–62	159, 250, 298, 304
Lipid P	120–180	250–380	67, 250, 294, 295, 298, 299, 300, 302	310–420	67, 188, 301	90–420	67, 158, 159, 247, 250, 296, 297, 298
Total protein-bound P	22–29	25–42	250, 298	30–50	301	11–43	250, 298, 301
RNA–P	10–11	4–5	250			4–5	159, 250
DNA–P	4–9	5–9	250, 312, 313, 314			5–6	159, 250
Phosphoprotein P*	2–3	2–3	250			2–3	250
Residue Organic P†	8–9	19–23	250			9–11	250

*Appears as inorganic P after mild alkaline hydrolysis. The phosphoprotein of Schmidt and Thannhauser.[248]

†Total protein-bound P minus (nucleic acid P plus phosphoprotein P). Referred to previously as residue organic phosphorus (ROP)[257,258] or 'inositide P.'[250]

Nucleoproteins

There are few reports in the literature on the isolation of either nucleoproteins or their constituent nucleic acids from tissue of the nervous system. Mention should be made, however, of the work of Halliburton,[210] who described the presence of a nucleoprotein in saline extracts of brain, and that of Levene,[259] who prepared nucleoprotein from calf brain. Nucleoprotein in lobster[260] and squid[261] nerves was studied by Schmidt and associates. The liponucleoprotein of Folch and Uzman[237] was referred to above.

Levene[262] reported that the nucleic acid of brain did not differ essentially from that of other tissues. More recently, Emanuel and Chaikoff[263] prepared deoxyribonucleic acid (DNA) from cattle cerebellum. This brain DNA resembled DNA prepared from kidney and spleen in chemical constitution, specific extinction and specific rotation, but it had a greater specific viscosity.

The concentration of ribonucleic acid (RNA) and DNA in gray matter and white matter of brain and in spinal cord and peripheral nerve is reported in Table IV. The difficulties of estimating nucleic acid in tissue from the nervous system were commented upon above. For more details, the reader is referred to the paper by Logan, Mannell and Rossiter.[250]

MINERALS

It is now generally believed that the discharge of a nerve cell and the conduction of a nerve impulse along the nerve fiber is inseparably linked with the passage of electrolytes across cell membranes. This topic is dealt with elsewhere in this volume. The following sections are concerned with the concentration of electrolytes in brain and nerve as a whole. The intimate changes in electrolyte concentration associated with nerve cell activity will not be discussed.

Brain.—Overton[264] developed the view that the water and electrolytes of most tissues are distributed between an intracellular space, containing a relatively high concentration of potassium and phosphate with little sodium and chloride, and an extracellular space, approximating to an ultrafiltrate of serum and containing a high concentration of sodium and chloride with little potassium. Much of the experimental evidence in favour of this theory was summarized by Peters.[265] Manery and Hastings[266] presented data to show that, whereas in some tissues, e.g., muscle, this concept could be correct, in others, e.g., blood or connective tissue, the concept could not apply. In these latter tissues a high proportion of the chloride must be in the intracellular space. The data for brain are consistent with the view that it is comprised of a chloride-free intracellular space and a chloride-containing

TABLE V

CONCENTRATION OF ELECTROLYTES IN BRAIN, SPINAL CORD AND PERIPHERAL NERVE OF VERTEBRATES

(m-moles/kg. wet tissue)

Constituent	Gray Matter	White Matter	Reference	Spinal Cord	Reference	Peripheral Nerve	Reference
Na⁺	50–90	45–100	266, 286, 304, 305, 307	55–85	267, 286, 304, 307	60–190	266, 269, 304
K⁺	55–100	45–100	286, 304, 305, 307	70–90	286, 304, 307	35–60	269, 304
Ca⁺	2.5–3.2	2.5–4.5	286, 307	4.5–8.0	286, 307	3.4–3.8	269, 315
Mg⁺	8.5–9.5	10.8–17.0	307	16.0–20.0	307	8.0	269
Cl⁻	31–62	25–51	266, 304, 305, 307	34–42	266, 304, 307	37–79	266, 269, 304

extracellular space. However, Manery and Hastings[266] stated the belief that the minute structure of this tissue is so complex that it would be "unreasonable to interpret" the data as evidence that brain is made up of a simple mixture of these two spaces.

There is also other evidence that much of the chloride of brain is intracellular. By long perfusion of a cat with Ringer-Locke solution, made up with an equivalent concentration of sulfate replacing the chloride, Amberson et al.[267] reduced the concentration of chloride in many of the tissues to extremely low values. Most of the chloride of tissues such as red cells, skeletal muscle, liver and kidney was found to be diffusible, and the concentration of chloride in the tissue varied with the concentration in the plasma. On the other hand, the chloride of the central nervous system (cerebrum, cerebellum and spinal cord) was retained. In further experiments Oster and Amberson[268] found that electrodialysis removed the chloride from brain tissue more slowly and less completely than from skeletal muscle. These two observations are consistent with the view that much of the brain chloride is intracellular.

Peripheral Nerve.—Fenn et al.[269] studied the electrolytes of frog, lobster and crab nerves. They suggested that the electrolytes may be divided between a "potassium space," probably inside the nerve fibers and a "sodium-chloride space," probably outside the fibers. Table VI,

TABLE VI

Probable Electrolyte Distribution in Frog Nerve
(*m-moles per 100 g. nerve or 100 ml. plasma*)
Data from Fenn, Cobb, Hegnauer and Marsh[269]

	Nerve	*Plasma*	*Nerve*	
			NaCl–Space	*K–Space*
Na	6.20	10.38	5.19	1.01
K	4.80	0.25	0.13	4.67
NH_4	0.19	—	—	0.19
Ca	0.36	0.20	0.10	0.26
Mg	0.80	0.30	0.15	0.65
Cl	3.70	7.43	3.7	0
PO_4	1.0	0.31	0.15	0.85
Lactate	0.80	0.80	0.40	0.40
HCO_3	1.08	2.54	1.27	0
S	0.35	—	—	0.35
H_2O	75	96	48	27
Cation equivalents	13.51	11.63	5.81	7.69
Anion equivalents	7.93	11.39	5.69	2.45

taken from their paper, shows the assumed distribution of electrolytes in frog nerve. The figures in the first two columns were obtained by direct measurement and those in the third column, the "sodium-chloride space," were derived by calculation on the assumption that this space contains 48 ml. of the 75 ml. water present in 100 g. of nerve and that the electrolytes in this space have the same concentration as in the plasma. The figure of 48 ml. was arbitarily chosen so that this space would contain all of the chloride in the nerve. The figures in the last column, the "potassium space," were obtained by subtracting the figures of the third column from the corresponding figures of the first column. As the authors state, this arbitary division of the nerve into two spaces is probably an undue simplification.

It can be seen from Table VI that, if the assumption of Fenn *et al.*[269] were true, the "sodium-chloride space" would contain nearly 85% of the sodium of the nerve, but much less of the calcium and magnesium and hardly any of the potassium. Much of the calcium, magnesium and potassium would be in the "potassium space." Bear and Schmitt[270] showed that the extruded axoplasm of the giant axon of the squid, which is pure intracellular material, contains a high concentration of potassium, thus confirming, in general terms, the theory of Fenn *et al.*[269] However, Bear and Schmitt[270] reported that the axoplasm of squid nerve also contains considerable chloride, showing that, for squid nerve at any rate, by no means all of the chloride is extracellular. This observation was confirmed by Steinbach.[271] Findings similar to those of Bear and Schmitt[270] were reported by Webb and Young,[272] who also investigated the electrolytes of squid nerve.

Anion Deficit.—If the equivalent concentration of cations and anions are added separately in the first four columns of Table VI, an important fact is revealed. In the plasma and in the "sodium-chloride space" the cations are slightly in excess of the anions, the difference being probably due to the presence of protein. In the whole nerve, however, the excess of cation over anion is great, the anion deficit being almost entirely in the "potassium space." Fenn *et al.*[269] suggested that much of the potassium is combined with some large indiffusible organic anion.

A similar anion deficit occurs in the axoplasm of squid nerve,[270,272] in lobster nerve,[273] and also in mammalian brain.[274] Silber,[275] Lewis[276] and Deffner and Hafter[277] showed that a part of the deficit in invertebrate nerve is made up by amino acids, notably aspartic acid, glutamic acid and taurine. Of particular interest is the finding of Koechlin[278] that a new substance isethionic acid (2-hydroxyethanesulfonic acid) is important in this regard in squid nerve. Tallan[279] showed that in mammalian brain a considerable part of the deficit is made up by N-acetyl-L-aspartic acid. Cystathionine also occurs in quite high concentrations in human brain.[280]

Despite these findings, however, a considerable portion of the anion deficit is still to be explained. In addition to the substances already mentioned, proteins, acid mucopolysaccharides and lipids have been suggested as additional sources of anion in tissue from the nervous system. The contribution of proteins in this regard is obvious. Recently the role of acid mucopolysaccharide has received some support, for Abood and Abul-Haj[197] isolated hyaluronic acid from frog nerve and provided evidence that it could bind K+.

The role of lipids in binding cation also is of considerable interest. Thudichum[1,2] observed that many lipid preparations contain inorganic cations. Koch and Pike[281] confirmed this observation and they suggested that phosphatides, especially "cephalins," might be important in the binding of cations. Subsequently Chargaff and Ziff[282] and Christensen and Hastings[283] reported that "cephalin," but neither phosphatidyl choline nor sphingomyelin, is active in this regard. The work of Folch[39,75] would indicate that both phosphatidyl serine and diphosphoinositide are responsible for this property of crude "cephalin." Phosphatidyl serine,[39] diphosphoinositide[75] and sulfatide[117] were isolated from brain as salts of Na+, K+, Ca++ or Mg++. The role of these acidic lipids in preserving electrolyte balance in the nervous system was the topic of a recent publication by Folch, Lees and Sloane-Stanley.[284]

Quantitative Determination of Minerals

The reported concentration of a number of minerals in gray matter and white matter of brain and in spinal cord and peripheral nerve is presented in Table V. Recently Ames and Nesbett[285] described a method for determining the electrolytes of a very small sample of brain tissue. In the same paper many recent publications on the quantitative determination of brain electrolytes are reviewed. Wender and Hierowski[286] have determined the electrolytes in the developing nervous system of the guinea pig and Aprison et al.[287] described the distribution of electrolytes in six different areas of the rabbit brain.

In addition to the minerals referred to in Table V, the concentration of iron, copper, and manganese in the white matter and the gray matter of the brain was studied by Tingey.[288] On a wet weight basis, iron is fairly evenly distributed between the gray matter and white matter. There is a greater concentration of copper, and a lower concentration of manganese, in gray matter than in white matter.

The technique of emission spectrography offers a more sensitive means of detecting certain elements than does chemical analysis. Scott and Williams[289] described the application of emission spectrography to the detection and determination of minerals in biological material.

They reported that there is a greater concentration of magnesium and phosphorus in white matter of the brain than in gray matter. These results were extended by Alexander and Myerson,[290] who reported that, on a wet weight basis, the concentration of sodium, potassium, copper, iron, calcium, magnesium and manganese in the white matter of the brain differs little from that in the gray matter, but that there is much more phosphorus in the white matter.

Microincineration

Gross chemical methods and methods of emission spectrography are of limited value, for they do not give any indication of the distribution of minerals within the nerve cell, or in the different parts of the nerve fiber. The technique of microincineration (see Scott[291] for references) has been remarkably successful in this respect. Scott[292] and Alexander and Myerson[293] reported that, in the nerve cells of the spinal cord, the greater part of the ash is concentrated in the nucleolus. For the most part, the remainder of the nucleus is free from ash, although the empty space of the nucleus is crossed with some ash-containing thread-like bands, which connect with the nucleolus. The ash of the cytoplasm appears to have a distribution similar to that of the Nissl granules, suggesting that the distribution of ash within the nerve cell is similar to the distribution of ribonucleic acid.

REFERENCES

1. THUDICHUM, J. L. W.: *A Treatise on the Chemical Constitution of the Brain.* London, Balliere, Tindall & Cox (1884).

2. THUDICHUM, J. L. W.: *Die Chemische Konstitution des Gehirns des Menschen und der Tiere.* Tübingen, Pietzcker (1901).

3. PAGE, I. H.: *Chemistry of the Brain.* Springfield, Ill., Thomas (1937).

4. GERARD, R. W.: *Physiol. Rev., 12:*469 (1932).

5. FOLCH, J. and LEBARON, F. N.: In *Metabolism of the Nervous System*, p. 67. Ed. D. Richter. London, Pergamon Press (1957).

6. McILWAIN, H.: *Biochemistry and the Central Nervous System*, 2nd Ed. London, Churchill (1959).

7. LEBARON, F. N.: *Ann. Rev. Biochem., 28:*579 (1959).

8. BLOOR, W. R.: *Biochemistry of the Fatty Acids.* New York, Reinhold (1943).

9. LEBARON, F. N., and FOLCH, J.: *Physiol. Rev., 37:*539 (1957).

10. HANAHAN, D. J.: *Lipide Chemistry.* New York, John Wiley & Sons (1960).

11. WITTCOFF, H.: *The Phosphatides.* New York, Reinhold (1951).

12. ROSSITER, R. J. and STRICKLAND, K. P.: In *Lipide Metabolism*, p. 69. Ed. K. Bloch. New York, John Wiley & Sons (1960).

13. FOLCH, J. and LEBARON, F. N.: *Canad. J. Biochem. Physiol., 34:*305 (1956).

14. FOLCH, J. and LEBARON, F. N.: In Symposium III. *Biochemistry of the Central Nervous System*, p. 157. Ed. F. Brücke. London, Pergamon Press (1959).

15. CARTER, H. E., GALANOS, D. S. and FUJINO, Y.: *Canad. J. Biochem. Physiol.*, *34*:320 (1956).

16. CARTER, H. E., GALANOS, D. S., GIGG, R. H., LAW, J. H., NAKAYAMA, T., SMITH, D. B. and WEBER, E. J.: *Federation Proc.*, *16*:817 (1957).

17. FOLCH, J.: *J. Biol. Chem.*, *146*:35 (1942).

18. FOLCH, J.: *J. Biol. Chem.*, *177*:497 (1949).

19. CHIBNALL, A. C. and CHANNON, H. J.: *Biochem. J.*, *23*:176 (1929).

20. Hokin, L. E. and Hokin, M. R.: *J. Biol. Chem.*, *233*:800 (1958).

21. BAER, E.: *J. Biol. Chem.*, *189*:235 (1951).

22. BAER, E. and KATES, M.: *J. Am. Chem. Soc.*, *70*:1394 (1948); *72*:942 (1950).

23. BAER, E., BUCHNEA, D. and NEWCOMBE, A. G.: *J. Am. Chem. Soc.*, *78*:232 (1956).

24. BAER, E. and BUCHNEA, D.: *Canad. J. Biochem. Physiol.*, *37*:953 (1959).

25. BAER, E., MAURUKAS, J. and RUSSELL, M.: *Science*, *113*:12 (1951).

26. BAER, E. and MAURUKAS, J.: *J. Biol. Chem.*, *212*:25,39 (1955).

27. BAER, E. and KATES, M.: *J. Biol. Chem.*, *175*:79 (1948); *185*:615 (1950).

28. BAER, E., STANCER, H. C. and KORMAN, I. A.: *J. Biol. Chem.*, *200*:251 (1953).

29. TATTRIE, N. H. and McARTHUR, C. S.: *Canad. J. Biochem. Physiol.*, *35*:1165 (1957).

30. LEVENE, P. A. and ROLF, I. P.: *J. Biol. Chem.*, *72*:587 (1927).

31. PANGBORN, M. C.: *J. Biol. Chem.* *188*:471 (1951).

32. THANNHAUSER, S. J., and BONCODDO, N. F.: *J. Biol Chem.*, *172*:135 (1948).

33. HANAHAN, D. J. and JAYKO, M. E.: *J. Am. Chem. Soc.*, *74*:5070 (1952).

34. HANAHAN, D. J.: *J. Biol. Chem.*, *211*:313 (1954).

34a. THOMPSON, R. H. S., NIEMIRO, R. and WEBSTER, G. R.: *Biochim. Biophys. Acta*, *43*:142 (1960).

34b. PAPADOPOULOS, N. M., CEVALLOS, W. and HESS, W. C.: *Arch. Neurol.*, *3*:677 (1960).

35. TATTRIE, N. H.: *J. Lipid. Res.*, *1*:60 (1959).

36. HANAHAN, D. J., BOCKEROFF, H. and BARRON, E. J.: *J. Biol. Chem.*, *235*:1917 (1960).

37. KLENK, E. and BÖHM, P.: *Ztschr. physiol. Chem.*, *288*:98 (1951).

38. DEBUCH, H.: *Ztschr. physiol. Chem.*, *304*:109 (1956).

39. FOLCH, J.: *J. Biol. Chem.*, *174*:439 (1948).

40. MARINETTI, G. V., ERBLAND, J. and STOTZ, E.: *Biochim. Biophys. Acta*, *30*:41 (1958).

41. WESTLEY, J., WREN, J. J. and MITCHELL, H. K.: *J. Biol. Chem.*, *187*:643 (1957).

42. WREN, J. J.: *Nature*, *185*:295 (1960).

43. FEULGEN, R. and ROSSENBECK, H.: *Ztschr. physiol. Chem.*, *135*:203 (1924).

44. FEULGEN, R., IMHÄUSER, K. and BEHRENS, M.: *Ztschr. physiol. Chem.*, *180*:161 (1929).

45. ANCHEL, M. and WAELSCH, H.: *J. Biol. Chem.*, *145*:605 (1942).

46. KLENK, E. and SCHUMANN, E.: *Ztschr. physiol. Chem.*, *281*:25 (1944).

47. THANNHAUSER, S. J., BONCODDO, N. F. and SCHMIDT, G.: *J. Biol. Chem.*, *188*:417 (1951).

48. SCHMIDT, G., OTTENSTEIN, B. and BESSMAN, M. J.: *Federation Proc.*, *12*:265 (1953).

49. BAER, E and STANCER, H. C.: *J. Am. Chem. Soc.*, *75*:4510 (1953).

50. KLENK, E. and DEBUCH, H.: *Ztschr. physiol. Chem.*, *296*:179 (1954).

51. KLENK, E. and DEBUCH, H.: *Ztschr. physiol. Chem.*, *299*:66 (1955).

52. RAPPORT, M. M., LERNER, B. ALONZO, N. and FRANZL, R.: *J. Biol. Chem.*, *225*:859 (1957).

53. RAPPORT, M. M. and FRANZL, R. E.: *J. Neurochem., 1*:303 (1957).
54. DEBUCH, H.: *J. Neurochem., 2*:243 (1958).
55. DEBUCH, H.: *Ztschr physiol. Chem., 311*:266 (1958).
56. GRAY, G. M.: *Biochem, J., 70*:425 (1958).
57. BLIETZ, R. J.: *Ztschr. physiol. Chem., 310*:120 (1958).
58. MARINETTI, G. V., ERBLAND, J. and STOTZ, E.: *J. Am. Chem. Soc., 80*:1624 (1958).
59. MARINETTI, G. V., ERBLAND, J. and STOTZ, E.: *J. Am. Chem. Soc., 81*:861 (1959).
60. MARINETTI, G. V., ERBLAND, J. and STOTZ, E.: *Biochim, Biophys. Acta, 33*:403 (1959).
61. DEBUCH, H.: *Ztschr. physiol. Chem., 314*:49 (1959).
62. ANSELL, G. B. and NORMAN, J. M.: *J. Neurochem., 1*:32 (1956).
63. DAWSON, R. M. C.: *Biochem, J., 75*:45 (1960).
63a. KLENK, E., DEBUCH, H. and DAUN, H.: *Ztschr. physiol. Chem., 292*:241 (1953).
63b. WEBSTER, G. R.: *Biochim. Biophys. Acta, 44*:109 (1960).
64. BERGMANN, H. and LIEBRECHT, E. M.: *Ztschr. physiol. Chem., 312*:51 (1958).
65. THIELE, O. W.: *Ztschr. physiol. Chem., 315*:117 (1959).
66. THIELE, O. W.: *Ztschr. physiol. Chem., 316*:137 (1959).
67. BRANTE, G.: *Acta physiol. scandinav.* (supp. 63), *18*:1 (1949).
68. DAWSON, R. M. C.: *Biochem. J., 56*:621 (1954).
69. WEISS, B.: *J. Biol. Chem., 223*:523 (1956).
70. EDGAR, G. W. F. and SMITS, G.: *J. Neurochem., 3*:316 (1959).
71. ANSELL, G. B. and SPANNER, S.: *Biochem. J., 79*:176 (1961).
72. CARTER, H. E., SMITH, D. B. and JONES, D. N.: *J. Biol. Chem., 232*:681 (1958).
73. SVENNERHOLM, J. and THORIN, H.: *Biochim. Biophys. Acta, 41*:371 (1960).
74. FOLCH, J. and WOOLLEY, D. W.: *J. Biol. Chem., 142*:963 (1942).
75. FOLCH, J.: *J. Biol. Chem., 177*:505 (1949).
76. HÖRHAMMER, L., WAGNER, H. and RICHTER, G.: *Biochem. Z., 331*:155 (1959).
77. HÖRHAMMER, L., WAGNER, H. and HÖLZL, J.: *Biochem. Z., 332*:269 (1960).
78. GRADO, C. and BALLOU, C. E.: *J. Biol. Chem., 236*:54 (1961).
79. ELLIS, R. B., KEMP, P. and HAWTHORNE, J. N.: *Biochem. J., 76*:43P (1960).
80. DITTMER, J. C. and DAWSON, R. M. C.: *Biochem. J., 81*:535 (1961).
81. HÖRHAMMER, L., WAGNER, H., and RICHTER, G.: *Biochem. Z., 330*:591 (1958).
82. HOKIN, L. E. and HOKIN, M. R.: *J. Biol. Chem., 233*:818 (1958).
83. STRICKLAND, K. P., THOMPSON, W., SUBRAHMANYAM, D. and ROSSITER, R. J.: *Biochem. J., 76*:41P (1960).
84. THOMPSON, W., SUBRAHMANYAM, D. and STRICKLAND, K. P.: *Federation Proc., 19*:234 (1960).
84a. TOMLINSON, R. V. and BALLOU, C. E.: *J. Biol. Chem., 236*:1902 (1961).
84b. BROCKERHOFF, H. and BALLOU, C. E.: *J. Biol. Chem., 236*:1907 (1961).
85. CARTER, H. E., HAINES, W. J., LEDYARD, W. E. and NORRIS, W. P.: *J. Biol. Chem., 169*:77 (1947).
86. THIERFELDER, H. and KLENK, E.: *Die Chemie der Cerebroside und Phosphatide.* Berlin (1930).
87. BRADY, R. O. and BURTON, R. M.: *J. Neurochem., 1*:18 (1956).
88. KISS, J., FODOR, G., and BÁNFI, D.: *Helvet. chim. acta, 37*:1471 (1954).
89. CARTER, H. E. and NORRIS, W. P.: *J. Biol. Chem., 145*:709 (1942).
90. SWEELEY, C. C. and MOSCATELLI, E. A.: *J. Lipid Res., 1*:40 (1959).
91. THANNHAUSER, S. J., BENOTTI, J. and BONCODDO, N. F.: *J. Biol. Chem., 166*:677 (1946).
92. RAPPORT, M. M. and LERNER, B.: *J. Biol. Chem., 232*:63 (1958).
93. FUJINO, Y. and NEGISHI, T.: *Nature, 184*:817 (1959).

94. ROUSER, G., BERRY, J. F., MARINETTI, G. V. and STOTZ, E.: *J. Am. Chem. Soc.*, *75*:310, 313 (1953).

95. SHAPIRO, D., FLOWERS, H. M. and SPECTOR-SHEFER, S.: *J. Am. Chem. Soc.*, *80*:2339 (1958).

96. KLENK, E.: *Ztschr. physiol. Chem.*, *235*:24 (1935).

97. THANNHAUSER, S. J. and SCHMIDT, G.: *Physiol. Rev.*, *26*:275 (1946).

98. CUMINGS, J. N., Ed.: *Cerebral Lipidoses*. Oxford, Blackwell Scientific Publications (1957).

99. THIERFELDER, H.: *Ztschr. physiol. Chem.*, *43*:21 (1904).

100. KLENK, E.: *Ztschr. physiol. Chem.*, *157*:291 (1926).

101. KLENK, E. and HÄRLE, R.: *Ztschr. physiol. Chem.*, *189*:243 (1930).

102. FOLCH-PI, J. and SPERRY, W. M.: *Ann. Rev. Biochem.*, *17*:147 (1948).

103. CHARGAFF, E., LEVINE, C. and GREEN, C.: *J. Biol. Chem.*, *175*:67 (1948).

104. HSIEN-GIEH, S., FAUST, C. E. and WILLIAMS, H. H.: *Federation Proc.*, *7*:161 (1948).

105. HALLIDAY, N., DEUEL, H. J., TRAGERMAN, L. J. and WARD, W. E.: *J. Biol. Chem.*, *132*:171 (1940).

106. DANIELSON, I. S., HALL, C. H. and EVERETT, M. R.: *Proc. Soc. Exper. Biol. & Med.*, *49*:569 (1942).

107. KLENK, E. and RENNKAMP, F.: *Ztschr. physiol. Chem.*, *272*:280 (1942).

108. ROSENBERG, A. and CHARGAFF, E.: *J. Biol. Chem.*, *233*:1323 (1958).

109. RADIN, N. S., BROWN, J. R. and LAVIN, F. B.: *J. Biol. Chem.*, *219*:977 (1956).

110. LONG, C. and STAPLES, D. A.: *Biochem. J.*, *73*:7P (1959).

111. CHIBNALL, A. C., PIPER, S. H. and WILLIAMS, E. F.: *Biochem. J.*, *30*:100 (1936).

112. KISHIMOTO, Y. and RADIN, N. S.: *J. Lipid Res.*, *1*:72 (1959).

113. SKIPSKI, V. P., ARFIN, S. M. and RAPPORT, M. M.: *Arch. Biochem.*, *82*:487 (1959).

114. CARTER, H. E. and GREENWOOD, F. L.: *J. Biol. Chem.*, *199*:283 (1952).

115. SHAPIRO, D. and FLOWERS, H. M.: *J. Am. Chem. Soc.*, *81*:2023 (1959).

116. FOLCH, J. and LEES, M.: *J. Biol. Chem.*, *191*:807 (1951).

117. BLIX, G.: *Ztschr. physiol. Chem.*, *219*:82 (1933).

118. THANNHAUSER, S. J., FELLIG, J. and SCHMIDT, G.: *J. Biol. Chem.*, *215*:211 (1955).

119. RADIN, N. S., MARTIN, F. B. and BROWN, J. R.: *J Biol. Chem.*, *224*:499 (1957).

120. LEES, M., FOLCH, J., SLOANE-STANLEY, G. H. and CARR, S.: *J. Neurochem.*, *4*:9 (1959).

121. JATZKEWITZ, H.: *Ztschr. physiol. Chem.*, *311*:279 (1958).

121a. AUSTIN, J. H.: *Neurology*, *10*:470 (1960).

121b. NORMAN, R. M., URICH, H. and TINGEY, A. H.: *Brain*, *83*:369 (1960).

122. ROSENBERG, A., HOWE, C. and CHARGAFF, E.: *Nature*, *177*:234 (1956).

123. BLIX, G.: *Skandinav. Arch. Physiol.*, *80*:46 (1938).

124. KLENK, E.: *Ztschr. physiol. Chem.*, *268*:50 (1941).

125. BLIX, G., GOTTSCHALK, A. and KLENK, E.: *Nature*, *179*:1088 (1957).

126. GOTTSCHALK, A.: *Yale J. Biol. Med.*, *28*:525 (1956).

127. GOTTSCHALK, A.: *The Chemistry and Biology of Sialic Acids and Related Substances*. Cambridge, Cambridge University Press (1960).

128. CORNFORTH, J. W., FIRTH, M. E. and GOTTSCHALK, A.: *Biochem. J.*, *68*:57 (1958).

129. CARROLL, P. M. and CORNFORTH, J. W.: *Biochim. Biophys. Acta*, *39*:161 (1960).

130. COMB, D. G. and ROSEMAN, S.: *J. Biol. Chem.*, *235*:2529 (1960).

131. LONG, C. and STAPLES, D. A.: *Biochem. J.*, *73*:385 (1959).

132. WARREN, L.: *J. Biol. Chem.*, *234*:1971 (1959).

133. LANDSTEINER, K. and LEVINE, P. A.: *J. Immunol.*, *10*:731 (1925).

134. LANDSTEINER, K. and LEVINE, P. A.: *Proc. Soc. Exper. Biol. & Med., 23*:343 (1926).
135. WALZ, E.: *Ztschr. physiol. Chem., 166*:210 (1927).
136. BLIX, G.: *Skandinav. Arch. Physiol., 80*:46 (1938).
137. KLENK, E.: *Ztschr. physiol. Chem., 273*:76 (1942).
138. KLENK, E.: *Ztschr. physiol. Chem., 288*:216 (1951).
139. BLIX, G., SVENNERHOLM, L. and WERNER, I.: *Acta chem. scandinav., 6*:358 (1952).
140. SVENNERHOLM, L.: *Acta chem. scandinav., 8*:1108 (1954).
141. SVENNERHOLM, L.: *Acta chem. scandinav., 9*:1033 (1955).
142. SVENNERHOLM, L.: *Acta chem. scandinav., 10*:694 (1956).
143. SVENNERHOLM, L.: *Nature, 177*:524 (1956).
144. KLENK, E. and SCHUMANN, E.: *Ztschr. physiol. Chem., 267*:128 (1940).
145. CUMINGS, J. N.: In *Cerebral Lipidoses*, p. 112. Ed. J. N. Cumings. Oxford, Blackwell Scientific Publications (1957).
146. TINGEY, A.: *J. Neurochem., 3*:230 (1959).
147. FOLCH, J., ARSOVE, S. and MEATH, J. A.: *J. Biol. Chem., 191*:819 (1951).
148. CHATAGNON, C. and CHATAGNON, P.: *Bull. Soc. chim. biol., 36*:373 (1954).
149. FOLCH, J., MEATH, J. A. and BOGOCH, S.: *Federation Proc., 15*:254 (1956).
150. ROSENBERG, A. and CHARGAFF, E.: *J. Biol. Chem., 232*:1031 (1958).
151. MELTZER, H. L.: *J. Biol. Chem., 233*:1327 (1958).
151a. WEICKER, H., DAIN, J. A., SCHMIDT, G. and THANNHAUSER, S. J.: *Federation Proc., 19*:219 (1960).
152. BOGOCH, S., *Biochem. J., 68*:319 (1958).
153. KLENK, E. and GIELEN, W.: *Ztschr. physiol. Chem., 319*:283 (1960).
154. GMELIN, L.: *Ztschr. physiol. Chem., 1*:119 (1824). (Cited by Page, 3).
155. ADAMS, C. W. M., and DAVISON, A. N.: *J. Neurochem., 4*:282 (1959).
156. CUMINGS, J. N.: *Brain, 76*:551 (1953).
157. CUMINGS, J. N.: *Brain, 78*:554 (1955).
158. JOHNSON, A. C., McNABB, A. R. and ROSSITER, R. J.: *Biochem. J., 45*:500 (1949).
159. McCAMEN, R. E. and ROBINS, E.: *J. Neurochem., 5*:18 (1959).
160. KONNIKOVA, G. S.: *Ukrain. Biokhim. Zhur., 22*:3 (1950); *C.A. 48*:12828c (1954).
161. LeBARON, F. N. and FOLCH, J.: *J. Neurochem., 4*:1 (1959).
162. WOODWARD, R. B., SANDHEIMER, F., TAUB, D., HEUSLER, K. and McLAMORE, W. M.: *J. Am. Chem. Soc., 74*:4223 (1952).
163. PAGE, I. H. and MÜLLER, E.: *Ztschr. physiol. Chem., 204*:13 (1932).
164. KOCH, E. M. and KOCH, F. C.: *J. Biol. Chem., 116*:757 (1936).
165. ERCOLI, A. and DE RUGGIERI, P.: *J. Am. Chem. Soc., 75*:3284 (1953).
166. FIESER, L. F.: *J. Am. Chem. Soc., 75*:4395 (1953).
167. FIESER, L. F. and BHATTACHARYYA, B. K.: *J. Am. Chem. Soc., 75*:4418 (1953).
168. POLYAKOVA, N. M.: *Doklady Akad. Nauk. S.S.S.R., 93*:321 (1953); *C.A. 48*:2858d (1954).
169. NEDZVETSKII, S. V., PANYUKOV, A. N. and SHPATS, T. A.: *Biokhimiya, 18*:315 (1953); *C.A. 48*:1511i (1954).
170. SILBERMAN, H. and SILBERMAN-MARTYNCEWA, S.: *J. Biol. Chem., 159*:603 (1945).
171. NICHOLAS, H. J., HILTIBRAN, R C. and WADKINS, C. L.: *Arch. Biochem. Biophys., 59*:246 (1955).
172. CHATAGNON, C., MORTREUIL, M., ZALTA, J. P. and CHATAGNON, P.: *Bull. Soc. chim. biol., 35*:419 (1953).
173. FOLCH, J., WEBSTER, G. R. and LEES, M.: *Federation Proc., 18*:228 (1959).
174. FOLCH, J. and LeBARON, F. N.: *Federation Proc., 12*:203 (1953).
175. LeBARON, F. N. and FOLCH, J.: *J. Neurochem., 1*:101 (1956).

176. LeBaron, F. N. and Rothleder, E. E.: *Proc. IVth Internat. Cong. Biochem. Vienna*, p. 206 (1958).

177. Huggins, C. G. and Cohn, D. V.: *J. Biol. Chem., 234*:257 (1959).

178. Baer, E., Maurukas, J. and Clark, D. D.: *J. Biol. Chem., 228*:181 (1957).

179. Dawson, R. M. C. and Dittmer, J. C.: *Biochem. J., 81*:540 (1961).

180. Klenk, E. and Montag, W.: *J. Neurochem., 2*:226 (1958).

181. Klenk, E. and Montag, W.: *J. Neurochem., 2*:233 (1958).

182. Klenk, E.: In Sympossium III. *Biochemistry of the Central Nervous System*, p. 146. Ed. F. Brücke. London, Pergamon Press (1959).

183. Johnston, P. V. and Kummerow, F. A.: *Proc. Soc. Exper. Biol. & Med., 104*:201 (1960).

184. Klenk, E.: *Ztschr. physiol. Chem., 153*:74 (1926).

185. Nieman, C.: *J. Am. Chem. Soc., 63*:3535 (1941).

186. Collins, F. D.: *Biochem. J., 72*:281 (1959).

187. Collins, F. D.: *Biochem. J., 72*:532 (1959).

188. McColl, J. D. and Rossiter, R. J.: *J. Exper. Biol., 29*:196, 203 (1952).

189. Lanfranchi, E.: *Arch. disc. biol., 24*:120 (1938).

190. Patterson, E. K., Dumm, M. E., and Richards, A. G.: *Arch. Biochem., 7*:201 (1945).

191. McColl, J. D. and Rossiter, R. J.: *J. Exper. Biol., 28*:116 (1951).

192. Grave, C.: Unpublished thesis (1941).

193. McColl, J. D., and Rossiter, R. J.: *J. Cell & Comp. Physiol., 36*:241, (1950).

194. Brante, G.: In *Biochemistry of Developing Nervous System*, p. 153. Ed. H. Waelsch. New York, Academic Press (1955).

195. Brante, G.: In *Metabolism of the Nervous System*, p. 112. Ed. D. Richter. London, Pergamon Press (1957).

196. Brante, G.: In Symposium III. *Biochemistry of the Nervous System*, p. 291. Ed. F. Brücke. London, Pergamon Press (1959).

197. Abood, L. G. and Abul-Haj, S. K.: *J. Neurochem., 1*:119 (1956).

198. Bairati, A.: *Experientia, 9*:461 (1953).

199. Hess, A.: *J. Comp. Neurol., 98*:69 (1953).

200. Freedman, B.: *Anat. Rec., 115*:265 (1953).

201. Eayrs, J. T.: In *Biochemistry of Developing Nervous System*, p. 443, Ed. H. Waelsch. New York, Academic Press (1954).

202. Diezel, P. B.: In *Cerebral Lipidoses*, p. 11. Ed. J. N. Cumings. Oxford, Blackwell Scientific Publications (1957).

203. Uzman, L. L.: *Arch. Path., 60*:308 (1955).

204. Brante, G.: In *Cerebral Lipidoses*, p. 164. Ed. J. N. Cumings. Oxford, Blackwell Scientific Publications (1957).

205. Wolman, M.: *J. Neurochem., 1*:370 (1957).

206. Richter, D.: *Brit. Med. J., 1*:1255 (1959).

207. Palladin, A. V. and Goryukhina, T. A.: *Fiziol Zhur., 33*:727 (1947); C. A. *44*:8976f (1950).

208. Nakamura, S., Hayashi, Y. and Tanaka, K.: *J. Biochem. (Japan), 41*:13 1954).

209. Polyakova, N. M. and Gotovtseva, O. P.: *Ukrain. Biokhim. Zhur., 29*:400 (1957); C. A. *52*:8256b (1958).

210. Halliburton, W. D.: *J. Physiol., 15*:90 (1894).

211. McGregor, H. H.: *J. Biol. Chem., 28*:403 (1917).

212. Dingman, W., Sporn, M. B. and Davies, R. K.: *J. Neurochem., 4*:154 (1959).

213. Palladin, A. V.: In *Metabolism of the Nervous System*, p. 456. Ed. D. Richter. London, Pergamon Press (1957).

214. PALLADIN, A. V. and POLYAKOVA, N. M.: In Symposium III. *Biochemistry of the Central Nervous System*, p. 185. Ed. F . Brücke. London, Pergamon Press (1959).
215. ROBERTSON, D. M.: *J. Neurochem., 1*:358 (1957).
216. LOWENTHAL, A., KARCHER, D. and VAN SANDE, M.: *Exper. Neurol., 1*:233 (1959).
217. ROBERTSON, D. M.: *J. Neurochem., 5*:145 (1960).
218. KARCHER, D., VAN SANDE, M. and LOWENTHAL, A.: *J. Neurochem., 4*:135 (1959).
219. KIYOTA, K.: *J. Neurochem., 4*:209 (1959).
220. POLYAKOVA, N. M.: *Doklady Akad. Nauk. S.S.S.R., 109*:1174 (1956); C. A. *51*:5238b (1957).
221. MISSERE, G., TONINI, G. and DE RISIO, C.: *Boll. soc. ital. biol. sper., 33*:491 (1957).
222. POLYAKOVA, N. M. and KABAK, K. S.: *Doklady Akad. Nauk. S.S.S.R., 122*:275 (1958); C. A., *53*:537b (1959).
223. DEUTICKE, H. J., HÖVELS, O. and LAUENSTEIN, K.: *Pflüger's Arch. ges. Physiol., 255*:46 (1952).
224. LI, T. P. and SHENG, P. K.: *Acta physiol. Sinica, 21*:292 (1957).
225. NEDZVETSKII, S. V. and RATNITSKAYA, S. S.: *Biokhimiya, 19*:677 (1954); C. A. *49*:6418e (1955).
226. PORTER, H. and FOLCH, J.: *Arch. Neurol. & Psychiat., 77*:8 (1957).
227. PORTER, H. and FOLCH, J.: *J. Neurochem., 1*:260 (1957).
228. PORTER, H. and AINSWORTH, S.: *J. Neurochem., 5*:91 (1959).
229. PORTER, H. and AINSWORTH, S.: *Proc. Soc. Exper. Biol. & Med., 98*:277 (1958).
230. ROBOZ, E. HENDERSON, N. and KIES, M. W.: *J. Neurochem., 2*:254 (1958).
231. KIES, M. W., ABOOD, E. C. and ROBOZ, E.: *J. Neurochem., 2*:261 (1958).
232. MAXFIELD, M.: *J. Gen. Physiol., 37*:201 (1953).
233. MAXFIELD, M. and HARTLEY, R. W.: *Biochim. Biophys. Acta, 24*:83 (1957).
234. DAVISON, P. F. and TAYLOR, E. W.: *J. Gen. Physiol., 43*:801 (1960).
235. MAXFIELD, M.: *J. Gen. Physiol., 34*:853 (1951).
236. KOECHLIN, B. A. and PARISH, H. D.: *J. Biol. Chem., 205*:597 (1953).
237. FOLCH, J. and UZMAN, L. L.: *Federation Proc., 7*:155 (1948).
238. CLOUET, D. H. and GAITONDE, M. K.: *J. Neurochem., 1*:126 (1956).
239. UZMAN, L. L.: *Arch. Biochem. Biophys., 76*:474 (1958).
240. UZMAN, L. L. and ROSEN, H.: *Arch. Biochem. Biophys., 76*:490 (1958).
241. EWALD, A. and KÜHNE, W.: (1877). Cited by Page, I. H.[3]
242. KÜHNE, W. and CHITTENDEN, R. H.: *Ztschr. Biol., 26*:291 (1889).
243. BLOCK, R. J.: *J. Biol. Chem., 94*:647 (1932).
244. STARY, Z. and ARAT, F.: *Biochem. Z., 329*:11 (1957).
245. KOENIG, H.: *J. Neurochem., 4*:93 (1959).
246. FINEAN, J. B., HAWTHORNE, J. N. and PATTERSON, J. D. E.: *J. Neurochem., 1*:256 (1957).
247. FOLCH, J., LEES, M. and CARR, S.: *Exper. Cell. Research*, Supp. 5, p. 58 (1958).
248. SCHMIDT, G. and THANNHAUSER, S. J.: *J. Biol. Chem., 161*:83 (1945).
249. FOLCH, J. and LEBARON, F. N.: *Federation Proc., 10*:183 (1951).
250. LOGAN, J. E., MANNELL, W. A. and ROSSITER, R. J.: *Biochem. J., 51*:470 (1952).
251. SCHNEIDER, W. C.: *J. Biol. Chem., 161*:293 (1945).
252. HAMMARSTEN, E.: *Acta med. scandinav.*, Supp. 196, *128*:634 (1947).
253. HEALD, P. J.: *Biochem. J. 73*:132 (1959).
254. HEALD, P. J.: *Biochem. J., 78*:340 (1961).
255. ENGELHARDT, V. A. and LISSOVSKAIA, N. P.: *Communications of the XIX Internat. Physiol. Cong.* Academy of Sciences, U.S.S.R., Moscow, p. 207 (1953).

256. VALIDIMIROV, G. E., IVANOVA, T. N. and PRAVDINA, N. I.: *Biokhimiya, 21*:155 (1956); C. A., *50*:10149b (1956).

257. FINDLAY, M., STRICKLAND, K. P. and ROSSITER, R. J.: *Canad. J. Biochem. Physiol., 32*:504 (1954).

258. MAGEE, W. L. and ROSSITER, R. J.: *Biochem. J., 58*:243 (1954).

259. LEVENE, P. A.: *Arch. Neurol. Psychopathol., 2*:3 (1899).

260. SCHMITT, F. O. and BEAR, R. S.: *Proc. Soc. Exper. Biol. & Med., 32*:943 (1935).

261. BEAR, R. S., SCHMITT, F. O. and YOUNG, J. Z.: *Proc. Roy. Soc. London, B., 123*:520 (1937).

262. LEVENE, P. A.: *J. Med. Research, 10*:204 (1903).

263. EMANUEL, C. F. and CHAIKOFF, I. L.: *J. Neurochem., 5*:236 (1960).

264. OVERTON, E.: *Pflüger's Arch. ges. Physiol., 92*:346 (1902).

265. PETERS, J. P.: *Body Water.* Springfield, Ill., Thomas (1935).

266. MANERY, J. F. and HASTINGS, A. B.: *J. Biol. Chem., 127*:657 (1939).

267. AMBERSON, W. R., NASH, T. P., MULDER, A. G. and BINNS, D.: *Am. J. Physiol., 122*:224 (1938).

268. OSTER, R. H. and AMBERSON, W. R.: *J. Biol. Chem, 131*:19 (1939).

269. FENN, W. O., COBB, D. M., HEGNAUER, A. H. and MARSH, B. S.: *Am. J. Physiol., 110*:74 (1934).

270. BEAR, R. S. and SCHMITT, F. O.: *J. Cell. & Comp. Physiol., 14*:205 (1939).

271. STEINBACH, H. B.: *J. Cell. & Comp. Physiol., 17*:55 (1941).

272. WEBB, D. A. and YOUNG, J. Z.: *J. Physiol., 98*:299 (1940).

273. SCHMITT, F. O., BEAR, R. S. and SILBER, R. H.: *J. Cell. & Comp. Physiol., 14*:351 (1939).

274. MANERY, J. F.: In *The Biology of Mental Health and Disease,* Chap. 10. New York, P. B. Hoeber (1952).

275. SILBER, R. H.: *J. Cell & Comp. Physiol., 18*:21 (1941).

276. LEWIS, P. R.: *Biochem. J., 52*:330 (1952).

277. DEFFNER, G. G. J. and HAFTER, R. E.: *Biochim. Biophys. Acta, 42*:200 (1960).

278. KOECHLIN. B. A.: *J. Biophys. Biochem. Cytol., 1*:511 (1955).

279. TALLAN, H. H.: *J. Biol. Chem., 244*:41 (1957).

280. TALLAN, H. H., MOORE, S. and STEIN, W. H.: *J. Biol. Chem., 230*:707 (1958).

281. KOCH, W. and PIKE, F. H.: *J. Pharmacol. & Exper. Therap., 2*:245 (1910).

282. CHARGAFF, E. and ZIFF, M.: *J. Biol. Chem., 131*:25 (1939).

283. CHRISTENSEN, H. N. and HASTINGS, A. B.: *J. Biol. Chem., 136*:387 (1940).

284. FOLCH, J., LEES, M. and SLOANE-STANLEY, G. H.: In *Metabolism of the Nervous System,* p. 174. Ed. D. Richter. London, Pergamon Press (1957).

285. AMES, A. and NESBETT, F. B.: *J. Neurochem., 3*:116 (1958).

286. WENDER, M. and HIEROWSKI, M.: *J. Neurochem., 5*:105 (1960).

287. APRISON, M. H., LUKENBILL, A. and SEGAR, W. E.: *J. Neurochem., 5*:150 (1960).

288. TINGEY, A. H.: *J. Ment. Sc., 83*:425 (1937).

289. SCOTT, G. H. and WILLIAMS, P. S.: *Anat. Rec., 64*:107 (1935).

290. ALEXANDER, L. and MYERSON, A.: *Arch. Neurol. & Psychiat., 39*:131 (1938).

291. SCOTT, G. H.: *Protoplasma, 20*:133 (1933).

292. SCOTT, G. H.: *Am. J. Anat., 53*:243 (1933).

293. ALEXANDER, L. and MYERSON, A.: *Am. J. Path., 13*:405 (1937).

294. JOHNSON, A. C., McNABB, A. R. and ROSSITER, R. J.: *Biochem. J., 43*:573 (1948).

295. JOHNSON, A. C., McNABB, A. R. and ROSSITER, R. J.: *Biochem. J., 44*:494 (1949).

296. JOHNSON, A. C., McNABB, A. R. and ROSSITER, R. J.: *Biochem. J., 43*:578 (1948).

297. RANDALL, L. O.: *J. Biol. Chem., 125*:723 (1938).

298. BODIAN, D. and DZIEWIATKOWSKI, D.: *J. Cell. & Comp. Physiol., 35*:155 (1950).

299. KOCH, W. and MANN, S. A.: *J. Physiol., 36:*36 (1907).
300. RANDALL, L. O.: *J. Biol. Chem., 124:*481 (1938).
301. SAMUELS, A. J., BOYARSKY, L. L., GERARD, R. W., LIBET, B. and BRUST, M.:
     *Am. J. Physiol., 164:*1 (1951).
302. ROBINS, E., EYDT, K. M., and SMITH, D. E.: *J. Biol. Chem., 220:*677 (1956).
303. RAPPORT, M. M. and LERNER, B.: *Biochim. Biophys. Acta, 33:*319 (1959).
304. TUPIKOVA, N. and GERARD, R. W.: *Am. J. Physiol., 119:*414 (1937).
305. STEWART-WALLACE, A. M.: *Brain, 62:*426 (1939).
306. ABDERHALDEN, E. and WEIL, A.: *Ztschr. physiol. Chem., 83:*425 (1913).
307. WEIL, A.: *Ztschr. physiol. Chem., 89:*349 (1914).
308. ABERCROMBIE, M. and JOHNSON, M. L.: *J. Neurol., Neurosurg. & Psychiat., 9:*113
     (1946).
309. ABDERHALDEN, E. and WEIL, A.: *Ztschr. physiol. Chem., 81:*207 (1912).
310. MAY, R. M.: *Bull. Soc. chim. biol., 30:*562 (1948).
311. LOGAN, J. E., MANNELL, W. A. and ROSSITER, R. J.: Unpublished observations.
312. HELLER, I. H. and ELLIOTT, K. A. C.: *Canad. J. Biochem. Physiol., 32:*584
     (1954).
313. KISSANE, J. M. and ROBINS, E.: *J. Biol. Chem., 233:*184 (1958).
314. MAY, L. and GRENELL, R. G.: *Proc. Soc. Exper. Biol. & Med., 102:*235 (1959).
315. TIPTON, S. R.: *Am. J. Physiol., 109:*457 (1934).

III

THE BIOCHEMISTRY OF THE BRAIN DURING EARLY DEVELOPMENT

WARREN M. SPERRY

MANY PAPERS containing information about the biochemistry of the brain during early development have been published since the subject was reviewed for the first edition of this book about a decade ago. Although the present review is restricted for the most part to these recent publications, limitations of space make it impossible to discuss all of them.* it is difficult to compare, correlate, and summarize the findings in this field for several reasons:

(a) The data have been obtained from different animal species; rats, mice, guinea pigs, chicks, rabbits, and humans have been more or less extensively studied, and there are some findings from at least 10 other species.

(b) Many investigators have studied two or more areas or structures of the brain; at the minimum, cortex and white matter, and at the maximum, a large number of areas in a few histochemical studies. Such investigations are much to be desired, but they increase the difficulty of the reviewer's task.

(c) In many papers, the data are reported as percentages of fresh tissue. One of the few facts, established with certainty, and with considerable precision in this field, is a large decrease in the concentration of water in the brain during its early development. The concentration of solids in whole brain nearly doubles and in white matter triples between embryonic and adult life (cf. pp.243-245, 1st Ed., for a detailed discussion). In the face of such large and rapid changes, it is difficult to interpret data based on wet weight, and for this reason, unless otherwise noted, only concentrations based on dry weight will be discussed in this review, in some instances calculated by the author from the original data.

(d) Some investigators have reported their data as amounts per

---

*References are included to all publications known to the author to contain information with a bearing on the subject of this chapter.

brain, others as amounts per unit of total nitrogen concentration, and a few have related their findings to deoxyribonucleic acid and, thence, to amounts of the substances studied per cell.

(e) Although more precise methods than some which have been used in the past (cf. pp.234-235, 1st Ed.) have been applied in this field during the period under review, there are still some analytical uncertainties which cloud the interpretation of the findings.

As in the past, the majority of studies during the period reviewed have been concerned with biochemical morphology, but there has been a gratifying increase in the investigation of enzymes, and modern techniques of biochemistry have been applied in several studies of metabolism during the early development of the brain.

BIOCHEMICAL MORPHOLOGY

Total Lipids.[8,15,16,20,30,45,57,97,107,108,110,123,157,165]—The elegant methods of Folch *et al.*[54,56] for extraction and purification have made possible more precise methods for the determination of total lipids of the brain[156] but other findings of Folch and his colleagues have added new uncertainties: (a) Strandin[53] is largely lost[54,56] during the purification procedures unless special steps are applied to recover it. (b) The discovery of proteolipids[55] raises the moot question as to whether or not the protein part of these complexes should be included in the weight of total lipids. (c) A phosphoinositide peptide is so firmly bound to trypsin-resistant protein that it is not removed by procedures commonly used for the extraction of lipids from brain tissue.[105] Fortunately, the amounts of these substances are relatively small in the adult brain, although little is known about them during early development. With due regard to these uncertainties, and to others which may apply to the total lipid data reported by most investigators, it may be stated with confidence that a large increase in the concentration of total lipids occurs during maturation of the brain in all species which have been studied. For example, increases from 18% in 1-day-old to 36% in 75 to 90-day-old mice, from 28% in 5-day-old to 42% in 40-day-old rats, and from 28.8% in 2-day-old to 50% in 2-year-old rabbits were reported by Folch-Pi,[57] Sperry,[157] and Davison and Wajda,[30] respectively. These data were selected because they were obtained with the best available methods and because the differences among them illustrate the difficulty of correlating the results obtained by different investigators in studies of different animal species.

Cholesterol.[7,22,30,57,63,107,110,123,130,157,161]—During the period of this review, further evidence was supplied for a marked increase in cholesterol concentration during development of the brain. For example, Folch-Pi[57] found 2.1% in 1-day-old and 7.6% in 75 to 90-day-old mice, Mandel and Bieth[107] reported a rise from 2.6% in 2-day-old rats to about 9% in adults, and extensive data of Fukuyama[63] show increases of about two-fold in the medulla, three-fold in the spinal cord, and four-fold in the cerebellum between birth and adulthood in the dog. Mihara,[123] in determinations of cholesterol (and several other lipids) at each month of fetal life in the human from the 4th to term, found about two-fold increases in cerebrum and spinal cord and about a 50% increase in medulla oblongatta to the highest concentration (6%) reported, but the increase in cerebellum was relatively small from (3.2 to 3.6%). In apparent disagreement with the results of most other investigators are the extensive data of Cumings et al.,[22] which show no consistent increase in cholesterol concentration in cerebral cortex of humans from the thirty-fourth week of fetal life to the twelfth year, and of Tingey[161] who also found no increase in human cortex between birth and adulthood.

Cholesterol Esters.—Most of the evidence previously reviewed (p.239, 1st Ed.) indicated that esterified cholesterol is absent from developing brain, as it is known to be from adult brain. In accord with this concept are most of the data obtained by Cumings et al.[22] in analyses of cortex and white matter of human brains through fetal life and infancy, but the findings of Mandel et al. are consistent in showing the presence of fairly large amounts of cholesterol esters in the brains of chick embryos[7,110] and of small amounts in the brains of rats[107] during the first week or two of post-natal life. Adams and Davison[1] also presented evidence, based in part on chromatography, for the presence of a considerable (up to 49%), but highly variable, portion of the cholesterol in esterified form in spinal cord and callosum of human and chick embryos, and of smaller amounts of cholesterol esters in these tissues of humans and in cord and whole brain of chicks during early post-natal life.

Total Phosphatides.[2,7,15,16,20,22,30,37,41,43,57,63,97,110,113,123,157,160,161,165]— Increases in phosphatide concentration in the brain and various parts thereof during maturation have been reported by most investigators in all species studied, but the rise is relatively small (usually about one-fifth to one-fourth in comparison with that of cholesterol, and there are some exceptions; e.g., the data of Cumings et al.[22] show no increase in human cerebral cortex and a rise which is questionable, because of large variations, in white matter between the tenth week of fetal and the twelfth year of post-natal life. Tingey[161] also found no appreciable change in phosphatide concentration in human cortex or white matter between birth and adulthood. Albrecht[2] reported little or no change in the ratio of lipid phosphorus to total nitrogen in mouse brain between birth and the sixth month of life.

Bernhard and Lindlar[6] found the unsaturated fatty acid composition of brain phosphatides to be about the same in 3-day-old and 22-month-old rats, the major components being monoenes (about 63%), tetraenes (about 17%), and hexaenes (about 15%), but Blancher and de Vaux-Saint-Cyr[10] observed a higher proportion of polyene, particularly hexaene, fatty acids in phosphatides of adult human brain than in those of premature infants.

Phosphatidyl Choline (Lecithin).[22,30,63,107,123,130,161]—This phosphatide has been estimated by difference on the basis of choline and sphingomyelin (see below) determinations. As might be expected, the findings are variable and to some extent inconsistent, but the preponderance of evidence indicates that the lecithin concentration does not increase, and may decrease, during development of the brain. At the extreme, Fukuyama[63] reported a decrease from about 8% in newborn to 0.6% in adult dog medulla and somewhat smaller, but still large, decreases in cerebellum and spinal cord. At the other extreme, is the finding by Mihara[123] of large increases in lecithin concentration in some parts of the human brain during fetal life.

Cephalins.[7,22,57,63,110,121,123,130,161]—The evidence concerning this ill-defined group of phosphatides is not conclusive, probably because of analytical difficulties. The majority of the few investigators who have presented data on what they have designated as "cephalin" found an increase in concentration during maturation of the brain, but there are wide variations in the magnitude of the reported rise. Tingey[161] found no change in what he called cephalin A in human white matter (10.5% in infants and 10.4% in adults) and a decrease from 9.4 to 7.8% in cortex. The interpretation of the results is complicated by Brante's[12] cephalin B (see Sphingomyelin).

The components of the cephalin fraction *(phosphatidyl ethanolamine, phosphatidyl serine,* and *phosphoinositide)* remain almost unstudied during maturation of the brain. The data of Mandel *et al.*[110] show no rise, and perhaps a decrease, in the concentration, based on wet weight, of ethanolamine plus serine in lipids from embryonic brains of chicks between the tenth and ninteenth days of incubation, and three determinations, reported by Folch-Pi[57] show little, if any, change in the concentration of phosphatidyl serine in mouse brain between the first and thirty-fifth days of life.

Plasmalogens.[15,16,30,43,57,97]—This phosphatide has been little studied, but the available evidence indicates that it increases markedly in concentration in the brain during early development. Folch-Pi[57] found about a three-fold increase in the concentration of plasmalogens in mouse brain between the first and thirty-fifth days of life and Davison and Wajda[30] reported almost a four-fold increase in rabbit brain between the second day of life and adulthood. Unfortunately, the more comprehensive data on rat brains, published by Korey and Orchen[97] and Erickson and Lands[43] are based on wet weight, but they appear to show an increase of about the same magnitude as those reported by Folch-Pi and Davison and Wajda. The results of Erickson and Lands[43] indicate that the maximal rate of accumulation of plasmalogen is not reached until about the twentieth to twenty-fourth days of life; from this finding these authors draw the important deduction that plasmalogen is not added to the Schwann cell membrane (in the formation of myelin) until after its characteristic spiral formation around the axon. But the data of Korey and Orchen,[97] when plotted in the same way (as μmoles/100 mg. fresh brain tissue) appear to show the maximal rate of increase between about the twelfth and twentieth days, i.e. during the period when the process of myelination is thought to be at its peak in the rat. (For further comments on the plasmalogens, see the following section.)

Phosphosphingosides (Sphingomyelin). [7,15,16,20,22,30,37,41,63,107,110,123,-130,161]—The interpretation of most studies of this phosphatide during maturation of the brain is clouded by an analytical uncertainty. The method of Schmidt *et al.*,[150] used in most of the work, depends on the fact that the phosphoglycerides, except plasmalogens, are much more easily split by dilute alkali than is sphingomyelin. A step which involves treatment with trichloracetic acid was included to cleave the acetal linkages, then thought to be present in the plasmalogens. Brante[12] found, however, and Dawson[32] confirmed, that the phosphatide fraction obtained by this method contained a considerable amount of material which is not sphingomyelin and which Brante called cephalin B. It now appears probable that the vinyl ether linkage, which Rapport and Franzl[141] have shown to be the structure present in plasmalogens, is not cleaved under the conditions of the original Schmidt *et al.*[150] method, and that Brante's cephalin B is, at least in part, unsplit, or partially split, plasmalogen. Schmidt *et al.*[151] have devised a modification of their method which avoids this difficulty and permits the determination of sphingomyelins, plasmalogens, and phosphoglycerides, but data obtained with it are not yet available.

With the original Schmidt *et al.*[150] method, most investigators have found a sharp increase, coinciding more or less closely with the time of most active myelination, in the concentration of alkali-resistant phosphatides, usually designated as "sphingomyelin," in the developing brain. There is one exception: The data of Cumings *et al.*[22] are quite variable and show no clear-cut change in "sphingomyelin" concentration from early fetal life to the twelfth year of age in either cerebral cortex or white matter of humans.

Edgar and Smits[41] attempted to correct for "cephalin B" by calculations based on choline determinations. The corrected data indicated the presence of a small amount (about 0.3%) of sphingomyelin in the telencephalons of rabbits 0 to 3 days old, as compared with 1.7% at 3 to 4 months and 2.2% at 1 to 2 years. In contrast with these values, Davison and Wajda[30] found 3.2% "sphingomyelin" in whole rabbit brain at 2 days, about 9% at 30 days, and a decrease to 4 to 6% at 81 days to 2 years of age. Edgar[37] also reported a decrease in "sphingomyelin" concentration in rabbit brain tissue after a maximum at 56 to 122 days after birth, but Edgar and Smits[41] concluded that it was the non-sphingomyelin, alkali-stable phosphatides which decreased.

Glycosphingosides: (a) *Cerebrosides.* [7,15,16,20,22,30,37,41,57,63,107,110,123,130,161,162,165]—These lipids were the first to be studied during development of the brain and they have been extensively investigated (cf. pp. 238-239, 1st Ed.). Unfortunately, most of the data, usually designated as concentrations of cerebroside, are open to question because of another analytical uncertainty which arises from the use of methods based on the determination of reducing sugar in acid hydrolyzates of brain lipids on the assumption that such sugar is all galactose from cerebrosides. But Klenk[93] discovered the presence in brain of another sugar-containing lipid, which he later named ganglioside, and it is now known that under the analytical conditions which have been used in most studies, reducing sugars from gangliosides are measured along with those from cerebrosides. This source of error is minimized in some investigations by the presence in normal brain of most of the gangliosides in grey matter and most of the cerebrosides in white matter. (For detailed discussions see publications by Edgar.[37-40])

Two procedures which avoid the foregoing source of error, at least in large part, are now available. (a) In the purification of lipids by the methods of Folch *et al.*,[54,56] the water-soluble gangliosides are largely removed. With this technique, Folch-Pi[57] found little or no cerebroside in whole mouse brain up to the seventh day of life; at 10 days the concentration was 1% and it increased rapidly and consistently thereafter, reaching 5.5% in adult mice. With a similar procedure for separating water-soluble glycolipids from the cerebrosides Uzman and Rumley[165] also found no cerebroside in mouse brain during the first 7 days of life, 1% at 10 days, and an increase thereafter, but the maximum was considerably lower than that reported by Folch-Pi[57] and the increase was much less consistent (e.g., 2.4% at 14 days and 1.6% at 16 days). (b) Radin *et al.*[139] devised a method in which cerebrosides are separated from other sugar-containing lipids by chromatography, and Cumings *et al.*[22] used it in extensive studies of cerebral white matter and cortex from human brains. In white matter there was a large increase from less than 1% cerebrosides at birth to an average of about 15% at 6 to 12 years. In cortex, the corresponding values were about 0.5% and 1.2%. Unfortunately, these data, although obtained with a method which appears to be the best available, are not clear-cut because of large fluctuations from the consistent rate of increase which might be expected with increasing age. For example, values of 10.6% at 10 months and 4.9% at 3 years are included. Cumings *et al.*[22] also determined "cerebrosides" in the same tissues by a method in which gangliosides were not removed, such as has been used in most studies (see above). As would be expected, the values in cortex were several times as large as those given by the Radin *et al.*[139] method. In white matter, during the first few days of life there was also a several-fold difference between the results yielded by the two methods, but this difference tended to decrease with increasing age. The range of "cerebroside" percentages, from about 5% at birth to 17% at 6 to 12 years was similar to those found with the "old" methods by most investigators in white matter. On the basis of such results, and other evidence, it is generally believed that cerebrosides are largely present in myelin.

Kishimoto and Radin[92] studied the fatty acids of cerebrosides isolated by chromatography[91] from the whole brains of rats from about 3 weeks of age to adulthood. The results are too complex for detailed description here, and the youngest age investigated is somewhat beyond the period of principal interest for this review.

(b) Gangliosides.[15,16,21,22,57,161,162,165]—There is much interest in these complex lipids, particularly because an error in their metabolism appears to underlie Tay-Sachs disease, but no unequivocal data have been published on their behavior in the normal brain during development. Folch-Pi[57] found 2.5% of strandin in the brains of 1-day-old and adult mice, with a rise to nearly 4% at the seventh day and a return to the adult level by the thirtieth day. It is known that strandin is closely related to the gangliosides, but it is not certain that the two are identical in the sense that strandin is a polymerized form of the monomeric glycolipids isolated by Klenk.[94] The concentrations of strandin found by Folch-Pi[57] in mouse brain are several times as high as the ganglioside concentrations reported by Klenk[95] in grey matter from normal human brains. Uzman and Rumley[165] separated the water-soluble glycolipids from the brains of mice during development and determined neuraminic acid in the solution as an indirect measure of gangliosides, but, as they point out, there is "no unanimity as to the neuraminic acid content of gangliosides". Their data resemble

those of Folch-Pi on strandin in showing about the same concentration (0.1 to 0.12%) of neuraminic acid of lipid origin in the brains of 1- to 5-day-old and adult mice, with some higher values (to 0.25% at 12 days) between the twelfth and forty-second days of life. Cumings *et al.*[22] also found about the same concentration (0.2%) of neuraminic acid from lipids in human cerebral cortex from foetuses, new-born infants, and a 12-year-old child, with higher values between the second month and seventh year of life. In a later study, Cumings *et al.*[21] obtained similar results for neuraminic acid in human cortex and also determined hexosamine from the lipids. The ratio between neuraminic acid and hexosamine was fairly constant, with a few exxceptions, from birth to the seventieth year of life in accord with Edgar's[39,155] suggestion that ganglioside be estimated from the hexosamine concentration. Tingey[162] also determined neuraminic acid and hexosamine from lipids in cortex and white matter of brains from normal newborn, 2½-year-old, and adult humans and from patients with lipidoses. The ganglioside concentrations, calculated from the two determinations, agreed fairly well in the majority of cases and showed a small rise from birth to adulthood in normal cortex and a large decrease in normal white matter.

Sulfatides.—No new studies of the sulfur-containing glycolipids in the brain during early development are known to the author (cf. p. 241, 1st Ed.). Presumably they would be included with the cerebrosides with the methods, based on reducing sugar determination, which have been most used.

Proteolipids.—Folch-Pi[57] reported little or no proteolipid protein in the brains of 1- and 4-day-old mice and a rapid increase from 0.5% at the seventh day to 1.0% at 19 to 30 days and 2.1% at 180 days. Uzman[163] found lipophilic peptides, soluble in chloroform-methanol, in 1-day-old mouse brain. The chromatographic and electrophoretic characteristics and amino acid composition of this mixture of large peptides changed considerably with increasing age, but a lipophilic protein, called neurosclerin, present in mouse brain in increasing amounts from birth to adulthood, did not change in composition. Alanine, glycine, and leucine, present in about equimolar amounts, made up about 40% of the total amino acid residues released on hydrolysis.[164]

Proteins and Amino Acids.[8,14,15,16,23,45,57,70,81-83,89,100,101,123,144-146,147,-163,164,167]—In the First Edition (p. 246) some fear was expressed that data on the total proteins of brain might have been affected by ignorance of the proteolipids whose existence had just been discovered[55] at the time of that review. This fear was unjustified since proteolipid protein constitutes only a small part of the total; less than 2% up to the thirtieth day of age and less than 4% in adult mice. Folch-Pi[57] found an increase in proteins (minus proteolipid protein) from about 8% of fresh brain tissue at birth to 12% in adult mice, but the values, expressed as percentage of dry weight, decreased from 65% at birth to 51% at 180 day of age. These results are in general agreement with most of those in the older literature (cf. pp. 246-247, 1st Ed.). Mihara[123] reported similar decreases in protein concentration in cerebrum and spinal cord during fetal life in the human, but in cerebellum and medulla oblongata there was little change.

Szepsenwol et al.[160] found no change in the concentration of protein phosphorus in wet brain during embryonic development in the chick.

Dahl and Samson[23] isolated the mitochondrial fraction from homogenates of brains from female rats, 1 to 50 days old, and determined the protein content. The concentration of mitochondrial protein in wet brain was constant during the first 5 days after birth and then increased sharply to a level over twice as high, reached at about the twentieth day; the increase was from 17% to about 26% of the total cerebral protein. On the assumption that the amount of deoxyribonucleic acid per cell is constant, the mitochondrial protein per cell increased by three-fold during the first 21 days and by about 20% during the twenty-first to fiftieth days of postnatal life.

The high concentration of glutamic acid in the brains of adult animals stimulated Waelsch[167] to study it and glutamine during early development. Although the concentrations of both amino acids in wet brain rose considerably between birth and the twenty-ninth day of life in rats, there was little, if any, increase in glutamic acid concentration, and possibly a small decrease in glutamine concentration, when the data were calculated on the basis of dry brain. These results suggested to Waelsch that the concentrations of glutamic acid and its amide are basic characteristics of the nervous tissue and not of its functional state. Results of Himwich and Himwich[81] are not in complete accord with Waelsch's concept; the increase in glutamic acid concentration which they reported, from 106 mg./100 gm. wet brain in newborn rats to 250 mg. in adults, is so large that there must have been some increase on a dry weight basis.

In striking contrast to the findings on glutamic acid are the data of Lajtha[100] on lysine; in a large number of analyses he found average concentrations of free lysine in whole brain of 81, 51, and 38 mg./100 gm. in new-born, 10-day-old, and adult mice, respectively. If it be assumed that the concentration of total brain solids was twice as high in Lajtha's adult mice as in his new-born mice, there was an approximately four-fold decrease in free lysine concentration in dry brain during maturation. There was no difference between young and adult mice in the lysine content of brain proteins. Similarly, the concentration of free leucine in fresh tissue was twice as high in brains of new-born mice as in those of adult mice.[101] R. B. Roberts *et al.*[147] reported an even larger difference between new-born and adult mice in the concentration of phenylalanine + leucine + isoleucine in the wet cortex; 6.2 and 2.5 μg./100 mg. tissue, respectively. They also found smaller concentrations of glycine, serine, and alanine in adult than in new-born cortex, but the differences were less marked. By contrast, the concentration of glutamic acid in adult mouse cortex was more than twice as high as it was at birth. R. B. Roberts *et al.* found no differences between new-born and adult mice in the concentrations of the amino acids which they determined in the proteins of brain cortex. E. Roberts *et al.*[145] and Roberts[144] reported a rapid increase in concentration of γ-aminobutyric acid (GABA) in wet brain during early development in mice, the adult level being reached at about the thirtieth day of life. Roberts *et al.*[146] reported the presence of GABA in the brains of chick embryos at the 4th day of incubation with an increase to the adult chick level (in wet brain) at the seventeenth to eighteenth day of incubation. Similar increases in GABA concentration were found in tadpole brains. No other amino acids showed comparable increases during early development of the brain in the three species studied.

Nucleic Acids.[2,8,9,14,23,46,70,84,108,109,111,113,133,135,160,165]—Further evidence (*cf.* p. 248, 1st Ed.) for a decrease in nucleic acid concentration during development of the brain was supplied by several investigators. The change is so large that it is usually evident when the concentrations are referred to fresh brain. At the extreme, Flexner and Flexner[46] found a decrease from about 70 mg. of DNA phosphorus/100 gm. wet brain cortex at the twenty-fifth day of gestation in the guinea pig embryo to about 10 mg./100 gm. at the forty-eighth day, with little change thereafter (the adult level averaged 6 mg./100 gm.). The decrease in RNA phosphorus was much less, but still substantial—from about 35 to 15 mg./100 gm. at the same ages, respectively. Palladin[133] obtained comparable results in rabbits: a decrease in DNA phosphorus from 368 mg./100 gm. dry whole brain in 16 to 20 day embryos to one-tenth of that concentration in adults. The corresponding values for RNA phosphorus were 416 and 166 mg./100 gm., respectively. By contrast, Mandel *et al.*[109] found a much smaller decrease in DNA in brains of chick embryos between the 10th and 19th days of incubation (from about 150 to 110 mg./100 gm. fresh tissue), and there was a substantial increase in RNA (from about 285 to 415 mg./100 gm.). Szepsenwol *et al.*[160] reported a still smaller decrease in DNA and increase in RNA during maturation of chick embryo brains.

Albrecht[2] found decreases in DNA and RNA concentrations in fresh brain during postnatal development in mice. The values for DNA were 380 mg./100 gm. at 1 to 2 days and 240 mg./100 gm. at 3 to 6 months of age. The corresponding values for RNA were 570 and 300 mg./100 gm. The data of Uzman and Rumley[165] are in fairly close agreement; they show 1.2% of total nucleic acid in fresh brain at 1 day of age and 0.6% in adult mice. On the basis of dry weight, the corresponding values are 8.2 and 2.8%. Dahl and Samson[23] reported a decrease from 256 mg. DNA per 100 gm. whole fresh brain in 1-day-old rats to 153 mg. at 50 days.

Mandel and Bieth[108] determined the amounts of DNA and RNA in the whole brain during development in several animal species. The amount of DNA per brain was at the adult level at birth in the guinea pig and reached the adult level at about 15 days of age in the rat, one month in the rabbit and cat, 5 months in the dog, and 1 year in man. The amount of RNA was always higher than that of DNA, except during the first 4 months of life in man, and it also plateaued at the adult level at an early age except in humans, in whom the adult level was four times that present at the 10th month of life. If the amount of DNA per cell is assumed to be constant, these results indicate that the maximal number of cells in the brain is reached at an early age and maintained at that number throughout the rest of life. The date of Uzman and Rumley[165] appear to be at variance with this assumption. In mice, they found the amount of DNA per brain to remain constant, or to decrease a little, during the first 7 days of postnatal life and then to rise sharply to a maximum over two-fold higher at the fourteenth day. There followed a rapid decrease to a minimum at the twentieth day only a little above the level at birth. After this there was a slow rise to an adult level which was considerably below the fourteenth-day maximum. The decrease in cell population between the fourteenth and twentieth days, indicated by these results, coincided with a decrease in brain weight owing to a large loss in water. This course of events may have been missed by Mandel and Bieth because they did not study as many ages as did Uzman and Rumley, and it is possible, although unlikely, that the apparent discrepancy resulted from a species difference between mice and the mammals studied by Mandel and Bieth.

Carbohydrates.—Although there have been far fewer studies of carbohydrates than of lipids during maturation of the brain, there is some histochemical evidence that polysaccharides may be of considerable importance. (Lipids of the ganglioside, or strandin type, designated as mucolipids by Rosenberg and Chargaff,[148] can, of course, be considered to be polysaccharides.) Wolman[171] reported the deposition in myelin of weakly acidic polysaccharides, as indicated by staining reactions, at the same time that lipids are deposited in the myelin of the rat brain. Hess[76] made the striking, but apparently unrelated, observation that the mucopolysaccharide of ground substance first appears in the brain of guinea pig embryos at the 45th day of gestation and increases in amount and intensity of staining to the adult level by the 50th day. This is just beyond the period of rapid maturation of the guinea pig brain as indicated by much other evidence (see below). On the other hand, Brante,[13] in biochemical studies of polysaccharides, found no striking differences between embryonic and adult brains in mice nor between brains of new-born calves and cows.

Serotonin.—Kato[87A] found large increases in serotonin concentration in wet brain during development in the rat.

Phosphorus.—Manina[112] studied the distribution of P^{32} in the brain by radioautography after subcutaneous injection of P_i^{32} into 18- and 20-day-old rat embryos and new-born, 10-day-old, and adult rats. Data are given in numbers of granules per unit area for several parts of the brain at 24 to 240 hours after P_i^{32} administration. The highest values were found in new-born rats.

Acid-soluble Phosphorus Compounds.—Bieth et al.[9] determined several compounds of this type during maturation of the brain in the rat and related the results to the phosphorus of DNA. The most striking result was an increase in the P_i/DNA-P ratio from 0.8 at 3 days to 1.8 to 2.0 at 8 days of age with little change thereafter.

Electrolytes.—At the time of the previous review there was some evidence (*cf.* p. 245, 1st Ed.) for decreases in Na+, K+, and Ca++ concentrations during development of the brain. Wender and Hierowski[169A] provided further strong evidence in recent studies of grey and white matter and spinal cord from guinea pigs. The decreases in Na+ and Ca++ were marked; e.g., from 178 m-equiv. Na+ per 100 gm. dry weight in white matter at the eighth to ninth weeks of gestation to 32 m-equiv. at the eighth to tenth months of post-natal life. The corresponding values for Ca++ were 13.3 and 3.0 m-equiv., respectively. K+ also decreased but not as much, the fetal and 8 to 10 month values in white matter being 68 and 29, respectively. Similar changes were found in spinal cord and grey matter, those in the latter being a little less striking than in the other two tissues. A large part of the total decreases in Na+ and Ca++ occurred between the last week of fetal life and the 3rd day of postnatal life. These findings are particularly striking when it is considered that the earliest determinations were carried out in fetuses well beyond the so-called "critical period" between the forty-first and forty-fifth days of gestation (see below).

Sulfur.—Gracheva et al.[73] injected methionine-S^{35} into pregnant rats and used radioautography to study the distribution of S^{35} in the central nervous system of the embryos.

ENZYMES

This section could have been included with the preceding one since most studies of enzymes in the brain during development have consisted of measurements of their concentrations in terms of activity units, but the importance of this work in its relation to the metabolism of the brain justifies its separate treatment. During the period covered by this review, information was published concerning at least 30 enzymes (Table I). The data were obtained from 15 animal species

TABLE I

ENZYMES STUDIED IN THE BRAIN DURING EARLY DEVELOPMENT

Enzyme	References
Acetylcholinesterase	4, 11A, 19, 42, 49, 71, 77, 80, 88, 117, 128, 136, 143
Acid phosphatase	19, 44, 49, 143
Adenosine diphosphatase	85, 87
Adenosine-3'-phosphatase	85, 87
Adenosine-5'-phosphatase	85, 87, 129
Adenosine triphosphatase	49, 85, 86, 87, 98, 132, 133
Alanine-ketoglutaric transaminase	106
Aldolase	47, 77, 133
Alkaline phosphatase	18, 19, 47, 143
Aspartic-ketoglutaric transaminase	106
Carbonic anhydrase	124, 143
Cytochrome oxidase	49, 50, 77, 98, 137
Deoxyribonuclease	133
Glucose-6-phosphate dehydrogenase	99
Glutamic decarboxylase	144, 145
Glutamic dehydrogenase	99
Glutamine synthetase	149
Glutamotransferase	149
Guanine deamidase	87
Hexokinase	133
Lactic dehydrogenase	99
Malic dehydrogenase	99
Monoamine oxidase	152A
Phosphoglucomutase	133
Phosphorylase	59
Pseudocholinesterase	42
Ribonuclease	133
Succinic dehydrogenase	50, 58, 60, 77, 96, 98, 126, 137
Succinoxidase	49, 50
Uridine triphosphatase	85

of which rats, guinea pigs, rabbits, and chicks were studied most extensively. In a large proportion of the investigations either one structure of the brain, such as cerebral cortex, was studied, or, more often, enzyme concentrations were measured in several parts of the brain.

In some histochemical studies information was obtained concerning the behavior of enzymes in a large number of areas. As would be expected, the data indicate large differences among species and among different structures of the brain both in the ages at which changes in the activities of various enzymes occur and in their maximal concentrations. It is obviously impossible within the available space to discuss all of the findings which have been published or to summarize them in general statements. Only a few of the more outstanding features of the data can be considered.

In all animal species, as far as they have been studied, there is a period during which there is rapid morphological and functional development of the brain and a more or less coincident increase in chemical metabolism. This "critical period," as Flexner[48] has called it, varies widely among species in the age at which it occurs, in its duration, and in other characteristics. It also varies within the same species among different structures of the brain. It has been most extensively studied by the Flexners and their colleagues in the guinea pig, in which the critical period occurs in the cortex between the forty-first and forty-fifth days of gestation.

Most of the published data show increases in enzyme concentrations during this critical period, but there are some exceptions. For example, Flexner and Flexner[44] found the concentration of acid phosphatase in dry cerebral cortex of guinea pigs to be maintained without appreciable change throughout gestation at a level higher than that present in adults. In contrast, Cohn and Richter[19] found a sharp but relatively small rise in the concentration of acid phosphatase during the first 10 days after birth in dry hypothalamus and cerebral cortex of rats. A slower decrease followed to the level present at birth, reached at 40 days. Similar findings were reported for alkaline phosphatase; Flexner et al.[47] found no evident change in its concentration during embryonic life in the guinea pig and a lower level in the adult, but in the rat, Cohn and Richter[19] found twice the adult level at birth, a sharp, but relatively small, rise during the first 10 or 15 postnatal days, and a large drop to the adult level at about 40 days in the hypothalamus, cortex, and thalamus. Glucose-6-phosphate dehydrogenase remained almost unchanged in relation to dry, lipid-free weight from birth to adulthood in all of the major cortical layers studied by Kuhlman and Lowry[99] in the rat.

Some of the reported increases in enzyme activity, related as a large majority of the data are to the wet weight of tissue, may represent only the decrease in water concentration which occurs during early development of the brain. For example, in the whole rat brain Kuhlman and

Lowry[99] found a two-fold increase in lactic dehydrogenase on the basis of wet weight between the tenth day of life and maturity; but on the basis of dry weight the increase was less than 10%.

The foregoing exceptions and uncertainties should not be over emphasized. In a large proportion of the investigations which have been reported definite increases in enzyme concentration were found during maturation of the brain; increases, that is, in percentage of dry tissue, or in percentage of wet tissue larger than can be explained by the decrease in water content. But there are considerable differences among enzymes in the patterns of the increases in relation to age. A good example is provided by the two enzymes which have been most extensively studied (Table I): succinic dehydrogenase and acetylcholinesterase. Flexner et al.[50] found the concentration of the former in guinea pig cortex to rise very rapidly during the "critical period"; from a low level, maintained up to about the fortieth day of gestation, it increased to the much higher adult level by the fiftieth day. In contrast, Kavaler and Kimel,[88] in Flexner's laboratory, observed a quite different pattern for acetylcholinesterase; the concentration began to rise at about the thirty-fifth day of gestation, and the rapidly ascending curve continued through the "critical period," with no evident break, to a maximum a little below the adult level, reached just before term. The concentration had reached about half of the adult level before muscular responses to electrical stimulation of cortex could be elicited and about 60% of the adult level before spontaneous electrical potentials of cortical origin appeared. These results do not appear to be in complete accord with the statement by Nachmansohn:[128] "One should expect in the embryo and during growth close relationships between the increase in the concentration of acetylcholinesterase and the period at which certain functions develop."

Similar differences among enzymes in their patterns of development in the brain were observed in the rat, in which the "critical period," although not as clearly defined as in the guinea pig, appears to begin at about the tenth day of postnatal life. Millichap[124] reported a six-fold rise (four-fold on dry weight) in the carbonic anhydrase concentration in cerebral hemispheres of rats between the tenth and twenty-fifth days of life. Hamburgh and Flexner[77] found the steepest rise in cytochrome oxidase and aldolase concentrations between the tenth and fifteenth days in the rat cerebral cortex, but the most rapid increase in acetylcholinesterase occurred before the tenth day. Cohn and Richter[19] also observed the steepest rise in acetylcholinesterase before the tenth day in rat cerebral cortex; in the hypothalamus there was a much larger increase from a higher level at birth to a maximum at the fifteenth day. In the rat as in the guinea pig the major part of the rise in acetylcholinesterase concentration appears to precede the "critical period" in the maturation of the brain.

Many other examples could be cited of differences among enzymes in their quantitative behavior during the maturation of the brain. The most extreme, discovered by Rudnick and Waelsch,[149] is the twenty-fold or more rise in glutamotransferase activity of the embryonic chick retina during a single day. A nice example of species differences is provided by data from Flexner's laboratory on cytochrome oxidase in guinea pigs and rats. In the former species, in contrast to the dramatic rise in succinic dehydrogenase during the "critical period" (see above), the concentration of cytochrome oxidase increased little, if at all on a dry weight basis, during the "critical period"; the major rise occurred just before term.[50] In the rat, on the other hand, the major increase in cytochrome oxidase took place between the tenth and fifteenth days of postnatal life, and this rise appears from the curves to have been somewhat greater on a percentage basis than that of succinic dehydrogenase during the same period.[77]

Although, in a broad sense the concentrations of a large proportion, but by no means all, of the enzymes which have been studied increase during maturation of the brain, the available data do not permit the general conclusion that there is a close, direct relation between enzyme concentrations and degree of functional development. In the writer's opinion, there is insufficient evidence to permit such a conclusion for any single enzyme. Perhaps such a direct relation should not be expected since enzymes are usually present in considerable excess, as for example, acetylcholinesterase in nerves.[128] Much more work must be done before changes in enzyme concentrations in the brain during early development are fully understood in their relation to metabolic and functional activity.

METABOLISM

Blood-Brain Barrier (BBB).—In a majority of recent investigations of metabolism in the brain during early development, isotopically labeled compounds were administered to intact animals, and the degree of labeling of the compounds under investigation in the brain was determined at various times thereafter. In interpreting the results of such experiments, especially when rates of metabolism at different ages are to be compared, account must be taken of the rate and extent of penetration of the labeled compound which was given (and of its metabolic products) across the BBB into the brain. Some consideration of the evidence concerning the BBB during early development is, therefore, necessary at this point.

Up to 1954, when Waelsch[168] reviewed the subject, studies with dyes, $P_i{}^{32}$, K^{42}, Cl^{36}, and thiocyanate all indicated that the BBB was absent in early life or much less effective than in the adult brain. Waelsch was careful to point out, however, that generalizations should be avoided until a considerably greater number of substances had been studied.

The finding of a rapid decrease in permeability of the BBB to P_i with increasing age in rats[161] and rabbits[5] is of particular importance here because $P_i{}^{32}$ has been used in a number of studies of brain metabolism during early development. Further evidence was supplied by Russian investigators.[112,114,154]

The permeability of the BBB to amino acids was studied by several investigators. Since the finding by Schwerin et al.[152] that the concentration of glutamic acid in the adult brain is not affected by large increases in the concentration in the plasma, it has been assumed that the BBB is impermeable to glutamic acid. Himwich and Himwich[81] and Himwich et al.[83] confirmed this in adult rats, but in 1-day-old rats the administration of glutamate caused a significant rise in the glutamic acid concentration in the brain. This result is in accord with the concept that the BBB is undeveloped in the young brain. By the tenth day of life, however, the permeability to glutamic acid, as measured in this way, had disappeared. The difference between young and mature brains in permeability of the BBB to lysine appears to be greater; Lajtha et al.[104] were able to cause its concentration to increase by 100% in day-old mice by raising the concentration in the plasma by 25- to 50-fold, whereas a significant increase in the adult brain could not be induced. On the other hand, Purpura and Carmichael[138] found the BBB to γ-aminobutyric acid to be as operative in new-born kittens as in adult cats.

When labeled amino acids are administered intravenously or intraperitoneally, a quite different picture emerges. Lajtha, Waelsch, and their colleagues, in a series of investigations,[101-104] found rapid penetration into the brain of C^{14} labeled lysine, leucine, and also of glutamic acid, in adult animals. Considerable radioactivity was present in the brain 2 to 3 minutes after injection of the labeled amino acid. Evidently, the BBB does not block the passage of amino acids from the plasma into the brain; it, or some other mechanism, prevents a net change in concentration in the adult brain.

The data of Lajtha and Waelsch show no consistent differences between young (new-born or 10-day-old) and adult mice in the rates of flux of labeled lysine or leucine from the plasma into the brain, but these investigators were careful to avoid the conclusion that no such differences exist because the flux rates are subject to large uncertainties resulting from rapid changes in the concentrations from which they are calculated; the labeled amino acids pass quickly from the plasma into the tissues. From similar experiments, Flexner *et al.*[52] and Roberts *et al.*[147] reached the conclusion that the rate of flux of glutamic acid from plasma to brain is about ten times greater in adult than in new-born mice. This finding is surprising because it stands in such marked contrast to previous thinking and also because, in other experiments by the same authors, glucose appeared to supply by synthesis *in situ* at least ten times as much glutamic acid in both new-born and adult cortex as was derived by flux of the amino acid from the blood.

Lipid Metabolism in Relation to Myelin Formation.—It has been assumed that the rapid metabolism of lipids in the brain during early life, as shown by the uptake of isotopic labels (D, P^{32}, and C^{14}), represents in large part the synthesis of lipids needed for growth and for formation of myelin, as contrasted with metabolic turnover (*cf.* p. 243, 1st Ed.). Indirect support for this assumption was provided by the failure of several investigators[11,115,131,158,159,166,169] to find appreciable labeling of cholesterol with deuterium or C^{14} in the adult brain *in vivo* or *in vitro*. This result suggested that cholesterol, synthesized and deposited in the brain during early development, remains inertly there for long periods of time, perhaps throughout life. More recently, however, McMillan *et al.*,[115] Nicholas and Thomas,[131] and Meltzer and Sperry[116] found appreciable labeling of cholesterol in the adult rat brain when acetate-1-C^{14} was injected directly into the brain tissue. or into the cisterna magna or the subarachnoid space, but the metabolism, indicated by these results, does not appear to represent turnover since cholesterol thus labeled in the adult brain remains there for at least a year with little decrease in radioactivity.[115,131] Apparently, the labeling under these conditions occurs during synthesis of cholesterol needed in the growth of the brain, which in the rat continues throughout life, and thus, it appears to be simply a continuation at a slower rate of the synthetic process which proceeds rapidly in the brain during early development.

Davison and his colleagues have provided important information concerning the fate of lipids deposited in the brain during early life. They[27,31] injected emulsions of cholesterol-4-C^{14} into the yolk sacs of newly hatched chicks and found a large proportion of the labeled cholesterol still present in the brain 502 days later. In similar studies,[28,31] a considerable part of cholesterol-4-C^{14}, injected intraperitoneally into 17-day-old rabbits, was retained in the brain up to a year later. By chemical degradation, the C^{14} was shown to be in the 4 position in cholesterol isolated from the chick and rabbit brains. Davison and Dobbing[25,26] injected P_i^{32} intraperitoneally into 16-day-old rats. The maximal incorporation of P^{32} into the total phosphatides of the whole brain was reached about 2 weeks later, and most of this labeled phosphatide was retained up to the eighty-sixth day of life. Davison et al.[29] injected DL-serine-3-C[14] intraperitoneally into 11-day-old rabbits and determined the radioactivity of lipid components of the whole brain at nine intervals, ranging from 1 to 192 days after the injection. Maximal labeling of cholesterol, cerebrosides, and sphingomyelin was reached by the third day, and there was little or no change from this level throughout the experiment except possibly for some decrease in sphingomyelin activity after 109 days. In the white matter of one rabbit 250 days after the serine was given, these lipids, and also the cephalin fraction, were labeled at levels about four times the corresponding values in grey matter, but the lecithin fraction was inactive. Finally, Davison[24] labeled brain lipids by injecting glycerol-1-C[14] into 13-day-old rats. At the 110th day after injection there had been little loss of the radioactivity incorporated into cholesterol and cerebrosides, but less than half of the initial amount was present in sphingomyelin, cephalin, and lecithin.

The foregoing findings show beyond doubt that a large proportion of the cholesterol molecules which are incorporated into the brain during early development remain inertly there, apparently throughout life, and the available evidence, although less extensive than that for cholesterol, indicates strongly that the same is true for a large proportion of cerebroside molecules and a smaller proportion of sphingomyelin and cephalin (plasmalogen?) molecules. There is much evidence for the assumption that these are the lipid components of myelin, and it is reasonable to assume, therefore, as Davison has, that the myelin structures are metabolically stable. If this is true, the proteins of myelin also would be expected to be stable. Indirect evidence for this assumption was provided by Furst et al.[64] in their finding of a very slow rate of incorporation of lysine-C[14] into the proteins of proteolipids.

de Almeida and Pearse[36] applied histochemical techniques to the study of lipids in relation to myelination in the rabbit brain.

Mechanism of Cholesterol Synthesis.—In slices and homogenates from brains of 10-day-old rats Grossi et al.[76] and Garattini et al.[67] observed far less incorporation of C[14] into cholesterol from mevalonate-2-C[14] than from acetate-1-C[14]. This finding is of considerable interest since the opposite result has been obtained in liver tissue by many investigators, including Garattini et al.[67] Grossi et al.[76] stated that they had obtained similar results in cell-free preparations and thus had ruled out a slow rate of passage of mevalonic acid into brain cells as the explanation. They suggested a deficiency in mevalonic kinase and decarboxylase in the preparations which they studied *in vitro*. In a later, preliminary report Garattini *et al.*[68] presented evidence for a similar difference between brain and other tissues *in vivo;* in 14 day-old rats the incorporation of C^{14} from mevalonate-2-C^{14} into cholesterol was far less in brain than in liver or kidney and considerably less than in lung, intestine, or heart, but the difference between mevalonate and acetate was not as striking as it was in the *in vitro* experiments and there was some indication that the rate at which mevalonic acid passed the BBB had an effect on the results.

Phosphatide Metabolism.—Miani *et al.*[122] repeated the classical experiments of Fries *et al.*[62] (*cf.* p. 242, 1st Ed.) with essentially the same results; there was a relatively large uptake of systemically administered $P_i{}^{32}$ into the phosphatides of various structures of the brain in new-born rats and a rapidly decreasing degree of labeling with increasing age. Such findings can not be interpreted in terms of phosphatide metabolism because of a rapid decrease in permeability to P_i of the BBB with increasing age (see above). Dawson and Richter[35] avoided this uncertainty, at least in large part, by relating the specific activity of the phosphatide phosphorus to that of the acid-soluble phosphorus of the brain 3 hours after giving $P_i{}^{32}$ to mice. The ratio decreased somewhat from the eighth day of life to adulthood, but Dawson[34] suggested that this may be explained by the smaller concentration of phosphatides in the young brain and he concluded that there is no evidence of any appreciably larger capacity of the nervous system to synthesize phosphatides in the young animal than in the adult. Manukyan,[114] on the other hand, in similar studies on the rabbit, found a fairly high relative specific activity of phosphatide phosphorus during embryonic life and quite large decreases in spinal cord, medulla oblongata, and cerebellum, and a smaller decrease in cortex, during postnatal life. Smirnov and Chetverikov[154] reported the uptake of P^{32} into phosphatides to be smaller than into phosphoproteins in young rabbit brains.

In important experiments, Miani and Bucciante[118-121] applied Dawson's[33] methods to the study of phosphatide metabolism in the brains of rats 3 to 13 days old. At intervals of 10 to 240 hours after admininstration of $P_i{}^{32}$ the hydrolytic products of brain phosphatides were separated, and the specific radioactivity of each fraction was determined. There was a sharp rise to maxima at about 20 hours and an equally rapid fall in the activities of the derivatives of phosphoinositides and "phosphatidic acid." This result might have been anticipated from Dawson's finding of active labeling of the same fractions in adult guinea pig brains *in vitro,* but there is a striking difference between the two experiments. Whereas Dawson[33,34] found little or no labeling of phosphatidylcholine, phosphatidylserine, or phosphatidylethanolamine in adult brains, the derivatives of all three became radioactive in the young rat brains, but the curves of activity rose and fell much more slowly than did those of the inositide and phosphatidic acid derivatives, the maxima being reached at 90 to 110 hours. The maximum for phosphatidylserine was about as high as for phosphoinositide. Phosphatidylcholine had the least activity. In identical experiments by Miani and Bucciante on 100 gm. rats the results were more nearly like those of Dawson. There was relatively little and very slow labeling of the three phosphoglycerides and the phosphoinositide and "phosphatidic acid" curves rose more slowly to somewhat lower maxima than were found in the very young rats.

Sixteen to twenty hours after administration of acetate-1-C^{14} to 10- to 13-day-old rats Korey and Orchen[97] observed the specific activity of the ether moiety of the brain plasmalogens to be more than twice as high as that of the total fatty acids of the brain. In similar experiments with palmitate-1-C^{14} the specific activity of the fatty acids was a little higher than that of the ether fraction. The incorporation of C^{14} from palmitate into plasmalogens was markedly depressed by unlabeled acetate or linoleate.

Ansell and Spanner found a relatively rapid incorporation of P^{32} into sphingomyelin in the brains of young rats during the "critical period." The effect of the BBB was avoided by relating the results to the specific activity of the acid-soluble phosphorus fraction.

Glycolipid Metabolism.—Rafelson *et al.*[140] incubated minced brain tissue from 1-day-old mice in the presence of glucose-U-C^{14} for 24 hours. More than 1% of the C^{14} was incorporated into the crude total lipids and over half as much into the proteins. No information was obtained concerning the manner in which the label was incorporated, but it may be assumed from more recent studies by Burton, Sodd, and Brady[14] and by Moser and Karnovsky[127] that some of it had found its way in the form of carbohydrate into glycolipids. In both of these investigations glucose-U-C^{14} or galactose-1-C^{14} was administered to rats[14] or mice[127] during early life (2- to 28-day-old rats; 3-day-old to 6-month-old mice), and the lipids were isolated from the brain, fractionated, and assayed for radioactivity at various intervals thereafter. Burton *et al.*[14] also included extensive *in vitro* studies in which cell free preparations of young rat brain tissue and subcellular fractions thereof were incubated with the labeled sugars and with the uridine diphosphate derivatives of glucose or galactose. The results are too complex for detailed review here; only the principal findings can be mentioned. Carbon from both galactose and glucose was incorporated into cerebrosides in rats and mice, largely as undegraded hexose. In rats there was no incorporation of glucose-U-C^{14}, measured 8 hours after administration, until about the fifth day of life; the maximal rate of incorporation into cerebrosides occurred at about the fifteenth day. In mice, galactose-1-C^{14} incorporation into cerebrosides, measured 1 hour after administration, was at the maximal rate at the third day and had declined considerably by the fifteenth day. The *in vitro* studies in rats[14] showed that uridine diphosphogalactose was the primary hexose donor to a lipid acceptor endogenous to the microsomal fraction. The specific activity of strandin, studied only in mice,[127] after administration of glucose-U-C^{14} was close to that of the total lipids throughout the period of study (3 to 180 days). After administration of glucose-6-C^{14} the specific activities of galactose, galactosamine, and glucose were in the ratios of 39:16:12, respectively.

The finding of Davison *et al.*[29] that C^{14} from DL-serine-3-C^{14} is incorporated into cerebrosides in the brains of young (11-day-old) rabbits (see above) was confirmed in rats by Garcia and Burton;[69] the maximal rate of labeling was reached between the fourteenth and eighteenth days of postnatal life. The gangliosides were also labeled.

Amino Acid and Protein Metabolism.—Winzler, Pearson, and their colleagues[125,140,153,170] studied the synthesis of protein-bound amino acids from various precursors by minced brain tissue from 1-day-old mice during incubation for 24 hours. C^{14} from glucose-U-C^{14} was incorporated into all essential amino acids, except threonine, and all non-essential amino acids, except proline. The same result was obtained *in vivo,* but the incorporation into essential amino acids, except histidine, was smaller than *in vitro.* C^{14} from acetate-C^{14} was incorporated *in vitro* into glutamic and aspartic acids, alanine, proline, serine, glycine, and only one essential amino acid, histidine. Formate-C^{14} was a precursor of serine, methionine, histidine, tyrosine plus phenylalanine, and cystine. C^{14} from labeled bicarbonate was incorporated only into glutamic and aspartic acids. C^{14} from glucose-1-C^{14} or glucose-6-C^{14} was incorporated into glutamic and aspartic acids, serine, proline, and alanine, and to a very small extent into methionine, tyrosine, and phenylalanine. These results show that carbons 1 and 6 of glucose are not incorporated into the essential amino acids by immature brain tissue. Other implications of these important experiments concerning the mechanisms of amino acid synthesis are beyond the scope of this review.

In experiments similar to those carried out *in vivo* by Winzler *et al.,*[170] Flexner *et al.*[52] failed to find incorporation of C^{14} from glucose-U-C^{14} into essential amino acids (except for small amounts in histidine) in the new-born mouse brain cortex, perhaps because a maximal time of only 7 hours after injection was used, whereas Winzler *et al.* gave glucose-U-C^{14} every 3 hours for a 24-hour period. Nonessential amino acids, particularly glutamic, were labeled with the maximum in the amino acid pool at 1 hour after injection.

In studies to which reference has been made (see BBB above), Lajtha et al.[101,103,104] measured the flux of lysine-C^{14} and leucine-C^{14} from the amino acid pool of the brain into proteins in 8-day old or new-born, respectively, as well as in adult, mice. In adults, the magnitude of the flux decreased sharply with increasing length of the interval (2 to 60 minutes) after the administration of the labeled amino acid. This result was considered to be a reflection of the presence in the brain of proteins with widely varying metabolic rates, those with the highest rates being measured mainly at the shortest intervals. In the lysine experiments with 8-day-old mice no such decrease in flux rate was observed; the rate was maintained at about the maximal adult level. This result indicates that only rapidly metabolizing proteins, as indicated by uptake of lysine, were being synthesized in the young brains. The turnover rate was very fast; the half-lifetimes varied from 2.2 to 3.4 minutes. In the leucine experiments the flux rate at 3 minutes after administration was about eight times as large in the young as in the adult brains and it decreased markedly as the intervals were increased, but at each interval it was much higher in the young brains. Lajtha[101] suggested that the difference between the lysine and leucine results is probably related to the use of 8-day-old mice in the former and new-born mice in the latter and not to a difference in the rates at which the two amino acids are incorporated. According to this interpretation a marked change in the pattern of protein synthesis occurs during the first few days after birth in the mouse brain.

Gaitonde and Richter used L-methionine-S^{35} as an indicator of protein metabolism in the brains of rats 15 to 150 days old. The labeled amino acid was injected intraperitoneally[65,142] or directly into the cerebrospinal fluid by cisternal puncture or injection into the subarachnoid space.[66] In both series of experiments the incorporation of S^{35} into brain proteins (ratio of specific activities of protein S and acid-soluble S) decreased with increasing age. Panchenko[134] found the rate of incorporation of methionine-S^{35} into proteins of various parts of the brain to be higher in young than in mature cats in all areas studied except the cortex.

The incorporation of C^{14} from glycine-C^{14} into proteins in homogenized brain tissue was considerably higher in chick embryos at the thirteenth day of incubation than in newly hatched chicks.[74]

Nucleic Acid Metabolism.—Manukyan[114] employed P^{32} as an indicator of DNA and RNA metabolism in cortex, cerebellum, medulla oblongata, and spinal cord of rabbits during the last 10 days of gestation and through postnatal life to adulthood. The results are plotted as ratios between the specific activities of nucleic acid P and P_i. The relative specific activity of DNA was low in all tissues studied and it showed little change with increasing age except for a fairly large decrease in cerebellum beginning at about the 10th postnatal day. The relative specific activity of RNA was much higher than that of DNA and higher than that of phosphatides (see above). It changed little with increasing age in cortex and cerebellum but rose considerably during postnatal life in medulla oblongata and spinal cord.

Adenosinetriphosphate Metabolism.—Gordon *et al.*[72] incubated homogenates of brains from chick embryos (17-day-old) or 1-day-old chicks with an excess of ATP and $P_i{}^{32}$ and determined the specific activity of ATP at intervals of 2 to 20 minutes. Equilibration was complete within 2 minutes. The specific activity was higher in the embryonic brain tissue but considerably lower at both ages than in corresponding experiments with homogenates of liver tissue.

Oxidative Metabolism.—Evidence for the high resistance of the young brain to anoxia was reviewed and discussed in detail by Himwich.[79] Changes in cerebral circulation and oxygen consumption which accompany maturation and aging in humans were reviewed by Kety.[90]

Greengard and McIlwain[75] showed that the rise in Qo_2 (*cf.* p. 254, 1st Ed.) of the cortex during the first month of life in the rat is markedly increased by electrical pulses; the same was true of lactic acid production. In the guinea pig the respiratory and glycolytic responses of cortical tissue to electrical stimulation *in vitro* increased sharply between the thirty-fifth and fifty-seventh days of gestation. These results are in accord with much other evidence concerning the "critical periods" of brain development in these species.

Flexner *et al.*[51] found, as would be expected, a marked rise in the Qo_2 of guinea pig cortex beginning at about the 40th day of gestation. The level at term was about four-fifths that of adults. The rate of glucose-C^{14} aerobic utilization by cortex tissue *in vitro* in bicarbonate buffer increased 4-fold between the thirty-eighth day of gestation and maturity but in phosphate buffer the increase was only two-fold. The corresponding increases in glucose oxidation were sixteen-fold in bicarbonate buffer and four-fold in phosphate buffer, the remainder of the glucose utilization being accounted for by lactate production. A substantial part of these changes occurred during embryonic life. A large proportion, usually over half, of the oxygen consumed could not be accounted for by glucose oxidation, as calculated from the specific activity of the CO_2 produced. This finding did not appear to be related to age. The rate of anerobic glycolysis was low up to about the forty-first day of gestation; it rose sharply to a maximum, reached at about the sixtieth day, considerably above the adult level.

Dahl and Samson[23] showed that mitochondria from new-born rat brains are capable of oxidative phosphorylation. The rate of oxygen utilization per unit weight of mitochondrial protein was constant up to the fiftieth day of life, whereas the synthesis of high-energy phosphate declined a little. These authors pointed out that the increase of Qo_2 of whole brain during development is proportional to the increase in mitochondrial protein (see above).

Abnormal Metabolism.—This chapter has been concerned with biochemical investigations of the developing normal brain. Such studies are essential to the eventual understanding of the biochemical abnormalities which underlie, or are major factors in, various diseases. For example, interest in the lipids of the brain during early life has been stimulated by the hope that knowledge concerning their relation to the formation of myelin would be of value in interpreting the process of demyelination in multiple sclerosis and other demyelinating diseases. Interest in the lipids has also been stimulated by the lipidoses, particularly Tay-Sachs and Niemann-Pick diseases, of which hereditary errors in the metabolism of lipids appear to be the primary causes. Although several studies of these diseases have been reported during the past 10 years, little has been added to the biochemical knowledge of them which was summarized in the first edition of this book (*cf.* pp. 256-7). The author predicts with some confidence that during the next decade the application of modern methods of biochemistry to the study of metabolism, particularly of the sphingolipids, in the normal, developing brain will lead to the understanding of the defective mechanisms which are responsible for the lipidoses and perhaps of other diseases which involve the central nervous system.

Conclusion.—In the first edition of this book, the chapter corresponding to this was concluded on a pessimistic note with the statement that there was great need for much more investigation of the biochemistry of the brain during early development. It is possible now to be a little more optimistic; during the past 10 years, as the preceding pages show, many such investigations have been reported, and there has been a considerable increase in knowledge in this field. But to a large degree this chapter has, of necessity, consisted, as did the first one, of a tabulation of more or less isolated investigations; few findings in this field have been so well established that they may be presented as accepted facts. It is to be hoped and expected that by the time this chapter is rewritten for the third edition, the application of modern techniques of biochemistry will have greatly increased our knowledge of the biochemical development of the brain and at the same time, through the resolution of uncertainties which now exist, made the subject much easier to review.

REFERENCES

1. ADAMS, C. W. M., and DAVISON, A. N.: *J. Neurochem., 4*:282 (1959).
2. ALBRECHT, W.: *Ztschr. Naturforsch., 11B*:248 (1956).
3. ANSELL, G. B., and SPANNER, S.: *Biochem. J., 73*:3P (1959).
4. APRISON, M. H., and HIMWICH, H. E.: *Am. J. Physiol., 179*:502 (1954).
5. BAKAY, L.: *Arch. Neurol. & Psychiat., 70*:30 (1953).
6. BERNHARD, K., and LINDLAR, F.: *Helvet. physiol. et pharmacol. acta, 14*:113 (1956).
7. BIETH, R., and MANDEL, P.: *Bull. Soc. chim. biol., 32*:109 (1950).
8. BIETH, R., MANDEL, P., and REVEL, J. P.: *J. physiol.* (Paris), *44*:214 (1952).
9. BIETH, R., MANDEL, P., and WEILL, J. D.: *Compt. rend. Soc. biol., 147*:1273 (1953).
10. BLANCHER, G., and DEVAUX-SAINT-CYR, C.: *Compt. rend. Soc. biol., 147*:266 (1953).
11. BLOCH, K.: *A Symposium on Steroid Hormones,* p. 39 E. S. Gordon, Ed. Lancaster, Pa.. Univ. Wisconsin Press (1950).
11A. BONICKION, A.: *J. Neurochem., 5*:195 (1960).
12. BRANTE, G.: *Acta physiol. scandinav., 18*:Suppl. 63 (1949).
13. BRANTE, G.: *Biochemistry of the Developing Nervous System,* p. 153. Waelsch, H., Ed. New York, Acad. Press, (1955).
14. BULANKIN, I. N., LANTODUB, I. YU., NOVIKOVA, N. M., PAPAKINA, I. K., and FRENKEL, L. A.: *Uchenye Zapiski Khar'kov. Univ. 53, Trudy Nauch.-Issledovatel. Inst. Biol., 21*:87 (1954); *Chem. Abstr., 50*:5055 (1956).
15. BÜRGER, M.: *Experientia,* Suppl. No. 4, 101 (1956).
16. BÜRGER, M.: *Die Medizinische,* 561 (1956).
17. BURTON, R. M., SODD, M. A., and BRADY, R. O.: *J. Biol. Chem., 233*:1053 (1958).
18. CHIQUONE, A. D.: *J. Comp. Neurol., 100*:415 (1954).
19. COHN, P., and RICHTER, D.: *J. Neurochem., 1*:166 (1956).
20. CROCKER, A.: Unpublished studies on human cerebrum.
21. CUMINGS, J. N., GOODWIN, H., and CURZON, G.: *J. Neurochem., 4*:234 (1959).
22. CUMINGS, J. N., GOODWIN, H., WOODWARD, E. M., and CURZON, G.: *J. Neurochem., 2*:289 (1958).
23. DAHL, D. R., and SAMSON, F. E., Jr.: *Am. J. Physiol., 196*:470 (1959).
24. DAVISON, A. N.: *Biochem. J., 74*:1P (1960)
25. DAVISON, A. N., and DOBBING, J.: *Lancet, 11*:1158 (1958).
26. DAVISON, A. N., and DOBBING, J.: *Biochem. J., 73*:701 (1959).
27. DAVISON, A. N., DOBBING, J., MORGAN, R. S., and WRIGHT, G. P.: *J. Neurochem., 3*:89 (1958).
28. DAVISON, A. N., DOBBING, J., MORGAN, R. S., and WRIGHT, G. P.: *Lancet, 1*:658 (1959).
29. DAVISON, A. N., MORGAN, R. S., WAJDA, M., and WRIGHT, G. P.: *J. Neurochem. 4*:360 (1959).
30. DAVISON, A. N., and WAJDA, M.: *J. Neurochem., 4*:353 (1959).
31. DAVISON, A. N., and WAJDA, M.: *Nature, 183*:1606 (1959).
32. DAWSON, R. M. C.: *Biochem. J., 56*:621 (1954).
33. DAWSON, R. M. C.: *Biochem. J., 57*:237 (1954).
34. DAWSON, R. M. C.: *Biochemistry of the Developing Nervous System,* p. 268. H. Waelsch, Ed. New York, Acad. Press. (1955).
35. DAWSON, R. M. C., and RICHTER, D.: *Proc. Roy. Soc.* (London), *B137*:252 (1950).
36. DEALMEIDA, D. F., and PEARSE, A. G. E.: *J. Neurochem., 3*:132 (1958).

37. EDGAR, G. W. F.: *Myelination Studied by Quantitative Determination of Myelin Lipids.* Utrecht, N.V. Drukkerij V/H L.E. Bosch and ZN (1955).

38. EDGAR, G. W. F.: *Acta anat., 27:*240 (1956).

39. EDGAR, G. W. F.: *Monatsschr. Psychiat. Neurol., 131:*274 (1956).

40. EDGAR, G. W. F.: *Acta anat., 31:*451 (1957).

41. EDGAR, G. W. F., and SMITS, G.: *J. Neurochem., 3:*316 (1959).

42. ELKES, J., and TODRICK, A.: *Biochemistry of the Developing Nervous System,* p. 309. H. Waelsch, Ed. New York, Acad. Press (1955).

43. ERICKSON, N. E., and LANDS, W. E. M.: *Proc. Soc. Exper. Biol. & Med., 102:*512 (1959).

44. FLEXNER, J. B., and FLEXNER, L. B.: *J. Cell. & Comp. Physiol., 31:*317 (1948).

45. FLEXNER, J. B., and FLEXNER, L. B.: *Anat. Rec., 106:*413 (1950).

46. FLEXNER, J. B., and FLEXNER, L. B.: *J. Cell. & Comp. Physiol., 38:*1 (1951).

47. FLEXNER, J. B., GREENBLATT, C. L., COOPERBAND, S. R., and FLEXNER, L. B.: *Am. J. Anat., 98:*129 (1956).

48. FLEXNER, L. B.: *The Biology of Mental Health and Disease,* p. 180. New York, Paul B. Hoeber (1950).

49. FLEXNER, L. B.: *Biochemistry of the Developing Nervous System,* p. 281 H. Waelsch, Ed. New York, Acad. Press (1955).

50. FLEXNER, L. B., BELKNAP, E. L., Jr., and FLEXNER, J. B.: *J. Cell. & Comp. Physiol., 42:*151 (1953).

51. FLEXNER, L. B., FLEXNER, J. B., and HELLERMAN, L.: *J. Cell. & Comp. Physiol., 47:*469 (1956).

52. FLEXNER, L. B., FLEXNER, J. B., and ROBERTS, R. B.: *J. Cell. & Comp. Physiol., 51:*385 (1958).

53. FOLCH, J., ARSOVE, S., and MEATH, J. A.: *J. Biol. Chem., 191:*819 (1951).

54. FOLCH, J., ASCOLI, I., LEES, M., MEATH, J. A. and LEBARON, F. N.: *J. Biol. Chem., 191:*833 (1951).

55. FOLCH, J., and LEES, M.: *J. Biol. Chem., 191:*807 (1951).

56. FOLCH, J., LEES, M., and SLOAN STANLEY, G. H.: *J. Biol. Chem., 226:*497 (1957).

57. FOLCH-PI, J.: *Biochemistry of the Developing Nervous System,* p. 121. H. Waelsch, Ed. New York, Acad. Press (1955).

58. FRIEDE, R. L.: *Arch. Psychiat. Nervenheilk., 196:*196 (1957).

59. FRIEDE, R.: *Ztschr. Physiol. Chem., 310:*4 (1958).

60. FRIEDE, R. L.: *J. Neurochem., 4:*101 (1959).

61. FRIES, B. A., and CHAIKOFF, I. L.: *J. Biol. Chem., 141:*479 (1941).

62. FRIES, B. A., CHANGUS, G. W., and CHAIKOFF, I. L.: *J. Biol. Chem., 132:*23 (1940).

63. FUKUYAMA, B.: *Igaku Kenkyu* (Acta Medica), *20:*59 (1950).

64. FURST, S., LAJTHA, A., and WAELSCH, H.: *J. Neurochem., 2:*216 (1958).

65. GAITONDE, M. K., and RICHTER, D.: *Biochem. J., 59:*690 (1955).

66. GAITONDE, M. K., and RICHTER, D.: *Proc. Roy. Soc., B145:*83 (1956).

67. GARATTINI, S., PAOLETTI, P., and PAOLETTI, R.: *Arch. Biochem. Biophys., 80:*210 (1959).

68. GARATTINI, S., PAOLETTI, P., and PAOLETTI, R.: *Arch. Biochem. Biophys., 84:*253 (1959).

69. GARCIA, L., and BURTON, R. M.: *Federation Proc., 19:*220 (1960).

70. GAYET, J., and SCHWANDER, J.: *Arch. sc. physiol., 9:*11 (1955).

71. GEREBTZOFF, M. A.: *Biochemistry of the Developing Nervous System,* p. 315. H. Waelsch, Ed. New York, Acad. Press, (1955).

72. GORDON, O. M., DONALDSON, K. O., and MARSHALL, L. M.: *Experientia, 11:*194 (1955).

73. GRACHEVA, N. O., KISELEVA, V. K., and LEBEDEVA, N. I.: *Uchenye Zapiski Leningrad, Gosudarst. Pedagog. Inst. im. A. I. Gertsena, 143:*319 (1958). *Chem. Abstr., 53:*17285 (1959).

74. GREENBURG, D. M., FRIEDBERG, F., SCHULMAN, M. P., and WINNICK, T.: *Cold Spring Harbor Symposia Quant. Biol., 13:*113 (1948).

75. GREENGARD, P., and MCILWAIN, H.: *Biochemistry of the Developing Nervous System,* p. 251. Waelsch, H., Ed. New York, Acad. Press (1955).

76. GROSSI, E., PAOLETTI, P., and PAOLETTI, R.: *Arch. internat. physiol. biochem.,* 66:564 (1958).

77. HAMBURGH, M., and FLEXNER, L. B.: *J. Neurochem., 1:*279 (1957).

78. HESS, A.: *J. Comp. Neurol., 102:*65 (1955).

79. HIMWICH, H. E.: *Brain Metabolism and Cerebral Disorders,* p. 124. Baltimore, Williams and Wilkins, (1951).

80. HIMWICH, H. E., and APRISON, M. H.: *Biochemistry of the Developing Nervous System,* p. 301. H. Waelsch, Ed. New York, Acad. Press (1955).

81. HIMWICH, H. E., and HIMWICH, W. A.: *Biochemistry of the Developing Nervous System,* p. 202. Waelsch, H. Ed. New York, Acad. Press (1959).

82. HIMWICH, W. A., and PETERSEN, J. C.: *Biol. Psychiat., Proc. Soc. Sessions Soc. Biol. Psychiat. San Francisco, 1958:*2 (pub. 1959).

83. HIMWICH, W. A., PETERSEN, J. C., and ALLEN, M. L.: *Neurology, 7:*705 (1957).

84. HUGHES, A., and FLEXNER, L. B.: *J. Anat., 90:*386 (1956).

85. JORDAN, W. K., and MARCH, R.: *Biochemistry of the Developing Nervous System,* p. 327. Waelsch, H., Ed. New York, Acad. Press (1955).

86. JORDAN, W. K., and MARCH, R.: *J. Histochem. Cytochem., 4:*301 (1956).

87. JORDAN, W. K., MARCH, R., and MESSING, R. A.: *Progress in Neurobiology: I. Neurochemistry,* p. 101. Korey, S., and Nurnberger, J. I., Eds. New York, Hoeber-Harper (1956).

87A. KATO, R.: *J. Neurochem., 5:*202 (1960).

88. KAVALER, F., and KIMEL, V. M.: *J. Comp. Neurol., 96:*113 (1952).

89. KELLY, B.: *Am. J. Physiol., 185:*299 (1956).

90. KETY, S.: *Biochemistry of the Developing Nervous System,* p. 208 Waelsch, H., Ed. New York, Acad. Press (1955).

91. KISHIMOTO, Y., and RADIN, N. S.: *J. Lipid Research, 1:*72 (1959).

92. KISHIMOTO, Y., and RADIN, N. S.: *J. Lipid Research, 1:*79 (1959).

93. KLENK, E.: *Ztschr. physiol. Chem., 235:*24 (1935).

94. KLENK, E.: *Ztschr. physiol. Chem., 268:*50 (1941).

95. KLENK, E.: *Biochemistry of the Developing Nervous System,* p. 397. H. Waelsch, Ed. New York, Acad. Press (1955).

96. KNOLLE, J.: *Ztschr. Zellforsch. u. mikroskop. Anat., 50:*183 (1959).

97. KOREY, S. R., and ORCHEN, M.: *Arch. Biochem. Biophys., 83:*381 (1959).

98. KREBS, E. M., PIGAREVA, Z. D., TCHETVERKOV, D. A., and POMASANSKAI, L. F.: *Cahiers Medicine Sovietque, 1:*20 (1953).

99. KUHLMAN, R. E., and LOWRY, O. H.: *J. Neurochem., 1:*173 (1956).

100. LAJTHA, A.: *J. Neurochem., 2:*209 (1958).

101. LAJTHA, A.: *J. Neurochem., 3:*358 (1959).

102. LAJTHA, A. BERL, S., and WAELSCH, H.: *J. Neurochem., 3:*322 (1959).

103. LAJTHA, A., FURST, S., GERSTEIN, A., and WAELSCH, H.: *J. Neurochem., 1:*289 (1957).

104. LAJTHA, A., FURST, S., and WAELSCH, H.: *Experientia, 13:*168 (1957).

105. LeBaron, F. N., and Folch, J.: *J. Neurochem.,* *1:*101 (1956).
106. Mallucci, L., and Tontodonati, T.: *Pediatria* (Naples), *66:*403 (1958).
107. Mandel, P., and Bieth, R.: *Bull. Soc. chim. biol., 33:*973 (1951).
108. Mandel, P., and Bieth, R.: *Compt. rend., 235:*485 (1952).
109. Mandel, P., Bieth, R., and Stoll, R.: *Bull. Soc. chim. biol., 31:*1335 (1949).
110. Mandel, P., Bieth, R., and Stoll, R.: *Compt. rend. Soc. biol., 143:*1224 (1949).
111. Mandel, P., Fruhling, L., and Weill, D.: *Experientia, 11:*226 (1955).
112. Manina, A. A.: *Doklady Akad. Nauk S.S.S.R., 126:*867 (1959).
113. Manukyan, K. G.: *Doklady Akad. Nauk S.S.S.R., 101:*1085 (1955).
114. Manukyan, K. G.: *Doklady Akad. Nauk S.S.S.R., 102:*567 (1955).
115. McMillan, P. J., Douglas, G. W., and Mortensen, R. A.: *Proc. Soc. Exper. Biol. & Med., 96:*738 (1959).
116. Meltzer, H. L., and Sperry, W. M.: Unpublished experiments.
117. Metzler, C. J., and Humm, D. G.: *Science, 113:*382 (1951).
118. Miani, N.: *Atti soc. med.-chir. Padova, 34:*26 (1956-57).
119. Miani, N.: *Experientia, 14:*34 (1958).
120. Miani, N., and Bucciante, G.: *Atti soc. med.-chir. Padova, 34:*48 (1956-57).
121. Miani, N., and Bucciante, G.: *Experientia, 14:*10 (1958).
122. Miani, N., Marini, L., and Amaducci, L.: *Arch. sc. biol., 39:*498 (1955).
123. Mihara, T.: *J. Biochem.* (Japan), *39:*155 (1952).
124. Millichap, J. G.: *Proc. Soc. Exper. Biol. & Med., 96:*125 (1957).
125. Moldave, K., Winzler, R. J., and Pearson, H. E.: *J. Biol. Chem., 200:*357 (1953).
126. Morikawa, N.: *Arch. hist. jap., 14:*165 (1958).
127. Moser, H. W., and Karnovsky, M. L.: *J. Biol. Chem., 234:*1990 (1959).
128. Nachmansohn, D.: *Chemical and Molecular Basis of Nerve Activity,* p. 38. New York, Acad. Press (1959).
129. Naidoo, D., and Pratt, O. E.: *Enzymologia, 16:*298 (1954).
130. Naka, S.: *Kyushu Memoirs M. Sc., 3:*203 (1953).
131. Nicholas, H. J., and Thomas, B. E.: *J. Neurochem., 4:*42 (1959).
132. Nikitin, V. N., and Golubitskaya: *Uchenye Zapiski Khar'kov Univ., 53, Trudy Nauch.-Issledovatel. Inst. Biol., 21:*143-151 (1954); *Chem. Abstr., 50:*5056 (1956).
133. Palladin, A. V.: *Biochemistry of the Developing Nervous System,* p. 177 H. Waelsch, Ed. New York, Acad. Press (1955).
134. Panchenko, L. F.: *Fiziol. Zhur. S.S.S.R., 44:*243 (1958); *Chem. Abstr., 52:*10340 (1958).
135. Parvis, P.: *Atti soc. ital. anat. XIII Convegno sociale,* 5 pp. (1951).
136. Pigareva, Z. D.: *Voprosy Biokhim. Nervnoi Sistemy, Kiev, Akad. Nauk Ukr. S.S.R., Sbornik 1957,* pp. 217-27; *Chem. Abstr., 53:*19084 (1959).
137. Pigareva, Z. D., and Chetverikov, D. A.: *Doklady Akad. Nauk. S.S.S.R., 78:*169 (1951).
138. Purpura, D. P., and Carmichael, M. W.: *Science, 131:*410 (1960).
139. Radin, N. S., Lavin, F. B., and Brown, J. R.: *J. Biol. Chem., 217:*789 (1955).
140. Rafelson, M. E., Jr., Winzler, R. J., and Pearson, H. E.: *J. Biol. Chem., 193:*205 (1951).
141. Rapport, M. M., and Franzl, R. E.: *J. Neurochem., 1:*303 (1957).
142. Richter, D.: *Biochemistry of the Developing Nervous System,* p. 225. Waelsch, H., Ed. New York Acad. Press (1957).
143. Richter, D., and Hullin, R. P.: *Biochem. J., 48:*406 (1951).

144. ROBERTS, E.: *Progress in Neurobiology. I. Neurochemistry* p. 11. Korey, S., and Nurnberger, J. I., Eds. New York, Hoeber-Harper (1956).
145. ROBERTS, E., HARMON, P. J., and FRANKEL, S.: *Proc. Soc. Exp. Biol. & Med., 78:*799 (1951).
146. ROBERTS, E., LOWE, I. P., GUTH, L, and JELINEK, B.: *J. Exper. Zool., 138:*313 (1958).
147. ROBERTS, R. B., FLEXNER, J. B., and FLEXNER, L. B.: *J. Neurochem., 4:*78 (1959).
148. ROSENBERG, A., and CHARGAFF, E.: *Biochim. et Biophys. Acta, 21:*588 (1956).
149. RUDNICK, D., and WAELSCH, H.: *Biochemistry of the Developing Nervous System,* p. 335. H. Waelsch, Ed. New York, Acad. Press (1955).
150. SCHMIDT, G., BENNOTTI, J., HERSHMAN, B., and THANNHAUSER, S. J.: *J. Biol. Chem., 166:*505 (1946).
151. SCHMIDT, G., OTTENSTEIN, B., SPENCER, W. A., KECK, K., BLIETZ, R., PAPAS, J., PORTER, D., LEVIN, M. L., and THANNHAUSER, S. J.: *A.M.A. J. Dis. Child. 97:*691 (1959).
152. SCHWERIN, P., BESSMAN, S. P., and WAELSCH, H.: *J. Biol. Chem., 184:*37 (1948).
152A. SHIMIZA, N., and MORIKAWA, N.: *Nature, 184:*Suppl. No. 9, 650 (1959).
153. SKY-PECK, H. H., PEARSON, H. E., and VISSER, D. W.: *J. Biol. Chem., 223:*1033 (1956).
154. SMIRNOV, A. A., and CHETVERIKOV, D. A. *Doklady Akad. Nauk. S.S.S.R., 90:*631 (1953).
155. SMITS, G., and EDGAR, G. W. F.: *J. Neuropath. & Exper. Neurol., 17:*269 (1958).
156. SPERRY, W. M.: *J. Biol. Chem., 209:*377 (1954).
157. SPERRY, W. M.: *Biochemistry of the Developing Nervous System,* p. 261. H. Waelsch, Ed. New York, Acad. Press (1955).
158. SPERRY, W. M., TAYLOR, R. M., and MELTZER, H. L.: *Federation Proc. 12:*271 (1953).
159. SRERE, P. A., CHAIKOFF, I. L., TREITMAN, S. S., and BURSTEIN, L. S.: *J. Biol. Chem., 182:*629 (1950).
160. SZEPSENWOL, J., MASON, J., and SHONTZ, M. E.: *Am. J. Physiol., 180:*525 (1955).
161. TINGEY, A. H.: *J. Ment. Sc., 102:*851 (1956).
162. TINGEY, A.: *J. Neurochem., 3:*230 (1959).
163. UZMAN, L. L.: *Arch. Biochem. Biophys., 76:*474 (1958).
164. UZMAN, L. L., and ROSEN, H.: *Arch. Biochem. Biophys., 76:*490 (1958).
165. UZMAN, L. L., and RUMLEY, N. K.: *J. Neurochem., 3:*170 (1958).
166. VAN BRUGGEN, J. T., HUTCHENS, T. T., CLAYCOMB, C. K., and WEST, E. S.: *J. Biol. Chem., 200:*31 (1953).
167. WAELSCH, H.: *Advances in Protein Chemistry,* Vol. 6, p. 299. New York, Acad. Press (1951).
168. WAELSCH, H.: *Biochemistry of the Developing Nervous System,* p. 187. Waelsch, H., Ed. New York, Acad. Press (1955).
169. WAELSCH, H., SPERRY, W. M., and STOYANOFF, V. A.: *J. Biol. Chem., 135:*291 (1940).
169A. WENDER, M., and HIEROWSKI, M.: *J. Neurochem., 5:*105 (1960).
170. WINZLER, R. J., MOLDAVE, K., RAFELSON, M. E., and PEARSON, H. E.: *J. Biol. Chem., 199:*485 (1952).
171. WOLMAN, M.: *Bull Research Council Israel, 6E:*163 (1957).

IV

THE HISTOCHEMISTRY OF THE MYELIN SHEATH

C. W. M. Adams

THE demyelinating diseases, in particular multiple sclerosis, have been a focus for research and speculation for the last eighty years, yet little headway has been made in our understanding of the pathogenesis of these diseases. Research into the demyelinating diseases has been mainly concerned with testing and disproving an array of aetiological hypotheses for multiple sclerosis rather than the investigation of the fundamental structural disorder of demyelination. It is proposed here to consider the histochemistry of normal and degenerating myelin with the aim that greater knowledge of the process of demyelination may suggest in which direction the aetiological agent for multiple sclerosis should be sought.

LIPIDS IN NORMAL MYELIN

(a) Histochemical Methods

Ranvier[1] in 1878 first used osmium tetroxide to stain the myelin sheath. Later Marchi[2] added Muller's fluid (potassium dichromate) to the osmium solution and found that only degenerating myelin was now stained. The mechanism of Marchi's method will be discussed later.

At about this time Weigert[3] noticed that myelin, after fixation in a mixture of dichromate and a copper salt, had a marked affinity for haematoxylin: the metallic salts formed a mordant with the myelin lipids to capture and bind the dye. This technique was subsequently modified[4-7] and later formed the basis of Baker's acid-haematin method for phospholipids.[8-10]

Following the publication of Lison's Histochimie Animale[11] in 1936, a greater variety of histochemical methods applicable to the analysis of myelin have slowly become available. These depend either on the chemical characterization of specific groups in the lipid molecule or

85

on the differing physical properties of lipids. These methods provide the only direct evidence of the chemical identity of the myelin lipids for in biochemical analyses it is impossible to obtain a sample of myelin uncontaminated by axon and, to a lesser extent, by connective tissue or glial elements. However, the histochemical demonstration of specific chemical groups in lipids may be impossible when the lipid is of hydrophobic nature and resists the penetration of aqueous reagents and dyes.[12] Fortunately myelin is an essentially hydrophilic mixture of lipids and these reservations are relatively unimportant in this case.

The specific chemical groups which can be identified in the myelin lipids are: the phosphatidyl group of phospholipids, the fatty acid ester link of the phosphoglycerides, the hexoses of cerebrosides, the α-β unsaturated group of plasmalogens, the basic groups of lipids, the ethylene bond of unsaturated lipids and the $\triangle^5$-stenol configuration of cholesterol. The histochemical detection of lipid carbonyl groups in myelin[13] is open to doubt on account of interference by other aldehydes.[14]

Phospholipids.—Phospholipid has been demonstrated in the myelin sheath by Baker's acid haematin method.[15,16] Baker showed that phospholipids were intensely stained by this method while cerebrosides gave only faint colours. Cain,[10] using highly purified lipid samples, claimed that phospholipids were the only lipids stained. However, there is still some doubt whether cerebroside may contribute slightly to the staining of myelin by acid haematin.[16-18] The view is widely held that the unsaturated groups of the fatty acids of phospholipid reduce the dichromate used in Baker's method to an insoluble lower oxide and that this accounts for the mordanting and subsequent staining of phospholipids with haematoxylin or haematin.[6,19] This explanation is probably incorrect as myelin is still stained by acid haematin after preliminary saturation of the reducing ethylene bonds of fatty acids by bromine.[20] Since phospholipids form a variety of complexes with metallic salts, it is more likely that chromate is captured and bound by phospholipids as a complex with the phosphatidyl group.

Okamoto[21] showed that phospholipids bind mercury after treatment with a solution of mercuric nitrate: the bound mercury was then demonstrated by diphenylcarbazone. By a series of preliminary extractions in solvents it was claimed that different classes of phospholipids could be identified. However, Edgar and Donker[22] found that these extractions were incomplete and, therefore, unreliable when applied to the myelin lipids.

Phosphoglyceride in myelin may be detected by an adaptation[23] of the ferric hydroxamate reaction for the lipid ester link. Since the reagents for this modification of the test are dissolved in water only hydrophilic lipids will react. Both phosphoglycerides and sphingolipids are hydrophilic but the latter are not stained as their fatty acids are bound to sphingosine, not by an ester link, but by an unreactive amide bond.

By the plasmal reaction[24,25] it has been shown that myelin is rich in plasmalogen phospholipids. This test depends on the hydrolysis of the a,β-unsaturated ether bond of plasmalogen[26] to fatty aldehyde which is stainable in the tissues by Schiff's reagent. Free aldehyde in the tissues or aldehyde formed by atmospheric oxidation of the ethylene bond (pseudo-plasmalogen) is excluded by preliminary aldehyde blockade and by using an unhydrolysed section as a control.

Copper phthalocyanin[27] demonstrates the basic groups of lipids and, probably, the guanidinyl group of arginine. At first the method was thought to stain only the choline-containing phospholipids—lecithin and sphingomyelin—but subsequent investigation[28] has shown that sphingomyelin is not stained unless the dye is dissolved in chloroform. Moreover, ganglioside is also stained and this raises doubt whether lipid-bound hexosamine and other weaker bases may not react with the dye as well as choline.

Glycolipids.—The hexoses of the myelin cerebrosides are mainly responsible for the positive periodic acid Schiff (PAS) reaction of the sheath. The prevention of staining by preliminary extraction of the myelin by lipid solvents suggests that the stained material is lipid and not a polysaccharide while the failure of aqueous extraction indicates that the PAS positive material is not ganglioside or water-soluble polysaccharide. It has been shown[29] that, if polysaccharides can be excluded, the PAS reaction of lipid mixtures is due to the hexoses of cerebrosides: preliminary acetylation prevented the reaction owing to the blockade of the reactive glycol groups of the carbohydrate. Likewise, the ethylene bond of the unsaturated fatty acid side chain of sphingomyelin is not PAS-positive when the tissues are oxidised by periodic acid for the standard time of 10 minutes.[38] However, with more prolonged oxidation at lower pH these ethylene bonds did become PAS-positive. From these observations it may be concluded that the lipid in myelin which is stained by the standard PAS reaction is cerebroside.

Bial's reagent (orcin-$FeCl_3$-HCl) has been used[31] for the detection of neuraminic acid in ganglioside and Molisch's reagent (a-naphthol-H_2SO_4) for the staining of the hexoses of ganglioside and cerebroside. Although cerebroside can be detected in myelin by the second method, both techniques tend to be rather too destructive to tissues for the accurate histological localisation of these lipids.

Unsaturated Groups.—The presence of unsaturated groups in the

fatty acid side chains of the myelin lipids is shown by the oxidation
of the ethylene bond to aldehyde by performic acid or, alternatively,
by the reduction of osmium tetroxide by these bonds. The performic
acid-Schiff reaction (PFAS[32,33]) is only successful when the lipids concerned are hydrophilic, as in myelin, for the reagents used in the test
are relatively insoluble in hydrophobic lipids such as neutral fat and
esterified cholesterol. With both the PFAS and osmium methods a
strong reaction is given by myelin.

   Cholesterol. The Schultz modification of the Liebermann-Burchard
reaction is too destructive to tissues to permit accurate localization of
cholesterol in the myelin sheath. This difficulty has been overcome
by the introduction of the perchloric acid-napthoquinone method[34]
which shows that there is abundant cholesterol within the myelin
sheath but only traces in unmyelinated areas. The distinction of free
from ester cholesterol by the formation of a non-Sudanophilic birefringent digitonide (Windhaus reaction) is seldom of practical value
in histochemistry due to interference by other lipids.[14]

(b) Histophysical Methods

   Virchow[35] was the first to draw attention to one of the characteristic
histophysical features of the myelin sheath, the formation of myelin
buds from the cut ends of unfixed medullated nerve fibres. The myelin
bud is an organized micellar outgrowth from the surface of a hydrophilic lipid resulting from the imbibition of water and the outward
orientation of the polar groups of these lipids.[36,37] Mixtures of lipids
which form buds must contain at least one hydrophilic type while
mixtures which bud most readily are composed of both strongly hydrophilic and hydrophobic sorts.[38] Triglycerides, cholesterol, cholesterol
esters and fatty acids are hydrophobic on account of their relatively
unpolarised fatty acid and sterolic hydroxyl groups while phospholipids, and to a lesser extent, glycolipids are hydrophilic owing to the
strongly polarised phosphatidyl group or the more weakly polarised
glycolic hydroxyl.

   The low surface tension and hydrophilic properties of the phospholipids in myelin, when compared with the high surface tension
of the globular hydrophobic fat of adipose tissue, is the key to many
of the different staining properties of the lipids of these two tissues.
Lipids which present polar groups to a water phase readily take up
polarised dyes or reagents in aqueous solution. Phospholipids, in contact with water, become orientated with the phosphatidyl group directed towards the aqueous phase while the paraffin chain of their
fatty acids is directed away from the water. Such hydrophilic or polar
lipids in myelin can be stained by aqueous solution of dyes, such as

the blue (oxazine) of Nile blue sulphate[39,40] Conversely hydrophobic lipids, such as the fats of adipose tissue, can only present their non-polar paraffin chains to a water surface. The mutual repellance between the paraffin chain and water promotes free energy (surface tension) at the interface and, hence, hydrophobic lipids coalesce to a globular form to lower the total surface-energy of the system.[41] Hydrophobic lipids are stained by dyes or reagents soluble in organic reagents but not by those soluble only in water. Thus, for example, they are stained by the red Sudan dyes, the red "fat"-soluble (oxazone) component of Nile blue sulphate and by organotropic fluorescent dyes.

It is not generally recognized that lipid-soluble stains, such as the Sudan dyes, are only absorbed by hydrophobic lipids when in liquid state. Solid crystalline lipids do not absorb these dyes.[42] In practice, the melting point of animal fats varies from —16°C. in the porpoise to 41°C. in mutton tallow,[43] so that if staining is carried out at 45°C. nearly all naturally-occurring mixtures of triglycerides will absorb these dyes.

Conversely, the physical characteristic of lipid birefringence can be detected only when the lipid is in crystalline state. Anisotropic lipid material in tissues warmed to about 50°C. is usually cholesterol since most other physiological mixtures of lipids are fluid at this temperature. However, the absence of birefringence cannot be taken to indicate that cholesterol is not present since the sterol may be dissolved in a liquid mixture of other lipids. For this reason birefringence is not a particularly useful tool for identifying lipids although, in general, it distinguishes between lipids of high and low melting point. Not all birefringence, moreover, is due to lipid crystals for the orderly or paracrystalline structure of the myelin sheath itself gives rise to birefringence owing to the plane of orientation of the lipid and protein layers in the sheath.[44]

Differential solubility of lipids would seem to be a useful technique for the histophysical identification of myelin lipids. However, traces of other lipids often increase the solubility of a lipid in a solvent.[45] Furthermore, some lipids are so firmly bound to protein that they can only be extracted by acidification of the solvent[46] or by the use of soaps, heat or very prolonged extraction in a chloroform-methanol mixture.[47] These and other limitations[22] tend to invalidate the detailed histochemical identification of myelin lipids by differential solubility.

The Marchi Reaction.—The Marchi reaction is a valuable histochemical method since information is gained about both the physical and chemical characteristics of lipids. Marchi[2] found that, when potassium dichromate was added to a solution of osmium tetroxide, only degenerating myelin was stained. Marchi's method has been modified by using potassium iodate[48] as the oxidant but, later, better results were obtained with potassium chlorate[49,50] and this modification is now in current use. However, no satisfactory explanation of the Marchi reaction was forthcoming. Lison[11] records that "cette addition de dichromate produit-elle resultats bizarres" and Cain[42] noted the "inexplicable behaviour of osmium tetroxide in the presence of dichromate. The difficulty is that osmium tetroxide alone stains all unsaturated lipids but in the presence of a polar oxidising agent only degenerating myelin and the fat of adipose tissue are stained.

An investigation[51] on the reactions between an OsO_4–$KClO_3$ mixture and simple unsaturated dicarboxylic acids showed that OsO_4 acted as a carrier for the oxidation of the unsaturated group of these acids and was not itself reduced in this system. The author[12] showed that hydrophilic lipids, such as phospholipids and myelin extracts, are permeable to both osmium tetroxide and polar oxidising agents such as chlorate. Conversely, hydrophobic lipids, for example, neutral fat and cholesterol esters, are impermeable to chlorate but absorb osmium (Table I). In this connection, osmium tetroxide behaves

TABLE I

PERMEABILITY OF LIPIDS TO OSMIUM TETROXIDE, POTASSIUM CHLORATE
AND HALOGENS

Reagents	Rate of Absorption (mm./hr.)			
	Hydrophilic Lipids	Hydrophobic Lipids		
	Myelin Lipids	Olive Oil	Oleic Acid	Cholesterol Oleate
OsO_4	0.92	0.48	0.58	0.52
$KClO_3$	0.96	<0.01	<0.01	<0.01
Br_2	1.20	0.58	0.53	ca. 0.50
I_2	0.66	0.16	0.16	0.14

similarly to a Sudan dye. From the observations on dicarboxylic acids it follows that potassium chlorate, which is absorbed by hydrophilic lipids, prevents the reduction of osmium by the hydrophilic lipids of normal myelin. Conversely, the hydrophobic lipids of degenerating myelin and adipose tissue reduce the absorbed osmium tetroxide since chlorate is not soluble in them.

This hypothesis of the mechanism of the Marchi reaction is supported by the detection of colourless partly reduced osmium (Os^{vi}) bound to normal myelin which had previously been treated with Marchi's fluid. It is inferred that the addition of chlorate to a solution of osmium tetroxide prevents the second stage of the reaction formulated in Fig. 1 and the chlorate is itself reduced instead. The addition compound formed in the first stage of the reaction can be detected by its reaction with α-naphthylamine to form a red chelate between the amine and Os^{vi}.[52] The combined technique of treating tissues with osmium tetroxide-potassium chlorate (Marchi fluid) followed by α-naphthylamine (OTAN method[53]) has a histochemical application in that hydrophilic lipids, such as those of normal myelin, are stained red while the hydrophobic lipids of degenerating myelin or adipose tissue are black. *In vitro* studies with pure lipid samples revealed that phosphoglyceride and phosphosphingoside are stained red, cerebroside faintly pink and neutral fats, fatty acids and cholesterol esters black. Cholesterol and fully saturated lipids such as tristearin were unstained.

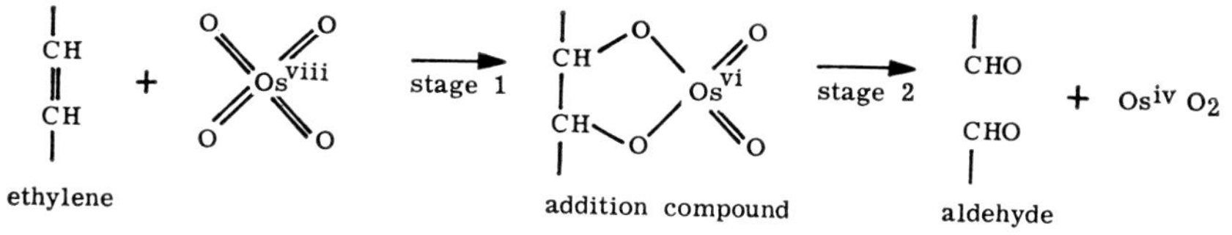

Fig. 1. Reactions between OsO$_4$ and the ethylene bond.

The hydrophobic lipid formed in degenerating myelin is probably mainly esterified cholesterol, since this ester first appears in the degenerating nerve at the time when the degeneration products become Marchi-positive.[54-57] Furthermore, in the plaques of multiple sclerosis, about 30-35% of the cholesterol is esterified[58-60] in contrast to the normal CNS of the adult human where cholesterol is present virtually only in its free form.[61] Similar amounts of esterified cholesterol were found in the Marchi-positive posterior columns of human cord undergoing Wallerian degeneration.[62] The conclusion that the Marchi reaction of degenerating myelin is due to the formation of hydrophobic cholesterol esters is supported by solubility studies on the Marchi substance.[63,64] According to Wolman[65,66] the formation of *neutral* mucopolysaccharide (myelosaccharide B) accounts for the Marchi reaction of degenerating myelin. It is most improbable, however, that the Marchi substance in the nervous system should be carbohydrate when, in the rest of the body, Marchi-stainable substances are all of lipid nature and never polysaccharide. Further evidence, in favour of cholesterol ester as the Marchi substance, has been obtained by histo-

chemical blockade of tissue reducing groups and by the chromatographic separation of degenerating myelin.[62] Blockade of the reducing
groups of protein, polysaccharide and hydrophilic lipid did not reduce
the osmiophilia of degenerating myelin but preliminary saturation by
bromine of the ethylene bonds of hydrophobic lipid prevented the
subsequent reduction of OsO_4. Of the fractions obtained by column
chromatography of degenerating myelin only the first, which eluted
cholesterol esters, was Marchi-positive. The cholesterol, phospholipid,
cerebroside and water-soluble fractions were all Marchi-negative as
were the aqueous and proteolipid phases obtained by preliminary
washing[67] of the crude extract.

Although certain amino acids reduce OsO_4 *in vitro*,[68] tissue proteins
are not stained black by short exposure to either Marchi's fluid or
OsO_4 alone. It is likely that, for full reduction of OsO_4 to OsO_2, both
oxygen atoms of the OsO_4 molecule must be reduced simultaneously.[62]
These requirements of spatial arrangements would be satisfied by the
ethylene bond of an unsaturated lipid or by a solution of a reducing
agent such as cysteine but not by a fixed tissue-protein (see Fig. 2).

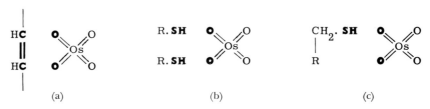

Fig. 2. Reactions between OsO_4 and reducing agents. (a) complete reduction
by the ethylene bond; (b) complete reduction by cysteine in solution; (c) slow
or incomplete reduction by -SH groups in protein.

LIPIDS DURING MYELINATION

Lipid droplets have been described in the neuropil before the onset
of myelination.[69,70] Likewise, diffuse metachomasia of the neuropil
before myelination has been atributed to the temporary storage of
sphingolipids there.[71] It has been suggested from biochemical evidence[72] that most of the lipids which are deposited in the newly-
formed myelin sheath are present as such or as lipid precursors before
myelination starts. However, in the author's experience stainable lipid
material in the kitten brain is only scanty before myelination and
differs in its histochemical characteristics from that in the developing
or mature sheath.

At the onset of myelination it has been claimed that sphingomyelin
is first laid down while a pyridine-insoluble lipid, tentatively identified

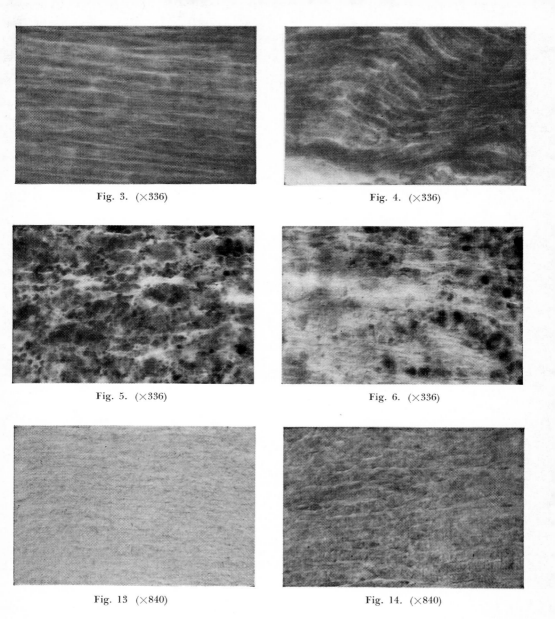

Fig. 3. (×336)

Fig. 4. (×336)

Fig. 5. (×336)

Fig. 6. (×336)

Fig. 13 (×840)

Fig. 14. (×840)

Fig. 3. Normal mouse sciatic nerve. The myelin sheath is stained red-brown (phospholipid). OTAN method, × 336.

Fig. 4. Mouse sciatic nerve 6 days after nerve section. The lipid fragments are stained similarly to the normal myelin sheath. OTAN method, × 336.

Fig. 5. Mouse sciatic nerve 12 days after nerve section. Some lipid fragments are now black (Marchi-positive cholesterol esters). OTAN method, × 336.

Fig. 6. Mouse sciatic nerve 16 days after nerve section. More fragments are now Marchi-positive while there is less phospholipid. OTAN method, × 336.

Fig. 13. Normal mouse sciatic nerve. Sudan IV and trypan blue, × 840.

Fig. 14. Mouse sciatic nerve 6 days after nerve section. Note dissociation of myelin lipid (orange) from protein (blue). Sudan IV and trypan blue, × 840.

as cerebroside, appears a few days later.[71] In the early phases of myelination the sheath and occasional surrounding lipid droplets are Marchi-positive as shown by the OTAN method.[73] This staining was attributed to the temporary presence of large amounts of esterified cholesterol during myelinogenesis. These esters, virtually disappear from the adult myelin sheath which by now is Marchi-negative.[61] The significance of these observations is discussed further in the next section.

LIPIDS IN DEMYELINATION

The chemico-structural mechanism of demyelination would appear to be a problem which could be readily solved by chemical analysis of the sectioned nerve or tract undergoing Wallerian degeneration. Such is not the case, however, for it has been shown that during the first eight days after nerve or cord section there are no significant chemical changes in the amount or nature of each of the myelin lipids.[56,57] During this preliminary phase the myelin sheath is undergoing physical fragmentation but from the foregoing biochemical analyses and from histochemical studies[15,16,74] it is clear that the lipid fragments have the same characteristics as the lipids of the normal sheath. Thus the granules, ovoids and ellipsoids in this early stage of degeneration are hydrophilic (OTAN method; Figs. 3 and 4) and contain plasmalogen (plasmal reaction), phospholipid (acid haematin method), phosphoglyceride (ferric hydroxamate reaction), lipid-bound carbohydrate (PAS method, reversed by lipid extraction), lipid-bound basic groups (copper phthalocyanin method), cholesterol (Schultz method) and lipid ethylene bonds (PFAS and OsO_4 methods).

After this initial period of physical fragmentation of the sheath the myelin lipids undergo chemical degradation. Thus, Rossiter and his co-workers[56,57,75] showed that sphingomyelin, cerebroside and lipid-bound phosphorus fell abruptly during the second week of degeneration and they were replaced by increasing amounts of esterified cholesterol. At this time some of the lipid fragments become hydrophobic and Marchi-positive (OTAN method; Fig. 5 and 6) owing to the accumulation of cholesterol esters in the degenerating nerve (see the section on the Marchi reaction). Correspondingly, during the second week of demyelination, lipid fragments with the staining characteristics of normal myelin begin to disappear and, by the 30th day after nerve section, they have become quite scanty.

The sequence of events during Wallerian degeneration of the peripheral nerve may be summarised as follows:

(1) An initial phase of physical disintegration of the sheath, which is the only event seen during the first eight days of degeneration.

(2) A stage of chemical degradation, resulting in the disappearance of the lipid components of normal myelin, which begins at the eighth day and lasts several weeks.

(3) A reparative phase, which starts when the demyelinating debris has been resorbed.

Two important problems are raised by Rossiter's observations on the chemical changes during Wallerian degeneration:

(a) Does the occurrence of esterified cholesterol indicate that the esterification of cholesterol is a primary process in demyelination or does it only reflect a secondary phase of chemical degradation of the myelin lipids to simpler esters?

(b) What processes are involved in the initial physical disintegration of the myelin sheath?

In Rossiter's view the accumulation of esterified cholesterol is a result of chemical degradation of the normal myelin lipids. Water-soluble degradation products such as phosphate, phosphoryl choline, glycerol, sphingosine, choline, ethanolamine and galactose are presumably reabsorbed. But the fatty acid side-chains of these polar lipids are not so readily reabsorbed and could be more easily rendered inert by esterification with the cholesterol set free from degenerating myelin. Free fatty acids in tissues either undergo esterification with cholesterol or, more slowly, are neutralised to form calcium soaps. According to this view, the formation of cholesterol esters is a secondary event which sheds no light on the primary processes of demyelination. The alternative view, that the esterification of cholesterol is a primary process, can only be advanced if the absence of ester during the first week after nerve section could be satisfactorily explained.

Cholesterol esterases are probably active during myelination for esterified cholesterol is temporarily present in the sheath during myelinogenesis[73] but the absence of these esters from the adult sheath[61] clearly indicates that the esters in the developing CNS are either removed intact or that they are de-esterified during the maturation of myelin. Deesterification, the more likely mechanism, would explain the unique feature of the adult sheath—that cholesterol is present only in its free state. If it is assumed that cholesterol esterase persists in the mature myelin sheath, enzyme would be available to promote esterification of cholesterol by reverse action during demyelination. The demonstration of cholesterol esterases by histochemical means would help to clarify this problem but, unfortunately, it has not yet been possible to devise a suitable method. The position remains that, from the limited information available, there is little evidence to suggest that cholesterol esterases are responsible for the initial disruption of the degenerating myelin sheath.

POLYSACCHARIDES AND METACHROMASIA IN MYELIN

Acid mucopolysaccaride has been demonstrated by the colloidal iron technique[76] in the neurilemma and axon of the peripheral nerve.[77] In the CNS a PAS-positive polysaccharide, which is insoluble in both water and lipid-solvents, is present in the "ground substance" or neuropil.[78] The polysaccharides of the brain have been analysed chemically[79] but their precise localisation was not determined.

Red-brown staining of peripheral nerve myelin with the Bicol method has been attributed[80] to weakly acidic mucopolysaccharide (myelosaccharide A) which increases, either in amount or in its accessibility to stains, during the very early phase of demyelination.[66] At a later stage of degeneration it has been claimed that this acid mucopolysaccharide is converted to a neutral sort (myelosaccharide B). Evidence was obtained to suggest that this acid mucopolysaccharide may be attached, through lipid, to a trypsin-digestible protein in the normal sheath.[81] Nevertheless, the identification of polysaccharide in myelin is still tentative and the PAS reaction of the sheath appear to be almost entirely due to lipid-bound carbohydrate.

Phospholipids and, possibly, sulphatides[82] are responsible for the blue staining of myelin with Bicol[81] and for the red-purple metachromasia of the sheath with cresyl violet and toluidine blue.[83,84] The red dichroic effect seen when myelin, stained by Sudan black, is viewed in polarised light is also due to phospholipid.[85] Ganglioside storage-products in Tay-Sachs disease develop a brown metachromasia with cresyl violet and toluidine blue,[84] probably on account of the neuraminic acid in the carbohydrate moiety of ganglioside.

MYELIN PROTEINS AND LIPID-PROTEIN COMPLEXES

The histological and histochemical characteristics of the myelin proteins were first investigated by Kühne and Chittenden[86] and Nageotte.[87] The neurokeratin which had previously been identified chemically[88] was thought to be located in the sheath and to be represented there by the protein net-work in myelin. Little more was known about the neurokeratins until it was shown by Folch and his colleagues[89,46] that two types of proteolytic-enzyme-resistant proteins are present in the brain. One, proteolipid, contains a lipid moiety and behaves like lipid as regards its solubilities while the other, trypsin-resistant protein residue (TRPR), remains in the tissues after lipid extraction but with lipid (diphosphoinositide) still attached to it.

In this section the histochemical characteristics of the myelin proteins will be discussed with emphasis on these questions:

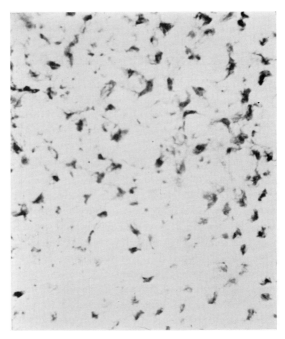

Fig. 7. Human sciatic nerve. Staining of the neurokeratin (TRPR) for tryptophane. pDMAB method, × 360.

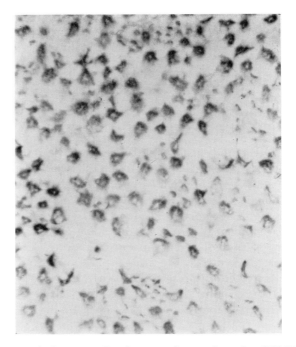

Fig. 8. Human sciatic nerve. Persistence of neurokeratin (TRPR) after extraction by chloroform-methanol. pDMAB method, × 360.

a) Can Folch's proteolipid protein and TRPR be identified histochemically in central and peripheral myelin?

b) Are there other proteins in myelin?

c) What forms of lipid-protein complexes are present in myelin?

Dissociation of lipid from protein or disruption of these lipid-protein bonds could account for the early physical disintegration of the degenerating sheath before the stage of chemical degradation of the myelin lipids (see the section on the lipids in demyelination). Accordingly another question will be raised:

d) What happens to these lipid-protein complexes during Wallerian degeneration?

Trypsin-resistant Proteins.—Histochemical investigations have shown that myelin contains a tryptophane-rich protein.[90] This protein in both the CNS and PNS is resistant to tryptic digestion.[91] Although there is no apparent difference in the histochemical amino acid patterns or enzyme digestibilities of the *trypsin-resistant* protein of myelin in either the CNS or PNS, yet that in central myelin, by reason of its solubility in chloroform-methanol, is mainly of proteolipid nature while the *trypsin-resistant* protein of peripheral myelin (Figs. 7, 8 and 9) resists this extraction and is, therefore, akin to Folch's TRPR.[92] On the other hand, Koenig[93] has claimed that the protein (neurokeratin) of peripheral myelin can be extracted by chloroform-methanol and is, accordingly, proteolipid. This claim was not substantiated by showing that the extractable material was resistant to tryptic and peptic digestion. Moreover, the tissues were stained by methods known to react with lipid rather than protein so that these observations have little direct relevance to myelin protein. Biochemical evidence also supports the view that the *trypsin-resistant* protein of peripheral myelin is a TRPR for only very small amounts of proteolipid appear to be present in the PNS, about a tenth of that in the CNS.[94-96]

The apparent absence of TRPR in sections of the CNS, which had been extracted in choroform-methanol and stained for protein,[92] must be due to the dispersal and hence dilution of this protein throughout both grey and white matter.[46] In contrast, TRPR can be recognised in peripheral myelin since it is concentrated in the myelin sheath only.

Trypsin-digestible Proteins.—Treatment of unfixed sections of brain and peripheral nerve with trypsin or pepsin[81,92] removes a large part of the lipid from myelin (Figs. 10, 11 and 12). This effect was attributed to the protease activity of these enzymes and not, in the case of trypsin, to an A-esterase action.[97] It was found[92] that the *trypsin-digestible* protein in myelin contains more histidine and tryrosine, but less tryptophane, than the *trypsin-resistant* myelin proteins (proteolipid and peripheral nerve TRPR). The loss of myelin

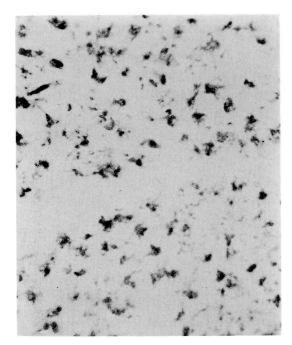

Fig. 9. Human sciatic nerve. Persistence of neurokeratin (TRPR) after tryptic digestion. pDMAB method, × 360.

Fig. 10. Human frontal cortex. Partial removal of myelin lipids by tryptic digestion. Sudan black, × 3.

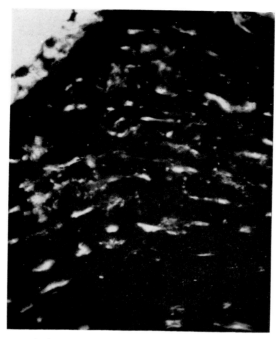

Fig. 11. Human sciatic nerve. The myelin lipids are stained black. Sudan black, × 360.

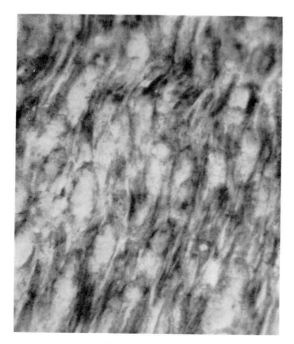

Fig. 12. Human sciatic nerve. Nearly complete removal of myelin lipids by tryptic digestion. Sudan black, × 360.

lipids after tryptic digestion suggests that there is a union between lipid and *trypsin-digestible* protein in the structure of the normal sheath.[81,92]

Lipid-protein Bonds.—The myelin sheath may be considered as a lamellar structure containing alternating bands of protein and lipid.[98,100] Although it is by no means certain which of these ultrastructural bands is lipid and which protein, yet the repeating two-layered lamellar pattern of myelin is confirmed by several independent techniques (polarisation microscopy, electron microscopy and x-ray diffraction). The myelin proteins and lipids are presumably arranged in such a way that not only is structural rigidity imparted to the sheath by protein-protein bonds and by lipid-lipid bonds in the circumferential axis of the lamella but also by protein-lipid bonds directed in a radial direction across the protein and lipid layers of each unit lamella. These lipid-protein bonds are probably hydrogen bonds or, alternatively, salt-linkages between phosphatidyl groups of phospholipid and free terminal amino-groups of protein. Such bonds probably account for the union between lipid and protein in the proteolipids, in the TRPR-diphosphoinositide complex and in the trypsin-digestible protein-lipid complex. No matter what their exact physicochemical nature is, these bonds may be of considerable importance in stabilising the myelin sheath in a radial direction.

TABLE II

THE CHARACTERISTICS OF LIPID-PROTEIN COMPLEXES IN MYELIN

Protein	Solubility in Chloroform-methanol	Digestibility by Trypsin	Associated Lipids	Site
Proteolipid	soluble	resistant	phospholipid cerebroside	CNS
TRPR	insoluble	resistant	phospholipid	peripheral nerve
Enzyme-digestible protein	insoluble	digested	phospholipid cerebroside	CNS and peripheral nerve

The lipids bound by proteolipid protein are phosphatides and cerebrosides,[89] while only phosphatide is associated with TRPR.[46] Phosphatide and cerebroside form at least a part of the lipid complex with the enzyme-digestible protein, since the specific staining of these lipids was much reduced after tryptic and peptic digestion.[92] The characteristics of the lipid-protein complexes in myelin, discussed in this section, are summarised in Table II.

Proteins in Demyelination.—Histochemical evidence[96] has indicated that there is dissociation or splitting of lipid from protein during the first week of Wallerian degeneration in the peripheral nerve (Figs. 13 and 14). This dissociation does not involve the *trypsin-resistant* proteins of either central or peripheral myelins, for the amounts of these proteins did not fall (Table III) until the secondary phase of demyelination at the time when the myelin lipids are chemically degraded (see the section on lipids in demyelination). Likewise there was no early fall in the phospholipid attached to the TRPR of the degenerating peripheral nerve. (No estimation was made of the amount of lipid in the proteolipids of the degenerating CNS.) Since there is apparently no change in the *trypsin-resistant* proteins, it may be deduced that the afore-mentioned lipid-protein dissociation involves only the trypsin-digestible myelin proteins. As a large part of the myelin lipids are attached to trypsin-digestible protein (see the previous section), proteolytic enzymes may have an important role in the early stages of demyelination.

TABLE III

TRYPSIN-RESISTANT PROTEINS IN THE DEGENERATING RAT SCIATIC NERVE AND CORD

Days after Section	Total Phospholipid†		Proteolipid Protein†		TRPR Protein†		TRPR Phospholipid†	
	Nerve	Cord	Nerve	Cord	Nerve	Cord	Nerve	Cord
0	5.20 ±0.48*	5.25 ±0.35	0.07 ±0.01	0.77 ±0.08	0.55 ±0.04	0.41 ±0.04	0.14 ±0.01	0.24 ±0.02
8	4.58 ±0.45	4.97 ±0.10	0.09 ±0.01	0.69 ±0.05	0.57 ±0.03	0.36 ±0.04	0.15 ±0.01	0.39 ±0.06
16	3.45	3.14	0.07	0.58	0.40	0.32	0.11	0.28

*Standard deviation.
†mg./100 mg. corrected wet weight.

MYELIN ENZYMES

Proteolytic Enzymes in Normal and Degenerating Myelin.—It has been shown biochemically that there is an increase in the activity of peptidase[101] and neutral protease[102,96] during Wallerian degeneration. The maximum activity was found during or after the second week of degeneration,[101,102] but some apparently increased activity was noted even by the first day after nerve section.[96] This increased protease activity in the degenerating nerve (Figs. 15, 16, and 17) was detected

Fig. 15. Normal mouse sciatic nerve. Protease activity is revealed as clear areas due to the digestion of the gelatin-silver film, × 96.

Fig. 16. Mouse sciatic nerve 4 days after nerve section. Increased protease activity. Gelatin-silver film, × 96.

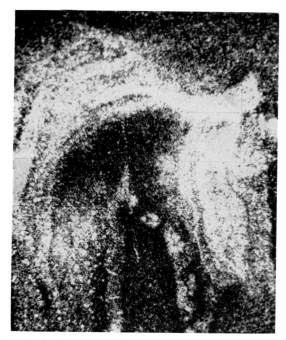

Fig. 17. As for Figure 16, but 6 days after nerve section.

histochemically by the digestion of a gelatin-silver emulsion on glass.[103] Further investigation[96] revealed that the increased activity of proteolytic enzymes in the first few days of demyelination is due more to increased availability or accessability of these enzymes than to increased synthesis. In ground-up samples of nerves there was, apparently, a considerable increase of proteolytic activity in the degenerating nerve but, when the samples were more fully extracted by *high speed centrifugation,* nearly as much enzyme was found in the normal as in the demyelinating tissue (Table IV). This suggests that proteolytic enzyme is a normal constituent of the peripheral nerve and that it is liberated into the axon or myelin sheath during degeneration and is then, accordingly, more easily extracted by simple grinding.

The protease of the peripheral nerve appears to be relatively stable to heat and storage and it is not markedly inhibited by chloroform, methanol or acetone.[104] However, after preliminary extraction by chloroform-methanol, sections of peripheral nerve failed, or nearly so, to digest gelatin in the histochemical test for protease. In the corresponding chemical estimations a large part of the enzyme was extracted by chloroform-methanol or chloroform-acetone. Part of this lipid-bound protease was recovered from the small proteolipid frac-

TABLE IV

THE EFFECT OF EXTRACTION METHODS ON THE PROTEASE ACTIVITY OF NORMAL AND
DEGENERATING MOUSE SCIATIC NERVE (μG. TYROSINE/100 MG. WET WEIGHT/HR.)

Extraction Method	Days after Section	Protease Activity	
		Normal Nerve	Degenerating Nerve
Ground-up nerves	3	207	370
	4 (a)	255	385
	4 (b)	186	405
Ground-up and centrifuged nerves	3	292	334
	4 (a)	335	364
	4 (b)	343	384

tion of the peripheral nerve (Table V). Its presence in the proteolipid
fraction suggests that a large part of the protease of the peripheral
nerve is in the myelin sheath but, in this respect, protease differs from
other myelin enzymes which appear to be attached to the neurokeratin.[105-107]

TABLE V

DISTRIBUTION OF PROTEASE ACTIVITY IN THE HUMAN FEMORAL NERVE AFTER
SEPARATION OF LIPIDS AND PROTEOLIPID FROM RESIDUE
(MG. TYROSINE/100 MG. WET WEIGHT/HR.).

Solvent	Fraction		Extraction Time	No. of Samples	% Age of Total Activity
$CHCl_3$–CH_3OH	extract		½–1 hr.	12	62.2
	residue				37.8
$CHCl_3$–CH_3OH	extract		18 hr.	4	58.6
	residue				41.4
$CHCl_3$–acetone	extract		18 hr.	2	73.6
	residue				26.4
$CHCl_3$–CH_3OH equilibrated with water	extract	$CHCl_3$ phase	18 hr.	2	17.2
		proteolipid			37.1
		aqueous phase			19.5
	residue		1 hr.		26.2
CH_3Cl_3–CH_3OH — H_2O (evaporated)	extract		1 hr.	12	27.5
	proteolipid protein				38.8
	residue				33.7

The liberation of protease within the myelin sheath in the early stages of degeneration would result in the disruption of lipid bound to *trypsin-digestible* protein as shown from experiments *in vitro* (Figs. 10, 11 and 12). This explains, in part, how fragmentation of myelin takes place in the early stages of demyelination without concomitant chemical degradation of the myelin lipids.[57] It is of interest that lysolecithin releases, amongst other enzymes, protease from brain homogenates[108] while CSF proteolytic enzymes are increased in lesions of the CNS which result in necrosis of brain tissue.[109] Ischaemic damage to the brain causes loss of protein from the neuropil[110,111] perhaps as a result of the release of protease.

Other Enzymes.—Histochemical studies reveal that adenosine-triphosphatase, adenosine-5-phosphatase (5-nucleotidase), alkaline phosphatase, creatine phosphatase, cytochrome oxidase, succinic dehydrogenase and pseudo-cholinestrase are enzyme constituents of the peripheral myelin sheath.[105-107] It has been stated[107,112] that acid phosphatase is confined to the axon but other investigators have identified the enzyme in the myelin sheath and neurilemma as well as the axon.[106,113] It has been suggested that the above-mentioned myelin enzymes, unlike protease, are located in the neurokeratin (TRPR) of the peripheral nerve[106] and, in particular, at the interstices of the neurokeratin net work.[107] Most workers, however, agree that the formation of the neurokeratin network is an artefact of fixation, resulting from the precipitation of the neurokeratin of the ultrastructural myelin lamellae by fixatives. Moreover, the reaction of these interstices with mitochondrial stains[107] is probably due to phospholipid bound by neurokeratin and does not necessarily indicate that mitochondria are present. These arguments, however, do not detract from the essential observations that these enzymes are bound to the neurokeratin elements of the peripheral myelin sheath.

Increased enzyme activity during demyelination is reflected in changes in the cell population of the degenerating nerve. Proliferation of Schwann or endoneurial cells begins within four days after nerve section, to be followed by an infiltration of macrophages into the degenerating nerve.[114,115] A sudden increase of DNA phosphorus during demylination[116] corresponds to this stage of cellular proliferation and infiltration.

Certain enzymes become more active during the first week of degeneration. Acid phosphatase, according to chemical estimation, increases during this period to reach a maximum at 16 days[117,118,101] Histochemical staining of the nerve for acid phosphatase (glycerophosphatase) decreases during demyelination[119,106] but this may be due to the different substrates used in the biochemical and histochemical methods.

When 6-benzoyl-2-naphthyl phosphate was used in place of glycero-phosphate as the histochemical substrate, some staining of Schwann cells occurred even at the forty-fifth day of degeneration. In this connection, there is some acid phosphatase (glycerophosphatase) activity in or around the lipid droplets engulfed by the microglia of the multiple sclerosis plaque.[120] Acid phosphatase, oxidase and peroxidase activities are increased in the focal lesions of experimental allergic encephalomyelitis;[121,122] the enzymes also appeared to be active immediately outside the histological limits of the focus.

Adenosine-5-phosphatase (5-nucleotidase) and adenosine-triphosphatase activity in the degenerating nerve appears to be largely in macrophages and the nuclei of Schwann cells.[106] Although biochemical estimation of β-glucuronidase in the degenerating nerve[123] shows the same pattern of increased activity as for acid phosphatase, yet the glucuronidase has not been satisfactorily demonstrated by histochemical means in the myelin sheath.[106]

Tributyrinase (ali-esterase) and pseudo-cholinesterase reach their maximum activity during the first week of demyelination when there is greatest proliferation of Schwann cells,[115] but a decrease was found in a "lipolytic" enzyme (ali-esterase) splitting methyl butyrate.[124] Pseudo-cholinesterase has been demonstrated histochemically in the myelin sheath[107] but sulphatase, lipase (tween substrate) and ali-esterase cannot be detected by these means.[106,74]

None of the enzymes which increase during demyelination have been shown to attack myelin lipids, or to cause demyelination *in vivo* or *in vitro*. Alkaline, but not acid, phosphatase can degrade lipid phosphate esters.[125] But alkaline phosphatase cannot be implicated in the demyelinating process, since the activity of this enzyme falls in the degenerating nerve, as has been shown in both biochemical and histochemical studies.[118,113,126]

THE PATHOLOGY OF THE DEMYELINATING DISEASES

The human demyelinating diseases, of which the most important is multiple sclerosis, are those conditions where the myelin sheath is predominantly affected, while the axon is to a greater or lesser extent spared. Thus Wallerian degeneration and the neuropathies resulting from avitaminoses or poisoning by organophosphorus compounds[127,128] do not belong to this group, for the axon degenerates pari passu with its sheath.

Apart from the simultaneous destruction of the axon in Wallerian degeneration, it has been stated that such secondary demyelination can be distinguished from the primary demyelination of multiple sclerosis by the way in which the sheath breaks down.[129] There is a

sharp non-anatomical border to the demyelination of multiple sclerosis and, in the early shadow of plaque of this disease, morphological
appearances suggest that the sheath first degenerates from the outside.
However, the myelin in the plaque of multiple sclerosis is broken
down into fine vesicles, granules, ovoids and balls as also occurs in the
peripheral nerve and cord undergoing Wallerian degeneration.[15,16]
From this limited evidence it would appear that the process of demyelination is similar in both conditions although the anatomical site at
which the sheath is first attacked may be different. Experiments on
Wallerian degeneration may, therefore, be relevant to the process of
demyelination in multiple sclerosis, but not necessarily to those factors
which determine the precise site of myelin destruction.

Aetiological Hypotheses for Multiple Sclerosis.—Both virus and
spirochaete[130-133] have been proposed as infective agents for multiple
sclerosis but transmission of the disease has not been satisfactorily
demonstrated in either a human community or the experimental animal. Nevertheless, it is of considerable interest that saprophytic organisms such as the *Nocardia* may cause demyelination *in vitro*.[134]

Focal venous thrombosis, resulting in local anoxia, was thought by
Putman[135,136] to be the initiating factor in multiple sclerosis but serial
section of 60 plaques from 5 cases of the disease did not support this
view.[137] The few thrombi found appeared to be a result rather than
the cause of the plaque.

Autoimmunisation or hypersensitisation of the brain against homologous, or possibly heterologous, CNS material is at present considered
as the most probable cause of multiple sclerosis. The difficulty in
equating allergic encephalomyelitis of the experimental animal to
multiple sclerosis is that the distribution and histological nature of
the lesions and the extent of demyelination are rather different in
the two diseases. Patients with multiple sclerosis, however, develop
abnormal immunological responses to the tuberculin protein[138] and
a condition, intermediate between experimental allergic encephalomyelitis and multiple sclerosis, developed in subjects who had been
inoculated with a rabies vaccine cultured on brain.[139]

Metabolic instability of the myelin sheath has been put forward as
the underlying biochemical defect in multiple sclerosis. In short-term
studies, a rapid fall occurs in the amount of labelled phospholipid[140]
or fatty acid[141] recovered from the brain after the injection of isotope.
On account of this apparently rapid turnover of myelin lipids, it was
suggested[141] that demyelinating diseases may result from a "displacement between synthesis and breakdown" of the components of myelin.
Demyelination could result when either synthesis is impaired or breakdown is speeded up. This hypothesis, however, can no longer be en-

tertained in the face of recent evidence from long-term studies that the myelin lipids are far more stable than was at first thought.[142-146] The fast turnover component appears to be mainly in the grey matter while the relatively stable fraction is in the white matter. It is apparent that the lipids of the normal adult myelin sheath, far from being metabolically unstable, are in fact extremely inert.

It has been suggested that a circulatory myelinolytic substance[147,148] or a myelinolytic enzyme released locally by oligodendroglia[149] might be the causative agent of multiple sclerosis. Other agents may be involved such as pressor amines diffusing from damaged tissues, the release of active enzymes by lytic agents[108] and the myelinolytic action of lecithinase,[150] lysolecithin[151] and other surface-active substances.[152]

Certain organophosphorus compounds, such as TOCP and DFP, cause secondary demyelination but this is not a result of their inhibition of pseudo-cholinesterase;[128] nor do these compounds inhibit amine oxidase, trypsin, lecithinase, cephalinase, alkaline phosphatase or pancreatic lipase.[153] The copper-containing enzyme, cytochrome oxidase, is considerably reduced in the brain and liver of swayback,[154] a demyelinating or dysmyelinating disease of lambs born on copper-deficient pastures.[155] Chronic sub-lethal cyanide and carbon monoxide intoxications produce focal demyelination in the experimental animal[156-158] as a result, presumably, of the inhibition of cytochrome oxidase. However, the levels of blood and urinary copper are normal in multiple sclerosis[159] so that copper deficiency cannot be implicated.

Purified lipase, administered by parenteral or intracerebral injection, was claimed to produce lesions resembling multiple sclerosis while the intracerebral introduction of proteolytic enzymes caused massive necrosis as well as demyelination.[160] Proteases were shown in histochemical studies[81,92] to disrupt a lipid-protein complex in myelin. These enzymes ar normal constituents of the peripheral nerve,[101,102,96] probably in the myelin sheath, and they appear to be released in the early stages of demyelination.[96,104] The serum is another source of proteolytic enzymes which could gain access to the myelin sheath as a result of damage to the endothelium of the cerebral capillaries. Although protease may be only one amongst a number of enzymes involved in demyelination, investigation of the circumstances leading to the introduction or release of proteolytic enzymes within the brain may be relevant to the pathogenesis of multiple sclerosis.

REFERENCES

1. RANVIER, M. L.: *Leçons sur l'histologie du systeme nerveux*, p. 91, Paris, Savy (1878).
2. MARCHI, V.: *Riv. sper. Freniat.*, 12:50 (1886).

3. WEIGERT, C.: *Fortschr. Med., 3:*236 (1885).
4. PAL, J.: *Ztschr. Wiss. Mikr., 6:*92 (1887).
5. KULTSCHITSKY, N.: *Anat. Anz., 4:*223 (1889).
6. SMITH, J. L. and MAIR, W.: *J. Path. Bact., 13:*14 (1909).
7. DIETRICH, A.: *Verhandl. deutsch. path. Gesellsch., 14:*263 (1910).
8. BAKER, J. R.: *Quart. J. Micr. Sc., 87:*441 (1946).
9. BAKER, J. R.: *Quart. J. Micr. Sc., 88:*463 (1947).
10. CAIN, A. J.: *Quart. J. Micr. Sc., 88:*467 (1947).
11. LISON, L.: *Histochimie Animale,* 1st Ed., p. 196. Paris, Gauthier-Villars (1936).
12. ADAMS, C. W. M.: *J. Neurochem., 2:*178 (1958).
13. ASHBEL, R., ALEXANDER, L. and RASKIN, N.: *J. Neuropath., 12:*293 (1953).
14. PEARSE, A. G. E.: *Histochemistry,* 2nd Ed., p. 357, London, Churchill (1960).
15. NOBACK, C. R. and MONTAGNA, W.: *J. Comp. Neurol., 97:*211 (1952).
16. NOBACK, C. R. and REILLY, J. A.: *J. Comp. Neurol., 105:*333 (1956).
17. PEARSE, A. G. E.: *Histochemistry,* 2nd Ed., p. 313, London, Churchill (1960).
18. ELFTMAN, H.: *J. Histochem. Cytochem., 2:*1 (1954).
19. GOMORI, G.: *Microscopic Chemistry,* p. 102. Chicago, Univ. Chicago Press (1952).
20. ADAMS, C. W. M.: Unpublished observation.
21. UEDA, M.: *Hyoyo J. M. Sc., 1:*117 (1952).
22. EDGAR, G. W. F. and DONKER, C. H. M.: *Acta neurol. belg., 57:*451 (1957).
23. ADAMS, C. W. M. and DAVISON, A. N.: *J. Neurochem., 3:*347 (1959).
24. FEULGEN, R. and VOIT, K.: *Pflüger's Arch. ges. Physiol., 206:*389 (1924).
25. CAIN, A. J.: *Quart. J. Micr. Sc., 90:*75 (1949).
26. RAPPORT, M. M.: In Korey: *The Biology of Myelin,* p. 282. New York, Hoeber (1959).
27. PEARSE, A. G. E.: *J. Path. Bact., 70:*554 (1955).
28. PEARSE, A. G. E.: *Histochemistry,* 2nd Ed., p. 318. London, Churchill (1960).
29. FISHER, E. R.: *Am. J. Path., 32:*721 (1956).
30. WOLMAN, M.: *Stain Tech., 31:*241 (1956).
31. DIEZEL, P. B., In Cumings: *Cerebral Lipidoses,* p. 11. Oxford, Blackwell (1957).
32. PEARSE, A. G. E.: *Quart. J. Micr. Sc., 92:*393 (1951).
33. LILLIE, R. D.: *Stain Tech., 27:*37 (1952).
34. ADAMS, C. W. M.: *Nature, 192:*331 (1961).
35. VIRCHOW, R.: *Virchows Arch., 6:*562 (1854).
36. LEATHES, J. B.: *Lancet, i:*957 (1925).
37. HÖBER, R.: *Physical Chemistry of Cells and Tissues,* 1st Ed., pp. 169, 272, London, Churchill (1945).
38. DERVICHIAN, D.: *Bull. Soc. chim. biol., Paris, 28:*433 (1946).
39. SMITH, J. L.: *J. Path. Bact., 12:*1 (1908).
40. CAIN, A. J.: *Quart. J. Micr. Sc., 90:*75 (1949).
41. DIXON, K. C.: *Quart. J. Exp. Physiol., 43:*139, (1958).
42. CAIN, A. J.: *Biol Rev., 25:*73 (1950).
43. HODGMANN, C. D.: *Handbook of Chemistry and Physics,* 31st Ed., p. 1266. Cleveland, Chemical Rubber Publishing Co., (1949).
44. SCHMIDT, W. J.: *Ztschr. Zellforsch., 23:*657 (1936).
45. LOVERN, J. A.: *The Chemistry of Lipids of Biological Significance,* p. 40. London, Methuen (1955).
46. LEBARON, F. N. and FOLCH, J.: *J. Neurochem., 1:*101 (1956).
47. BERENBAUM, M. C.: *Quart. J. Micr. Sc., 99:*231 (1958).
48. BUSCH, C. K.: *Neurol. Zentralbl., 17:*476 (1898).

49. SWANK, R. L. and DAVENPORT, H. A.: *Stain Tech.*, *9*:11 (1934).
50. SWANK, R. L. and DAVENPORT, H. A.: *Stain Tech.*, *10*:87 (1935).
51. ZELIKOFF, M. and TAYLOR, H. A.: *J. Am. Chem. Soc.*, *72*:5039 (1950).
52. WINGFIELD, H. C. and YOE, J. H.: *Analyt. Chim. Acta*, *14*:446 (1956).
53. ADAMS, C. W. M.: *J. Path Bact.*, *77*:648 (1959).
54. METTLER, F. A.: *Stain Tech.*, *7*:95 (1932).
55. METTLER, F. A. and HANADA, R. E.: *Stain Tech.*, *17*:111 (1942).
56. JOHNSON, A. D., MCNABB, A. R. and ROSSITER, R. J.: *Arch. Neurol. Psychiat.*, Chicago, *64*:105 (1950).
57. ROSSITER, R. J.: In Elliott, Page and Quastel: *Neurochemistry*, 1st Ed., p. 696. Springfield, Ill., Thomas (1955).
58. CUMINGS, J. N.: *Brain, 76*:551 (1953).
59. CUMINGS, J. N.: *Brain, 78*:554 (1955).
60. RODNIGHT, R.: *J. Neurochem., 1*:207 (1957).
61. ADAMS, C. W. M. and DAVISON, A. N.: *J. Neurochem., 5*:293 (1960).
62. ADAMS, C. W. M.: *J. Histochem. Cytochem., 8*:262 (1960).
63. HURST, E. W.: *Brain, 48*:1 (1925).
64. WOLFGRAM, F. and ROSE, A. S.: *Neurology, 8*:839 (1958).
65. WOLMAN, M.: *J. Histochem. Cytochem., 4*:195 (1956).
66. WOLMAN, M.: *J. Neurochem., 1*:370 (1957).
67. FOLCH, J., LEES, M. and SLOANE-STANLEY, G. H.: *J. Biol. Chem., 226*:497 (1957).
68. BAHR, G. F.: *Exper. Cell Res., 7*:457 (1954).
69. SATTLER, C. H.: *Arch. Ophth., 90*:271 (1915).
70. BEMBRIDGE, B. A.: *Tr. Ophth. Soc., U.K., 76*:311 (1956).
71. DE ALMEIDA, D. F. and PEARSE, A. G. E.: *J. Neurochem., 3*:132 (1958).
72. UZMAN, L. L. and RUMLEY, M. K.: *J. Neurochem., 3*:170 (1958).
73. ADAMS, C. W. M. and DAVISON, A. N.: *J. Neurochem., 4*:282 (1959).
74. ADAMS, C. W. M.: *M.D. thesis, University of Cambridge*, p. 91 (1959-1960).
75. JOHNSON, A. D., MCNABB, A. R. and ROSSITER, R. J.: *Biochem. J., 45*:500 (1949).
76. ABUL-HAJ, S. K. and RINEHART, J. F.: *J. Nat. Cancer Inst., 13*:232 (1952).
77. ABOOD, L. G. and ABUL-HAJ, S. K.: *J. Neurochem., 1*:119 (1957).
78. HESS, A.: *J. Comp. Neurol., 98*:69 (1953).
79. BRANTE, G.: In Richter: *Metabolism of the Nervous System*, p. 112. London, Pergamon Press (1957).
80. WOLMAN, M.: *Neurology, 6*:636 (1956).
81. WOLMAN, M. and HESTRIN-LERNER, S.: *J. Neurochem., 5*:114 (1960).
82. WISLOCKI, G. B. and SINGER, M.: *J. Comp. Neurol., 92*:71 (1950).
83. LANDSMEER, J. M. F. and GIEL, R.: *J. Histochem. Cytochem., 4*:69 (1956).
84. HIRSCH, T. and PEIFFER, J.: In Cumings: *Cerebral Lipidoses*, p. 68. Oxford, Blackwell (1957).
85. DIEZEL, P. B.: *Die Stoffwechselstörungen der Sphingolipoide*, p. 38. Berlin, Springer-Verlag (1957).
86. KÜHNE, W. and CHITTENDEN, R. H.: *Ztschr. Biol., 26*:291 (1890).
87. NAGEOTTE, J.: *C. R. Soc. Biol.*, Paris, *69*:628 (1910).
88. EWALD, A. and KÜHNE, W.: *Verhandl. naturh.-med. Ver., Heidelb., 1*:457 (1874).
89. FOLCH, J. and LEES, M.: *J. Biol. Chem., 191*:807 (1951).
90. ADAMS, C. W. M.: *J. Clin. Path., 10*:56 (1957).
91. ADAMS, C. W. M.: *Proc. Roy. Soc. Med., 51*:339 (1958)
92. TUQAN, N. A. and ADAMS, C. W. M.: *J. Neurochem., 6*:327 (1961).
93. KOENIG, H.: *J. Neurochem., 4*:93 (1959).

94. FINEAN, J. B., HAWTHORNE, J. N. and PATTERSON, J. D. E.: *J. Neurochem.*, *1*:256 (1957).

95. FOLCH, J., LEES, M. and CARR, S.: *Exper. Cell Res.*, *5*:suppl. 58 (1958).

96. ADAMS, C. W. M. and TUQAN, N. A.: *J. Neurochem.*, *6*:334 (1961).

97. ALDRIDGE, W. N.: *Ann. Rep. Progr. Chem.*, *53*:294 (1956).

98. SCHMITT, F. O. and BEAR, R. S.: *J. Cell. Comp. Physiol.*, *9*:261 (1937).

99. FERNANDEZ-MORAN, H.: *Exper. Cell Res.*, *1*:309 (1950).

100. ENGSTRÖM, A. and FINEAN, J. B.: *Biological Ultrastructure*, pp. 217, 235. New York, Acad. Press (1958).

101. McCAMAN, R. E. and ROBINS, E.: *J. Neurochem.*, *5*:32 (1959).

102. PORCELLATI, G. and CURTI, B.: *J. Neurochem.*, *5*:277 (1960).

103. ADAMS, C. W. M., FERNAND, V. S. V. and SCHNIEDEN, H.: *Brit. J. Exper. Path.*, *39*:393 (1958).

104. ADAMS, C. W. M. and BAYLISS, O. B.: *J. Histochem. Cytochem.*, *9*:473 (1961).

105. BECKETT, E. B. and BOURNE, G. H.: *J. Neuropath.*, *17*:199 (1958).

106. WOLFGRAM, F. and ROSE, A. S.: *Neurology*, *10*:365 (1960).

107. TEWARI, H. B. and BOURNE, G. H.: *Nature*, *186*:645 (1960).

108. MARPLES, E. A., THOMPSON, R. H. S. and WEBSTER, G. R.: *J. Neurochem.*, *4*:62 (1959).

109. CHAPMAN, L. F. and WOLFF, H. G.: *Arch. Int. Med.*, *103*:86 (1959).

110. DIXON, K. C.: *J. Path. Bact.*, *66*:251 (1953).

111. DIXON, K. C.: *J. Path. Bact.*, *69*:251 (1955).

112. WOLF, A., KABAT, E. A. and NEWMAN, W.: *Am. J. Path.*, *19*:423 (1943).

113. SAMORAJSKI, T.: *J. Histochem. Cytochem.*, *5*:15 (1957).

114. ABERCROMBIE, M. and JOHNSON, M. L.: *J. Anat.*, London, *80*:37 (1946).

115. CAVANAGH, J. B. and WEBSTER, G. R.: *Quart. J. Exper. Physiol.*, *40*:12 (1955).

116. LOGAN, J. E., MANNELL, W. A. and ROSSITER, R. J.: *Biochem. J.*, *51*:482 (1952).

117. HEINZEN, B.: *Anat. Rec.*, *98*:193 (1947).

118. HOLLINGER, D. M., ROSSITER, R. J. and UPMALIS, H.: *Biochem. J.*, *52*:652 (1952).

119. LASSER, A. M. and BUEKER, E. D.: *Anat. Rec.*, *97*:395 (1947)

120. ADAMS, C. W. M.: Unpublished observations.

121. ROIZIN, L. and KOLB, L. C.: In: *Premier Congrès International des Sciences Neurologiques*, p. 57. Brussels, Les Editions Acta Medica Belgica (1957).

122. ROIZIN, L.: *J. Neuropath.*, *8*:381 (1949).

123. HOLLINGER, D. M. and ROSSITER, R. J.: *Biochem. J.*, *52*:659 (1952).

124. LUMSDEN, C. E.: *Quart. J. Exper. Physiol.*, *37*:45 (1952)

125. STRICKLAND, K. P., THOMPSON, R. H. S. and WEBSTER, G. R.: *J. Neurol., Neurosurg. Psychiat.*, *19*:12 (1956).

126. MARCHANT, J.: *J. Anat.*, Lond., *83*:227 (1949).

127. CAVANAGH, J. B.: *J. Neurol., Neurosurg. Psychiat.*, *17*:163 (1954).

128. CAVANAGH, J. B. and THOMPSON, R. H. S.: *Brit. M. Bull.*, *10*:47 (1954).

129. McALPINE, D., COMPSTON, N. D. and LUMSDEN, C. E.: *Multiple Sclerosis*, p. 208. Edinburgh, Livingstone (1955).

130. KUHN, P. and STEINER, G.: *M. Klinik.*, *13*:1007 (1917).

131. STEINER, G.: *Nervenarzt*, *1*:457 (1928).

132. STEINER, G.: *J. Neuropath.*, *13*:221 (1954).

133. ICHELSON, R. R.: *Proc. Soc. Exper. Biol. Med.*, *95*:57 (1957).

134. SCHATZ, A. and ADELSON, L. M.: Proceedings of the First International Congress of Neurological Sciences (Brussels, 1957). London, Pergamon Press, p. 38 (1959).

135. PUTNAM, T. J.: *Arch. Neurol. Psychiat.*, Chicago, *33*:929 (1935).

136. PUTNAM, T. J.: *Arch. Neurol. Psychiat.*, Chicago, *37:*1298 (1937).
137. DOW, R. S. and BERGLUND, G.: *Arch. Neurol. Psychiat.*, Chicago, *47:*1 (1942).
138. SMITH, H. V. ESPIR, M. L. E., WHITTY, C. W. M. and RUSSELL, W. R.: *J. Neurol., Neurosurg. Psychiat.*, *20:*1 (1957).
139. UCHIMURA, Y. and SHIRAKI, H.: *J. Neuropath.*, *16:*139 (1957).
140. DAWSON, R. M. C. and RICHTER, D.: *Proc. Roy. Soc.*, B., *137:*252 (1950).
141. SPERRY, W. M. and WAELSCH, H.: *Res. Nerv. & Ment. Dis. Proc.*, *28:*255 (1950).
142. DAVISON, A. N., DOBBING, J., MORGAN, R. S. and PAYLING WRIGHT, G.: *J. Neurochem.*, *3:*89 (1958).
143. DAVISON, A. N., DOBBING, J., MORGAN, R. S. and PAYLING WRIGHT, G.: *Lancet*, *i:*58 (1959).
144. DAVISON, A. N., MORGAN, R. S., WAJDA, M. and PAYLING WRIGHT, G.: *J. Neurochem.*, *4:*360 (1959).
145. DAVISON, A. N. and DOBBING, J.: *Biochem. J.*, *75:*565 (1960).
146. DAVISON, A. N. and DOBBING, J.: *Biochem. J.*, *75:*571 (1960).
147. MARBURG, O.: *Jb. Psychiat. Neurol.*, *27:*213 (1906).
148. MARBURG, O.: In Bumke and Foerster: *Handbuch der Neurologie*, Vol. 33, p. 546. Berlin (1935).
149. LUMSDEN, C. E.: *Brit. M. J.*, *i:*1035 (1951).
150. MORRISON, L. R. and ZAMECNIK, P. C.: *Arch. Neurol. Psychiat.*, Chicago, *63:*367 (1950).
151. WEBSTER, G. R.: *Nature*, *180:*660 (1957).
152. AYRES, W. W.: *Am. J. Path.*, *34:*590 (1958).
153. EARL, C. J., THOMPSON, R. H. S. and WEBSTER, G. R.: *Brit. J. Pharmacol.*, *8:*110 (1953).
154. HOWELL, J. McC. and DAVISON, A. N.: *Biochem. J.*, *72:*365 (1959).
155. INNES, J. R. M. and SHEARER, G. D.: *J. Comp. Path.*, *53:*1 (1940).
156. HURST, E. W.: *Australian J. Exper. Biol. M. Sc.*, *18:*201 (1940).
157. HURST, E. W.: *Australian J. Exper. Biol. M. Sc.*, *20:*297 (1942).
158. LUMSDEN, C. E.: *J. Neurol., Neurosurg. Psychiat*, *13:*1 (1950).
159. MANDELBROTE, B. M., STANIER, M. W., THOMPSON, R. H. S. and THRUSTON, M. N.: *Brain,* *71:*212 (1948).
160. VOGEL, F. S.: *J. Exper. Med.*, *93:*297 (1951).

V

BLOOD FLOW AND METABOLISM OF THE HUMAN BRAIN IN HEALTH AND DISEASE

Seymour S. Kety

The fundamental importance of studies *in vitro* of the metabolism of nervous tissue cannot be exaggerated. It is only when the manifold variables which enter into this complex process can be controlled, when individual components can be isolated and modified, that a basic understanding of the process can be acquired. In addition, however, it is frequently necessary to confirm the findings of *in vitro* techniques by observations on the whole organ, disturbed as little as possible by the procedures used to study it, and intact in structure and function. For this reason, study of the living brain *in vivo* offers important complementary information to *in vitro* studies. Moreover, if knowledge is to be acquired concerning the metabolic derangements in human cerebral disease it is necessary that investigation include studies of the metabolism of the human brain.

Most estimates of the oxygen usage of the brain as a whole are based upon the following relationship derived from the familiar Fick formula:

$$Q_{O_2} = CBF \times (A\text{-}V)_{O_2}$$

where Q_{O_2} represents oxygen consumption, CBF, cerebral blood flow, and $(A\text{-}V)_{O_2}$, the concentration difference for oxygen between arterial and cerebral venous blood. If blood flow is expressed as ml. per 100 gm. of brain per minute and $(A\text{-}V)_{O_2}$ as ml. of O_2 per ml. of blood, the

TABLE I

CEREBRAL CIRCULATION AND METABOLISM: NORMAL VALUES IN HEALTHY YOUNG MEN

	Per 100 gm. per Minute	For Whole Brain per Minute
Blood Flow	54 ml.	750 ml.
Oxygen Consumption	3.3 ml.	46 ml.
Glucose Consumption	5.4 mg.	76 mg.

113

oxygen consumption is obtained as ml. O_2 per 100 gm. of brain per minute. Cerebral venous blood can be obtained in animals from the torcular herophili or in man and lower primates from the superior bulb of the internal jugular vein as it emerges from the skull. In animals cerebral blood flow has been controlled by a perfusion technique[1] or directly measured by a bubble flow meter.[2] In man the nitrous oxide method[3] offers a means for quantitative measurement of cerebral blood flow. It is of interest that values for cerebral oxygen consumption obtained *in vivo* by these three techniques show a good degree of consistency within themselves as well as a remarkable agreement at levels of functional inactivity with the best values obtained *in vitro*[4] (see also Chapter VIII).

Since the rate of cerebral circulation is one of the two factors which enter into the calculation of cerebral oxygen consumption and, more important, because cerebral metabolism and function are dependent on it, a discussion of the cerebral circulation seems warranted.

PHYSIOLOGY, NORMAL AND PATHOLOGICAL

The rate of cerebral blood flow like that of the circulation through any organ depends upon only two factors, although each of these may in turn be the resultant of a host of other variables. These two factors are: (a) the pressure head or the difference between the arterial and venous pressures at the level of the cranium, and (b) the resistance or hindrance imposed on the flow of blood through the vessels of the brain.

Blood Pressure

Recent investigation does not substantiate the earlier belief that cerebral blood flow passively follows changes in arterial blood pressure. Studies in intact human beings have strengthened the concept that a normal arterial blood pressure is zealously maintained by numerous homostatic mechanisms such as the carotid sinus reflex and central control of peripheral vascular tone, and that as long as the mean arterial blood pressure remains above a critical minimum level, cerebral blood flow is actually regulated intrinsically by changes in cerebrovascular resistance.

Cerebrovascular Resistance

Reference has already been made to this important factor as the predominant regulator of cerebral blood flow at blood pressures above the shock level. It represents the resultant of all factors tending to impede the flow of blood through the brain and includes intracranial pressure, blood viscosity, organic changes in as well as the functional tone of cerebral vessels.

Intracranial Pressure.—The thin-walled vessels of the brain, immersed in cerebrospinal fluid, accurately reflect change in pressure within that medium. When the intracranial pressure rises, as it does, for example, in space-taking lesions of the brain, these vessels are compressed and the cerebrovascular resistance increases to a comparable degree.[5] This should result in a proportionate reduction in cerebral blood flow except that the rise in blood pressure which accompanies increased intracranial pressure tends partially to compensate for the increased resistance and to preserve a normal blood flow. With excessive increases in cerebrospinal fluid pressure, however, to levels above 400 mm. of water, the rise in blood pressure is inadequate and there results a significant cerebral circulatory insufficiency.

Blood Viscosity.—Although relatively constant under most conditions, the viscosity of the blood, largely dependent on the proportion of erythrocytes, may vary widely from the normal in anemia and polycythemia. Since a viscous fluid offers more frictional resistance in its flow through narrow tubes, marked changes in viscosity will be reflected in alternations in cerebrovascular resistance. In severe anemias of all types there is a reduction in this resistance and a corresponding increase in cerebral blood flow;[6] this acts as a compensatory mechanism tending to maintain a normal state of oxygen delivery. Conversely in polycythemia vera, there may be a threefold increase in blood viscosity and a corresponding increase in cerebrovascular resistance. Indeed, we have observed in this condition a cerebral blood flow of 22 ml./100 gm. of brain per minute, the lowest value recorded in any living patient. Because of the high oxygen concentration of this blood and since the CO_2 carrying capacity is closely related to the hemoglobin content, such patients are able to maintain in their brains normal exchanges of these two gases in spite of the severe reduction in blood flow.[7]

Organic Change in Cerebral Vessels.—Examination of the brains of patients who have suffered from the senile psychoses usually reveals marked sclerosis and narrowing of the lumen of cerebral arteries and a good deal of parenchymal atrophy. It has usually been assumed that cerebral arteriosclerosis imposes a resistance to the flow of blood through the brain and that the resultant decrease in nutrition has led to the functional and anatomical changes in the brain substance. Recent observations in senile psychotic individuals made during life have strengthened that theory.[8] The cerebrovascular resistance was found to be significantly increased with a resultant decrease in cerebral circulation. Probably on that basis the oxygen consumption of the brain was found to be depressed with resultant mental aberration. Meningovascular syphilis has also been found to be associated with a decreased blood flow on the basis of an augmented vascular resistance in the brain,[9] a clinical confirmation of the vascular changes seen in such brains at necropsy.

Cerebrovascular Tone.—In this function resides the fundamental regulation of cerebral nutrition in most normal and pathological states. By constriction or dilation of the flood gates of the cerebral circulation either locally or generally, a remarkable degree of homeostasis is maintained in all but the most abnormal circumstances. Alterations in cerebrovascular tone may be achieved by certain neurogenic mechanisms, by humoral agents or by a number of drugs.

The *neurogenic control* of the cerebral circulation is still only poorly defined. The sympathetic innervation to cerebral vessels originates in the thoracic lumbar outflow and ascends via the cervical sympathetic chains traversing the stellate ganglion. There is also anatomical evidence for vasodilator fibres originating in the medulla and traversing the facial and greater superficial petrosal nerve. Granting the existence of such cerebrovascular innervations, one finds the evidence for their exact functions vague and equivocal. In anesthetized animals stimulation of the cervical sympathetic chain may produce evidence of mild cerebral vasoconstriction[10] although this is not common to all species or preparations. Evidence for a normal tonic constrictor effect from the cervical sympathetics was not found in man[11] where bilateral procaine block of the stellate ganglia, although followed by signs of sympathetic paralysis in the face and eyes, produced no change in cerebrovascular resistance or blood flow.

In contrast to the vague neurogenic control, chemical substances exert striking and well recognized effects upon cerebrovascular tone. A large number of experiments on lower animals have demonstrated the ability of carbon dioxide to dilate cerebral vessels. Quantitative measurements performed in normal young men have resulted in the conclusion that increases in blood carbon dioxide tension achieved by breathing this gas in 5 to 7% concentration result in a great acceleration of cerebral blood flow averaging 75% above the normal value.[12] This increased flow is the result of a decrease in cerebrovascular resistance. Clinical application of such concentrations of carbon dioxide is to be found in anesthesiology where recovery from ether anesthesia may be hastened not only by the respiratory stimulation produced but also by the accelerated cerebral blood flow which hastens the removal of the anesthetic from the brain. The addition of carbon dioxide to inspired gas will also enable an individual to tolerate extremely low oxygen tensions.[13] Conversely, a decrease in blood carbon dioxide tension produced by moderate hyperventilation, was followed by a marked constriction of cerebral blood vessels and a reduction in blood flow by approximately one third.[12] As a result of this there could be demonstrated a definite degree of cerebral anoxia, the cerebral venous oxygen saturation falling from a normal value of 63% to a mean of 43%. The derangements in and loss of consciousness which accompanies clinical hyperventilation can be explained on the basis of cerebrovascular constriction and cerebral anoxia.

Oxygen tension is another important factor in the regulation of cerebrovascular resistance. The breathing of a mixture containing 10% oxygen produces a marked increase in cerebral blood flow, even though the blood pressure falls somewhat.[12] The cerebral vasodilation produced by this low-oxygen mixture is equal to that following 5 to 7% CO_2 inhalation and occurs in spite of a significant decrease in arterial CO_2 tension brought about by anoxic hyperpnea. It must therefore be concluded that hypoxia has as powerful a dilator action on cerebral vessels as therapeutic concentrations of carbon dioxide. In asphyxia where both factors are operating in the same direction, one would expect a marked increase in cerebral blood flow. This is found to be the case in severe pulmonary disease where serious anoxemia and hypercapnia converge to cause a more than twofold increase in cerebral circulation.[7] Tensions of oxygen above that of room air appear to cause a slight constriction of cerebral vessels. The inhalation of 85% to 100% oxygen is associated with a 13% decrease in cerebral blood flow on the basis of a moderate increase in cerebrovascular resistance.[12] Recent studies indicate that with tensions of oxygen greater than one atmosphere a more severe constriction of cerebral vessels occurs.[14]

A most important aspect of cerebral homeostasis consists in an adjustment of circulation to local metabolic needs. The mechanism whereby this adjustment is accomplished has not been definitely elucidated but the fact that at least three products of metabolism (decrease in oxygen tension, increase in hydrogen ion concentration and in carbon dioxide tension) are dilators to cerebral vessels, suggests these substances as possible agents.

In addition to those endogenous substances, there are numerous drugs which presumably affect cerebrovascular tone. The experimental evidence in some cases, however, is fairly indirect. On the basis of a large number of experiments in animals and man by different groups, cerebral vasodilator properties have been ascribed to nitroglycerine, acetylcholine, histamine, alcohol, caffeine, ether and papaverine. On the other hand cerebral vasoconstriction may, under certain experimental circumstances, be produced by epinephrine, caffeine, ergotamine and posterior pituitary extract. Since in the animal experiments the dosages employed and the routes of administration were far removed from clinical usage, and in the studies in man cerebral blood flow was often measured by methods of questionable veracity, it is fair to state that the effects of drugs in therapeutic dosage on the human cerebral circulation are plargely undetermined. Recently histamine has been shown consistently to dilate the cerebral vessels in man although, because of its tendency to reduce the blood pressure, it does not always significantly increase cerebral blood flow.[15] Aminophylline administered intravenously in therapeutic dosage produces a consistent constriction of cerebral vessels, a significant reduction in cerebral blood flow and a resultant cerebral anoxia.[16] Similar results have been obtained with caffeine.[15] Some interesting differences in the behavior of the cerebral circulation to epinephrine and norepinephrine have been demonstrated,[17] the former increasing the blood pressure without cerebral vasoconstriction, thus increasing blood flow significantly.

There are a few clinical diseases in which there is a characteristic increase in cerebrovascular tone, the mechanism of which is still obscure. Essential hypertension is associated with a high cerebrovascular resistance which in some cases may be more than double the normal

TABLE II

PHYSIOLOGICAL AND PATHOLOGICAL STATES INVOLVING ALTERATIONS IN CEREBROVASCULAR RESISTANCE AND BLOOD FLOW

Condition	Mean Arterial Blood Pressure (mm. Hg)	Cerebral Blood Flow	Cerebral O_2 Consumption	Cerebrovascular resistance (mm. Hg)
		(ml./100 gm./min.)		(ml./100 gm./min.)
Normal	85	54	3.3	1.6
Hyperventilation	98	34	3.7	2.9
CO_2 (5–7%)	93	93	3.3	1.1
O_2 (85–100%)	98	45	3.2	2.2
O_2 (10%)	78	73	3.2	1.1
Increased Intracranial Pressure	118	34	2.8	3.5
Primary Polycythemia	108	25	3.0	4.3
Anemia	78	79	3.3	1.0
Cerebral Arteriosclerosis	121	41	2.8	3.0
Cerebral Hemangioma	75	164	3.3	0.5
Essential Hypertension	159	54	3.4	3.0

value.[18] Cerebral blood flow, however, remains normal, since the increased resistance parallels the increase in mean arterial blood pressure. A number of possibilities present themselves by which to explain this inordinately high tone of cerebral vessels and the hypertension. The increased resistance may be primary and the hypertension a compensatory adjustment brought about by cerebral anoxia. This is unlikely since there is no evidence of a restricted cerebral circulation in essential hypertension, whereas in other conditions such as high intracranial pressure or cerebral arteriosclerosis, where the hypertension is probably compensatory, some degree of cerebral ischemia exists to initiate and maintain this mechanism. A second possibility is that the increased cerebrovascular tone is a homeostatic response on the part of these vessels to a hypertension originating elsewhere, a response which serves to prevent an excessive cerebral blood flow. If this were the case then a sudden fall in blood pressure in hypertensive patients to normal levels should be promptly followed by a comparable relaxation of cerebral blood vessels and the maintenance of a normal blood flow through the brain. When, by differentially blocking the sympathetic innervation to the lower part of the body in hypertensives, such a fall in blood pressure is achieved, there is not an immediate and complete relaxation of cerebral vessels with the result that cerebral blood flow is significantly decreased and some degree of cerebral anoxia is acutely produced.[19] On the basis of these considerations it appears that the increased cerebrovascular resistance in essential hypertension is neither primary nor secondary in the brain but rather a reflection of a uniform increase in vascular tone throughout the body.

THE ENERGY METABOLISM OF THE NORMAL BRAIN

The brain appears to derive its energy, at least in the normal state, almost entirely from aerobic processes. It utilizes oxygen at a rate which is among the highest in the body, having a mean value in normal man close to 3.5 ml./100 gm. of brain per minute. For a human brain of average weight, this corresponds to a total oxygen consumption of approximately 50 ml. per minute or about 20% of the basal oxygen requirements for the body as a whole. It is interesting to calculate from the oxygen consumption and the respiratory quotient of the human brain, its normal rate of energy utilization which is very close to 20 watts.

Nature of Substrate Normally Utilized

A wealth of evidence points to glucose as the normal source for the substrates of cerebral oxidations.

The first evidence that cerebral metabolism was somewhat unusual in comparison with that of other organs was the rather consistent finding of a respiratory quotient for the brain which was very close to unity. Although instantaneous values obtained in any individual may fluctuate widely on either side of unity, this is not unexpected in view of the rather large errors in any estimate, dependent upon the ratio of two differences and because of the many intervening processes between oxygen utilization and carbon dioxide release. Means of large numbers of determinations in the same individual or in a population of normal individuals usually reveal no systematic deviation from unity, which is also the case for hypoglycemic and diabetic dogs and animals in severe ketosis.

The unusual respiratory quotient pointed to carbohydrate as the predominant substrate source for brain oxidation, and, indeed, a significant arteriovenous difference for glucose was demonstrated early and has been repeatedly confirmed. The methods which have been used are not entirely specific for glucose. They have, however, become increasingly more specific in recent times so that, although the absolute levels of so-called blood glucose in arterial and venous blood have shown a systematic decrease through the years, the difference has remained remarkably constant. If the substance which disappears is not glucose, no one has been able to suggest a tenable hypothesis of what else it may be. There is some variance in the mean values obtained by various groups for the normal utilization of glucose by the human brain, but the average lies close to 5 mg./100 gm. of brain per minute, or about 70 mg. per minute for the brain as a whole. There has been little success in the demonstration of a significant cerebral arteriovenous difference for any substrate other than glucose.

The evidence still appears to be quite good that the intact brain utilizes glucose predominantly as its normal source of substrate and energy with no evidence for the significant utilization of any other substrate for this purpose, that glucose is essential for the complete, normal functioning of the human brain and that few substances, if any, can substitute for glucose in this respect even under unusual circumstances. There are no doubt many processes and, perhaps, several alternative pathways which intervene between the primary uptake of glucose and its ultimate utilization; yet, because of the unique features of the exchange between capillary and brain or some special characteristics of cerebral metabolism, it seems that glucose alone under normal and even quite abnormal circumstances can serve as the source of these processes.

THE OXYGEN CONSUMPTION OF THE BRAIN IN VARIOUS CONDITIONS

It is of interest to examine the rate of utilization of oxygen by the brain as one index of its over-all metabolic activity in various physiological and pathological states.

Changes in Temperature

The influence of temperature change upon cerebral oxygen consumption *in vivo* is not well defined. There appears to be a significant reduction in oxygen consumption in dogs subjected to hypothermia[20] and comparable results have been reported in man.[21] With regard to the effects of increased temperature, a significant increase in the arteriovenous oxygen difference has been reported by Himwich and associates[22] in man, while another group studying asymptomatic neurosyphilis found no increase in either arteriovenous oxygen difference or cerebral oxygen utilization during induced fever.[23]

Age

There appears to be some correlation of cerebral oxygen consumption with age in man. The youngest group averaging five years of age has been reported by Kennedy[24] who found an oxygen consumption of 5.1 ml./100 gm. per minute. This is to be compared with an average value of 3.5 in young adults (Table I). This function does not appear to decrease with advancing age in specially selected healthy populations.[25]

The Supply of Nutrient Materials

Oxygen.—The supply of oxygen and glucose to the brain by way of the arterial blood flow is, of course, an important limiting factor in cerebral metabolism and function.[26] Although relatively mild anoxia will produce subtle symptoms of mental dysfunction and a reduction in venous oxygen saturation to 24% is incompatible with consciousness,[27] no decrease in cerebral oxygen consumption has been detected during the inhalation of 10% oxygen even in the presence of mental symptoms.[12] Davies has demonstrated that the cortex will continue to use oxygen at a normal rate until the cortical oxygen tension has fallen to surprisingly low values.[28]

Glucose.—Hypoglycemia produces a marked decrease in cerebral oxygen consumption well correlated with arterial blood glucose and with mental state.[29,30] After prolonged hypoglycemic coma, irreversible by glucose, there is a persistent decrease in oxygen utilization by the brain.[31]

Cerebral Blood Flow.—Although blood pressure and cerebral blood flow are limiting factors in the supply of nutrient materials to the brain, there are sufficient homeostatic adjustments possible so that changes in these functions are not always well correlated with changes in oxygen consumption. Because of the ability of cerebral vessels to dilate in response to an increase in carbon dioxide tention or decrease in oxygen tension,[12] the cerebral circulation would be expected to adjust itself to metabolic needs both locally and generally, over a wide range of circulatory insults. In addition, even in the case of a moderate reduction in blood flow, the brain is able to extract more oxygen from the blood which traverses it without an interference with metabolism or function. Many series of studies have demonstrated that in patients with essential hypertension and even in normotensives[32] a reduction in blood pressure achieved by a variety of procedures is associated with no change in cerebral oxygen consumption while the blood flow is undiminished,[33-36] or even when it is significantly reduced.[19] One study has demonstrated that at the time when syncope occurs as the result of a markedly reduced blood pressure the cerebral circulation has fallen to about 30 ml./100 gm. per minute from a normal of about 54 without any immediate reduction in cerebral oxygen consumption.[37]

The Effect of Hormones

Adrenal Medullary and Cortical Hormones.—With one or two notable exceptions, most hormones appear to exert surprisingly little effect upon the over-all oxygen consumption of the brain. Although norepinephrine was shown to have no demonstrable effect upon cerebral metabolism, epinephrine produced a highly significant increase in cerebral oxygen consumption[17] when given intravenously in doses sufficient to produce a significant rise in blood pressure, and, in most subjects, feelings of anxiety. Adrenocorticotrophic hormones[38-40] as well as cortisone[39] appear to exert no significant effect upon cerebral oxygen consumption in man.

Thyroid.—The long-accepted principle that the thyroid hormone accelerates the metabolism of all body tissues was challenged for the first time when Sokoloff and his associates[41] and Scheinberg[42] independently discovered that in patients with severe hyperthyroidism oxygen consumption by the brain was normal even though the total body oxygen consumption was elevated to an average of 50% above normal. A third group has recently confirmed these observations.[43] Any hypothesis which purports to explain the mechanism of action of thyroid hormone must be compatible with its lack of effect on the oxygen consumption of the intact brain. In clinical hypothyroidism, one group has reported a significant reduction in cerebral oxygen consumption[44] while no change in that value was found by another.[43]

Cerebral Oxygen Consumption in Altered Cerebral Function

Coma.—There is evidence that in many states where there may be expected to be a generalized depression of metabolism resulting in altered functional activity, a significant reduction in cerebral oxygen uptake is found which is usually well correlated with functional derangement. In one of the first quantitative studies of cerebral metabolism on the intact brain performed by Schmidt and his associates in the monkey under light barbiturate anesthesia, a mean value of 3.7 ml. of oxygen per 100 gm. per minute was obtained when the animal was in its best condition and exhibiting spontaneous movements. This value fell with evidence of functional depression to a mean of 1.7 in those animals who had absent reflexes and were artificially ventilated.[45] In coma of various types, there is a profound decrease in cerebral oxygen utilization; a mean value of 2.2 ml./100 gm. per minute has been reported in uremic coma[46] and of 1.7 in diabetic coma.[47] In the latter case, a good correlation was found between the depth of coma and the cerebral oxygen consumption.

Anesthesia.—In anesthesia this function is also significantly depressed. A value 2.1 ml. of oxygen per 100 gm. per minute has been reported in thiopental anesthesia by two different groups[48,49] and an average of 2.2 has been obtained in severe acute alcohol intoxication.[50] These findings are in accord with the reduced Q_{o_2} found *in vitro* with many anesthetics and are considerably more pertinent since they are not subject to the criticism that the concentration of anesthetic employed may have been unrealistic. Neither these studies nor those *in vitro*, however, justify the conclusion that the mechanism of action of barbiturate anesthesia is by a primary depression of the oxidative metabolism of the brain. The work of Larrabee[51,52] suggests that this action may be upon synaptic transmission which would still explain these findings in man, since a large share of the oxygen consumption by the brain in the conscious state may be dependent upon interactions among neurons.

Conditions Associated with Increased Cerebral Metabolic Activity.— A great increase in cerebral oxygen consumption to nearly double the normal value has been reported in the monkey during convulsions,[45] a slight increase in cortical Q_{o_2} secondary to electrical changes,[28] while a significant decrease in this function has been observed in man in the post-convulsive depressed state.[29] There is reason to believe that anxiety may be associated with a moderate increase in cerebral oxygen consumption.[53] There may be some association between the anxiety and the increased cerebral oxygen consumption associated with epinephrine infusion.[17]

Conditions Associated with No Change in Cerebral Oxygen Consumption.—Although an overwhelming interference with cerebral metabolic activity should and, indeed, does result in serious alterations in mental function, the reverse is by no means the case and many al-

terations in the functional activity of the brain are found to be un-
associated with detectable changes in oxygen consumption. Mangold
and associates[54] have found a slight increase in cerebral blood flow
and no change in cerebral oxygen consumption during normal sleep,
rendering untenable the theory of cerebral ischemia to explain that
phenomenon and demonstrating that sleep is quite different from
coma or narcosis. No increase in this function is produced by the performance of mental arithmetic.[55] In a study of 30 patients with
various forms and durations of schizophrenia, cerebral oxygen consumption, as well as cerebral blood flow and other functions studied,
was found to be completely normal and showed no correlation with
duration or severity of the disease.[29].

TABLE III

CONDITIONS INVOLVING ALTERATIONS IN MENTAL STATE OR CEREBRAL METABOLISM

Condition	Mental State	Mean Arterial Blood Pressure (mm. Hg)	Cerebral Blood Flow (ml./100 gm./min.)	Cerebral O₂ Consumption (ml./100 gm./min.)	Cerebrovascular resistance (mm. Hg)
Normal, Awake	Alert	85	54	3.3	1.6
Normal, Asleep	Asleep	90	65	3.4	1.5
Schizophrenics	Alert—inac-cessible	95	54	3.3	1.7
Schizophrenics, Narcosynthesis	Alert—more accessible	95	54	3.3	1.8
Cerebral Arterio-sclerosis	Confused	121	41	2.8	3.0
Diabetic Acidosis	Confused	86	45	2.7	2.1
Insulin Hypo-glycemia	Confused	86	61	2.6	1.4
Brain Tumor	Comatose	122	34	2.5	3.6
Pentothal Anes-thesia	Comatose	78	60	2.1	1.3
Insulin Coma	Comatose	93	63	1.9	1.5
Diabetic Coma	Comatose	66	65	1.7	1.1

A number of drugs which produce definite changes in mental state
have been found not to produce a generalized effect upon oxidative
metabolism of the brain. Among these are chlorpromazine[56] and alcohol[50,56] in doses sufficient to produce mild intoxication. In pentothal
semi-narcosis there was no change in cerebral oxygen consumption
even though a remarkable improvement in the accessibility of patients
with schizophrenia and in their ability to communicate was demonstrated.[29] The psychotomimetic, lysergic acid diethylamide, has not
been shown to affect the oxidative metabolism or the glucose consumption of the brain in subjects who are actively hallucinating under the
drug.[57]

These findings are not at all surprising when one realizes the numerous, complex, and as yet poorly defined processes which must occur between the release of energy by way of oxidative metabolism and its final utilization in normal, mental function. The biochemical changes which may lie at the root of some of these subtle alterations in function may be sharply localized to areas within the brain so small as not to produce an effect in over-all measurements. Important defects, however, may surely lie beyond oxidation, or, indeed, beyond biochemistry. For the brain is neither a pump nor a motor and its current counterparts seem to be instruments of computation and communication. In such an instrument, although a defective power supply will produce dysfunction, meaningfulness of content and accuracy are by no means always correlated with the power used.

REFERENCES

1. GEIGER, A. and MAGNES, J.: *Am. J. Physiol., 149:*517 (1947).
2. DUMKE, P. R. and SCHMIDT, C. F.: *Am. J. Physiol., 138:*421 (1943).
3. KETY, S. S., and SCHMIDT, C. F.: *J. Clin. Invest., 27:*476 (1948).
4. ELLIOTT, K. A. C.: *J. Neurophysiol., 11:*473 (1948).
5. KETY, S. S., SHENKIN, H. A. and SCHMIDT, C. F.: *J. Clin. Invest., 27:*493 (1948).
6. SCHEINBERG, P.: *J. Clin. Invest., 28:*808 (1949).
7. KETY, S. S.: Unpublished observations.
8. FREYHAN, F. A., WOODFORD, R. B. and KETY, S. S.: *J. Nerv. & Ment. Dis., 113:*449 (1951).
9. PATTERSON, J. L., JR., HEYMAN, A. and NICHOLS, F. T., JR.: *J. Clin. Invest., 28:*803 (1949).
10. SCHMIDT, C. F. and HENDRIX, J. P.: *A. Res. Nerv. & Ment. Dis., Proc., 18:*229 (1938).
11. HARMEL, M. H., HAFKENSCHIEL, J. H., AUSTIN, G. M., CRUMPTON, C. W. and KETY, S. S.: *J. Clin. Invest., 28:*415 (1949).
12. KETY, S. S. and SCHMIDT, C. F.: *J. Clin. Invest., 27:*484 (1948).
13. GIBBS, F. A., GIBBS, E. L. and LENNOX, W. G.: *J. Aviation Med., 14:*250 (1943).
14. LAMBERTSON, C. J., KOUGH, R. H., COOPER, D. Y., EMMEL, G. L., LOESCHCKE, H. H. and SCHMIDT, C. F.: *J. Appl. Physiol., 5:*471 (1953).
15. SHENKIN, H. A.: *J. Appl. Physiol., 3:*465 (1951).
16. WECHSLER, R. L., KLEISS, L. M. and KETY, S. S.: *J. Clin. Invest., 29:*28 (1950).
17. KING, B. D., SOKOLOFF, L. and WECHSLER, R. L.: *J. Clin. Invest., 31:*273 (1952).
18. KETY, S. S., HAFKENSCHIEL, J. H., JEFFERS, W. A., LEOPOLD, I. H. and SHENKIN, H. A.: *J. Clin. Invest., 27:*511 (1948).
19. KETY, S. S., KING, B. D., HORVATH, S. M., JEFFERS, W. A. and HAFKENSCHIEL, J. H.: *J. Clin. Invest., 29:*402 (1950).
20. ROSOMOFF, H. L. and HOLADAY, D. A.: *Am. J. Physiol., 179:*85 (1954).
21. FERUGLIO, F. S., RUIU, P. and RUIU, L.: *Minerva Med., 45:*1655 (1954).
22. HIMWICH, H. E., BOWMAN, K. M., FAZEKAS, J. F. and GOLDFARB, W.: *Am. J. M. Sc., 200:*537 (1939).

23. HEYMAN, A., PATTERSON, J. L. and NICHOLS, F. T.: *J. Clin. Invest.*, *29*:1335 (1950).
24. KENNEDY, C., SOKOLOFF, L. and ANDERSON, W.: *Am. J. Dis. Child.*, *88*:813 (1954).
25. DASTUR, D. K., LANE, M. H., HANSEN, D. B., KETY, S. S., BUTLER, R. N., PERLIN, S. and SCKOLOFF, L.: In *Biological and Behavioral Aspects of Normal Aging in Man*. NIMH Monograph. U.S. Government Printing Office (in press).
26. ROSSEN, R., KABAT, H. and ANDERSON, J. P.: *Arch. Neurol. & Psychiat.*, *50*:510 (1943).
27. LENNOX, W. G., GIBBS, F. A. and GIBBS, E. L.: *Arch. Neurol. & Psychiat.*, *34*:1001 (1935).
28. DAVIES, P. W. and REMOND, A.: A *Res. Nerv. & Ment. Dis., Proc.*, *26*:205 (1947).
29. KETY, S. S., WOODFORD, R. B., HARMEL, M. H., FREYHAN, F. A. APPEL, K. E. and SCHMIDT, C. F.: *Am. J. Psychiat.*, *104*:765 (1948).
30. HIMWICH, H. E., BOWMAN, K. M., DALY, C., FAZEKAS, J. F., WORTIS, J. and GOLDFARB, W.: *Am. J. Physiol.*, *132*:640 (1941).
31. FAZEKAS, J. F., ALMAN, R. W. and PARRISH, A. E.: *Am. J. M. Sc.*, *222*:640 (1951).
32. STONE, H. H., MACKRELL, T. N. and WECHSLER, R. L.: *Am. J. M. Sc.*, *228*:112 (1954).
33. BESSMAN, A. N., ALMAN, R. W. and FAZEKAS, J. F.: *Arch. Int. Med.*, *89*:893 (1952).
34. CRUMPTON, C. W. and QUILL, R.: *J. Clin. Invest.*, *31*:622 (1952).
35. HAFKENSCHIEL, J. H., CRUMPTON, C. W., MOYER, J. H. and JEFFERS, W. A.: *J. Clin. Invest.*, *29*:408 (1950).
36. HAFKENSCHIEL, J. H. and FRIEDLAND, C. K.: *J. Clin. Invest.*, *32*:655 (1953).
37. FINNERTY, F. A., WITKIN, L. and FAZEKAS, J. F.: *J. Clin. Invest.*, *33*:1227 (1954).
38. SCHIEVE, J. F., SCHEINBERG, P. and WILSON, W. P.: *J. Clin. Invest.*, *30*:1527 (1951).
39. SENSENBACH, W., MADISON, L. and OCHS, L.: *J. Clin. Invest.*, *32*:372 (1953).
40. ALMAN, R. W. and FAZEKAS, J. F.: *Arch. Neurol. & Psychiat.*, *65*:680 (1951).
41. SOKOLOFF, L., WECHSLER, R. L., MANGOLD, R., BALLS, K. and KETY, S. S.: *J. Clin. Invest.*, *32*:202 (1953).
42. SCHEINBERG, P.: *J. Clin. Invest.*, *29*:1010 (1950).
43. SENSENBACH, W., MADISON, L., EISENBERG, S. and OCHS, L.: *J. Clin. Invest.*, *33*:1434 (1954).
44. SCHEINBERG, P., STEAD, E. A., BRANNON, E. S. *and* WARREN, J. V.: *J. Clin. Invest.*, *29*:1139 (1950).
45. SCHMIDT, C. F., KETY, S. S. and PENNES, H. H.: *Am. J. Physiol.*, *143*:33 (1945).
46. HEYMAN, A., PATTERSON, J. L. and JONES, R. W.: *Circulation*, *3*:558 (1951).
47. KETY, S. S., POLIS, B. D., NADLER, C. S. and SCHMIDT, C. F.: *J. Clin. Invest.*, *27*:500 (1948).
48. WECHSLER, R. L., DRIPPS, R. D. and KETY, S. S.: *Anesthesiology*, *12*:308 (1951).
49. HIMWICH, W. A., HOMBURGER, E., MARESCA, R. and HIMWICH, H. E.: *Am. J. Psychiat.*, *103*:689 (1947).
50. BATTEY, L. L., HEYMAN, A. and PATTERSON, J. L.: *J.A.M.A.*, *152*:6 (1953).
51. LARRABEE, M. G.: In *The Biology of Mental Health and Disease*, p. 384. New York, Hoeber (1952).
52. LARRABEE, M. G. and POSTERNAK, J. M.: *J. Neurophysiol.*, *15*:91 (1952).

53. KETY, S. S.: *Am. J. Med., 8:*205 (1950).

54. MANGOLD, R., SOKOLOFF, L., CONNER E., KLEINERMAN, J., THERMAN, P. G. and KETY, S. S.: *J. Clin. Invest., 34:*1092 (1955).

55. SOKOLOFF, L., MANGOLD, R., WECHSLER, R. L., KENNEDY, C. and KETY, S. S.: *J. Clin. Invest., 34:*1101 (1955).

56. FAZEKAS, J. F., ALBERT, S. N. and ALMAN, R. W.: *Am. J. M. Sc., 230:*128 (1955).

57. SOKOLOFF, L., PERLIN, S., KORNETSKY, C. and KETY, S. S.: *Ann. New York Acad. Sc., 66:*468 (1957).

VI

METABOLISM AND FUNCTION
IN THE BRAIN*

Alexander Geiger

The steady progress attained during the last decade in the knowledge of biochemical functions of the brain is attested by numerous reviews in this volume. Nevertheless, the possibility of constructing a plausible and inclusive scheme of the chemical mechanism of the excitation process and of other aspects of the physiological functions of the living brain seems, at this time, rather remote.

However, by grouping biochemical data in relation to various experimentally-induced physiological states of the brain, inferences can now be attempted in the hope that they may disclose sequences of biochemical events which occur during and following the excitation process.

It is obvious that, at present, all efforts seeking to integrate biochemical and physiological functions are greatly limited by the lack of suitable direct methods. Thus, the limitations of methods used and the deviations from physiological conditions caused in the process of obtaining the data, together with the complexity of the object, are the sources of much frustration. When metabolic functions of the brain are studied on the whole organ, with the method of Kety and Schmidt, or with a perfusion method, only such changes can be unequivocally observed which markedly affect a considerable portion of the brain, such as excitation of the whole brain by electroshock or by metrazol, or the effects of such narcotic drugs which affect the rate of oxygen consumption of a great number of brain cells. Some drugs in high enough concentrations may affect the metabolic *pattern* of the whole brain, or of large parts of it, in such a way that even if the total amount of oxygen utilized remains unaltered, the relative proportion of exo-

*The author is indebted to the National Institute of Neurological Diseases and Blindness, National Institutes of Health, United States Public Health Service, and to the National Multiple Sclerosis Society, whose generous support has made our work possible.

128

genous and endogenous substrates oxidized may be changed. The same drug, in lower concentrations, may affect only small areas with high affinity for the drug, which, in turn, may propagate its effect by nervous conduction to a wider area within the brain. The interpretation of the observed biochemical changes is further complicated by the heterogeneity of brain tissue within the same area—i.e., by the various compartmentalized pools of metabolites created by the anatomical relationship of blood capillaries to glial cells and to neurons.

The correlation of the *in vitro* metabolism of isolated brain slices with physiological functions is also fraught with sources of misinterpretation. To mention only one of them, sectioning of an axon is followed by chromatolysis, accompanied by an abnormal rate of protein turnover in the soma, as has been shown by Hydén and his colleagues.[1] This will hamper attempts seeking to characterize protein metabolism under varied physiological conditions in isolated brain slices. The metabolic rate of the whole brain under various physiological conditions, its blood flow rate, oxygen utilization, and glucose consumption have been reviewed in this volume. A few selected aspects have also been reviewed recently by the author.[2]

CARBOHYDRATES

Of the carbohydrate metabolism of the brain, only a few selected aspects—and mainly those which are affected by variations of physiological conditions—are considered here.

Only glucose and mannose are able to maintain brain functions when added to the blood.[3-5] Maltose, which was found by Mann and Magath to be also effective, could not maintain brain functions in brain perfusion experiments. Fructose was found by Stone[6] and Klein[7] not to be able to sustain brain metabolism because of insufficient rate of penetration. As was shown by Geiger and Magnes,[8] this sugar is not metabolized in the perfused brain *in vivo*, even when added in very high concentrations to the perfusing blood. The inability of the brain to metabolize this sugar is probably due to the low affinity of the brain hexokinase to fructose.[9] The question why some of the hexoses, or their intermediary metabolites can not maintain brain functions *in vivo is* complicated by the mechanism of uptake of each of these compounds into the brain. It is rather remarkable that although most of the metabolic steps involving glucose breakdown are known, the first reaction—namely, the mechanism of uptake of these sugars into the cell, is obscure. A number of hypotheses concerning the mechanism of active transport of glucose into tissue other than brain have been proposed.

In perfusion experiments, with glucose added to the simplified blood, the brain could be kept alive for a limited time only—for 60 to 90 minutes. Lactic acid steadily accumulated in the brain cortex until its concentration reached 0.35–0.40%. The glucose content of the cerebral cortex progressively diminished in spite of high glucose concentrations in the blood. High concentrations of lactic acid in the brain cortex and the disappearance of glucose from it usually co-incided with the disappearance of electric signs of brain activity. In-creased aerobic glycolysis was followed at a later stage by an impair-ment of glucose uptake. However, when a fresh isolated liver was inserted into the brain perfusion circuit, the preparation has been maintained for up to 4 hours in good functional condition without showing disturbances in its carbohydrate metabolism. Addition of a fresh liver extract in Ringer's solution improved glucose uptake and oxidation for a comparatively short period of time. As shown by the effect of added liver extract, disturbances in brain metabolism and function resulted, at least in part, from the lack of substances which are normally contributed by the liver.

In perfusion experiments without the liver, when the entire glucose taken up from the blood was transformed into lactic acid, oxygen consumption persisted at a relatively high rate. The continued oxygen consumption under these conditions indicated oxidation of non-carbo-hydrate compounds in the brain.[5] If glucosamine was added to the perfusion blood at a time when glucose uptake was blocked, this amine was taken up and phosphorylated by the brain.[10] After many futile attempts to isolate the active substances which are contributed by the liver to the maintenance of brain function and normal carbo-hydrate metabolism in the brain, it was finally found that the addition of two nucleosides, uridine and cytidine, to the perfusion blood in the absence of liver maintained normal functions and carbohydrate metab-olism in the brain up to 5 hours.[11] During these longlasting perfusion experiments, it was found advantageous to change the perfusion blood from time to time to avoid an excessive accumulation of metabolic breakdown products in the blood.

Recent experiments have indicated that the central nervous system utilizes glucose only if this is taken up from the blood, across the blood-brain barrier, and not if introduced via the cerebrospinal fluid.[12] When the blood sugar level of anesthetized cats was reduced by insulin until the disappearance of the patellar reflex, subsequent perfusion of the spinal subarachnoid space with Ringer's solution containing 100 to 600 mg. % of glucose, between a lumbar and a cisternal tap, failed to restore the reflexes, which were, however, restored by intra-venous glucose injections. These experiments, as much as liver-free perfusion experiments, point to a specific mechanism located somewhere between the blood capillaries of the brain and brain cells, which make the glucose "acceptable" to the latter. The part played by diffusion and by chemical transport of glucose in and out of red blood cells has been calculated by kinetic studies.[13-19] Inability of diffusion to account for placental glucose transfer has also been shown.[15] Phosphorylation was thought to be part of the transport mechanism in the intestinal absorption of sugars.[20-22] It has been shown, however, that the glucose transfer mechanism in the intestine is more complex.[23]

Various mechanisms have been proposed for the chemical transport mechanism of sugars into living cells. Mutarotase catalyzes the alpha-beta interconversion of sugars[24] and it is suggested to convert the sugars into a "preferentially absorbed form," supposedly a free alde-hyde. This enzyme has been found in liver and kidney and brain. The Michaelis-Menten constant of this enzyme in the brain, as calculated, corresponds to the average rates at which glucose is utilized in the brain.[25] The role of insulin in glucose transport across cell boundaries, as postulated for other tissue,[26,27] cannot be easily reconciled in the brain with the fact that insulin does not penetrate into the brain from the blood.[28] Nevertheless, insulin added to the perfusion blood in perfusion experiments slightly increased sugar oxidations in the brain.[29]

Considering the effect of cytidine and uridine on sugar uptake and oxidation by the brain,[11] the polysaccharide synthesis via glucuronic acid and glucosamine requires attention as another possible glucose transport mechanism. Observations made during recent years on the mechanism of action of penicillin as reported recently,[30,31] may be pertinent to these considerations.

Glucose transport in other organs and possibly in the brain is possi-bly interconnected with cation transport or with the concentration of various cations inside and outside of the cell.[32] In recent observations of Csaky and Zollicoffer,[33] resorption of glucose from a loop of in-testine perfused *in situ* with glucose dissolved in isosmotic solutions of Na_2SO_4, or Li_2SO_4, or K_2SO_4, or $MgSO_4$ (upper jejunum of a rat), was rapid from sodium sulphate solution, but it was inhibited by 75 to 90% when the sodium was replaced by lithium or potassium or magnesium.

The possibility of proteins or peptides participating in the first steps of glucose metabolism (possibly in their transport) is indicated by recent findings of Walaas *et al.*[34] According to these authors, C^{14} glucose is very rapidly (within seconds) incorporated into a glucosan-peptide complex in the diaphragm of the rat. No such compound has yet been demonstrated in the brain. It was shown by Wertheimer *et al.*[35] that in the blood serum of starved rats a protein is present which inhibits glucose incorporation into glycogen of rat diaphragm. Similarly, a globulin fraction has been isolated from normal blood serum[36] which inhibits glucose uptake by the diaphragm of normal rats. This protein acts like an antagonist of insulin. Recently, Rafaelson[37] reported that insulin increased the glucose uptake by the spinal cord and by peripheral nerves of alloxan diabetic rats, when the cord and nerves were incubated *in vitro* in physiological saline solution. According to these authors, insulin also increased the glucose uptake of brain cortex slices possessing an intact, pia-covered surface, whereas slices not covered by pia having artificial surfaces were uninfluenced by insulin. Recently, Magnes and Hestrin reported that insulin increased somewhat the glucose uptake of the perfused cat's brain.[38] Experiments with radioactive insulin have shown, however, no noticeable penetration of insulin into the brain.[39]

In the perfused brain of the cat *in vivo,* substances derived from the liver were necessary in maintaining glucose uptake and carbohydrate utilization in the brain.[40] It was also shown that cytidine and uridine play a role in this process and are probably part of the active substances furnished by the liver.[41] It was shown recently by Allweiss and Magnes that 5-hydroxytryptophane or 5-hydroxytryptamine (serotonin), when added to the perfusion blood, increased the glucose content of the cat's brain cortex in perfusion experiments.

During convulsive activity of the brain, at the time of increased metabolic rate, the glucose uptake into the brain is drastically reduced, or completely inhibited (Geiger *et al.*[43]). After the cessation of convulsions, glucose is taken up at a steadily increasing rate for a considerable time—usually 15 to 20 minutes. During the period of increased rate of glucose uptake, much more glucose is taken up from the blood, than can be accounted for by oxygen uptake or lactic acid production, and the glucose taken up in excess of lactic acid production and oxygen consumption is not found as such in the brain. During the time of this increased glucose uptake there is increased synthesis of glycolipids, and the glycolipid content of the brain cortex, at about an hour following convulsions seems to be greater than it was before convulsions.[44]

Brain perfusion experiments with uniformly C^{14} labeled glucose have also shown an increased rate of incorporation of glucose carbon into the lipids, glycolipids, as well as the phospholipids, during, and mainly after, convulsions.[45]

The information available on the nature and amounts of free and combined carbohydrates present in the brain *in vivo* is not satisfactory. Even the normal glucose concentration is not known with certainty, due to a very rapid glycolysis occurring in the excised tissue. Thus, one minute after death, about 8 mg. % of "true glucose was found in brain tissue of rats by Gey.[46] In the author's laboratory, using a technique of freezing the brain cortex *in situ* by applying a slight pressure with a metal container filled with dry ice and acetone (thus simultaneously stopping the blood flow and freezing the cortex), glucose concentrations of up to 50 mg. % were found (with glucose oxidase) in the brain cortex of cats in nembutal narcosis, in addition to an equal amounts of reducing substances other than glucose. Most of the latter consisted of various carbohydrates.[47] Analyses of the carbohydrate composition of the giant nerve fibers of the squid have been reported.[48]

The role of the glycogen, and the extent of its turnover rate in the brain is not known. In earlier experiments of Kerr and his colleagues,[49] a reduction of brain glycogen was found during hypoglycemia and following metrazol convulsions. According to more recent studies of Russian authors,[50-52] only a comparatively small part of the glycogen of the brain (about 20%) is turned over at a comparatively fast rate, while the bulk seems to have a very low turnover rate. In liver and muscle,[35] glycogen turnover is not a replacement of the whole pre-existing glycogen with new, but a displacement of peripherally situated glucosyl residues. In brain-perfusion experiments, with the perfusion blood devoid of any glucose, about 20 mg. % of glycogen remained in the brain after 2 hours of glucose-free perfusion.[54] Among all the organs investigated, the brain alone cannot produce a co-factor: 3, 5-cyclic adenosine monophosphate which is necessary for the synthesis of phosphorylase-A from the 2 phosphorylases B.[55] The formation of this co-factor from ATP in the presence of magnesium by subcellular particulates of liver, heart, and skeletal muscle, is markedly accelerated by glucagon and epinephrine. However, epinephrine did not stimulate the generation of co-factor in the brain.

In a normal animal, and also in brain perfusion experiments *in vivo,* the amount of oxygen consumed and lactic acid produced by the brain is equivalent to the amount of glucose taken up from the blood, as pointed out by Himwich,[56] and by the author. This relationship holds for most conditions *in vivo,* unless they very much deviate from the normal. In narcosis, the reduction of glucose uptake was found to parallel the reduced oxygen consumption.[57] However, in hypoglycemia, the glucose consumption was more reduced than the oxygen utilization,[58] indicating oxidation of other substrates. During incipient liver coma, the glucose uptake of the brain was much more reduced than its oxygen consumption, thus indicating that most of the oxygen taken up by the brain was used for the oxidation of substances other than glucose.[59]

In perfusion experiments, during metrazol- or electroshock-induced convulsion, the great increase of oxygen consumption is accompanied by a drastically reduced uptake of glucose from the blood. During this period, the glucose content of the brain is markedly reduced, but most of the glucose utilized by the brain is transformed to lactic acid. (A high rate of lactic acid production in the brain during convulsion was repeatedly reported previously.) In view of the fact that lactic acid production accounts for most of the glucose utilized, the simultaneous large increase of the oxygen consumption (at least twice the resting rate) has to be accounted for by the oxidation of other substances. In perfusion experiments, using uniformly C^{14} labeled glucose, the extra CO_2 produced by the brain during convulsions—i.e., the amount over the resting level—was derived from non-glucose sources in the brain.[60] A number of brain functions, and the ability of the brain to respond to metrazol with convulsions and increased rate of CO_2 production, are also maintained during glucose-free perfusion.[58,61]

The various pathways of glucose utilization and the fate of the glucose in the brain are under investigation. It was generally assumed that the glycolytic pathway and the tricarboxylic cycle are the main mechanisms by which carbohydrates are utilized in the brain[62] and little or no importance was attributed to the oxidation of the hexose-6-phosphate via the shunt. However, most of the intermediates of the glucose-6-phosphate-oxidase pathway were found to be present in the brain[63] and nervous tissue. Recently it was shown that the pentose phosphate pathway in brain and retina can be stimulated to increased activity by various chemicals.[64-65]

The partial utilization of the glucose entering the brain for synthetic reactions was seen in numerous *in vitro* experiments and in perfusion experiments. Although the oxygen consumption equals the glucose uptake minus lactic acid production in brain perfusion experiments *in vivo*, substances other than glucose are constantly oxidized, as could be seen when uniformly C^{14} labeled glucose was present in the perfusion blood. At least some of the non-carbohydrate substances in the brain are simultaneoulsy incorporating C^{14} derived from glucose, indicating a resynthesis by utilization of the glucose C^{14}. Sachs[66] found, in experiments with C^{14}-labeled glucose, that part of the respiratory CO_2 of the brain of normal and schizophrenic humans is derived from non-glucose sources. In these experiments, the proportion of non-glucose-C to glucose-C^{14} in the CO_2 was significantly different between schizophrenic and normal individuals. It was recently shown by All-weiss and Magnes[67] in brain perfusion experiments with uniformly labeled C^{14} glucose, that only about 30% of the carbon dioxide produced by the brain was derived from the glucose taken up from the blood. The findings of Allweiss and Magnes were confirmed in extensive studies of this author and his colleagues, using the brain perfusion technique.[68] In these experiments, the pool of carbohydrates and of carbohydrate intermediates in the brain reached an equilibrium with the labeled glucose of the blood during the first 20 to 25 minutes of the perfusion. After equilibration of blood- and brain-glucose and intermediates, in perfusion experiments continued for four hours or more, the carbon dioxide produced by the brain at any time contained only 25 to 30% of C^{14} derived from glucose, indicating admixture of large amounts of cold carbon at a constant, steady rate. The cold carbon obviously derived from the oxidation of such endogenous substances which, being present in very large amounts, do not become appreciably radioactive during the experimental period. Such large pools in the brain are mainly lipids and proteins.

It was also shown in brain homogenates and slices[69,63,70] that not more than about 60% of the oxygen consumed was due to the oxidation of carbohydrates, and that non-carbohydrates were oxidized, together with glucose.

In perfusion experiments with uniformly C^{14}-labeled glucose[68,71] during convulsions, when the total carbon dioxide production of the brain increased about two-fold, the amount of $C^{14}O_2$ derived from glucose did not increase over the resting value—even decreased in some experiments—indicating that the excess CO_2 produced by the brain during convulsions was due to the oxidation of non-carbohydrates, probably proteins and lipids. This was also borne out by the sharply increased rates of C^{14} incorporation into proteins and lipids under these conditions.[45]

AMINO ACIDS

The study of the metabolism and role of the amino acids in brain received great impetus from the discovery of Florey, Elliott et al.,[72-74] and Roberts et al.[75] of the role of γ-amino-butyric acid as an inhibitory substance of nervous activity. This question, and the amino acid metabolism are dealt with elsewhere in this volume. I would like, however, to consider a few aspects of the amino acid metabolism, in which a bearing on physiological functions may be discernible. The transport mechanism of amino acids across cell boundaries, especially in the form proposed by Christensen's group[76] may have a bearing on ion movements across the nerve cell boundaries. Their findings show that the uptake of glycine by Ehrlich mouse ascites, carcinoma cells, is dependent on potassium flux in and out of the cell. The authors suggest that potassium behaves like an amino acid in this respect. Earlier experiments[77] indicated a similar relationship of the glutamic acid and potassium transport in and out of brain slices, respiring in a glucose media. The amino-acid transport mechanism proposed earlier by Christensen *et al.*,[78-79] i.e., a complex Schiff-base formation between pyridoxal-amino-acid-metal, may also be suggestive in connection with experiments of Curtis *et al.*,[80] in which chelation of cations in spinal neurons (by an ionophoretic technique) excited interneurons, Renshaw cells and motoneurons.

In the adult animal's brain cortex, the nonessential amino acids are being produced at a rapid rate, paralleling the turnover of the tricarboxylic cycle.[81-83] Thus, there is an efflux of endogenous nonessential amino acid from the cells into the intercellular spaces and into the blood stream, as was seen in recent experiments, in the author's laboratory. On the other hand, as shown by Lajtha *et al.*,[85-87] amino acids added to the blood are exchanged fairly rapidly with the free amino acids in the brain. Thus, the efflux and influx of nonessential amino acids from and into brain cells, with the accompanying movement of K^+ ions, may well be a part of the excitation process.

Some acidic α-amino acids applied directly, excite spinal neurons of the cat.[88] According to Purpura *et al.*,[89] a number of Ω-amino acids of carbon-chain length of 2 to 5 are selective inactivators of depolarizing excitatory synapses of superficial dendrites. Longer chain Ω-amino acids inactivate the hyperpolarizing, inhibitory axodendritic synapses. Ω-guanidino acids have effects similar to the former. α-amino acids seem to antagonize the effect of Ω-amino- or of Ω-guanidino acids. Edwards and Kuffler made similar studies on the isolated crayfish receptor sensory cell,[90] and found that guanidino acids block sensory discharges as effectively as does GABA.

The role of glutamine and asparagine in convulsive states has been discussed in detail in a review.[91]

Both L-asparagine and L-glutamine increased the bound acetylcholine in slices of cerebral cortex respiring in an atmosphere containing 10 per cent oxygen *in vitro*.[92] Epileptogenic samples of brain cortex behaved like hypoxic brain cortex. Otherwise lethal seizures, induced by pentylenetetrazol or by 3-methyl 3-ethyl glutarimide, could be prevented by L-asparagine administered orally in doses of 3 mM/kg. to experimental animals,[93] or by intraperitoneal administration of asparagine or glutamine when seizures were induced by methionine sulphoximine.[91] In brain perfusion experiments the relative concentrations of potassium and sodium in the brain cortex usually parallel the level of integrity of the physiological functions. When these deteriorate during hypoxia, anemia, exhaustive stimulation, and a number of metabolic poisons, the sodium concentration increases in the brain cortex while the potassium concentration decreases proportionally.[94] No significant change in the free amino acid concentration of the brain was observed during and after metrazol convulsions in perfusion experiments with uniformly C^{14}—labeled glucose.[83] The rate at which glutamic and aspartic acid were labeled also remained the same as in the resting state. Only in a small number of experiments was a slight increase of the aspartic acid concentration observed.

Increased production of ammonia in the brain, or increased uptake from the blood, is manifested by increased glutamine synthesis.[87] Glutamine, in contrast to glutamic acid, can penetrate into the brain in comparatively large amounts, as shown by Schwerin and Waelsch.[95,96] Waelsch[97] has shown that brain cortex slices depleted of glutamine and glutamic acid could resynthesize these amino acids from added glucose. Since then, similar observations have been repeatedly published.[91]

A rather high rate of amino acid production from C^{14}—labeled glucose injected into intact mice, or added to glycolyzing brain slices has been demonstrated.[81,82,92]

The labeling of glutamic acid, glutamine, GABA, aspartic acid and alanine by C^{14} derived from uniformly C^{14}—labeled glucose under the effect of various chemicals which influence metabolic activity has been investigated by Quastel's group on brain slices.[99,100] Protoveratrine, like high K-concentrations and electric impulses, increased the respiratory rate and the yield of labeled glutamic acid, glutamine and GABA. According to these investigators, this drug acts by immobilizing Ca. This, in turn, accelerates the turnover of pyruvate to acetyl-CoA by an increase in the ratio of $K+/Ca+$.

As far as the utilization of the nonessential amino acids at rest and during activity, for purposes other than protein synthesis, is concerned, the existing data are not sufficiently indicative of the difference between the utilization and *de novo* synthesis, on one hand, and conversion of the a-keto-acids by transamination, on the other. Brain perfusion experiments *in vivo*,[83,101] indicate that exchange equilibrium between the keto-acids of the tricarboxylic acid cycle and glutamic- and aspartic-acids is reached fairly rapidly. After 45 to 50 minutes of perfusion with uniformly C^{14}—labeled glucose, these amino acids contain as much C^{14} as the corresponding keto acids of the tricarboxylic cycle and the respiratory CO_2. The large pool of acetyl-aspartic acid in the brain seems to be comparatively inert, as very little C^{14} is incorporated into this compound as compared to aspartic acid. As shown by Lajtha *et al.*,[85,86] labeled amino acids of the blood exchange freely and rapidly with the free amino acids of the brain. Thus, the rapid amino acid exchange between blood and brain in living animals makes it difficult to decide whether, after the intravenous administration of C^{14}—labeled glucose, the labeled nonessential amino acids found in the brain were produced in the brain or were exchanged for those produced elsewhere in the organism. Brain perfusion experiments are well-suited to show the production of nonessential free amino acids in the living brain. Although the nonessential amino acids were produced in the brain at a high rate, as mentioned before, none of the essential amino acids—with the possible exception of valine—could be produced in the brain of adult cats in these experiments.

PHYSIOLOGICAL ROLE OF PROTEIN AND NUCLEIC ACID METABOLISM

Interest in functional aspects of the protein metabolism of the central nervous system goes back to the experiments of Soula[102] at the beginning of this century, and of Baglioni[103] during its first decade, followed by the work of Winterstein[104,105] and Mitolo[106] in the late 'teens and early 'twenties. These authors demonstrated that the release of non-protein nitrogen by frog spinal cord is considerably accelerated during excitation over the resting figures. Similar results were obtained later on the brain cortex of narcotized cats by Geiger, Dobkin and Magnes.[107] Hydén and his colleagues[1] have demonstrated with highly refined techniques the effect of exhaustive stimulation *in vivo,* on the protein- and nucleic acid-metabolism, of various types of neurons in the CNS of rats. These changes involved both the proteins and the lipids of the Purkinje cells. The studies of Brattgard *et al.*[108] have shown that during the early postnatal period the mass per volume of the retinal ganglion cells increased by about 100% if the newborn rabbits received adequate light stimulation, but no such change occurred in the absence of stimulation. These questions are dealt with elsewhere in this volume.

A not inconsiderable incorporation of radioactive precursors into proteins of the brain has been observed by a number of investigators.[87,98,109,110] In brain perfusion experiments with a simplified blood containing C^{14}—labeled glucose, the rate of incorporation of labeled carbon into the brain proteins sharply increased during and following convulsions evoked by metrazol or by electroshock.[68]

Proteins of various subcellular fractions incorporated labeled precursors at different rates.[111,112,45] The specific activity of the proteins was highest in the microsomal fraction, and next highest in the nuclei, indicating a relatively high metabolic rate of proteins in the microsomes. Similar conclusions were drawn from brain perfusion experiments, with a blood not containing any glucose.[58] Of the subcellular units of the brain cortex sampled at various intervals during the perfusion,[113] the greatest loss in substance was sustained by the microsomes. Only when about 60% of the microsomal nucleoproteins and lipids were used up by the brain did physiological activity cease. The loss sustained by the mitochondrial fraction was proportionally much smaller and affected mostly the lipid fraction.

It was reported recently by Chapman et al.[114] that a proteolytic enzyme is released from the brain into the CSF, which produces from serum globulin a bradykinin-like hypotensive polypeptide on incubation.

Pope[115] described the abundant occurrence and distribution of a dipeptidase in human cortex. Vladimirov et al.[116] and Palladin[117] have noted a changed incorporation rate only after a certain time interval following convulsions. Ungar et al.[118] observed a reversible denaturation of brain proteins during stimulation. On the basis of these and similar observations, a mechanism of the excitation process has been proposed.[119]

On the basis of Ungar's experiments, which show reversible denaturation of proteins after electrical stimulation in the nerve cells, Fischer and Zeman[120] tried to develop a histochemical method capable of distinguishing between inactive and stimulated nerve cells. Their staining method was based on the fact that protein in the denatured state has more ionized tyrosine hydroxyl and cysteine sulfhydryl groups available than in the inactive state, and that iodination will further increase their affinity for basic dyes. They report that surfaces of neurons of excited nervous tissue were consistently stained more intensively by methylene blue than non-excited or depressed nerve cells. Similar findings were made by these authors in brain sections of young DBA-2 mice, after seizures of one minute duration were produced by sonic vibrations. The authors also report that chlorpromazine hydrochloride follows the same pattern of differential sorption on the nerve cells as does methylene blue. The authors in this connection quote Bodoni's observation of 1899[121] of the tranquilizing action of methylene blue on agitated mental patients. In the work of Nachmansohn et al.[122] special receptor proteins for acetylcholine are postulated.

An increasing number of radioautographic studies are being performed with the object of studying protein- and nucleic acid-turnover in resting and stimulated brain. The technique of Messier and Le-Blond[123] appears to be the most useful method. McLean et al., using S^{35} methionine, found a reduced incorporation of radioactive precursors into proteins in certain brain areas after insulin shock.[124,125] They emphasize parallelism between radioautographic darkening and the extent of Nissl staining. X-irradiation showed no change between control and experimental animals, while infection and depressant drugs decreased the radioactivity of brain proteins. Insulin-convulsion caused a noticeable decrease in incorporation of S^{35}, particularly after administration of dextrose. Incorporation of S^{35} methionine into gray matter was considerably higher than into white; hippocampus and the granular layer of cerebellar cortex were particularly dark; supraoptic nucleus, habenula, and pontine nuclei were darker than other formations. These findings were confirmed and extended.[126] These authors suggest that brain areas having motor functions generally show the greater darkening, while sensory areas show a lesser grain density. Individual nerve cells within most areas show similar degree of darkening, except the Purkinjé cells, which were divided into three groups according to their contents of RNA and protein, corresponding to their functional phases.

If the observed blackening of individual brain cells is an indication of the protein turnover rate, the proteins of neurons turn over faster than glia and white matter, based on equal weights. Koenig[127] injected adenine and orotic-C^{14} acid into rats, and found that nuclear RNA becomes tagged earlier than cytoplasmic RNA. In this work, the radioactivity of neurons and of supporting tissue could be extracted from the slides by ribonuclease digestion. After the third day, supporting tissue cells exhibited RNA-ase resistant activity, which, however, could be extracted by DNA-ase, indicating labeled DNA. Similar were the findings of Beuttas et al.,[128] who examined the incorporation of C^{14}—labeled leucine into proteins of various brain areas in the mouse at rest, during narcosis, during convulsions, and following specific stimuli. In both, the resting and stimulated brains, the heaviest incorporation of uniformly C^{14}—labeled leucine was found in the proteins of the Purkinje cells, the neurons of the hippocampus, hypothalamic nuclei, and brain cortex, mainly the pyriform cortex. In these experiments, the amounts of uniformly C^{14}—labeled amino acids incorporated after stimulation were consistently lower than in the resting state, irrespective of whether stimulation immediately preceded sacrifice of the animals, or if an hour elapsed between the stimulation and killing of the animals. These observations were in accord with other radioautographic studies, but at variance with observations made on the cat's brain by counting the C^{14} in the isolated proteins. This divergency of results was found to be caused by large protein losses incurred during the histological preparation of the brain slices used for autography. These experiments clearly demonstrated the unsuitability of methods involving the usual histological procedures for radioautographic studies of this kind. As pointed out previously by Hydén,[1] during the process of embedding, alcohol extraction, etc., protein losses in the neuron amount to 70%. In the author's laboratory, simultaneous treatment of slides and of homogenized brain material, derived from the same brain with various concentrations of alcohol, has shown a loss of 30 to 50% of the proteins. It seems, therefore, that more proteins are lost during the histological preparation of the brain sections than during the chemical isolation of the proteins. Even with the latter procedure, losses average about 20%. These experiments indicated, however, that such proteins of the brain which would not be alcohol-soluble after formaldehyde treatment in the "resting" brain cells become alcohol-soluble after stimulation.

The role of protein metabolism in brain functions received new interpretation recently in a number of laboratories.[120,130,119]

The structural functions and concentrations of nucleic acid in brain cells under various physiological conditions have been reviewed recently.[1,131,132] The observations made with cytochemical methods support the view that stimulation of neurons causes increased nucleoprotein production and utilization by the brain cells. Similar observations were made on tissue cultures of adult brain cells by R. S. Geiger.[133-136] The effects on neurons and on glial cells of stimulation by electric current and by drugs were followed continuously with time-lapse photography and phase-contrast optics. Metrazol and electric stimulation act on cytoplasmic granules of neurons, nucleus and nucleolus by increasing their motility. It bands granules around the nucleus and aggregates them in the perikaryon and dendrites, the latter acquiring a knobby appearance. Changes occur in the size and refractivity of the nucleus and nucleolus. Neurites become more motile and their end feet swell. The nucleolus becomes motile, and secretes nucleoproteins into the cytoplasm. The oligodendroglia become more motile, and from those present as perineuronal satellites, transfer of cytoplasmic material becomes more frequent. Addition of *sodium barbital* in concentration of 25 γ/ml. to the culture medium caused rapid intracellular changes in the neurons and a slight contraction of the neuron. Practically the entire cytoplasm appeared to become free of mitochondria (phase contrast, vital staining with Janus Green). The mitochondria began to reappear after 15 minutes, reduced in size and more uniformly dispersed throughout the cytoplasm. This process was reversible on washing, the mitochondria assumed their original size and distribution. Recovery was accompanied by increased nucleolar activity and concentration of perinuclear granules, other than mitochondria. The granules in the glia appeared unaffected by barbital.

The early effect of stimulation on the nucleus has recently been discussed by Ruska *et al.*[137] These authors consider the endoplasmic reticulum to be endowed with the properties of the cell membrane, which can conduct the excitation into the cell interior to the nucleus in the same way as excitation spreads on the exterior boundary of the cell.

When brain cortex of the cat (in Nembutal narcosis) was stimulated through the brachial plexus for 5 to 30 seconds, and the ipsilateral sensory motor area was frozen *in situ during* the stimulation (serving as control), and the controlateral side frozen *after* the completion of stimulation, differences were seen between the composition of nitrogenous substances in the areas frozen in the "resting" state and those frozen after stimulation.[43]

Stimulation for 20 seconds at 60 cpm. produced the following chemical changes per gram wet tissue: a) nonprotein nitrogen increased; b) nuclei acid nitrogen decreased; c) lipid nitrogen decreased. Amino-nitrogen increased in the lipid and nucleic acid fractions and decreased in the acid-soluble fraction. These chemical changes were proportional to the number of effective stimuli and were reversible at rest. It is concluded that nucleic acids and lipids are metabolized in the brain cortex during activity. When, after similar stimulation, the purine- and pyrimidines were isolated from the hydrolyzed nucleic acid extracts of the brain cortex, it was found that the nucleic acids of the stimulated areas consistently contained higher amounts of cytidine and adenine than the "resting" areas, when the uridine and guanine concentrations remained constant.[138] These changes probably indicate new synthesis. It was shown recently[139,140] that when homogenates of liver or Ehrlich's ascites tumor cells were incubated with C^{14}—labeled ATP, the RNA became labeled to some extent in the inner nucleotides, but predominantly in the terminal nucleotides. In order to attach the adenine nucleotide to the RNA, the preceding group must be a cytidine or a cytidylic acid end-group. When the cytidylic acid end-groups are missing, they must be introduced through the reaction of the RNA with CTP before the adenylic group can be attached. Terminal adenylate group of the soluble RNA fraction may be split off by reactions with pyrophosphate to form ATP. Hecht *et al.*[140] have concluded that the end-unit containing cytosine and adenine nucleotides provides a functional grouping in the soluble RNA which is required for its action as a carrier of activated amino acids in protein synthesis.

The changes in the nucleotide-composition of nucleic acids in neurons in the "resting" state and after stimulation have recently been studied by Grenell and Hydén (141), who found that in *nerve cells* cytosine was lower in the RNA produced after stimulation than before, but increased in the *glia* after stimulation, in spite of a decrease in the RNA concentration. After administration of a new compound: 1,3,3'tricyano,2-amino propene, to rabbits, a large increase of RNA was found in the nerve cells, with a simultaneous decrease of RNA in the glia.[141] These changes were also accompanied by a decrease of cytosine and increase of adenine in the neuronal RNA and a remarkable increase of cytosine in the glial RNA.

It was reported by Mihailovich et al.[142] that after electroshock there is a decrease in the RNA content of the brain, but not in the DNA content. These authors examined several brain areas, such as frontal cortex, occipital cortex, cerebellar cortex, caudate nucleus, midbrain, and medulla, and found that shock applied once, reduced the DNA content by about 20 to 25% in these areas. However, repeated shock treatment did not alter this picture.

The observed changes in nucleotide ratios in the nucleic acids of the neurons (and glia) combined with the increased turnover rate of some proteins, following stimulation, suggest that certain changes in the composition of the proteins synthesized after the stimulation, on the basis of a changed nucleic acid "template" could be expected. These changes in the protein composition could be a coding mechanism for the memory engram. This idea has been further developed by Hydén,[1] and is at the time of writing a part of the subjects discussed in a symposium organized by F. O. Schmitt on "Molecular Specificity and Biological Memory."

In a recent report of McIlwain,[143] gangliosides added to the incubation mixture restored the excitability to brain slices which (by previous treatment) had lost their ability to respond with increased metabolic rate to electric pulses.

The role of brain lipids is described elsewhere in this volume.

METABOLIC PATTERN

The data presented in the foregoing pages show that practically all of the chemical components of the brain, "free" or "bound" are involved to a larger or smaller extent, in its overall metabolism. On the other hand, only glucose is taken up by the brain from the blood in sufficient amounts to satisfy its metabolic requirements, as indicated by the fact that the glucose uptake of the brain from the blood equals its oxygen consumpion pius lactic acid production. Thus, practically all the chemical processes of the brain, including the synthetic processes referred to previously, are supported by glucose, with minor additions of co-factors, accessory substances, and essential amino acids. It was shown in the preceding pages that in brain-perfusion experiments with "simplified blood" in which uniformly C^{14}-labeled glucose was the only substrate offered to the brain, the respiratory CO_2 of the brain contains a large proportion of carbon derived from the oxidation of endogenous non-carbohydrate substances, and that all the nonessential amino acids, proteins, and lipids were produced by the brain, using glucose as a primary substrate. The relative proportions in which glucose and various other endogenous compounds participate in the oxidative metabolism vary under changing physiological conditions (as under the effect of stimulation or of drugs) even if the total oxidation rate remains constant. This raises the question whether the relative proportion of the various substrates (endogenous substrates and glucose) utilized by the brain under various physiological conditions can be regarded as characteristic of any particular physiological conditions.

In the "resting" state, with uniformly C^{14}-labeled glucose as the only substrate in the "simplified" perfusion blood, the proportion of C^{14} in the respiratory CO_2, pyruvate, glutamate, and aspartate reaches a constant figure after the initial exchange of glucose and its intermediary metabolites has been accomplished during the first 30 to 50 minutes of perfusion. From there on, even in perfusion experiments lasting 4 to 5 hours, this proportion of C^{14} to total C remains constant, indicating a steady influx of metabolites from non-carbohydrate sources into the glycolytic and tricarboxylic cycles at a constant rate. After the initial exchange of metabolites was accomplished, analysis of metabolites in blood and brain samples taken at various time intervals showed the following picture: The respiratory CO_2 contained 25 to 30% of $C^{14}O_2$. The lactic acid carbon in the brain contained only about 50% of C^{14}. Glutamic acid C had the same C^{14} concentration as the CO_2, while the label in the brain-aspartic acid was consistently lower—about 65% of the glutamic acid. These findings indicated that a major dilution of the glycolytic intermediaries of the glucose C^{14} occur before the pyruvic acid stage. Further dilution of the pyruvic carbon in the tricarboxylic cycle, as shown by the specific activities of the CO_2 and glutamate, indicates the influx of the cold carbon, probably via acetyl CoA or succinyl-CoA.

Stimulation of the brain by electroshock, metrazol, or through the brachial pleus, nearly doubled the total respiratory CO_2-output of the brain, but the C^{14}-output remained constant at the "resting" level, thus greatly reducing the C^{14} concentration in the respiratory CO_2. The C^{13} concentration in the lactic acid, also, remained around 50%, as in the "resting" state, indicating that the dilution occurred in the tricarboxylic acid cycle by influx of cold carbon from a large pool which did not become appreciably radioactive during the preceding perfusion time. No significant effects on the label of glutamic acid was seen, although that of the aspartic was diminished. Some drugs (among them isoniazide, iproniazide, phenyl cyclopropylamine) influenced this pattern in the direction of increased proportional participation of glucose-C^{14} in CO_2 and lactate formation, presumably by blocking the influx of cold carbon from pools which otherwise dilute the pyruvic acid. In these experiments, the C^{14} concentration in the respiratory CO_2 and in the pyruvic acid (or brain lactic acid) increased steadily and linearly until, after 2 hours of perfusion, the carbon of these compounds reached a C^{14} concentration of up to 85% of that of the glucose. The C^{14} concentration in glutamic and aspartic acids and in alanine did not follow that in the CO_2, but their radioactivity remained at the "resting" level (i.e., 25 to 30% C^{14}), indicating a possible inhibition of transaminases by these drugs.

These experiments demonstrate the flexibility of the metabolic pattern of the brain, and indicate their possible usefulness for the study of the metabolic correlates of physiological functions. It should be pointed out that at the present time labeled glucose seems to be the only substrate which is capable of uncovering this pattern. Labeled amino acids, when added to the perfusion blood, show anomalies which can, as indicated by the studies of Lajtha et al.,[145] be attributed to compartmentalization of various free amino acids within the neurons or between neurons and glia cells. When uniformly C^{14}-labeled aspartic acid was added to the blood, and the C^{14} concentration of the respiratory CO_2 was compared to that of the aspartic acid in the brain cortex, it was found soon after the start of the perfusion that the C^{14} concentration in the respiratory CO_2 equalled and later exceeded that in the aspartic acid of the brain. These experiments indicated[144] that when C^{14}-aspartate is added to the perfusion blood a gradient of C^{14}-aspartate between the capillaries and the neurons exists for many hours the aspartic acid having a much higher activity in the blood capillaries, and probably in the astrocytes and other glial cells surrounding the capillaries, than the neurons which are not directly adjacent to the capillaries. Thus, it is very likely that the CO_2 produced by some of the glial cells had a much higher C^{14} concentration than that produced by the neurons. Such a gradient, with the concomitant heterogeneity of label in the metabolite "pools" of various cells, would make the study of the metabolic pattern with any amino acid impossible. Fortunately, this is not the case with glucose, as within a comparatively short time after the addition of labeled glucose to the perfusing blood the specific activity of the glucose in the brain equals that in the blood.

The most convenient tool for the study of the brain's "metabolic pattern" is labelled glucose perfused through the brain. This approach will reflect only such changes as involve comparatively large parts of the brain.

REFERENCES

1. HYDÉN, H: In *The Cell*, p. 215. J. Bracket and A. E. Mirsky, Ed., New York, Acad. Press. (1960).
2. GEIGER, A.: *Physiol. Rev., 38*:1 (1958).
3. MANN, C. F. and MAGATH, T. B.: *Arch. Int. Med., 30*:171 (1922).
4. MADDOCK, S., HAWKINS, J. E. and HOLMES, E.: *Am. J. Physiol., 175*:53 (1939).
5. GEIGER, A., MAGNES, J., TAYLOR, R. M. and VERALLI, M.: *Am. J. Physiol., 177*:138 (1954).
6. STONE, W. E.: *Biochem. J., 32*:1908 (1939).
7. KLEIN, J. R. and OLSEN, N. S.: *J. Biol. Chem., 167*:1 (1946).
8. GEIGER, A. and MAGNES, J.: *Federation Proc., 8*:1, (1949).
9. SOLS, A. and CRANE, R. K.: *J. Biol. Chem., 210*:58 (1954).
10. GEIGER, A., MAGNES, J. and DOBKIN, J.: *Abstr. 19th Internat. Physiol. Congr.*, p. 383. Montreal (1953).
11. GEIGER, A. and YAMASAKI, S.: *J. Neurochem., 1*:93 (1956).
12. WOLFF, P. H. and TSCHIRGI, R. D.: *Am. J. Physiol., 184*:220 (1956).
13. LEFEVRE, P. G. and LEFEVRE, M. E.: *J. Gen. Physiol., 35*:891 (1952).
14. REINWEIN, D., KALMAN, C. F. and PARK, C. L.: *Federation Proc., 16*:237 (1957).
15. WIDDAS, W. F.: *J. Physiol., 118*:23 (1952).
16. WIDDAS, W. F.: *J. Physiol., 125*:163 (1954).
17. WILBRANDT, W.: *Arch. Exper. Path. u. Pharm., 212*:9 (1950).
18. WILBRANDT, W.: *J. Cell. & Comp. Physiol., 47*:137 (1956).
19. WILBRANDT, W., FREI, S. and ROSENBERG, T.: *Exper. Cell Res., II*:59 (1956).
20. HELE, M. D.: *Biochem. J., 55*:864 (1953).
21. LOURAN, M.: *Compt. rend Soc. biol., 238*:842 (1954).
22. VERZAR, F. and McDOUGALL, E. T.: *Absorption from the Intestine*. London, Longmans (1936).
23. HESTRIN-LERNER, S. and SHAPIRO, B.: *Biochem. et biophys. acta, 12*:553 (1954); *Ibid., 13*:54 (1954).
24. KESTON, A. S.: *Science, 120*:355 (1954).
25. KESTON, A. S.: *Federation Proc., 16*:203 (1957).
26. LEVINE, R. and GOLDSTEIN, M. S.: In *Major Metabolic Fuels*, Vol. 5, p. 73. Brookhaven Symp. Biol. (1952).
27. PARK, C. R., BORNSTEIN, J. and POST, R. L.: *Am. J. Physiol., 182*:12 (1955).
28. HAVGAARD, N., McVAUGHAN, HAVGAARD, E. S. and STADIE, W. J.: *Biol. Chem., 208*:549 (1954).
29. ALLWEISS, C. and MAGNES, J.: *Abstr. 20th Internatl. Physiol. Congr.* (1956).
30. PARK, J. T. and STROMINGER, J. L.: *Science, 125*:95 (1957).
31. STROMINGER, J. L.: *J. Biol. Chem., 224*:532 (1957).
32. KREBS, H. A. and EGGLESTON, L. O.: *Biochem. J., 44*:2 (1949).
33. CSAKY, T. Z. and ZOLLICOFFER, L.: *Am. J. Physiol., 198*:1056 (1960).
34. WALAAS, O., BORREBACK, B., KRISTIANSEN, T. and WALAAS, E.: *Biochem. Biophys. Acta, 40*:562, (1960).
35. BERMAN, E. R. and WERTHEIMER, E.: *Am. J. Physiol., 198*:1075 (1960).
36. VARGAS, L., TAYLOR, R. W. and RANDLE, P. J.: *Biochem. J., 77*:43 (1960).
37. RAFAELSON, O. J.: *Lancet*, p. 941 (Nov. 1, 1958).
38. ALLWEISS, C. and MAGNES, J.: *Abstr. 20th Internatl. Physiol. Congr.* (1956).
39. RAFAELSON, O.: *Lancet*, p. 1941 (1958).
40. GEIGER, A., MAGNES, J., TAYLOR, R. M. and VERALLI, M.: *Am. J. Physiol., 177*:138 (1954).

41. GEIGER, A. and YAMASAKI, S.: *J. Neurochem., 1:*93 (1956).

42. MAGNES, J. and HESTRIN-LERNER, S.: *J. Neurochem., 5:*128 (1960).

43. GEIGER, A., YAMASAKI, S. and LYONS, R.: *Am. J. Physiol., 184:*239 (1956).

44. GEIGER, A.: In Waelsch, *Neurochemistry*, p. 245. Great Britain, Chapel River Press, (1958).

45. GEIGER, A., HORVATH, N. and KAWAKITA, Y.: *J. Neurochem., 5:*311 (1958).

46. GEY, K. F.: *Biochem. J., 64:*145 (1956).

47. GOMBOS, G., WHITNEY, G. and GEIGER, A.: Unpublished observations.

48. DEFFNER, G. and HAFTER, R.: *Biochim. Biophys. Acta, 42:*189 (1960); *Ibid., 42:*200 (1960).

49. KERR, S. E., HAMPEL, C. W. and GHANTUS, J. J.: *J. Biol. Chem., 119:*405 (1946).

50. KHAIKINA, B. I. and KRACHKO, L. S.: *Ukraim. Biokhim. Zhur., 29:*10 (1957).

51. PROKHORAVA, M. I.: *Chem. Abstr., 50:*7268 (1956).

52. SVORAD, D.: *Nature, 181:*775 (1958).

53. STETTEN, M. R. and STETTEN, P.: *J. Biol. Chem., 207:*331 (1954; *J. Biol. Chem., 213:*723 (1955).

54. STETTEN, DEWITT, JR., and STETTEN, M. R.: *Physiol. Rev., 40:*505 (1960).

55. SUTHERLAND, E. W. and RALL, T. W.: *J. Biol. Chem., 232:*1077 (1958); *Biol. Chem. 232:*1065 (1958).

56. HIMWICH, H. E.: *Brain Metabolism and Cerebral Disorders.* Baltimore, Williams & Wilkens (1951).

57. KETY, S. S.: In *Neurochemistry*, p. 294. K. A. C. Elliott, I. H. Page, and J. H. Quastel, Eds. Springfield, Ill., Thomas (1955).

58. GEIGER, A., MAGNES, J. and GEIGER, R. S.: *Nature, 170:*754 (1952).

59. ERBSLÖH, F., BERNSMEIER, A. and HILLESHEIM, H. R.: *Arch. Psychiat. u. Ztschr. ges. Neurol., 196:*611 (1958).

60. GEIGER, A., MAGNES, J. and DOBKIN, J.: *Federation Proc., 13:*52 (1954).

61. GRENELL, R. G. and DAVIES, P. W.: *Federation Proc., 9:*52 (1950).

62. BLOOM, B.: *Proc. Soc. Exper. Biol. & Med., 88:*317 (1955).

63. DIPIETRO, D. and WEINHOUSE, E.: *Arch. Biochem. Biophys., 80:*268 (1959).

64. COHEN, L. H. and NOELL, W. K.: *J. Neurochem., 5:*253 (1960).

65. HOSKIN, F. C. G.: *Biochim. et Biophys. Acta, 40:*309 (1960).

66. SACHS, W.: *J. Appl. Physiol., 10:*37 (1957); *14:*849 (1959).

67. ALLWEISS, C. and MAGNES, J.: *J. Neurochem., 2:*326 (1958).

68. GEIGER, A., KAWAKITA, Y. and BARKULIS, S. S.: *J. Neurochem., 5:*323 (1960).

69. SUTHERLAND, V. C., BURBRIDGE, T. N. and ELLIOTT, H. W.: *Am. J. Physiol., 180:*195 (1955).

70. WENNER, C. E. and WEINHOUSE, S.: *J. Biol. Chem., 222:*399 (1956).

71. ALLWEISS, C. and MAGNES, J.: *Nature, 181:*626 (1958).

72. FLOREY, E.: *Arch. internat. physiol., LXII:*5 (1954).

73. ELLIOTT, K. A. C. and FLOREY, E.: *J. Neurochem., 1:*181 (1956).

74. BAZEMORE, A., ELLIOTT, K. A. C. and FLOREY, E.: *Nature, 178:*1052 (1956).

75. ROBERTS, E. and FRANKEL, S.: *J. Biol. Chem., 187:*55 (1950).

76. RIGGS, T. R., WALKER, L. M. and CHRISTENSEN, H. N.: *J. Biol. Chem., 233:*1979 (1958).

77. KREBS and EGGLESTON: *Biochem. J., 44:*2 (1949).

78. CHRISTENSEN, H. N.: In *Amino Acid Metabolism*, p. 63, W. D. McElroy and B. Glass, Eds. Baltimore, John Hopkins Press (1955).

79. CHRISTENSEN, H. N. and RIGGS, T. R.: *J. Biol. Chem., 220:*265 (1956).

80. CURTIS, D. R., PERRIN, D. D. and WATKINS, J. C.: *J. Neurochem., 6:*1 (1960).

81. BELOFF-CHAIN, A., CATANZARO R., CHAIN, E. B., MASI, I. and POCCHIARI, R.: *Proc. Royal Soc. B., 144*:22 (1955).

82. KINI, M. M. and QUASTEL, J. H.: *Nature, 184*:252 (1959).

83. BARKULIS, S. S., GEIGER, A., KAWAKITA, Y. and AGUILAR, V.: *J. Neurochem., 5*:339 (1960).

85. LAJTHA, A., FURST, S. S., GERSTEIN, A. and WAELSCH, H.: *J. Neurochem., 1*:289 (1957).

86. LAJTHA, A., FURST, S. S. and WAELSCH, H.: *Experientia, 13*:168 (1957).

87. WAELSCH, H.: In *Metabolism of the Nervous System.* D. Richter, Ed. Pergamon Press London (1957).

88. CURTIS, D. R., PHILLAS, J. W. and WATKINS, J. C.: *J. Physiol., 150*:656 (1960).

89. PURPURA, D. P., GIRADO, M., SMITH, T. G., CALLAN, D. A. and GRUNDFEST, H.: *J. Neurochem., 3*:238 (1959).

90. EDWARDS, C., *et al.: J. Neurochem., 4*:19 (1950).

91. TOWER, D. B.: In the *Neurochemistry of Nucleotides and Amino Acids*, p. 173. R. O. Brady and D. B. Tower, Eds. New York, John Wiley & Sons (1960).

92. TOWER, D. B. and ELLIOTT, K. A. C.: *J. Appl. Physiol., 5*:375 (1953).

93. HAWKINS, J. A. and SARETT, L. H.: *Clin. Chim Acta, 2*:481 (1957)

94. GEIGER, R. S., MAGNES, J. and GEIGER, A.: Unpublished observations.

95. SCHWENTIN, P., BESSMAN, S. T. and WAELSCH, H.: *J. Biol. Chem., 184*:37 (1950).

96. WAELSCH, H., MAGNES, J., SCHWETIN, P. and GEIGER, A.: Unpublished observations.

97. WAELSCH, H.: *Lancet, 257*:1 (1949).

98. WINZLER, R. J., MOLDAVE, T., RAFELSON, M. E. and PERSON, H. E.: *J. Biol. Chem., 199*:485 (1952).

99. QUASTEL, J. H. and KINI, M. M.: *Proc. Internat. Congr. Biochem., IV, 3*:90 (1959).

100. KINI, M. M. and QUASTEL, J. H.: *Science, 131*:412 (1960)

101. OTSUKI, S., GOMBOS, G., SCRUGGS, W., WHITNEY, G. and GEIGER, A. Unpublished observations.

102. SOULA, L. C.: *J. physiol. et path. gen., 15*:267 (1913).

103.. BAGLIONI, S. Z.: *Allgem. Physiol., 4*:384 (1904).

104. WINTERSTEIN, H. Z.: *Physiol. Chem., 110*:212 (1918).

105. WINTERSTEIN, H. Z. and HIRSCHBERG, E.: *Biochem. Ztschr., 158*:401 (1926).

106. MIOTLO, M.: *Fisiol. e. med. Rome, 7*:2 (1930).

107. GEIGER, A., DOBKIN, J. and MAGNES, J.: *Science, 118*:655 (1953).

108. BRAATGARD, S. O., EDSTRÖM, J. E. and HYDÉN, H.: *J. Neurochem., 1*:316 (1957).

109. GAITONDE, M. K. and RICHTER, D.: *Biochem. J., 59*:690 (1955).

110. ROBERTS, R. B., FLEXNER, J. B. and FLEXNER, L. B.: *J. Neurochem., 4*:78 (1959).

111. RICHTER, D.: In *Biochemistry of the Central Nervous System*, p. 173. F. Brücke, Ed. London, New York, Paris, and Los Angeles, Pergamon Press (1958).

112. WAELSCH, H.: *J. Nerv. & Ment. Dis.*, 126:33 (1958).

113. ABOOD, L. G. and GEIGER, A.: *Am. J. Physiol., 182*:557 (1955).

114. CHAPMAN, L. F., RAMOS, A., CORRADO, A., FORTES, V. and SYMMES, D.: *Arch. Neurol., 3*:43 (1960).

115. POPE, A.: *J. Neurochem., 4*:31 (1959).

116. VLADIMIROV, G. E. and URINSON, A. P.: *Biokhimiya, 22*:655, (1957).

117. PALLADIN, A. V. and POLJAKOWA: In *Biochemistry of The Central Nervous System*, p. 185, F. Brücke, Ed. London, New York, Paris, Los Angeles, Pergamon Press (1958).

118. UNGAR, G., ASCHEIM, E., PSYCHOYOS, S. and ROMANO, D. V.: *J. Gen. Phyisol.*, *40*:635 (1957).

119. UNGAR, G.: *J. physiol.*, *49*:1235 (1957).

120. FISCHER, R., and ZEMAN, W.: *Nature, 183*:1377 (1959).

121. BODONI, P.: *Semaine med.*, *7*:56 (1899).

122. NACHMANSOHN, D.: In *Biochemistry of the Central Nervous System*, p. 34, F. Brücke, Ed. London, New York, Paris, and Los Angeles, Pergamon Press (1958).

123. MESSIER, B. and LeBLOND, C. P.: *Proc. Soc. Exper. Biol. & Med., 96*:7 (1957).

124. MacLEAN, P. D., FLANIGAN, S., FLYNN, J. P., KIM, C. and STEVENS, J. R.: *Yale J. Biol. & Med., 28*:380 (1955-56).

125. FLANIGAN, S., GABRIELI, E. R. and MacLEAN, P. D.: *A.M.A. Arch. Neurol. & Psychiat., 77*:588 (1957).

126. OEHLERT, W., SCHULTZE, B. and MAURER, W.: *Bietr. path. Anat. u. Allgem. Path., 119*:No. 3, 343 (1958).

127. KOENIG, H.: *Biochem. Cytol., 4* (6):785 (1958).

128. BEUTTAS, J., BALABAN, M. and GEIGER, A.: *Federation Proc., 19*:No. 1, Pt. 1 (1960).

129. KATZ, J. J., and HALSTEAD, W.: In Halstead, *Brain and Behavior: A Symposium.* U. of Calif. Press (1950).

130. HYDÉN, H.: In *Biochemistry of the Central Nervous System*, p. 64, F. Brücke, Ed. London, New York, Paris, and Los Angeles, Pergamon Press (1958).

131. EINARSON, L.: In *Modern Scientific Aspects of Neurology*. London, Arnold, (1960).

132. *The Neurochemistry of Nucleotides and Amino Acids.* R. Brady and D. B. Tower, Eds. New York, John Wiley & Sons (1960).

133. GEIGER, R. S.: *Nature, 182*:1674 (1958).

134. GEIGER, R. S.: *Exper. Cell Res., 14*:541 (1958).

135. GEIGER, R. S.: *Federation Proc., 17*:No. 1 (1958).

136. GEIGER, R. S.: *J. Neuropsychiat., 1*:185 (1960).

137. RUSKA, H., EDWARDS, G. A. and CAESAR, R.: *Experimenta, 14*:117 (1958).

138. GEIGER, A.: In *Metabolism of the Nervous System*. D. Richter, Ed. Pergamon Press (1957).

139. STEPHENSON, M. L., SCOTT, J. F., and HOAGLAND, M. D.: *Federation Proc., 16*:275 (1957).

140. HECHT, L. I., ZAMECNEK, B. S., STEPHENSON, M. L. and SCOTT, J. F.: *Biol. Chem., 233*:954 (1958).

141. GRENELL, R. G. and HYDÉN H.: Personal communication (1961).

142. MYHAILOVICH, B. D., JANKOVIC, M., PETROVI, M. and ISAKOVICH: *Experimentia, 14*:144 (1958).

143. McILWAIN, H.: *Biochem. J., 76*:167 (1960).

144. GOMBOS, G., OTSUKI, S., GEIGER, A. SCRUGGS, W. and WHITNEY, G.: In preparation.

145. LAJTHA, A., BERL, S. and WAELSCH, H.: In *Inhibition of the Nervous System and γ-Amino butyric Acid*, p. 460. Oxford, London, New York, Paris, Pergamon Press (1960).

VII

METABOLISM OF GLUCOSE AND OXYGEN IN MAMMALIAN SYMPATHETIC GANGLIA AT REST AND IN ACTION

Martin G. Larrabee and Jack D. Klingman

I. INTRODUCTION

Since Langley and Dickinson in 1889 described the block of transmission through sympathetic ganglia caused by local application of nicotine, many investigators have studied the pharmacology of these ganglia. The classical papers of Dale on choline esters and of Feldberg and his colleagues on the relation of acetylcholine to transmission processes deserve special mention because they have contributed in the development of stimulating concepts of broad biological significance. Despite such extensive pharmacological studies and several physiological investigations of synaptic properties in ganglia,[10,19,20,52] including the remarkable effects of a virus infection,[16,17] measurements of metabolism in sympathetic ganglia have been limited until recently to the formation and release of acetylcholine,[42] to the effects of oxygen-lack and circulatory arrest,[3,11] and to a few preliminary and non-quantitative reports on relative rates of oxygen uptake under various conditions.[53] Several investigators have reported that certain ganglia from several species of mammals retain the capacity for axonal conduction and synaptic transmission for many hours after excision when kept in appropriate bathing solutions at body temperature or cooler.[12,21,47] It is thus possible to study ganglionic metabolism in an environment which is reproducible and adjustable, and to take advantage of a relatively simple and readily-isolated mammalian neuronal system which includes nerve fibers, cell bodies, and synapses. Moreover, the nerve cells in an isolated ganglion are normally at

Preparation of this chapter and much of the work discussed was supported by a research grant (B-702) from the Institute of Neurological Diseases and Blindness of the National Institutes of Health, U. S. Public Health Service.

150

rest, so that neuronal activity is under experimental control and can readily be induced and measured by standard electrical techniques.

II. GENERAL METHODS

Most of the experiments described here were performed in our own laboratory, usually on superior cervical ganglia excised from adult rats with body weights usually between 180 and 220 gm. The preparations were ordinarily kept at about 37° and were either immersed or dipped frequently into a physiological solution containing the following materials, with concentrations given in millimoles per liter: NaCl, 136; KCl, 5.6; $CaCl_2$, 2.22; $MgCl_2$, 1.2; $NaHCO_3$, 16.2; NaH_2PO_4, 1.2; glucose, 5.5. The solution was equilibrated with 5% CO_2, 95% O_2, giving a pH about 7.4 at 37°. It was kept sterile, usually at least to the moment of contact with the preparation and with the moist chamber. Sometimes the whole experiment was conducted aseptically.[48] In order to minimize the possibility of anoxia at the core of the preparation,[48] immersion fluids were always kept in motion around the ganglion and entry of air into the moist chamber was carefully prevented.

Since the preparation weighed only 0.5 to 1 mg. when wet, and only 100 to 300 μg. when dried, special procedures had to be developed for the various metabolic measurements.[50,57]

The following methods involving glucose uniformly labeled with carbon-14 have not been described previously. (A) Isotopic measurements of glucose and lactate exchanges were made by dipping ganglia for 1-hour periods into about 25 μl. of solution containing labeled glucose. The solution was then dried on paper, and the glucose and lactate were separated by one-dimensional chromatography and counted. The amounts of glucose removed and lactate added by the tissue were calculated by comparison with control samples.[41] (B) Labeled carbon dioxide was measured by continually collecting the CO_2 from fluid which had flowed past the tissue at a controlled rate and transporting this CO_2 past a Geiger counter.[40] The measurements were made about 3 hours after placing the preparation in the solution containing labeled glucose, to permit the rate of labeled CO_2 production to approach the maximum value (Fig. 1). (C) Acid products with volatility similar to acetic acid were isolated from the bathing fluid in a specially-constructed planchet-to-planchet microstill and were measured by their radioactivity.[49] (D) Incorporation of labeled carbon into chemical constituents of the tissue was determined by incubating ganglia with uniformly labeled glucose for various times, grinding in cold acetone, and spreading the ground material on a planchet. Alternatively, incubated ganglia were digested and fully oxidized, the resultant CO_2 being trapped in alkali and counted. Counting rates from 27 preparations showed a relatively rapid initial rise during the first 2 hours, followed by an approximately linear rise for the next 8 hours. The initial rapid rise was ignored and the rate of incorporation was calculated from the subsequent linear rise.

This procedure should prevent intraganglionic glucose, lactate, CO_2, and other rapidly turning-over constituents of carbohydrate metabolism from contributing to the estimate of the incorporation rate.[41]

Metabolic poducts measured by these tracer methods were expressed in terms of amount of material derived from labeled glucose, rather than the total amount of material produced from all sources. Thus for a given component X,

Moles of carbon in X derived from labeled glucose =

$$\frac{\text{CPM found in X}}{\text{CPM/mole of carbon in glucose}} \times \frac{\text{Counting efficiency for glucose}}{\text{Counting efficiency for X}}$$

III. SURVIVAL OF EXCISED PREPARATIONS

Under conditions of excision, various properties of the rat ganglia remained nearly constant for many hours. Constant production of labeled CO_2 and constant content of labeled potassium, continuing for 8 or more hours after equilibration, are shown in Figures 1 and 2. Rate of oxygen uptake, measurement of which began about one hour after excision, did not decline more than 2% per hour over the first 10 hours.[48] The only metabolic rate found to change significantly with time was the aerobic conversion of glucose to lactate, which progressively increased over a period of 5 hours.[38] However, the amount of glucose left over for other uses, such as oxidation and incorporation into the tissue, did not change with time. Progressive decline in ATP content has been observed (Table VI).[59]

The action potential recorded from the postganglionic nerve was well maintained, signifying continued capacity for impulse conduction and synaptic transmission.[48,53] In fact, the height of the action potential increased for the first 10 to 15 hours in many preparations kept in relatively large volumes of stirred solution (30 ml. or more). In one series of 34 preparations, for example, the majority still yielded action potentials greater than the inital value 10 hours after excision and none had fallen below 50%.[68] Times for 50% decline in response in these 34 experiments were distributed fairly uniformly from 11 to 49 hours, with an average of 30 hours. This average is comparable to that similarly estimated for rat ganglia left in the body after section of the preganglionic nerve.[53]

IV. METABOLIC RATES AT REST

Rates of various exchanges between excised rat ganglia and the bathing fluid are given in Table I. Since they were determined after a steady state of exchange had been approached, they are measures of the rates of production or utilization within the tissue. *All tracer measurements concerned only the carbon of glucose,* since this was the only

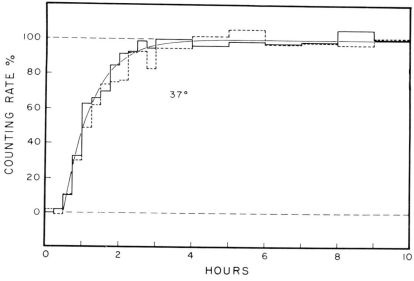

Fig. 1. Output of labeled CO_2 from superior cervical ganglia excised from rats, as a function of time after transfer from a solution containing unlabeled glucose to one containing glucose labeled uniformly with C-14.[39,40] Rate of output is proportional to counting rate. Dashed and solid lines represent two different preparations. Smooth curve is a plot of the equation: (Counting rate)/ (final counting rate) $= (1-e^{-(t-0.5)/0.75})$ where t is expressed in hours. This shows that the rise in counting rate can be fitted approximately by a single exponential.

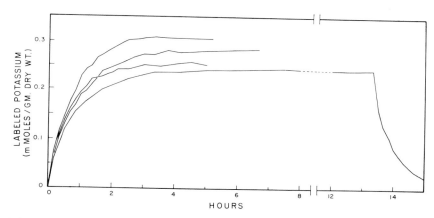

Fig. 2. Content of labeled potassium in several excised sympathetic ganglia, as a function of time after transfer to solution containing K-42.[9] Each curve refers to a single preparation (37°).

labeled material provided. For example, the CO_2 determined by tracer methods measured only that which derived its C from the labeled glucose.

In order to obtain an estimate of lactate production which was limited to lactate formed from glucose, thus eliminating endogenous sources, the ratio of labeled lactate produced to labeled glucose consumed was determined in four experiments. The ratio of the amounts in moles was 0.47 ± 0.04 (mean $\pm$ s.e.m.). Lactate produced from glucose was calculated by multiplying this ratio by the glucose uptake, with the result entered on line 6 in Table I.

TABLE I

METABOLIC RATES IN SUPERIOR CERVICAL GANGLIA EXCISED FROM RATS

($\mu mol./gm.$ dry weight/hr.)

(Mean $\pm$ s.e.m. or individual rates)

	Temperature	Rate	No.	Method*	Ref.
		A. Oxygen Uptake			
1	36°	300 ± 9	23	Flow respirometer	48
2	24°	111 ± 8	10	Flow respirometer	48
		B. Glucose Uptake			
3	36°	68 ± 3	46	Chemical	38, 41
4	23°	26 ± 1	35	Chemical	18
		C. Lactate Output			
5	36°	38 ± 2	46	Chemical	38
6	36°	32 ± 3	—	Combined (see text)	
7	23°	15 ± 1	35	Chemical	18
		D. Carbon Dioxide Output			
8	37°	260 ± 6**	13	Tracer	40
		E. Output of Acids with Volatility Similar to Acetic (Expressed as acetate)			
9	37°	1.0, 2.1, 2.4	3	Tracer	49
		F. Incorporation of Carbon from Glucose (Expressed as carbon)			
10	36°	48 ± 11	16	Tracer	41
		G. Ammonia Output			
11	37°	2.2 ± 0.5	16	Microdiffusion	57, 66, 67

*All tracer measurements reported in this article were made using uniformly labeled glucose (obtained from Nuclear Chicago Corp.). A few results with specifically labeled glucose will be reported elsewhere.[40]
**Lower rates for CO_2 production previously implied in abstracts have since been found not to be comparable with the other metabolic data. The dry weights of tissue in those experiments were considerably heavier than in all other series of experiments, presumably due to inclusion of more connective tissue when excising the preparations, giving too low a value for CO_2 production per unit weight.

Partitioning of Carbon. From results such as those in Table I it is possible to determine the proportions in which the carbon of glucose is partitioned between various metabolic channels at 36-37°. The relevant metabolic rates are summarized in Table II, where all have been converted into a common coinage—namely, the micromoles of carbon involved in each component per gram per hour. The only exception is in the units for oxygen, which are micromoles of O_2 per gram per hour, since one mole of O_2 is equivalent to one mole of C in oxidation of glucose. These units facilitate comparisons and aid the drawing up of balance sheets.

Part A of Table II shows that the carbon of glucose has been well accounted for: 64% appeared as CO_2, 24% appeared as lactate, 12% was retained in various chemical constituents of the tissue, and a trivial amount (1%) was possibly put out as acids of intermediate volatility, such as acetate. The total carbon accounted for agrees excellantly with that consumed as glucose. This gives reassurance that the various measurements are reasonably correct and that all the major destinations of the carbon have been included.

TABLE II

METABOLIC BALANCE CALCULATIONS USING DATA SELECTED FROM TABLE I

(36-37°. Mean ± s.e.m.)

Part A			$\mu mol.\ C/gm.$ $dry\ wt./hr.$	Per Cent of Glucose Carbon
1	Glucose uptake, Table I, line	3	407 ± 16	
2	CO_2 output	8	260 ± 6	64
3	Lactate output	6	96 ± 10	24
4	Incorporation	10	48 ± 11	12
5	Volatile acid output	9	4 ± 1	1
6	Sum of 2, 3, 4, 5		408 ± 16	100
Part B			$\mu mol.\ O_2/gm.$ $dry\ wt./hr.$	Per Cent of O_2 uptake
7	Oxygen uptake, Table I, line	1	300 ± 9	
			$\mu mol.\ C/gm.$ $dry\ wt./hr.$	
8	CO_2 output, Table I, line	8	260 ± 6	87
9	Incorporation	10	48 ± 11	16
10	Sum of 8 and 9		308 ± 13	103
11	Difference from O_2 uptake		8 ± 16	

In preliminary investigations using paper chromatography,[45] the carbon incorporated into the tissue was traced to several amino acids, as expected,[4,5] and several lipids and other compounds (Fig. 4 and Table V).

Metabolic Balance. In part B of Table II comparisons are made with the rate of oxygen uptake. Eighty-seven per cent of the oxygen is accounted for by the production of labeled CO_2. This figure does not represent the respiratory quotient of the tissue, since only the carbon coming more or less directly from glucose is measured. Because the respiratory quotient can be assumed not to exceed unity in the steady state, not more than about 13% of the total CO_2 produced could have come from substrates which had remained unlabeled during the preliminary incubation period (at least 3 hours).

An interesting calculation can be made by assuming that the tissue is in a steady state in the sense that the concentrations of materials within it are staying constant and that the rate of carbon incorporation represents replacement of unlabeled carbon, which is being lost by oxidation of endogenous substrates. In this case the rate of unlabeled CO_2 production would equal the rate of carbon incorporation. When this rate is added to the measured rate of labeled CO_2 production in order to obtain an estimate of total CO_2 production, the rate of oxygen uptake is fully accounted for, at least within the limits of accuracy of the measurements (Table II, part B). Some support for the hypothesis of a steady state is thus obtained.

The evidence for a steady state applies only to materials concerned in carbohydrate metabolism and only during the first five or ten hours after excision. Clearly some progressive changes occur even during this time, since the bathing fluid provides nothing which could replace the nitrogen lost as ammonia (Table I, line 11). Later there is a failure of axonal conduction and synaptic transmission, certainly indicating a profound change from the condition of the freshly excised preparation.

If the carbon from endogenous substrates is being continually replaced by labeled carbon from glucose, it is relevant to inquire why there is no progressive rise in rate of labeled CO_2 production after the fourth hour in experiments such as the two shown in Fig. 1. Perhaps the substrate pools are so large, or the pathways to them from glucose are so indirect, that the specific activity within the pools remains too low to be detected in the CO_2 coming from them, even up to the tenth hour. At all events, the results imply that most of the materials being oxidized can be divided into those in which the carbon has all been replaced from glucose during 3 or 4 hours of incubation, and those in which no more than a small fraction has been replaced as late as the tenth hour.

V. SOME COMPARISONS WITH OTHER NERVOUS TISSUES

Many of the foregoing results on carbohydrate metabolism in ganglia are qualitatively similar to those found in perfused brain by Geiger and his colleagues[25,27] and by Allweis and Magnes.[2] Significant

TABLE III

COMPARISON OF METABOLIC RATES IN RESTING SYMPATHETIC GANGLIA WITH SOME OTHER NERVOUS TISSUES AT 35-37°

($\mu mol.$ C or O_2/gm. dry weight/hr.)

Species	Tissue	State	Glucose Uptake	CO_2 Output	Lactate Output	Pyruvate Output	"Acetate" Output	O_2 Uptake	References
Human	Brain	Natural circ.	547*		64*	12*		481*	33
Human	Brain	Natural circ.	490†		2*	6*		470†	43
Rat	Cerebral cortex	Sliced						500	23
Rat	Brain	Homogenate	488**	323**	138**	3**	22**‡	352**	24
Rat	Ganglia	Excised	407	260¶	96¶	0¶‖	4¶‡	300	Table II
Rat	Peroneal nerve	Excised						72**	14
Rat	Various nerves	Excised						30–90	48

*Calculated from published A-V differences per unit volume of blood, assuming blood flow = 750 ml. per minute, and dry weight of brain = 280 gm.

†Calculated from published rates per 100 gm. of brain per minute, assuming normal weight of brain = 5 times dry weight.

**Calculated from published rates per unit wet weight, assuming wet weight = 5 times dry weight.

‡Product, isolated by distillation procedures which would collect acids with a volatility similar to acetic acid, was not fully identified.

¶Output of carbon from uniformly labeled glucose was measured by tracer methods. Therefor these are not total rates.

‖Indicated by absence of counts in pyruvate region of chromatogram of bathing solution.[40]

quantitative differences are that only 20-30% of the carbon in the consumed glucose appeared as CO_2 in the perfused brain, compared to about 60% in excised ganglia, and that the CO_2 derived from labeled glucose accounted for only 20-30% of the oxygen consumed by brain, compared to about 85% in ganglia. It would be interesting to know whether these differences persist under natural conditions or whether the metabolism of one or the other tissues has been modified by the change to the experimental situation.

Various metabolic rates for sympathetic ganglia excised from rats are compared with rates found in some other nervous tissues in Table III. The ganglionic rates are nearer to those of brain than to those of peripheral nerve.

VI. METABOLIC CHANGES ACCOMPANYING ACTIVITY

1. Changes in Oxygen Uptake

Rate of Change. With the onset of activity, neuronal metabolism promptly begins to change. This was shown in perfused sympathetic ganglia of cats by measuring the oxygen concentration with a suitably polarized platinum electrode thrust into the ganglion. The rate of decline of oxygen concentration when the perfusion was stopped indicated the rate of oxygen utilization.[53] When 2 to 4 volleys of impulses at a frequency of 12 per second were initiated by preganglionic stimulation, the rate of oxygen uptake accelerated without measurable latency, certainly in less than 1 second, and reached a maximum from which the rate started to fall after less than 5 seconds. How much earlier the maximum rate was actually passed could not be determined due to lags inherent in the method. Prompt acceleration of oxygen uptake following the start of repetitive activity has also been observed in frog nerve[8,13] and is presumably a general characteristic of nervous tissue. Similarly prompt formation of inorganic phosphate in brain, caused by electrical stimulation, has been reported.[15,32]

When the preganglionic nerve was continuously stimulated, the rate of oxygen uptake by an excised rat ganglion increased to reach a new steady level after a few minutes. When stimulation was stopped, the oxygen uptake promptly declined, returning to the resting level with a time constant no greater than 2 minutes at either 23° or 36°.[48] This recovery was rapid compared to that in type-A fibers of frog nerve, which exhibited a time constant of about 18 minutes at 20°.[8] The difference between the two tissues thus persisted even when the rat ganglion was cooled nearly to the temperature of the frog nerve. Others have reported that the return of oxygen uptake to the resting level is also more rapid in type-A fibers of the rat (common peroneal nerve) than in type-A fibers of frogs following repetitive stimulation.[14] Although the authors do not state values for the rat nerve, one of their illustrations indicates a time constant for recovery which is less than 5 minutes at 25°. Thus different recovery rates may be characteristic of different species, and it has been speculated that possibly "quicker return to resting rate represents an adaptation in a higher organism either for metabolic economy or for earlier readiness for renewed action."[48]

Frequency of Activity. The steady rate of oxygen consumption attained during continual activity increased with the frequency of stimulation. In excised sympathetic ganglia the maximum increase, about 50% above the resting level, was produced at 15 per second. The increase fitted an exponential function of frequency, which was the same as that applied to frog nerve in the analysis of Brink, Bronk, Carlson and Connelly,[8] except that the frequencies required were about one-eighth of those for frog nerve. Thus at a given low frequency (e.g., 5 per second) the rate of oxygen uptake increased much more above the resting level in rat ganglia than in frog nerve. On the other hand the rate in rat ganglia reached a maximum at about 15 per second, whereas it continued to rise up to a frequency of 100 or more per second in the frog nerve. Analysis showed that the extra amount of oxygen consumed per volley of impulses became less as the frequency rose in both nerve and ganglion. This reduction was not caused by limitations in diffusion of oxygen or of glucose, or by a failure of response. Thus the reduction in oxygen used per volley represents an increasing efficiency in terms of oxygen used per nervous action; in addition, it may signify an inability of the metabolic system to keep up with the demand and may explain why the response begins to fail in both frog nerve and rat ganglion when the frequency of stimulation is raised above that at which the maximum rate of oxygen uptake is reached.

The difference in frequency parameters just described seems to be characteristic not of species but of the type-A fibers in somatic nerves compared with neurons of the sympathetic nervous system. Thus the limiting rate of oxygen uptake was reached at a relatively high frequency in type-A fibers of the phrenic, saphenous, and peroneal nerves in rats, as well as in type-A fibers of sciatic nerves in frogs. On the other hand the limit was reached at lower frequencies in type-C fibers of the inferior cardiac sympathetic nerves of cats and in type-B fibers in cervical sympathetic trunks of rabbits, as well as in sympathetic ganglia of rats, rabbits, and cats.[14,48,53] If this indeed represents a difference between the metabolic limitations on frequencies of action, it would be physiologically appropriate in view of evidence that type-A fibers are normally called upon to conduct impulses at frequencies higher than those occurring in the sympathetic nervous system.

Temperature and pH. The increment in oxygen consumption caused by activity in ganglia was affected relatively little by changing the temperature from 25° to 35° or the hydrogen ion concentration from pH 6.9 to pH 7.4.[18]

2. Changes in Substrate Utilization

Glucose Uptake. Since glucose satisfies the substrate requirements of an excised ganglion at rest, it is reasonable that the uptake of this material is accelerated during activity (Fig. 3). Other investigators

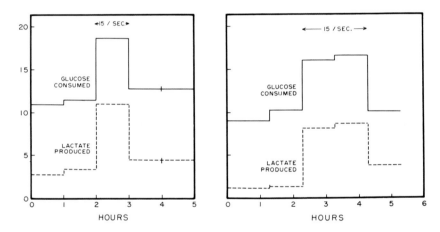

Fig. 3. Rates of glucose uptake and lactate output by two ganglion preparations, at rest and during repetitive supramaximal stimulation of the preganglionic nerve.[38] Ordinate indicates milligrams of material per gram dry weight per hour (36°).

have observed increases in glucose uptake associated with electrical stimulation or with activity induced by convulsant drugs in spinal cords and nerves excised from frogs,[34,35] in slices of guinea pig brain,[61] and in perfused cat's brain.[25,28] No such increase could be demonstrated in a few experiments on rabbit ganglia, but the precision of the method was poor, so that the possibility of a moderate increase was not excluded.[53] Holmes, Gerard, and Solomon[36] reported that the depletion of reducing substances in nerves from frogs or rabbits was not accelerated during stimulation, but this is not relevant in the present context since the nerves were supported in a gas phase; hence uptake of glucose from the bathing fluid was not studied.

Evidence Against Accelerated Oxidation of Glucose in Ganglia, Nerve, and Brain. The increased rate of glucose uptake during activity might be assumed to represent a metabolic response which supplies additional substrate for oxidative generation of energy. However, the rate of lactate output was found to accelerate nearly as much as did the rate of glucose uptake in excised ganglia at 36-37° (Fig. 3; Table IV). Similar findings have been reported for both sliced[61] and perfused[28] brain. This suggests that the extra glucose is mostly converted to lactate.

TABLE IV

INCREMENT IN METABOLIC RATES CAUSED BY ACTIVITY IN SUPERIOR CERVICAL GANGLIA EXCISED FROM RATS (36-37°)

(μmol. C or O_2/gm. dry weight/hr. Mean ± s.e.m. (No. of obs.))

		5/sec.	10/sec.	Ref.
1.	Increment in glucose carbon taken up	104 ± 34 (9)*	145 ± 32 (8)†	38
2.	Increment in lactate carbon put out	87 ± 22 (9)*	138 ± 24 (8)†	38
3.	Glucose increment less lactate increment	17 ± 10 (9)*	7 ± 15 (8)†	38
4.	Increment in CO_2 from labeled glucose	52 ± 11**	Not measured	40
5.	Increment in O_2 uptake	78 ± 12 (5)‡	113 ± 17 (5)¶	48

*Average of 3 at 3 per second, 3 at 6 per second, and 3 at 10 per second.
†Average of 3 at 6 per second, 3 at 10 per second, and 2 at 15 per second.
**This increment was obtained by multiplying the average resting rate of labeled CO_2 production (Table I, line 8) by the average fractional increase in labeled CO_2 production (0.21 ± .04) caused by stimulation at 5 per second in 10 experiments.
‡Interpolation between 4 per second and 8 per second in 5 experiments.
¶Interpolation between 8 per second and 15 per second in 5 experiments.

More direct evidence against accelerated glucose oxidation has been reported by other investigators who measured output of labeled CO_2 from nervous tissues supplied with glucose containing C-14. No increase in production of labeled CO_2 was found by Mullins[62] during electrical stimulation of frog nerves, or by Geiger, Kawakita, and Barkulis[27] during convulsive activity produced by Metrazol in perfused cat brains. The extra oxygen consumed during activity must have been used to oxidize endogenous substrates, since labeled glucose was the only substrate provided in the bathing or perfusion solution.†

Evidence for Accelerated Oxidation of Glucose in Sympathetic Ganglia. In contrast to the foregoing observations, clear-cut evidence for accelerated oxidation of glucose during activity in excised sympathetic ganglia has been obtained by tracer methods using uniformly labeled glucose. On the average of ten experiments in which the pre-

---

†Recent experiments, performed since this chapter was written, have consistently shown increased output of labeled CO_2 during stimulation of frog nerves supplied with uniformly labeled glucose,[50a] in conflict with the results of Mullins.

ganglionic nerve was stimulated maximally for 30 minutes at a frequency of 5 per second, the rate of labeled CO_2 production increased by 21% during the period of activity. Neither this percentage increase in labeled CO_2 output nor the absolute increase differed significantly from the corresponding values for the increase in rate of oxygen uptake at the same frequency of activity (Table IV). Therefore these tracer experiments on ganglia failed to support the previous conclusion that active neurons oxidize substrates which are endogenous to the isolated tissues.*

Another observation on ganglia seems to be at variance with those reported for frog nerves, where Mullins[62] found that production of labeled CO_2 could be increased by stimulation after previous soaking in labeled glycine, alanine, or glutamate. This indicated that oxidation of these amino acids was accelerated, in agreement with earlier reports of increased ammonia production from frog nerves during activity.[30] In the case of rat ganglia, however, no increase in ammonia production was found during activity,[57] either with the usual bathing solution containing glucose, or after addition of glutamate. (Glutamate was tried because this substance considerably increased the resting rate of ammonia production, indicating that it could be metabolized by a ganglion.[57]) Thus amino acids are presumably not oxidized at a significantly accelerated rate during activity in ganglia.

Discussion of Apparently Conflicting Results. It is necessary to explain how sufficient additional glucose could be available for oxidation during activity in a ganglion, even though the rate of lactate output increased nearly as much as did the rate of glucose uptake. Statistical control confirmed that the small amount by which the increase in glucose uptake exceeded that in lactate production was indeed significantly less than the amount of glucose needed for the observed increase in output of labeled CO_2 (Table IV). Possibly some of the extra lactate came from endogenous sources, thus sparing some glucose for CO_2 production. Alternatively, enough glucose carbon might have been made available by stopping incorporation during activity and deflecting this carbon traffic into CO_2 production. However, there was if anything an increase in the rate of incorporation during activity rather than a decrease (Table V). Three out of four experiments were in reasonable quantitative agreement, suggesting a small increase in

---

*Previous conclusions in abstracts that the absolute increase in labeled CO_2 production by ganglia was considerably less than the increase in O_2 uptake are now believed to be in error for reasons given in a footnote to Table I. Newer data have led to altered conclusions and to a critical reexamination of older evidence by other investigators for qualitative changes in neuronal metabolism during activity, mentioned elsewhere in this section.

TABLE V

INCORPORATION OF CARBON FROM GLUCOSE BY SUPERIOR CERVICAL GANGLIA EXCISED FROM RATS DURING INCUBATION IN SOLUTION CONTAINING UNIFORMLY LABELED GLUCOSE FOR 4 HOURS AT 37°

(μmol. C/gm. wet weight)

	A	B	C	D
	Average of Three Typical Experiments		*One "Atypical" Experiment*	
	Resting	*Active**	*Resting*	*Active**
Water extract	59	+ 8	77	+ 16
Lipid extract	31	+ 1	31	+ 31
Phenol extract	7	+ 2	15	+ 16
Residue	13	− 1	10	+ 55
Total	110	+10†	133	+118†

*Difference between a ganglion of which the preganglionic nerve was stimulated supramaximally 10 times per second throughout the 4 hour incubation and the control ganglion, from the other side of the same animal, which was kept at rest in the same vessel. At end of the incubation, ganglia were rapidly cooled, blotted, weighed and frozen. Subsequently they were extracted successively with acetone, water, ethanol-ether and phenol. The water extract and the lipid extract (combined acetone and ethanol-ether extracts) were chromatogrammed on paper treated with silicic acid and scanned radiographically (see Fig. 4).

†Total increments in the individual experiments, stated in the order in which they were performed, were + 118 ("atypical" experiment), +26, −3, +6.

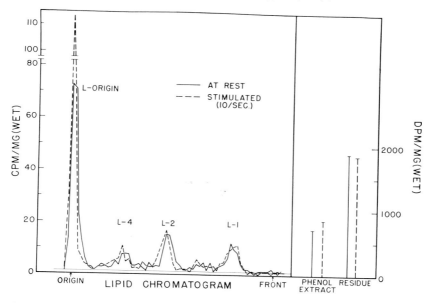

Fig. 4. Radioactivity in chromatograms of lipid extracts of two ganglia which had been kept for 4 hours at 37° in solution containing glucose uniformly labeled with C-14. To the right is shown radioactivity in a phenol extract and in the residue. For further details on stimulation and extraction procedures, see footnote to Table V.

rate of incorporation. In a fourth experiment incorporation was so much higher in the stimulated ganglion that the result can hardly be considered typical (column D). Examination of various tissue extracts, including chromatograms of the water and lipid extracts, revealed no conspicuous effect on any particular component in the three "typical" experiments (Table V and Fig. 4).

Regardless of the metabolic mechanism, labeled CO_2 was certainly produced faster during activity than during rest in excised ganglia and the amount was enough to account for the accompanying acceleration of oxygen consumption. This result contrasts with those already cited for excised frog's nerve and perfused cat's brain. Dissimilarities in experimental conditions as well as species must be considered. In the perfused cat's brain, there may have been some limitation in rate of glucose oxidation even in the resting state, since lactate production was about 40% of the glucose utpake, and only about one-third of the CO_2 put out derived its carbon from the labeled glucose. In the experiments on frog nerves there could possibly have been an inadequate supply of glucose, since the nerves were suspended in a gas phase for several hours after the preliminary soak in solution containing labeled glucose.

Glucose Metabolism at Reduced Temperature and Reduced pH. Results on excised ganglia which differ in part from the observations described above, but gave further evidence for increased oxidation of glucose during activity, were found when the temperature was reduced to 23° and the pH of the bathing fluid was less than 7.1.[18] Unlike the results at 36°, glucose uptake was accelerated substantially more during activity than was the lactate output, so that considerable extra glucose was left over to serve as possible substrate (Fig. 5). The amount of glucose thus available was greater during the first half-hour of stimulation than later and was on the average about twice as great during this initial period if the pH were low (6.7-7.1) than when it was high (7.1-7.4). Another difference from the results at 36° was that the acceleration of glucose metabolism continued during the first half-hour of recovery after stopping stimulation (Fig. 5). This may represent replacement of endogenous materials oxidized during activity, suggested for brain by Geiger.[25] When pH as well as temperature was reduced, the total extra glucose taken up in connection with the $2\frac{1}{2}$ hours of activity, including the recovery period as well as the period of stimulation, was more than enough to provide both the extra lactate put out and the substrate needed for the amount of extra oxygen consumed.[18]

An increase in production of labeled CO_2 from labeled glucose occurred during activity in ganglia at the reduced temperature, although the data are too few to justify quantitative comparison with the increase in oxygen uptake. At all events, interpretations are simpler in these experiments than in those at body temperature, since the glucose and the lactate studies agree with the CO_2 measurements in indicating increased oxidation of glucose during activity.

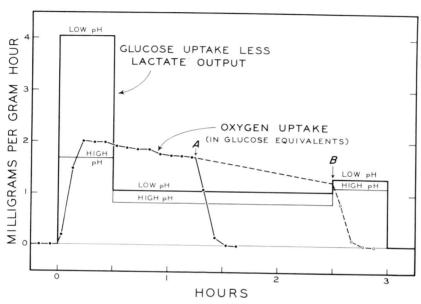

Fig. 5. Time course of metabolic increments in excised ganglia at reduced temperature (23°), caused by repetitive supramaximal stimulation of the preganglionic nerve for 2½ hours at a frequency of 5 per second.[18] Averages of several experiments. During measurements of oxygen uptake stimulation was stopped after 1.25 hours, but the dashed lines indicate the time course to be expected with 2.5 hours of stimulation. "High pH" = 7.4 to 7.1; "low pH" = 7.1 to 6.7. Ordinate indicates amounts of materials in equivalent mg of glucose per gram dry weight per hour.

VII. GLUCOSE-LACK

Metabolic measurements described above demonstrate that glucose is certainly the major and perhaps the only substrate oxidized by an excised sympathetic ganglion in the resting state. Therefore, it is not surprising that capacity for transmission through a ganglion is lost when the supply of glucose is withdrawn, in a time which varies from a few minutes to more than an hour depending on the frequency of activity. Conduction along the preganglionic nerve fibers of the rat's superior cervical ganglion, failed almost as rapidly as did transmission involving synapses.[53] Since both failed much more rapidly without glucose than did conduction along myelinated fibers in peripheral nerves of the same species, the relative sensitivity to glucose-lack seems to be a characteristic of the type of nerve cell involved rather than a characteristic of a particular physiological process such as synaptic transmission.[37]

The finding that lack of glucose has but little selective effect on synaptic transmission compared to axonal conduction in sympathetic ganglia is similar to a previous observation on lack of oxygen. Synaptic transmission in these ganglia was found to be no more sensitive to anoxia than was conduction along many of the preganglionic fibers leading to them.[11,53]

Acetylcholine Output. Effects of glucose deprivation were studied in perfused ganglia of cats by Kahlson and MacIntosh.[42] Failure of transmission during glucose lack and the restoration following return to glucose were correlated with failure and recovery of acetylcholine production, thus implicating processes of synaptic transmission. However, the subsequent finding that conduction in preganglionic fibers is sensitive to lack of glucose permits an explanation of these observations which does not assume that acetylcholine release is primarily affected. If this substance is a product of activity in the preganglionic fibers, but not necessarily involved in synaptic transmission, then failure of preganglionic conduction would obviously prevent its release. Such conduction failure would moreover bring the postsynaptic cells to rest, despite continued repetitive preganglionic stimulation, and would permit the ganglion cells to retain or even to regain responsiveness, since rest was shown to favor recovery in the absence of glucose. This would explain why injected acetylcholine or potassium chloride elicited a response after the preganglionic stimulation had become ineffective.

Oxygen Uptake. If failure of function in the absence of glucose be ascribed to loss of substrate for the oxidative generation of energy, then a corollary to be expected is a decline in rate of oxygen consumption, just as has been reported for brain tissue after glucose withdrawal under some, although not all, conditions.[25,28,31,43,65] There was indeed a small slowing of oxygen uptake after removal of glucose from a resting ganglion, but neither the magnitude nor the time course seemed adequate to account for the failure of response (Fig. 6). During the first hour, while the height of response was still maintained, the rate of oxygen consumption progressively dropped about 15%. During the second hour, while the response progressively failed, there was a temporary rise of oxygen uptake, almost back to the control level, followed by a later secondary decline.[57] Thus the oxidative accompaniment of failing function was actually a rise in the rate of oxygen consumption rather than the expected fall. Moreover, the preliminary slowing of oxygen uptake could be equaled or exceeded by suitable applications of poisons such as azide or iodoacetate (the latter in the presence of lactate) without causing a failure of transmission as rapid as that found after removal of glucose.

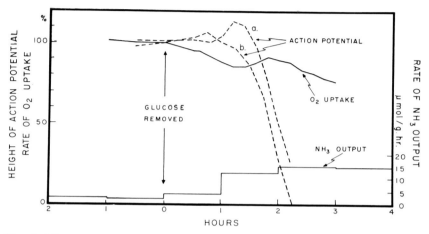

Fig. 6. Effects of glucose-lack on O_2 uptake, NH_3 output,[66,67] and height of the postganglionic action potential evoked by a supramaximal stimulus to the preganglionic nerve.[57] Action potentials for curve *a* recorded during the oxygen measurements, for *b* during the ammonia measurements. Averages of several experiments, all on preparations kept at rest except for an occasional test stimulus. Ammonia output is expressed on a dry weight basis (36-37°).

Following withdrawal of glucose, oxidative processes apparently shift to endogenous substrates, with relatively little change in rate. Since the energy yield per molecule of oxygen does not vary greatly from one material to another, it is doubtful whether the rate of energy production in a ganglion is reduced enough by withdrawal of glucose to account for the functional failure.

ATP Content. It was thought that the energy produced oxidatively in the absence of glucose might not be effectively transferred into energy storage systems such as ATP and certain other organic phosphates. Therefore the ATP contents of ganglia were measured by the highly specific luciferase method[69] after extraction in cold 5% perchloric acid (Table VI).[59] The concentration in freshly excised ganglia was approximately one-third of that estimated for brain by Heald.[32a] When ganglia were kept at 37° in control solution containing glucose, there was a slow decline in ATP content. Most significant in the present context is the finding that this rate of decline was not accelerated by removal of glucose. The ATP concentration did decline rapidly in the absence of oxygen.[59] However there is no explanation in the ATP results for the failure of response in the absence of glucose; this failure was complete within 3 hours in these as in other experiments.

TABLE VI

ATP CONTENT OF SUPERIOR CERVICAL GANGLIA EXCISED FROM RATS[59]
($\mu mol./gm.$ wet weight. Mean $\pm$ s.e.m. (No. of obs.))

Incubation Time at 37°	Fresh	3 Hours	12 Hours
Controls	$1.02 \pm .07(9)$	$.70 \pm .04(5)$	$.35 \pm .03(3)$
No glucose		$.80 \pm .11(5)$	$.43 \pm .04(4)$

Potassium Content. The ability of ganglion cells to maintain ionic

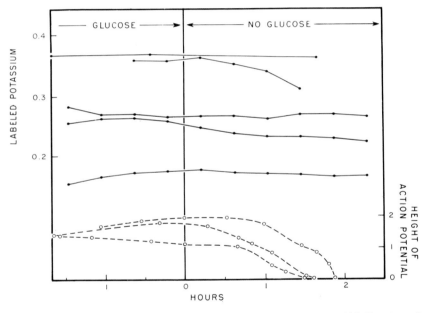

Fig. 7. Content of labeled potassium in excised ganglia (solid lines) and height of the postganglionic action potentials evoked by an occasional supra-maximal stimulus to the preganglinoic nerve (dashed lines), before and after removal of glucose from the bathing solution.[9] Several hours before removal of glucose the preparations were placed in solution containing K-42, which was continued at the same concentration in the glucose-free solution. Ordinate on left indicates ganglionic content of labeled potassium in milli-moles per gram dry weight. Height of action potential is given in arbitrary units. Potassium content and action potentials were measured in different preparations in the same apparatus. (37°).

concentration gradients across their membranes in the absence of glucose was investigated by tracer methods, using K-42.[9] As already shown above, the K-42 content of the tissue comes into equilibrium with that of the bathing fluid in about three hours (Fig. 2). The effect of withdrawing glucose after equilibrium had been attained is shown for several preparations by the solid lines in Figure 7. Although there was a marked decline in one preparation and a smaller drop in another, there was no consistent effect of significant magnitude.

The ability of ganglion cells not only to maintain a high internal concentration of potassium without glucose, but in addition to reconcentrate potassium after considerable loss, was demonstrated by temporary removal of oxygen from several preparations which had first been equilibrated with K-42 in the presence of glucose and then deprived of glucose for 1½ to 2 hours.[9] Anoxia for 20 to 30 minutes caused a rapid fall in potassium content; restoration of oxygen—still without glucose—was followed by a rise of K-42. In experiments where the K-42 content was constant before removal of oxygen, recovery attained approximately the original level (Fig. 8).

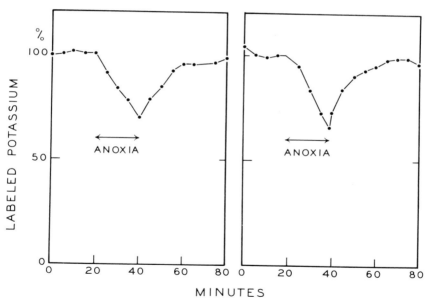

Fig. 8. Decline in the ganglionic content of labeled potassium caused by removal of oxygen and recovery following return to oxygen, all in the absence of glucose.[9] Ganglia were first equilibrated in solution containing the labeled potassium, which was continued at the same concentration throughout the remainder of the experiment. Glucose was removed about 2 hours before start of anoxia (37°).

Discussion. We are thus left with a presumed metabolic defect caused by glucose withdrawal, the mechanism of which is not revealed either in oxygen uptake, in ATP content, or in potassium content. Possibly there were in fact relatively large changes in one of these variables in a region of the nerve cell which was so circumscribed that the change was undetected amidst the total metabolism of the whole tissue. However, such localization cannot be ascribed solely to synaptic structures, since impulse conduction in the preganglionic nerve trunk is also sensitive to glucose-lack.

Other possibilities are that the abnormal metabolism either fails to produce some essential substance, such as acetylcholine,[42] or consumes some essential constituent of the cell. Clues in the latter direction may be contained in the acceleration of ammonia production which we and others have reported during glucose-lack in various nervous tissues (Fig. 6),[44,57] and the large loss of microsomal RNA and the spilling of amino acids into glucose-free perfusion fluid by brain reported by Abood and Geiger.[1] But it is not clear how these changes could affect conduction and transmission without more conspicuous effects on either the oxygen uptake, ATP content, or potassium content of a ganglion.

VIII. CONDITIONS INFLUENCING SURVIVAL IN THE ABSENCE OF GLUCOSE

Frequency of activity. Rats vs rabbits. The effect of repetitive stimulation on the rate of failure of transmission after removal of glucose has been studied at 36-37° in ganglia excised from both rats and rabbits.[53] Survival was shortened by repetitive stimulation, to a degree which increased with the frequency of stimulation. A striking difference between rats and rabbits was observed: without repetitive stimulation, rat ganglia failed in about two hours, but rabbit ganglia retained their responsiveness for very much longer times. The latter was shown both by extrapolation from failure times at various low frequencies, and by a single experiment in which a rabbit ganglion at rest gave undiminished responses to occasional test stimuli for nearly three hours without glucose. The rabbit ganglion could readily be made to fail by relatively low frequencies of repetitive stimulation (e.g., 2 per second).

Temperature. Effects of temperature changes were studied on rat ganglia, with a surprising result on repetitively stimulated preparations.[53] Although resting preparations failed more slowly at low temperatures than at high ($Q_{10} = 2.6$ from 20° to 40°), survival of those stimulated as infrequently as once every 10 seconds was nearly independent of temperature ($Q_{10} = 1.1$ from 20° to 33°). At 6 per second no temperature effect at all could be detected from 20° to 40°. A possible explanation is that the extra metabolic requirements associated with each nerve impulse are independent of temperature, especially since the increase in rate of oxygen consumption associated with repetitive activity is affected much less by temperature changes than is the resting rate, both in rat ganglia[18] and in rat peripheral nerve.[14]

Alternative Substrates. Kahlson and MacIntosh[42] tested the ability of a number of substances to substitute for glucose in sympathetic ganglia of cats, by injecting small quantities into the perfusion fluid entering a superior cervical ganglion, after the response to repetitive preganglionic stimulation had failed in the absence of glucose. Contraction of the nictitating membrane served as a measure of transmission. Relative effectiveness was estimated by determining the amounts on a weight basis required to give equal restorations of response (Table VII). The

TABLE VII

Effectiveness of Various Substances in Restoring Transmission in a Perfused Ganglion Lacking Glucose (Kahlson and MacIntosh[42])

Substances Which Restored Response	Rel. Effectiveness	Substances Which Did Not Restore Response	
A. Monoaldohexoses		*C. Disaccharides*	*E. Other Substances*
Glucose	100	Lactose	Acetate
Mannose	60	Maltose*	Acetaldehyde
Galactose	5	Sucrose	Acetoacetate
			d–l–glyceraldehyde
B. Other Substances		*D. Other Sugars*	Succinate
Lactic acid	< 50	Arabinose	$MgCl_2$
Pyruvic acid	< 50	Fructose	PO_4^{2-}
			Adrenalin
			Aneurin
			Ascorbic acid

*A weak effect of maltose was ascribed to contamination with glucose.

materials tested were applied only briefly, so that ability to maintain responsiveness for long periods was not investigated; conversely some of the ineffective materials might have become effective if continuously supplied. The relative effectiveness of the various monosaccharides may be related to their ability to traverse cell membranes, since Wilbrandt[70] has found that at low concentrations (30 mM) the rates of entry into erythrocytes fall in the same order as in Table VII.

Bioassay of the venous effluent in these experiments showed that restoration of transmission was closely correlated with reappearance of acetylcholine, which had disappeared from the effluent fluid simultaneously with the failure of transmission after glucose removal. However, as already indicated, these findings can be interpreted by assuming that the primary effect is on conduction in the preganglionic nerve, rather than on the release of acetylcholine.

A number of possible substrates have also been tested on superior cervical ganglia excised from rats by determining survival times in solutions containing known concentrations (Table VIII). Among the materials tested, only lactate maintained the response about as well as did glucose. Glutamine was the only other substance which delayed failure significantly, although it was not nearly as effective as glucose. Glutamate was tested because it had previously been found to greatly increase ammonia output from ganglia in the presence of glucose, suggesting that glutamate could be metabolized, as mentioned earlier. However, as shown in the table, there was no indication that this substance could substitute for glucose in maintaining transmission; correspondingly it did not cause an increase in ammonia output in the absence of glucose.[57] Presumably glutamate can enter the cells of a ganglion only in the presence of glucose, as others have found in various tissues.

TABLE VIII

SURVIVAL OF SUPERIOR CERVICAL GANGLIA EXCISED FROM RATS WHEN SUPPLIED WITH VARIOUS SUBSTRATES (36-37°C)

Substrate*	Concentration (g/1)	No. of Preparations	Ave. Survival Time (hr.)†	Reference
Series A. Ganglia at Rest				
1. None	——	4	1.7	53
2. Glucose	1	4	16	37, 53
3. Lactate	0.5	2	12	37
Series B. Ganglia at Rest				
4. None	——	21	1.6	68
5. Glucose	1	18	32	68
6. Glutamine	0.5–2	10	6.3	68
7. Glutamate	1–2	2	2.0	68
8. Creatine phosphate	0.3	1	1.8	68
9. Creatine phosphate	·5	1	1.3	68

*Except for omission of glucose, the bathing solution was the same as that described in the section on General Methods.
†Time required for postganglionic action potential elicited by a supramaximal preganglionic stimulus to fall to half its initial height.

The ability of various substrates to support function in brain and spinal cord, summarized by Kety,[43] differ considerably from results on ganglia, perhaps in part because of the blood-brain barrier.

IX. ANESTHETICS

An important theory of anesthetic action proposes that the characteristic depressant effects on nerve cells caused by these agents is mediated by a metabolic disturbance.[64,65] It was thought that the simple neuronal system provided in a sympathetic ganglion might offer a favorable preparation in which to seek evidence concerning this metabolic hypothesis, especially since it had been found that these ganglia share a characteristic of the central nervous system with regard to many anesthetics, in that synaptic transmission is blocked by lower concentrations than is conduction of impulses along the axons leading to and from the synaptic regions.[58] Several anesthetics, moreover, including ether, chloroform, and chloretone were found to affect transmission in concentrations as low as those required for surgical anesthesia.[55] However, not all anesthetics blocked synaptic transmission selectively. In general there was an increase with molecular weight both in potency (measured by the molarity required for 50% reduction in action potential) and in selectivity (ratio of concentration required for block of axons to that for block of synapses).

In agreement with the observations of Quastel and his colleagues[64,65] on excised brain tissue, all agents tested were found to reduce the resting rate of oxygen uptake when applied to ganglia in sufficient concentrations.[54] In superior cervical ganglia excised from rats, pentobarbital, chloretone, and 2-hexanol impaired oxygen uptake even at concentrations just sufficient to cause a 50% reduction in the postganglionic response elicited by a supramaximal stimulus to the preganglionic nerve. Pentobarbital and chloretone increased the rate of glucose uptake, and pentobarbital was found to increase lactate production.[22] However, the correlation between effects on transmission and effects on metabolism was by no means universal. At concentrations reducing the postganglionic reponse by 50%, oxygen uptake was not slowed by ether in rat ganglia,[22] or by any of seven agents tried on ganglia from rabbits.[54] Thus the few correlations observed may be no more than coincidences in the concentrations required to cause two independent effects. This is supported by results with chloretone, which affects the resting oxygen uptake of rabbit ganglia and frog nerves at similar concentrations, but blocks the electrical responses at concentrations which differ considerably between the two preparations.[6,54]

When frog nerve was stimulated repetitively,[6] or when brain slices were exposed to dinitrophenol or 100 mMKCl,[30a] the increased rate of oxygen uptake which resulted was more affected by low concentrations of anesthetics than was the unstimulated oxygen consumption. Consequently it has been proposed that anesthetics act primarily on an aspect of metabolism that is relatively quiescent in resting neurons. This suggestion was made more plausible by earlier evidence of a qualitative change in metabolism accompanying the shift from rest to activity. However, some of the evidence for qualitative change has been questioned above, and other evidence, based on experiments with azide, has been reappraised by Brink.[7] Moreover, in excised ganglia, where activity can be better controlled than in brain and where sensitivity to anesthetics is much higher than in frog nerve, metabolic effects on repetitively stimulated preparations could be interpreted as a consequence rather than a cause of suppression of neuronal activity.[54,56] A similar interpretation has been advanced by Kety[43] for observations on brain *in situ*.

The question whether an anesthetic acts by disturbing neuronal metabolism remains unsettled,[56] although it may be significant that considerable careful investigation on many different neuronal systems has failed to yield incontrovertible evidence in favor of such a mechanism. The importance of measuring effects on activity and effects on metabolism under identical conditions has been emphasized by observations on excised sympathetic ganglia.[54]

REFERENCES

1. ABOOD, L. G., and GEIGER, A.: *Am. J. Physiol., 182*:557 (1955).
2. ALLWEIS, C., and MAGNES, J.: *J. Neurochem., 2*:326 (1958).
3. BARGETON, D.: *Am. J. Physiol., 121*:261 (1938).
4. BARKULIS, S. S., GEIGER, A., KAWAKITA, Y., and AGUILAR, V.: *J. Neurochem., 5*:339 (1960).
5. BELOFF-CHAIN, ANNE, CATANZARO, R., CHAIN, E. B., MASI, I., and POCCHIARI, F.: *Proc. Roy. Soc., B 144*:22 (1955).
6. BRINK, F.: In *Nerve Impulse, Trans. Second Cont.* Nachmansohn, D. Ed. New York, Macy (1951).
7. BRINK, F.: In *The Metabolism of the Nervous System.* Richter, D., Ed. New York, Pergamon (1957).
8. BRINK, F., JR., BRONK, D. W., CARLSON, F. D., *and* CONNELLY, C. M.: *Cold Spring Harbor Symp. Quant. Biol., 17*:53 (1952).
9. BRINLEY, F. J., JR.: Ph.D. Thesis, Johns Hopkins Univ. (1961).
10. BRONK, D. W.: *J. Neurophysiol., 2*:380 (1939).
11. BRONK, D. W., LARRABEE, M. G., and GAYLOR, J. B.: *J. Cell. & Comp. Physiol., 31*:193 (1948).
12. BROWN, G. L., and PASCOE, J. E.: *J. Physiol., 118*:113 (1952).
13. CONNELLY, C. M., BRONK, D. W., and BRINK, F. JR.: *Rev. Scient. Instruments, 24*:683 (1953).
14. CRANEFIELD, P. F., BRINK, F., and BRONK, D. W.: *J. Neurochem., 1*:245 (1957).
15. DAWSON, R. M. C., and RICHTER, D.: *Am. J. Physiol., 160*:203 (1950).
16. DEMPSHER, J., LARRABEE, M. G., BANG, F. B., and BODIAN, D.: *Am. J. Physiol., 182*:203 (1955).
17. DEMPSHER, J., and RIKER, W. K.: *J. Physiol., 139*:145 (1957).
18. DOLIVO, M., and LARRABEE, M. G.: *J. Neurochem., 3*:72 (1958).
19. ECCLES, J. C.: *J. Physiol., 101*:465 (1943).
20. ECCLES, J. C.: *J. Physiol., 103*:27 (1944).
21. ECCLES, ROSAMOND: *J. Physiol., 117*:181 (1952).
22. EDWARDS, C., and LARRABEE, M. G.: *J. Physiol., 130*:456 (1955).

23. ELLIOTT, K. A. C.: In *Neurochemistry*. Elliott, K. A. C., Page, I. H., and Quastel, J. H., Eds. Springfield, Ill., Thomas (1955).

24. ELLIOTT, K. A. C., SCOTT, D. B. M., and LIBET, B.: *J. Biol. Chem., 146*:251 (1942).

25. GEIGER, A.: *Physiol. Rev., 38*:1 (1958).

26. GEIGER, A., HORVATH, N., and KAWAKITA, Y.: *J. Neurochem., 5*:311 (1960).

27. GEIGER, A., KAWAKITA, Y., and BARKULIS, S. S.: *J. Neurochem., 5*:323 (1960).

28. GEIGER, A., MAGNES, J., and DOBKIN, J.: *Federation Proc., 13*:52 (1954).

29. GEIGER, A., MAGNES, J., and GEIGER, R. S.: *Nature, 170*:754 (1952).

30. GERARD, R. W.: *Physiol. Rev., 12*:469 (1932).

30a. GHOSH, J. J., and QUASTEL, J. H.: *Nature, 174*:28 (1954).

31. GRENELL, R. G., and DAVIES, P. W.: *Federation Proc., 9*:52 (1950).

32. HEALD, P. J.: *Biochem. J., 57*:673, (1954).

32a. HEALD, P. J.: *Phosphorus Metabolism of Brain*. New York, Pergamon (1960).

33. HIMWICH, W. A., and HIMWICH, H. E.: *J. Neurophysiol., 9*:133 (1946).

34. HIRSCHBERG, ELSE, and WINTERSTEIN, H.: *Ztschr. physiol. Chem., 100*:185 (1917).

35. HIRSCHBERG, ELSE, and WINTERSTEIN, H.: *Ztschr. physiol. Chem. 108*:27 (1919).

36. HOLMES, E. G., GERARD, R. W., and SOLOMON, E. I.: *Am. J. Physiol., 93*:349 (1930).

37. HOROWICZ, P., and LARRABEE, M. G.: *Federation Proc., 13*:72 (1954).

38. HOROWICZ, P., and LARRABEE, M. G.: *J. Neurochem., 2*:102 (1958).

39. HOROWICZ, P., and LARRABEE, M. G.: *The Physiologist, 1*:No. 4, 37 (1958).

40. HOROWICZ, P., and LARRABEE, M. G.: *J. Neurochem.* (In press, 1961).

41. HOROWICZ, P., and LARRABEE, M. G.: In preparation (1962).

42. KAHLSON, G., and MACINTOSH, F. C.: *J. Physiol., 96*:277 (1939).

43. KETY, S. S.: In *The Metabolism of the Nervous System*. Richter, D., Ed. New York, Pergamon (1957).

44. KIMURA, Y., and ITO, K.: *Sc. Papers Coll. Gen. Education, Univ. of Tokyo, 2*:157 (1952).

45. KLINGMAN, J., LARRABEE, M. G., and HOROWICZ, P.: *Federation Proc. 18*:82 (1959).

46. LANGLEY, J. N., and DICKINSON, W. L.: *Proc. Roy. Soc., 46*:423 (1889).

47. LARRABEE, M. G.: *Am. J. M. Sc., 217*:355 (1949).

48. LARRABEE, M. G.: *J. Neurochem., 2*:81 (1958).

49. LARRABEE, M. G.: *Analyt. Biochem., 1*:151 (1960).

50. LARRABEE, M. G.: In *Methods in Medical Research*, Vol. 9. Quastel, J. H., Ed. Chicago, Year Book Publishers (1961).

50a. LARRABEE, M. G.: In *Biophysics of Physiological and Phamacological Actions*. Shanes, A. M., Ed. Am. Assoc. for Advancement of Science. (In press, 1961).

51. LARRABEE, M. G., BRINLEY, F. J., JR., HOROWICZ, P., KLINGMAN, J., and LOONEY, G.: *Federation Proc., 19*:299 (1960).

52. LARRABEE, M. G., and BRONK, D. W.: *J. Neurophysiol., 10*:139 (1947).

53. LARRABEE, M. G., and BRONK, D. W.: *Cold Spring Harbor Symp. Quant. Biol., 17*:245 (1952).

54. LARRABEE, M. G., GARCIA RAMOS, J., and BÜLBRING, EDITH.: *J. Cell. & Comp. Physiol., 40*:461 (1952).

55. LARRABEE, M. G., and HOLADAY: *J. Pharm. & Exper. Therap., 105*:400 (1952).

56. LARRABEE, M. G., and HOROWICZ, P.: In *Molecular Structure and Functional Activity*. Grenell, R. G., and Mullins, L. J., Eds. Washington, Am. Inst. Biol. Sc., (1956.)

57. LARRABEE, M. G., HOROWICZ, P., STEKIEL, W., and DOLIVO, M.: In *Metabolism of the Nervous System*. Richter, D., Ed. New York, Pergamon Press, (1957).
58. LARRABEE, M. G., and POSTERNAK, J. M.: *J. Neurophysiol., 15*:91 (1952).
59. LOONEY, G., LARRABEE, M. G., and KLINGMAN, J. D.: Unpublished observations (1960).
60. MCILWAIN, H.: *Biochemistry and the Central Nervous System*. Boston, Little, Brown, and Co. (1959).
61. MCILWAIN, H., ANGUIANO, G., and CHESHIRE, J. D.: *Biochem. J., 50*:12 (1951).
62. MULLINS, L. J.: *Am. J. Physiol., 175*:358 (1953).
64. QUASTEL, J. H.: *Physiol. Rev., 19*:135 (1939).
65. QUASTEL, J. H.: In *The Biology of Mental Health and Disease*. New York, Hoeber, (1952).
66. STEKIEL, W. J.: Ph.D. Thesis, Johns Hopkins Univ. (1957).
67. STEKIEL, W. J., and LARRABEE, M. G.: *Federation Proc., 16*:124 (1957).
68. STEKIEL, W. J., LARRABEE, M. G., TEXTER, J., LOONEY, G., and KLINGMAN, J. D.: Unpublished observations (1958).
69. STREHLER, B. L., and MCELROY, W. D.: In *Methods in Enzymology*, Vol. 3. Colowick, S. P., and Kaplan, N. O., Eds. New York, Academic Press, (1957).
70. WILBRANDT, W.: *J. Cell & Comp. Physiol., 47*:137 (1956).

VIII

BRAIN TISSUE RESPIRATION
AND GLYCOLYSIS

K. A. C. ELLIOTT AND L. S. WOLFE

UNDER SUITABLE conditions excised brain, like any other tissue, will consume oxygen, evolve carbon dioxide, and carry on a number of metabolic activities for many hours. In this chapter an attempt is made to summarize present information concerning respiration and glycolysis by adult mammalian brain tissue *in vitro*. Work on the respiration of central nervous tissue up to 1939 has been reviewed by Quastel.[1] The purpose of the studies of isolated cell-containing tissue *in vitro* has been to discover the metabolic behaviour and potentialities of the integrated tissue in order to interpret and predict physiological events. These studies enable only over-all reactions, which involve many intermediate reactions and alternate pathways, to be appraised. Intermediate steps and enzymic mechanisms underlying brain tissue respiration and glycolysis are discussed by other contributors to this volume.

Isolated brain tissue slices lack a capillary circulation, no evidence of functional activity has been reported to occur in them and they are no longer in their natural environment. The preparation of these slices necessarily involves damage to neuronal and glial processes. Further the slices when placed in saline media show considerable swelling[2] and also lose some soluble constituents to the suspending medium.[3,4] Consequently the physiological significance of the observations is not completely certain. However, many of these deficiencies of the approach can be compensated for by appropriate experimental techniques. The studies of McIlwain and his co-workers (see ref. 4) on the preparation and maintenance of the composition of isolated cerebral tissues and the biochemical criteria available for comparing tissue *in vivo* and *in vitro* have clearly demonstrated the value of isolated tissue for the study of the chemical requirements, exchanges and syntheses occurring in cerebral tissue. The recent demonstration by Li and McIlwain[5] and Hillman and McIlwain[6] that high, maintained,

177

resting potentials can be recorded from slices of mammalian cerebral cortex *in vitro,* and that the tissue can be depolarized by potassium ions and L-glutamate, is further evidence that physiologically significant mechanisms are preserved in the isolated tissue.

METHODS, MEDIA AND NOMENCLATURE

Most of the work on respiration and glycolysis has been carried out by manometric measurements of the absorption of oxygen and evolution of carbon dioxide by means of the well-known Barcroft or Warburg apparatus or modifications of these. In many cases these methods have been supplemented by chemical determinations of changes in various substances in the tissue and medium. Recently polarographic techniques for the measurement of changes in oxygen consumption have been used and have advantages in the study of certain preparations.[8,236]

Slices of cerebral cortex are most commonly used; they are suspended in media designed to resemble either plasma[9-12] or cerebrospinal fluid[13] in inorganic composition and osmotic pressure. Krebs[14] introduced media containing lactate, pyruvate, fumarate and glutamate as well as glucose in addition to the usual inorganic ions of his previous media and in these media he obtained much higher respiration rates for brain and other tissues than in media containing only glucose as substrate. (See, however, below.) It is at present difficult to decide which medium represents the most physiological environment. Inorganic constituents of the medium have specific metabolic effects and therefore a medium suitable for the particular experiment should be chosen. The bicarbonate-CO_2 buffer is the most "physiological," but phosphate is more convenient for many purposes and other buffers such as glycylglycine or tris-(hydroxymethyl) aminomethane can be used. Methods of preparation of slices are described in the original publications and in practical manuals.[7,12,20,238]

McIlwain and Buddle[15] have described a mechanical device for preparing slices or chopped up brain. The oxygen uptake by suspensions of the chopped tissue was within 3% of that of slices and markedly greater than that of homogenates. Suspensions of cerebral cortex prepared by light homogenization in isotonic media respire at 70% of the rate of slices and when dilute show similar anaerobic glycolytic activity.[13,16,17] However, such suspensions show less aerobic glycolysis than slices. High potassium concentrations stimulate respiration, aerobic glycolysis and acetylcholine synthesis in slices but not in suspensions. Suspensions prepared in hypotonic media require for maximal activity the addition of various cofactors but when appropriately supplemented may show higher activity than slices. These preparations which are very useful for studies of enzymes, are not considered further in this chapter.

Comparison of respiratory rates reported for slices by different workers is made difficult by variations in the method of obtaining the reference weight of tissue. In most earlier work tissue was removed from the medium after the experimental period and dried. Leaching out of soluble material as well as fragmentation lowered the dry weight so that the results were high. This difficulty is partly corrected by adding trichloracetic acid and collecting the slices and precipitate on glass filters.[18] In other cases the weight of the wet slices is determined before use and the dry weight is deduced from wet weight-dry weight determinations on comparable samples. This method is inaccurate because of the variable swelling and the difficulty of removing adherent fluid without damaging brain slices.[19] Fluid can be removed without damaging the tissue by suspending the slices on the platinum wire used for weighing on a torsion balance and gently dabbing the tissue several times on the convex surface of a clean dry watch glass.[12] True fresh weights of tissue can be obtained by cutting slices in a humid chamber without wetting.[20]

The metabolic activities of main concern in this discussion are: (1) oxygen uptake; (2) carbon dioxide evolution which is usually expressed in terms of the ratio of carbon dioxide evolved to the oxygen uptake (i.e., respiratory quotient or R.Q. $= Q_{CO_2}/-Q_{O_2}$); (3) anaerobic, and (4) aerobic glycolysis which refer to the splitting of carbohydrate with the production of lactic acid in the absence or presence, respectively, of oxygen. In manometric work these activities are commonly expressed in terms of Warburg's "Q" values which are microliters of gas at N.T.P. evolved per milligram dry weight of tissue per hour. Uptakes of gas are therefore negative (i.e., $- Q_{O_2}$). Results are frequently expressed in terms of milliliters per gram of fresh tissue per hour, and many determinations of gas exchange *in vivo* are expressed as milliliters per 100 gm. tissue per minute. The most informative units for expressing respiratory rates are millimoles or micromoles per gram of fresh tissue per hour but it is only recently that such units have come into common usage.

THE NORMAL RATE OF OXYGEN UPTAKE

Krebs and Johnson[21] have listed determinations of respiratory rates of brain and other tissues of animals published up to 1938. Table I lists results of some determinations of the rate of oxygen uptake by rat brain tissue under various conditions. Table II shows rates for cerebral cortex from various mammals. There is no relation of the respiration rate to body weight of individual animals within a species but for different species of mammals the rate per unit weight of tissue decreases with increasing size of animal.[22] Slices from the lateral aspect of the hemisphere respire 10 to 20% less actively than slices from the dorsal aspect. Surface slices respire slightly less actively than second slices.[13]

TABLE I

EXAMPLES OF OXYGEN UPTAKE RATES BY RAT BRAIN SLICES

Medium* Containing Ca mM	Mg mM	Buffer	$-Q_{O_2}$† μl./mg. dry/hr. Mean Range	Basis for Dry Weight	Refer- ence
1.8	—	Bicarbonate	13.2 (10.0–16.2)	Final dry wt.	(23)
2.5	1.2	Bicarbonate	⎰14.1 (12.0–16.6) ⎱ 9.8 (5.6–11.6)	Final dry wt. ⎱ Initial dry wt.‡⎰	(19)
1.2	1.3	Bicarbonate	11.2 (10.2–12.2)	Fresh wt.	(13)
1.7	0.8	Phosphate	11.5 (9.0–13.2)	Final dry wt.	(24)
—	—	Phosphate	18.0 (15.8–20.0)	Final dry wt.	(24)
—	1.3	Phosphate	17.1 (15.0–21.5)	Fresh wt.	(13)
—	—	Phosphate	⎧15.8	Fresh wt.⎫	
—	—	Phosphate	⎨10.7 (Homoge- ⎩ nized)	Fresh wt.⎬ ⎭	From Fig. 4 in (16)

In media containing pyruvate, glutamate and fumarate   (14)

—	1.2	Phosphate	26.3 (20.2–35.8)	Final dry wt.	
2.5	1.2	Low Phos. and Bicarb.	19.2 (17.9–20.8)	Final dry wt.	

*All media were isotonic and contained Na, Cl, and K in physiological concentrations.
†Figures for bicarbonate medium are the average over 60 to 90 mins. Figures for phosphate medium give the rate for the first 30 mins.
‡Dry weight estimated from the initial wt. of slices, wet with saline, and the wet/dry weight ratio determined on other similar slices.

TABLE II

AVERAGE RESPIRATION RATES ($-Q_{O_2}$) OF BRAIN CORTEX SLICES FROM THE VARIOUS ANIMALS

Animal	Elliott[13] "Complete Saline"*	Krebs[14] "Supple- mented Medium"†	Animal	Elliott[13] "Complete Saline"*	Krebs[14] "Supple- mented Saline"
Mouse	14.2	22.9	Dog	7.0	14.8
Rat	11.2	19.2	Sheep		11.3
Guinea pig	8.7	17.4	Man	6.1	
Rabbit	7.4	15.1	Beef	5.3	12.1
Cat	8.4	15.5	Horse		10.5

Both media contained glucose.
*Medium containing 1.3 mM Ca, other salts and bicarbonate, 25 mM, buffer in presence of 5% CO_2, 95% O_2. Based on fresh (unmoistened) weight and fresh wt./dry wt. ratio = 5.
†Medium containing 2.5 mM Ca, other salts, and low, 3.6 mM bicarbonate, in presence of 100% O_2. With added pyruvate, glutamate and fumarate. Based on final dry weight.

Table III shows some comparative average figures for the respiration rates of various parts of dog and beef brain in glucose-saline-phosphate medium.[25],[26] Considerably lower rates were obtained for cortex, caudate nucleus, thalamus and cerebellum of newborn dogs.[26] The respiration rate of the newborn rat cerebral hemisphere was lower than that of the adult.[27] White matter respires at half or less of the rate of

TABLE III

AVERAGE OXYGEN UPTAKE RATES BY VARIOUS PARTS OF THE BRAIN (ML. PER GRAM PER HOUR)

Beef Brain Slices[25]		Dog Brain* Mince[26]	
Cerebral cortex	1.7	Cerebral cortex	1.16
Cerebellar cortex	2.55	Cerebellum	1.4
Corpus striatum	1.98	Caudate nucleus	1.36
Thalamus	1.17	Thalamus	1.01
Cornu ammonis	1.26	Mid brain	0.92
Globus pallidus	0.36	Medulla	0.69

*Efforts made to eliminate white matter.

grey matter.[4],[16],[25],[28] Little is known of the respiration of more specific regions of the cortex. Heller and Elliott[29] have estimated the relative respiratory capacities of neurons and glia by comparing the cell density and $- Q_{O_2}$ of cerebral cortex, cerebellar cortex, corpus callosum and glial tumours. Per unit weight, both cerebral and cerebellar cortices respire more actively than white matter. Per cell nucleus, the rate is highest in the cerebral cortex and lower in the white matter. But the average cell in white matter which contains no nerve cells is more active than the average cell in the cerebellar cortex which contains numerous small neurones. Oligodendroglia which predominate in white matter, appear to respire more actively than astrocytes. At least 70% of the cerebral cortex respiration is accounted for by neurones.

TABLE IV

RESPIRATION RATES OF VARIOUS RAT TISSUES IN BICARBONATE-SALINE-GLUCOSE MEDIUM

Tissue	$-Q_{O_2}$	Tissue	$-Q_{O_2}$
Brain cortex slices	10–16	Intestinal mucosa, intact	12
Retina intact	22–33	Diaphragm intact	7–8
Kidney cortex slices	21–24	Lung slices	8
Liver slices	8–17	Pancreas slices	4
Spleen slices	11–12	Tumors, slices	6–14
Testis, teased out	11–12	Whole resting animal	4.8–6.0

(From Krebs and Johnson.[21])

The respiration rate of brain tissue under ordinary conditions *in vitro* is not, as often stated, exceptionally high. Retina and kidney cortex, for instance, respire more actively and several other tissues are nearly as active as is shown in Table IV. Tissues not listed in this table respire considerably less actively at least *in vitro*. Electrical stimulation of slices increases the respiratory rate to levels close to that of normal cerebral cortex *in vivo* (see Chapter IX).

SUBSTRATES OF RESPIRATION

There is general agreement that the brain *in situ* under normal physiological conditions respires almost exclusively at the ultimate expense of glucose (see, e.g., ref. 31). Brain slices and suspensions in a suitable medium provided with glucose and oxygen will respire at a nearly constant rate for hours. The respiratory quotient of slices approaches unity, the theoretical value for complete combustion of carbohydrate.* Balance sheets based on determinations of oxygen uptake, carbon dioxide evolution, lactic acid and other changes have shown that the respiration of brain suspensions[34] and slices[35] can be accounted for to within 80 to 90% by glucose consumption. Experiments with suspensions[34] and with slices[36] have shown that added glucose is used in preference to endogenous substrates. As will be discussed in other chapters, it is now recognized that a considerable fraction of the glucose is utilized indirectly, amino acids and other substances being intermediate products (see, e.g., refs. 36, 36a, 237).

The glucose that is utilized directly in the mammalian brain is metabolized almost entirely by the Embden-Meyerhof pathway and under normal conditions the direct oxidative pathway (hexosemonophosphate shunt) is of little importance.[37,38] However, certain inhibitors such as arsenite and menadione[39] can alter the normal metabolic pathways in a manner which permits a greater participation of the direct oxidative pathway. Glucose metabolism by the Embden-Meyerhof pathway involves a series of non-oxidative reactions and one oxidative step leading to the production of pyruvic acid. Under anaerobic conditions the oxidative step is balanced by reduction of pyruvic acid to lactic acid, while under aerobic conditions most of the pyruvic acid is oxidized through the tricarboxylic acid cycle to carbon dioxide and water. As might be expected both lactate and pyruvate can take the place of glucose as substrates for oxidation. With slices the oxygen

---

*There has been some disagreement concerning the exact figure for the R.Q. of slices (e.g., Dickens and Simer[23] found an average of 0.98; Elliott and Baker[32] found 0.86 but later figures of Elliott *et al.*[19] (see also ref. 33) averaged 0.94). With suspensions the R.Q. usually averages 0.91.[13,34]

uptake rates with glucose, lactate and pyruvate are about the same, but with pyruvate the R.Q. is raised to about 1.2, the theoretical value for the complete oxidation of pyruvic acid.[19] With brain suspensions[34] pyruvate gives a higher respiration rate than glucose and it appears to be used preferentially when pyruvate and glucose are present together, while lactate does not compete successfully with glucose.

Intermediate products of glycolysis such as hexosediphosphate and hexose-6-phosphate[40] and phosphoglycerate[41] are only slowly oxidized by brain tissue *in vitro* possibly because of the lack of phosphate acceptors. Fumarate and malate are similarly slowly oxidized by brain slices.[19] Of all tissues studied only kidney cortex slices[42] are able to rapidly consume added amounts of intermediates of the tricarboxylic acid cycle.[42] With brain and most other tissues except kidney cortex, added succinate is oxidized rapidly only to fumarate, which is converted non-oxidatively to malate, and only slowly further.[19,40] Succinate added to the suspending medium of brain and other tissues causes a considerable increase in oxygen uptake but there is not a corresponding increase in the tissue content of phosphocreatine.[4] Quastel and Wheatley[40] showed that the maximum rate of succinate oxidation occurs when the tissue is depleted of other oxidizable material. Lactate, for instance, spares the oxidation of succinate. Added α-ketoglutarate is also oxidized presumably to succinate, fumarate and malate and slowly further (pigeon brain suspensions[43]).

Loebel[44] (see also refs. 30, 40, 45) showed that fructose and mannose increase respiration of isolated cerebral tissues. However, relatively high concentrations are needed. Galactose[40] is also utilized but less actively and mannitol, arabinose and xylose scarcely at all. Sucrose is quite inert. Brain tissue contains a small amount of glycogen which decreases rapidly in insulin-treated animals[46,47] and during preparation of cerebral tissues for *in vitro* studies.[48] Studies with brain suspensions[34] indicate that added glycogen is not directly utilized but must first be hydrolyzed to glucose. Brain tissue synthesizes little if any glycogen from lactate, pyruvate, citrate, glutamate or glucose-1-phosphate.[49,50] With glucose as substrate glycogen-like material has been obtained *in vitro* but the synthesis is slow and the material not as labile as true glycogen.[48,51,52]

In the absence of added substrate the respiration rate of brain tissue falls off. Studies with brain suspensions[34] (see also ref. 53) have shown that endogenous glucose and lactate are consumed and oxidation of non-carbohydrate material becomes apparent. Consumption of non-carbohydrate material is completely suppressed in the presence of pyruvate, almost completely by glucose and considerably by lactate. Takagaki, Hirano and Tsukada[54] studied the ammonia formation in brain cortex slices of guinea pig in a glucose-free medium. They found that ammonia formation was accompanied with a decrease of glutamic acid content. More than half of the endogenous oxygen consumption could be related to a decrease in glutamic acid content. In the presence of glucose or other oxidizable substrates ammonia formation and the decrease of glutamic acid content were suppressed. Brain perfusion experiments with glucose-free fluids (see ref. 55 and Chapter VI) have also shown that metabolism and function in the absence of glucose can continue for a short time by the oxidation of non-carbohydrate materials and 'structural' components (e.g., nucleic acids and lipids). L-glutamic acid will support the respiration of brain tissue[42] and appeared to be the only amino acid which would do so.[56] Support of oxygen uptake by γ-aminobutyric acid and succinic semialdehyde has been reported;[57,58] in the authors' laboratory only a slight effect of γ-aminobutyric acid is found.

No evidence of fat oxidation by brain under normal conditions has been adduced. It has been possible to cause rapid oxidation of the phospholipid in brain or liver suspensions by the addition of small amounts of iron salt or an iron-protein complex, especially when ascorbic acid is also added.[59] Crude fractionation indicated that the 'cephalin' fraction was affected. Petrushka, Quastel and Scholefield[60] reported a stimulation of respiration of rat brain cortex slices by heated snake venom (phospholipase A) followed by a marked decrease in respiratory activity after one hour. The effects are thought to be a consequence of an attack on the phospholipid groups in brain cell membranes. With liver and kidney slices the effects were small or absent.

The following substances have been found to be oxidized by brain tissue: α-glycerophosphate,[61] β-hydroxybutyrate,[62] acetoacetate,[63,64] acetopyruvate,[65] ethyl alcohol,[66] various amines (see below). No substance has been found to support brain oxygen uptake as actively as glucose, pyruvate or lactate with the exception of succinate and substances like p-phenylene diamine which are oxidized very rapidly by brain and other tissues.[40,53] p-Phenylene diamine is oxidized directly by the cytochrome oxidase-cytochrome c system and has been used for estimating the activity of this system[67] but it is not a substrate of physiological significance.

The following substances are not oxidized by brain: butyric and crotonic acids,[68] α-ketoadipate,[63] α-hydroxyacetoacetate,[69] gluconate[40] and glycerol (Elliott, unpublished).

Acetic acid is produced in the oxidation of added pyruvate by brain tissue.[34] With rat brain suspensions about 14% of the pyruvate metabolized was converted to acetate. Small amounts appear when glucose or lactate is the added substrate. But acetic acid is not oxidized by brain slices or suspensions.[19,34] It is possible that acetic acid is formed from a labile precursor and represents only an artefact of the *in vitro* conditions.

The effect of the enriched media of Krebs[14] in increasing respiration rates is difficult to understand and has not been confirmed by others.[71] Pyruvate, lactate and fumarate do not increase the respiration of brain slices when glucose is present[19] and, in our experience, glutamate does so only slightly if at all (see ref. 71).

ANAEROBIC GLYCOLYSIS

Brain tissue, like a number of other tissues, carries on active glycolysis or more precisely glucolysis under anaerobic conditions. That is to say it causes glucose to undergo a series of reactions resulting in the production of two molecules of lactic acid from one molecule of glucose. The actual rate of glucose utilization, by brain and some other tissues, under anaerobic conditions is several times the rate under aerobic conditions. While glycolysis makes some energy available for biological processes, the energy yield per glucose molecule is far less than in complete oxidation. In glycolysis 54 kilocalories are released or two units of high energy phosphate are produced, while in complete oxidation about 690 kilocalories are released or about 38 units of high energy phosphate produced.

In Table V results of some determinations of anaerobic glycolysis rates are assembled. Rates, often falling rapidly with time and varying from 3.5 to 25 μl. of carbon dioxide liberated by lactic acid from bicarbonate-buffered medium per milligram dry weight per hour, have been reported for glycolysis by rat cerebral cortex slices under apparently similar conditions (see Table V). With slices the average rate per unit weight of tissue does not vary greatly between species though it increases appreciably with size of animal. Since the rate of respiration decreases with size, the glycolytic activity relative to respiratory activity increases considerably with size of animal.[13]

Chesler and Himmich[47] find that anaerobic glycolytic activity of grey matter from different parts of adult cat and dog brain decreases in the following order: caudate nucleus, cortex, thalamus, corpus quadrigemina, cerebellum, medulla, spinal cord. In infant brain the activities of the first three parts are much smaller than in the adult, and the activities of the latter three parts are considerably higher. These findings and determinations at intermediate ages lead the authors to conclude that "the part of the brain exhibiting the highest glycolytic rate advances in a rostral direction as growth proceeds." White matter has low glycolytic activity.[28]

TABLE V

SOME VALUES FOR THE ANAEROBIC GLYCOLYSIS RATES OF VARIOUS TISSUES IN THE
BICARBONATE-SALINE-GLUCOSE MEDIUM

Rat Tissue Slices	$Q_{CO_2}^{N_2}$	Refer-ence	Rat Tissue Slices[21]	$Q_{CO_2}^{N_2}$
Brain cortex	9.0–25.2*	72	Intestinal mucosa (intact)	13.5
Brain cortex	3.5–10.5	73	Bone marrow	21
Brain cortex	5.7–21.4	17	Leucocytes	20
			Red cells	0.35
Retina (intact)	88	21	Adrenal	4
Testis (teased out)	7–15	19, 21	Pituitary	13
Kidney papilla	33.5	21	Cartilage	1.4–1.9
Kidney cortex	4–7	21	Placenta	11–18
Liver	1–7	21	Embryo (whole)	10–32
Spleen	8–10	21	Tumours	11–42

AVERAGES OF MEASUREMENTS BY A UNIFORM PROCEDURE[13] (SEE ALSO[19])

Animal	Cortex Slices†			Tissue	Suspensions‡		
	Plain	$Q_{CO_2}^{N_2}$ With Pyru-vate	Ratio Pyr $Q_{CO_2}^{N_2}$ $-Qo_2$		Plain	$Q_{CO_2}^{N_2}$ With Pyru-vate	Ratio Pyr $Q_{CO_2}^{N_2}$ $-Qo_2$
Mouse	2.8	7	0.5	Whole brain	6.0	8.0	1.0
Rat	4.4	7.7	0.7	Whole brain	6.0	8.4	1.4
Guinea pig	6.8	10.1	1.2	Whole brain	6.7	7.6	1.7
Rabbit	7.0	8.0	1.2	Whole brain	4.6	5.3	1.5
Cat	6.8	11.0	1.3	"Cortex"¶	4.8	6.4	1.6
Monkey				"Cortex"¶	4.8	5.1	1.7
Dog	10.5	13.3	1.9	"Cortex"¶	4.9	5.2	1.6
Man	10.4	11.7	1.8	"Cortex"¶	5.7	6.3	2.1
Beef				"Cortex"¶	4.4	5.4	2.1

*First 15 to 20 minutes. Others are average rates over longer periods.
†These rates appear lower than usual largely because the fresh weight divided by 5 was used as basis for calculation.
‡The rate with suspensions is affected by dilution. The dilution was constant.
¶Containing some white matter.

Though fructose is readily oxidized, Loebel[44] showed that it is scarcely glycolyzed at all by brain tissue.* The same is true for most other glycolytically active tissues while embryonic and tumour tissues vary in their activity toward fructose.[76] Methyl glyoxal is converted to lactate by brain and other tissues at a high rate.[77]

Many workers have observed that the rate of glycolysis by slices or suspensions of brain and other glycolyzing tissues is markedly increased by the presence in the medium of small amounts of pyru-

*Meyerhof[75] found that brain homogenates can carry on fructolysis provided adenosinetriphosphate, phosphocreatine or phosphate donors are added. Conditions comparable to those of his experiments are unlikely to occur in the intact tissue.

vate.[17,19,73,78] The extent of the increase is variable and often more marked than in the examples in Table V. With rat brain suspensions, maximum stimulation is obtainable over a brief period with concentrations as low as 0.05 mM although such small amounts rapidly disappear from the medium.[17] A final concentration of 2 mM pyruvate gives maximum and sustained stimulation of anaerobic glycolysis. A higher rate of glycolysis is usually obtained if anaerobic conditions are established after a period of aerobiosis.[79,80] Pappius *et al.* have found further that the stimulatory effect of pyruvate on anaerobic glycolysis is apparent in media containing sodium, choline, lithium or potassium as the main cation but the stimulation by a preliminary period of aerobiosis does not occur in the lithium or potassium media.

Elliott and Rosenfeld[80] have proposed a mechanism for the action of added pyruvate. Increased pyruvate concentration leads to the formation of lactate and oxidized coenzyme I (NAD). The increased availability of the oxidized coenzyme would cause accelerated formation of 3-phosphoglycerate from glyceraldehyde-3-phosphate and further metabolism of the extra 3-phosphoglycerate would lead to the formation of pyruvate so that the elevated pyruvate concentration would be maintained.

The effect of previous aerobiosis is explained by Pappius *et al.*[83] as due to the production or restoration in the tissue of adenosine triphosphate. The concentration of this substance, which is necessary for the initiaton of glycolysis, determines the rate of glycolysis in slices. The variability in the observed rates of anaerobic glycolysis is probably largely due to variations in the previous access of the tissue to oxygen, in the course of ordinary manipulations of the tissue. It is believed that results of oxygen uptake measurements are far less variable because, under aerobic conditions, the concentration of adenosine triphosphate is less likely to be a limiting factor.

While the respiration rate per unit weight of isotonic suspensions is almost independent of tissue concentration, provided adequate diffusion of oxygen can occur,[16] the glycolytic activity decreases with increase in concentration.[17] This does not seem to be due to the destruction of coenzyme I (NAD) since added nicotinamide does not stimulate glycolysis.[84] It may be due to the action of proteolytic enzymes.[85] Even with slices glycolysis falls off markedly if too large a weight of slices is placed in a given volume of medium. This is probably partly due to inhibition by accumulating lactate.

In general, glycolytic activity is more sensitive than respiration to many factors. It is more variable under apparently uniform conditions. A large number of agents affect glycolysis; some simply inhibit it, some cause an increase in aerobic glycolysis without affecting anaerobic glycolysis, and other increase aerobic glycolysis and inhibit anaerobic glycolysis.

AEROBIC GLYCOLYSIS

Suppression of glycolysis under aerobic conditions occurs to varying extents with almost all tissues capable of active anaerobic glycolysis.

If respiration occurs at the expense of complete oxidation of lactic acid, or a precursor of lactic acid, then 3 molecules of oxygen taken up should prevent the accumulation of 1 molecule of lactic acid. However, in most tissues which are capable of active anaerobic glycolysis, more lactic acid accumulation is suppressed under aerobic conditions than can be accounted for by the oxygen consumed. This suppression of glycolysis under aerobic conditions is commonly referred to as the "Pasteur effect" since Pasteur drew attention to the similar situation in which the production of alcohol by yeast cells is depressed under aerobic conditions. The effect is often referred to in terms of the Meyerhof "Oxidation Quotient" which is given by

$$O.Q. = \frac{\text{Anaerobic glycolysis } (Q\,_{L}^{N_2}) - \text{aerobic glycolysis } (Q\,_{L}^{O_2})}{\text{Oxygen uptake } (-Q_{O_2})}$$

If this quotient is less than 3, no Pasteur effect need be assumed. But values greater than 3 indicate either resynthesis of lactic acid to carbohydrate or suppression of the glycolytic process. The mechanism of the Pasteur effect has been the subject of intense discussion and numerous theories. Recently Gatt and Racker[86] have studied the Pasteur effect and also the inhibition of oxygen consumption by the presence of glucose ("the Crabtree effect") with mitochondrial preparations. Their work indicates that these effects are due to competition between oxidative phosphorylation and glycolysis for cofactors such as inorganic phosphate and adenine nucleotides. When either inorganic phosphate or adenine nucleotides were present in suboptimal concentrations the respiring mitochondria inhibited glycolysis and the glycolysis of glucose inhibited mitochondrial respiration.

Studies on glycolysis by Balazs and Lagnado[87] show that glycolysis by brain mitochondria is inhibited by the presence of oxygen as a result of inactivation of triose phosphate dehydrogenase (an — SH enzyme) and by consequent diminution of the amount of adenosine triphosphate available for the initiation of glycolysis.

In some tissues the suppresion of glycolysis is only partial. This is particularly so with cancer tissue and was the basis of Warburg's theory of cancer metabolism. But aerobic glycolysis is active also in retina, kidney medulla, jejunal mucous membrane, testis and to a lesser extent in various other tissues.

Most workers have observed only slight accumulation of lactic acid with brain tissue under aerobic and otherwise normal conditions.

However, the suppression of glycolysis of brain tissue takes time to occur. With cortex lices prepared and kept until used in a glucose-containing medium, fairly active aerobic glycolysis has been observed during the first few mintues.[19] With slices cut and kept in a humid chamber without moistening quite high rates of aerobic glycolysis, continuing for 30 to 90 minutes, have been obtained.[13] These rates were almost equal to the anaerobic rate obtained with mouse or rat cortex but relatively less wih larger animals. In all cases the aerobic glycolysis of brain finally decreases to a low value while the respiration rate continues high. With isotonic suspensions glycolysis is strongly inhibited by aerobic conditions though, again, the inhibition takes some time to become complete.[13,34]

It should be noted that increase in glycolysis rate will occur under any circumstances when the tissue is insufficiently provided with oxygen, as when slices of the ordinary thickness are incubated under oxygen tensions appreciably less than one atmosphere (in air for instance) or if suspensions are too dense for adequate diffusion of oxygen into the medium. The increased glycolysis then observed is not truly aerobic glycolysis but is a result of some tissue being under virtually anaerobic conditions. Such conditions are also produced when a tissue is prevented from using oxygen by poisoning of relevant enzyme systems with cyanide or other agents.

FACTORS AFFECTING RESPIRATION AND GLYCOLYSIS

Oxygen Tension

Provided a minimum concentration of oxygen is present, the rate of oxygen uptake by brain is not initially affected by oxygen tension. However, at oxygen tensions of one atmosphere or higher a toxic effect of oxygen gradually becomes apparent.[16,18,92,93] This effect is discussed in Chapter XXXV of this volume.

The lower limit of oxygen tension which will support the full oxygen uptake cannot be determined with sliced tissue since, in such preparations, diffusion rates rather than enzyme activities limit the oxygen uptake rate. With dilute brain suspensions, the full rate of oxygen uptake occurs at oxygen tensions as low as 0.6% of an atmosphere[88] (0.005 mM dissolved oxygen). Anaerobic glycolysis does not occur until the oxygen tension is reduced to the point where oxygen uptake is diminished.[88,89] Similar results have been obtained with bone marrow[90] but with several other tissues glycolysis appears to increase before respiration has been diminished by low oxygen tension.[91]

Deprivation of oxygen, glucose being present, causes a very slow loss of subsequent respiratory activity. Deprivation of both oxygen and glucose at 38° C. causes a rapid loss of glycolytic capacity.[17,72,80] The

effects of oxygen deprivation on the subsequent respiration and anaerobic glycolysis by brain slices are greatly reduced if the temperature is low and is nearly or completely prevented at $0°$.[80] As mentioned
earlier, anaerobic glycolysis is more rapid when there has been a brief
period of previous aerobic conditions or when a trace of oxygen is
still present. The loss of glycolytic activity during the period of deprivation of oxygen and substrate at $38°C$ can be largely reversed by brief
aerobiosis.[80] Pappius *et al.*[83] showed that the rate of glycolysis is correlated with the amount of pyrophosphate, presumably adenosine triphosphate available in the tissue. In the absence of glucose and oxygen the level of pyrophosphate falls rapidly but can be raised again
by a period of aerobiosis in the presence of glucose. In an ice-cold
medium or at $38°C$ in the absence of any medium the level of pyrophosphate is preserved.[83]

Substrate Concentration

The respiration rate of brain suspensions at the expense of glucose
is unaffected by the glucose concentration over a wide range. It is
not depressed until the concentration is as low as 2 mg./100 ml., i.e.,
0.1 mM.[88] Concentrations over 10 mM sometimes inhibit slightly.[34]
Pyruvate will support maximum respiration at about as low a concentration as glucose, but a higher concentration of L-lactate (7 mM)
is required.[88] Anaerobic glycolysis is unaffected by glucose concentration at least between 1 and 17 mM. However, with slices the rate
falls when the concentration is lowered to about 4 mM because of inadequate diffusion. Lactic acid accumulating during glycolysis, or
added to the medium, inhibits the rate with slices or suspensions to a
variable extent.[17,72] This inhibition does not occur in the presence of
added pyruvate.[17]

As already mentioned deprivation of both oxygen and glucose, so
that neither respiration nor glycolysis can occur, causes very rapid but
largely reversible loss of the glycolytic capacity of brain slices or suspensions. If oxygen is available and no added substrate, irreversible
loss of activity occurs slowly.

Temperature

Field, Fuhrman and Martin[94] found a temperature coefficient (Q_{10})
of 2.13 for the average respiration rate of rat cortex slices at temperatures between 10 and $40°C$. At $40°$ the rate diminished reversibly with
time, at higher temperatures the loss of activity was more rapid and
was largely irreversible. Dixon[95] found much higher rates of anaerobic
and aerobic glycolysis with rabbit cortex slices at $45°$ than at $37.5°$.

The anaerobic glycolysis rate fell off rapidly but reversibly at 45°. Brain removed from hyperthermic animals respires, at 39°, at the normal rate.[96]

Brain slices[97] or whole brain[14] may be kept in saline media at nearly 0°C. for an hour or more without loss of respiratory, or glycolytic activity subsequently measured at the physiological temperature. The respiratory activity of brain slices kept in ice-cold glucose-phosphate medium for up to 16 hours decreases by only 25% with little increase in aerobic glycolysis (see ref. 234).

Hydrogen Ion Concentration

The respiration rate of brain slices rises rapidly with the pH of the medium up to 6 or 7 and continues to rise up to pH 9-9.5, and falls off sharply in more alkaline medium.[98] However, it has been shown[99] that the pH of the fluids within a slice is not the same as that of the surrounding medium so that effects of pH cannot be properly assessed with slices. With suspensions,[99] the respiration shows an optimum at pH 7.0-7.5 and the rate falls off with increase or decrease of pH. The inhibitory effect of pH outside the optimal range, particularly on the alkaline side, rapidly becomes irreversible.

The optimum pH for anaerobic glycolysis by brain suspensions[84] is about 7.0 in the absence of added pyruvate. But in the presence of pyruvate the rate increases with pH up to about 7.3 and remains maximal at least up to pH 7.9. The small aerobic glycolysis of suspensions ceases below pH 6.6 and increases with pH at least up to 7.3. Birmingham and Elliott[84] suggested that the increase in lactate accumulation occurring at higher pH with slices under aerobic conditions was due to decreased lactic acid utilization. But Domonkos and Huszak[100] regard it as due to a greater glycolytic activity.

Electrolytes

The effects of electrolytes on brain metabolism *in vitro* is discussed in Chapter X and will be considered only briefly here. The early studies by Dickens and Greville[24] on slices have been largely confirmed by Elliott and Libet[16] with suspensions.

In a medium lacking calcium and magnesium ions the respiration is initially considerably more rapid than in the complete medium but the rate falls off rather rapidly to below that in the complete medium. Restoration of calcium to the medium depresses but stabilizes the metabolism; magnesium behaves similarly but less effectively, particularly with slices.[14,24,101] There is a similarity between the effects of omitting calcium and that of increasing potassium.[102]

With sodium as the only cation, the aerobic glycolysis is increased and the anaerobic glycolysis depressed.[24] In supplemented cell free brain preparations sodium inhibits respiration and glycolysis strongly.[103,104] Takagaki and Tsukada[104] found that the aerobic lactic acid formation and glucose utilization of slices metabolizing glucose in a sodium-free medium, (sodium replaced by choline), was increased with little change in oxygen uptake. When pyruvic acid instead of glucose was substrate the respiration was almost twice the control. These effects were peculiar to brain tissue and were not observed in slices of liver, kidney or diaphragm. Apparently the glycolytic and oxidative systems are influenced independently by the ionic composition of the medium.[105] Anaerobic glycolysis by slices is increased if sodium is replaced by choline or potassium but slightly depressed in a lithium medium.[82]

The addition of 100 mM potassium to an already isotonic medium was shown by Ashford and Dixon[106] and Dickens and Greville[24] to cause a striking but variable and transitory increase in respiration and aerobic glycolysis and inhibition of anaerobic glycolysis by cerebral cortex slices. Other tissues are not similarly affected. When brain slices metabolize glucose or pyruvate aerobically in normal balanced media they maintain high tissue concentrations of phosphocreatine. McIlwain[107] and Acs, Balázs and Straub[108] showed that high potassium concentration or the presence of gluatmine diminished the phosphocreatine content of brain slices. Findlay, Magee and Rossiter[109] found that the incorporation of radioactive phosphorus into lipids and pentose nuclic acid in brain slices was inhibited by high potassium concentrations. McMurray, Berry and Rossiter[110] found similar effects on the incorporation of ^{32}P into lipids of mitochondria. These results suggest that potassium ions in high concentrations uncouple phosphorylation. Kovách and Fonyó[111] have studied the incorporation of ^{32}P into adenosine triphosphate and phosphocreatine in brain slices in the presence of 50 mM potassium and came to similar conclusions.

By using cortex slices which have been depleted of potassium by brief storage at O° in potassium-free medium, Elliott and Bilodeau (to be published) have shown that potassium in concentrations as low as 4 mM, in isotonic medium, markedly stimulate and stabilize respiration; maximum effect is obtained with 60 mM potassium. Aerobic glycolysis is *depressed* by 10 mM potassium but increased by higher concentrations. Anaerobic glycolysis is *stimulated* by 10 mM potassium and inhibited by higher concentrations. All effects, especially those of potassium concentrations above 60 mM, are greatly modified by the presence or absence of calcium and by variations of sodium concentration.

The ability of brain slices to concentrate potassium during incubation is dependent upon the presence of sodium in the medium; concentration fails if other univalent anions are substituted for sodium.[81,82]

Weil-Malherbe[112] showed that ammonium ion (33 mM), exerts effects on the metabolism of brain slices similar to those of potassium. Gore and McIlwain[102] found similar but smaller effects.

Studies on the effects of anions are few. Thomas and McIlwain[113] found that glycolysis and respiration in the presence or absence of stimulating agents (e.g., high potassium, electrical pulses) were not affected by replacing the chloride in the medium with nitrate. If the chlorides were replaced by acetate, respiration was normal initially but fell within two hours and glycolysis was high. Potassium salts then did not stimulate respiration but increased further the glycolysis.

Phosphate, which is commonly used as a buffer *in vitro,* causes a temporary acceleration of respiration of brain suspensions but the rate falls rather rapidly.[17,84] This was observed in media without calcium. The bicarbonate-carbon dioxide system causes a small but appreciable inhibition of respiration, about 10% with 20 mM bicarbonate and 16% at 40 mM, the pH being kept constant by changing the carbon dioxide tension.[84] Anaerobic glycolysis occurs at the same rate in either buffer and has not been studied in the absence of buffer.[84] With slices of cortex, Craig found no difference in respiration rates under 1,5, and 20% carbon dioxide, the pH being maintained at 7.5 by changing the bicarbonate concentration.[114] With slices of medulla the respiration decreased at the high carbon dioxide concentration.

Vitamins

The work of Peters and his colleagues on the relation of thiamine to brain tissue respiration and carbohydrate metabolism can be only briefly summarized here (see ref. 115 and Chapter XII). Brain tissue from pigeons suffering from avitaminosis B_1 respire at a smaller than normal rate in the presence of glucose, lactate or pyruvate. Addition of thiamine to the medium *in vitro* raises the respiration rate to normal. With avitaminous brain and lactate or glucose as substrate, pyruvate accumulates in the medium but disappears on the addition of thiamine. Peters called the effect of thiamine on the oxidation of pyruvate the "Catatorulin" effect. Though thiamine pyrophosphate (cocarboxylase) is not immediately effective with brain mince, this is apparently due to failure to penetrate to active sites. It is now established that thiamine pyrophosphate is the coenzyme of keto-acid metabolism. Similar effects of the vitamin deficiency and the addition of thiamine have been obtained with rat brain.[116]

Although other B vitamins are concerned as parts of coenzymes in brain and other tissue metabolism, their effects on metabolism in intact tissue have not been reported. Most of the vitamins are firmly bound in the tissue. McIlwain, Thomas and Bell[117] showed that cozymase is maintained in cerebral tissue metabolizing aerobically but is lost under anaerobic conditions and is not restored by the addition of nicotinic acid, nicotinamide or cozymase. Ascorbic acid, however, is readily lost from and taken up by cerebral tissues. It is most actively concentrated in the tissue when oxygen and glucose are present.

Hormones

Insulin does not appear to exert any direct action on brain tissue metabolism. Insulin added *in vitro,* or administered to the animal, does not obviously affect the respiration rate of brain suspensions.[16,34] The respiration rate of tissue removed from an insulinized animal falls off more rapidly than normally in the absence of added substrate, but this is due to the tissue containing less glucose and lactate than normally.[47,118] Rafaelsen[119] using isolated pieces of rat spinal cord has reported that insulin in the incubation medium increased the aerobic glucose uptake and that in alloxan-diabetic rats the glucose uptake was decreased but was increased by the addition of insulin to the medium. Heller and Hesse[120] have shown that insulin when added *in vitro* to rat sciatic nerves is capable of stimulating respiration probably by enhancing the utilization of glucose, endogenous or exogenous. Rafaelsen[119] showed that insulin increased the glucose uptake of brain cortex slices, but only those having one intact pia-covered surface (i.e., first slices).

Cohen and Gerard[121] found that the rate of oxygen consumption by minced brain from hyperthyroid rats was, initially, about 30% higher than normal without added substrate and that the effects of added glucose or other substrates were increased. Brophy and McEachern[123] found no increases with slices though increases were noted with kidney slices and diaphragm. Peters and Rossiter[122] found that thiamine appreciably increased pyruvate oxidation by minced brain from hyperthyroid rats.

With hypophysectomized rats, McLeod and Reiss[124] observed no changes in the respiration rate of cortex slices but a 25% increase in average rate of anaerobic glycolysis. Administration of adrenocorticotrophic hormone brought the anaerobic glycolysis back to normal.[125] Thyrotrophic hormone given to hypophysectomized animals caused some increase in respiration but this fell off later and no obvious effect was observed with normal animals.[124] Crismon and Field[126] found no change in the respiration of brain slices from adrenalecto-mized rats.

Deoxycorticosterone, progesterone, testosterone, and stilbestrol in-hibit oxygen uptake by brain suspensions.[127] Eisenberg, Gordon and H. W. Elliott[128] found that the respiration rate of brain suspensions from castrated rats was 32% above normal and was brought nearly to normal by treating the animals with testosterone or various deriva-tives, with progesterone or with deoxycorticosterone acetate. Testos-terone *in vitro* caused less inhibition in castrated untreated animals. Respiration of brain from estradiol proprionate-treated animals was elevated.

Protoveratrine

With guinea pig cortex slices Wollenberger[129] found that extremely low concentrations (0.004-0.01 mM) of protoveratrine, veratridine and cardiac glycosides cause large increases in the respiratory and aerobic glycolytic rate and completely inhibit anaerobic glycolysis. The effects are restricted to brain tissue. Nicotinamide and pyruvate prevent the effect on anaerobic glycolysis. The same changes are found in cerebral cortex from animals poisoned with protoveratrine. The effects are more pronounced in phosphate than in bicarbonate buffered media and are not observed with suspensions or homogenates. Wollenber-ger[130] pointed out that there is a striking parallel between the action of protoveratrine, potassium ions and electrical impulses on brain cortex metabolism. Protoveratrine will not act in potassium free media and prevents the uptake of potassium by washed cerebral cor-tex slices. Strophanthin-G (ouabain) also completely inhibits potas-sium accumulation which can be partially restored by adding calcium or magnesium ions.[132] Bilodeau and Elliott (unpublished) find that if slices are treated with protoveratrine in potassium-free medium, the stimulatory effect on respiration of potassium, subsequently added, is lost. The protoveratrine stimulation of rat brain respiration is highly sensitive to narcotics and is diminished by malonate.[131] Pro-toveratrine and ouabain probably act on the neuronal membrane inducing changes in the cationic balance by removal of bivalent ca-tions from the membrane.

Glutamic Acid

Glutamic acid has been mentioned earlier as a substrate for respira-tion. Weil-Malherbe[112] found that 1 to 10 mM glutamic acid caused a gradual inhibition of anaerobic glycolysis by brain slices and an in-crease in aerobic glycolysis. The effects were greater in the presence of lactate or succinate but were reversed by pyruvate. Both isomers of glutamic acid, and glutamine and β-hydroxyglutamic acid, behave similarly. Brain is the only tissue tested which is affected. The action of glutamate is probably connected with the fact that slices of brain cortex re-accumulate lost potassium when incubated in the presence of oxygen and glucose (Pappius and Elliott[81]) and more potassium is accumulated when L-glutamate is present (Terner, Eggleston and Stern[133]). Stern *et al.*[134] found that, in the presence of glucose and oxygen, brain slices will absorb glutamic acid or glutamine from the suspending medium until the concentration in the tissue is considerably higher than in the medium. Similar accumulation of glutamate occurs in several other tissues. Woodman and McIlwain[137] found that L-glutamate, L-aspartate, γ-aminobutyric acid, asparagine and α- and β-alanine depress the level of phosphocreatine in brain tissue respiring in the presence of glucose is reduced. Hillman and McIlwain[6] found that L-glutamate depolarizes neurones in brain cortex slices whereas D-glutamate has no effect. Some of the effects of L-glutamate may be related to potassium accumulation (but see ref. 135) and others to amidation of glutamic acid. Strecker[138] has presented evidence showing that the glutamic acid-glutamine system is capable of regulating directly or indirectly the levels of adenosinetri- and adenosinediphosphate, and controlling the rates of glycolysis and respiration. Stern *et al.*[134] found that added adenosine triphosphate abolishes the inhibition of anaerobic glycolysis by glutamate.

D-Glutamate (10 mM) is not metabolized;[135,137] it inhibits the metabolism of L-glutamic acid and the synthesis and breakdown of glutamine in brain slices.[136]

Maleic Acid

Weil-Malherbe[112] found that maleic acid (20 mM) exerts a variable inhibition of respiration with gradual increase in aerobic glycolysis to the anaerobic level. This effect was accelerated by glutamate, citrate or glutathione and abolished by pyruvate. Similar effects on aerobic glycolysis occurred with some other tissues.

Various Nitrogenous Compounds

Warburg[139] found that, with a number of tissues, ethyl isocyanide causes aerobic glycolysis to reach the anaerobic level without affecting respiration or anaerobic glycolysis. Phenylhydrazine (2.5 mM), phenosafranine and related compounds (0.01 mM), guanidine and methyl guanidine (1 mM) and 1:11-undecanediamidine and decamethylenediguanidine (0.01-0.001 mM) have similar effects on brain tissue[140]:

the respiration rate is usually raised while the aerobic acid formation equals or exceeds the anaerobic.

The bacterial pigment pyocyanine accelerates the respiration of various tissues.[141] With brain cortex slices, Young[142] observed increases in respiration at 0.1 mM or higher concentration followed by inhibition. In the absence of added substrate there was no acceleration. Anaerobic and aerobic glycolysis could also be increased.

A number of redox indicator dyes[143,144] and dinitrophenols[143,145-148] in low concentrations (0.01 mM) increase the respiration of brain and other tissue slices in the presence of glucose but inhibit in the absence of added substrate. Some also cause an increase in aerobic glycolysis, often transitory. Inhibition of tissue respiration, sometimes accompanied by increased glycolysis, sets in sooner or later with all these substances, particularly in higher concentrations. The effects of 2:4-dinitrophenol are similar to the effects of increase in potassium concentration, omitting calcium ions or adding glutamate. McIlwain[149] showed that it decreases the concentration of phosphocreatine in tissue slices and Findlay et al.[109] that it inhibits the incorporation of ^{32}P into phosphorus fractions in brain slices. Dinitrophenol stimulates respiration of minced rat brain in the presence of glucose, lactate, or pyruvate but not with succinate, citrate or fumarate.[147]

Iron Compounds

Panimon, Horwitt and Gerard[150] observed acceleration of oxygen uptake by iron salts in media of low pH, and great acceleration by ferrous orthophenanthroline in neutral media, with brain and other tissue suspensions. Iron salts or an iron-protein complex in the presence of ascorbic acid at first stimulate and then inhibit respiration.[59] This action is unaffected by cyanide but is inhibited by epinephrine and other phenols and by serum and stimulated by histidine and other amino acids.

Neurotropic Agents

The effects of narcotics, tranquilizers, anaesthetics, aliphatic aldehydes and alcohols on respiratory metabolism have been extensively studied by Quastel and his coworkers (see refs. 131, 151, 153, 154) and are discussed elsewhere in this volume. In general these substances at moderate concentrations appreciably inhibit the oxygen uptake of brain and other tissues[155] at the expense of glucose, pyruvate, lactate or glutamate. Succinate and paraphenylenediamine oxidation are not inhibited. This and other observations[156,157] indicate that the locus of action of the drugs is not in the cytochrome system. The inhibitory effects are usually reversible. As a result the effects are not observed in tissue removed from narcotized animals and suspended in narcotic-free medium.[158] Potassium-stimulated respiration is inhibited by much lower concentrations of these drugs than is respiration in an ordinary medium.[158a]

Webb and Elliott[155] found that the inhibition of respiration of brain suspensions and slices by narcotic agents was accompanied by a considerable increase in aerobic glycolysis. With increasing narcotic concentration the rate of glycolysis increased as the respiration was inhibited until, at about 60% inhibition of respiration, a maximum was reached which was slightly greater than the normal rate of anaerobic glycolysis. With higher drug concentrations the rate of glycolysis fell. Anaerobic glycolysis was scarcely affected unless the concentration of the drug was high enough to inhibit aerobic glycolysis. The effects of concentrations of the drug which increased aerobic glycolysis were reversible, but concentrations which inhibited both glycolysis and respiration produced irreversible effects. When maximum glycolysis and 40% of the normal respiration rate were obtained with the narcotic agents, the glucose consumption was three times the normal rate. The effect of narcotic agents was not specific for brain and similar effects were found with testis and kidney cortex slices. The oxidation of glutamic acid was inhibited by these agents in kidney cortex as in brain.

Convulsant drugs such as metrazol, picrotoxin, strychnine, convulsant barbiturates and caffeine have little effect on respiration or glycolysis until very high concentrations are reached.[155,159,161] McIlwain and Greengard found no antagonism between the effects of the convulsant $\beta\beta$-methylglutarimide (Megimide) and butabarbitone on respiration and glycolysis in isolated cerebral tissues. However, the respiratory response of brain slices to electrical pulses was considerably more sensitive to narcotic agents than the unstimulated respiration.[160,161] Lisovskaya and Livanova[162] have examined the effects of depressants, sedatives and analeptics on the metabolism of slices of rat cerebral cortex at pharmacological concentrations. Reserpine, strychnine, Metrazol, and phenamine had no effect on respiration, adenosine triphosphate levels or phosphoprotein metabolism. Depressants such as phenylurethane had no effect on oxygen uptake but inhibited the resynthesis of adenosine triphosphate. The most striking results were obtained with chlorpromazine which at 2.5×10^{-3} M strongly inhibited respiration, completely inhibited the accumulation of adenosine triphosphate and markedly reduced the incorporation of P_{32} into phosphoprotein.

Amines

Quastel and Wheatley[163] found that certain amines, particularly tyramine, phenylethylamine derivatives, mescaline and also indole and skatole, caused marked inhibition of brain tissue respiration at the expense of glucose, lactate or glutamate but not of succinate except in the case of tyramine. Histamine had no effect. The effect with indole was not reversible but complete or partial reversibility was found with other substances. Pugh and Quastel[164,165] showed that brain and other tissues can cause the oxidation of amines to aldehydes through the action of amine oxidase. Some amines are not oxidized and inhibit the oxidation of others. Among these Mann and Quastel[166] found that phenylmethylethylamine (bezedrine) in 0.001% concentration prevented the inhibition which ordinarily followed the addition of toxic amines. It appears that the aldehyde oxidation products of the toxic amines are the actual inhibitors of respiration and benzedrine prevents the formation of these aldehydes.

Various Inhibitors

The respiration of brain tissue, like that of all other tissues, is strongly depressed by cyanide[167,168,169] or azide.[170] Tissues thus inhibited show glycolysis rates approaching the anaerobic level in the presence of oxygen. Carbon monoxide at 18 times the partial pressure of oxygen does not inhibit the respiration of retina or other tissues (brain not studied) but increases aerobic glycolysis to the anaerobic level.[171] Pyrophosphate does not affect the metabolism of brain slices.[172]

Iodoacetate strongly inhibits respiration and anaerobic glycolysis by brain slices[40,173] although the inhibition of respiration develops more slowly than of glycolysis.[174] With washed suspensions[175] the oxidation of glucose in inhibited more rapidly than that of pyruvate or lactate.[175] Fluoride inhibits glycolysis[176] and the oxidation of glucose by brain tissue but not that of lactate.[53] Glyceraldehyde strongly inhibits respiration at the expense of glucose, and glycolysis by brain slices.[177]

Decanoate and other fatty acids initially stimulate and then gradually inhibit the respiration of rat brain slices in the presence of glucose[235] (see also ref. 189, pigeon brain). Aerobic glycolysis is stimulated.

Hydroxymalonate,[178] a lactic dehydrogenase inhibitor, inhibits the oxidation of lactate by brain slices more strongly than that of glucose or pyruvate. It also inhibits anaerobic glycolysis. Nicotine and nicotinic acid[179] inhibit lactate and pyruvate oxidation more strongly than that of glucose.

Brain tissue has been shown to be inhibited to various extents, by

malonate,[180-182] triiodobenzoate,[175] para-aminophenol,[183] oxazolidine-
diones,[184] atabrine,[185] trivalent arsenicals (reversed by thiols),[186,187]
2:3-dimercaptopropanol,[188] and diisopropyl fluorophosphate, tetraethylpyrophosphate and methylfluoroacetate (frog brain).[190] Sodium
fluoroacetate has little effect on the respiration of frog or rat
brain.[190,191]

Both aerobic and anaerobic glycolysis of brain slices are inhibited by
2-deoxy-d-glucose (10 mM) and oxygen consumption is inhibited to a
lesser extent.[192,193] The primary effect of this substance appears to be
at the hexokinase stage possibly causing a depletion of adenosine triphosphate by the formation of 2-deoxyglucose-6-phosphate. The inhibition of anaerobic glycolysis can be relieved by the addition of 3 mM
adenosine triphosphate or 5 mM glucose-6-phosphate.

Electrical Stimulation

McIlwain[194] has found that application of electrical pulses to cerebral cortex slices or fragments causes an increase up to 100% in the
oxygen uptake and induces a variety of metabolic changes very similar to the effects of electrical stimulation of brain tissue *in situ*. The
results and interpretation of experiments using this technique are considered by Professor McIlwain in Chapter IX.

RELATIONSHIP OF STUDIES *IN VITRO* TO OBSERVATIONS *IN VIVO*

The oxygen consumption by the brain of man and other animals is
discussed in another article in this volume (see also Kety[195]). Slices
represent the most nearly physiological preparation for *in vitro* studies
but they constitute only local samples whereas determinations *in vivo*
refer to the whole brain. Suspensions of whole brain in a complete
medium, corrected for loss of activity due to homogenization, might
give a better comparison with figures obtained *in vivo* but whole brain
suspensions only from small animals have been studied. Suspensions
of grey matter respire at about 70% of the rate of grey matter slices.[13]
If rates obtained on whole brain suspensions are corrected for a similar loss and for about 10% loss of activity during preparation[13] an approximate value for "slices of whole brain" is obtained. Such estimates
for whole brain average about 80% of the rates for cortex slices with
rat, mouse, guinea-pig and rabbit. This fraction of the values for cortex
slices from other animals may represent roughly the figure for "slices
of whole brain" of these other animals. In Table VI estimates obtained
in this way are compared with rates determined *in vivo*. The *in vitro*
estimates correspond to the values found *in vivo* in conditions of de-

pressed functional activity. McIlwain[4,30] has compared the respiration of slices of human grey and white matter with estimates of the respiratory activity of these tissues calculated from an estimate of the proportions of grey and white matter and determinations of the oxygen uptake of the whole brain *in vivo*. The respiratory rate for cerebral cortex *in vivo* is 120 μmoles O_2/g./hr. and *in vitro* 55 μmoles O_2/g./hr. The difference between these two rates is considered to be related to the level of functional activity of the tissues in the two circumstances. The increased respiration of brain tissue *in vitro* obtained on electrical stimulation is comparable to the respiration of physiologically active brain *in vivo*.

TABLE VI

OXYGEN UPTAKE BY WHOLE BRAIN IN VITRO AND IN VIVO — Q_{O_2} (MICROLITERS PER MG. DRY WEIGHT PER HOUR)

	In Vitro (Estimated)	In Vivo			Reference
Cat	6.8	No reflexes 6.9	Conscious? 12–15	Convulsing 15–21	(228)
Monkey	5.9	Depressed (Hemorrhage) 5.6	"Normal" 11.1 (Mean)	Convulsing 19.5	(232)
Man	4.8	Coma Diabetic, Insulin 5.1 5.7	Resting 9.9		(233)

The mechanism by which the rate of oxygen usage is controlled and varied with functional activity is not known. It is probable that it is related to changes in the concentrations of phosphate compounds.[196] The effects of high potassium, deprivation of calcium and electrical stimulating in increasing respiration rates, may be related to the variations of metabolic activity *in vivo*. Davies and Grenell[197] have demonstrated the effectiveness of potassium in increasing the oxygen uptake of locally perfused brain *in vivo*.

The *in vitro* observation that brain will consume other materials if it is deprived of glucose has been confirmed by Kety.[198] They found that while the rate of oxygen consumption is much decreased, the ratio of oxygen consumed to glucose utilized is greatly increased in human brain during insulin hypoglycemia. Grenell and Davies[199] have reported that oxygen uptake of local cortical areas in the cat is maintained at the full rate in spite of local perfusion with glucose-free solution. In studies with the cat brain perfused *in situ* Geiger[200] has clearly shown that non-carbohydrate substrates are oxidized in the absence of glucose though dysfunction ensues when glucose is not available to replace these substances. The glutamic acid, glutamine and γ-aminobutyric acid contents of brain decrease during insulin hypoglycemia, suggesting that these substances are among the materials consumed under such conditions.[201,201a]

Although brain tissue *in vitro* will respire at maximum rate in the presence of extremely low glucose concentrations, symptoms of hypoglycemia and even stupor and convulsions can occur when the blood glucose concentration is still appreciable. This emphasizes the fact that the concentrations of metabolites at tissue cells *in vivo* are not necessarily the same as those of the blood since such materials have to diffuse from the capillaries and over an appreciable distance to the cells.

Fructose, lactate, pyruvate, glutamate and succinate can all support oxygen uptake by brain *in vitro*. But Mann and Magath[202] and Wortis *et al.*[203] found that injected lactate would not prevent or alleviate hypoglycemic convulsions in hepatectomized dogs and would not rouse patients from insulin coma. Maddock, Hawkins and Holmes[204] found that fructose, pyruvate, glutamate and succinate, unlike glucose, mannose or maltose, would not restore normal cortical potentials when injected into hepatectomized, eviscerated dogs. Mayer-Gross and Walker[205] found that injection of large amounts of glutamic acid sometimes roused patients from insulin coma but this did not seem to be due to the oxidizability of glutamate and the nature of the effect was obscure.[138]

There are possible explanations for the failure of these substances to replace glucose. Klein, Hurwitz and Olsen[206] found that the rate of transfer of fructose, lactate, glutamate and succinate from blood to brain is much lower than that of glucose, and might not be sufficient to support respiration. Pyruvate did penetrate to the brain tissue rapidly[211] and was converted there to lactate but *in vitro* studies[34] have shown that relatively high concentrations of lactate are required for the full rate of respiration. Meyerhof[207] has shown that under conditions likely to exist in brain, the affinity of fructose for hexokinase is much lower than that of glucose. Added succinate is oxidized rapidly by brain through one step only and it seems unlikely that it would support function effectively. Glutamate, *in vitro* is not used as actively as glucose; if glucose is present it is usually scarcely used.

Studies on brain suspensions[99] indicate that changes in blood pH within the extreme limits of pathological variation (pH 6.9-7.8) are unlikely to affect brain oxygen uptake *in situ* appreciably. Patients in severe diabetic acidosis show a considerable decrease in cerebral oxygen utilization in spite an adequate oxygen supply.[208] This is probably partly related to the acidosis but is better correlated with the accompanying ketosis.

Gurdjian, Webster and Stone[209] found that in morphinized dogs variations in carbon dioxide tension *in vivo,* in the presence of adequate oxygen, caused no significant changes in the concentration of glucose, lactate and phosphate esters in the brain. Experiments with brain suspensions[84] show that wide variations in bicarbonate or carbon dioxide tension have detectable but not marked direct effects on brain respiration and glycolysis. Carbon dioxide added to the inspired gas mixture diminishes the changes occurring in the electrocardiogram during hypoxia, but the effect is due to the improved oxygenation of the blood (Bohr effect) and the improved cerebral circulation caused by the carbon dioxide.

In muscle, glycolysis can serve as an inefficient but rapid method for producing energy-rich phosphate compounds when these have been used up during functional activity faster than they can be provided by oxygen supply and respiration. This seems to be true also for brain since lactic acid accumulates in brain under conditions of hyperactivity,[210,211] as well as in hypoxia,[212,213] and cyanide poisoning.[214,215]

Himwich and his co-workers[216] believe that anaerobic glycolysis is an important source of energy in brains of newborn animals. Newborn animals survive much longer periods of anoxia than do adults;[217] the survival time is increased by increase in blood sugar level and considerable amounts of lactic acid are found in their brains after anoxia.[216] Though the glycolytic activity of infant brain is lower than that of the adult, the respiratory activity is still lower. Glycolytic activity appears nearly adequate for the lower energy demands in the newborn.[26,27]

Glycolysis is possibly concerned in other functions. Even under aerobic conditions the brain forms some lactic acid. With human subjects under resting conditions Gibbs, Lennox, Nims and Gibbs[218] found that lactic acid equivalent to an average of 16% of glucose consumed was added to the blood stream by the brain. Richter and Dawson[219] found that the lactic acid content of rat brain, although still considerable, was decreased during sleep and anaesthesia and was increased in excitement. Glycolysis is possibly concerned in the regulation of the pH and of cerebral circulation either in the brain as a whole or in local regions. Aerobic lactic acid production decreases as the pH is lowered. Anaerobic glycolysis also decreases below pH 7.0 which suggests that the development of acidity in anoxic tissue is self-limiting. But the production of acid during hypoxia, local or general, also tends to counteract the anoxic condition since the lowered pH and the concomitant release of carbon dioxide would tend to dilate cerebral blood vessels.[220,221] Further, it is to be expected that the intracellular acidosis would strongly affect functional activity. The increase in gly-

colysis which accompanies the decrease in respiration in the presence
of narcotics is perhaps an important aspect of the action of such drugs.

While some glycolysis probably occurs under fully aerobic conditions, it seems likely that in local regions it is often increased towards
the anaerobic level. The oxygen tension, measured at the cortex surface, varies and is extremely low at points distant from visible blood
vessels.[222] A very brief decrease in blood supply near such a region,
or an increase in demand due to increased activity, could lead to oxygen lack and the onset of a high rate of glycolysis.

Numerous substances, often in low concentration, increase glycolysis
under aerobic conditions to anaerobic levels *in vitro* without decreasing the oxygen uptake. It is possible that this might occur *in vivo*
under the influence of endogenous substances and provide a mechanism for increasing energy production or controlling pH, or might affect
function in useful or pathological ways. Dickens[140] suggests that the
tetanic convulsive effect of guanidine may be connected with its effect
on aerobic glycolysis.

The effects of high potassium on respiration and glycolysis are of
special interest. The problem of the meaning of these results in terms
of *in vivo* mechanism has recently been discussed by Grenell.[223] Potassium is released from the cell during nervous activity and this may
be part of the mechanism which stimulates the extra respiration associated with activity. This increase in respiration and glycolysis would
provide further energy necessary for recovery and further functional
activity. Dixon[224] suggests that the leakage of potassium, which occurs
when the supply of glucose and oxygen is cut off, may be a factor responsible for ischemic injury. The loss of intracellular potassium
would interfere with enzymic processes dependent on this ion and the
increased potassium in the intercellular fluid may cause irritation of
other cells.

Elevated temperature raises the respiration rate *in vitro* and this
is in agreement with the finding of Himwich *et al.*[225] that the cerebral
oxygen consumption is elevated in patients undergoing fever therapy.
Field, Fuhrman and Martin[94] consider that the irreversible loss of respiratory activity of rat brain which occurs *in vitro* at temperatures
over 40° is a factor in the loss of reflexes and death of animals at such
temperatures. On the other hand, death due to cold is believed to be
due to decrease in blood and oxygen supply to the brain.[97]

Scheinberg[226] has reported studies on patients which show, in
agreement with the results of Brophy and McEachern[123] on slices, that
the oxygen uptake of brain does not, like that of other tissues, increase
in hyperthyroidism. But clinical signs of mental dysfunction in myxe-

dema may be due to decreased cerebral metabolism resulting from increased cerebral vascular resistance.

The inhibitory effect of narcotics on brain respiration is paralleled by studies *in vivo*. Cerebral oxygen consumption has been shown to be decreased during pentothal or ether anesthesia in patients[195,227] and by various barbiturates in the cat brain perfused *in situ*.[228] Local oxygen uptake is strongly inhibited by local perfusion with pentobarbital.[199] However, inhibitory effects on respiratory metabolism do not necessarily represent the sole or even the main action of narcotics. These drugs exert *in vitro* several other effects of possibly equal significance, namely, stimulation of lactic acid production, increase in rate of glucose consumption and, at concentrations likely to be effective *in vivo*, inhibition of free acetylcholine synthesis.[229] *In vivo* an accumulation of bound acetylcholine occurs[230,231] which suggests interference with release of the active form. Possibly a combination of these effects underlies narcotic action.

In general it may be concluded that the results of *in vitro* studies on brain metabolism, where subject to experimental test, have been confirmed by results of work *in vivo* or at least are not in conflict with them. *In vitro* studies have indicated possible modes of action of various agents and may be expected to lead the way in opening up new approaches in the study of nervous and mental diseases. The great advantage of the *in vitro* experimental methods are their ease of control, speed and relative reproducibility.

REFERENCES

1. QUASTEL, J. H.: *Physiol. Rev., 19*:135 (1939).
2. PAPPIUS, H. M., and ELLIOTT, K. A. C.: *Canad. J. Biochem. & Physiol., 34*:1007 and 1053 (1956).
3. WINTERSTEIN, H.: In *Bethe's Handbuch der Normalen und Pathologischen Physiologie*, Vol. 9, pp. 365 and 515. Berlin, Springer (1929).
4. MCILWAIN, H.: *Neurology, 8*:32, suppl.1 (1958); *Proc. 4th Internat. Congr. Biochem., 3*:46 (1959); *Biochemistry and the Central Nervous System*. London, J. & A. Churchill (1959).
5. LI, C-L., and MCILWAIN, H.: *J. Physiol., 139*:178 (1957).
6. HILLMAN, H. H., and MCILWAIN, H.: *Proc. Physiol. Soc.*, p. 20, April 22-23 (1960).
7. UMBREIT, W. W., BURRIS, R. H. and STAUFFER, J. F.: *Manometric Techniques*, Minneapolis, Burgess Pub. Co. (1957).
8. CHANCE, B.: *Ciba Foundation Symposium*, p. 91 (1959).
9. WARBURG, O.: *Biochem. Ztschr., 152*:51 (1924).
10. KREBS, H. A., and HENSELEIT, K.: *Ztschr. physiol. Chem., 210*:33 (1932).
11. KREBS, H. A.: *Ztschr. physiol. Chem., 217*:191 (1933).
12. MCILWAIN, H.: *Biochem. J., 49*:382 (1951).
13. ELLIOTT, K. A. C., and HENDERSON, N.: *J. Neurophysiol., 11*:473 (1948).
14. KREBS, H. A.: *Biochim. biophys. Acta, 4*:249 (1950).

15. McIlwain, H., and Buddle, H. L.: *Biochem. J.*, *53*:412 (1953).
16. Elliott, K. A. C., and Libet, B.: *J. Biol. Chem.*, *143*:227 (1942).
17. Elliott, K. A. C., and Henry, M.: *J. Biol. Chem.*, *163*:361 (1946).
18. Stadie, W. C., Riggs, B. C., and Haugaard, N.: *J. Biol. Chem.*, *160*:191 (1945).
19. Elliott, K. A. C., Greig, M. E., and Benoy, M. P.: *Biochem. J.*, *31*:1003 (1937).
20. Elliott, K. A. C.: In *Methods in Enzymology*. New York, Acad. Press (1955).
21. Krebs, H. A., and Johnson, W. A.: *Tabulae biol.*, *19*:Part 3, 100 (1948).
22. Elliott, K. A. C.: In *Biology of Mental Health and Disease*, p. 54. New York, Hoeber (1952).
23. Dickens, F., and Simer, F.: *Biochem. J.*, *25*:985 (1931).
24. Dickens, F., and Greville, G. D.: *Biochem. J.*, *29*:1468 (1935).
25. Dixon, T. F., and Meyer, A.: *Biochem. J.*, *30*:1577 (1936).
26. Himwich, H. E., and Fazekas, J. F.: *Am. J. Physiol.*, *132*:454 (1941).
27. Himwich, H. E., Baker, Z., and Fazekas, J. F.: *Am. J. Physiol.*, *125*:601 (1939).
28. Krebs, H. A., and Rosenhagen, H.: *Ztschr. ges. Neurol. u. Psychiat.*, *134*:643 (1931).
29. Heller, I. H., and Elliott, K. A. C.: *Canad. J. Biochem. physiol.*, *33*:395 1955); in *Metabolism of the Nervous System*, p. 286. D. Richter, Ed. London, Pergamon (1957).
30. McIlwain, H.: *Biochem. J.*, *55*:618 (1953); *J. Neurol., Neurosurg. & Psychiat.*, *16*:257 (1953).
31. Gibbs, E. L., Lennox, W. G., Nims, L. F., and Gibbs, F. A.: *J. Biol. Chem.*, *144*:325 (1942).
32. Elliott, K. A. C., and Baker, Z.: *Biochem. J.*, *29*:2433 (1935).
33. Baker, Z., Fazekas, J. F., and Himwich, H. E.: *J. Biol. Chem.*, *125*:545 (1938).
34. Elliott, K. A. C., Scott, D. B. M., and Libet, B.: *J. Biol. Chem.*, *146*:251 (1942).
35. McIlwain, H., Anguiano, G., and Cheshire, J. D.: *Biochem. J.* 50:12 (1951).
36. Sutherland, V. C., Burbridge, T. N. and Elliott, H. W.: *Am. J. Physiol.*, *180*:195 (1956).
36a. Beloff-Chain, A., Catanzaro, R., Chain, E. B. Masi, I., and Pocchiari, F.: *Proc. Roy. Soc. London*, S. B. *144*:22 (1955).
37. Bloom, B.: *Proc. Soc. Exper. Biol. & Med.*, *88*:317 (1955).
38. Sacks, W.: *J. Appl. Physiol.*, *10*:37 (1957).
39. Hoskin, F. C. G.: *Biochem. biophyso acta*, *40*:309 (1960).
40. Quastel, J. H., and Wheatley, A. H. M.: *Biochem. J.*, *26*:725 (1932).
41. Jowett, M., and Quastel, J. H.: *Biochem. J.*, *31*:275 (1937).
42. Elliott, K. A. C.: *Physiol. Rev.*, *21*:267 (1941).
43. Krebs, H. A., and Johnson, W. A.: *Biochem. J.*, *31*:645 (1937).
44. Loebel, R. O.: *Biochem. Ztschr.*, *161*:219 (1925).
45. Dickens, F., and Greville, G. D.: *Biochem. J.*, *27*:832 (1933).
46. Kerr, S. E.: *J. Biol. Chem.*, *116*:1 (1936).
47. Kerr, S. E., and Ghantus, M.: *J. Biol. Chem.*, *116*:9 (1936).
48. McIlwain, H., and Tresize, M. A.: *Biochem. J.*, *63*:250 (1956).
49. Benoy, M. P. and Elliott, K. A. C.: *Biochem. J.*, *31*:1268 (1937).
51. Le Baron, F. N.: *Biochem. J.*, *61*:80 (1955).
52. Kleinzeller, A., and Rybová, R.: *J. Neurochem.*, *2*:45 (1957).
53. Holmes, E. G.: *Biochem. J.*, *24*:914 (1930).
54. Takagaki, G., Hirano, S., and Tsukada, Y.: *Arch. Biochem. Biophys.*, *68*:196 (1957).

55. Geiger, A., Magnes, J., and Geiger, R. S.: *Nature*, London, *170:*754 (1952).
56. Weil-Malherbe, H.: *Biochem. J., 30:*665 (1936).
57. McKhann, G. M., and Tower, D. B.: *Am. J. Physiol., 196:*36 (1959).
58. Tsukada, Y., Nagata, Y., and Takagaki, G.: *Proc. Japan Acad., 33:*510 (1957).
59. Elliott, K. A. C., and Libet, B.: *J. Biol. Chem., 152:*617 (1944).
60. Petrushka, E., Quastel, J. H. and Scholefield, P. G.: *Canad. J. Biochem. & Physiol., 37:*975 (1959).
61. Quastel, J. H., Tennenbaum, M., and Wheatley, A. H. M.: *Biochem. J., 30:*1668 (1936).
62. Jowett, M., and Quastel, J. H.: *Biochem. J., 29:*2182 (1935).
63. McGowan, G. K., and Peters, R. A.: *Biochem J., 31:*1637 (1937).
64. Mann, P. J. G., Tennenbaum, M., and Quastel, J. H.: *Biochem J., 32:*253 (1938).
65. Krebs, H. A., and Johnson, W. A.: *Biochem. J., 31:*772 (1937).
66. Robertson, J. D., and Stewart, C. P.: *Biochem. J., 26:*65 (1932).
67. Elliott, K. A. C., and Greig, M. E.: *Biochem. J., 32:*1407 (1938).
68. Quastel, J. H., and Wheatley, A. H. M.: *Biochem. J., 27:*1753 (1933).
69. Weil-Malherbe, H.: *Biochem. J., 32:*1032 (1938).
70. Long, C.: *Biochem. J., 32:*1711 (1938).
71. Pappius, H., and Elliott, K. A. C.: *Canad. J. Biochem. & Physiol., 32:*484 (1954).
72. Dickens, F., and Greville, G. D.: *Biochem. J., 27:*1134 (1933).
73. Blum, E., Appel, H., and Couciero, P.: *Ztschr. physiol. Chem., 220:*186 (1933).
74. Chesler, A., and Himwich, H. E.: *Am. J. Physiol., 142:*541 (1944).
75. Meyerhof, O.: *Arch. Biochem., 13:*485 (1947).
76. Dickens, F., and Greville, G. D.: *Biochem. J., 26:*1251 and 1546 (1932).
77. Jowett, M., and Quastel, J. H.: *Biochem. J., 28:*162 (1934).
78. Mendel, B., Baugh, M., and Strelitz, F.: *Klin. Wochschr., 10:*118 (1931).
79. Rosenthal, O.: *Biochem. Ztschr., 207:*263 (1929).
80. Elliott, K. A. C., and Rosenfeld, M.: *Canad. J. Biochem. & Physiol., 36:*721 (1958).
81. Pappius, H. M., and Elliott, K. A. C.: *Canad. J. Biochem. & Physiol., 34:*1053 (1956).
82. Pappius, H. M., Rosenfeld, M., Johnson, D. M., and Elliott, K. A. C.: *Canad. J. Biochem. & Physiol., 36:*217 (1958).
83. Pappius, H. M., Johnson, D. M., and Elliott, K. A. C.: *Canad. J. Biochem. & Physiol., 37:*999 (1959).
84. Birmingham, M. K., and Elliott, K. A. C.: *J. Biol. Chem., 189:*73 (1951).
85. Krimsky, J., and Racker, E.: *J. Biol. Chem., 179:*903 (1949).
86. Gatt, S., and Racker, E.: *J. Biol. Chem., 234:*1075 and 1024 (1959).
87. Bálazs, R., and Lagnado, J. R.: *J. Neurochem., 5:*1 (1959).
88. Elliott, K. A. C., and Henry, M.: *J. Biol. Chem., 163:*351 (1946).
89. Craig, F. N., and Beecher, H. K.: *J. Neurophysiol., 6:*135 (1943).
90. Warren, C. O.: *J. Cell & Comp. Physiol., 19:*193 (1942).
91. Laser, H.: *Biochem. J., 31:*1671 (1937).
92. Mann, P. J. G., and Quastel, J. H.: *Biochem. J., 40:*139 (1946).
93. Dickens, F.: *Biochem. J., 40:*145 (1946).
94. Field, J., 2nd, Fuhrman, F. A., and Martin, A. W.: *J. Neurophysiol., 7:*117 (1944).
95. Dixon, K. C.: *Biochem. J., 30:*1483 (1936).

96. REISS, C. N., FIELD, J., HALL, V. E., and GOLDSMITH, M.: *Am. J. Physiol.*, *157*:283 (1949).
97. FUHRMAN, F. A., and FIELD, J., 2nd: *Am. J. Physiol.*, *139*:193 (1943).
98. CANZANELLI, A., GREENBLATT, M., ROGERS, G. A., and RAPPORT, D.: *Am. J. Physiol.*, *127*:290 (1939).
99. ELLIOTT, K. A. C., and BIRMINGHAM, M. K.: *J. Biol. Chem.*, *177*:51 (1949).
100. DOMONKOS, J., and HUSZÁK, I.: *J. Neurochem.*, *4*:238 (1959).
101. CANZANELLI, A., ROGERS, G., and RAPPORT, D.: *Am. J. Physiol.*, *135*:309 (1942).
102. GORE, M. B. R., and McILWAIN, H.: *J. Physiol.*, *117*:471 (1952).
103. RACKER, E., and KRIMSKY, I.: *J. Biol. Chem.*, *161*:453 (1945).
104. TAKAGAKI, G., and TSUKADA, Y.: *J. Neurochem.*, *2*:21 (1957)
105. TSUKADA, Y., and TAKAGAKI, G.: *Nature*, London, *175*:725 (1955).
106. ASHFORD, C. A., and DIXON, K. C.: *Biochem. J.*, *29*:157 (1935).
107. McILWAIN, H.: *Biochem. J.*, *52*:289 (1952).
108. ACS, G., BÁLAZS, R. and STRAUB, F. B.: *Kiserletes Orvostudomany*, *5*:466 (1953).
109. FINDLAY, M., MAGEE, W. L., and ROSSITER, R. J.: *Biochem. J.*, *58*:236 (1954).
110. McMURRAY, W. C., BERRY, J. F., and ROSSITER, R. J.: *Biochem. J.*, *66*:629 (1957).
111. KOVÁCH, A. G. B., and FONYÓ, A.: In *The Biochemical Response to Injury*, p. 151. Oxford, Blackwell (1960).
112. WEIL-MALHERBE, H.: *Biochem. J.*, *32*:2257 (1938).
113. THOMAS, J., and McILWAIN, H.: *J. Neurochem.*, *1*:1 1956).
114. CRAIG, F. N.: *J. Gen. Physiol.*, *27*:325 (1944).
115. PETERS, R. A.: *Lancet*, 1161 (1936); *Chem. & Indust.*, *59*:373 (1940); *Brit. Med. Bull.*, *9*:116 (1953).
116. O'BRIEN, J. R., and PETERS, R. A.: *J. Physiol.*, *85*:454 (1935).
117. McILWAIN, H., THOMAS, J., and BELL, J. L.: *Biochem. J.*, *64*:332 (1956).
118. ELLIOTT, K. A. C.: *Proc. Soc. Exper. Biol. & Med.*, *63*:234 (1946).
119. RAFAELSEN, O. J.: *Lancet*, *2*:941 (1958); *J. Neurochem.*, *7*:33, and 45 (1961).
120. HELLER, I. H., and HESSE, S.: *Lancet*, *2*:406 (1960).
121. COHEN, R. A., and GERARD, R. W.: *J. Cell. & Comp. Physiol.*, *10*:223 (1937).
122. PETERS, R. A., and ROSSITER, R. J.: *Biochem. J.*, *33*:1140 (1939).
123. BROPHY, D., and McEACHERN, D.: *Proc. Soc. Exper. Biol. & Med.*, *70*:120 (1949).
124. MACLEOD, L. D., and REISS, D. S.: *Endocrinology*, *41*:437 (1947).
125. REISS, M., and REES, M.: *Biochem. J.*, *34*:820 (1940).
126. CRISMON, J. M., and FIELD, J. 2nd: *Am. J. Physiol.*, *130*:231 (1940).
127. GORDON, G. S., and ELLIOTT, H. W.: *Endocrinology*, *41*:517 (1947).
128. EISENBERG, E., GORDON, G. S., and ELLIOTT, H. W.: *Science*, *109*:337 (1949); *Federation Proc. 9*:269 (1950).
129. WOLLENBERGER, A.: *Federation Proc.*, *9*:326 (1950); *J. Pharmacol.*, *97*:311 (1949).
130. WOLLENBERGER, A.: *Biochem. J.*, *61*:68,77 (1955).
131. QUASTEL, J. H.: *Biochemistry of the Central Nervous System*, Vol. III, p. 90. F. Brücke, London, Pergamon (1959).
132. GÁRDOS, G.: *J. Neurochem.*, *5*:199 (1960).
133. TERNER, C., EGGLESTON, L. V., and KREBS, H. A.: *Biochem. J.*, *47*:139 (1950).
134. STERN, J. R., EGGLESTON, L. V., HEMS, R., and KREBS, H. A.: *Biochem. J.*, *44*:410 (1949).
135. TAKAGAKI, G., HIRANO, S., and NAGATA, Y.: *J. Neurochem.*, *4*:124 (1959).
136. KREBS, H. A.: *Biochem. J.*, *29*:1951 (1935).

137. WOODMAN, R. J., and MCILWAIN, H.: *Biochem. J., 81*:83 (1961).
138. STRECKER, H. J.: In *Metabolism of the Nervous System*, p. 459 D. Richter, Ed. London, Pergamon (1957).
139. WARBURG, O.: *Biochem. Ztschr., 172*:432 (1926).
140. DICKENS, F.: *Biochem. J., 28*:537 (1934); *30*:1233 (1936); *33*:2017 (1939).
141. FRIEDHEIM, E. A. H.: *Biochem. J., 28*:173 (1934).
142. YOUNG, L.: *J. Biol. Chem., 120*:659 (1937).
143. ELLIOTT, K. A. C., and BAKER, Z.: *Biochem. J., 29*:2396 (1935).
144. DICKENS, F.: *Biochem. J., 30*:1064 (1936).
145. DODDS, E. C., and GREVILLE, G. D.: *Nature*, London, *132*:966 (1933).
146. PEISS, C. N., and FIELD, J.: *J. Biol. Chem., 175*:49 (1948).
147. TYLER, D. B.: *J. Biol. Chem., 184*:711 (1950).
148. TSUKADA, Y., TAKAGAKI, G., and HIRANO, S.: *Biochem. J.* (Japan), *45*:489 (1958).
149. MCILWAIN, H.: *Biochem. J., 52*:289 (1952).
150. PANIMON, F., HORWITT, M. K., and GERARD, R. W.: *J. Cell. & Comp. Physiol., 17*:1 and 17 (1941).
151. QUASTEL, J. H., and WHEATLEY, A. H. M.: *Proc. Roy. Soc. London, B, 112*:60 (1932); *Biochem. J., 31*:565 (1937).
152. JOWETT, M., and QUASTEL, J. H.: *Biochem. J., 31*:565 (1937).
153. JOWETT, M.: *J. Physiol., 92*:322 (1938).
154. BEER, C. T., and QUASTEL, J. H.: *Canad. J. Biochem. & Physiol., 36*:531 and 543 (1958).
155. WEBB, J. L., and ELLIOTT, K. A. C.: *J. Pharmacol., 103*:24 (1951).
156. MICHAELIS, M., and QUASTEL, J. H.: *Biochem. J., 35*:518 (1941).
157. GREIG, M. E.: *J. Pharmacol., 87*:185 (1946).
158. WORTIS, S. B.: *Arch. Neurol. & Psychiat., 33*:1022 (1935).
158a. GHOSH, P. N., and QUASTEL, J. H.: *Nature*, London, *74*:28 (1954).
159. ANGUIANO, G., and MCILWAIN, H.: *Brit. J. Pharmacol., 6*:448 (1951).
160. GREENGARD, O., and MCILWAIN, H.: *Biochem. J., 61*:61 (1955).
161. MCILWAIN, H., and GREENGARD, O.: *J. Neurochem., 1*:348 (1957).
162. LISOVSKAYA, N. P., and LIVANOVA, N. B.: *Biokhimiya, 24*:799 (1959).
163. QUASTEL, J. H., and WHEATLEY, A. H. M.: *Biochem. J., 27*:1609 (1933); *28*:1521 (1934).
164. PUGH, C. E. M., and QUASTEL, J. H.: *Biochem. J., 31*:286 and 2306 (1937).
165. BLASCHKO, H., RICHTER, D., and SCHLOSSMANN, H.: *Biochem. J., 31*:2187 (1937).
166. MANN, P. J. G., and QUASTEL, J. H. *Nature*, Lond., *144*:943 (1939).
167. DIXON, M., and ELLIOTT, K. A. C.: *Biochem. J., 23*:812 (1929).
168. ALT, H. L.: *Biochem. Ztschr., 221*:498 (1930).
169. VAN HEYNINGEN, W. E.: *Biochem. J., 29*:2036 (1935).
170. HOLLINGER, N., FUHRMAN, F. A., LEWIS, J. J., and FIELD, J.: *J. Cell. & Comp. Physiol., 33*:223 (1949).
171. LASER, H.: *Biochem. J., 31*:1677 (1937).
172. GREIG, M. E., and MUNRO, M. P.: *Biochem. J., 33*:143 (1939).
173. BARKER, S. B., SHORR, E., and MALAEN, M.: *J. Biol. Chem., 129*:33 (1939).
174. FUHRMAN, F. A., and FIELD, J., 2nd: *J. Cell. & Comp. Physiol., 21*:307 (1943).
175. BERNHEIM, F., and BERNHEIM, M. L. C.: *J. Biol. Chem., 138*:501; *140*:441 (1940).
176. DICKENS, F., *and* ŠIMER, F.: *Biochem. J., 23*:936 (1929).
177. BAKER, Z.: *Biochem. J., 32*:332 (1938).

178. Jowett, M., and Quastel, J. H.: *Biochem. J., 31:*275 (1937).
179. Baker, Z., Fazekas, J. F., and Himwich, H. E.: *J. Biol. Chem., 125:*545 (1938).
180. Quastel, J. H., and Wheatley, A. H. M.: *Biochem. J., 25:*119 (1931).
181. Greville, G. D.: *Biochem. J., 30:*877 (1936).
182. Tyler, D. B.: *Proc. Soc. Exper. Biol. & Med., 49:*537 (1942).
183. Bernheim, F., Bernheim, M. L. C., and Michel, H. O.: *J. Pharmacol. & Exper. Therap., 61:*311 (1937).
184. Fuhrman, F. A., and Field, J., 2nd: *J. Cell. & Comp. Physiol., 19:*351 (1942); *J. Pharmacol., 77:*229 (1943).
185. Wright, C. I., and Sabine, J. C.: *J. Biol. Chem., 155:*315 (1944).
186. Gordon, J. J., and Quastel, J. H.: *Biochem. J., 42:*337 (1948).
187. Peters, R. A., and Wakelin, R. W.: *Biochem. J., 40:*513 (1946).
188. Barron, E. S. G., Miller, Z. B., and Meyer, J.: *Biochem. J., 41:*78 (1947).
189. Peters, R. A., and Wakelin, R. W.: *Biochem. J., 32:*2290 (1938).
190. Brooks, V. B., Ransmeier, R. E., and Gerard, R. W.: *Am. J. Physiol., 157:*299 (1949).
191. Webb, J. L., and Elliott, K. A. C.: *Canad. J. Res., 26:*239 (1948).
192. Woodward, G. E., and Hudson, M. T.: *Cancer Res., 14:*599 (1954).
193. Tower, D. B.: *J. Neurochem., 3:*185 (1958).
194. McIlwain, H.: *Biochem. J., 49:*382; *50:*132 (1951).
195. Kety, S. S.: *Am. J. Med., 8:*205 (1950).
196. McIlwain, H., and Gore, M. B. R.: *Biochem. J., 50:*24 (1951).
197. Davies, P. W., and Grenell, R. G.: *Federation Proc., 9:*29 (1950).
198. Kety, S. S., Lukens, F. D., Woodford, R. B., Harmel, M. H., Freyhan, F. A., and Schmidt, C. F.: *Federation Proc., 7:*64 (1948).
199. Grenell, R. G., and Davies, P. W.: *Federation Proc., 9:*52 (1950).
200. Geiger, A.: *Physiol. Rev., 38:*1 (1958).
201. Dawson, R. M. C.: *Nature,* London, *164:*1097 (1949).
201a. Cravioto, R. O., Massieu, G., and Izquiero, J. J.: *Proc. Soc. Exper. Biol. & Med., 78:*856 (1951).
202. Mann, F. C., and Magath, T. B.: *Arch. Int. Med., 30:*171 (1922).
203. Wortis, J., Bowman, K. M., Goldfarb, W., Fazekas, J. F., and Himwich, H. E.: *Am. J. Physiol., 125:*551 (1939).
204. Maddock, S., Hawkins, J., Jr., and Holmes, E.: *Am. J. Physiol., 125:*551 (1939).
205. Mayer-Gross, W., and Walker, J. W.: *Biochem. J., 44:*92 (1949).
206. Klein, J. R., Hurwitz, R., and Olsen, N. S.: *J. Biol. Chem., 164:*509 (1946); *167:*1 (1947).
207. Meyerhof, O.: *Arch. Biochem., 13:*485 (1957).
208. Kety, S. S., Polis, B. D., Nadler, C. S., and Schmidt, C. F.: *J. Clin. Investigation, 27:*500 (1948).
209. Gurdjian, E. S., Webster, J. E., and Stone, W. E.: *Am. J. Physiol., 156:*149 (1949).
210. Stone, W. E., Webster, J. E., and Gurdjian, E. S.: *J. Neurophysiol., 8:*233 (1945).
211. Klein, J. R., and Olsen, N. S.: *J. Biol. Chem., 167:*747 (1947).
212. Fazekas, J. F., and Himwich, H. E.: *Am. J. Physiol., 139:*366 (1943).
213. Gurdjian, E. S., Stone, W. E., and Webster, J. E.: *Arch. Neurol. & Psychiat., 51:*472 (1944).
214. Albaum, H. G., Tepperman, J., and Bodansky, O.: *J. Biol. Chem., 164:*45 (1946).

215. OLSEN, N. G., and KLEIN, J. R.,: *J. Biol. Chem.*, *167*:739 (1947).
216. HIMWICH, H. E., BERNSTEIN, A. O., HERRLICH, H., CHESLER, A., and FAZEKAS, J. F.: *Am. J. Physiol.*, *135*:387 (1942).
217. FAZEKAS, J. F., ALEXANDER, F. A. D., and HIMWICH, H. E.: *Am. J. Physiol.*, 134:281 (1941).
218. GIBBS, E. L., LENNOX, W. G., NIMS, L. F., and GIBBS, F. A.: *J. Biol. Chem.*, *144*:325 (1942).
219. RICHTER, D., and DAWSON, R. M. C.: *Am. J. Physiol.*, *154*:73 (1948).
220. NIMS, L. F., GIBBS, E. L., and LENNOX, W. G.: *J. Biol. Chem.*, *145*:189 (1942).
221. KETY, S. S., and SCHMIDT, C. F.: *J. Clin. Investigation*, *27*:484 (1948).
222. RÉMOND, A., DAVIES, P. W., and BRONK, D. W.: *Federation Proc. 5*:86 (1946).
223. GRENELL, R. G.: In *Biochemistry of the Central Nervous System*, Vol. III, p. 115. F. Brücke, Ed. Pergamon Press (1959).
224. DIXON, K. C.: *Biochem. J.*, *44*:187 (1949); *J. Physiol.*, *110*:87 (1949).
225. HIMWICH, H. E., BOWMAN, K. M., GOLDFARB, W., and FAZEKAS, J. F.: *Science*, *90*:398 (1939).
226. SCHEINBERG, P.: *Federation Proc.*, *9*:113 (1950).
227. HIMWICH, W. A., HOMBURGER, E., MARESCA, R., and HIMWICH, H. E.: *Am. J. Physiol.*, *149*:517 (1947).
228. GEIGER, A., and MAGNES, J.: *Am. J. Physiol.*, *149*:517 (1947).
229. McLENNAN, H., and ELLIOTT, K. A. C.: *J. Pharmacol.*, *103*:35 (1951).
230. TOBIAS, J. M., LIPTON, M. A., and LEPINAT, A. A.: *Proc. Soc. Exper. Biol. & Med.*, *61*:51 (1946).
231. ELLIOTT, K. A. C., SWANK, R. L., and HENDERSON, N.: *Am. J. Physiol.*, *162*:469 (1950).
232. SCHMIDT, C. F., KETY, S. S., and PENNES, H. H.: *Am. J. Physiol.*, *143*:33 (1945).
233. KETY, S. S., and coworkers: *J. Clin. Investigation*, *27*:476 (1948); *27*:500 (1948); *Am. J. Psychiat.*, *104*:765 (1948).
234. WOLFE, L. S., and McILWAIN, H.: *Biochem. J. 78*:33 (1961).
235. AHMED, K., and SCHOLEFIELD, P. G.: *Biochem. J. 81*:45 (1961).
236. STRICKLAND, E. H., ZIEGLER, F. D., and ANTHONY, A.: *Nature*, *191*:969 (1961).
237. ALLWEIS, C. L., GAINER, H., and CHAIKOFF, I. L.: *Arch. Biochim. Biophys.*, *92*:159 (1961).
238. McILWAIN, H., *Biochem. J.*, *78*:213 (1961).

IX

ELECTRICAL PULSES AND THE *IN VITRO* METABOLISM OF CEREBRAL TISSUES

HENRY MCILWAIN

A BIOCHEMICAL investigator who employs preparations which are not intact animals but derived from them, must appraise the relationship between his material and some relevant part or function of the whole animal. The brain *in situ* exhibits interchange of two types with the remainder of an animal: of chemical substances and of electrical impulses. The cerebral traffic of substances and pulses *in vivo* are linked, forming two major aspects of cerebral functioning. Their linkage is difficult to investigate in the whole animal, and this gave impetus to the studies now to be described. *In vitro,* the interchange of substances can be simulated by interchange between tissue-fragments and an ambient nutrient saline. This is well known and is described elsewhere in this book. The present chapter describes the replacement of the second interaction by providing the isolated tissue with an environment of fluctuating electrical potential gradients.

It will be noted that each *in vitro* surrogation can be made by relatively simple means, resolving anatomical difficulties which at first sight appear overwhelming. Thus the nutrient saline is not applied through the innumerable blood capillaries, but at artificially created surfaces. The electrical potential gradients are not applied by the normal pathways of afferent impulses, but to saline which surrounds the tissue. Applying impulses in this way is a typical electrophysiological technique; only exceptionally are potentials directly applied as *in vivo* across the individual nerve membrane or at a defined synaptic structure.

Studies of the metabolic response of isolated cerebral tissues to electrical pulses are made in close relationship with two other types of study. These are: (1) examination of tissue composition; and (2) measurement of resting potentials in the isolated tissue. Regarding (1), it was the discovery that cerebral tissues can maintain *in vitro* a pattern of labile constituents analagous to those native to the brain *in vivo*[1-3] which led to attempts to modify metabolism by pulses.[4] In particular, the isolated tissue maintains energy-rich phosphates, known *in vivo* to undergo rapid change when electrical pulses are applied to the head. These phosphates are largely broken down during isolation of the tissue, but are recovered when the carefully prepared, cell-containing tissue is incubated with oxygen and glucose. Moreover, such tissues also recover a large part of their normal high, internal concentration of potassium salts and they extrude sodium salts. (2) Microelectrode techniques, applied to isolated tissues in oxygenated glucose salines, show that the differential ion concentrations are indeed effective in maintaining resting potentials in the tissue.[5,6] These potentials depend on a variety of metabolic factors and indicate that neural elements in the tissue are in a condition in which they can be discharged or depolarized by applied pulses.

MULTIPLICITY OF METABOLIC RESPONSES TO APPLIED ELECTRICAL PULSES

Experimental arrangements for applying pulses to isolated cerebral tissues are epitomized in Figure 1 and described in detail else-

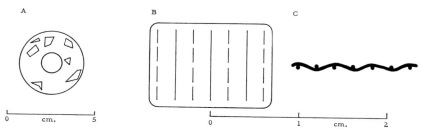

Fig. 1. Relationship between tissue and electrodes in two fashions of applying electrical pulses: *A,* tissue fragments between concentric electrodes such as can be fitted to a tube or manometer-vessel. *B,* Tissue slice between grid electrodes as used in a manometric vessel or in a quick-transfer apparatus (plan). *C,* Elevation of *B.*

where.[3,4,7-13] The metabolic responses to pulses are manifold, occurring together in the same piece of tissue, and interrelated in fashions which are still the subject of investigation. They include in probable order of immediacy: ion movements, carrier and phosphate changes, and respiratory and substrate changes.[14,15] The increase in respiration, a consequence of applying pulses *in vitro* with all substrates which support normal response, and also observed *in vivo*, has been a convenient characteristic to investigate first in finding conditions for *in vitro* experiments. Factors then found to condition response are: (1) electrical

characteristics of the pulses applied; (2) the tissue being studied; (3)
the substrates provided, and (4) inorganic constituents of the tissue's
environment. In the following description these factors are considered
individually, it being assumed unless otherwise stated, that during the
investigation of one characteristic others have been kept approximately
optimal.

REQUIREMENTS FOR RESPIRATORY RESPONSE

Electrical Characteristics of Applied Pulses

Response to sine-wave currents is shown in Figure 2.[9,16,17] Two parameters are concerned: frequency and voltage. Interpolation shows an
optimal frequency of about 80 cycles per second at which response is
obtained with minimum current; the threshold potential is then
about 0.4 v(r.m.s.). This is with electrodes 2 mm. apart, an arrangement which is recommended when sine-wave currents are employed.

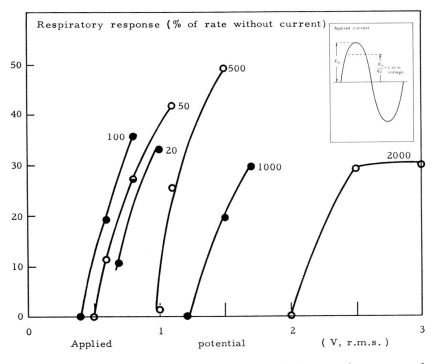

Fig. 2. Increase in respiration of guinea pig cerebral cortex in oxygenated
glucose salines, between electrodes 2 mm. apart,[16] on application of sine-wave
alternating current. Frequency of current (cycles/sec.) is given near each
curve.

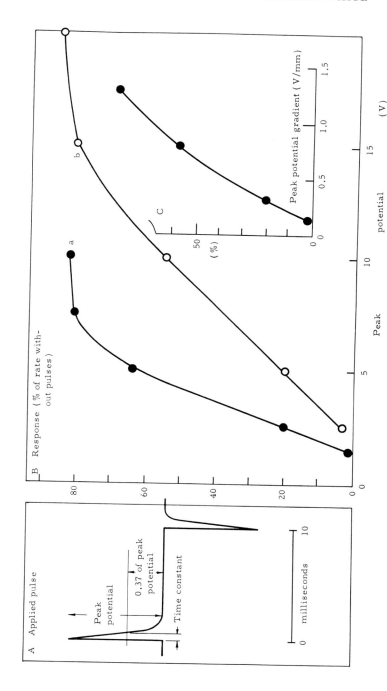

Fig. 3. *A*: Time-voltage relationships in condenser pulses. *B*: Respiratory response to pulses of time-constant 0.3 msec., applied to guinea pig cerebral cortex at 100 per second in vessels with electrodes 5.3 (*a*) and 10.5 (*b*) mm. apart. *C*: Combines the findings of *a* and *b*, expressed as potential gradients.[16]

It is important to note that these characteristics correspond closely to, or are just lower than, the optima and threshold found for excitation of the mammalian cerebral cortex *in situ*.[4,16]

Pulses of exponential time-voltage relationships, produced by charge and discharge of condensers, proved much more effective stimuli from the point of view of the electrical energy expended to obtain a given response.[4,9,13,16] Variables here, with a given electrode arrangement and a continuous series of pulses, are: their peak potentials, their frequency, and their duration which is expressed as a time-constant (time taken for the potential to fall to $1/e$ or 0.37 of its peak value). The voltage-response curve is shown in Figure 3, referring to pulses of 0.3 msec. time-constant, applied at 100 per second. Pulses of these characteristics have been used often in subsequent work (e.g., refs. 17-21) and can cause the respiration of a wide variety of cerebral tissues to increase about two-fold. The potential required for this depends on the electrodes to which the pulses are applied, as is shown in Figure 3. Figure 3C summarizes the results of both experiments of Figure 3B, and shows that potential gradient rather than potential is the conditioning factor in the instances studied, when gradients of 0.2v/mm or greater, caused stimulation. Maximum response was reached with gradients of some 1.5v/mm.

Effects of the time-constant of the pulses and their frequency of application, are interrelated. Figure 4A shows respones to pulses in which the two characteristics are varied independently while potential is kept constant. Clearly, response increases with increasing pulse-frequency, at least up to 1000 per second. However, when (Fig. 4B) response was plotted against the product of pulse-frequency and duration, the pulses of lesser frequency were found most effective in causing respiratory response. Such results may indicate a refractory period or an overlapping of the respiratory effect of one pulse with that of a succeeding one.

In the preceding experiments, pulses have been applied at chosen frequencies for periods of 30 to 60 minutes. When a continuous series of pulses is interrupted so that for intervals of 1 to 40 seconds no pulses are being applied, respiration does not necessarily fall in direct relationship to the length of the unstimulated intervals. These results can be interpreted to mean that the respiratory effect of pulses persists for a brief period after their application has ceased. The effect of the pulses in the instance investigated behaved as though their respiratory action decayed with a time-constant of 2.7 seconds. This value, though derived by an indirect method, is very markedly shorter than corresponding values for other parts of the nervous system for which data are available.[16] Thus ganglia and peripheral nerve show time constants

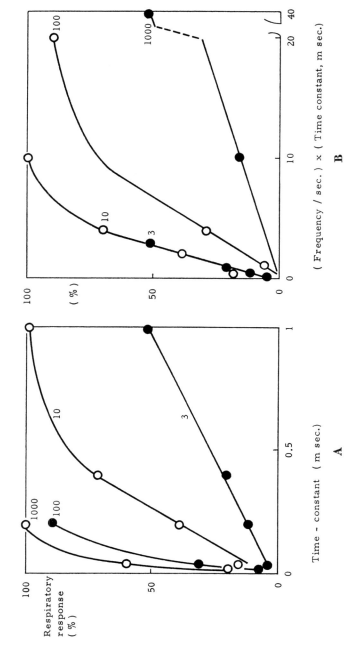

Fig. 4. Respiratory response of guinea pig cerebral cortex to condenser pulses of peak potential gradient 1.8 V/mm. and of varying duration and frequency. Frequency (pulses per second) is quoted on the diagrams.

of about 2 to 4 minutes. Such values emphasize the immediacy of the association in cerebral tissues between stimulus and metabolic response, in keeping with the susceptibility of the brain to anoxia and related metabolic hazards.

Comparison of the various electrical characteristics required in pulses for stimulation of the isolated tissue affords many close correlations with pulses which stimulate the brain *in situ*.[4,16] The information of this section is also fundamental to the use of electrical pulses with the isolated tissue. It must be noted that the different forms of simuli are not by any means equivalent in their results. Thus marked differences are found in susceptibility to drugs, between tissues exposed to different pulse types or sequences.[10,17,22] Anticonvulsants were more active in tissue stimulated with relatively high-frequency sine waves than with other stimuli. With interrupted bursts of pulses, the action of protoveratrine proved synergistic, which was not the case with other types of pulses. Statements have loosely been made that the actions of increased concentrations of potassium salts parallel those of electrical pulses, but this is not the case, as the varying effect of pulses indicate (see also Fig. 5). A drug which suppresses the action of several types of pulses may have no effect on tissue treated with potassium salts.[23] In other instances, as with interrupted bursts of pulses or with the local application of pulses,[21,24] corresponding data with potassium salts is not available.

Tissues Responding

It was early shown[25] that metabolic response to pulses in the present experimental arrangement was exhibited by excitable tissues, neural and muscular, but was not shown by, for example, kidney. Tissue from many parts of the brain have been shown to respond.[3,13,18,20,21,24,26,27] These include cerebral cortex, subcortical white matter, medulla, hypothalamus, cerebellum, and also spinal cord and spinal ganglia. When examined in the brain as a whole, metabolic response was small at an early stage of development,[28] but appeared in the foetal guinea pig and infant rat at about the stage shown by other investigations to be that of the appearance of selective ion permeability. Of species, cerebral cortex from the rat, guinea pig, rabbit, cat, monkey and man show similar responses with glucose as substrate; response with other substrates is noted subsequently.

Special interest attaches to the behaviour of human cerebral tissues obtained during neurosurgery.[3,10,13,26,27] Tissues considered on other grounds to be normal gave responses similar to those from other animal species. Diminished response was found in several instances in tissue associated with neoplasms. Differences were not recognized in tissues obtained at leucotomy for mental disease. Experimental modification of cerebral tissues in experimental animals by freezing caused diminution of response.[27] Also, pretreatment of the isolated tissue in a number of fashions impairs its ability to respond to pulses when, subsequently, it is placed under conditions normally adequate for response.[14,19,30,31] The treatments which so acted were: keeping the tissue at 0° for some hours in ordinary media, or briefer incubation in media which lacked oxygen or lacked glucose. Recovery of response in such modified tissues has been sought with a view to understanding chemical factors involved in repsonse.[14,31]

Mechanical damage to the tissue can also cause diminution and loss of response. The relation of loss to fineness of subdivision was shown in experiments with a mechanical chopper.[32] In ground and homogenized tissue, and also in subcellular particles, no response to pulses has been established.[33] (Contrary reports have come from investigators who also find response in liver preparations. Careful appraisal of accuracy and of likely artefacts,[15,33] renders these reports doubtful; they have been in part withdrawn but are still quoted.)

Substrates and Response

Applied pulses with glucose as substrate greatly increase the formation of both its normal metabolic products, lactic acid and carbon dioxide.[34] Search for lesser products has not been extensive, but balance studies with cerebral cortex indicated that with as without pulses the two products accounted, to within 6%, for the glucose consumed. For maximal response glucose was required at or above 2 mM; applied pulses rendered the tissue markedly more susceptible to lowered glucose concentration.[35] Fructose and lactate were effective but were required at markedly higher concentrations for comparable results.[3,35] Details of concentration were examined in the rabbit and in man;[36] results at 5 mM and greater were similar in the various species quoted in Table I.

Among acids of the tricarboxylic cycle, pyruvate was fully effective in supporting respiratory response, but most others have proved ineffective. Of the amino acids so far examined, none has been found fully effective. With tissue from laboratory animals, aspartic acid, asparagine, γ-aminobutyric acid, a hydroxy derivative and an aminocaproic acid did not support response. Partial response was however found with glutamic acid: of 0 to 17% in the guinea pig but a markedly larger response in human cerebral cortex. Correlation has been noted between the abilities of different substrates to maintain labile phosphates in the tissue, and their abilities in supporting response to pulses.[3,14,36,41,42] Oxalacetate supported both.[42a]

TABLE I

Substrates and the Respiratory Response of Mammalian Cerebral Cortex to Electrical Pulses

Compound	Response (concentrations: mM)	Species; Literature Reference
Glucose	Maximal; requires 2	Rabbit, sheep, monkey, man, rat, guinea pig, cat[3,26,35,37,38]
Fructose	Maximal; requires 10	Rabbit, guinea pig[35]
Fructose–1:6–di-phosphate	None at 2	Rabbit[35]
Lactate	Maximal; requires 5–10	Rabbit, guinea pig, rat, man[3,35,37]
Pyruvate	Maximal; observed at 5–33	Guinea pig, rat, man[37,39]
α–Ketoglutarate	None; tested at 5–20	Guinea pig[36,39]
Citrate	None; tested at 5–20	Guinea pig, man[37,39]
Fumarate	None; tested at 5–20	Guinea pig, man[37,39]
Succinate	None; tested at 5–30	Guinea pig, man, monkey[37,39]
Glutamate	0–10%; 17%; observed at 5–30 14–60%; observed at 15–30	Guinea pig, rat[37,39,40] Man[37]
Aspartate	None; tested at 7	Guinea pig, rat[36]
Asparagine	None; tested at 7–30	Guinea pig, rat[36]
γ–Aminobutyrate	None; tested at 6–33	Guinea pig, rat, cat[36]
γ–Amino–β–hy-droxybutyrate	None; tested at 8–33	Guinea pig, rat[36]
δ–Aminocaproate	None; tested at 8–33	Guinea pig, rat[36]

Substrates were examined in phosphate- or glycylglycine-buffered salines in experiments of 1 to 2 hours duration.

Ionic Environment Response

Media can be made appreciably hyper and hypo-tonic and response is retained, though it may be depressed;[43] great alteration in the constituent anions is also compatible with response. In particular, chloride ions can be completely replaced by nitrate, largely replaced by sulphate, and twelve-fold variation made in phosphate level, with retention of response.[43,44]

In marked contrast is the dependence of response on the presence of sodium salts. Isotonic media in which sodium salts were at 15 mM in place of the normal 120-130 mM, gave little or no respiratory response to pulses. Pulses also had less effect in media high in potassium or ammonium salts, in which respiration was already raised. Calcium or magnesium salts could be increased or diminished several fold, and response retained.[43,45] In many of these instances also, relationships were found between tissue phosphates and response.

CHANGES IN TISSUE COMPOSITION WITH
APPLIED PULSES

The promptest responses to pulses which have been detected *in vitro* by direct chemical methods, are, naturally, constituents of the tissue rather than of the medium surrounding it. Those which have been investigated in most detail are shown in Figure 5. In such experiments, carefully prepared tissue slices are first incubated in oxygenated glucose salines until the components concerned have reached stable values approaching those *in vivo*[12] (see above). The experiments are carried out in a quick-transfer apparatus so that the tissue can be rapidly fixed at a chosen, brief, interval after applying pulses.[11,12] Tissue lactate and glucose are then seen to undergo extremely rapid changes in level within seconds of the commencement of pulses. The changes are already falling in rate after 10 seconds of pulses; lactate reaches its peak value at 40 seconds and thereafter falls, presumably by diffusion to the medium surrounding the tissue, where its accumulation has already been noted. The change in glucose also is most rapid in the first few seconds. Thus commencing with 2.5 mM glucose in the medium, the level in the slice before pulses were applied was 1.3 μmoles/g., which fell to 0.4 mM after application of pulses for 20 seconds. Thereafter the rate of change fell. Accelerated entry from the medium may contribute to this, but it is also likely that the balance between glycolysis and respiration changes in favour of respiration. Approximately stoichiometric balance is found between lactate formed and glucose consumed when pulses are first applied; it is notable that the level of a glycogen-like material in the slice does not contribute to these changes. In this, the situation in the isolated tissue differs from that obtaining when pulses are applied to the brain *in situ,* but in other respects the similarity between the two situations is close, and extends to the numerical values found for the rates of change.[3,15]

Tissue Phosphates

Between applied pulses and changes in glucose, lactate or oxygen many systems are clearly involved. Correlation with tissue phosphates, noted at several points in this account, prompted their direct investigation and those first studied are shown in Figure 5. Change is again extremely rapid, alterations in level of inorganic orthophosphate (P), adenosine triphosphate (ATP) and phosphocreatine (CrP) being largely complete in 5 seconds. During this time adenosine triphosphate has fallen from and returned to its initial value, even during the continued application of pulses; the greatest net change in phosphate is represented by: (1) CrP $\longrightarrow$ Cr + P. When however the metabolism of phos-

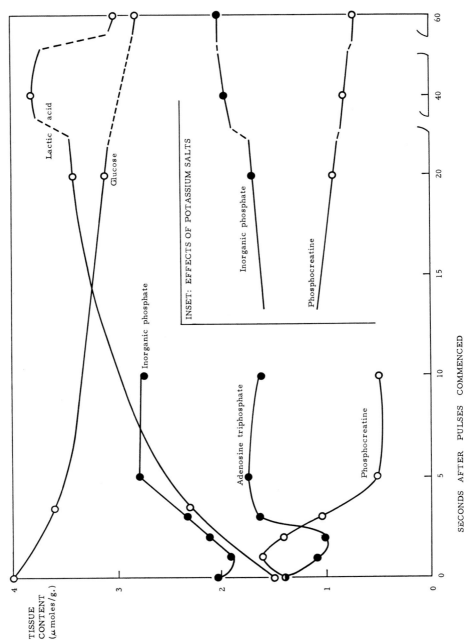

Fig. 5. Change in tissue constituents on applying pulses. Guinea pig cerebral cortex was incubated in quick transfer electrodes[11,12] for 30 to 40 minutes, and at zero time on the diagram pulses were applied. After the brief periods shown, different tissue samples were fixed and extracted for analysis.[46,47]

phocreatine is examined in cell-free systems, reaction (1) is notably absent and phosphocreatine is mainly removed by the Lohmann reaction[48] with adenosine diphosphate (ADP): (2) Crp + ADP ⟶ Cr + ATP. Occurrence of this reaction in slices on application of pulses would be consistent with the transitory changes in adenosine triphosphate recorded in Figure 5. Presumably therefore the pulses have made available adenosine diphosphate.

The nature of the reactions yielding inorganic phosphate and other phosphates with pulses, have been explored with the use of isotopic phosphate (Table II). After a brief period of exposure to labelled

TABLE II

PHOSPHATE EXCHANGE INDUCED BY PULSES IN GUINEA PIG CEREBRAL CORTEX

Phosphate Fraction	Tissue Content (μmoles P/g. wet tissue)	Specific Activities of P Relative to P of Medium			Literature Reference
		Before Pulses	After Pulses	Change (%)	
1. Orthophosphate	1.12	199	160	−20	49
2. γ–P of adenosine triphosphate	1.2	111	44	−60	49
3. Phosphocreatine	1.15	92	40	−57	49
4. Acid-insoluble residue	——	2.02	2.55	+26	49
5. Phosphoprotein from 4	1.16	41	54.5	+33	50
6. Phosphoserine from 5	——	3.02	3.91	+30	19
7. Guanosine nucleotides	0.5	27	40	+48	51

Guinea pig cerebral cortex was incubated in quick transfer electrodes[11,12] for 30 to 40 minutes,[32] P added as orthophosphate and incubation continued for 3 minutes before transfer to a phosphate-free medium and application of pulses for 10 seconds. The specific activities are not necessarily comparable in the different experiments.

orthophosphate, pulses for 10 seconds caused a major redistribution in the newly entered phosphate. It was lost from P, CrP and ATP, and gained by acid-insoluble material. A major component of this fraction, which was enriched in isotope by pulses, proved to be phosphoprotein, and the phosphoserine derived from it was also enriched. A lesser amount of guanosine nucleotides also increased in activity, and like the phosphoprotein did not change in total amount. Presumably, therefore, these components are taking part in cyclic changes and are likely to be the source of the unlabeled phosphate gained by P, ATP, and CrP; it is also an intriguing possibility that they are concerned in the tissue's performance of osmotic work.[52,15]

No other agent has been found to have the effects on tissue composition which are caused by pulses and recorded in Figure 5; in view of incorrect statements, it is to be noted that the action of potassium salts differs,[47] as is shown in Figure 5 inset.

Other Observations

The effects of pulses which are illustrated in Fig. 1 are all readily reversible when application of pulses is stopped. The rates of change which obtain on applying and on stopping pulses have been measured and carefully appraised in comparison with comparable changes in the brain *in situ,* as has been reviewed elsewhere.[3,15] Irreversible changes follow the application of pulses anaerobically or in absence of an adequate substrate.[14,29] In tissue maintained aerobically and with glucose, pulses cause loss of acetylcholine and when eserine is present, pulses increase the acetylcholine accumulating in the medium.[53] For observation of respiratory and other responses to pulses, the volume of fluid in which a given weight of tissue is incubated is not critical, and may be decreased to 1% of that normally employed.[54]

Tissue stimulated electrically has proved particularly sensitive to added agents, including many drugs which affect the brain *in vivo.* This greater sensitivity is not purely dependent on increase in respiration or substrate utilization, for in several instances no comparable sensitivity is found when these processes are similarly increased by potassium salts or by 2:4-dinitrophenol.[23] It has been stated without adequate appraisal that potassium salts simulate electrical pulses, but the differences between the effects of these agents seem more interesting than the resemblances. The ability of electrically stimulated tissue to simulate *in vivo* situations is further illustrated by the fashion in which it reveals a difference caused by hypoglycaemia[55] and is highly sensitive to depressant drugs:[24,56-58] observations which emphasize, as indicated above, that electrical pulses restore to the isolated tissue a normal element of its *in vivo* environment.

REFERENCES

1. GORE, M., IBBOTT, F. and McILWAIN, H.: *Biochem. J., 47:*121 (1950).
2. McILWAIN, H., BUCHEL, L. and CHESHIRE, J.: *Biochem. J., 48:*12 (1951).
3. McILWAIN, H.: *Biochemistry and the Central Nervous System.* London, Churchill (1959).
4. McILWAIN, H.: *Biochem. J., 49:*382 (1951).
5. LI, C.-H., and McILWAIN, H.: *J. Physiol., 139:*178 (1957).
6. HILLMAN, H. and McILWAIN, H.: In preparation (1960).
7. McILWAIN, H.: *Biochem. J., 50:*132 (1951).
8. FORDA, O., and McILWAIN, H.: *Brit. J. Pharmacol., 8:*225 (1953).
9. AYRES, P. J. W., and McILWAIN, H.: *Biochem. J., 55:*607 (1953).
10. McILWAIN, H.: *EEG Clin. Neurophysiol., 6:*93 (1954).

11. HEALD, P. J. and McILWAIN, H.: *Biochem. J., 63*:231 (1956).
12. McILWAIN, H.: Submitted for publication (1960).
13. RODNIGHT, R., and McILWAIN, H.: In preparation (1960).
14. McILWAIN, H. and GORE, M. B. R.: *Biochem. J., 54*:305 (1953).
15. McILWAIN, H.: *Physiol. Rev., 36*:355 (1956).
16. McILWAIN, H.: *J. Physiol., 124*:117 (1954).
17. GREENGARD, O., and McILWAIN, H.: *Biochem. J., 61*:61 (1955).
18. BOLLARD, B. M. and McILWAIN, H.: *Biochem. J., 66*:651 (1957).
19. HEALD, P. J.: *Biochem. J., 68*:580 (1958).
20. McILWAIN, H. and GREENGARD, O.: *J. Neurochem., 1*:348 (1957).
21. BOLLARD, B. M. and McILWAIN, H.: *Biochem. Pharmacol., 2*:81 (1959).
22. WOLLENBERGER, A.: *Biochem. J., 61*:77 (1955).
23. McILWAIN, H.: *Brit. J. Pharmacol., 6*:531 (1951).
24. KURAKOWA, M.: *J. Neurochem.*, in press (1960).
25. KRATZING, C. C.: *Biochem. J., 50*:253 (1951).
26. McILWAIN, H., AYRES, P. J. W. and FORDA, O.: *J. Ment. Sc., 98*:265 (1952).
27. BRIERLEY, J. B. and McILWAIN, H.: *J. Neurochem, 1*:109 (1956).
28. GREENGARD, P. and McILWAIN, H.: *Proc. Internat. Neurochem. Symp., 1*:251 (1955).
29. McILWAIN, H.: *Biochem. J., 63*:257 (1956).
30. McILWAIN, H. and MARKS, N.: *Biochem. J., 73*:401 (1959).
31. McILWAIN, H.: *Biochem. J., 73*:514 (1959).
32. McILWAIN, H. and BUDDLE, H. L.: *Biochem. J., 53*:412 (1953).
33. NARAYANASWAMI, A. and McILWAIN, H.: *Biochem. J., 57*:663 (1954).
34. McILWAIN, H., ANGUIANO, G. and CHESHIRE, J. D.: *Biochem. J., 50*:18 (1951).
35. McILWAIN, H.: *Biochem. J., 55*:618 (1953).
36. McILWAIN, H.: Unpublished.
37. McILWAIN, H.: *J. Neurol., Neurosurg. & Psychiat., 16*:257 (1953).
38. SETCHELL, B. P.: *Biochem. J., 72*:265, 275 (1959).
39. KRATZING, C. C.: *Biochem. J., 54*:312 (1953).
40. KRATZING, C. C.: *Biochem. J., 62*:127 (1956).
41. McILWAIN, H.: *Biochem. Soc. Symp., 8*:27 (1952).
42. RODNIGHT, R. and McILWAIN, H.: *Biochem. J., 57*:649 (1954).
42A. WOODMAN, R. J. and McILWAIN, H.: Submitted for publication (1961).
43. GORE, M. B. R. and McILWAIN, H.: *J. Physiol., 117*:471 (1952).
44. THOMAS, J. and McILWAIN, H.: *J. Neurochem., 1*:1 (1956).
45. McILWAIN, H.: *Biochem. J., 52*:289 (1952).
46. McILWAIN, H. and TRESIZE, M. A.: *Biochem. J., 63*:250 (1956).
47. HEALD, P. J.: *Biochem. J., 57*:673 (1954).
48. NARAYANASWAMI, A.: *Biochem. J., 52*:295 (1952).
49. HEALD, P. J.: *Biochem. J., 63*:242 (1956).
50. HEALD, P. J.: *Biochem. J., 66*:659 (1957).
51. HEALD, P. J.: *Biochem. J., 67*:529 (1957).
52. HEALD, P. J.: *Phosphorus Metabolism of the Brain.* London, Pergamon (1960).
53. ROWSELL, E. V.: *Biochem. J., 57*:666 (1954).
54. RODNIGHT, R. and McILWAIN, H.: *Biochem. J., 57*:649 (1954).
55. SETCHELL, B. P.: *Biochem. J. 72*:265, 275 (1959).
56. WALLGREN, H.: Private communication.
57. McILWAIN, H.: *Biochem. J., 53*:403 (1953).
58. McILWAIN, H. and GREENGARD, O.: *J. Neurochem., 1*:348 (1957).

X

EFFECTS OF ELECTROLYTES ON
BRAIN METABOLISM

J. H. QUASTEL

VARIOUS ASPECTS of brain metabolism *in vitro* are greatly affected by the electrolyte composition of the medium surrounding brain tissue when it is incubated either aerobically, or anaerobically, at 37°. These effects are now assuming considerable importance as they may reflect the changes of metabolism that occur in the nervous system *in vivo* during excitation by sensory stimulation or during depression due to lack of such stimulation.

OXYGEN CONSUMPTION OF THE BRAIN *IN VITRO*

Some of the earliest results on the respiratory activity of the brain *in vitro* are due to Warburg and his colleagues,[1] who had, in 1923, introduced the tissue slice techinque for the study of *in vitro* metabolism. Rat brain cortex in presence of a glucose-Ringer medium at 37° C. yielded an oxygen quotient (Q_{o_2} = cmm. O_2 taken up per mg. dry weight tissue per hour) of 10.7 while retina gave the high figure of 30.7. Although higher figures for the Q_{o_2} of brain cortex slices have been recorded, both in normal physiological media[2] and in media fortified by the addition of a variety of substances that are consumed by the brain,[3] the values are usually lower than those calculated from those obtained by the study of the brain *in vivo*. Estimates of *in vitro* respiratory rates of whole brain, made by Elliott,[4] approximate to the values found *in vivo* in conditions of diminished functional activity but are considerably less than normal values *in vivo* (about one-half). Some typical values are quoted in Table I. It is evident that respiratory rates of brain tissue *in vitro*, examined in normal physiological media, do not reflect the rates obtained in the brain *in situ*. Nevertheless, it is possible by stimulation of isolated brain tissue, by alteration of the cationic concentration in the medium surrounding the brain tissue, or by electrical stimulation, to increase respiratory rates to approximately

226

those found *in vivo*. It should be noted that the potassium content of brain slices is dependent on the sodium content of the incubating medium; replacement of the sodium by choline or lithium leads to loss of brain potassium.[37]

TABLE I

OXYGEN UPTAKE BY WHOLE BRAIN *In Vivo* AND *In Vitro*[4]

	In Vitro Estimated	Qo_2 In Vivo Lack of Reflexes	Normal
Cat	6.8	6.9	12–15
Monkey	5.9	Depressed (Hemorrhage) 5.6	11.1
Man	4.8	Coma Diabetic Insulin 5.1 5.7	9.9

Ashford and Dixon[5] using slices of rabbit brain cortex found that the addition of 0.1 M KCl (but not that of 0.1 M NaCl) to a normal Ringer-glucose medium in which the slices were incubated aerobically at 37° would increase the rates of oxygen consumption and of aerobic glycolysis but would decrease the rate of anaerobic glycolysis. Moreover the stimulations of aerobic metabolism by potassium ions addition were reversible, but the anaerobic inhibition was irreversible. Dickens and Greville,[6] confirming these facts with rat brain cortex slices, found that in experiments using a Ringer phosphate medium (containing 0.12 M NaCl, 2.4 mM KCl, 1.7 mM CaCl$_2$, 0.8 mM MgCl$_2$ and 0.01 M glucose), where solid KCl was weighed into the side bulb of a Warburg manometer vessel and only washed into the main vessel 30 to 40 minutes after the commencement of the experiment, there was a greatly increased rate of respiration, which was not steadily maintained. In fact in 90 minutes after the addition of the KCl the respiration was little higher than in the control. When the KCl was added to the medium in the vessels at the commencement of the experiment there was a larger, and more sustained, increase in the rates of respiration and aerobic glycolysis. Rubidium and cesium salts at 0.1 M gave effects similar to those of potassium, whereas sodium and lithium chlorides had only slight effects and magnesium chloride had none. So far as changes in the cationic composition of the medium, in which the brain slices were incubated, on the rate of oxygen consumption were concerned, it was found that whilst the addition of K$^+$ raised the respiration, the addition of Ca^{++} + Mg^{++} lowered the respiration, that the omission of Ca^{++} resulted in a high but unsteady respiration, and that with Na$^+$ as the only cation present the initial respiration was high but fell very rapidly. Canzanelli et al[7] have concluded that Ca^{++} and K$^+$ are the only cations controlling respiration, the Ca^{++} acting antagonistically to K$^+$.

The phenomenon in which stimulation respiration is brought about by an increase of the K+/Ca++ ratio in the medium surrounding the brain tissue does not occur in a homogenate or a fine mince; it is evident that it is linked with the integrity of the brain cell membranes.

TABLE II

Substrate 0.01 M	Qo$_2$ (Rat Brain Cortex Slices) in Ringer-phosphate Medium	
	5 mM KCl Present	105 mM KCl Present
Glucose	12.5	20.5
Fructose	12.6	20.0
Sodium pyruvate	13.2	18.8
Sodium lactate	11.8	16.8
Sodium L–glutamate	7.5	7.0
Sodium succinate	10.8	9.0

Cationic stimulation of brain cortex respiration takes place with the identical substrates that permit responses to applied oscillating electrical impulses.[8] Some typical results are shown in Table II.[9] It is not confined to glucose as substrate but occurs with fructose, sodium pyruvate and sodium lactate; however, not with sodium succinate nor, apparently, with sodium-L-glutamate. Nevertheless, using radioactive sodium glutamate-l-C^{14}, it is possible to show a definite effect of increased K$^+$ on the breakdown of glutamate in presence of rat brain cortex slices.

Respiration of brain slices in presence of L-glutamate is not as re-

TABLE III

EFFECTS OF 100 MM KCl ON THE AEROBIC METABOLISM OF L–GLUTAMATE (USING GLUTAMIC ACID–1–C^{14}) BY RAT BRAIN CORTEX SLICES IN 90 MINUTES INITIAL ACTIVITY 10^5 C/MIN.[10]

	L–glutamate–1–C^{14} 10 mM		L–glutamate–1–C^{14} + Glucose 10 mM 10 mM	
	5 mM KCl	105 mM KCl	5 mM KCl	105 mM KCl
Oxygen consumed cmm./10 mg. dry weight tissue	216	278	186	340
C^{14}O$_2$ formed c/min./mg. dry weight	1450	1930	763	1560

sponsive to electric impulses as it is in presence of glucose, but human brain tissue, which consumes glutamate at a relatively vigorous rate, is responsive to the application of electric impulses in presence of the amino acid.[8] The addition of potassium ions can stimulate the aerobic metabolism of L-glutamate in presence of rat brain cortex slices though the effect is not large except in presence of glucose.[10] This can be seen in the values quoted in Table III, where glutamate containing a labelled carboxyl group was used.

EFFECTS OF MALONATE

Whereas the respiration of unstimulated brain cortex slices in the presence of glucose is but little affected by the presence of malonate, whose well known inhibitory effect on succinate oxidation makes it a potent inhibitor of the citric acid respiratory cycle, potassium-stimulated brain respiration is highly malonate sensitive. Results of Takagaki et al.[11] on the effects of malonate and of high concentrations of potassium ions on glucose utilization and lactic acid formation by brain cortex slices in presence of glucose are shown in Table IV. They

TABLE IV

METABOLISM OF GLUCOSE (3.3 MM) IN GUINEA PIG BRAIN CORTEX SLICES[11]
Values are given in micromoles per gram tissue per hour

Additions	Oxygen Uptake	Lactate Formed	Glucose Utilized	Glucose Oxidized (calculated)
Nil	56.5 ± 5.5	17.1 ± 2.6	18.1 ± 2.1	9.6
Malonate 10 mM	42.9 ± 2.1	24.7 ± 4.0	20.5 ± 2.7	8.2
KCl 100 mM	94.4 ± 8.1	59.4 ± 5.9	51.0 ± 4.2	21.3
Malonate 10 mM + KCl 100 mM	36.9 ± 1.8	68.4 ± 1.6	51.2 ± 3.3	17.0

show that malonate suppresses stimulation of respiration but has no adverse effect on potassium-stimulated aerobic glycolysis. The stimulation of oxygen uptake by brain cortex slices by increased K$^+$ is shown also by the increased rate of formation of C^{14}O$_2$ when uniformly labelled glucose (i.e., glucose-U-C^{14}) is present as a substrate. It is possible to demonstrate a value of approximately 6.0 for the ratio of potassium-stimulated oxygen uptake to potassium-stimulated glucose breakdown. This is the theoretical value for complete oxidation of glucose to CO$_2$ and water. A typical experimental result is shown in Table V.[10]

The malonate inhibition of potassium-stimulated brain cortex respiration which may be reversed by oxalacetate[10] indicates the impor-

TABLE V

EFFECTS OF K^+ ON OXYGEN UPTAKE AND GLUCOSE–U–C^{14} BREAKDOWN TO $C^{14}O_2$
(BY 10 MG. DRY WEIGHT RAT BRAIN CORTEX SLICE IN ONE HOUR)

Micromoles O_2 Taken Up for Glucose Consumption*		Micromoles Glucose Converted to $C^{14}O_2$		Calculated Micromoles O_2 Taken Up, Equivalent to Glucose Converted to $C^{14}O_2$	
5 mM KCl	105 mM KCl	5 mM KCl	105 mM KCl	5 mM KCl	105 mM KCl
3.4	6.6	0.47	1.05	2.8	6.3

*Corrected for endogenous oxygen uptake.

tant role of the citric acid cycle in stimulated brain respiration. This is shown perhaps more clearly in the results given in Table VI,[12] which indicate that the percentage malonate inhibition of $C^{14}O_2$ from pyruvate-2-C^{14} (i.e., oxidation of the acetyl moiety of the molecule) is considerably greater than that from pyruvate-1-C^{14} (i.e., where only the carboxyl group is labelled) both in the absence and presence of an increased potassium ion concentration. That malonate inhibits the latter process indicates that part of the $C^{14}O_2$ derived from pyruvate-1-C^{14} is formed after its fixation and metabolism by the citric acid cycle.

TABLE VI

EFFECTS OF KCl AND MALONATE ON PYRUVATE METABOLISM IN RAT BRAIN CORTEX SLICES

Substrate	Q_{O_2}		$C^{14}O_2$ Formed in 1 hour (Expressed as Counts/ min./mg. dry weight)	
	5 mM KCl	105 mM KCl	5 mM KCl	105 mM KCl
(1) Pyruvate–1–C^{14}				
(a) without malonate	14.2	19.8	1166	2008
(b) with 10 mM malonate	8.0	9.2	903	1342
(2) Pyruvate–2–C^{14}				
(a) without malonate	14.2	19.8	481	1040
(b) with 10 mM malonate	8.0	9.2	258	336

Neither cationic stimulation, nor appreciable malonate inhibition, occurs in a brain homogenate respiring in glucose media. Evidently the stimulation of metabolism by changed cationic (K+/Ca++) balance is inherently associated with events taking place at the brain cell membrane. The facts recorded lead to the conclusion that one rate limiting step, which is accelerated by increased K^+/Ca^{++}, is conversion in brain of pyruvic acid into acetyl-CoA the oxidation which is accomplished by the citric acid cycle.

EFFECTS OF ELECTROLYTES ON BRAIN ORGANIC PHOSPHATES

Increased K^+/Ca^{++} in the medium bathing brain slices have the effects of diminishing brain phosphocreatine and adenosine triphosphate whilst increasing brain adenosine diphosphate and phosphate ions.[13,14] Similar phenomena occur on the application of oscillating electrical impulses.[13] It seems that inorganic phosphate is not derived directly from the phosphocreatine or adenosine triphosphate,[15] but indirectly *via* guanosine derivatives and phosphoproteins. Excitation of the brain,[16] like electrical stimulation,[13] increases the brain ADP/ATP ratio.

MODE OF ACTION OF INCREASED K^+/Ca^{++} ON BRAIN RESPIRATION

It is known that metabolic energy, in the form of ATP, derived from respiration, is required for transport of ions against a concentration gradient at the nerve cell membrane. It is assumed that the reverse process, i.e., the stimulation of respiratory activity by ionic movements at the nerve cell membrane, occurs by the initiation of series of reactions resulting in the accumulation of ADP or phosphate. The latter substances are now known to play key roles in the regulation of respiratory and glycolytic processes. The increased concentration in the nerve cell of ADP (or phosphate ions), as a result of the increased K^+/Ca^{++} ratio in the surrounding medium, leads to increased mitochondrial respiration, which results in an increased rate of oxygen uptake by the brain slices and in increased rates of mitochondrial biosyntheses dependent on mitochondrial ATP. Brain phosphocreatine acts as a "buffer" substance, yielding phosphate to ADP, as the concentration of ADP is increased as a result of cationic stimulation. Thus the level of phosphocreatine falls, in presence of increased K^+/Ca^{++}, and its buffering action diminishes as its level decreases. These facts have considerable significance when considering the mode of action of hypnotics and other depressants that affect brain oxidations and phosphorylations.

The increased rate of mitochondrial respiration, as a result of cationic, or electrical, stimulation is accompanied by an increased turnover of the citric acid cycle. This results in a variety of changes, among which may be mentioned:

(a) Increased rate of synthesis of acetylcholine.[17]

(b) Altered labelling of phospholipids and phosphoproteins after exposure to labelled phosphate.[18,19]

(c) Increased rate of synthesis of glutamine and altered labelling of radioactive amino acids derived from glucose.[12]

EFFECTS OF ELECTROLYTES ON BRAIN CARBOHYDRATE-AMINO ACID INTERRELATIONS

It is now well known that when radioactive glucose is metabolized by brain cortex *in vitro* radioactive amino acids are formed. A mince of the brain of one day old mice when incubated with glucose uniformly labelled with C^{14} (i.e., glucose-U-C^{14}) incorporates radioactivity in all amino acids of brain protein with the exception of threonine.[20] Rat brain cortex slices can covert glucose-C^{14} into labelled glutamic, aspartic and γ-aminobutyric acids.[21] It is evident that glucose during its normal metabolism in the brain cell produces intermediates, the α-ketonic acids (see Fig. 1).[12] that undergo conversion to amino acids largely at the expense of organic nitrogen already available in the brain cell. In these reactions, transaminations play a major role and by reason of these reactions amino acid interconversion stake place. The amino acids play a vital role in brain function, not only for the maintenance of ionic balance in the cell but because they give rise to amines that are physiologically active and because they take part in the biosynthetic changes that maintain the structure of the cell.

TABLE VII

FORMATION OF LABELLED AMINO ACIDS FROM 5mM GLUCOSE–U–C^{14} AND 5mM FRUCTOSE-U-C^{14} IN PRESENCE OF RAT BRAIN CORTEX SLICES AND EFFECTS OF K^+ (12) INCUBATION TIME = 1 HR.

Values expressed as counts/minute/100 mg. wet tissue

Amino Acid Formed	Glucose–U–C^{14} Initially 10^6 c/min.		Fructose–U–C^{14} Initially 10^6 c/min.	
	5 meq./1 K^+	105 meq./1 K^+	5 meq./1 K^+	105 meq./1 K^+
Glutamic acid	5057	5516	4784	942
Glutamine	1289	2397		
γ Aminobutyric acid	966	1491	739	271
Alanine	657	794	374	224
Aspartic acid	1318	1183	2159	2127

Experiment[12] shows that a not inconsiderable fraction, possibly amounting to 10%, of glucose is converted into amino acids. Typical experimental results are shown in Table VII.

In a normal Ringer medium, there is a labelling of glutamic acid, glutamine, γ-aminobutyric acid, aspartic acid and alanine in the presence of glucose-U-C[14] and of fructose-U-C[14]. The labelling of glutamic acid, with both sugars, is highest among the amino acids investigated, aspartic acid showing the next highest activity. It may be noted that the ratios of radioactive glutamate, glutamine, and γ-aminobutyrate found that rat brain cortex in presence of glucose-U-C[14] (and of increased potassium ions to stimulate respiration to the level found *in vivo*) are 1:0.44:0.27 which approximate to the ratios of these amino acids normally found in adult rat brain cortex[23] namely 1:0.43:0.17. It is noteworthy also that the labelling of aspartic acid, on incubation with fructose-U-C[14] greatly exceeds that found after incubation with glucose-U-C[14].

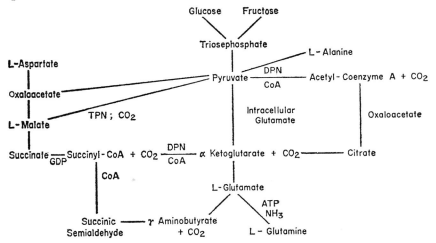

Fig. 1 .

It is evident from Figure 1 that labelled pyruvate, derived from glucose-U-C[14] may transaminate with existing glutamic acid to give rise to labelled alanine and α-ketoglutaric acid (short-circuiting the citric acid cycle) which is metabolized in the normal way. Thus the labelled pyruvate may undergo a variety of reactions that will yield all the labelled amino acids mentioned in Table VI. The glutamic acid, in the cell, is maintained, however, because the labelled amino acids in their turn transminate with the unlabelled α-ketoglutarate to reform unlabelled glutamate. Thus a complex series of reactions takes place resulting ultimately in a steady-state, the net effect of which is the conversion of glucose to carbon dioxide and water. There will be no net synthesis of amino acids, for nitrogen is not added to the system, but a redistribution of the existing amino acids, which will all be in dynamic equilibrium. With fructose, as seen in Table VI, the steady-state of the amino acids at any given time will differ from that obtaining with glucose. Moreover the steady-state will vary with the electrolyte balance in the medium bathing the brain cortex slices and with the respiratory conditions. The distribution of the amino acids (e.g., as given in Table VII) may be explained on the conclusions that the main respiratory path of glucose lies along the citric acid cycle, that transaminations are largely responsible for the formation of the amino acids and that the effect of increased K^+ is indirectly to stimulate the citric acid cycle and particularly the rate of conversion of pyruvate to acetyl-CoA. With such an interpretation,[12] it is possible to understand the larger yield of labelled aspartate from fructose-U-C^{14} than from glucose-U-C^{14} because fructose is less able than glucose to yield sufficient pyruvate and therefore acetyl-CoA to remove oxalacetate as citrate. More oxalacetate is, therefore, transaminated to aspartate. The effect of increased K^+/Ca^{++} is seen particularly in increased yields of glutamine (whose formation is dependent on available ATP in the mitochondria) and of glutamate and γ-aminobutyrate as a result of increased turnover of α-ketoglutarate (For further details, see Kini and Quastel.[12])

EFFECTS OF ELECTROLYTES ON BRAIN GLYCOLYSIS

Anaerobic

Just as a potassium-calcium antagonism occurs in the stimulation of brain respiration, it also occurs in the stimulation of anaerobic brain glycolysis but the effects are reversed. Some typical results[24] are shown in Table VIII. The presence of calcium ions is apparently essential

TABLE VIII

EFFECTS OF POTASSIUM AND CALCIUM IONS ON ANAEROBIC GLYCOLYSIS

KCl	CaCl₂	Anaerobic Glycolysis of Guinea Pig Brain Cortex Slices $Q^{N_2}_{CO_2}$
0	0	4.7
0	1 mM	11.9
4 mM	0	4.1
4 mM	1 mM	8.0

for brain glycolysis;[25] yet the low anaerobic glycolytic rate of rat brain slices may be greatly increased by the addition of pyruvate or of certain organic bases.[25] The effects of the latter substances cannot be explained in terms of DPN-ase inhibitions; they seem, in some way, to replace Ca^{++} at the brain cell membrane.[25]

Aerobic

It is well known[5,6] that increased K^+ stimulates aerobic glycolysis of brain *in vitro*. The reason for this stimulation is not known with certainty. The transfer of phosphate from phosphopyruvate to ADP to pyruvate and ATP[26-28] is markedly accelerated by potassium and ammonium salts, and inhibited by sodium chloride. Possibly the stimulation of ADP formation by increased K^+ is responsible for an increased rate of the above transfer reaction and hence increased pyruvate formation and increased glycolysis. But increased K^+ may act by increasing the ratio $DPNH_2/DPN$ by its indirect accelerating effect (in brain slices) on the oxidation of pyruvate to acetyl-CoA by DPN.

The acceleration of aerobic brain glycolysis by increased K^+ is presumably related to the increased lactic acid formation in brain during convulsions[29] or after electrical stimulation.[8]

SIMILARITIES BETWEEN THE EFFECTS OF CATIONIC AND ELECTRICAL STIMULATION ON BRAIN METABOLISM *IN VITRO*

There is a pronounced similarity between the effects of cationic (increased $K+/Ca++$) stimulation and electrical stimulation (by oscillating impulses) on brain metabolism *in vitro*, so much so that there is little doubt that both methods of stimulation have a common basis of action, namely cationic changes at the neuronal membrane. The following is a summary of some of the results that point to this conclusion:

(1) Both methods raise the respiratory rate of brain tissue *in vitro* to the value found *in vivo*.

(2) The substrates that permit responses to electrical impulses (glucose, fructose, pyruvate, lactate) are the same as those which allow cationic stimulation of respiration to occur.[8,9]

(3) Both methods result in a fall of brain phosphocreatine and adenosine triphosphate.[13] Excitation of the brain is known to increase the ADP/ATP ratio.[16]

(4) Both methods result in a release of free acetylcholine from "bound" acetylcholine and an acceleration of the rate of synthesis of acetylcholine.[17,30]

(5) Both methods result in increased aerobic glycolysis of brain.[11,31]

This phenomenon has its parallel in the increased formation of lactic acid in the brain in the living animal when brain excitation occurs.

(6) Both methods result in decreased anaerobic glycolysis of brain.

(7) Both forms of stimulated respiration are highly sensitive to barbiturates and other hypnotics.[9,12,32]

(8) Both forms of stimulated respiration are more inhibited by alcohol[33,34] and by chlorpromazine,[35,36] at pharmacologically active concentrations, than the unstimulated respiration.

REFERENCES

1. WARBURG, O., POSENER, K. and NEGELEIN, E.: Biochem. Ztschr., 152:309 (1924).
2. JOWETT, M. and QUASTEL, J. H.: Biochem. J., 37:1101 (1937).
3. KREBS, H. A. and JOHNSON, W. A.: Tabulae Biol., 19:100 (1948).
4. ELLIOTT, K. A. C.: The Biology of Mental Health and Disease, Symposium, p. 54. New York, Hoeber (1952).
5. ASHFORD, C. A. and DIXON, K. C.: Biochem. J., 29:157 (1935).
6. DICKENS, F. and GREVILLE, G. D.: Biochem. J., 29:1468 1935).
7. CANZANELLI, A., ROGERS, G. and RAPPORT, D.: Am. J. Physiol., 135:309 (1942).
8. McILWAIN, H.: J. Neurol., Neurosurg. & Psychiat., 16:257 (1953) ; Biochem. J., 55:619 (1953).
9. GHOSH, J. J. and QUASTEL, J. H.: Nature, 174:28 (1954) .
10. PARMAR, S. and QUASTEL, J. H.: In Quastel, J. H., Biochemistry of the Central Nervous System, p. 40. Brücke, F., Ed. Proc. 4th Inter. Congress Biochem. Vienna. New York, Pergamon, (1959).
11. TAKAGAKI, G., HIRANO, S. and TSUKADA, Y.: J. Biochem. (Japan), 45:41 (1958).
12. KINI, M. M., and QUASTEL, J. H.: Nature, 184:252 (1959); Science, 131:412 (1960) .
13. DAWSON, R. M. C. and RICHTER, D.: Am. J. Psychiat., 160:203 (1950).
GORE, M. B. R. and McILWAIN, H.: J. Physiol., 117:471 (1952) .
HEALD, P. J.: Biochem. J., 57:673 (1954).
HEALD, P. J. and McILWAIN, H.: Biochem. J., 63:231 (1956).
14. GONDA, O. and QUASTEL, J. H.: Proc. Can. Fed. Biol. Soc., 4:26 (1961) and Biochem. J., 84: In press (1962).
15. HEALD, P. J.: Biochem. J., 66:659; 67:529 (1957).
16. SHAPOT, V. S.: Metabolism of the Nervous System, Symposium, p. 257. Richter, D., Ed. New York, Pergamon (1957).
17. MANN, P. J. G., TENNENBAUM, M. and QUASTEL, J. H.: Biochem. J., 33:822 (1939) .
18. ROSSITER, R.: Canad. J. Biochem. & Physiol., 33:477 (1955).
19. YOSHIDA, H. and QUASTEL, J. H.: Biochem. Biophys. Acta, 57:67 (1962).
20. SKY-PECK, H. H., PEARSON, H. E., and VISSER, D. W.: J. Biol. Chem., 223:1033 (1956).
21. BELOFF-CHAIN, A., CATANZARO, R., CHAIN, E. B., MASI, I. and POCCHIARI, F.: Proc. Roy. Soc. London, B 144:22 (1955) .
22. QUASTEL, J. H. and QUASTEL, D. M. J.: Chemistry of Brain Metabolism in Health and Disease. Springfield, Ill., Thomas (1961).
23. BERL, S. and WAELSCH, H.: J. Neurochem., 3:161 (1958) .
24. QUASTEL, J. H., and WHEATLEY, A. H. M.: J. Biol. Chem., 199:1xxx (1937).
25. ADAMS, D. H. and QUASTEL, J. H.: Proc. Roy. Soc. London, B 145:472 (1956).

26. UTTER, M. F.: *J. Biol. Chem.*, *185*:499 (1950).
27. MUNTZ, J. A. and HURWITZ, J.: *Arch. Biochem.*, *32*:124, 137 (1951).
28. LARDY, H. A. and ZIEGLER, J. A.: *J. Biol. Chem.*, *159*:343 (1945).
29. OLSEN, N. S. and KLEIN, J. R.: *A. Nerv. & Ment. Dis. (Proc.) 26*:118 (1946).
30. ROWSELL, E. V.: *Biochem. J.*, *57*:666 (1954).
31. MCILWAIN, H.: *Physiol. Rev.*, *36*:355 (1956).
32. LEWIS, J. L. and MCILWAIN, H.: *Biochem. J.*, *57*:680 (1954).
33. BEER, C. T. and QUASTEL, J. H.: *Canad. J. Biochem. & Physiol. 36*:543 (1958).
34. WALLGREN, H. and KULONEN, E.: *Biochem. J. 75*:150 (1960).
35. LINDAN, O., QUASTEL, J. H. and SVED, S.: *Canad. J. Biochem. & Physiol.*, *35*:1135, 1145 (1957).
36. MCILWAIN, H. and GREENGARD, O.: *J. Neurochem.*, *1*:348 (1957).
37. PAPPIUS, H. M., ROSENFELD, M., JOHNSON, D. M., and ELLIOTT, K. A. C.: *Canad. J. Biochem. Physiol.*, *36*:217 (1958).

XI

MECHANISMS OF CARBOHYDRATE METABOLISM IN THE BRAIN

G. D. Greville

Physiological function should be taken into account when biochemical mechanisms are considered. The devotion of energy produced in carbohydrate metabolism to synthesis of ATP,* the energy currency, is common to all tissues, but in each organ the currency is spent in a way suited to that organ's particular functions. Thus in liver it supports chemical syntheses, in the kidney osmotic activity and in muscle mechanical work. The brain does not contract, its secretions are introverted and subtle, and its synthetic activities, though vital, are small in scale. Its energy production is directed almost solely to promoting the occult processes of nervous transmission, and its metabolism, as we know it, is relatively simple in scope. In this concentration on the requirements of its own particular function brain is perhaps most closely related to muscle.

The pathways and mechanisms of carbohydrate catabolism are, on the whole, the common property of the several tissues. The particular features of brain are therefore not to be sought so much in unique routes or processes as in the control of metabolic rates and in the relative importances of the various familiar pathways. Material for such considerations will, it is hoped, be provided in the survey which follows.

Abbreviations: ADP, ATP, adenosine-5'-diphosphate, triphosphate; CoA, coenzyme A; DNP, 2,4-dinitrophenol; 2-DOG, 2-deoxy-D-glucose; DPN, diphosphopyridine nucleotide; $DPNH_2$, $TPNH_2$, reduced forms of DPN, TPN; FDP, D-fructose-1,6-diphosphate; G- (followed by numeral), glucose- (e.g., G-1-P); α-GP, glycerol-1-phosphate; α-KG, α-ketoglutarate; NDP, NTP, nucleoside-5'-diphosphate, triphosphate; -P (preceded by numeral), -phosphate (e.g., G-6-P); PEP, phosphoenolpyruvate; 6-PFK, 6-phosphofructokinase; PGI, phosphoglucose isomerase; P_i, inorganic orthophosphate; PPP, pentose phosphate pathway; TCC, tricarboxylic acid cycle; TPN, triphosphopyridine nucleotide; UDP, UTP, uridine-5'-diphosphate, triphosphate; UDPG, uridine diphosphate-D-glucoside.

GLYCOGEN FORMATION AND BREAKDOWN

Brain glycogen is very similar to liver glycogen,[1] but is said to be even more highly branched.[2] Intracellular degradation of glycogen involves collaboration between (glucosan) phosphorylase and amylo-1:6-α-glucosidase, which break the 1:4 and 1:6 links respectively (Fig. 1, IV and VI). Phosphorylase was detected and studied in rabbit brain tissue in 1938,[3] and the glucosidase has been reported to be present in the same material.[4] Studies with liver have shown that synthesis of glycogen may be achieved by the combined action of phosphorylase and glucosan transglucosylase (branching factor) (Fig. 1, IV and V). Whether both enzymes are involved in glycogen synthesis in brain was left undecided by the finding[5] that partially purified brain phosphorylase synthesized material which, like glycogen, gave a brown colour with iodine. However, in the histochemical test for phosphorylase, polysaccharide synthesized in different parts of the brain gives different colours with iodine ranging from purple to brown;[6] this is consistent with different ratios of branching factor to phosphorylase activity in different regions. Furthermore, elegant histochemical experiments on

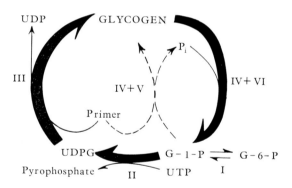

Fig. 1. The glycogen cycle. I, Phosphoglucomutase (216, 2240): II, UDPG pyrophosphorylase (88, 3540); III, UDPG glycogen transglucosylase (32, 187); IV, glucosan phosphorylase (38, 300: glycogen breakdown); V, glucosan transglucosylase; VI, amylo-1:6-α-glucosidase. For each enzyme the first value in the parentheses gives the activity (μmol./g. tissue/hr.) in rat-brain extracts, the second that in rat-liver extracts[8,10] (III at pH 8.5, the others at pH 7.4).

polysaccharide synthesis from G-1-P in rabbit brain, with α- and β-amylase to characterize the material formed and $HgCl_2$ to inhibit the putative branching factor, seem to have shown the presence of this enzyme in nervous tissue.[7]

However, it is by no means certain that the phosphorylase-branching factor pathway is operative in the living cell, and evidence for a route from G-1-P to glycogen via UDPG has recently been obtained[8] (Fig. 1). This path has been welcomed since, if glycogen is degraded by one enzyme system and synthesized by another, a difficulty is resolved, namely that activation of liver phosphorylase, a reversible enzyme, by adrenaline and glucagon always leads to glycogen breakdown. Activities of the enzymes of the glycogen cycle have been determined in rat-brain extracts (legend to Fig. 1). They are similar to the activities in spleen and lung, but only 2 to 15% of those in liver and muscle. However, the UDPG enzymes (Fig. 1, II, III) in rat and rabbit[8a] brain should be well capable of carrying the whole of glycogen synthesis* (maximum rate for guinea-pig brain *in vitro*, 1 μmol. glucose/g. tissue/hr.[9]).

In liver tissue, phosphorylase is inactivated enzymically with loss of phosphate. The enzymic reactivation is stimulated by adenosine-3',5'-phosphate (cyclic adenylate); formation of this from ATP is catalysed by cyclizing enzyme, which in turn is stimulated by adrenaline and glucagon. Brain phosphorylase too seems to exist in active and inactive forms. In brain the specific activity of phosphorylase-inactivating enzyme is relatively low,[12] but that of cyclizing enzyme is high. Like its counterpart in liver, brain cyclizing enzyme is stimulated by adrenaline.[13] The main action of cyclic adenylate in brain may not be on phosphorylase, however, since it can affect other enzymes as well, e.g., 6-PFK (T. E. Mansour).

GLYCOLYSIS

Twenty years ago it had already been shown, by the use of extracts and study of the intermediary reactions, that the conversion of carbohydrate to lactic acid in brain tissue proceeds through the Embden-Meyerhof pathway.[14-21] In the next stage, in the succeeding decade, the necessary conditions for maximal rates of anaerobic glycolysis in homogenates and "extracts" of brain were established. (Homogenates were made with water or salt solutions and "extracts" were the supernatants obtained from them by low-speed centrifugation.) In general, these had to be "fortified" by addition of Mg^{++}, P_i, DPN, nicotinamide, phosphate donors and acceptors and pyruvate. These are discussed separately in the next paragraph but first it should be stated that brain tissue is very active with respect to two enzymes, DPNase (coenzyme nucleosidase)[22] and ATPase, which destroy two coenzymes of glycolysis.

---

*There is a hint of yet another pathway of glycogen synthesis in brain, from maltose through oligosaccharides.[11]

Both enzymes are largely attached to subcellular particles, unlike the glycolytic enzymes which, with the exception of hexokinase, are almost entirely in the supernatant fraction obtained by high-speed centrifugation of brain homogenates. Homogenates therefore behave somewhat differently to the (almost) particle-free "extracts."

(a) Mg^{++} *ion* is essential as activator for several glycolytic enzymes. (b) P_i[19] is required as a substrate for glyceraldehyde-3-P dehydrogenase. (c) *DPN* links the two dehydrogenases. It may be saved from destruction by inhibition of the DPNase by *nicotinamide,*[22] which is naturally needed more with homogenates than with "extracts."[23] It is quite unnecessary with rat-brain homogenates in isotonic, Ca^{++}-containing media.[24] (d) *Phosphate donors and acceptors.*[25,26] Per mole of glucose, 2 moles of ATP are needed (by hexokinase and 6-PFK) and also 4 moles of ADP (by phosphoglycerate and pyruvate kinases). For maximal glycolytic rates, therefore, an optimal ATP/ADP ratio must be maintained. Furthermore, the net synthesis of 2 moles of ATP must be matched by an equivalent breakdown by ATPase (or other dephosphorylating system). Homogenates, with high ATPase, glycolyse slowly with hexose (a phosphate acceptor) but rapidly with FDP (a donor). The reverse applies with "extracts," which lack ATPase. Creatine (acceptor) accelerates glycolysis of FDP in "extracts," and creatine phosphate (donor) that of hexose in homogenates. Hexose, FDP and ATP together form a balanced system commonly used with both "extracts" and homogenates. (e) An adequate *pyruvate* concentration must be maintained to ensure that the re-oxidation of $DPNH_2$ is not rate-limiting (e.g., ref. 27). If fluoride is present, addition of pyruvate is essential to circumvent the inhibited enolase.

The greater part of the hexokinase of rat-brain homogenates is fixed in the particles and only about one-fifth is found in the clear supernatant obtained by high-speed centrifugation (p. 243). The anaerobic glucolysis of the latter is limited by lack of hexokinase to 25-30% of that of the homogenate, but can be raised to 100% by addition of the particles[28,29] (cf. ref. 30). Rate studies with "extracts" may therefore be highly misleading.

Rat-brain homogenates "fortified" with the cofactors indicated above may reach an anaerobic glycolysis ($Q_{CO_2}^{N_2}$) of 60-80 μl./mg. dry tissue/hr.[23,31] This is 3 to 9 times that of slices of cerebral cortex in glucose. ($Q_{CO_2}^{N_2}$ values of 36 and 47 were found for "fortified" homogenates of rat spinal cord and medulla respectively.[23]) Clearly the glycolytic enzymes of brain cells *in vitro* are working at far below their capacity. The high rates obtained with homogenates are partly due to the addition of FDP as substrate, but aside from this one may consider the factors which could limit the activity of glycolytic enzymes within the cell structure: these factors might also be operative *in vivo.* Possible restraints are as follows. (a) Inadequate rate of transport of glucose into the cell or lactate out of it. (b) Inadequate concentrations of cofactors in the cell. Pyruvate needs special mention. Addition of pyruvate accelerates[32] or maintains[33] the anaerobic glucolysis of brain slices. A trace of O_2 in the gas phase leads to slight accumulation of pyruvate and a similar result.[27] Anaerobic pre-incubation of slices in absence of added substrate causes loss of glycolytic power[33]; this seems to be associated with removal of pyruvate and breakdown of ATP; and the anaerobic glucolysis can be restored by temporary exposure of the slices to O_2 (which results in resynthesis of ATP) followed by addition of pyruvate,[34,21,35,36] but not by the latter alone.[33,35] In general, the pyruvate level is seen as an important factor in the regulation of anaerobic glucolysis.[27] (c) An unsuitable ATP/ADP ratio. (d) Segregation of enzymes in different cell compartments. Thus hexokinase is apparently associated with the mitochondria and may not be fully accessible to ATP or glucose from the cell sap. It has been suggested that the basal metabolism of glucose is handled by the hexokinase of the cell sap and that for more active metabolism the mitochondrial hexokinase comes into action.[29] (e) Restriction of diffusion of substrates or cofactors through the cell sap due to the presence of structures such as the endoplasmic reticulum, although some cytologists believe that movements of the latter may aid the transport of solutes.

Enzymes of the glycolytic pathway will now be considered.

Hexokinase.—Good evidence of transphosphorylation from ATP to glucose was obtained when interference by ATPase was avoided by use of aqueous extracts of fresh brain in presence of iodoacetate[19] or of acetone-dried brain with fluoride.[20] (Brain ATPase is damaged by acetone and inhibited by fluoride). Later experiments showed the product of the phosphate transfer to be hexose-6-P.[37,38] Preparations of brain hexokinase seem to be of two types, soluble and particulate. The enzyme has been obtained in clear solution by extraction of acetone-dried homogenates of ox-brain cortex.[37,39] Slight purification was achieved by fractionation with $(NH_4)_2SO_4$.[40,41] The preparations phosphorylated D-glucose, D-fructose and D-mannose, but not L-glucose, D-galactose, L-sorbose or various pentoses.[39] Na^+ was inhibitory with glucose but not with fructose.[39]

Particulate hexokinase was prepared by treatment, first with lipase and then with deoxycholate, of particles obtained by differential centrifugation of calf-brain homogenates.[42] The preparations were free from interfering enzymes and were used for extensive enzymological studies. The hexokinase was dependent on Mg^{++} and was inhibited by heavy metals and agents which react with SH-groups. ADP inhibited by competition with ATP.[43] Sixteen compounds, sugars and derivatives, acted as substrates,[44] including D-glucose, D-mannose, D-fructose, D-galactose (which probably yielded the 6-phosphate like the others), D-glucosamine (cf. ref. 45) and 2-DOG. Michaelis constants and maximum velocities were determined. It was concluded that the substrate specificity involves the ring structure and the OH groups at C atoms 1, 3, 4 and 6 of the D-glucopyranose molecule.

G-6-P (cf. ref. 46) and five other compounds, all of them 6-phosphates except L-sorbose-1-P,[47] inhibited brain hexokinase non-competitively.[48] Differences between the structures of the substrates and inhibitors suggested that brain hexokinase has a binding site for hexose-6-P different from those for carbohydrate substrate and ATP.* With glucose as substrate, activity decreases with time unless the G-6-P is removed. Addition of PGI and 6-PFK leads to a steady rate, which is only maximal if these enzymes are in large excess.[42] The apparent activation (in brain extracts) of hexokinase observed by Weil-Malherbe and colleagues on addition of erythrocyte lysates and muscle extracts was largely due to the 6-PFK which these contained.[50] In enzyme studies, 2-DOG as a substrate for hexokinase offers the advantage of a non-inhibitory product which, furthermore, is inert towards PGI and G-6-P dehydrogenase.[44] In the living cell, however, inhibition of hexokinase by G-6-P may provide a mechanism for regulation of glucose utilization.

Of the hexokinase activity of homogenates of rat brain in sucrose media 85 to 90% is associated with the particles.[42,29] Lower values (35 to 75%) are given for other tissues.[42] The percentages of the activity in rat-brain homogenates found in the mitochondrial fraction is given variously as 30,[51] 50[42] and 75.[29] Such variation is not unexpected since this fraction is ill-defined (p. 252). Sub-fractionation in dense media has led to considerable separation of hexokinase and succinate dehydrogenase from esterase, cholinesterase and lactate dehydrogenase.[29] The association of hexokinase with succinate dehydrogenase, considered a mitochondrial marker, suggests that brain particulate hexokinase is indeed a mitochondrial enzyme. The hexokinase of the supernatant fraction may not be an artifact: no soluble hexokinase could be released from the mitochondrial fraction by freezing and thawing.[29]

Other Glycolytic Enzymes.—Little has been done on the isolation and purification of the glycolytic enzymes in brain. PGI (G-6-P ⇌ fructose 6-P),[52] phosphoglucomutase (G-1-P + glucose-1,6-diphosphate ⇌ glucose-1,6-diphosphate + G-6-P),[52] and aldolase (FDP ⇌ glyceraldehyde-3-P + dihydroxyacetone phosphate)[53] from rabbit brain have been

---

*UTP can replace ATP as phosphate donor (R. K. Crane, cited by ref. 49).

purified about 25-fold by fractionation with ammonium sulphate. 6-PFK (fructose-6-P + ATP $\longrightarrow$ FDP + ADP) from dog, ox, and rabbit brain has been partially purified;[54,52] it needs for activity $(NH_4)^+$ and a divalent cation.[54] Finally, ox-brain L-lactate dehydrogenase has been purified 100-fold; it is competitively inhibited by oxalate and oxamate.[55]

Aldolase[56] and lactate dehydrogenase[57] have been observed in extracts of human brain. Many studies, involving assays on the microscale, have been made of the distribution of individual glycolytic enzymes in different areas of the brain and in the various layers of cerebral and cerebellar cortex and Ammon's horn. The following references may be cited: aldolase,[58-60,52] hexokinase,[60,52] lactate dehydrogenase,[57-63] 6-PFK,[60,52] phosphoglucomutase,[60,52] phosphorylase,[60,52] and PGI.[60,52] PGI and lactate dehydrogenase have been assayed even in single large nerve cell bodies.[64,65]

Inhibitors of Anaerobic Glycolysis.—Besides fluoride and iodoacetate, some other inhibitors are of interest. (a) Na^+ inhibits the glucolysis of brain homogenates: this is due to inhibition of hexokinase and pyruvate kinase and stimulation of ATPase.[66,67] Homogenates are therefore best studied in Na^+-free media. (b) *L-Glyceraldehyde* inhibits brain glucolysis, possibly through condensation with triose phosphate, catalysed by aldolase, to form L-sorbose-1-phosphate which inhibits hexokinase.[47] (c) *2-DOG* lowers the anaerobic glucolysis of brain slices.[68,69] 2-DOG-6-P, which is formed by hexokinase from 2-DOG and ATP (p. 243), inhibits purified kidney PGI by competition with G-6-P (A.N. Wick and colleagues). Addition of 2-DOG to brain slices leads to accumulation of 2-DOG-6-P, as would be expected since the latter is not attacked by PGI. This is accompanied by depletion of pyrophosphate, and the inhibition of anaerobic glycolysis is overcome by addition of ATP or G-6-P.*[69] The effect of 2-DOG on brain glucolysis therefore seems to be due to the depletion of ATP, resulting from 2-DOG-6-P formation, and, possibly, to inhibition of PGI. (d) *Ferrous salts* partially inactivate glyceraldehyde-3-P dehydrogenase in brain homogenates.[71] This hardly affects the glycolysis of FDP, since the dehydrogenase is, apparently, normally in excess. The reduction in ATP synthesis, however, causes cessation of glycolysis when glucose is substrate, a vicious circle being set up in which diminished phosphorylation of glucose leads to still less synthesis of ATP. Thus a small inhibition of one, non-limiting, step in the glycolytic chain may

---

*It is interesting that inhibition of respiration by 2-DOG is not relieved by these substances, as this indicates that brain-cell membranes *in vitro* are more permeable under anaerobic than under aerobic conditions[69] (cf. ref. 70).

lead to a disproportionate effect on another stage, finally resulting in failure of the whole system.

Mannose.—Injection of this sugar prevents development of abnormal cortical potentials in hepatectomized animals.[72] It is readily glycolysed by brain tissue.[73] It is presumably led to the glycolytic pathway by hexokinase, for which it is a good substrate,[44] and phosphomannose isomerase (mannose-6-P $\rightleftharpoons$ fructose-6-P), which seems to have about the same activity in brain as in other tissues.[74]

Fructose.—This sugar moves sluggishly from blood to brain.[75] It will not support normal cerebral electrical activity in hepatectomized animals.[72] It is utilized very slowly by perfused brain,[76] even when forced in by a high concentration gradient.[77] The catabolism of this sugar by brain tissue *in vitro* is therefore of limited interest, save as an exercise in enzymology. With brain cortex slices, fructose is oxidized as rapidly as glucose, but paradoxically, it is not converted to lactic acid under anaerobic conditions.[73,78] The incorporation of ^{14}C from fructose into respiratory CO_2 by brain tissue preparations is greater than that from glucose.[79,80]

Crude brain hexokinase, like yeast hexokinase, converts fructose to its 6-phosphate, and brain, unlike some tissues, seems to lack both fructokinase which forms the 1-phosphate and 1-phosphofructokinase which removes it.[40] As further evidence that fructose is phosphorylated by the same enzyme in brain tissue as is glucose, (a) glucose prevents fructose utilization by slices;[80] (b) N-acetylglucosamine competitively inhibits phosphorylation of both sugars in extracts of acetone-dried brain;[45] and (c) 2-DOG inhibits oxidation of both sugars by slices.[68]

Otto Meyerhof and colleagues,[25,81,82] seeking a cause for the low fructolysis of brain tissue, found that with isotonic homogenates, as with slices, fructolysis was much slower than glucolysis. With "extracts," in which the ATPase activity is low (p. 241), it was not. The difference between the sugars could be abolished in the homogenates if ATP was continuously added, or obtained in the "extracts" if the concentration of ATP or sugar was decreased. The feeble fructolysis of brain was therefore ascribed to the low affinity of fructose for hexokinase,* the effect of which appears at reduced ATP or sugar concentrations. The cessation of fructose utilization on passing from aerobic to anaerobic conditions—an inversion of the Pasteur effect (p. 259)—might then be due to a decrease, in the absence of respiratory-chain phosphorylation, in the concentration of ATP available to the hexokinase. Uncoupling of oxidative phosphorylation might produce

---

*The affinity of fructose for (particulate) brain hexokinase is only 0.5% of that of glucose.[44]

the same result. 4,6-Dinitro-o-cresol, 10^{-5}M, which accelerates the respiration of brain cortex slices with glucose, has little effect with fructose—an inconclusive finding (Greville, unpublished). It may be mentioned that it has been proposed that less, rather than more, ATP is available to the hexokinase under aerobic conditions than under anaerobic (p. 259).

Galactose.—This sugar is utilized by the brain *in situ* at a negligible rate[83] and will not prevent development of abnormal cortical potentials in hepatectomized animals.[72] Galactose depresses the respiration of brain slices below the endogenous value.[73] Anaerobically, it is glycolysed by brain slices and homogenates slowly in comparison with glucose, but the rates become equal if the galactose concentration is raised.[25]

The following reaction scheme has been proposed[84,49] for galactose metabolism in brain:

(1)   Galactose + ATP → galactose-1-phosphate + ADP;
(2)   Galactose-1-phosphate + UDPG → G-1-P + UDP-galactoside.
UDP-galactoside is also formed from glucose as follows:
(3)   Glucose + ATP → G-6-P + ADP;
(4)   G-6-P ⇌ G-1-P;
(5)   G-1-P + UTP ⇌ UDPG + pyrophosphate (p. 239);
(6)   UDPG ⇌ UDP-galactoside.

Reaction (1) is catalysed by galactokinase (found in brain[85]), (2) by uridylyl transferase (found in brain: K. Kurahashi, cited by ref. 49) and (6) by UDP-galactoside-4-epimerase (galactowaldenase) (found in brain[86]). Reactions (1), (2), (6), (5) and (4) in sequence will provide a route from galactose to the glycolytic pathway. The slowness of galactose metabolism in brain is ascribed[49] to the low velocity of reactions (1) and (2) in this tissue. On the other hand, formation of UDP-galactoside from glucose or galactose is of importance in the synthesis of cerebral galactolipids. The "microsomal" fraction of young rat brain contains the enzymes necessary for the incorporation of glucose or galactose into galactolipid, which most probably proceeds through the pathways indicated above, together with

(7)   UDP-galactoside + ("microsomal") acceptor lipid → neutral galactolipid
           + UDP.[84]

RESPIRATION

Tricarboxylic Acid Cycle.—That carbohydrate oxidation in brain tissue proceeds through the TCC was first suggested by the finding[87] that malonate decreases the respiration of cerebral cortex slices in presence of glucose. More direct evidence was: (a) fumaric or other C_4-dicarboxylic acid is needed for oxidation of pyruvate by dialysed dispersions of pigeon or rabbit brain,[18] and (b) citrate and α-KG are formed from oxaloacetate by minced sheep brain under anaerobic conditions.[88] In Chapter 12 Sir Rudolph Peters discusses this conclusion further.

Pyruvate Dehydrogenase.—As is made clear in Chapter 12, there is little doubt that pyruvate dehydrogenase in brain catalyses the reaction

(8) $\qquad$ Pyruvate + CoA + DPN → acetyl CoA + CO_2 + $DPNH_2$

by a mechanism involving thiamine pyrophosphate and lipoate similar to that in other tissues. In this reaction sequence lipoate is the immediate H acceptor, and is reoxidized by DPN:

(9) $\qquad$ Reduced lipoate + DPN → oxidized lipoate + $DPNH_2$.

Reaction (9) is catalysed by lipoate dehydrogenase, which in pig heart is identical with the flavoprotein diaphorase ($DPNH_2$ + dye → DPN + leuco-dye) extractable from that organ (V. Massey). Brain tissue shows strong diaphorase-like activity,[89] but one of the enymes responsible has no lipoate dehydrogenase activity.[89a]

An interesting feature of pyruvate metabolism in brain is the dismutation[90] (see also Chapter 12)

(10) $\qquad$ 2 Pyruvate → lactate + acetate + CO_2.

Presumably this is the result of reaction (8), catalysed by pyruvate dehydrogenase, being followed by reaction (11) catalysed by lactate

(11) $\qquad$ $DPNH_2$ + pyruvate ⇌ DPN + lactate,

dehydrogenase, the acetyl CoA formed in reaction (8) being converted to acetate, possibly by a deacylase. The formation of acetate becomes prominent when entry of acetyl CoA into the TCC is prevented by absence of O_2[91] or presence of malonate.[92] A similar limited oxidation of pyruvate occurs in liver when the TCC is blocked, but here the acetyl CoA yields acetoacetate, which is not formed by brain.[93] With brain suspensions, some acetate formation, equivalent to about 20% of the pyruvate disappearance, occurs even in presence of O_2 and absence of inhibitors.[94,92] Little acetate is formed with glucose as substrate,[93] presumably because the steady-state pyruvate level is too low.

Anaerobically, with brain slices and minces, 2 moles of pyruvate yield one mole each of lactate and CO_2 in accordance with the dismutation equation (10). With slices 80% of the theoretical acetate is formed, but only 10% with minces: the balance is largely found as succinate.[91] Particles from the ciliate *Tetrahymena pyriformis* are said to catalyse the reversible synthesis of succinate from acetyl CoA by reaction (12)[95] (cf. ref. 96).

(12) 2 Acetyl CoA + 2 ADP + 2 P_i + DPN ⇌ succinate + 2 CoA + 2 ATP + $DPNH_2$.

The $DPNH_2$ is re-oxidized by pyruvate in presence of lactate dehydrogenase (equation 11). Succinate formation is much slower than succinate cleavage to acetyl CoA, but an indication that the latter can take place with brain homogenates[95] suggests the possibility that reactions (12) and (11) are together responsible for the anaerobic formation of succinate in minces mentioned above, since all the necessary reactants are to hand.

Acetate is not oxidized at a detectable rate by rat-brain slices[97] or homogenates,[93] and it is not utilized by sheep brain *in vitro*.[98] This last finding is interesting since acetate is the chief energy-source in ruminants.

Citrate condensing enzyme catalyses the reaction

(13)   Acetyl CoA + oxaloacetate → citrate + CoA.

In various animal species its activity, per mg. of protein, is higher in brain than in liver or kidney, but much lower than in heart muscle.[99] Reaction (13) can be reversed under certain conditions, but there is

(14)   Citrate + CoA + ATP → acetyl CoA + oxaloacetate + ADP + P_i,

another reaction (14), which is catalysed by *citrate cleavage enzyme*. This is active in brain tissue of various species.[100,101] Wollemann[100] has deduced that reaction (14) is catalysed in brain tissue by condensing enzyme together with CoA phosphokinase (CoA + ATP → CoA-phosphate + ADP). Srere,[101] however, could not reproduce the evidence, and has also obtained cleavage enzyme (from chicken liver) free from condensing enzyme. The equilibrium in reaction (13) is unfavourable for acetyl CoA formation, and possibly the synthesis of acetylcholine from citrate[102] may involve the cleavage enzyme rather than the condensing enzyme as once supposed (e.g., ref. 103).

Aconitase.—The activity, measured by the conversion of cisaconitate to citrate, in extracts of rat brain is about one-eighth of those of kidney cortex.[104] The enzyme has also been demonstrated in rabbit[103] and pigeon[105] brain. It is largely (85%) in the mitochondrial fraction of rabbit-brain homogenates.[106] When pigeon brain slices are incubated aerobically, an appreciable portion of their aconitase passes into the medium. Penetration of citrate into these slices is very poor, and citrate accumulating during pyruvate metabolism is almost completely retained in them.[107] It may be held in the mitochondria, since the bulk of the citrate in liver is found in the mitochondrial fraction.

Isocitrate dehydrogenase activity, apparently TPN-linked, has been found in extracts of brain, although much lower than in those of kidney, liver and heart.[108] The activity, measured by TPN reduction, in the mitochondrial fraction of rabbit cerebral cortex is twice that in the supernatant fraction. The "mitochondrial" activity, probably limited by poor permeation by TPN, is trebled by disruption of the particles by various means. Sonic disintegration releases the enzyme in soluble form.[109] There is said to be some DPN-linked activity.[194]

α-Ketoglutarate dehydrogenase, which catalyses the reaction

$$\text{(15)} \qquad \text{α-KG} + \text{CoA} + \text{DPN} \rightarrow \text{succinyl CoA} + CO_2 + \text{DPNH}_2,$$

is similar to pyruvate dehydrogenase. It has been detected in brain tissue of various animal species.[91] Anaerobically, brain slices and mince perform the dismutation

$$\text{(16)} \qquad 2\ \text{α-KG} \rightarrow \text{α-hydroxyglutarate} + \text{succinate} + CO_2.$$

which is analogous to that with pyruvate (equation 10), the DPNH_2 formed in reaction (15) being re-oxidized with the aid of α-hydroxyglutarate dehydrogenase.[91] Reaction (15) is followed in the TCC by

$$\text{(17)} \qquad \text{Succinyl CoA} + \text{NDP} + P_1 \rightarrow \text{succinate} + \text{CoA} + \text{NTP},$$

catalysed by *succinyl CoA synthetase,* which has been reported to be in ox-brain tissue.[100]

Succinate dehydrogenase activity in brain tissue has been much studied during the last 30 years.[110] In homogenates of rat[111,112] and rabbit[106] brain, as with other tissues, it is found largely in the mitochondrial fraction. Succinate dehydrogenase can be extracted from mitochondria of various tissues as a soluble flavoprotein, but the brain enzyme does not seem to have been characterized as yet.[113]

Fumarase from rabbit brain has been purified 20-fold and its kinetics have been studied.[53] It is concentrated in, and firmly bound to, the mitochondrial fraction of rabbit-brain homogenates.[106] *Malate dehydrogenase* is very active in brain tissue of various animal species.[114,115] The ox-brain enzyme has been purified 50-fold and is specific for L-malate.[55] From liver homogenates two quite different malate dehydrogenases can be obtained, one from the mitochondrial fraction and one from the supernatant (C.J.R. Thorne). With rat brain, there is an active malate dehydrogenase in the supernatant,[116] but whether this differs in its properties from the "mitochondrial" enzyme[111] is not known.

γ-Aminobutyrate Shunt.—In brain tissue the reactions shown below form a shunt around that part of the TCC between α-KG and succinate:[116a]

α-KG + γ-aminobutyrate → L-glutamate + succinic semialdehyde

Isotope studies indicate that in cat cerebral cortex slices about 40% of the traffic between α-KG and succinate passes through this shunt.[116b]

Distribution.—Studies have been made, by quantitative michrochemical techniques, of the distribution of fumarase[58,59] and malate dehydrogenase[57-62] in different areas of the brain and in the various layers of cerebral and cerebellar cortex and Ammon's horn. The distribution of succinate dehydrogenase, also, in brain has been surveyed by several workers using histochemical staining techniques (e.g., refs. 117-121).

Respiration of Homogenates.—The question as to which substances must be added to cell-free preparations of brain in order to obtain maximal respiratory rates, initially of importance because of the information it gave regarding the mechanisms of carbohydrate oxidation in that tissue, later became more of practical interest. It was found in 1939 that oxidation of pyruvate by dialysed dispersions of pigeon and rabbit brain was activated by a C_4-dicarboxylic acid, ATP or AMP and P_i.[18] (P_i was needed also for dehydrogenation of pyruvate with methylene blue as H acceptor.[122]) In absence of adenine nucleotide the utilization of pyruvate was diminished and its oxidation less complete.[18] Omission of dicarboxylic acid, on the other hand, led to less complete oxidation without decreased utilization.[123] Homogenates of rat brain in water showed high respiratory rates on addition of glucose, FDP, DPN, nicotinamide, ATP, cytochrome c and fumarate[124] (cf. ref. 66); the most important cofactors for respiration were the same as those for glycolysis with homogenates (p. 241), namely DPN and a stable phosphate donor (FDP).[124] It was uncertain whether pyruvate was utilized, but it was later found to be oxidized by mouse brain in a similar system provided that the DPN level was adequate.[125] DPN was needed with "fine" homogenates made with a tightly-fitting Potter-Elvehjem device but not with "coarse" ones with a loosely-fitting instrument: the former type of homogenate had a higher DPNase activity than the latter. Some authors[125,80] have noted a stimulation of respiration by Mg^{++}. The respiratory rates, on a dry-weight basis, of the fortified rat and mouse brain homogenates noted above, were 2 to 3 times those of slices.

In a recent study of the oxidation of ^{14}C-glucose by isotonic rat brain homogenates, the workers[80] omitted FDP in order to escape dilution of the isotope. They also avoided addition of nicotinamide. As might be expected, ATP as well as DPN became most important. With the further addition of 10^{-4}M-fumarate, cytochrome c and Mg^{++} satisfactory respiratory rates were obtained. Use of an isotonic medium stimulated and prolonged the glucose oxidation although it did not increase the rate of oxygen uptake.

The respiratory rate of isotonic homogenates of rat brain was independent of O_2 pressure down to 4 mm. Hg and of glucose concentration down to 10^{-4}M.[126] With the water homogenates of rat brain mentioned above, the aerobic glycolysis was as large as the anaerobic, i.e., there was no Pasteur effect.[124] On the other hand, briefly-homogenized suspensions in isotonic media show a low aerobic glycolysis.[127,24] The respiration of homogenates in glucose, like glycolysis, is inhibited by Na^+,[66] but recent workers have not all omitted Na^+ from their media.

Endogenous Respiration.—With the fortified rat and mouse brain homogenates mentioned above[124,66,125] omission of substrate reduced the respiratory rate to about one-third. With isotonic brain suspensions the ratio is considerably higher, and three-fourths of the endogenous respiration is concerned with the oxidation of non-carbohydrate materials.[93] Endogenous non-carbohydrate respiration is of great significance in the brain *in vivo,* and in cat brain perfused with glucose-free fluid can even support prolonged evoked activity with increased O_2 consumption.[128] The substrates of endogenous brain respiration are not known for certain, but there is evidence that both proteins and lipids may be utilized.[128] Brain tissue is capable of oxidizing fatty acids *in vitro* (references[80]) and two of the necessary enzymes have been shown to be present in it.[129]

Fate of Glucose.—Chemical analyses have indicated that with isotonic suspensions addition of glucose largely suppresses the oxidation of endogenous non-carbohydrate material,[93] but isotopes have disclosed that the situation is more complex. Thus with rat[80] and human[130] brain slices in presence of ^{14}C-glucose the amount of glucose carbon converted to CO_2 during the first hour corresponded to only about one half of the oxygen uptake. A similar result was obtained with fortified homogenates.[80] The fate of ^{14}C-glucose has been studied with slices of rat[131] and cat[69] cerebral cortex. (Rather unusual media were used which would cause abnormally high respiration and, particularly, aerobic glucolysis.) The results indicate that 60 to 70% of the glucose metabolized was converted to lactate, 20% to CO_2 and most of the remainder to α-amino-acids and derivatives (glutamine, glutamic, γ-aminobutyric and aspartic acids and alanine) which would arise from TCC intermediates (see also ref. 132). Qualitatively similar results were obtained with other parts of the brain[133] and with fructose.[134,132] It was found with perfused cat brain that non-carbohydrate constituents are oxidized simultaneously with glucose from the blood, and that a substantial part of the glucose metabolized is used for resynthesis of these compounds.[128] The O_2 consumption corresponds to that necessary to oxidize the glucose taken from the blood, as is found with the intact brain *in situ* after allowance for the small lactate production. Thus whilst the respiration of the brain is virtually entirely supported by glucose from the blood,[135] only about one-third of this is oxidized directly to CO_2, the remainder being converted first to stored non-carbohydrate materials which are subsequently oxidized (cf. ref. 128a). In the steady state the utilization of these substances, probably protein and lipid, matches their formation from glucose. It would seem that in slices lipid synthesis is negligible since glucose carbon is recovered almost completely in other substances.

Mitochondria.—Studies of oxidations by brain mitochondria have been bedevilled by the impossibility of separating homogeneous fractions from homogenates in dilute sucrose solutions. Fractions in which mitochondria were concentrated were first prepared from brain in 1952,[136,111] and many workers have followed this lead. Such preparations are a subcellular compote of mitochondria, in various degrees of preservation, with a high proportion of unidentified particles, as electron micrographs bear graphic witness.[137] In contrast with the much greater homogeneity achieved with liver (G.H. Hogeboom and W.C. Schneider) and particularly brown fat (J.D. Lever and J.B. Chappell), this situation arises from the peculiar nature of brain tissue, especially the possession by the neurone of long processes which must be torn by the homogenizer into pieces of various sizes. If very gentle homogenization is used the mitochondria are not freed.[138] Subfractionation by centrifugation in a density gradient yields much purer mitochondrial fractions,[139,29] but the dense media used probably make the particles unsuitable for metabolic studies (cf. ref. 136). So until there are further improvements in fractionation and cell rupture, such studies will continue to be made in a micro-minestrone (called here "mitochondrial fraction"), the composition of which depends on the skill and habits of the operator.

Brain mitochondrial fractions vigorously oxidize the various TCC intermediates:[136,141,142,138] pyruvate oxidation is "sparked" by malate or fumarate. (Citrate is feebly oxidized;[136,143,138] this may be due to poor penetration, since Ca^{++}, which inhibits with other substrates,[144] stimulates with citrate.[143]) Respiration is not increased by addition of cytochrome c, DPN (see, however, ref. 145), TPN, thiamine pyrophosphate or lipoic acid, but adenine nucleotide is needed.[136,138] Respiration declines rather rapidly with time;[141,138,146] this is not seen with liver mitochondria. Co^{++} and glutathione stabilize when both are added.[141] Fatty acids[147] and acetaldehyde[145] inhibit the oxidation of pyruvate "sparked" by malate. The action of phospholipase A in heated snake venon on the mitochondrial structure causes initially a stimulation of respiration[148] (cf. ref. 149).

Brain mitochondrial fractions contain glycolytic enzymes and, unlike those from liver and kidney for example, show respiration and anaerobic glycolysis when glucose is added, up to 25% and 10% respectively of the activity of the homogenate.[143,51,80,138,150-6,29] It is not yet settled whether these enzymes belong to the mitochondria or to contaminating particles. A subfraction obtained by density-gradient centrifugation of a brain mitochondrial fraction consisted mostly of pinched-off nerve endings containing synaptic vesicles and occasional mitochondria.[140] Part at least of the glycolytic activity of crude mito-chondrial fractions might thus reside in entrapped cell sap in these and similar artifacts (cf. ref. 29), although, while much of the activity can be extracted with water, some remains associated with insoluble matter despite disruption of the particles by a detergent.[152]

Oxidative Phosphorylation.—Phosphorylation coupled to respiration has been shown with brain homogenates (e.g., refs. 157-159) and mito-chondrial fractions (e.g., refs. 136, 142, 160-162). The P/O ratios (atoms P esterified/atom O consumed) were comparable with those found with other tissues and were reduced (i.e., phosphorylation was un-coupled) by DNP,[163,144] azide, phenosafranine and other dyes,[163] fatty acids,[147] heated snake venom[164] and certain P-containing antichol-inesterases.[165] Coupled phosphorylation has also been shown when the electron transport was between substrate and ferricyanide[160] or fer-rocytochrome c and O_2.[166] Respiratory control, i.e., limitation of res-piration by lack of ADP, occurs with brain mitochondrial fractions as with those of other tissues, as evidenced by acceleration of O_2 uptake on addition of ADP,[156] ATP with potato apyrase or hexokinase and glucose,[138] uncoupling agents (DNP, dicoumarol)[138,156] or Ag+ (see below).[167] Treatment of brain mitochondrial fractions with a detergent yielded particles much smaller than mitochondria which still showed oxidative phosphorylation with various substrates.[144] They differed from the mitochondrial fraction in that ADP could not be replaced as phosphate acceptor by other NDP's, and in that their phosphoryla-tion was much less susceptible to inhibition by Ca++.

Adenosine Triphosphatase.—ATPase is important in carbohydrate metabolism because it affects the levels of ADP and P_i in the cell and hence the metabolic rates. It may also have a nuisance value; for example, brain particles give low P/O ratios unless the ATPase is inhibited by fluoride. Brain ATPase activity is largely associated with subcellular particles, and is stimulated by Ca++ or Mg++ (see ref. 168 for references; also ref. 169). Distribution studies in the cerebral cortex suggest that Ca++ and Mg++ activate separate ATPases with different cytological locations.[170] Interest attaches to ATPase activity evoked in mitochondria by DNP, since this is believed to involve enzymes of the oxidative phosphorylation mechanism. DNP stimulates ATPase activity of brain mitochondrial fractions, but only when the particles have come in contact with ethylenediaminetetra-acetate.[171,167,172] $Ag+$ also stimulates under these conditions.[167]

Hydrogen (Electron) Transport.—The mitochondrial respiratory chain, simplified and with uncertainties, may be shown thus (cyt. = cytochrome; FP = flavoprotein):

$$
\begin{array}{ccccccc}
& Amytal & & Antimycin\ A & & & \\
Substrate \to & DPN \ +\to\ ?FP_1 \to & cyt.b \ +\to & cyt.c_1 \to & cyt.c \to & cyt.a(a_3) \to & O_2 \\
& \uparrow & & \uparrow\ \uparrow & & & \\
Pyruvate & & & & & & \\
\alpha\text{-}KG \to & FP_2 & \alpha\text{-}GP \to & ?FP_3\ FP_4 \leftarrow succinate & & &
\end{array}
$$

Hydrogen transport in brain has had relatively little attention. The absorption bands of cytochromes a, b and c are to be seen in cerebral cortex.[173] The small particles made from brain mitochondrial fractions (p. 253) gave a difference spectrum, closely resembling that of submito-chondrial particles from liver (C. Cooper and A.L. Lehninger), which indicated that cytochromes a, b and c and flavoprotein were reduced on addition of oxidizable substrate and HCN.[144] The potential activity of *cytochrome oxidase* in rat and sheep brain, as in other tissues, is greatly in excess of requirements,[174-176] but in human it may be rate-limiting.[177] Its distribution in the cerebrum indicates localization mainly in perikarya and dendrites, and probably reflects that of mito-chondria; activity in white matter is low.[178,177] Brain cytochrome oxidase activity is reduced in copper deficiency in rats[179] and swayback lambs.[180] The *cytochrome* c content of mitochondria is a rough meas-ure of their respiratory capacity: per g. of protein the cytochrome c of rat brain mitochondrial fractions is only about 0.6 of that of liver,[181] but the brain fractions probably contain a smaller proportion of mito-chondria. The turnover of cytochrome c (atoms O/sec./mol. cyto-chrome c) in brain mitochondrial fractions with pyruvate as substrate is 50 to 100% of that in other tissues.[181] The *flavin nucleotide* concen-tration in brain is only about one-tenth of that in liver, kidney and heart and comparable to that of skeletal muscle; brain is however much more resistant than the other tissues to depletion in riboflavin deficiency.[182-184] Flavin-adenine-dinucleotide predominates.[182] The *DPN* concentration in brain is one-half–one-third of that in liver, kidney and heart.[185-187,65] About one-seventh of brain DPN is in the mitochondrial fraction[187] where the amount per g. of protein is less than with heart, liver and kidney, although the ratio DPN/cytochrome c is nearer to that in the other tissues.[188] With the brain mitochondria in the controlled state (respiration inhibited by lack of ADP) in presence of pyruvate all their DPN is in the oxidized form. In the controlled state the DPN of heart, liver and kidney mitochondria is largely as $DPNH_2$ in presence of the DPN-independent substrate succinate; this phenomenon is not completely understood, but it is noteworthy that it does not occur with brain.[188]

The rate of oxidation of DPNH$_2$ by cerebral-cortex homogenates is twice the highest rate of cerebral respiration observed *in vivo* or *in vitro*,[189] but in homogenates part of the H transport may be by extra-mitochondrial DPNH$_2$-cytochrome *c* reductase, and whether this happens in the cell is not known. In brain the DPNH$_2$-cytochrome *c* reductase activity is greatest in the mitochondrial fraction.[190] The oxidation of DPNH$_2$ by brain homogenates is partially sensitive to antimycin *A* and amytal; the distribution of the sensitive activity among various fractions is consistent with localization in the mitochondria, whereas the insensitive activity has a different distribution and may be largely extra-mitochondrial.[191]

In brain mitochondrial fractions the *TPN* content is low (about one-fifth of the DPN): over 50% is as TPNH$_2$.[187,188] TPNH$_2$ is produced by isocitrate dehydrogenase and may be oxidized (a) directly by TPNH$_2$-cytochrome *c* reductase or (b) indirectly through DPN-TPN transhydrogenase (TPNH$_2$ + DPN ⇌ DPNH$_2$ + TPN). In liver route (b) seems to be used exclusively, but in brain this transhydrogenase activity is very low[192,193] and route (a) may be followed,[194] although this is probably extra-mitochondrial.[191] DPN transhydrogenase is active in brain; this enzyme transfers H from one molecule of DPN to another, and possibly between free and bound DPN in mitochondria.[195]

In brain mitochondria, α-GP and succinate dehydrogenases are probably linked to the respiratory chain at the level of cytochrome *b*. As evidence, α-GP rapidly reduces cytochrome *b* (L. Packer, cited by ref. 196), aerobic oxidation of α-GP is inhibited by antimycin, and α-GP reduces fumarate with antimycin present.[196]

The Glycerol-1-phosphate Cycle.—In animal tissues there are two dehydrogenases which convert α-GP to dihydroxyacetone phosphate, for in addition to the mitochondrial enzyme (preceding paragraph) there is a DPN-dependent one in the cell sap. Skilfully-isolated mitochondria are almost impermeable to DPNH$_2$. If this applies *in vivo*, the re-oxidation by the mitochondrial respiratory chain of DPNH$_2$ formed during glycolysis in the cell sap needs special machinery. Estabrook and Sacktor, and Bücher and colleagues, have proposed the following cyclical mechanism for insect flight muscle, in which the mitochondrial α-GP dehydrogenase activity is very high. DPNH$_2$, formed during glycolysis, is re-oxidized by the α-GP dehydrogenase of the cell sap:

(18)   Dihydroxyacetone phosphate + DPNH$_2$ → α-GP + DPN.

The α-GP passes into the mitochondria, where it is re-oxidized by the dehydrogenase which is joined to the respiratory chain. The resulting dihydroxyacetone phosphate presumably returns to the cell sap. Thus, in effect, the H atoms of the $DPNH_2$ of the cell sap are oxidized to water in the mitochondria.

In considering whether this cycle applies to brain, one notes that this tissue contains a very active mitochondrial α-GP dehydrogenase.[197,196] Indeed, in a sucrose-containing medium, α-GP is oxidized almost as fast as succinate or α-KG by rat-brain mitochondrial fractions whereas with heart, liver and kidney it is oxidized very slowly compared with the other substrates[181] (cf. ref. 198). The situation regarding the DPN-dependent α-GP dehydrogenase is, however, uncertain. In rat brain it is reported (1) to be absent,[29] (2) to have one-fourteenth[116] and (3) one-fourth[199] of the activity of lactate dehydrogenase. It was not found in ox brain.[200] It has been suggested that the rapid oxidation of α-GP by the mitochondria of brain may be of special functional significance in that organ,[198] but whether this is in connexion with an α-GP cycle remains to be seen.

PYRUVATE-CARBOXYLATION PATHWAYS

In animals CO_2 fixation into pyruvate may occur through two* reactions:

(19) $$CO_2 + PEP + NDP \rightleftharpoons oxaloacetate + NTP,$$

catalysed by PEP carboxykinase (oxaloacetate carboxylase), and

(20) $$CO_2 + pyruvate + TPNH_2 \rightleftharpoons L\text{-malate} + TPN,$$

catalysed by the malic enzyme. These reactions may be important in carbohydrate metabolism (a) as factors which partly determine the amount of oxaloacetate available to react with acetyl CoA, (b) as stages in the synthesis of certain amino-acids from hexose, and (c) as steps in glycogenesis, by forming, together with malate → oxaloacetate, a "dicarboxylic acid pathway" from PEP to pyruvate which is thermodynamically more satisfactory than the single step catalysed by pyruvate kinase (H.A. Krebs, M.F. Utter).

Evidence has been obtained that minced brain from day-old mice can fix $^{14}CO_2$ into pyruvate to yield, ultimately, labelled aspartate and glutamate.[201] Hsu and Utter[202] have measured the specific activities of the two CO_2-fixing enzymes in five rat tissues. The amount of

---

*The importance of the oxaloacetate synthetase system of M. F. Utter and D. B. Keech (1960) and of the liver oxaloacetate decarboxylase of L. M. Corwin (1959) has not yet been assessed.

PEP carboxykinase in brain is very low compared with that in liver and kidney. The malic enzyme concentration in brain is, however, similar to that in heart, kidney and liver, and higher than that in skeletal muscle. The malic enzyme activities of these rat tissues are considerably lower than that of avian liver, but ox brain is almost as active as pigeon liver (J.R. Stern, cited by ref. 203). Whether the dicarboxylic acid pathway is operative even in liver and kidney is still uncertain;[202] in any case it seems to be unlikely in brain since the PEP carboxykinase content is so low. On the other hand, the malic enzyme reaction in brain may well serve the functions (a) and (b) outlined above.

PENTOSE PHOSPHATE PATHWAY (PPP)

The PPP offers a way of glucose oxidation other than the Embden-Meyerhof (E-M) glycolytic route with subsequent TCC. The finding that brain tissue *in vitro* oxidizes glucose in presence of inhibitors of glycolysis (iodoacetate, fluoride, glyceraldehyde) or of pyruvate oxidation (nicotine) has been taken to imply the existence of some such alternative route in this tissue (p. 85 of ref. 135). However, observations of this type are rather difficult to interpret. In particular, partial inhibition of glyceraldehyde-3-P dehydrogenase will strongly inhibit anaerobic glucolysis due to reduction of ATP synthesis (p. 244) but may not affect aerobic metabolism if oxidative phosphorylation can supply the necessary ATP.[71]

The PPP comprises an oxidative portion (21), involving the TPN-linked G-6-P and 6-phosphogluconate dehydrogenases, and an anaerobic portion (22) involving transketolase and transaldolase:

(21) $3 \text{ G-6-P} + 6 \text{ TPN} \rightarrow 3 \text{ pentose phosphate} + 3 \text{ CO}_2 + 6 \text{ TPNH}_2;$
(22) $3 \text{ Pentose phosphate} \rightarrow 2 \text{ fructose-6-P} + \text{triose phosphate}.$

A cycle may be formed if some of the fructose-6-P is converted to G-6-P. Brain contains the enzymes necessary for operation of the PPP. Rat and rabbit brain extracts oxidize G-6-P and 6-phosphogluconate[204] and convert ribose-5-P to hexosemonophosphate.[205,206] Brain homogenates have been found to convert G-6-P to ribulose phosphate, an intermediate in the oxidative path, and ribose-5-P to sedoheptulose phosphate, an intermediate in the anaerobic path.[207] In rat brain, however, the specific activity of 6-phosphogluconate dehydrogenase[206] and the TPN content[185,187] are very low compared with those in liver, a tissue in which the PPP is believed to operate. Rabbit brain is not deficient in this enzyme.[208]

Studies using ^{14}C-glucose have been made with various tissues in attempts to determine what proportion of the glucose metabolized passes through the PPP. Usually, the incorporation of ^{14}C from G-6-^{14}C into the respiratory CO_2 has been compared with that from G-1-^{14}C. If the ratio (C-6/C-1) is unity it is considered that the E-M pathway is used exclusively. If the ratio is lower, the preferential conversion of C-1 into CO_2 is thought to indicate operation of the PPP.* C-6/C-1 ratios close to 1 have been found with slices of rabbit,[209] guinea-pig,[210] rat (B.W. Agranoff and R.O. Brady, cited by ref. 69) and cat[69] brain and with human brain *in situ*.[211] These experiments, therefore, give no indication that the PPP is operative in brain. Incorporation of ^{14}C into lactate formed by aerobic glucolysis may also be used, and results with slices of cat brain[69] (C-6/C-1 = 1.03) as well as with those of rat[80] and human[130] brain have been taken to indicate almost exclusive use of the E-M pathway.

With rat-brain homogenates, addition of TPN markedly increased the incorporation into CO_2 of ^{14}C from G-1-^{14}C but had little effect on that from uniformly-labelled glucose.[80] With guinea-pig brain slices, low concentrations of arsenite (an inhibitor of the TCC) and of Synkavite (sodium menadiol diphosphate) greatly reduced the C-6/C-1 ratio.[210] These findings suggest that the PPP, or part of it, may come into operation in brain under abnormal conditions.

---

*By the E-M route C-1 and C-6 of glucose both form the β-C of pyruvate, so G-1-^{14}C and G-6-^{14}C each give the same yield of $^{14}CO_2$, made in the TCC (C-6/C-1 = 1). Most authors assume for simplicity that when G-6-P enters the PPP CO_2 is formed from C-1 alone, although this is most unlikely unless only the oxidative part (21) is working. C-6/C-1 will then, if G-6-P enters both the E-M pathway and the PPP, equal (yield of $^{14}CO_2$ from G-1-^{14}C by E-M pathway)/(yield of $^{14}CO_2$ from G-1-^{14}C by both pathways). It will not give the proportion of the G-6-P entering the E-M pathway, since the ^{14}C must undergo much greater dilution and diversion in the E-M route and TCC than in the PPP. If (21) and (22) are followed by complete conversion of both the fructose-6-P and the triose phosphate to G-6-P which enters the PPP, then in the stationary state C-6/C-1 = 1 and the PPP cannot be detected by C-6/C-1 measurements. It is likelier, however, that the fructose-6-P equilibrates with G-6-P and becomes available to both pathways whereas the triose phosphate yields pyruvate. This situation is analysed by J. Katz and H. G. Wood (*J. Biol. Chem.*, 235:2165 [1960]) who allow for the influence of routes of disposal of G-6-P other than the E-M and PPP. A given value of C-6/C-1 will not then represent a unique proportion of G-6-P entering the PPP. The PPP will convert C-6 of G-6-P to C-3 of triose phosphate, and an important factor is the fraction of this C-3 which is oxidized to CO_2 (N). As $N \to 1$, C-6/C-1 for the PPP $\to 1$, so the higher N the less easily is the PPP detected. A low N exaggerates the effect of the PPP on C-6/C-1 ratios. Katz and Wood conclude that $^{14}CO_2$ yields from G-6-^{14}C and G-1-^{14}C by themselves give no useful quantitative and very limited qualitative information on the patterns of glucose metabolism. Incorporation into a triose phosphate derivative such as lactate involves the consideration that labelled triose phosphate arises from both G-6-^{14}C and G-1-^{14}C by the E-M route (C-6/C-1 = 1) but only from G-6-^{14}C by the PPP (C-1/C-6 = 0). The factor N is no longer implicated, and C-6/C-1 values are more informative than those for CO_2.

THE PASTEUR EFFECT

The Pasteur effect is a regulatory mechanism shown by a lower rate of carbohydrate consumption under aerobic than under anaerobic conditions.[212] The decreased carbohydrate breakdown necessarily involves decreased lactate accumulation. The effect is shown well by brain slices, the rate of glucose utilization in O_2 being about one-third of that in N_2[212,213] and the aerobic glucolysis being small compared with the anaerobic. In the Pasteur effect, O_2 acts indirectly through the respiration, since on abolition of the latter by HCN the glycolytic rate rises to the anaerobic value. However, many agents and conditions cause large increases in aerobic glucolysis and glucose utilization (apparent inhibition of the Pasteur effect) with no inhibition, and in some cases increase, of the respiration. These include (a) DNP, (b) phenosafranine and other compounds with rings containing N, (c) veratrine alkaloids, (d) guanidine and derivatives, (e) cation imbalance in the medium (high K^+ or low Ca^{++}), (f) (NH_4^+), (g) nicotinamide, (h) certain thiols and (i) electrical impulses. All these act on brain tissue[213-5] which is particularly susceptible; indeed (d) and (e) affect brain only, and this tissue is more sensitive than others to (f). (a), (e), (h) and (i) all lower the energy-rich phosphate and raise the P_i level in brain slices.[213]

The respiration may operate through more than one mechanism to cause the inhibition of carbohydrate consumption which forms the Pasteur effect. It seems that in muscle the respiration can decrease the permeability of the cell membrane to glucose and, independently, the rate of catabolism of glucose within the cell (P.J. Randle). For the latter effect F. Lynen and E. Racker, from studies of yeast and ascites tumour cells respectively, give the following explanation. Oxidative phosphorylation in the mitochondria removes P_i so less is available to the glyceraldehyde-3-P dehydrogenase in the cell sap. The consequent diminution in glycolytic ATP synthesis leads to slowed glucose phosphorylation, ATP formed in the mitochondria not being readily available to the hexokinase. Inhibition of the Pasteur effect by DNP is then to be expected. This postulated "compartmentation" of ATP, accepted also by B. Chance and B. Hess, is unpalatable in view of the seeming dependence of certain extra-mitochondrial biosyntheses on oxidative phosphorylation, but must be accepted *faute de mieux*.

Inhibition by O_2 of glucose consumption and lactate formation has been observed[153-6] with brain mitochondrial fractions, which are capable of glycolysis (p. 252). Evidence was obtained that the depression of lactate production was partly caused by an inhibition of glyceraldehyde-3-P dehydrogenase not due to lack of P_i or phosphate acceptors.

The aerobic inhibition of glucose consumption was abolished by respiratory-chain inhibitors, DNP and ATP, and was attributed to restricted availability of mitochondrial ATP (see above). Addition of liver mitochondria to brain supernatant fraction slowed the aerobic glucose consumption and lactate formation;[216] this was attributed to inhibition of 6-PFK.[217] Connexion with the Pasteur effect depended on the finding that the mitochondria did not inhibit glycolysis under anaerobic conditions;[216] this could not be confirmed in manometric experiments.[30] TPN addition inhibited glycolysis of brain supernatant fraction; this was attributed to accumulation of 6-phosphogluconate which inhibits PGI, with consequent accumulation of G-6-P which in turn inhibits hexokinase.[218] This offers another possible mechanism for the Pasteur effect. Clearly there are many ways in which the respiratory machinery can interfere with the glycolytic, but work with cell-free preparations is unlikely to show which are responsible for the Pasteur effect in the living cell. With brain it remains also to be seen whether permeability changes are involved.

In detecting or evaluating enzymic pathways in brain tissue results are obtained to which a variety of cytological and histological elements have simultaneously contributed. For instance, even if brain mitochondria were freed from other subcellular particles they would still be a mixture derived from perikarya, axons, dendrites and vascular and glial cells. In homogenates the contents of all these structures may be thrown together and pathways non-existent in the living cell may conceivably be brought into being; at best, metabolic rates per unit weight of tissue are averages of those of the various structures represented. This last is true even of measurements with intact-cell preparations. A start has been made in assaying enzymes in specific histological regions and even single cell bodies, as noted above. This approach must be pursued and extended to the evaluation of metabolic pathways and H transport and phosphorylation sequences. Without this the mechanisms of brain metabolism cannot be fully elucidated.*

REFERENCES

1. KERR, S. E.: *J. Biol. Chem.*, *123*:443 (1938).
2. GONCHAROVA, E. E.: *Doklady Akad. Nauk. S.S.S.R.*, *112*:899 (1957).
3. CORI, G. T., COLOWICK, S. P. and CORI, C. F.: *J. Biol. Chem.*, *123*:375, (1938).
4. KHAĬKINA, B. I. and GONCHAROVA, K. O.: *Ukrain. Biokhim. Zhur.*, *21*:239 (1949).
5. CORI, G. T. and CORI, C. F.: *J. Biol. Chem.*, *135*:733 (1940).
6. SHIMIZU, N. and OKADA, M.: *J. Histochem. & Cytochem.*, *5*:459 (1957).
7. TAKEUCHI, T.: *J. Histochem. & Cytochem.*, *6*:208 (1958).

*The writer is grateful to Miss Elizabeth Grantham for valued secretarial assistance.

8. LELOIR, L. F., OLIVAŔRIA, J. M., GOLDEMBERG, S. H. and CARMINATTI, H.: *Arch. Biochem. & Biophys., 81*:508 (1959).

8a. BRECKENRIDGE, B. M. and CRAWFORD, E. J.: *J. Biol. Chem., 235*:3054 (1960); *J. Neurochem., 7*:234 (1961).

9. LeBARON, F. N.: *Biochem. J., 61*:80 (1955).

10. VILLAR-PALASI, C. and LARNER, J.: *Arch. Biochem. & Biophys., 86*:270 (1960).

11. GIRI, K. V., NAGABHUSHANAM, A., NIGAM, V. N. and BELVADI, B.: *Science, 121*:898 (1955).

12. WOSILAIT, W. D. and SUTHERLAND, E. W.: *J. Biol. Chem., 218*:469 (1956).

13. SUTHERLAND, E. W. and RALL, T. W.: *Pharmacol. Rev., 12*:265 (1960).

14. MAZZA, F. P. and MALAGUZZI-VALERI, C.: *Arch. Sc. Biol., Napoli, 21*:443 (1935).

15. EULER, H. v., GÜNTHER, G. and VESTIN, R.: *Hoppe-Seyler's Ztschr. physiol. Chem., 240*:265 (1936).

16. MALAGUZZI-VALERI, C.: *Arch. Sc. Biol., Napoli, 22*:77 (1936).

17. MEYERHOF, O.: *Bull. Soc. chim. biol., 20*:1335 (1938).

18. BANGA, I., OCHOA, S. and PETERS, R. A.: *Biochem, J., 33*:1980 (1939).

19. GEIGER, A.: *Biochem., J., 34*:465 (1940).

20. OCHOA, S.: *J. Biol. Chem., 141*:245 (1941).

21. MACFARLANE, M. G. and WEIL-MALHERBE, H.: *Biochem. J., 35*:1 (1941).

22. MANN, P. J. G. and QUASTEL, J. H.: *Biochem. J., 35*:502 (1941).

23. UTTER, M. F., WOOD, H. G. and REINER, J. M.: *J. Biol. Chem., 161*:197 (1945).

24. BIRMINGHAM, M. K. and ELLIOTT, K. A. C.: *J. Biol. Chem., 189*:73 (1951).

25. MEYERHOF, O. and GELIAZKOWA, N.: *Arch. Biochem., 12*:405 (1947).

26. MEYERHOF, O. and WILSON, J. R.: *Arch. Biochem., 14*:71 (1947).

27. ELLIOTT, K. A. C. and HENRY, M.: *J. Biol. Chem., 163*:361 (1946).

28. ROSSITER, R. J.: *Canad. J. Biochem. & Physiol, 35*:579 (1957).

29. JOHNSON, M. K.: *Biochem. J., 77*:610 (1960).

30. CREMER, J. E.: *Biochim. et Biophys. Acta, 41*:155 (1960).

31. LePAGE, G. A.: *Cancer Res., 10*:77 (1950).

32. MENDEL, B., BAUCH, M. and STRELITZ, F.: *Klin Wschr., 10*:118 (1931).

33. DICKENS, F. and GREVILLE, G. D.: *Biochem. J., 27*:1134 (1933).

34. QUASTEL, J. H. and WHEATLEY, A. H. M.: *J. Biol. Chem., 119*:80 (1937).

35. ELLIOTT, K. A. C. and ROSENFELD, M.: *Canad. J. Biochem. & Physiol., 36*:721 (1958).

36. PAPPIUS, H. M., JOHNSON, D. M. and ELLIOTT, K. A. C.: *Canad. J. Biochem. & Physiol., 37*:999 (1959).

37. COLOWICK, S. P., CORI, G. T. and SLEIN, M. W.: *J. Biol. Chem., 168*:583 (1947).

38. MEYERHOF, O. and RANDALL, L. O.: *Arch. Biochem., 17*:171 (1948).

39. WIEBELHAUS, V. D. and LARDY, H. A.: *Arch. Biochem., 21*:321 (1949).

40. SLEIN, M. W., CORI, G. T. and CORI, C. F.: *J. Biol. Chem., 186*:763 (1950).

41. RACKER, E.: *J. Biol. Chem., 167*:843 (1947).

42. CRANE, R. K. and SOLS, A.: *J. Biol. Chem., 203*:273 (1953).

43. SOLS, A. and CRANE, R. K.: *J. Biol. Chem., 206*:925 (1954).

44. SOLS, A. and CRANE, R. K.: *J. Biol. Chem., 210*:581 (1954).

45. HARPUR, R. P. and QUASTEL, J. H.: *Nature*, London, *164*:693 (1949).

46. WEIL-MALHERBE, H. and BONE, A. D.: *Biochem. J., 49*:339 (1951).

47. LARDY, H. A., WIEBELHAUS, V. D. and MANN, K. M.: *J. Biol. Chem., 187*:325 (1950).

48. CRANE, R. K. and SOLS, H.: *J. Biol. Chem., 210*:597 (1954).

49. BURTON, R. M.: In *The Neurochemistry of Nucleotides and Amino Acids*, p. 51. R. O. Brady and D. B. Tower, Eds. New York, John Wiley (1960).

50. LONG, C. and THOMSON, A. R.: *Biochem. J., 61:*465 (1955).
51. BALÁZS, R. and LAGNADO, J. R.: *J. Neurochm., 5:*1 (1959).
52. BUELL, M. V., LOWRY, O. H., ROBERTS, N. R., CHANG, M-L. W., and KAPPHAHN, J. I.: *J. Biol. Chem., 232:*979 (1958).
53. LOWRY, O. H., ROBERTS, N. R., WU, M.-L., HIXON, W. S. and CRAWFORD, E. J.: *J. Biol. Chem., 207:*19 (1954).
54. MUNTZ, J. A.: *Arch. Biochem. & Biophys., 42:*435 (1953).
55. WINER, A. D.: *Biochem. J, 76:*5P (1960).
56. GREVILLE, G. D. and LEHMANN, H.: *J. Physiol., 102:*357 (1943).
57. TYLER, H. R.: *Proc. Soc. Exper. Biol. & Med., 104:*79 (1960).
58. ROBINS, E. and SMITH, D. E.: *As. Res. Nerv. & Ment. Dis., Proc., 32:*305 (1953).
59. ROBINS, E., SMITH, D. E., EYDT, K. M. and MCCAMAN, R. E.: *J. Neurochem., 1:*68 (1956).
60. ROBINS, E., SMITH, D. E. and JEN, M. K.: *Progr. Neurobiol,* Vol. 2, p. 205. S. R. Korey and J. I. Nurnberger, Eds. New York, Hoeber (1957).
61. STROMINGER, J. L. and LOWRY, O. H.: *J. Biol. Chem., 213:*635 (1955).
62. ROBINS, E., ROBERTS, N. R., EYDT, K. M., LOWRY, O. H. and SMITH, D. E.: *J. Biol. Chem., 218:*897 (1956).
63. BENNETT, E. L., KRECH, D., ROSENWEIG, M. R., KARLSSON, H., DYE, N. and OHLANDER, A.: *J. Neurochem., 3:*153 (1958).
64. LOWRY, O. H., ROBERTS, N. R. and CHANG, M-L. W.: *J. Biol. Chem. 222:*97 (1956).
65. LOWRY, O. H., ROBERTS, N. R. and KAPPHAHN, J. I.: *J. Biol. Chem., 224:*1047 (1957).
66. RACKER, E. and KRIMSKY, I.: *J. Biol. Chem., 161:*453 (1945).
67. UTTER, M. F.: *J. Biol. Chem., 185:*499 (1950).
68. WOODWARD, G. E. and HUDSON, M. T.: *Cancer Res., 14:*599 (1954).
69. TOWER, D. B.: *J. Neurochem., 3:*185 (1958).
70. STERN, J. R., EGGLESTON, L. V., HEMS, R. and KREBS, H. A.: *Biochem. J., 44:*410 (1949).
71. RACKER, E. and KRIMSKY, I.: *J. Biol. Chem., 173:*519 (1948).
72. MADDOCK, S., HAWKINS, J. E. and HOLMES, E.: *Am. J. Physiol., 125:*551 (1939).
73. LOEBEL, R. O.: *Biochem. Ztschr., 161:*219 (1925).
74. KIZER, D. E. and MCCOY, T. A.: *Proc. Soc. Exper. Biol. & Med., 103:*772 (1960).
75. KLEIN, J. R., HURWITZ, R. and OLSON, N. S.: *J. Biol. Chem., 164:*509 (1946).
76. ALLWEIS, C. and MAGNES, J.: *J. Neurochem., 2:*326 (1958).
77. GEIGER, A., MAGNES, J., TAYLOR, R. M. and VERALLI, M.: *Am. J. Physiol., 177:*138 (1954).
78. DICKENS, F. and GREVILLE, G. D.: *Biochem. J., 27:*832 (1933).
79. WENNER, C. E., DUNN, D. F.: and WEINHOUSE, S.: *J. Biol. Chem., 205:*409 (1953).
80. DiPIETRO, D. and WEINHOUSE, S.: *Arch. Biochem. & Biophys., 80:*268 (1959).
81. MEYERHOF, O. and WILSON, J. R.: *Arch. Biochem., 17:*153 (1948).
82. MEYERHOF, O. and WILSON, J. R.: *Arch. Biochem., 19:*502 (1948).
83. PAGE, I. H.: *Chemistry of the Brain,* p. 146. London, Baillière, Tindall & Cox, (1937).
84. BURTON, R. M., SODD, M. A. and BRADY, R. O.: *J. Biol. Chem., 233:*1053 (1958).
85. LELOIR, L. F.: *Advances Enzymol., 14:*193 (1953).
86. MAXWELL, E. S., KALCKAR, H. M. and BURTON, R. M.: *Biochim. et Biophys. Acta, 18:*444 (1955).
87. GREVILLE, G. D.: *Biochem. J., 30:*877 (1936).

88. KREBS, H. A., EGGLESTON, L. V., KLEINZELLER, A. and SMYTH, D. H.: *Biochem. J.*, *34*:1234 (1940).
89. DEWAN, J. G. and GREEN, D. E.: *Biochem. J.*, *32*:626 (1938).
89a. GIUDITTA, A. and STRECKER, H. J.: *Biochim. et Biophys. Acta*, *48*:10 (1961).
90. KREBS, H. A. and JOHNSON, W. A.: *Biochem. J.*, *31*:645 (1937).
91. WEIL-MALHERBE, H.: *Biochem. J.*, *31*:299, 2080, 2202 (1937).
92. WEBB, J. L. and ELLIOTT, K. A. C.: *Canad. J. Res.*, *26E*:239 (1948).
93. ELLIOTT, K. A. C., SCOTT, D. B. M. and LIBET, B.: *J. Biol. Chem.*, *146*:251 (1942).
94. LONG, C.: *Biochem. J.*, *32*:1711 (1938).
95. SEAMAN, G. R. and NASCHKE, M. D.: *J. Biol. Chem.*, *217*:1 (1955).
96. GUZMAN BARRON, E. S. and GHIRETTI, F.: *Biochim. et Biophys. Acta*, *12*:239 (1953).
97. ELLIOTT, K. A. C., GREIG, M. E. and BENOY, M. P.: *Biochem. J.*, *31*:1003 (1937).
98. McCLYMONT, G. L. and SETCHELL, B. P.: *Australian J. Biol. Sc.*, *9*:184 (1956).
99. OCHOA, S., STERN, J. R. and SCHNEIDER, M. C.: *J. Biol. Chem.*, *193*:691 (1951).
100. WOLLEMANN, M.: *Acta Physiol. Acad. Sc. Hung.*, *10*:171 (1956).
101. SRERE, P. A.: *J. Biol. Chem.*, *234*:2544 (1959).
102. FELDBERG, W. and MANN, T.: *J. Physiol.*, *104*:411 (1946).
103. PERSKY, H. and GUZMAN BARRON, E. S.: *Biochim. et Biophys. Acta*, *5*:66 (1950).
104. JOHNSON, W. A.: *Biochem. J.*, *33*:1046 (1939).
105. COXON, R. V.: *Biochem. J.*, *55*:545 (1953).
106. SHEPHERD, J. A. and KALNITSKY, G.: *J. Biol. Chem.*, *207*:605 (1954).
107. COXON, R. V.: *Bull. Soc. chim. belg.*, *65*:68 (1956).
108. ADLER, E., EULER, H. V., GÜNTHER, G. and PLASS, M.: *Biochem. J.*, *33*:1028 (1939).
109. SHEPHERD, J. A.: *J. Histochem. & Cytochem.*, *4*:47 (1956).
110. QUASTEL, J. H.: *Physiol. Rev.*, *19*:135 (1939).
111. ABOOD, L. G., GERARD, R. W., BANKS, J. and TSCHIRGI, R. D.: *Am. J. Physiol.*, *168*:728 (1952).
112. ALDRIDGE, W. N. and JOHNSON, M. K.: *Biochem. J.*, *73*:270 (1959).
113. GIUDITTA, A. and SINGER, T. P.: *J. Biol. Chem.*, *234*:666 (1959).
114. GREEN, D. E.: *Biochem. J.*, *30*:2095 (1936).
115. LONG, C.: *Biochem. J.*, *39*:143 (1945).
116. DELBRÜCK, A., SCHIMASSEK, H., BARTSCH, K. and BÜCHER, T.: *Biochem. Ztschr.*, *331*:297 (1959).
116a. ROBERTS, E.: In *Inhibition in the Nervous System and Gamma-aminobutyric Acid*, p. 144. E. Roberts, Ed. Oxford, Pergamon Press (1960).
116b. McKHANN, G. M., ALBERS, R. W., SOKOLOFF, L., MICKELSEN, O. and TOWER, D. B.: *ibid*, p. 169.
117. RUTENBURG, A. M., WOLMAN, M. and SELIGMAN, A. M.: *J. Histochem. & Cytochem.*, *1*:66 (1953).
118. NEUMANN, K. and KOCH, G.: *Hoppe-Seyler's Ztschr. physiol. Chem.*, *295*:35 (1953).
119. MUSTAKALLIO, K. K.: *Ann. med. exper. et biol. Fenniae*, *32*:175 (1954).
120. SHIMIZU, N. and MORIKAWA, N.: *J. Histochem. & Cytochem.*, *5*:334 (1957).
121. FRIEDE, R.: *J. Histochem. & Cytochem.*, *6*:347 (1958).
122. LONG, C.: *Biochem. J.*, *37*:215 (1943).
123. LONG, C.: *Biochem. J.*, *40*:278 (1946).
124. REINER, J. M.: *Arch. Biochem.*, *12*:327 (1947)

125. LARNER, J., JANDORF, B. J. and SUMMERSON, W. H.: *J. Biol. Chem.*, *178*:373 (1949).
126. ELLIOTT, K. A. C. and HENRY, M.: *J. Biol. Chem.*, *163*:351 (1946).
127. ELLIOTT, K. A. C. and HENDERSON, N.: *J. Neurophysiol.*, *11*:473 (1948).
128. GEIGER, A.: *Physiol. Rev.*, *38*:1 (1958).
128a. BARKULIS, S. S., GEIGER, A., YAWAKITA, Y. and AGUILAR, V.: *J. Neurochem.*, *5*:339 (1960).
129. VIGNAIS, P. M., GALLAGHER, C. H. and ZABIN, I.: *J. Neurochem.*, *2*:283 (1958).
130. SUTHERLAND, V. C., BURBRIDGE, T. N. and ELLIOTT, H. W.: *Am. J. Physiol.*, *180*:195 (1955).
131. BELOFF-CHAIN, A., CATANZARO, R., CHAIN, E. B., MASI, I. and POCCHIARI, F.: *Proc. Roy. Soc., London*, *B144*:22 (1955).
132. KINI, M. M. and QUASTEL, J. H.: *Nature*, London, *184*:252 (1959).
133. CHAIN, E. B., LARSSON, S. and POCCHIARI, F.: *Proc. Roy. Soc., London*, *B152*:283 (1960).
134. BELOFF-CHAIN, A., CANTANZARO, R., CHAIN, E. B., MASI, I. and POCCHIARI, F.: *Ann. Acad. Sc. Fenniae*, Ser. AII, No. *60*:412 (1955).
135. HIMWICH, H. E.: *Brain Metabolism and Cerebral Disorders*. Baltimore, Williams & Wilkins (1951).
136. BRODY, T. M. and BAIN, J. A.: *J. Biol. Chem.*, *195*:685 (1952).
137. PETRUSHKA, E. and GIUDITTA, A.: *J. Biophys. Biochem. Cytol.*, *6*:129 (1959).
138. ALDRIDGE, W. N.: *Biochem. J.*, *67*:423 (1957).
139. WHITTAKER, V. P.: *Biochem. Pharmacol.*, *1*:351 (1958-9).
140. GRAY, E. G. and WHITTAKER, V. P.: *J. Physiol.*, *153*:35P (1960).
141. CHRISTIE, G. S., JUDAH, J. D. and REES, K. R.: *Proc. Roy Soc., London*, *B141*:523 (1953).
142. BERGER, M., STRECKER, H. J. and WAELSCH, H.: *Nature*, London, *177*:1234 (1956).
143. GALLAGHER, C. H., JUDAH, J. D. and REES, K. R.: *Biochem. J.*, *62*:436 (1956).
144. ABOOD, L. G. and ALEXANDER, L.: *J. Biol. Chem.*, *227*:717 (1957).
145. BEER, C. T. and QUASTEL, J. H.: *Canad. J. Biochem. & Physiol.*, *36*:531 (1958).
146. ALDRIDGE, W. N. and PARKER, V. H.: *Biochem. J.*, *76*:47 (1960).
147. SCHOLEFIELD, P. G.: *Canad. J. Biochem. & Physiol.*, *34*:1211, 1227 (1956).
148. PETRUSHKA, E., QUASTEL, J. H. and SCHOLEFIELD, P. G.: *Canad. J. Biochem. Physiol.*, *37*:975, 989 (1959).
149. BRAGANCA, B. M. and QUASTEL, J. H.: *Biochem. J.*, *53*:88 (1953).
150. DU BUY, H. G. and HESSELBACH, M. L.: *J. Histochem. & Cytochem.*, *4*:363 (1956).
151. ABOOD, L. G., BRUNNGRABER, E. and TAYLOR, M.: *J. Biol. Chem.*, *234*:1307 (1959).
152. BRUNNGRABER, E. G. and ABOOD, L. G.: *J. Biol. Chem.*, *235*:1847 (1960).
153. BALÁZS, R. and RICHTER, D.: *Biochem. J.*, *68*:5P (1958).
154. BALÁZS, R.: *Biochem. J.*, *72*:561 (1959).
155. BALÁZS, R. and RICHTER, D.: *Biochem. J.*, *74*:30P (1960).
156. BALÁZS, R. and RICHTER, D.: *Biochem. J.*, *76*:67P (1960).
157. OCHOA, S.: *J. Biol. Chem.*, *138*:751 (1941).
158. COLOWICK, S. P., KALCKAR, H. M. and CORI, C. F.: *J. Biol. Chem.*, *137*:343 (1941).
159. BERRY, J. F. and MCMURRAY, W. C.: *Canad. J. Biochem. & Physiol.*, *35*:799 (1957).
160. ABOOD, L. G. and ROMANCHEK, L.: *Biochem. J.*, *60*:233 (1955).

161. PENNIALL, R., KALNITSKY, G. and ROUTH, J. I.: *Arch. Biochem. & Biophys.,* *64*:390 (1956).
162. SETCHELL, B. P.: *Biochem. J., 72*:265 (1960).
163. CASE, E. M. and McILWAIN, H.: *Biochem. J., 48*:1 (1951).
164. ARAVINDAKSHAN, J. I. and BRAGANCA, B. M.: *Biochim. et Biophys. Acta, 31*:463 (1959).
165. STRICKLAND, K. P., THOMPSON, R. H. S. and WEBSTER, G. R.: *Biochem. J.,* *62*:512 (1956).
166. DAWKINS, M. J. R., JUDAH, J. D. and REES, K. R.: *Biochem. J., 72*:204 (1959).
167. CHAPPELL, J. B. and GREVILLE, G. D.: *Nature,* London, *174*:930 (1954).
168. NAIDOO, D. and PRATT, O. E.: *Biochem. J., 62*:465 (1956).
169. LAGNADO, J. R., BALÁZS, R. and RICHTER, D.: *Biochem. J., 73*:18P (1959).
170. HESS, H. H. and POPE, A.: *J. Neurochem., 3*:287 (1959).
171. MAXWELL, R. E. and NICKEL, V. S.: *Proc. Soc. Exper. Biol. & Med., 86*:846 (1954).
172. BAIN, J. A.: *Progr. Neurobiol.,* Vol. 2, p. 139. S. R. Korey and J. I. Nurnberger, Eds. New York, Hoeber (1957).
173. HUSZÁK, S.: *Biochem. Ztschr., 298*:137 (1938).
174. ELLIOTT, K. A. C. and GREIG, M. E.: *Biochem. J., 32*:1407 (1938).
175. SCHNEIDER, W. C. and POTTER, V. R.: *J. Biol. Chem., 149*:217 (1943).
176. GALLAGHER, C. H. and BUTTERY, S. H.: *Biochem. J., 72*:575 (1959).
177. HESS, H. H. and POPE, A.: *J. Neurochem., 5*:207 (1960).
178. POPE, A., HESS, H. H., WARE, J. R. and THOMSON, R. H.: *J. Neurophysiol., 19*:259 (1956).
179. GALLAGHER, C. H., JUDAH, J. D. and REES, K. R.: *Proc. Roy. Soc.,* London, *B145*:134, 195 (1956).
180. HOWELL, J. McC. and DAVIDSON, A. N.: *Biochem. J., 72*:365 (1959).
181. KLINGENBERG, M. and SLENCZA, W.: *Biochem. Ztschr., 331*:334 (1959).
182. BESSEY, O. A., LOWRY, O. H. and LOVE, R. H.: *J. Biol. Chem., 180*:755 (1949).
183. BURCH, H. B., LOWRY, O. H., PADILLA, A. M. and COMBS, A. M.: *J. Biol. Chem., 223*:29 (1956).
184. SCHAUS, R. and KIRK, J. E.: *J. Gerontol., 11*:147 (1956).
185. GLOCK, G. E. and McLEAN, P.: *Biochem. J., 61*:388 (1955).
186. JEDEIKIN, L. A. and WEINHOUSE, S.: *J. Biol. Chem., 213*:271 (1955).
187. JACOBSON, K. B. and KAPLAN, N. O.: *J. Biol. Chem., 226*:603 (1957).
188. KLINGENBERG, M., SLENCZA, W. and RITT, E.: *Biochem. Ztschr., 332*:47 (1959).
189. McILWAIN, H. and TRESIZE, M. A.: *Biochem. J., 65*:288 (1957).
190. BRODY, T. M., WANG, R. I. H. and BAIN, J. A.: *J. Biol. Chem., 198*:821 (1952).
191. GIUDITTA, A. and STRECKER, H. J.: *J. Neurochem., 5*:50 (1959).
192. KAPLAN, N. O., COLOWICK, S. P. and NEUFELD, E. F.: *J. Biol. Chem., 205*:1 (1953).
193. HUMPHREY, G. F.: *Biochem. J., 65*:546 (1957).
194. VIGNAIS, P. V. and VIGNAIS, P. M.: *Biochim. et Biophys. Acta, 47*:515 (1961).
195. STEIN, A. M., KAPLAN, N. O. and CIOTTI, M. M.: *J. Biol. Chem., 234*:979 (1959).
196. RINGLER, R. L. and SINGER, T. P.: *J. Biol. Chem., 234*:2211 (1959).
197. GREEN, D. E.: *Biochem. J., 30*:629 (1936).
198. SACKTOR, B., PACKER, L. and ESTABROOK, R. W.: *Arch. Biochem. & Biophys., 80*:68 (1959).
199. BOXER, G. E. and SHONK, C. E.: *Cancer Res. 20*:85 (1960).
200. GREEN, D. E., NEEDHAM, D. M. and DEWAN, J. G.: *Biochem. J., 31*:2327 (1937).

201. MOLDAVE, K., WINZLER, R. J. and PEARSON, H. E.: *J. Biol. Chem.*, *200:*357 (1953).
202. UTTER, M. F.: *Ann. New York Acad. Sc. 72:*451 (1959).
203. OCHOA, S., VEIGA SALLES, J. B. and ORTIZ, P. J.: *J. Biol. Chem.*, *187:*863 (1960).
204. DICKENS, F. and GLOCK, G. E.: *Biochem. J.*, *50:*81 (1951).
205. SABLE, H. Z.: *Biochim. et Biophys. Acta, 8:*687 (1952).
206. GLOCK, G. E. and MCLEAN, P.: *Biochem. J.*, *56:*171, (1954).
207. GORDON, M., HAWLEY, P. and GAITONDE, M. K.: *Neurology, 8:*Suppl. 1, 75 (1958).
208. HORECKER, B. L. and SMYRNIOTIS, P. Z.: *J. Biol. Chem.*, *193:*371 (1951).
209. BLOOM, B.: *Proc. Soc. Exper. Biol. & Med.*, *88:*317 (1955).
210. HOSKIN, F. C. G.: *Arch. Biochem. & Biophys.*, *91:*43 (1960).
211. SACKS, W.: *J. Appl. Physiol.*, *10:*37 (1957).
212. DIXON, K. C.: *Biol. Rev., Cambridge Phil. Soc., 12:*431 (1937).
213. MCILWAIN, H.: *Biochemistry and the Central Nervous System*, 2nd Ed. London, Churchill (1959).
214. DICKENS, F.: In *The Enzymes*, 1st Ed, Vol. 2, part i, p. 672. J. B. Sumner and K. Myrbäck, Eds. New York, Acad. Press (1951).
215. MCILWAIN, H.: *Biochem. J., 71:*281 (1959).
216. AISENBERG, A. C., RENAFARGE, B. and POTTER, V. R.: *J. Biol. Chem.*, *224:*1099 (1957).
217. AISENBERG, A. C.: *J. Biol. Chem., 234:*441 (1959).
218. POTTER, V. R. and NIEMEYER, H.: In *Regulation of Cell Metabolism*, p. 230. Ciba Foundation Symposium (1959).

XII

SIGNIFICANCE OF THIAMINE IN THE METABOLISM AND FUNCTION OF THE BRAIN

R. A. Peters

THE DIRECT connexion of thiamine deficiency with a convulsive stage and with cellular oxidations was not only the first instance of the *in vitro* action of a vitamin but, the writer thinks, it brought to a focus the ideas generated by Hopkins' address on the dynamic action of biochemical substances and the predominant significance of enzymes. It also provided a firm foundation for the progress of neurochemistry in the enzyme field. Knowledge of the relation of thiamine to the oxidation of pyruvate in brain started with the finding of a fault in the disposal of lactate, especially associated with the lower parts of the pigeon brain.[1] From this it was found that there was a depression of oxygen uptake in Ringer-phosphate solutions in the presence of lactate or glucose, not present when succinate was the substrate. This lowering of the oxygen uptake in brain tissue occurred only in the pigeon made deficient in thiamine and only when the acute signs of opisthotonus appeared. The condition was reversed specifically by addition of thiamine *in vitro* as well as *in vivo*. The convulsions induced at the acute stage of a deficiency could be cured with great rapidity, within 20 to 30 minutes, by injection of a thiamine solution into the subarachnoid space of the bird. In this time it was difficult to conceive of a histological change, and the condition was considered to be that of a pure biochemical lesion, a term introduced to describe this state. The absence of detectable histological change was found in Oxford[2] and was subsequently confirmed in extended work in Boston.[3]

Further investigation of the phenomenon led to the discovery that there was a change in pyruvate metabolism. This metabolite accumulated in the avitaminous animal, and disappeared in the brain even *in vitro* on adding the vitamin. The Oxford results on the pigeon

267

were confirmed in the chick[4] in the USA. In the terminal stages of thiamine deficiency there was an increased amount of pyruvate in the blood[5] which was found also in beri-beri patients.[6] It was tempting to think that the increase of pyruvate in the brain tissue was the immediate cause of the convulsions; but injected pyruvate disappears with great speed[7] and the more balanced view is that the convulsions are induced by the dysfunction of the nerve cells caused by failure in the energy metabolism.

It was a lucky circumstance that this work developed with thiamine and the pigeon's brain, as this vitamin and tissue show the biochemical lesion better than any other yet found. It appears that, in the pigeon, the critical loss of thiamine in an acute deficiency occurs first in the brain. The brain deficiency is less easily shown in the rat. It was demonstrated originally in a lactate-pyrophosphate medium, but was even then less marked.[8] Sometimes it cannot be demonstrated. The reason for this is not clear; it is possible that in many rats thiamine may be lowered critically first in the heart, as is often the case in clinical beri beri.

Leaving out much detail the next step was initiated by the identification of the cofactor for alcoholic fermentation in yeast as thiamine-pyrophosphate (TPP);[8a] this cofactor had been found to be necessary for the complete action of the enzyme carboxylase in yeast which decarboxylates α-keto acids like pyruvate and is therefore an essential step in alcoholic fermentation.

$$CH_3CO\ COOH \rightarrow CH_3.CHO + CO_2 \rightarrow CH_3CH_2OH$$

It became necessary to decide whether thiamine acted as such in brain or after conversion by the brain tissue to thiamine diphosphate.

First came the question whether the brain tissue contained thiamine diphosphate and, if so, under what circumstances this varied. The diagram (Fig. 1) shows that the thiamine diphosphate in brain tissue decreases during the period of rice feeding in which the diet is deficient in thiamine. Except after dosing with thiamine, the brain contained little of the free vitamin.[9] The initiation of convulsions was found to be associated with a further fall in TPP content amounting to 0.8 μg./g. This shows how small the change can be between a functioning brain and one in which the metabolism is wrong.

The results obtained in Oxford were confirmed and extended in Holland to other birds,[10] and have been extended more recently by the finding that the thiamine analogue pyrithiamine induces convulsions together with a rapid fall in TPP content of brain in the rat;[11] this was in contrast to a deficiency in the diet in which case the thiamine content of the brain was retained better than that of other tissues. Forced feeding with carbohydrate in pigeons, oddly enough, gave a higher thiamine concentration in brain at death (viz. 1.26 μg./g.) than without carbohydrate (0.81 μg./g.).[12] Feeding with thyroid tissue or thyroxine lowers the content of TPP in rats' brain, unless there is excess thiamine in the diet,[13] an important pointer for clinical medicine.

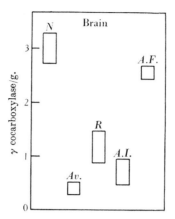

Fig. 1. Cocarboxylase in pigeon's brain. *N,* normal. *Av.,* avitaminous (with symptoms). R, rice-fed (no symptoms). *A.I.,* avitaminous after injection of vitamin B_1. *A.F.,* avitaminous fed vitamin B_1 for 3 days. Ordinates: mean $\pm 2\epsilon$. (Courtesy, Ochoa, S. and Peters, R. A.: *Biochem. J.,* 32:1510 (1938).)

The thiamine diphosphate was decreased in brain during convulsions; but this fact alone did not show that it was the active component of the pyruvate oxidase system. Final proof came by using instead of 'brei' a 'dispersion' of pigeon brain, made by grinding in 1% KCl in a mortar, reinforced with Mg, ATP and fumarate.[14] In this way from the avitaminous brains a dispersion was obtained in which the extra respiration in pyruvate was induced by thiamine diphosphate and not by thiamine. This proved the point that thiamine must be converted by brain tissue to the diphosphate even *in vitro* before it became the active cofactor. No other step appears to be necessary.

The 'dispersions' of pigeon brain were much more unstable than the 'brei,' but they made possible an analysis of some of the biochemical factors needed for pyruvate oxidation. Whereas the brei needed only buffers and pyruvate for oxidation (and, when avitaminous, thiamine), and whereas fumarate addition made no difference in O_2 uptake, brain dispersions required reinforcement with fumarate as well as Mg, phosphate and an adenine nucleotide. Until recently, active dispersions could be obtained from rabbit and guinea pig brains, but not from the rat; however active dispersions can be made from the latter by modern methods, using sucrose.[15]

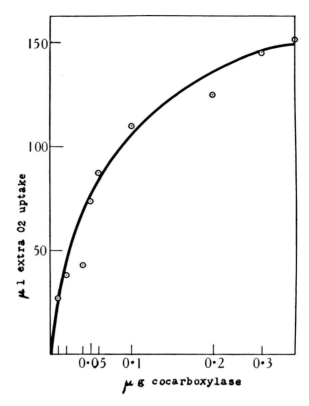

Fig. 2. Pyruvate oxidase system, homogenate of avitaminous pigeon brain tissue; relation between the amount of cocarboxylase (aneurin pyrophosphate) added and the increase of oxygen consumption (Banga, Ochoa and Peters[44]).

Though it was realized that complete oxidation of pyruvate needed a 'battery of enzymes,' and though the need for fumarate was suggestive, it was for a long time not possible to reconcile certain experimental facts with the oxidation of pyruvate via the Krebs tricarboxylic acid cycle. There was firstly the fact that no vitamin effect with succinate could be shown with brei from the avitaminous brain which showed this well with pyruvate and lactate. The oxidation of succinate and pyruvate, as also of α-ketoglutarate and pyruvate was additive.[16] If pyruvate oxidation passed through a succinate stage, why was there no vitamin effect, and especially why was there no inhibition with excess of succinate? The writer now thinks that the brei as prepared must include in addition to stable mitochondria oxidising via the citric acid cycle, separate particles containing the succinoxidase system which are probably damaged mitochondria.[17] This would reconcile these apparent contradictions and may prove biochemically important.

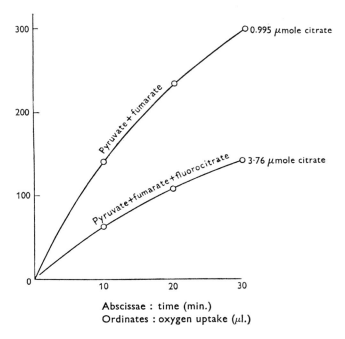

Abscissae : time (min.)
Ordinates : oxygen uptake (μl.)

Fig. 3. The effect of citrate inhibitor (fluorocitrate) on the oxygen uptake and citrate accumulation in homogenates of pigeon brain. As shown by the lower curve, the addition of fluorocitrate lowers oxygen uptake by stopping the metabolism of citrate, which therefore accumulates. (Courtesy, Peters, R. A. and Wakelin, R. W.: *J. Physiol., 119:*421 (1953).)

A second obstacle was the fact that reinforcement of the dispersion with succinate, fumarate and malate much enhanced pyruvate oxidation; with α-ketoglutarate the effect was less, and with citrate it could be negligible; this latter point was against oxidation via the cycle unless it could be shown that it was due to lack of permeability. That this must be so can be shown very clearly by using fluoro-citrate to block aconitase. Pyruvate oxidation decreases with accumulation of citrate. The effect does not occur with brei, which appears to be impermeable even to fluorocitrate. Small accumulation of citrate and α-ketoglutarate can also be shown in dispersions during pyruvate oxidation. The above facts are given in some detail to show how a recognition of separate anatomical parts of the cell can reconcile apparently contradictory facts. We can say now that much of pyruvate oxidation in brain normally passes through the tricarboxylic acid cycle, which means that TPP also is in control at the α-ketoglutarate stage. During an avitaminosis in the pigeon this TPP is not affected.

The stage in the oxidation of pyruvate involving TPP is the initial decarboxylation. In yeast, on the whole, α-keto acids are decarboxylated irrespective of the length of chain. With the pigeon brain brei, in addition to pyruvate, α-ketobutyrate was decarboxylated, but after this there was no further reaction; in contrast to yeast, the effects with α-ketovalerate were much smaller. α-Ketobutyrate competes with pyruvate for the active centre concerned (18a). After decarboxylation, the product from α-ketobutyrate was not oxidised further; on the other hand, that from pyruvate in the presence of the appropriate factors

TABLE I

COMPARISON OF CO_2 EVOLUTION BY YEAST AND O_2 UPTAKE FOR BRAIN WITH α–KETO ACIDS ($\mu l.$)

Keto Acid	Yeast CO_2 Evolution*	Brain O_2 Uptake†	RQ‡	Mol. Oxidised**
Pyruvate	316	696	1.3	45.4
α–ketobutyrate	396	171	2.3	45.7
α–ketovalerate	273	18	——	

*In 25 minutes.
†Per gram per hour over 3 hours.
‡$\dfrac{CO_2}{O_2}$.
**In 3 hours.

(From data of Long and Peters and of McGowan.)

can be oxidized via the citric acid cycle. In the absence of these factors, it is converted irreversibly to acetate, which does not increase the oxygen uptake of brain. The metabolism of pyruvate by brain brei was accounted for quantitatively in terms of the following 3 equations.[18b]

$$67\% \quad 2CH_3.CO.COOH + 5O_2 = 6CO_2 + 4H_2O$$
$$19.5\% \quad 2CH_3.CO.COOH + O_2 = 2CH_3.COOH + 2CO_2$$
$$10\% \quad 2CH_3.CO.COOH + H_2O = CH_3 CHOH COOH + CH_3COOH$$

Since it would now be believed that the metabolism of pyruvate goes through acetyl-SCoA, it seems that brain tissue cannot form propionyl-SCoA. The observations recorded up to this point make clear that thiamine as the pyrophosphate is concerned in the first stage of pyruvate oxidation. In dealing with subsequent stages it is relevant to make what may appear to be a digression.

A development of much interest took place during the war when it was discovered in Oxford that the pyruvate oxidase system of brain tissue and that part sensitive to thiamine was especially sensitive to the action of certain mono-substituted tervalent arsenicals as well as to dichlordiethyl sulphone. The sensitivity was much greater when pyruvate was a substrate than, for instance, when succinate was substrate. These researches and analyses of compounds of arsenicals with kerateine (reduced keratin) led to the idea that the arsenical lewisite was combined to form a ring with two contiguous SH groups. The ring

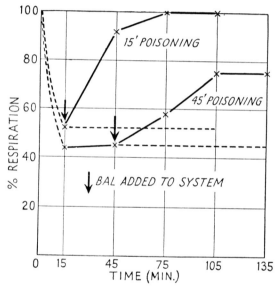

Fig. 4. Reversibility of toxicity of lewisite to the pyruvate oxidase system in brain brei from the pigeon. Substrate pyruvate. Sufficient lewisite oxide was added to the brain brei to produce a decrease in respiration of approximately 50%. BAL was added at the points indicated by the arrows after 15 and 45 minutes of respiration. (Data of Stocken and Thompson, 1941.)

hypothesis was made more definite by the practical finding that British Anti-Lewisite (BAL, 2,3-dimercaptopropanol), which is capable of forming a five-membered ring with arsenic[20] acted as an antidote by removing the arsenical lewisite from its combination with a component in the pyruvate oxidase system; further no monothiol compound would act as antidote *in vitro* or *in vivo*. The nature of this component was obscure for some years. It was not possible to see how the apo-enzyme could contain on its protein two contiguous -SH groups. Some ten years later than the experiments in Oxford, workers in the U.S.A.[21] concluded that in some bacterial systems the pyruvate oxidase system required a dithio compound, 6,8-dithiooctanoic acid, which is now called lipoic acid. This can also exist in dithiol form.

$$CH_2.CH_2.CH.(CH_2)_4.COOH$$
$$\quad | \qquad\ |$$
$$\ SH \quad\ SH$$

Lipoic acid

It satisfies the criterion that after poisoning with arsenite the inhibition in the bacterial system can be reversed by BAL. Sometimes a dithiol such as BAL accelerates oxidation. Lipoic acid has been found in liver tissue, but the writer has found no record of its presence in brain. A dithiol, however, fits in so well with the behaviour of brain tissue and arsenicals so far as the BAL work goes that it is unlikely that some similar dithiol is not part of the pyruvate oxidase system in brain together with TPP. *Ceteris paribus* it would be a component of α-ketoglutarate oxidation by analogy with research on these two systems in muscle tissue.[22] Hence we reach the conclusion that pyruvate is oxidised in brain tissue by the tricarboxylic acid cycle; its entry is initiated by conversion to a C_2 fragment for which at least TPP and a dithio compound as well as an apoenzyme are required.[26]

Other forms of thiamine are known. With the opening of the thiazole ring there can be oxidation to a disulphide. It is not known whether this -SH/-S-S system is functional; when the disulphide is used in a brain system *in vitro* it is rapidly converted back to thiamine.

Before closing it should be mentioned that in man Wernicke's syndrome bears a close relation to phenomena seen in partial deficiency of thiamine in pigeons. (For general reviews see refs. 24 and 25.)

REFERENCES

1. The following took part in the early work in Oxford, H. W. Kinnersley, N. Gavrilescu, R. Passmore, A. P. Meilklejohn, H. M. Sinclair, R. H. S. Thompson, J. R. P. O'Brien. See Reviews by Peters, R. A.: *Lancet 1*:1161 (1936); *Chem. & Ind., 59*:373 (1940).
2. CARLETON, H. M.: Unpublished.
3. SWANK, R. L.: *J. Exper. Med., 71*:683 (1940).
4. SHERMAN, H. C. and ELVEHJEM, C. A.: *Am. J. Physiol., 117*:142 (1936).
5. THOMPSON, R. H. S. and JOHNSON, R. E.: *Biochem. J., 29*:694 (1935).
6. PLATT, B. S. and LU, G. D.: *Biochem. J., 33*:1525 (1939).
7. LU, G. D. and NEEDHAM, D. M.: *Biochem. J., 33*:1544 (1939).
8. O'BRIEN, J. R. P. and PETERS, R. A.: *J. Physiol., 85*:454, (1935)
8a. LOHMANN, K. and SCHUSTER, P.: *Biochem. Ztschr., 294*:188 (1937).
9. OCHOA, S. and PETERS, R. A.: *Biochem. J., 32*:1510 (1938).

10. WESTENBRINK, H. G. K. and GOUDSMIT, J.: *Enzymol.*, *5*:307 (1938); WESTENBRINK, H. G. K. and VAN LEER, I. S.: *Arch. Néer. Physiol.*, *25*:536 (1940); VILLELA, G. G., et al.: *Arch. Biochem.*, *23*:81 (1949).

11. KOEDAM, J. C.: *Biochem. Biophys. Acta*, *29*:333 (1958); DE CARO, C. A. R., et al.: *Experimentia*, *12*:300 (1956).

12. GRUBER, M.: *Biochem. Biophys. Acta*, *7*:480 (1951).

13. PETERS, R. A. and ROSSITER, R. J.: *Biochem. J.*, *33*:1146 (1939).

14. BANGA, I., OCHOA, S. and PETERS, R. A.: *Biochem. J.*, *33*:1109, 1980 (1939).

15. McGOWAN, G. K. and PETERS, R. A.: *Biochem. J.*, *31*:1637 (1937).

16. BRODY, T. M. and BAIN, J. A.: *J. Biol. Chem.*, *195*:685 (1952); ALDRIDGE, W. N.: *Biochem. J.*, *67*:423 (1957).

17. Suggested by Dr. J. B. Chappell.

18. (a) LONG, C. and PETERS, R. A.: *Biochem. J.*, *33*:759 (1939); (b) LONG, C.: *Biochem. J.*, *32*:1711 (1938).

19. PETERS, R. A., STOCKEN, L. A. and THOMPSON, R. H. S.: *Nature*, London, *156*:616 (1945); see also PETERS, R. A.: Dohme Lectures I. *Bull Johns Hopkins Hosp.*, *97*:1 (1955).

20. STOCKEN, L. A. and THOMPSON, R. H. S.: *Biochem. J.*, *40*:535 (1946).

21. GUNSALUS, I. C. and others; see under METTZLER.[24]

22. GREEN, D. E., WESTERFELD, W. W., VENNESLAND, B. and KNOX, W. E.: *J. Biol. Chem*, *145*:69 (1942).

23. PETERS, R. A.: *Nature*, London, *158*:707 (1946) (for references also).

24. Review. METTZLER, P. E.: *The Enzymes*, 2nd Ed., Vol. 2, New York Acad. Press 1960.

25. Review. JANSEN, B. C. P.: *Vitamins & Hormones*, *VII*:83 (1949).

26. GAL, E. M. and RAZEVSKA, D. E. have now proved the presence of Lipoic Acid in Brain. *Arch. Biochem. Biophys. 89*:253, (1960).

XIII

THE TURNOVER OF PROTEINS AND LIPIDS *IN VIVO* IN THE BRAIN

DEREK RICHTER

THE CONCEPT of the dynamic state of body constituents has developed mainly as a result of experiments with isotopic tracers. The use of labelled metabolites made it possible to measure the rates of metabolic processes occurring *in vivo* and it was found that proteins, lipids and other cell constituents are continually being broken down and resynthesized (Schoenheimer[1]). By this process of constant renewal the living cell is able to repair the damage caused by stress or injury and maintain its characteristic structural organization unimpaired. This balanced process of continuous turnover which has been revealed only by the use of isotopes, must clearly be distinguished from the net increase in the amount of a constituent, such as occurs during growth or during glandular secretion: but since there is no evidence to the contrary, it is believed that similar pathways of synthesis are involved. In other words, the net synthesis of new protein and lipid during growth and secretion are likely to be effected by the same synthetic mechanisms that operate in the normal dynamic turnover of cell constituents. The processes concerned in dynamic turnover are sometimes written in the form of a simple reversible reaction,

$$\text{precursor} \rightleftharpoons \text{cell constituent},$$

but it must be understood that a number of intermediate steps are generally involved and the pathway of degradation may not be simply a reversal of the synthetic process.

In the steady state of equilibrium the amino acids and other metabolites concerned in dynamic turnover are present at constant concentration although continually being replaced, and they have been regarded as forming 'metabolic pools.' The rate of replacement is expressed by the turnover rate, v which may be defined as the flux of metabolite through the metabolic pool (Reiner[2]), or

$$v = \frac{\text{amount of metabolite replaced per min.}}{\text{total amount of metabolite in pool}}$$

The turnover may also be expressed in terms of the half-life $t_{\frac{1}{2}}$ of a cell constituent on the assumption that we are dealing with first order reactions.

$$t\frac{1}{2} = \frac{\text{concentration of product} \times \ln 2}{\text{flux of metabolite}}$$

I. TURNOVER OF PROTEIN

(1) The Composition of the Amino Acid Pool

The free amino acid pool of the brain contains the nine amino acids essential for growth in the rat, and also arginine, proline and tyrosine, at concentrations similar to those in the blood plasma. Glutamic acid, aspartic acid, glycine, alanine and threonine are present in relatively large amounts, which suggests that these amino acids may have other functions in the brain besides serving as building blocks for protein synthesis (Ansell and Richter;[3] Tallan *et al.*;[4] Waelsch[5]).

Attempts to measure the utilization of amino acids in the brain *in vivo*, by analysing samples of the blood entering and leaving the brain have given evidence of a small but significant conversion of glutamic acid into glutamine in the blood traversing the brain (Adams *et al.*[6]); but the net utilization of amino acids in the brain is probably small under normal physiological conditions (Kety[7]). Kamin and Handler[8] showed that the concentrations of methionine, histidine, lysine and arginine in the brain can be increased by raising the concentration in the blood plasma in the dog: but the concentrations of glutamic acid, tyrosine and other amino acids in the brain cannot be raised by elevating the blood level. It has been concluded that this may be because these amino acids penetrate only very slowly through the blood-brain barrier (Waelsch[5]). On the other hand Roberts *et al.*[9] found that glutamic acid and phenylalanine penetrate at an appreciable rate through the blood-brain barrier in the mouse: the flux of these amino acids from plasma to cortex was greater in the adult than in the new-born and of the order of 25 per cent of the flux from plasma to liver. Chirigos *et al.*[10] have recently reported that the passage of tyrosine into the brain is inhibited by other amino acids: the rates of entry are also different for the D- and L-isomers. They conclude that the transport of amino acids across the blood-brain barrier may be effected by an 'active' process and not by simple diffusion. Experiments with tissue slices incubated in physiological saline have shown that isolated brain tissue is able to take up glutamic acid and other amino acids from the surrounding medium against a concentration gradient.[11,12] It would, therefore, appear that the concentrations of amino acids in the amino acid pool of the brain are not determined simply by the levels in the blood.

The amino acids in the amino acid pool come partly from the blood; but a part may also be formed in situ in the brain. Experiments with ^{14}C-glucose have shown that brain tissue has a very considerable capacity for synthesizing amino acids from carbohydrate (Beloff-Chain et al.;[13] Kini and Quastel[14]). Bush[15] found that 3 minutes after injecting pyruvate-2-^{14}C into rats, 53% of the ^{14}C in the brain was combined in the glutamate fraction: Roberts et al.[9] found the rate of conversion of glucose carbon into amino acid carbon in vivo is 10 to 20 times faster in the brain than in the liver. Winzler[16] and his colleagues were even able to show an incorporation of ^{14}C from ^{14}C-glucose into the essential amino acids in the 1-day-old mouse brain. The brain is known to contain active transaminases which can catalyse the conversion of one amino acid into another (Cohen and Hekhuis[17]) and systems that can form cystine from methionine (Gaitonde and Richter[18]). Sporn et al.[19] have recently shown that the rat brain can convert proline into glutamic acid, aspartic acid, alanine, arginine ornithine and γ-aminobutyric acid. The brain is, therefore, not directly dependent on amino acids supplied by the blood for replenishing the amino acid pool.

(2) The Incorporation of Amino Acids into the Proteins of the Brain

The metabolic pathway of protein synthesis in the brain is believed to be similar to that in other organs. The amino acids are first 'activated' by combination with ATP to form amino acyl adenylates, after which they are transferred to the soluble RNA. They are then integrated in specific sequence into the organized nucleoprotein structure of the microsomes, where they are linked to form peptide chains.

In the earlier investigations with the aid of isotopes it was found that labelled amino acids injected in vivo were readily taken up into the proteins of the liver, kidney and other organs; but they were taken up only very slowly by the brain (Friedberg and Greenberg;[20] Tarver and Morse[21]). These experiments led to the view that the proteins of the brain are metabolically inert, resembling in this respect the connective tissue proteins such as collagen. However, Friedberg et al.[22] noted that there was a greater uptake of amino acid in the brain after intrathecal injection than after administration by intraperitoneal injection. This suggested that the low rate of uptake of labelled amino acids into the brain might be due to the blood-brain barrier rather than to the inertness of the brain proteins. Gaitonde and Richter[23,24] obtained further evidence on this point by measuring the specific radioactivity in the amino acid pool as well as in the proteins of the rat brain after administering ^{35}S-L-methionine. They found that, although the total uptake of labelled amino acid into the brain after intraperitoneal injection was small, the specific radioactivity of the proteins was high in comparison with that in the amino acid pool: the rate of incorporation of methionine into the brain proteins must therefore be relatively high.

TABLE I

MEAN HALF-LIFE OF BRAIN PROTEINS[25,26]

Animal	Amino Acid	Injection	Period of Exchange (min.)	Half-life (days)
Rat	^{35}S–methionine	Cisternal	20–60	14
Mouse	^{14}C–lysine	Intravenous	45	10

The high rate of turnover of the brain proteins was confirmed in further experiments in which the blood-brain barrier was by-passed by injecting the labelled amino acid directly into the cerebrospinal fluid (Gaitonde and Richter[25]). Under these conditions ^{35}S-methionine penetrates rapidly into the brain tissue and a high rate of incorporation was observed. As had been found for the liver and other organs, the calculated turnover rate depended on the time allowed for incorporation. This is because the tissue proteins are not homogeneous: in short-term experiments the turnover corresponds to that of the metabolically active proteins, while in long-term experiments the turnover is determined mainly by proteins that are more slowly metabolized. Estimates of the mean turnover rate of the mixed proteins of a heterogeneous organ such as the brain are useful only for purposes of rough comparison. Calculations based on the uptake *in vivo* of ^{35}S-L-methionine during a period of 20 to 60 minutes indicated a mean half-life of the order of 14 days for the mixed proteins of the rat brain. Values of the same order ranging from 6.2 to 15.2 days were obtained by Lajtha *et al.*[26] for the half-life of the proteins of the mouse brain determined for a similar period by means of ^{14}C-lysine injected by the intraperitoneal or intravenous route. These figures may be compared with estimates of 6 days for the half-life of the proteins in visceral organs and a much longer period for the carcass proteins of the rat.[27] Experiments with shorter incorporation times give lower values for the calculated half-life. Lajtha *et al.*[26] have reported mean half-life values as low as 2.8 days for the total proteins of the mouse brain in experiments with incorporation times of 2 minutes; but errors due to diffusion and compartmentation are likely to be considerable in experiments of very short duration.[28]

(3) The Localization of Amino Acid Incorporation in the Brain

The brain is a composite organ made up of regions differing widely in structure, function and chemical composition: it is therefore of interest to know something of the distribution in the brain of the proteins that are metabolically active. One approach to this problem is to find out where the amino acids are incorporated, by measuring the uptake of a labelled amino acid in samples taken by dissection from different regions of the brain. Experiments with ^{14}C-lysine[29] and ^{35}S-methionine[30-32] have shown that the labelled amino acids are incorporated to a greater extent in regions containing gray matter than in those containing white: the specific activity of proteins in the cerebellum and cerebral cortex is high in comparison with corpus callosun.

While it is reasonable to attribute the higher uptake of labelled amino acid in the gray matter to the higher metabolic activity of the proteins, clearly the uptake of a labelled amino acid is not a measure of the rate of protein synthesis. The actual incorporation depends on the specific radioactivity of the amino acid incorporated and, especially in experiments of short duration, the specific radioactivity of the free amino acid may be expected to vary in different parts of the brain. Furst et al.[29] tried to determine the mean half-life times of the proteins in different regions by calculating these with reference to the specific radioactivity of free amino acid in the tissue: but this gave higher turnover rates for proteins of the white matter than for those of the cortex. They concluded that in the white matter the labelled amino acid incorporated in the proteins is in a different 'compartment' from most of the free amino acids of the tissue. In other words, the free amino acids in the tissue are not all contained in the amino acid pool concerned in protein synthesis. The specific activity of the amino acid incorporated is, therefore, higher than the calculated value and the estimated half-life values are unreliable. Further evidence of compartmentation in the brain has been obtained in experiments on the incorporation of ^{14}C-glutamic acid (Berl et al.[33]).

The localization of amino acid incorporation has also been studied by the autoradiographic method. Autoradiograms prepared from brain sections after the injection of ^{35}S-methionine agreed with measurements by biochemical methods in indicating a higher incorporation in the gray matter than in the white. In regions such as the cerebellar cortex and Ammon's horn the pattern of incorporation corresponded closely to the arrangement of nerve cell layers and gave evidence that the labelled amino acid is incorporated mainly in the bodies of the nerve cells (Cohn et al.;[34] Richter et al.[32]). A relatively large amount of labelled amino acid was found in the supraoptic and paraventricular nuclei of the hypothalamus, regions known to be concerned in neuro-secretion.

Measurements of the uptake of labelled amino acids in isolated cell particles obtained from brain tissue by differential centrifugation have shown that, as in other organs, most of the initial incorporation is in the microsomes: the uptake into the proteins of the nuclei, mitochondria and soluble protein fraction is relatively slow.[29,35] The protein giving the highest rate of incorporation is a liponucleoprotein which can be separated from the microsomes by extraction with solvents: it contains 47% of lipids and 1.9% of nucleic acids. It corresponds in properties to the nucleoprotein of the Nissl granules and was found to have a half-life time of the order of 50 to 90 minutes (Clouet and Richter[35]). The lowest rate of incorporation was found in the proteolipids, which are a main constituent of the myelin sheath.[29,35,36]

Very little is known about the nature or distribution of the systems concerned in the breakdown of the proteins that are continually being synthesized in the cell. Apart from a cathepsin, which has a pH optimum at pH 3.5, the brain contains a relatively unstable 'neutral' proteinase which is more active in the gray matter than the white (Ansell and Richter[37,38]). A proteinase requiring an energy-source and most active in the mitochondria has also been described (Lajtha[39]).

(4) Factors Affecting Protein Turnover in the Brain

Greenberg *et al.*[40] found that ^{14}C-glycine is incorporated into the proteins at a very high rate in brain homogenates of the chick embryo: the uptake in brain tissue of the 13-day embryo is about twice as active as in the liver. With increasing age the activity falls off, and in the newly hatched chick, brain and liver tissue incorporate amino acids at similar rates. Measurements of the uptake of ^{35}S-methionine and ^{14}C-lysine in animals of different age *in vivo* have shown that the incorporation is greater in young animals than in the adult.[25,5]

In experiments in which ^{35}S-methionine was administered by intra-cisternal injection it was found that the incorporation of amino acid was decreased in narcosis with ether or pentobarbitone.[25] Electrical stimulation of the brain produced little effect under these conditions, but insulin coma produced a significant decrease of 25% in amino acid incorporation. There have been a number of reports of changes produced by drugs and other agents in the specific radioactivity of the brain proteins after labelled amino acids have been administered by intraperitoneal or intravenous injection: but the interpretation of the experimental data is often difficult. Changes in specific activity suggesting a change in protein turnover may be due in fact to temporary changes in the brain circulation or alterations in the permeability of the blood-brain barrier, producing a change in amino acid flux; and we do not know how drugs or other treatments may affect the distribution of amino acids in the incorporation and storage pools in the tissue.

Little work has been carried out as yet on the incorporation of metabolites other than amino acids; but Heald[41] has reported experiments showing that stimulation increases the incorporation of ^{32}P-phosphate into phosphoproteins in the brain.

II. TURNOVER OF LIPIDS

(1) Cholesterol

In the earlier studies, in which metabolites labelled with isotopes were administered to animals, it was found that the lipids of the brain were labelled to a smaller extent than the lipids of most other organs. This was found by Changus et al.[42] for ^{32}P and by other investigators using ^{15}N-choline,[43] ^{15}N-ethanolamine,[43] triglyceride labelled with deuterium[44,45] and heavy water.[46] In most of these investigations the uptake of isotope was measured in the total lipids, but Waelsch et al.[46] isolated the unsaponifyable fraction (mainly cholesterol) of the adult rat brain and found that the incorporation of deuterium from heavy water into this fraction was negligible, while there was an appreciable incorporation in the unsaponifyable fraction of liver and intestine. On the other hand, they found that in young growing rats there was a rapid incorporation of deuterium from heavy water into the unsaponifyable fraction as well as the fatty acids of the brain. Bloch et al.[47] administered cholesterol labelled with deuterium to an adult dog, but found no labelling of the brain cholesterol after six days, although there was labelling of cholesterol in other organs.

More recent experiments using acetate-1-^{14}C and octanoate-1-^{14}C have confirmed the view that cholesterol is synthesized in the brain of the young animal during the period of growth, but there is little or no synthesis of cholesterol in the adult brain (Van Bruggen et al.;[48] Sperry et al.;[49] McMillan et al.[50]). On the other hand, a small but significant biosynthesis of cholesterol from acetate-1-^{14}C and mevalonate-2-^{14}C has been reported in brain slices in vitro (Grossi et al.[51]). The possibility of cholesterol synthesis in the adult brain cannot therefore be entirely excluded.

Davison et al.[52,53] found that 4-^{14}C-cholesterol injected into the yolk sac of newly hatched chicks or administered by intraperitoneal injection to the 17-day-old rabbit appears in the cholesterol of the brain as well as in other organs. It would therefore appear that the brain cholesterol is not all synthesized *in situ*. Whereas the labelled cholesterol quickly disappeared from heart, liver and plasma, it persisted for more than a year in the brain: chemical degradation studies showed that the ^{14}C was still present in the 4-position.

Cholesterol esters are not present to any considerable extent in the adult brain: but Adams and Davison[52] have found that they occur in relatively high concentration at the sites of active myelination. The peak concentration of esters coincides with the initial stages of myelin formation; this suggests that they may serve as a precursor of the cholesterol deposited in the tissue.

(2) Fatty Acids

The fatty acids in the brain are present mainly combined in the phospholipids and other complex lipids: only very small amounts of triglyceride are present. The early experiments with deuterated triglyceride and with heavy water established that the fatty acids of the brain are labelled in the young growing animal and also at an appreciable rate in the adult, although less readily in the brain than in other organs.[44-46] The labelling of fatty acids in the brain with ^{14}C-acetate administered by intraperitoneal injection *in vivo* is also appreciable in young animals, but very slow in the adult (Nicholas and Thomas[55]): incorporation is greater if the ^{14}C-acid is administered by intracerebral injection. Klenk[56] has found a considerable rate of labelling of saturated and unsaturated fatty acids with ^{14}C-acetate in brain slices *in vitro,* and Grossi *et al.*[51] have observed a labelling of fatty acids with butyrate-1-C^{14}, mevalonate-2-C^{14} and glucose-U-C^{14} in slices of adult rat brain. Under these conditions a part of the ^{14}C is released as $^{14}CO_2$. Volk *et al.*[57] found an oxidation of octanoate-1-^{14}C and palmitate-1-^{14}C by brain slices. These observations give support to the view that the fatty acids of the brain can be utilized as a source of energy under suitable conditions.

(3) Phosphatides

The work of Hevesy[58] and others[59] showed that ^{32}P-phosphate is incorporated into the phospholipids of the brain, but in the adult the uptake of ^{32}P is much less in the brain than in other organs. These experiments were at first taken to mean that the turnover of phospholipids is relatively inactive in the brain: but other experiments suggested that the slow uptake of ^{32}P in the brain might be due rather to the blood-brain barrier.[60] Dawson and Richter[61] found that if the uptake of ^{32}P in the phospholipids was related to the specific activity in the soluble precursor fraction in the tissue, the rate of turnover of phospholipid phosphorus appeared to be relatively rapid: the rate of incorporation of ^{32}P in the phospholipids of the mouse brain corresponded to a complete exchange of all the phospholipid P in 70 hours. The view that the blood-brain barrier is the main limiting factor in the uptake of ^{32}P-phosphate in the brain *in vivo* is supported by the work of Borell and Örström,[62] who measured the uptake of [32]P *in vivo* in different regions of the rabbit brain: they found a relatively high rate of incorporation in the region of the pineal body and in other parts where the blood-brain barrier is known to be relatively permeable to metabolites.

Most of the work on ^{32}P incorporation has dealt with the uptake into total phospholipid. Ansell and Dohmen[63] have recently measured the incorporation of ^{32}P-phosphate into individual phospholipids of the rat brain and found that there are considerable differences in turnover rate: the most active incorporation *in vivo* was in the phosphoinositide fraction. This is followed in order of activity by phosphatidic acid > phosphatidyl-choline > phosphatidylethanolamine > phosphatidyl serine. The position of phosphatidic acid agrees with the view that it may serve as a precursor of α,β-diglycerides: these then react with cytidine diphosphate choline and cytidine diphosphate ethanolamine to give the complete phosphatide molecules. The elucidation of the pathways of phospholipid synthesis in the brain has developed mainly as a result of work with labelled metabolites *in vitro*: this work has been reviewed by Rossiter[64] and by Dawson.[65] The first step is believed to be the esterification of glycerophosphate with two molecules of fatty acid to form the phosphatidic acid (Kornberg and Pricer[66]). This reaction has been shown to take place in liver preparations in the presence of ATP and coenzyme A, which first 'activates' the fatty acid by the formation of an acyl CoA derivative. The subsequent steps in which cytidine triphosphate reacts with phosphorylcholine, phosphorylethanolamine or phosphorylserine to form cytidine diphosphate choline, etc. have been worked out mainly by Kennedy[67] and his collaborators. This work is still in active progress and it appears possible that other pathways of phospholipid synthesis may also operate.

The turnover of phospholipids in the brain depends to some extent on the physiological conditions. The rate of turnover is decreased in thiopentone anaesthesia and in insulin coma. Recent work has shown that the turnover of phosphorylethanolamine is more sensitive to insulin hypoglycaemia than is that of phosphorylcholine.[68] Interest attaches also to the stimulating effect of acetylcholine on the formation of phosphatidic acid (Hokin and Hokin[69]). They have suggested that the phosphatidic acids may be concerned in the transport of ions across the lipid membranes: this offers a possible explanation of the high turnover rate of phosphatidic acid in the brain.[70] It has recently been shown that the synthesis of phospholipids is sensitive to the action of drugs of the chlorpromazine series;[63,64] drugs of this class affect the incorporation of acetate-1-^{14}C and glucose-U-^{14}C as well as ^{32}P *in vivo* at very low dose levels and it has been suggested that their pharmacological properties may depend on this action.[71]

REFERENCES

1. SCHOENHEIMER, R.: *The Dynamic State of Body Constituents.* Cambridge, Mass., Harvard Univ. Press (1946).
2. REINER, J. M.: *Arch. Biochem. Biophys., 46:*53, 80 (1953).
3. ANSELL, G. B. and RICHTER, D.: *Biochem. J., 57:*70 (1954).
4. TALLAN, H. H., MOORE, S. and STEIN, W. H.: *J. Biol. Chem., 211:*927 (1954).
5. WAELSCH, H.: In *Metabolism of the Nervous System,* p. 431. D. Richter, Ed. London, Pergamon Press (1957).
6. ADAMS, J. E., HARPER, H. A., GORDAN, G. S., HUTCHIN, M. and BENTINCK, R. C.: *Neurology, 5:*100 (1955).
7. KETY, S. S.: In *Metabolism of the Nervous System,* p. 221. D. Richter, Ed. London, Pergamon Press (1957).
8. KAMIN, H. and HANDLER, P.: *J. Biol. Chem., 188:*193 (1951).
9. ROBERTS, R. B., FLEXNER, J. B. and FLEXNER, L. B.: *J. Neurochem., 4:*78 (1959).
10. CHIRIGOS, M. A., GREENGARD, P. and UDENFRIEND, S.: *J. Biol. Chem., 235:*2075 (1960).
11. STERN, J. R., EGGLESTON, L. V., HEMS, R. and KREBS, H. A.: *Biochem. J., 44:*410 (1949).
12. NEAME, K. D.: *J. Neurochem., 6:*358 (1961).
13. BELOFF-CHAIN, A., CATANZARO, R., CHAIN, E. B., MASI, I. and POCCHIARI, F.: *Proc. Roy. Soc. B., 144:*22 (1955).
14. KINI, M. M. and QUASTEL, J. H.: *Nature, 184:*252 (1960).
15. BUSH, H.: *Cancer Res. 15:*365 (1955).
16. WINZLER, R. J., MOLDAVE, K., RAFELSON, M. E. and PEARSON, H. E.: *J. Biol. Chem., 199:*485 (1952).
17. COHEN, P. P. and HEKHUIS, G. L.: *J. Biol. Chem., 194:*497 (1941).
18. GAITONDE, M. K. and RICHTER, D.: In *Metabolism of the Nervous System,* p. 449. D. Richter, Ed. London, Pergamon Press (1957).
19. SPORN, M. B., DINGMAN, W. and DEFALCO, A.: *J. Neurochem., 4:*141 (1959).
20. FRIEDBERG, F. and GREENBERG, M. D.: *J. Biol. Chem., 168:*411 (1947).
21. TARVER, H. and MORSE, L. M.: *J. Biol. Chem., 173:*53 (1948).
22. FRIEDBERG, F., TARVER, H. and GREENBERG, M. D.: *J. Biol. Chem., 173:*355 (1948).
23. GAITONDE, M. K. and RICHTER, D.: *Biochem. J., 55:*viii (1953).
24. GAITONDE, M. K. and RICHTER, D.: *Biochem. J., 59:*690 (1955).
25. GAITONDE, M. K. and RICHTER, D.: *Proc. Roy. Soc. B., 145:*83 (1956).
26. LAJTHA, A., FURST, S., GERSTEIN, A. and WAELSCH, H.: *J. Neurochem., 1:*289 (1957).
27. SPRINSON, D. B. and RITTENBERG, D.: *J. Biol. Chem., 180:*715 (1949).
28. STONER, H. B., HEATH, D. F. and COLLINS, O. M.: *Biochem. J., 76:*135 (1960).
29. FURST, S., LAJTHA, A. and WAELSCH, H.: *J. Neurochem., 2:*216 (1958).
30. LODIN, Z. and KOLOUSEK, J.: *Physiol. Bohemslovenica, 5:*43 (1956).

31. PALLADIN, A. V., BELIK, Y. V. and KRACHKO, L. I.: *Biokhimiya*, *22*:334 (1957).
32. RICHTER, D., GAITONDE, M. K. and COHN, P.: In *Structure and Function of the Cerebral Cortex*, p. 340. D. B. Tower and J. P. Schadé, Eds. Amsterdam, Elsevier (1960).
33. BERL, S., LAJTHA, A. and WAELSCH, H.: *J. Neurochem. 7*:186 (1961).
34. COHN, P., GAITONDE, M. K. and RICHTER, D.: *J. Physiol., 126*:7P (1954).
35. CLOUET, D. E. and RICHTER, D.: *J. Neurochem., 3*:219 (1959).
36. GAITONDE, M. K.: *Biochem. J., 80*:277 (1961).
37. ANSELL, G. B. and RICHTER, D.: *Biochim. Biophys. Acta, 13*:87 (1954).
38. ANSELL, G. B. and RICHTER, D.: *Biochim. Biophys. Acta, 13*:92 (1954).
39. LAJTHA, A.: In *The Regional Chemistry, Physiology and Pharmacology of the Nervous System*, p. 25. S. S. Kety and J. Elkes, Eds. New York, Pergamon Press (1961).
40. GREENBERG, D. M., FRIEDBERG, F., SCHULMAN, M. P. and WINNICK, T.: *Cold Spring Harbor Symposia on Quantitative Biology, 8*:113 (1948).
41. HEALD, P. J.: *Biochem. J., 73*:132 (1959).
42. CHANGUS, G. W., CHAIKOFF, I. L. and RUBEN, S.: *J. Biol. Chem., 126*:493 (1938).
43. STETTEN, DE W.: *J. Biol. Chem., 140*:143 (1941).
44. CAVANAGH, B. and RAPER, H. S.: *Biochem. J., 33*:17 (1939).
45. SPERRY, W. M., WAELSCH, H. and STOYANOFF, V. A.: *J. Biol. Chem., 135*:281 (1942).
46. WAELSCH, H., SPERRY, W. M. and STOYANOFF, V. A.: *J. Biol. Chem., 135*:291 (1940).
47. BLOCH, K., BERG, B. M. and RITTENBERG, D.: *J. Biol. Chem., 149*:511 (1943).
48. VAN BRUGGEN, J. T., HUTCHENS, T. T., CLAYCOMB, C. K. and WEST, E. S.: *J. Biol. Chem., 200*:31 (1953).
49. SPERRY, W. M., TAYLOR, R. M. and MELTZER, H. L.: *Federation Proc., 12*:271 (1953).
50. McMILLAN, P. J., DOUGLAS, G. W. and MORTENSEN, R. A.: *Proc. Soc. Exper. Biol. & Med., 96*:738 (1957).
51. GROSSI, E., PAOLETTI, P. and PAOLETTI, R.: *Arch. internat. physiol. et biochem., 66*:564 (1958).
52. DAVISON, A. N., DOBBING, J., MORGAN, R. S. and PAYLING WRIGHT, G.: *J. Neurochem., 3*:89 (1958).
53. DAVISON, A. N., DOBBING, J., MORGAN, R. S. and PAYLING WRIGHT, G.: *Lancet, 1*:658 (1959).
54. ADAMS, C. W. M. and DAVISON, A. N.: *J. Neurochem., 3*:347 (1959).
55. NICHOLAS, H. J. and THOMAS, B. E.: *J. Neurochem., 4*:42 (1959).
56. KLENK, E.: *Ztschr. physiol. Chem., 302*:268 (1955).
57. VOLK, M. E., MILLINGTON, R. H. and WEINHOUSE, S.: *J. Biol. Chem., 195*:493 (1952).
58. HEVESY, G.: *Advances Enzymol., 7*:111 (1947).
59. CHAIKOFF, I. L.: *Physiol. Rev., 22*:291 (1942).
60. STRICKLAND, K. P.: *Canad. J. M. Sc., 30*:484 (1952).
61. DAWSON, R. M. C. and RICHTER, D.: *Proc. Roy. Soc. B., 137*:252 (1950).
62. BORELL, V. and ÖRSTRÖM, A.: *Biochem. J., 41*:398 (1947).
63. ANSELL, G. B. and DOHMEN, H.: *J. Neurochem., 2*:1 (1957).
64. ROSSITER, R.: In *Metabolism of the Nervous System*, p. 355. D. Richter, Ed. London, Pergamon Press (1957).
65. DAWSON, R. M. C.: *Biol. Rev., 32*:188 (1957).
66. KORNBERG, A. and PRICER, W. E.: *J. Biol. Chem., 204*:329, 345 (1953).

67. KENNEDY, E. P. and WEISS, S. B.: *J. Am. Chem. Soc.*, 77:250 (1955).
68. ANSELL, C. B. and SPANNER, S.: *J. Neurochem.*, 4:325 (1959).
69. HOKIN, L. E. and HOKIN, M. R.: *J. Biol. Chem.*, 233:818, 822 (1958).
70. HOKIN, L. E. and HOKIN, M. R.: *J. Biol. Chem.*, 234:1387 (1959).
71. GROSSI, E., PAOLETTI, P. and PAOLETTI, R.: *J. Neurochem.*, 6:73 (1960).

XIV

AMINO ACID AND PROTEIN METABOLISM

H. Waelsch

This article deals with the metabolism of amino acids and proteins in the nervous system, an aspect of neurochemistry covered in several recent reviews.[1-3]

The metabolism of certain amino acids leading to the formation of pharmacologically active amines is discussed in the appropriate chapters.

AMINO ACID METABOLISM

The Pool of Free Amino Acid

The pool of free amino acids of the brain is the source from which both amines and proteins are derived and to which amino acids liberated in the breakdown of proteins are returned. Its composition is unique for the central nervous system. The composition of the free amino acid pool of cat and rat brain based on some selected recent analyses[4-7] is shown (Table I). The concentration of free glutamic acid in mammalian brain is higher than in any other organ (0.01 molar). In addition, brain has a high concentration of γ-aminobutyric acid (0.002 molar), of acetyl aspartic acid (0.006 molar), and in man, of cystathionine, the condensation product of serine and homocysteine (up to 0.0025 molar[8]). The three last mentioned compounds do not occur in any significant concentration in other tissues of the mammalian body. The dicarboxylic amino acids have the additional function of compensating partially for the anionic deficit in tissues. In the invertebrate nerve, this is accomplished by a large concentration of aspartic acid (133 μmoles/gm. in lobster nerve[9]), or of the hydroxyl analogue of taurine, isothionic acid (220 μmoles/gm. in axon of giant squid[10]). The amide of cysteic acid was isolated recently from lobster nerve.[11,12]

Origin of the Amino Acids

As in other organs, the carbon skeleton of the non-essential amino

288

acids is derived in nervous tissue through the citric acid cycle and ultimately from glucose. Active transaminases present in the brain catalyze the reversible amination and deamination of essential and non-essential amino acids.[13] Recent experiments suggest the participation of glutamine also in transamination reactions in cerebral tissue[14] similar to those observed in liver and kidney extracts.[15]

TABLE I

CONCENTRATIONS OF FREE AMINO ACID ON THE BRAIN OF CAT AND RAT
(*micromoles/gm. tissue*)

| Compound | Animal | |
	Rat	Cat
Leu	.2	.14
Phe	.06	.07
Try	.03	
Val	1.0	.18
His	.08	.06
Lys	.02	.14
Ileu		.09
Tyr	.1	.06
Met	.08	.1
Thr	1.0	.22
Arg	.2	.08
Asp		2.2
Asp—NH$_2$		.1
Acetyl—Asp	5.0	6.0
Glu	10.0	8.7
Glu—NH$_2$	4.0	3.4
Gly	1.3	1.3
Ala	.6	1.0
γ–NH$_2$ Bu	2.0	2.3
Pro		.14
Cy		.04
Ser	1.1	.72
GSH		.9
Tau		2.0

Uptake of Amino Acids by the Brain from the Blood

When the concentration of glutamic acid[16] or proline[17] is raised in the blood of animals, no significant increase in the concentration of the respective amino acid is found in the brain at different time intervals after administration of the amino acids. A net uptake of glutamine from the circulating blood can be demonstrated under comparable experimental conditions.[16] Similarly, after the administration of lysine[18] and leucine[19] only small increases in the concentrations of the respective amino acids in the brain are observed with greatly increased blood concentration. On the other hand, the blood brain barrier appears not to interfere greatly with the uptake of tyrosine[20] by the brain from the blood. Apparently only the fully developed blood-brain barrier of the mature brain is able to protect the brain from increased concentrations of some of the blood amino acids, since net uptake by the immature brain of amino acids excluded by the mature brain has been demonstrated.[18,19,21]

The exchange of the amino acids between blood and brain is quite rapid, independently of whether or not increased blood concentrations result in a net uptake by the brain[22] (Table II). Half of the free lysine of the brain is replaced by blood lysine within one hour, as shown

TABLE II[22-24]
TURNOVER RATE OF FREE AMINO ACIDS

	Flux*	Half-life Time (minutes)	µg. Substance/gm. Fresh Tissue	
			Plasma	Organ
Lysine				
Young brain	1.1–1.5	21–29	49	51
Adult brain	0.7–5.2	5–43	50	38
Adult liver	6.0–29	2.2–10	50	92
Leucine				
Adult brain	0.1–3.0	3–65	17	9.6
Adult liver	0.6–5.8	4–45	17	42
Glutamic Acid				
Adult brain	0.15–4.0	200–5000	15	1500

*Flux = µg. amino acid/gm. fresh tissue/minute exchanged.

with the aid of the C^{14} labeled amino acid. Comparable high exchange rates have been found also for leucine and glutamic acid.[23-25] We are probably dealing with a general phenomenon, since with other cells exchange of amino acids was shown to be considerably more rapid than one-directional active transport.[26,27] These findings suggest that slow changes of the pool of free amino acids can be effected despite the restraining action of the blood-brain barrier; otherwise the replenishment of the essential amino acids of the cerebral pool of free amino acids would be impossible. Since it is difficult to ascertain what portion of the amino acids liberated from protein breakdown is re-used for protein synthesis and other purposes, the extent of their net uptake has not been estimated.

Experiments in which the amino acid concentration in blood is raised to an unphysiological level may elicit an aspect of the blood-brain barrier not operative under physiological conditions. For determining the uptake of amino acids of the brain under physiological conditions, accurate measurements of the arterio-venous differences would be required.

Glutamic Acid and its Metabolic Derivatives

Glutamic acid occurs in the brain in concentrations exceeding those found in other organs; together with the glutamic acid occurring in glutamine and glutathione, this amino acid accounts for close to 50% of the α-amino nitrogen of the protein-free filtrates of cerebral tissue.[28] Many other observations point to the important role of this dicarboxylic amino acid and its metabolic derivatives—glutamine and γ-aminobutyric acid—in the metabolism of nervous tissue in relation to function in health and disease.

The carbon skeleton of glutamic acid—in the form of ketoglutaric acid—is derived from glucose through the citric acid cycle; the keto acid is aminated to the amino acid either by transamination with other amino acids or by free ammonia in a reductive amination catalyzed by glutamic dehydrogenase. Both transaminases and glutamic dehydrogenase are very active in brain tissue. The latter enzyme is responsible for one of the two principal mechanisms for the removal of ammonia in the central nervous system.

The above discussed origin of the major portion of the carbon skeleton of cerebral glutamic acid from glucose is supported by the results of *in vitro, in vivo,* and perfusion experiments in which the incorporation of the carbon atoms of C^{14} labeled glucose or pyruvic acid was studied. Furthermore, labeled carbon dioxide is incorporated *in vivo* into cerebral aspartic and glutamic acids, a fact which attests to the operation of carbon dioxide fixation in brain tissue.[29] Although *in vitro* experiments cannot supply quantitative values for conversions which occur *in vivo,* they attest to the rapid incorporation of glucose or pyruvate carbon atoms into glutamic acid and its metabolic derivatives.

After 20 minutes of incubation with pyruvate-2-^{14}C as substrate 42% of the metabolized pyruvate was recovered in glutamic acid in *in vitro* studies with rat cerebral cortex and 53% *in vivo* 3 minutes after the intravenous administration of pyruvic acid.[30,31] If the citric acid cycle is interrupted and the flow of ammonia acceptors stopped, an increase of the ammonia level in the brain results.[32] The rapid utilization of glucose carbon for the synthesis of cerebral aspartic and glutamic acid has been documented extensively by the use of brain cortex slices.[33-36] (For a comparison of the utilization of glucose and fructose see ref. 36.) From an analysis of the free amino acid of the cortex of the cat brain perfused with "simplified blood" containing C^{14} glucose, it was concluded that despite the rapid incorporation of glucose carbon into dicarboxylic amino acids a large portion of the tricarboxylic cycle intermediates was supplied by endogenous carbon sources.[37]

Experiments in which C^{14}-glucose was administered to mice led to the estimate that about 10 times as much glutamic acid is derived in the brain from glucose as is supplied as such from the circulating blood.[38]

Evidence mentioned previously[16] shows that at least in animal experiments administered glutamic acid cannot penetrate the blood-brain barrier, but it has also been claimed that an arterio-venous difference can be observed in man, which may suggest glutamic acid uptake by the mammalian brain under physiological conditions.[39]

Glutamic Acid as a Respiratory Substrate in Nervous Tissue

Early experiments with brain cortex slices suggested a unique position for glutamic acid in cerebral metabolism, since it was the only amino acid oxidized of thirteen tested.[40] In the intact animal rapid metabolism of other amino acids (proline, alanine, aspartic acid, arginine) can be demonstrated.[41]

The presence of active transaminases implies that the carbon skeletons of amino acids other than glutamic acid are available for oxidation by brain tissue. Up to the present time there is no clear-cut evidence of the oxidation by slices fortified by various essential cofactors, of amino acids other than glutamic acid. Oxidation of glutamic acid by cortex slices from guinea pig brain does not support the regeneration of creatine phosphate; the slices, correspondingly, do not respond to electrical stimulation in the presence of glutamic acid. Under the same experimental conditions slices from human cortex do respond.[42-44] It appears feasible that glutamic acid plays a special role in the metabolism of the human brain and that, from the evolutionary point of view, the efficacy of glutamic acid utilization is a parameter of the functional refinement of the central nervous system. This possibility is of some interest in view of the claim quoted above of the ability of the human brain to take up glutamic acid and of the still controversial effects of glutamic acid administration in man.

When glutamic acid is incubated with brain slices it is oxidized without the appearance of free ammonia; instead an increase of the concentration of glutamine is found.[40] Other mechanisms for the metabolism of glutamic acid involve transamination reactions directly or after decarboxylation to γ-aminobutyric acid and are not accompanied by the appearance of ammonia.

Since glutamic acid can serve as substrate for respiration of brain cortex slices, the question has been raised whether it can do so *in vivo*. Decreases of glutamic acid concentration have been reported in the rat brain after strychnine convulsions,[45] in hypoglycemic coma,[46] in thiopental anesthesia (with a slight increase in glutamine),[47] and in epileptogenic foci in cat cortex produced *in vivo* by freezing.[48]

It has been asserted that slices of cerebral cortex of animals after induced epileptogenic seizures and cerebral cortex slices from human epileptogenic foci show upon incubation a decrease in glutamic acid levels in contrast to control slices, in which a significant increase was observed under the same conditions.[49,50]

Although in hypoglycemia the decrease of glutamic acid may be suggestive of its function as a respiratory substrate, the decrease was relatively minor and less than in situations where no deprivation of glucose could be assumed, such as in anesthesia or in experimentally induced epilepsy.

Glutamine Metabolism

The major mechanism[51] for the fixation of free ammonia in the central nervous system is the formation of glutamine from glutamic acid and ammonia, an adenosine triphosphate-requiring reaction catalyzed by glutamine synthetase.[52-55] This enzyme is highly active in the brain and appears to be concentrated in the microsomal and mitochondrial fractions, as identified by fractional centrifugation.[56,57] Glutamine synthetase from brain tissue cannot be separated from glutamotransferase, which catalyzes the replacement of the amide group by hydroxylamine or hydrazine.[58] A possible function of the transferase system in peptide synthesis has been considered.[58] Glutamine penetrates the blood-brain barrier of adult animals with greater ease than glutamic acid[16] and may therefore serve as a supply of cerebral ammonia and glutamic acid.

The concentration of amide nitrogen in brain slices remains steady in the absence of glucose but rises in its presence.[59] The effect is even more pronounced if the medium contains, in addition to glucose, ammonium ions and either ketoglutarate or pyruvate.[40] After exhausting exercise or electric stimulation a decrease in the level of cerebral glutamine *in vivo*, with or without a corresponding decrease of that of glutamic acid, has been observed in animals.[60-62] These conditions are likely to lead to increased ammonia production in the brain. In epileptogenic foci produced in the cortex of cats, a comparable decrease of glutamic acid, glutamine, and glutathione, but not of γ-aminobutyric acid, is found, but without a corresponding increase in the ammonia concentration.[48,63]

Marked increase of glutamine concentration was found in rat, dog, and cat brain after an infusion of ammonium salts.[64,65,51]

Glutamic Acid Uptake by Tissue Slices

Brain slices lose potassium ions to the suspending medium during their preparation and especially during their storage at temperatures below 37°. This leakage is stopped and to some extent reversed on subsequent incubation of the slices in a glucose-bicarbonate medium under aerobic conditions. If the medium contains, in addition, glutamic acid, the uptake of potassium is accelerated.[66] This effect of glutamic acid is dependent on the buffers used and has been related to an increase of the intracellular space.[67]

Brain slices respiring in a medium containing glucose and glutamic acid are capable of accumulating glutamic acid against a concentration gradient.[68] The accumulation of glutamic acid in cortex slices is accompanied by an approximately equivalent migration of potassium.[66] This observation cannot be transposed to *in vivo* conditions in which the blood-brain barrier regulates potassium migration between blood and brain, since the half-life time of brain potassium has been estimated as approximately 24 hours,[69] a rate of migration considerably lower than that obtained with tissue slices. On the other hand, the findings with tissue slices suggest a possible role of the dicarboxylic acid in the maintenance of the intracellular ionic milieu.

The Compartments of Glutamic Acid Metabolism in the Brain

Recent studies of the metabolism of intracisternally administered glutamic acid and also of intercerebrally synthesized glutamic acid demonstrated that the metabolism of glutamic acid *in vivo* occurs in tissue or cellular compartments. In experiments of short duration it was found that glutamine formed from the C^{14}-labeled glutamic acid had up to five times higher specific activity than the precursor amino acid[70] (Table III). Analogous results were obtained after the carotid infusion of N^{15}-ammonium acetate into cats. Subsequent comparison of the N^{15} concentration of the α-amino group of glutamic acid and glutamine[51] showed that the ratio of the N^{15} concentration was about 10:1 although the glutamic acid moiety of glutamine had presumably been formed from newly synthesized glutamic acid. It seems likely that only a fraction of the total tissue glutamic acid is metabolically highly active; the bulk of the dicarboxylic amino acid is relatively inert with a half-life time of several hours.

Similarly in a study of the effect of GABA on the normalization of experimentally produced paroxysmal activity it could be shown that a large portion of the tissue GABA does not participate in this action, and that only a small fraction is pharmacologically active.[48,63]

A more complete understanding of metabolic compartments or pools is essential for quantitative estimates of *in vivo* metabolism and the turnover rates of the various metabolites and also for establishing a relationship between the intermediary metabolism and the structure of any organ.[56,71]

TABLE III[70]

INTRACEREBRAL GLUTAMIC ACID INJECTION INTO RATS

Time	Subs.	Specific Activity (counts/min. μmole)			Total Counts in 1 gm. Fresh Tissue	
		Plasma	Brain	Liver	Brain	Brain Total (glu + gline)
¼'	Glu*	—	7,700	—	77,000	92,000
	Gline*	—	3,300	—	15,000	
1'	Glu	180,000	5,500	200	51,000	84,000
	Gline	1,200	7,300	66	33,000	
2'	Glu	130,000	3,200	800	32,000	91,000
	Gline	2,200	12,000	600	59,000	
5'	Glu	34,000	2,700	770	27,000	97,000
	Gline	6,100	14,000	760	70,000	
15'	Glu	8,900	2,200	190	22,000	77,000
	Gline	6,500	11,000	280	55,000	
30'	Glu	3,300	2,100	180	21,000	58,000
	Gline	870	7,300	240	37,000	
60'	Glu	1,500	1,900	61	19,000	44,000
	Gline	410	5,000	130	25,000	

*Glu = glutamic acid. Gline = glutamine.
In each experiment two rats were injected via the cisterna magna with uniformly labeled C^{14} glutamic acid (0.02 ml. of a solution containing 40 μc. and 4 μmole/ml. in 0.9% saline). Each point is the average of two expermients.
Glutamine is formed from a glutamic acid pool of higher than average specific activity.

Many of the metabolic compartments which can be demonstrated *in vivo* may have been eliminated in tissue slices, where metabolism may therefore simulate the qualitative but not the quantitative aspects of *in vivo* metabolism. Compartmentalization of metabolic events in brain and other organs probably is one of the main aspects of control of metabolism.

Glutamic Acid and Its Derivatives and the Convulsive States

The apparent participation of γ-aminobutyric acid in the mechanism of suppression of seizures with relatively simple paroxysmal activity is the most recent indication that glutamic acid and its metabolic derivatives may play a role in the metabolic mechanism related to the convulsive state. More than 18 years ago an effect of glutamic acid administration on petit mal attacks was reported.[72] As a consequence of these observations, the action of glutamic acid in mental defectives was tested.[73] This was followed by attempts to influence epileptic seizures by the administration of glutamine and asparagine;[74] a trial with γ-aminobutyric acid in epileptics was reported recently.[75] The clinical efficacy of the administration of glutamic acid, which has been extended to other diseases of the nervous system, has been under discussion since its first clinical trials.[28,76] The results are contradictory, and at present it appears that despite the large amount of biochemical and physiological work stimulated by these observations, the therapeutic effects are mainly of theoretical interest.

Animal experimentation also has suggested a close connection between glutamic acid metabolism and the convulsive state. After the discovery of the effect of glutamic acid on petit mal epilepsy, attempts were made to design antimetabolites which would block the metabolism of glutamic acid. The methionine sulfoxide developed for this purpose[77] was superseded when it was found that methionine sulfoximine was the agent in bleached flour which produced running fits in dogs. The sulfoximine has since become a useful tool for the production of convulsions in animals.[78,79] Its action, as that of methionine sulfoxide, is overcome by glutamine and by methionine.

The question arises whether the effects of glutamic acid, glutamine, etc., can all be explained by the final conversion to γ-aminobutyric acid, which is the real effective agent.[80] Although this question cannot be answered at present, it may be noted that both glutamic acid and γ-aminobutyric acid are kept out of the brain by the blood-brain barrier. The possibility that glutamic acid was effective only in those cases in which a lesion with lowered barrier permitted the entrance of dicarboxylic amino acid is suggested by the fact that mental defectives with a secondary deficiency seemed to be more susceptible to the action of the amino acid.[73]

PROTEIN METABOLISM

Introductory Remarks

In studying the metabolism of the proteins of the nervous system (as of any other organ) we attempt to answer two questions: (1) Are there any aspects of protein metabolism which differentiate this organ from any other? (2) Is there any evidence for a link between the metabolism of proteins or their components or metabolic derivatives, and the function of the organ?

Investigations on the protein metabolism of the nervous system are carried out on one of the structurally most heterogeneous organs in the mammalian body. It contains different cells from layer to layer with a varying ratio of neuronal and non-neuronal elements. A special problem is presented by the metabolism of axonal proteins, which are sometimes at long distances from the cell body.

Peptide Metabolism

Glutathione, the tripeptide present in all tissues, occurs in the central nervous system in concentrations of 1 to 2 μmole/gm. It may be synthesized with the participation of adenosine triphosphate[81] or by transpeptidation from γ-glutamyl peptides.[82] A substituted amino acid occurring in high concentration, acetyl aspartic acid (80-120 mg./100 gm.[83]), can be synthesized from aspartic acid and acetyl CoA by an enzyme system occurring in brain extracts.[84,85] The slow turnover[86] of acetyl aspartic acid represents a puzzling feature of the metabolism of this dicarboxylic amino acid.

Specialized areas of the brain are characterized by the presence of peptides which are recognized by their hormonal activities. Up to the present, nothing is known about the mechanism of the biological synthesis of these peptides. It will be of considerable interest to know whether they are produced as products of the synthetic or degradative metabolism of proteins or whether their synthesis is due to specific enzymes or combinations of enzymes.

Since only small amounts of amino acids other than those derived from glutathione and acetyl aspartic acid are liberated upon hydrolysis of protein-free filtrates of brain tissue of the cat,[4] it is unlikely that peptides of unknown composition occur in brain tissue in high concentration. The same appears to be true for the hypothalamus, whereas a considerable amount of peptides beyond those accounted for by oxytocin, vasopressin, or intermedin are present in the posterior pituitary.[87] The concentration, nature, and mechanism of synthesis of these peptides occurring in two areas of the brain are of particular interest, since it has been suggested that neurohormones of peptide nature are synthesized in the hypothalamus and are stored in the posterior pituitary. Recent experiments on the *in vivo* synthesis and turnover of vasopressin appear to be inconsistent with such a simple two-compartment relationship between the hypothalamic nuclei and the neurohypophysis.[88]

Mechanism of Protein Synthesis in Brain

Studies on the mechanism of protein synthesis in mammalian tissues have been carried out during recent years with preparations of organs such as liver, pancreas, mammary gland, and muscle. The first three organs are characterized by the production of large amounts of protein to be excreted.

If the cell body of the neuron is called upon to produce the proteins of the axon directly or to provide the machinery for axonal protein synthesis, the neuron may have to be considered a secretory cell, just as liver or pancreas cells. In histological studies the close packing (as in a secretory cell) of the components of the perikarya was noted.[89]

In most of the studies on protein synthesis, the incorporation of an added labeled amino acid into a protein fraction of the cell is taken as a measure of protein synthesis *in vivo* and *in vitro*. The sequence of events leading to protein synthesis is visualized today as involving: (1) carboxyl activation of amino acids in an adenosine triphosphate-requiring reaction by the action of a soluble activating enzyme with formation of amino acyl adenylates; (2) transfer of the amino acyl moiety to soluble ribonucleic acid; (3) transfer of the amino acyl moiety from the ribonucleic acid to ribosomes with the formation of peptide bonds. The overall reaction is, therefore, incorporation of activated amino acids into ribosomes. A number of amino acid activating enzymes catalyzing step (1) have been found in extracts from brain tissue.[90] The incorporation of labeled amino acid into microsomal protein has been demonstrated to occur in extracts of brain cortex[91] (Table IV). Owing to the structural complexity of the organ

TABLE IV[91]

In Vitro INCORPORATION OF C^{14}–L–LEUCINE INTO RAT BRAIN CORTEX
PARTICULATE FRACTIONS

	Time (min.)	Counts/min. mg. Protein
O time	0	2
Complete system	5	39
Complete system	15	55
Complete system	30	84
Complete system	60	97
No ATP, GTP, CP, CP enzyme added	15	4
No Microsome added	15	7
No supernatant added	15	12
No GTP added	15	16
Nuclei instead of Microsomes	15	19
Mitochondria instead of microsomes	15	18

The complete system consists of 0.3 ml. microsomes (or nuclei or mitochondria) (3 mg. protein), 0.2 ml. pH 5.2 supernatant (2 mg. protein), 10 μmole creatine phosphate (CP), 1.0 μmole of adenosine triphosphate (ATP), 0.25 μmole of guanosine triphosphate (GTP), 0.1 μmole 1–leucine ^{14}C (4 x 10^5 counts/min.), and creatine transphosphorylase (CP enzyme).

the preparation of homogeneous fractions of nuclei, mitochondria, and microsomes from brain presents many difficulties. Ribosomes prepared from brain homogenates in the presence of desoxycholate show a composition similar to that of those prepared from liver. The incorporation of labeled amino acids into ribosomes from guinea pig brain proceeds at a rate equal to, if not higher than, into liver ribosomes.[92] This finding confirms the high potential for protein synthesis of brain tissue, which was deduced from *in vivo* experiments.

If labeled amino acids are administered to animals and brain homogenates are subsequently fractionated into nuclear, mitochondrial, and microsomal proteins, a higher rate of incorporation of label into microsomal proteins of all brain areas is found,[93] in agreement with results obtained with other organs[94] (Table V). Fractionation of the microsomal proteins from various organs including brain obtained in such an experiment yields protein fractions with a considerably higher specific activity, i.e., shorter half-life time, than the bulk of the microsomal proteins (cf. refs. 95, 96). Although subject to great variations, the data demonstrate heterogeneity of synthetic rates within the various protein fractions of microsomes. Different incorporation rates of radio methionine into salt or alkali soluble protein fractions of grey and white matter have also been shown.[97] Although the microsomes of brain tissue show a higher rate of incorporation of amino acid, nuclear and mitochondrial proteins also incorporate labeled amino acid, in agreement with results obtained with subcellular particles from other organs.

The question of exchange of an amino acid versus synthesis of a new peptide linkage has been discussed extensively in studies on the incorporation of amino acids into cellular protein fractions and has been decided in favor of the latter. Definitive evidence can come only from a demonstration of net synthesis of a protein. Exchange of free amino acids with brain protein-bound amino acids was suggested recently when it was found that the rates of *in vivo* incorporation of amino acids did not parallel their concentration on the respective proteins.[38,98] In view of the uncertainties of turnover rates and composition of protein fractions analyzed, data obtained with the present methods are too crude to decide whether, and to what degree, an amino acid is incorporated into a protein by an exchange mechanism.

Turnover of Proteins in the Mature Nervous System

Labeled amino acids administered systemically to animals are incorporated into the brain proteins at a lower rate than into the proteins of most other organs. These findings were explained initially by

TABLE V[93]

RELATIVE SPECIFIC ACTIVITIES OF PARTICULATE FRACTIONS FROM VARIOUS MONKEY BRAIN AREAS

Fraction	Cortex	Cerebellum	Thalamus-hypothalamus	Pons Medulla	Cord	White Matter
Whole homogenate	0.26 = 1.0	0.18 = 1.0	0.18 = 1.0	0.13 = 1.0	0.1 = 1.0	0.19 = 1.0
Cell debris, nuclei, etc.	0.97	1.12	0.53	0.80	0.77	0.67
Mitochondria	0.82	1.21	0.80	1.04	1.07	0.86
Large microsomes	1.33	2.61	1.44	1.27	1.43	1.88
Intermediate and small microsomes	3.86	3.20	2.13	1.82	1.80	2.73
Supernatant	1.47	1.15	1.10	1.17	1.17	1.20

Specific activity of whole homogenate = average for area = 1.0. Relative specific activity for fractions = $\dfrac{\text{specific activity of cell fraction}}{\text{specific activity of whole homogenate}}$.

the assumption that the metabolic rate of brain proteins is below that of most organs; it was also suggested that the proteins of the brain are not in a dynamic state.

Today, however, good evidence is available from several laboratories which shows that the metabolic activity, i.e., turnover of cerebral proteins, is comparable to that in other tissues. The observed low incorporation rate into brain proteins of labeled amino acids administered systemically was due, first, to poor penetration of amino acids not heavily labeled, and second, to the short exposure of the brain to the labeled compound in the circulating blood. A lack of turnover of brain proteins was also deduced from the finding that after administration of C^{14} glycine to pregnant mother animals, radioactivity was recovered in the brain of the young at several months of age, while liver showed no activity.[99] The small residual activity might have been located in myelin lipids (or myelin proteins), since, according to accumulating evidence, components of the myelin deposited during maturation of the nervous system have a very slow metabolism.[100] After intracisternal administration labeled amino acids are incorporated significantly into the brain proteins.[101,102] Owing to the rapid exchange of the pool of free amino acids with those of the blood, a significant incorporation of amino acids into brain protein is also obtained after systemic administration of amino acids of high specific activity. The latter approach has the obvious advantage of simulating more closely the physiological situation than intracisternal administration of amino acids. On the basis of results obtained in experiments in which S^{35}-methionine[103] was administered intracisternally to rats, an average half-life time of 13 days was calculated for brain proteins from experiments of 20 to 60 minute duration. In those experiments no definite knowledge as to the specific activity of the precursor, methionine, in the cerebral pool of free amino acid was available. With S^{35}-methionine as the labeled amino acid and the specific activity of free blood plasma methionine as reference, a half-life of rabbit brain proteins of 6.2 days (4.0 for liver) and 8.9 days for rat brain (2.8 days for liver) was reported from other laboratories.[103,104]

In another series of experiments, C^{14}-lysine and leucine administered systemically were employed.[105-108] These amino acids are metabolically inert during the experimental period, and use was made of the fact that after intravenous administration the exchange is rapid enough to lead to a satisfactory labeling of the lysine or leucine in the pool of free amino acid of the brain. By direct determination of the specific activity of the free as well as protein bound amino acids in the brain tissue itself, more detailed information as to the relative turnover rates of the proteins was obtained (Table VI). The half-life times calculated

TABLE VI[22,23]

HALF-LIFE TIME (IN DAYS) OF PROTEINS OF ORGANS OF IMMATURE AND ADULT MICE AS MEASURED WITH C^{14} LYSINE AND C^{14} LEUCINE

Time after Injection (min.)	Brain				Liver				Muscle			
	Adult Lysine	Adult Leucine	8 d. Lysine	1 d. Leucine	Adult Lysine	Adult Leucine	8 d. Lysine	1 d. Leucine	Adult Lysine	Adult Leucine	8 d. Lysine	1 d. Leucine
2	2.8	3.8		0.7	0.9	0.4		0.2	3.5	5.1		0.9
3												
5	3.5	8.1	3.4	1.2	1.3	0.9	1.7	0.4	7.6	7.1	2.4	1.5
10	5.5	11	2.2	1.7	2.6	1.3	1.1	0.7	7.6	14	1.7	2.0
20	6.2	15	3.0	2.4		2.4	2.7	1.4	10	24	2.5	2.9
30	6.9	20		3.0		3.9		2.0	13	28		3.2
45	10	24	2.4	3.3		5.7		4.0	17	30	2.3	4.1
60	15	27		4.1				4.7	24	34		5.0

Adult: 100-120 days; 8 d. = 8 days old; 1 d. = less than 24 hours old C_3H mice.

for brain proteins are longer than for liver proteins but are shorter than for muscle proteins. Furthermore, the half-life time of the proteins of all organs analyzed depends on the time interval between administration of the amino acid and killing of the animal and is longer in experiments of longer duration.

The dependence of half-life times on the duration of the experiments can be explained by the heterogeneity of turnover rates of the different protein fractions. The proteins with short half-life will be measured in experiments in which the animals were exposed to the isotopic amino acids for only a short period of time, while in experiments of longer duration the protein fractions of slow metabolism will predominate.

The spectrum of turnover rates of organ protein which is observed when the time of exposure to the isotopic amino acid is varied provides an overall characterization of protein metabolism of an organ for comparative purposes and thereby a more biological interpretation of the concept of the dynamic state of body proteins than an average half-life time does.

The spectrum of turnover rates was determined for the proteins of different parts of the brain also.[93] As in the previous experiments, the calculation of half-life time was based on the specific activities of protein lysine and of the free lysine in the respective areas of the monkey brain (Table VII). As expected the metabolic heterogeneity is found

TABLE VII[93]

HALF-LIFE TIMES OF PROTEINS IN MONKEY BRAIN AREAS

	Half-life Time (days) Calculated from Different Time Points		
	5'	10'	45'
Cord	10.6	9.5	18.5
White	3.9	4.0	8.7
Medulla–Pons	6.6	6.7	13.7
Thalamus–Hypothalamus	6.1	7.8	16.8
Cerebellum	5.4	7.6	14.1
Cerebral cortex	5.5	6.7	12.7

also for the proteins of each brain area investigated. The apparent high metabolic rate of the proteins of white matter is noteworthy and may be interpreted as showing the failure of the administered labeled amino acid to mix with the free lysine present in the structure. If the administered C^{14}-lysine is used preferentially for protein synthesis, the spuriously low values for the specific activity of the total free lysine would result in high values of turnover rates. The proteins of the cortical areas have somewhat higher metabolic activity than those of the underlying older parts of the brain. Decreasing rates of incorporation of radiomethionine into proteins of grey matter, white matter, and nerve, in that order, have also been reported.[109-111] Further information about the rate of protein turnover in various parts of the brain was gained by autoradiographic methods.[112,113] With all its technical simplicity and impressive visual results, this method measures total activities instead of specific activities of proteins or the protein-bound amino acid and is unable to estimate the specific activities of the precursor amino acid. An apparently higher rate of incorporation into the protein of a particular area may reflect an actual higher rate of protein turnover or a higher specific activity of the precursor amino acid in the particular pool. While in many cases results obtained by radioautography correspond to differences in turnover rate, checks by independent methods are necessary for the confirmation of such an interpretation.

By the autoradiographic method, higher rates of incorporation in brain areas rich in cell bodies than in areas rich in white matter were found.[114] Autoradiography of brain parts after S^{35}-methionine administration showed isotope incorporation in the following descending order: cerebellum, cortex, pons, spinal cord, peripheral nerve.[115] Grey matter was twice as active as white, after 24 hours. The sequence of metabolic activities in the different brain parts thus parallels the results obtained by other methods. In the spinal cord the highest activity was in the motor cells of the anterior horn. Nerve cells have been reported to lose incorporated S^{35}-methionine or H^3-glycine faster than other cell types in the brain.[116] Ganglion cells were found to be among the most active cells in the body in incorporating methionine, their activity being comparable to that of glandular epithelia of the pancreas and the reticuloendothelial cells in the spleen.[104,113]

The differences in turnover rates of protein from different parts of the brain relate roughly to ratios of cellular to non-cellular elements. The higher metabolic action of proteins of grey matter than those of white matter suggests that the neurons contain some of the proteins with a high renewal rate. Such arguments are, at present, indirect and assume a rate of protein metabolism of glia lower than that of neurons irrespective of the location and characteristics of the particular glia species. It has been pointed out previously that rates of incorporation of labeled amino acids into nuclear, mitochondrial, microsomal, and soluble proteins vary widely. Each of these fractions will contain proteins of differing turnover rates. Therefore, the heterogeneity of protein metabolism will be related primarily to the distribution and concentration of the proteins of subcellular units. Enough information about differences in the concentration of various enzymes or proteins in various brain structures is available today[117-120] to suggest that the presence of such specific proteins in varying amounts will also contribute to the heterogeneous metabolic rates of the proteins of the brain, although such differences may not be demonstrable with the methods available. The spectrum of turnover rates will extend from the protein of the ribosomes with the highest turnover rates to proteolipids[93,121] and other proteins with very long half-life times.

The best approximation to the real values of turnover rates of proteins can obviously be obtained only if the rate of incorporation of the labeled amino acid into proteins is based on the determination of the specific activity of the protein-bound amino acid itself after hydrolysis of the protein and is related to the specific activity of the precursor amino acid in the pool of free amino acids in the organ or part of the organ to be studied. This conclusion is reinforced by the finding that despite the administration of large amounts of amino acids intracellular pools supply more than half of the amino acids for newly synthesized liver proteins.[122] Turnover values of organ proteins based on calculation from radioactivities found in blood or indirect estimates of specific activities of free amino acids in organs have to be accepted with caution; for example, no direct data are available on the re-use of amino acids liberated by protein breakdown in an organ.[122]

Whereas at the present time the direct determination of the specific activity of the precursor free amino acid in an organ gives the closest approximation to a calculation of renewal rates of proteins in this organ, this approach suffers from other uncertainties, particularly in short-time experiments. The significance of the values of turnover rates obtained in short-time experiments has to be scrutinized further with consideration of the local pool of free amino acids drawn upon for synthetic purposes and the compartments for protein synthesis existing in the cell. In a previous section the evidence for the compartmentalization of glutamic acid metabolism has been summarized. Similar consideration may apply to the interpretation of protein turnover in short-time experiments, particularly if the labeled amino acids have a preferred access to the site of protein synthesis. More will have to be known about the mechanism of protein synthesis, the spacial relationship of the responsible enzymes, and the local pool of metabolites and coenzymes before the accuracy of the determined rates of turnover can be appraised.

Protein Metabolism in Nerve

The question of the origin of the proteins of the nerve axon has attracted increasing attention during recent years. Several attempts have been made to decide experimentally whether these axonal components are synthesized locally along the axon or originate in the perikarya and are transported through the axon by axonal flow. The strongest support for axonal flow and consequently for the synthesis of the axonal proteins in the perikarya derives from constriction experiments of Weiss and Hiscoe.[123] Enlargement of the nerve proximal to the constriction cuff and emergence distal to the cuff of a nerve with a diameter essentially corresponding to the opening of the cuff was observed. This finding was interpreted as a damming up of the viscous jelly-like axonal content synthesized in the perikarya. A rate of flow of 1 mm. per day was calculated, a figure of an order of magnitude of that estimated for nerve regeneration and also neuro-secretory movement from the hypothalamus to the posterior lobe of the hypophysis. The observation[124,125] that the proximal portion of the nodes of Ranvier is larger in most nerves than the distal part was interpreted as additional confirmation of the existence of proximo-distal flow of axoplasm. A considerably faster movement along the axon of radioactive sodium and copper was found after its injection into the nerve (80 mm. per day). This fast flow is assumed to proceed in the endoneural spaces.[126] Since the original experiments of Weiss and Hiscoe, considerable circumstantial evidence has been accumulated in support of the concept of axonal flow. Most of the evidence is based on the analysis of enzyme concentrations in the proximal and distal part of a cut nerve. It has been established by several investigators (for a review, see ref. 127) that choline acetylase disappears from the distal part of the sectioned nerves.[128-130] The increase of choline acetylase in the proximal part with a decrease distal to the section is taken as evidence that the enzyme is derived from the cell body of the neuron.[131] Acetylcholinesterase, but not pseudo-cholinesterase, shows different behavior in the two segments.[132] Lipolytic esterase increased in the proximal stump of the two segments with a decrease in the distal stump; after reunification of the stumps the zone of highest esterase activity passed into the upper portion of the distal segment, a finding which was related to outgrowth of regenerating neurites.[133] A detailed histochemical study of succinic dehydrogenase and DPN and TPN diaphorases during the regenerative cycle following interruption of the sciatic nerve of the rat and the central descending tracts of the cat showed changes in enzyme concentration and accumulation in the central stump. These observations were interpreted as demonstrating axonal flow of the enzymes synthesized in the cell body.[134] The observation that pseudo-cholinesterase does not follow the pattern of acetylcholinesterase in the distal and proximal portion of a cut nerve suggests that because of its localization in the Schwann cells the former enzyme is not under the same metabolic control as the true cholinesterase. Similar consideration may apply to the site of synthesis of acetic thiokinase[129] or cholinekinase,[135] neither of which follows the pattern of choline acetylase or true cholinesterase in the degenerating cut nerve. Extracts of acetone-dried powders of degenerating cat sciatic showed undiminished thiokinase activity up to 16 days after sectioning, with an increase in enzyme activity after this time. Choline acetylase had already disappeared 8 days after sectioning. These findings may suggest that acetyl-CoA for acetylcholine synthesis is supplied by the Schwann cells, whereas choline acetylase as an axonal protein disappears when the supply from the nerve cell is interrupted.

These experiments do not clarify the basic question: Is the damming up of axoplasm or the increase of the concentration of enzymes in the proximal stump of the cut nerve the result of local biosynthetic events or an expression of the synthetic activity of the cell body with subsequent axoplasmic flow?

The problem of the origin of axonal components was also approached with the aid of isotopes. After administration of P^{32} phosphate to frogs and cats, a gradient of radioactivity was found in nerves.[136,137] Because of the high metabolic activity of the Schwann cells and the multiple metabolic route of phosphate into rapidly metabolized components of the nerve, such as phosphoinositides or phosphoprotein, the significance of the observed gradient is difficult to assess. It may be an expression of the intensity of local energy-yielding processes (e.g., possibly related to the distribution of mitochondria) which are directly linked to the rate of incorporation of phosphate into organic linkage. Stronger support for synthesis of axonal proteins in the cell body and migration into the axon comes from experiments in which C^{14}-lysine was administered to frogs and the specific activity of the protein-bound lysine of the upper and lower parts of the sciatic plexus and nerve determined at different time intervals after the administration of the labeled amino acid.[138] A proximo-distal gradient (reversing itself after 38 days) of the specific activity of protein bound lysine was noted during the first 4 weeks (Table VIII). While the experiments with frogs led to the establishment of a proximo-distal gradient, a similar experiment with a spider monkey[91] showed an equal distribution of incorporated C^{14}-lysine along the nerve. On the other hand, results analogous to those found with C^{14}-lysine incorporation into the proteins of the sciatic nerve of the frog were obtained when the progression of radioactivity was determined in the proteins of the ulnar and sciatic nerves of the cat after cisternal administration of S^{35}-methionine and C^{14}-glycine.[139]

TABLE VIII[138,91]

LYSINE INCORPORATION INTO SCIATIC NERVE PROTEINS
(*Rana p.*)

Days	Liver	Cord	Sciatic Plexus		Sciatic Nerve	
			Upper	Lower	Upper	Lower
8	220		100	51	28	25
17	150		100	73	29	35
28	260	130	100	83	63	63
38	300	170	100	100	100	116

Frogs were killed at the indicated days after the injection of C^{14}–lysine. The proteins of the upper and lower parts of the sciatic plexus and sciatic nerve were purified by conventional methods and the radioactivity measured.

Several attempts have been made recently to elucidate the origin of axonal proteins by a study of the recovery of acetylcholinesterase after inhibition by organophosphates. A synthesis of true cholinesterase in the perikarya and subsequent transport along the axon has been suggested by Dale.[140] This suggestion finds support in the observation[141] that during development the enzyme appeared first in the cell bodies, and also in the studies on enzyme activities in the two parts of a cut nerve summarized above. Additional evidence for synthesis of the enzyme by the cell body was recently obtained[142] when it was shown that the distribution of the enzyme paralleled that of the Nissl bodies and that after irreversible inhibition the enzyme reappeared first in the cytoplasm and only later in the processes. It was reasoned that cholinesterase was probably synthesized in the endoplasmic reticulum and then transported via canaliculi to the cell surface and to the processes. When the resynthesis of acetylcholinesterase in frogs after intracerebral injection of an organophosphorous inhibitor was studied, a progressive proximo-distal inhibition of the acetylcholinesterase in the plexus sciaticus and sciatic nerve was found. On the other hand, the enzyme activity returned first in the distal part of the sciatic nerve and recovery progressed in a distal-proximal direction, pseudo-cholinesterase recovering evenly along the nerve.[143]

In experiments on cats it could be shown that after irreversible inactivation by diisopropyl-fluorophosphate, acetylcholinesterase activity returned uniformly along the hypoglossal and cervical sympathetic nerve trunks.[144]

If the reappearance of the true cholinesterase can be ascribed to resynthesis of the enzyme protein or of its active site and not to re-activation of the enzyme, the distal-proximal recovery of the enzyme could be explained by the growth of the endoplasmic reticulum into the axon after shedding the nucleoprotein granules. During migration of the enzyme its concentration may be too low or it may be in an inactive form and its determination possible only after it accumulated in the distal portion of the nerve, this accumulation progressing in a distal-proximal direction. The force behind axonal flow and migration of protein into the axon would then be the expansion of the endo-plasmic reticulum, which in growing into the axon would disintegrate.

In a study of the action of the same inhibitor on acetylcholinesterase in the rat brain, observations were made which indicate the general effect of such "specific" enzyme inhibitors on protein metabolism.[145] The rate of turnover of proteins in the caudate nucleus of the rat during the recovery phase after inhibition of cholinesterase with an irreversible inhibitor exceeds the rate of the normal control. These results show clearly the difficulty in assigning inhibition of a specific enzyme a particular functional significance *in vivo*.

The experimental evidence summarized and discussed above does not contradict the concept of the origin of axonal constituents or neu-rohormones in the perikarya with flow through the axon. Some ob-servations such as the distal-proximal recovery of acetylcholinesterase in frog sciatic nerve or its even recovery in cat nerves can be fitted into this concept by the utilization of additional hypotheses. It is of interest to remember that recent studies of the synthesis of vasopressin[88] in the hypothalamic-hypophysial axis, if to be interpreted by the concept of neurosecretory migration, would suggest a rapidity of flow not in ac-cord with the data on the rate of production of this hormone. It is apparent from the data available that local metabolism must play a considerable role in the synthesis or modification of axonal components which may be derived in part by axonal flow. The question may also be asked as to the origin of structural units responsible for the local metabolic activity. It may well be that the metabolic apparatus such as mitochondria, responsible for metabolism along the axon, originates in the perikarya and migrates through the axon transported by the expanding endoplasmic reticulum.

The hypothesis that the axonal components are at least in part de-rived from the perikarya of the nerve cells by axonal flow and that neurosecretion is a specialized case of this mechanism suggests that the phenomenon of axonal flow may be a general property of the neuron. The components of the axon being rejuvenated continuously have to be removed by metabolism either during migration or at the end organs; thereby the metabolism of the nerve cell body may have specific influences on the metabolic environment of the synapse and the neuromuscular junction.

The Breakdown of Proteins in Brain (in vitro)

Proteinases in cerebral tissue have been known for a long time, and this tissue appears to contain more peptidases than muscle. The proteinases are more active at an acidic pH (3.6) than at a more neutral pH (6.6).[146] A proteinase with a pH optimum at 7.4 was found to be more active in white than in grey matter, whereas cathepsins with an optimal pH of 3.5-3.8 were more active in grey.[147-149] The quantitative distribution of dipeptidase in cortical layers suggests that the cell bodies of neurons and glia are the principal sites of peptidase activity in the cerebral cortex.[119,120]

Nuclei and mitochondria contain less peptidase than the lighter cytoplasmic particles.[150] The mitochondrial fraction of brain cortex exhibits a higher proteinase activity than other subcellular fractions[149] (Table IX). The lability of proteins to proteinase action in the central

TABLE IX[149]

DISTRIBUTION OF PROTEINASE ACTIVITY IN RAT BRAIN PARTICULATE FRACTIONS

	$\mu Mole\ N/hr.$	
	pH 3.8	pH 7.6
Nuclei	28	14
Mitochondria	42	33
Microsomes	6	3
Supernatant	5	8
Mitochondria and Nuclei	74	30
Mitochondria and Microsomes	40	11
Mitochondria and Supernatant	91	62

100 mg. protein/fraction added. The solubilized N in the supernatant was measured by Kjeldahl determination.

nervous system increase in the order: frog, pigeon, rat, cat.[151] In brain, as in other organs, the role of proteinase in protein metabolism has not been elucidated. We do not know to what degree the catabolic phase of protein turnover is an energy-requiring process; if findings with liver have an analogy in the nervous tissue, proteinase may, under normal conditions, be enclosed in lysozyme-like particles and may be active only under conditions of injury or stress. It is of interest in this connection that the appearance of proteolytic activity in nerves has been claimed after extensive, but not after short, stimulation.[152]

Protein Metabolism in the Developing Brain and During Excitation and Depression

Under normal conditions the amount of protein of the adult nervous system degraded over finite time periods is compensated by the amount synthesized. In brain as in other organs, this steady state condition does not hold true during growth, when the anabolic phase outweighs the catabolic phase, and so deposition of new protein occurs. Under a variety of experimental and abnormal conditions, such as extreme stimulation, convulsions, exhaustion, and glucose deprivation of the perfused brain, the catabolic phase has a higher rate than the anabolic, which results in an uncompensated degradation of proteins, sometimes followed during recovery by an overshooting of the synthetic phase. The different facets of the protein metabolism under non-steady state conditions are discussed below.

(A) The Developing Brain: Recent studies have concerned themselves with the development of the mature enzyme pattern in relation to function. The activities of a number of enzymes, among them phosphatases, cholinesterase,[153-155] succinoxidase, succinic dehydrogenase, cytochrome oxidase, apyrase,[154,155] and glutamo-synthetase,[156,157] increase concomitantly with or prior to myelinization. The protein content increases in all areas of the maturing brain.[158,159] The amino acid composition of brain proteins also differs in young and adult animals, a fact which indicates a disproportionate increase of a particular protein or the appearance of new protein species.[158,160,161,105]

No decisive evidence is available to show whether or not the rate of flux of free amino acids from blood plasma to brain is dependent on the age of the animal. Estimation of the rapid exchange rates of lysine[106] (Table II), leucine,[105] and glutamic acid[138,162] is not sufficiently accurate for a determination of differences in flux rates between young and adult animals. It has been claimed that the rate of flux of phenylalanine, leucine, and isoleucine mixtures is about twice as great in adult as in newborn.[38,98] The flux of glutamic acid from plasma to brain is assumed to be ten times greater in adult cortex than in newborn, in spite of the fact that in both cases ten times as much glutamic acid is derived from glucose as from blood glutamic acid. This increased rate of flux in adults of amino acids from blood into brain has not been found to parallel the turnover rates of protein.

It appears that the proteins of the immature brain have a higher average turnover rate than those of the mature organ[102,105,106,163] (Table VI). The data are a composite of turnover rates of many proteins, the rapid synthesis of newly formed protein superimposed on the turnover rates of the proteins already deposited.

All parts of the immature brain (cat), except cortex, showed a higher rate of methionine incorporation than the corresponding parts of the mature brain.[110,164] For a full appraisal of these data, a knowledge of the specific activity of the precursor amino acid, in this case S^{35}-methionine, in the pool of free amino acid would be necessary.

(B) Protein Metabolism in Excitation and Depression: Participation of protein in different functional states may entail changes in the configuration of these macromolecules, by folding, unfolding, masking, unmasking of certain active sites or by cleavage of peptide bonds, leading to partial or complete breakdown to amino acids or peptides. Most studies available today on the effect of stimulation were carried out under extreme conditions, such as exhaustive stimulation or convulsions, and the changes observed may be the result of unspecific stress on tissue metabolism not directly related to the nature of the stimulation.

Furthermore, many of the methods applied did not permit quantitative evaluation or any conclusion as to the rates of the reactions involved. This criticism holds true for radioautographic assessment of rate of incorporation of amino acid into proteins without knowledge of the pool size and specific activity of the precursor amino acids. For this reason, only some of the investigations will be mentioned—these mainly in order to show the trend of research probably to be intensified in the near future.

Extensive studies[165-170] on cytochemical changes in neurons under graded *in vivo* stimulation utilized ultraviolet spectrophotometry in combination with microchemical techniques. All findings attest to the high metabolic activity of cytoplasmic nucleic acids and proteins. After increased motor activity or electrical, auditory or vestibular excitation the respective ganglion cells show similar quantitative changes. After mild stimulation an increase in protein content was noted, whereas after exhausting stimulation the protein concentration decreased to a fraction of the concentration found under resting conditions. Return to a normal concentration after the stimulation took several weeks. The authors conclude that under functional stimulation the turnover of proteins is increased, with a prevalence under moderate conditions of the anabolic phase, and under intense stimulation leading to fatigue and exhaustion, of the catabolic phase. It is pointed out that the quantitative evaluation of the earlier data obtained by microspectrophotometry is made difficult by changes of the volume of the neurons under stress.[170]

In recent studies, an increase of 10% in the protein concentration, but a considerably greater increase of cytochrome oxidase and succinic oxidase activity, was observed in the ganglion cells of the Deiters' nucleus upon vestibular stimulation. The oligodendroglia showed the reverse changes, a fact which suggests to the authors that the nerve cells and the surrounding oligodendrocytes represent a symbiotic metabolic unit.[169] Extensive metabolic changes were noted in experiments with the perfused cat brain.[171] After 50 to 60 minutes of glucose free perfusion about 50% of the microsomes disappeared from the cortex accompanied by a corresponding reduction in nucleic acids, while the concentration of amino acids and nucleotides increased in the perfusate. Closely related is the observation on the intact cat that stimulation of the brachial plexus resulted in an increase of nonprotein nitrogen.[172] This change was reversible within a few minutes. A relation between protein metabolism and stimulus is supported by the observation that stimulus was necessary for the full protein complement in developing retinal ganglion cells.[173] The protein content of non-stimulated cells was half that of the controls, and in addition these cells contained very little, if any, nucleoproteins, a finding possibly explained by the fact that the cells of animals reared in darkness failed to develop.

TABLE X

CHANGES IN RATE OF PROTEIN METABOLISM UNDER DIFFERENT EXPERIMENTAL CONDITIONS

Experimental Conditions	Labeled Amino Acid Employed	Observed Change	Reference
Electric stimulation	methionine	−	102
Electric stimulation	methionine glycine	+	175
Electric stimulation	glycine	+	176
Electroconvulsive shock	proline	no change	177
Narcosis (ether pentobarbitone)	methionine	−	102
Narcosis (amytal)	glycine	−	175
Narcosis (amytal)	glycine	−	176
Narcosis and hypothermia	methionine	−	102
Narcosis (medinal-urethane)	methionine	no change	163
Hypoglycemia	methionine	−	102
Phenamine excitation	methionine	+	163
Exhaustion	methionine	−	174
Sleep after exhaustion	methionine	+	174

During exhausting activity a decrease of S^{35}-methionine incorporation into proteins of the rat brain was observed, with an increased rate of incorporation during sleep following the exhaustion.[174] The effect of anesthesia and other experimental conditions on the turnover of brain protein is not clear. Contradictory findings on increased and decreased rates of metabolism have been reported (Table X). In order to arrive at a definite conclusion, the dependence of protein turnover on the experimental period, as well as the precursor-product relationship, will have to be known.

It is at present difficult to visualize by what mechanism the extensive changes in protein metabolism would be primary concomitant reactions of functional activity of the central nervous system. The extensive changes with slow recovery as found after acoustic stimulation and the disappearance of microsomal protein in the perfused brain suggest that we are dealing with the influence of exhausting stimulation on metabolism but not with a biochemical mechanism directly related to functional activity.

Such a mechanism may relate to physico-chemical properties of brain proteins or macromolecules in general. Indications in this direction were found when changes in configuration of nerve and cortex proteins were studied after direct and indirect stimulation.[152,178,179] Modifications of the ultraviolet absorption in alkaline solution of the respective proteins were observed which were reversible after short stimulation. Prolonged stimulation, in addition to causing structural changes, also resulted in breakdown of protein, and the appearance of proteolytic activity. It seems, therefore, that short stimulation leads to reversible changes in configuration of brain and nerve proteins, and intensive stimulation results in additional breakdown of proteins.

Protein-bound SH showed an increase during stimulation,[178] pointing to a structural rearrangement of proteins participating in the mechanism of excitation, a finding in line with the suggested importance of protein-bound SH groups for nervous activity.[179]

Phosphoproteins may play a role in the binding and release of cations; therefore the turnover of the phosphate moieties of such proteins under conditions of stimulation and depression of the nervous system is of interest. Increased rates of phosphate turnover of cerebral phosphoprotein with activity were found upon excitation by electric shock or in camphor-induced convulsions,[175,176,180-183] and also in brain slices in potassium-rich media, an effect peculiar to brain.[184]

The participation of amide groups of proteins in functional activity of the nervous system is to be considered, since they have recently been demonstrated to be metabolically active.[185-187] It should be noted that ammonia liberated by brain cortex slices cannot be accounted for by the known ammonia-liberating enzymatic reactions. Excitation of nerve and brain tissue is accompanied by ammonia release, *in vitro* and *in vivo*;[188,189] this was elaborated by *in vivo* experiments in which animals were found to have after excitation an increase of ammonia and in narcosis a decrease in the ammonia concentration.[191] No claim was made in these experiments as to a participation of protein amide groups in ammonia metabolism. On the other hand, it has been claimed that after exhausting exercise the proteins of the rat brain show a decrease of amide groups relative to the total protein nitrogen.[191-194] These results, which show a low level of significance, could be explained by the disappearance of a protein fraction particularly rich in amide nitrogen. The metabolic activities of protein amide groups are of interest because the removal of these groups would modify the physical properties and configuration of the protein and because by a cycle of de- and reamidation proteins may act as ion carriers.

REFERENCES

1. WAELSCH, H.: In *Metabolism of the Nervous System*, p. 431 D. Richter, Ed. Oxford, Pergamon Press (1957).
2. WAELSCH, H. and WEIL-MALHERBE, H.: In *Psychiatrie der Gegenwart*, Vol. 7. Springer (1961).
3. WAELSCH, H. and LAJTHA, A.: *Physiol. Rev.*, in press (1961).
4. TALLAN, H. H., MOORE, S. and STEIN, W. H.: *J. Biol. Chem.*, 211:927 (1954).
5. SCHURR, P. E., THOMPSON, H. T., HENDERSON, L. M., WILLIAMS, J. N., JR., and ELVEHJEM, C. A.: *J. Biol. Chem.*, 182:39 (1950).
6. ANSELL, G. B. and RICHTER, D.: *Biochem. J.*, 57:70 (1954).
7. BERL, S., and WAELSCH, H.: *J. Neurochem.*, 3:161 (1958).
8. TALLAN, H. H., MOORE, S. and STEIN, W. H.: *J. Biol. Chem.*, 230:707 (1958).
9. SILBER, R. H.: *J. Cell. & Comp. Physiol.*, 18:21 (1941).
10. KOECHLIN, B. A.: *J. Biophys. Biochem. Cytol.*, 1:511 (1955).
11. DEFFNER, G. G. J. and HAFTER, R. E.: *Biochim. Biophys. Acta*, 42:200 (1960).
12. DEFFNER, G. G. J. and HAFTER, R. E.: *Biochim. Biophys. Acta*, 35:334 (1959).
13. AWAPARA, J., and SEALE, B.: *J. Biol. Chem.*, 194:497 (1952).
14. GUHA, S. R. and GHOSH, J. J.: *Ann. Biochem. & Exper. Med.*, 19:33 (1959).
15. MEISTER, A., and TICE, S. V.: *J. Biol. Chem.*, 187:173 (1950).
16. SCHWERIN, P., BESSMAN, S. P., and WAELSCH, H.: *J. Biol. Chem.*, 184:37 (1950).
17. DINGMAN, W., and SPORN, M. B.: *J. Neurochem.*, 4:148 (1959).
18. LAJTHA, A.: *J. Neurochem.*, 2:209 (1958).
19. LAJTHA, A. and TOTH, J.: *J. Neurochem.*, in press (1961).
20. CHIRIGOS, M. A., GREEGARD, P. and UDENFRIEND, S.: *J. Biol. Chem.*, 235:2075 (1960).
21. HIMWICH, W. A., PETERSEN, J. C. and ALLEN, M. L.: *Neurology*, 7:705 (1957).
22. LAJTHA, A., FURST, S., GERSTEIN, A. and WAELSCH, H.: *J. Neurochem.*, 1:289 (1957).
23. LAJTHA, A.: *J. Neurochem.*, 3:358 (1959).
24. LAJTHA, A., BERL, S. and WAELSCH, H.: *J. Neurochem.*, 3:322 (1959).
25. WAELSCH, H.: *J. Nerv. & Ment. Dis.*, 126:33 (1958).
26. HEINZ, E.: *J. Biol. Chem.*, 225:305 (1957).
27. HEINZ, E., and WALSH, P. M.: *J. Biol. Chem.*, 233:1488 (1958).
28. WAELSCH, H.: *Adv. Protein Chem.*, 6:301 (1951).
29. BERL, S., CLARKE, D. D., TAKAGAKI, G., PURPURA, D. P. and WAELSCH, H.: *Federation Proc.*, 20:I, 342 (1961).
30. BUSCH, H.: *Cancer Res.*, 15:Suppl. 3, 365 (1955).
31. BUSCH, H., GOLDBERG, M. H. and ANDERSON, D. C.: *Cancer Res.*, 16:175 (1956).
32. BENITEZ, D., PSCHEIDT, G. R. and STONE, W. E.: *Am. J. Physiol.*, 176:488 (1954).
33. WAELSCH, H.: *Lancet*, July 2 (1949).

34. Chain, E. B.: *Brit. M. J.*, *2*:709 (1959).
35. Krebs, H. A. and Bellamy, D.: *Biochem. J.*, *75*:523 (1960).
36. Kini, M. M. and Quastel, J. H.: *Nature*, *184*:252 (1959).
37. Barkulis, S. S., Geiger, A., Kawakita, Y. and Aguilar, V.: *J. Neurochem.*, *5*:339 (1960).
38. Roberts, R. B., Flexner, J. B. and Flexner, L. B.: *J. Neurochem.*, *4*:78 (1959).
39. Adams, J. E., Harper, H. A., Gordan, G. S., Hutchin, M. and Bentinck, R. C.: *Neurology*, *5*:100 (1955).
40. Weil-Malherbe, H.: *Biochem. J.*, *30*:665 (1936).
41. Sporn, M. B., Dingman, W. and Defalco, A.: *J. Neurochem.*, *4*:141 (1959).
42. McIlwain, H.: *J. Ment. Sc.*, *97*:674 (1951).
43. McIlwain, H., Ayres, P. J. W. and Forda, O.: *J. Ment. Sc.*, *98*:265 (1952).
44. McIlwain, H.: *J. Neurol., Neurosurg. & Psychiat.*, *16*:257 (1953).
45. Haber, C., and Saidel, L.: *Federation Proc.* *7*:47 (1948).
46. Dawson, R. M. C.: *Biochem. J.*, *47*:386 (1950).
47. Dawson, R. M. C.: *Biochem. J.*, *49*:138 (1951).
48. Berl, S., Purpura, D. P., Girado, M. and Waelsch, H.: *J. Neurochem.*, *4*:311 (1959).
49. Tower, D. B.: *Neurology*, *5*:113 (1955).
50. Tower, D. B.: In *Proceedings of the Fourth International Congress of Biochemistry*, p. 213. F. Brücke, Ed. London, Pergamon Press (1959).
51. Takagaki, G., Berl, S., Clarke, D. D., Purpura, D. P. and Waelsch, H.: *Nature*, *189*:326 (1961).
52. Krebs, H. A.: *Biochem. J.*, *29*:1951 (1935).
53. Speck, J. F.: *J. Biol. Chem.*, *179*:1405 (1949).
54. Elliot, W. H.: *Biochem. J.*, *49*:106 (1951).
55. Lajtha, A., Mela, P. and Waelsch, H.: *J. Biol. Chem.*, *205*:553 (1953).
56. Waelsch, H.: In *Proceedings of the Fourth International Congress of Biochemistry*. Vol. III: Biochemistry of the Central Nervous System, p. 36. F. Brücke, Ed. London, Pergamon Press (1959).
57. Ghosh, J. J. and Waelsch, H.: Unpublished.
58. Waelsch, H.: *Advances Enzymol.*, *XIII*:237 (1952).
59. Weil-Malherbe, H., and Green, R. H.: *Biochem. J.*, *61*:210 (195).
60. Vrba, R.: *Physiol. Bohemoslov.*, *4*:397 (1955).
61. Gray, I., Johnston, J. M. and Spearing, C. W.: *Federation Proc.*, *15*:265 (1956).
62. Tsukada, Y., Takagaki, G., Sugimoto, S. and Hirano, S.: *J. Neurochem.*, *2*:295 (1958).
63. Berl, S., Takagaki, G., and Purpura, D. P.: *J. Neurochem.*, *7*:198 (1961).
64. Du Ruisseau, J. P., Greenstein, J. P., Winitz, M. and Birnbaum, S. M.: *Arch. Biochem. Biophys.*, *68*:161 (1957).
65. Clark, G. M., and Eiseman, B.: *New England J. Med.*, *259*:178 (1958).
66. Terner, C., Eggleston, L. V. and Krebs, H. A.: *Biochem. J.*, *47*:139 (1950).
67. Elliott, K. A. C.: *Canad. J. Biochem. & Physiol.*, *33*:466 (1955).
68. Stern, J. R., Eggleston, L. V., Hems, R. and Krebs, H. A.: *Biochem. J.*, *44*:410 (1949).
69. Katzman, R., and Leiderman, P. H.: *Am. J. Physiol.*, *175*:263 (1953).
70. Berl, S., Lajtha, A. and Waelsch, H.: *J. Neurochem.*, *7*:186 (1961).
71. Waelsch, H.: In *Structure and Function of the Cerebral Cortex*, Elsevier Pub. Co. (1960).
72. Price, J. C., Waelsch, H. and Putnam, T. J.: *J. A. M. A.*, *122*:1153 (1943).
73. Albert, K., Hoch, P. and Waelsch, H.: *J. Nerv. & Ment. Dis.*, *114*:471 (1951).

74. TOWER, D. B.: *Neurology, 5:*113 (1955).
75. TOWER, D. B.: In *Inhibition in the Nervous System and γ-Aminobutyric Acid.* E. Roberts, Ed. London, Pergamon Press (1960).
76. KLINGMÜLLER, V.: Biochemie, Physiologie und Klink der Glutaminäure. Aulendorf i. Württ., Editio Cantor (1955).
77. WAELSCH, H., OWADES, P., MILLER, H. K. and BOREK, E.: *J. Biol. Chem., 166:*273 (1946).
78. MISANI, F., and REINER, L.: *Arch. Biochem., 27:*234 (1950).
79. TOWER, D. B.: *Neurochemistry of Epilepsy.* Springfield, Ill., Thomas (1960).
80. WAELSCH, H.: *Postgrad. Med., 27:*645 (1960).
81. JOHNSTON, R. B., and BLOCH, K.: *J. Biol. Chem., 188:*221 (1951).
82. FODOR, P. J., MILLER, A., NEIDLE, A. and WAELSCH, H.: *J. Biol. Chem., 203:*991 (1953).
83. TALLAN, H. H., MOORE, S. and STEIN, W. H.: *J. Biol. Chem., 219:*257 (1956).
84. GOLDSTEIN, F. B.: *Biochim. Biophys. Acta, 33:*583 (1959).
85. GOLDSTEIN, F. B.: *J. Biol. Chem., 234:*2702 (1959).
86. JACOBSON, K. B.: *Federation Proc., 17:*248 (1958).
87. WINNICK, T., WINNICK, R. E., ACHER, R. and FROMAGEOT, C.: *Biochim. Biophys. Acta, 18:*488 (1955).
88. SACHS, H.: *J. Neurochem., 5:*297 (1960).
89. PALAY, S. L., and PALADE, G. E.: *J. Biophys. Biochim. Cytol., 1:*69 (1955).
90. LIPMANN, F.: In *The Metabolism of the Nervous System,* p. 329. D. Richter, Ed. Oxford, Pergamon Press (1957).
91. LAJTHA, A.: In *Chemical Pathology of the Nervous System,* p. 268. J. Folch, Ed. Oxford, Pergamon Press (1961).
92. ACS, G., NEIDLE, A., and WAELSCH, H.: *Biochim. Biophys. Acta, 50:*403 (1961).
93. FURST, S., LAJTHA, A. and WAELSCH, H.: *J. Neurochem., 2:*216 (1958).
94. KELLER, E. B., ZAMECNIK, P. C. and LOFTFIELD, R. B.: *J. Histochem. Cytochem., 2:*378 (1954).
95. CLOUET, D. H. and RICHTER, D.: *J. Neurochem., 3:*219 (1959).
96. SACHS, H. and WAELSCH, H.: *Biochim. Biophys, Acta, 21:*188 (1956).
97. KRAVCZYNSKI, J. and SILICZ, T.: *Chem. Abst., 51:*10697 (1957).
98. FLEXNER, L. B., FLEXNER, J. B. and ROBERTS, R. B.: *J. Cell. & Comp. Physiol., 51:*385 (1959).
99. STILL, J. W.: *J. Hered., 48:*202 (1957).
100. WAELSCH, H., SPERRY, W. M. and STOYANOFF, V. A.: *J. Biol. Chem., 135:*291 (1940).
101. FRIEDBERG, F., TARVER, H. and GREENBERG, D.: *J. Biol. Chem., 173:*355 (1948).
102. GAITONDE, M. K. and RICHTER, D.: *Proc. Roy. Soc., 145:*83 (1956).
103. MAURER, W.: *Wien. Ztschr. Inn. Med., 38:*393 (1957).
104. NIKALAS, A., QUINCKE, E., MAURER, W. and NEYEN, H.: *Biochem. Ztschr., 330:*1 (1958).
105. LAJTHA, A.: *J. Neurochem., 3:*358 (1959).
106. LAJTHA, A., FURST, S., GERSTEIN, A. and WAELSCH, H.: *J. Neurochem., 1:*289 (1957).
107. LAJTHA, A. and FURST, S.: In *Ultrastructure and Cellular Chemistry of Neural Tissues.* p. 195. New York, Hoeber-Harper (1957).
108. LAJTHA, A., FURST, S. and WAELSCH, H.: *Experientia, 13:*168 (1957).
109. PALLADIN, A. V., POLYAKOVA, N. V. and SILICH, J. P.: *Chem. Abst., 51:*16792b (1957).
110. PANTCHENKO, L. F.: *J. Physiol. U.S.S.R., 44:*243 (1958).

111. Silich, J. P.: *Ukrain. Biokhim. Zhur., 29*:166, 171 (1957; *Chem. Abst., 51*:16785c (1957).

112. Lodin, Z and Kolousek, J.: *Physiol. Bohemoslovenica, 5*:43 (1956).

113. Niklas, A. and Oehlert, W. *Beitr. Path. Anat., 116*:92 (1956).

114. Cohn, P., Gaitonde, M. K. and Richter, D.: *J. Physiol., 126*:7P, (1954).

115. Fischer, J., Kolousek, J. and Lodin, Z.: *Nature, 178*:1122 (1956).

116. Koenig, H.: *J. Biophys. Biochem. Cytol., 4*:785 (1958).

117. Dixon, K. C.: *J. Physiol., 120*:267 (1953).

118. Palladin, A. V., and Poljakowa, N. M.: *Doklady Akad. Nauk. USSK* 107:568 (1956).

119. Pope, A.: *J. Neurophysiol., 15*:115 (1952).

120. Pope, A.: *J. Neuropath. & Exper. Neurol., 14*:39 (1955).

121. Davison, A. N.: *Biochem. J., 78*:272 (1961).

122. Loftfield, R. B. and Harris, A.: *J. Biol. Chem., 219*:151 (1956).

123. Weiss, P. and Hiscoe, H. B.: *J. Exper. Zool., 107*:315 (1948).

124. Lubinska, L.: *Nature, 173*:867 (1954).

125. Lubinska, L. and Ukaszewska, I.: *Acta Biol. Exper., 17*:115 (1955).

126. Weiss, P., Wang, H., Taylor, C. A. and Edds, M. V.: *Am. J. Physiol., 143*:521 (1945).

127. Hebb, C. O.: *Physiol. Rev., 37*:196 (1957).

128. Banister, J. and Scrase, M.: *J. Physiol., 111*:437 (1950).

129. Berry, J. F. and Rossiter, R. J.: *J. Neurochem., 3*:59 (1958).

130. Feldberg, W.: *Physiol. Rev., 25*:596 (1945).

131. Hebb, C. O. and Waites, M. H.: *J. Physiol., 132*:667 (1956).

132. Sawyer, C. H.: *Am. J. Physiol., 146*:246 (1946).

133. Lumsden, C. E.: *Quart. J. Exper. Physiol., 7*:1 (1952).

134. Friede, R. L.: *Exper. Neuro., 1*:441 (1959).

135. Berry, J. F., McPherson, C. F. and Rossiter, R. J.: *J. Neurochem., 3*:65 (1958).

136. Ochs, S. and Burger, E.: *Am. J. Physiol., 194*:499 (1958).

137. Samuels, A. J., Boyarsky, L. L., Gerard, R. W., Libet, B. and Brust, M.: *Am. J. Physiol., 164*:1 (1951).

138. Waelsch, H.: *J. Nerv. & Ment. Dis., 126*:33 (1958).

139. Koenig, H.: *Tr. Am. Neurol. A.,* 162 (1958).

140. Dale, H. H.: *Proc. Staff Meet., Mayo Clin., 30*:5 (1955).

141. Lewis, P. R. and Hughes, A. F. W.: In *The Metabolism of the Nervous System,* p. 511. D. Richter, Ed. Oxford, Pergamon Press (1957).

142. Fukuda, T. and Koelle, G. B.: *J. Biophys. Biochem. Cytol., 5*:433 (1959).

143. Clouet, D. H. and Waelsch, H.: In *The Regional Chemistry, Physiology and Pharmacology of the Nervous System.* p. 243. S. Kety and J. Elkes, Eds. Oxford, Pergamon Press (1961); *J. Neurochem.,* in press.

144. Koenig, E. and Koelle, G. B.: *Science, 132*:1249 (1960).

145. Clouet, D. H. and Waelsch, H.: *Federation Proc., 20*:307 (1961).

146. Kies, M. W. and Schwimmer, S.: *J. Biol. Chem., 145*:685 (1942).

147. Ansell, G. B., and Richter, D.: *Biochim. Biophys. Acta, 13*:87 (1954).

148. Ansell, G. B., and Richter, D.: *Biochim. Biophys. Acta, 13*:92 (1954).

149. Lajtha, A.: In *The Regional Chemistry, Physiology and Pharmacology of the Nervous System.* p. 25. S. Kety and J. Elkes, Eds. Oxford, Pergamon Press (1961).

150. Hanson, H. and Tendis, N.: *Arch. ges. Inn. Med., 9*:224 (1955).

151. Li, C.-T.: *Dodlady Akad. Nauk, USSK 120*:650 (1958); *Chem. Abst., 52*:17453c (1958).

152. UNGAR, G., ASCHHEIM, E., PSYCHOYOS, S. and ROMANO, D. V.: *J. Gen. Physiol.,* 40:635 (1957).
153. COHN, P. and RICHTER, D.: *J. Neurochem., 1*:166 (1956).
154. FLEXNER, L. B.: *The Harvey Lectures, 47*:156 (1952).
155. FLEXNER, L. B.: In *Biochemistry of the Developing Nervous System,* p. 281. H. Waelsch, Ed. New York, Acad. Press. (1955).
156. RUDNICK, D. and WAELSCH, H.: *J. Exper. Zool., 129*:309 (1955).
157. RUDNICK, D. and WAELSCH, H.: In *Biochemistry of the Developing Nervous System,* p. 335. H. Waelsch, Ed. New York, Acad. Press (1955).
158. CLOUET, D. H. and GAITONDE, M. K.: *J. Neurochem., 1*:126 (1956).
159. KELLEY, B.: *Am. J. Physiol., 185*:299 (1956).
160. BLOCK, R. J.: *J. Biol. Chem., 120*:467 (1937).
161. LAJTHA, A.: *J. Neurochem., 2*:209 (1958).
162. LAJTHA, A., BERL, S. and WAELSCH, H.: *J. Neurochem., 3*:322 (1959).
163. PALLADIN, A. V., BELIK, YA. V. and KRACHKO, L. I.: *Biokimia, 22*:359 (1957).
164. PANTCHENKO, L. F.: *Uchenye Zapiski, Moskov. Med. Inst., 6*:41 (1957); *Chem. Abst., 52*:20518d (1958).
165. HAMBERGER, C. A. and HYDEN, H.: *Acta Oto-laryng., 61*:Suppl. (1945).
166. HYDEN, H.: *Acta physiol. scandinav., 6*:Suppl. 17 (1943).
167. HYDEN, H.: In *Neurochemistry.* Elliott *et al.,* Eds. Springfield, Ill., Thomas (1955).
168. HYDEN, H.: In *Biochemistry of the Central Nervous System,* p. 64. F. Brücke, Ed. Oxford, Pergamon Press (1959).
169. HYDEN, H., LVTRUP, S. and PIGON, A.: *J. Neurochem., 2*:304 (1958).
170. HYDEN, H.: In *The Cell,* Vol. IV, p. 215. J. Brachet and A. E. Mirsky, Eds. New York, Acad. Press (1960).
171. ABOOD, L. G. and GEIGER, A.: *Am. J. Physiol., 182*:557 (1955).
172. GEIGER, A., YAMAKAKI, S. and LYONS, R.: *Am. J. Physiol., 184*:239 (1956).
173. BRATTGARD, S.-O.: *Acta radiol., 96*:Suppl. 1 (1952).
174. SHAPOT, V. S.: In *Metabolism of the Nervous System,* p. 257. D. Richter, Ed. Oxford, Pergamon Press.
175. VLADIMIROV, G. E. and URINSON, A. P.: *Biokhimia, 22*:709 (1957).
176. NECHAEVA, G. A., SADIKOVA, N. V. and SKVORTSEVICH, V. A.: *Voprosy Biokhim. Nervoi Sistemy Sbornik, 31:* (1957); Chem. Abst., *53*:1500b (1959).
177. DINGMAN, W., SPORN, M. B., and DAVIES, R. K.: *J. Neurochem., 4*:154 (1959).
178. UNGAR, G. and ROMANO, D. V.: *Proc. Soc. Exper. Biol. & Med., 97*:324 (1958).
179. UNGAR, G. and ROMANO, D. V.: *Federation Proc., 18*:162 (1959).
180. HEALD, P. J.: *Biochem. J., 66*:659 (1957).
181. HEALD, P. J.: *Biochem. J., 68*:580 (1958).
182. VLADIMIROV, G. E.: *Fiziol. Zhur. S.S.S.R., 39*:3 (1953); *Chem. Abst., 47*:4983e (1953).
183. VLADIMIROV, G. E.: *Voprosy Biokhim. Nervoi Sistemy Sbornik,* 247 (1957); *Chem. Abst., 53*:1502d (1959).
184. TUSUKADA, Y., TAKAGAKI, G. and HIRANO, S.: *J. Biochem., 45*:489 (1958).
185. CLARKE, D. D., MYCEK, M. J., NEIDLE, A. and WAELSCH, H.: *Arch. Biochem. Biophys., 79*:338 (1959).
186. MYCEK, M. J., CLARKE, D. D., NEIDLE, A. and WAELSCH, H.: *Arch. Biochem. Biophys., 84*:528 (1958).
187. MYCEK, M. J. and WAELSCH, H.: *J. Biol. Chem., 235*:3513 (1960).
188. WINTERSTEIN, H. and HIRSCHBERG, E.: *Biochem. Ztschr., 156*:138 (1925).
189. TASHIRO, S.: *Am. J. Physiol., 60*:519 (1922).

190. RICHTER, D. and DAWSON, R. M. C.: *J. Biol. Chem., 176:*1199 (1948).

191. VRBA, R.: *Uspekhi Sovremennoi Biol., 41:*321 (1956).

192. VRBA, R.: *Rev. Czechoslovak Med., 3:*81 (1957).

193. VRBA, R. and FOLBERGROVA, J.: *J. Neurochem., 4:*338 (1959).

194. VRBA, R., FOLBERGROVA, R. V. and KANTUREK, V.: *J. Neurochem., 2:*187 (1958).

XV

AMMONIA METABOLISM IN THE BRAIN*

H. Weil-Malherbe

THE INVOLVEMENT of nitrogen metabolism in nervous cell function is evident from the reactions leading to the appearance and disappearance of ammonia in the brain. It is now well established that nervous activity is accompanied by a liberation of ammonia and that the rate of this process is correlated with the intensity of nervous activity.

AMMONIA LEVELS IN THE BRAIN *IN VIVO*

The steady formation of ammonia by excised peripheral frog nerve and its increase upon electrical stimulation of the nerve was first demonstrated by Tashiro.[1] Winterstein[2] made similar observations with rabbit nerve; he further showed that ammonia formation was depressed by nerve section, anoxemia and anaesthesia. Ammonia levels in the brain of experimental animals have been studied by several authors using the technique of rapid freezing: a significant rise of the ammonia concentration in rat brain was found after convulsions produced by the injection of drugs, such as camphor,[3] picrotoxin[4] or pentamethylenetetrazole,[5] by electrical stimulation of the brain,[4] anoxia[4] or high oxygen pressure.[6] In some instances[4,6] the rise occurred in the preconvulsive phase; this effect was particularly marked in the brains of dogs after the injection of methyl fluoroacetate[7] where the ammonia concentration rose steadily and reached a maximum at the time seizures developed. An approximately linear increase of the ammonia level up to about three times normal was observed in rabbit brain during the first 15 minutes of ischaemia.[8]

The level of ammonia in the brain was also raised, in the absence of convulsive activity, as a result of central stimulation of a milder degree, produced, for instance by painful electrical stimulation of the

---

*The term ammonia is used in this article to denote the sum of ammonium ions and free base.

extremities,[9,10] by certain conditioned reflexes,[9,10] by tumbling in a revolving drum[11] or by the injection of corticotrophin[12] or amphetamine.[13]

Changes in the opposite direction are produced by anaesthesia and sleep. Richter and Dawson[4] found a progressive drop and finally a practically complete disappearance of ammonia in the brains of rats under nembutal anaesthesia for periods of up to 90 minutes. According to Vladimirova,[9] the ammonia concentration of rat brain decreases by about 50% during natural sleep.

AMMONIA FORMATION BY BRAIN TISSUE *IN VITRO*

Provided post mortem changes are suppressed by rapid freezing *in situ,* values of 0.2-0.3 μmoles of ammonia per gram of fresh brain tissue are found in mice,[14] rats,[4,10] rabbits,[8] and dogs.[7] If the heads are severed and freezing is delayed for a few seconds, the ammonia level is approximately doubled.[4] This initial burst is followed by a further output of ammonia. Three minutes after death, a value of 2 μmoles/gm. has been found in cat brain.[15] In slices of rat brain cortex, fixed about 20 minutes after death, it is usual to find about 5 μmoles/gm.[16]

When brain tissue is homogenized in hypotonic bicarbonate buffer solution at pH 7.4, a strong formation of ammonia ensues which, within a few minutes after death, leads to a concentration three times as high as that found in slices of cerebral cortex and 60 to 80 times as high as the *in vivo* level, but there is little or no further increase upon subsequent incubation of the homogenate. In brain slices, on the other hand, ammonia is formed at a fairly steady rate for at least 5 hours in a glucose-free medium; whereas the initial ammonia content of brain slices (together with suspension medium) is less than a third of that of a brain homogenate, after incubation it is twice as high as in the homogenate. A brain homogenate prepared in isotonic saline is intermediate between slices and hypotonic homogenate, both as regards initial concentration and subsequent formation of ammonia. These results emphasize the importance of the integrity of cellular structure; while comparatively well preserved in slices, the structure of cells is largely destroyed in the isotonic homogenate; that of mitochondria, on the other hand, is still more or less intact; in the hypotonic homogenate mitochondria, too, are severely damaged. The requirement of intact mitochondria for ammonia formation suggests the involvement of oxidative phosphorylation. This is borne out by the fact that absence of oxygen or the presence of inhibitors, such as 2:4-dinitrophenol, virtually reduces the ammonia formation of brain slices to the level found in hypotonic homogenates.[16]

The question arises whether the post mortem formation of ammonia is in any way connected with the ammonia formation resulting from activity *in vivo*. In contrast to the findings on peripheral nerve,[1,2] electrical stimulation of brain slices[17] or of the excised superior cervical ganglion[18] did not increase the output of ammonia. Nevertheless, the fact that at least a fraction of the post mortem ammonia formation of brain slices is dependent on endergonic reactions indicates that the process is not entirely autolytic. It is conceivable, therefore, that the same mechanism operates *in vivo*.

THE ORIGIN OF CEREBRAL AMMONIA FORMED *IN VIVO* AND *IN VITRO*

In view of the possible significance of the liberation of ammonia for nervous function, the nature of the ammonia precursor is of great interest; yet this seemingly simple problem is still unsolved.

The work of Embden,[19] Parnas[20] and others (e.g., ref. 21) on ammonia formation in muscle, which identified the acid-soluble adenosine nucleotides as the principal precursors, suggested a similar mechanism for the ammonia formation in brain *in vivo*, especially since enzymes for the deamination of adenosine[22] and 5'-adenylic acid[22-24] are present in the brain. However, little or no breakdown of ATP was found in brain during fluoroacetate poisoning in spite of a greatly increased formation of ammonia.[7,25] According to Koransky,[26] the increase of inosinic acid in the brain of rats after a convulsion accounts for only about one-tenth of the ammonia formation.

The ammonia formation of brain slices *in vitro* by far exceeds the amount which could theoretically be formed by the complete deamination of the acid-soluble fraction of adenosine and adenosine phosphates in brain. Far from being completely deaminated, pre-formed adenosine phosphates contained in brain slices seem to be fairly resistant to deaminase action,[27] a fact which is confirmed by the observation that ATP, hydrolysed during the preparation and initial storage of brain slices, is fully resynthesized when the slices are incubated in glucose-saline.[28]

A mechanism exists in muscle whereby the amino group of aspartic acid is transferred to inosinic acid, resulting in its amination to adenylic acid.[29,30] Evidence has been obtained that a similar system exists in brain, but from present indications its activity does not seem to be sufficient to account for the ammonia formation of brain slices on the basis of a cyclic amination and deamination involving adenylic acid.[31]

Another possibility to be considered is the deamination of glutamine and glutamic acid. Although glutamine added to the incubation medium is rapidly deaminated by brain slices, the pre-formed glutamine contained within the slices remains practically unchanged during aerobic as well as anaerobic incubation.[16] D-Glutamic acid, an inhibitor of glutaminase, at a concentration of 2 mM, completely blocks the deamination of added glutamine by brain slices without affecting the spontaneous ammonia formation of brain slices in a substrate-free medium.[16] These observations seem to rule out soluble glutamine as a precursor of ammonia; in any case, its complete deamination would only account for about 10% of the amount formed by brain slices in 5 hours.

L-Glutamic acid which occurs in brain in relatively high concentration has repeatedly been claimed to be a precursor of ammonia. Yet, when glutamic acid is added to brain slices, it is oxidized without the appearance of ammonia; instead the concentration of amide-N increases.[32,33] The underlying reaction may be formulated thus:

$$2 \text{ Glutamic acid} + \tfrac{1}{2} O_2 \rightarrow \text{Glutamine} + \alpha\text{-Ketoglutaric acid} + H_2O,$$

indicating that the rate of deamination is limited by the rate of glutamine synthesis. This limitation is explained by the fact that the equilibrium of the glutamic dehydrogenase system is strongly in favor of the reductive amination of ketoglutarate.[34] Other mechanisms for the oxidation of glutamic acid, directly or after decarboxylation to γ-amino-butyric acid, involve transamination reactions and are not accompanied by the appearance of ammonia.

Brain contains other ammonia-producing enzymes, *viz.* glucosamine 6-phosphate deaminase,[35-36] guanine and guanosine deaminases[37,38] and amine oxidase.[39] Although these enzymes may have important functions to perform, their contribution to ammonia production is presumably slight because the concentration of the substrates is low, as in the case of amines, or remains unchanged during the period of incubation, as in the case of hexosamines.[40]

It is now generally recognized that the proteins, nucleoproteins and lipids of the nerve cell are no longer to be regarded as mere structural units but have a rapid turnover and actively participate in the various functional activities of the cell. Geiger *et al.*[41] showed that increased activity of cat brain cortex increased the non-protein nitrogen (NPN) in the active area. An increase of NPN was also found in incubated brain slices; like ammonia formation, it was inhibited by anoxia and abolished by destruction of the cellular structure.[16]

Vrba[42] reported that physical exhaustion lowered the level of protein-bound amide groups in rat brain; this reaction, in his view, accounts for some or all of the ammonia formed during nervous activity *in vivo*. An enzyme, transglutaminase, has recently been described which brings about the liberation of protein-bound amide groups by direct hydrolysis or by an exchange reaction with amines or protein amino groups[43]. Such a reaction may contribute to, but cannot fully account for, the ammonia formation in brain slices.[40,44]

In summary, there are indications that the formation of ammonia by nervous tissue *in vivo* and *in vitro* is due to reactions involving proteins and nucleoproteins; however, detailed information about the nature of its precursors and the mechanism of its liberation is lacking.

UTILIZATION OF AMMONIA IN BRAIN

It has been known for many years[45,46] that, in contrast to the rapid formation of ammonia in a substrate-free medium, brain slices form very little ammonia in a medium containing glucose. This was originally attributed to a "sparing effect" of glucose on the consumption of endogenous substrates and thus to a suppression of autolytic reactions, but it has since become evident that another mechanism which only functions in the presence of glucose is at least equally important. This mechanism results in the incorporation of ammonia in the amino groups of glutamic acid and other amino acids and in the amide group of glutamine.

The facts on which the concept of the "ammonia-binding mechanism" in brain are based are as follows:

α-Ketoglutarate is derived from glucose through the citric acid cycle. It combines with ammonia to form glutamic acid, an exergonic reaction catalysed by glutamic dehydrogenase. It has been shown that brain slices, supplied with ^{14}C-glucose, incorporate 10 to 20% of the ^{14}C utilized into non-carbohydrates, principally amino acids. Of the incorporated ^{14}C, about 75% is found in glutamic acid and its derivatives, glutamine[76] and γ-aminobutyric acid, with aspartic acid and alanine accounting for the rest.[47,48,76] Similar results were obtained with pyruvate, labelled in the C_2 or C_3 position, as substrate.[49,48] If the citric acid cycle is interrupted by fluoroacetate poisoning and the flow of ammonia acceptors thereby stopped, an increase of the ammonia level in the brain results.[7]

The concentration of amide nitrogen in brain slices remains steady in the absence of glucose, but rises in its presence.[16] The effect is even more pronounced if the medium contains, in addition to glucose, ammonia together with ketoglutarate or pyruvate.[33] An increase of the level of cerebral glutamine *in vivo*, with or without a corresponding decrease of glutamic acid concentration, has been observed in rats after physical exercise,[50] after tumbling in a revolving drum[11] and after electrical stimulation of the extremities.[10] These conditions are likely to lead to increased ammonia production in the brain.

From these observations, the following picture emerges (Fig. 1): one molecule of ammonia combines with α-ketoglutarate to form L-glutamate; a second molecule of ammonia thereupon combines with glutamate to form glutamine. The amide group of glutamine represents the electrically neutral transport form of ammonia in the organism. It is significant in this connection that glutamine passes much more freely through the blood-brain barrier than glutamic acid.[51]

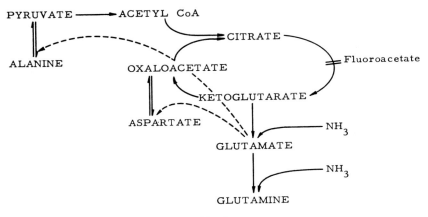

Fig. 1.

This main stream of ammonia disposal is assisted by an auxiliary mechanism utilizing transamination to pyruvate and oxaloacetate. The transaminases catalysing these reactions have a high level of activity in brain tissue; other transaminations, by comparison, occur at a negligible rate.[52] The fact that the keto acids functioning as amino acceptors in brain transaminations are especially those arising during glucose oxidation is certainly not a coincidence and suggests that one of the principal functions of these systems is the temporary accommodation of ammonia when its formation exceeds the capacity of glutamine synthesis. Reversal of the transamination reaction results in the resynthesis of glutamic acid from aspartic acid and alanine; these reactions may be expected to occur when the ammonia production has abated.

The functioning of the ammonia-binding mechanism of the brain is important not only for the removal of ammonia produced within the brain, but also for the neutralization of ammonia reaching the brain from outside. Only passing reference can be made to the dramatic pharmacological effects of injected ammonium salts on the central nervous system (for further information cf. refs. 53-57). High plasma levels of ammonia produced in experimental animals by infusion of ammonium salts[56,58] or by hepatectomy[59] were shown to lead to an increase of the glutamine concentration in the brain. The plasma level of ammonia is frequently increased in patients with widespread liver damage and has been incriminated as an important factor in the causation of hepatic encephalopathy and hepatic coma (cf. ref. 60). In cases where the ammonia level in the plasma is raised, significant amounts of ammonia are taken up by the brain,[61,62] especially when associated with alkalosis: in this condition, a greater proportion of ammonia exists in the undissociated form which passes more freely through the blood-brain barrier. Thus, the absence of correlation of hepatic coma with blood ammonia levels, which has frequently been commented upon, may, in some cases, be due to differences in plasma pH.[63] A closer correlation exists between hepatic coma and ammonia levels in the CSF.[64]

SOME CONSEQUENCES OF THE AMMONIA-BINDING MECHANISM

While the reductive amination of ketoglutarate is, thermodynamically, a spontaneous reaction, the synthesis of glutamine from glutamic acid and ammonia requires energy supplied in the form of ATP.[65] Inhibitors of ATP-synthesis, such as 2,4-dinitrophenol, therefore inhibit the ammonia-binding mechanism and increase the ammonia formation of brain slices in a glucose-containing medium[66,67] in contrast to their effect in the absence of glucose where they inhibit the formation of ammonia.[16] On the other hand, the consumption of ATP in glutamine synthesis is probably the explanation for some effects of ammonia (or glutamic acid) on the metabolism of brain slices. Synthetic and other reactions depending on ATP, such as anaerobic glycolysis, incorporation of labelled phosphate into various phosphate esters, synthesis of acetylcholine, fixation of CO_2 and responses to electrical pulses are inhibited.[68-73] As might be expected, the concentration of high-energy phosphates is depressed by ammonia as well as by glutamate;[74,28] consequently, energy producing reactions, i.e. respiration and glycolysis, are accelerated.[33,68]

Another substance utilized in the ammonia-binding mechanism is ketoglutarate and its continued withdrawal towards glutamate probably reduces the supply of dicarboxylic acids necessary for the functioning of the citric acid cycle.[75] It has indeed been shown that the concentration of pyruvate increases about threefold and that of ketoglutarate decreases by one third in the brain of dogs treated with ammonia.[56] Similarly, the aerobic accumulation of lactic acid observed when brain slices are incubated in a medium containing glucose and ammonia[68] may partly be due to an increased utilization of glucose and partly to a malfunction of the citric acid cycle.

It thus appears that many of the effects that might be attributed to a toxic action of ammonia are in reality the results of a detoxification mechanism. This is not to deny the toxicity of ammonia itself. Indeed, the fact that the synthesis of glutamine has priority over many other energy-consuming reactions and the further fact that the synthesis of glutamate proceeds in spite of the risk of a depletion of dicarboxylic acids suggest that the intracellular accumulation of ammonia has to be prevented even though a high price may have to be paid for it.

REFERENCES

1. TASHIRO, S.: *Am. J. Physiol., 60:*519 (1922).
2. WINTERSTEIN, H.: *Naturwissenschaften, 21:*22 (1933).
3. VLADIMIROVA, E. A.: *Physiol. Zh. SSSR, 25:*848 (1938).
4. RICHTER, D., and DAWSON, R. M. C.: *J. Biol. Chem., 176:*1199 (1948).
5. TORDA, C.: *J. Pharmacol., 107:*197 (1953).
6. GERSHENOVICH, Z. S., and KRICHEVSKAYA, A. A.: *Doklady Akad. Nauk S.S.S.R., 95:*387 (1954); *Chem. Abst., 48:*8909 (1954).
7. BENITEZ, D., PSCHEIDT, G. R., and STONE, W. E.: *Am. J. Physiol., 176:*488 (1954).
8. THORN, W., and HEIMANN, J.: *J. Neurochem., 2:*166 (1958).
9. VLADIMIROVA, E. A.: *Dokl. Akad. Nauk SSSR, 95:*905 (1954).
10. TSUKADA, Y., TAKAGAKI, G., SUGIMOTO, S., and HIRANO, S.: *J. Neurochem., 2:*295 (1958).
11. GRAY, I., JOHNSTON, J. M., and SPEARING, C. W.: *Federation Proc., 15:*265 (1956).
12. TORDA, C., and WOLFF, H. G.: *Federation Proc., 11:*163 (1952).
13. LUSENKO, V. S.: *Fiziol. Zh., Kiev, 2:*53 (1956).
14. NATHAN, D. G., and WARREN, K. S.: *Arch. Biochem. Biophys., 81:*377 (1959).
15. KREBS, H. A., EGGLESTON, L. V., and HEMS, R.: *Biochem. J., 44:*159 (1949).
16. WEIL-MALHERBE, H., and GREEN, R. H.: *Biochem. J., 61:*210, (1955).
17. ROWSELL, E. V.: *Biochem. J., 57:*666 (1954).
18. LARRABEE, M. G., HOROWICZ, P., STEKIEL, W., and DOLIVO, M.: In *Metabolism of the Nervous System,* p. 208. D. Richter, Ed. New York, Pergamon Press (1957).
19. EMBDEN, G., and WASSERMEYER, H.: *Ztschr. physiol. Chem., 179:*161, 226 (1928).
20. PARNAS, J. K., and MOZOLOWSKI, W.: *Biochem. Ztschr., 184:*398 (1927).
21. BENDALL, J. R., and DAVEY, C. L.: *Biochem. Biophys. Acta, 26:*93 (1957).
22. CONWAY, E. J., and COOKE, R.: *Biochem. J., 33:*479 (1939).
23. MUNTZ, J. A.: *J. Biol. Chem., 201:*221 (1953).
24. WEIL-MALHERBE, H., and GREEN, R. H.: *Biochem. J., 61:*218 (1955).
25. DAWSON, R. M. C., and PETERS, R. A.: *Biochem. Biophys. Acta, 16:*254 (1955).
26. KORANSKY, W.: *Arch. exper. Path. u. Pharmakol., 228:*140 (1956).
27. TSUKADA, Y., and TAKAGAKI, G.: *Nature,* London, *173:*1138 (1954).
28. ÁCS, G., BALAZS, R., and STRAUB, F. B.: *Kisérletes Orvostudomány, 6:*1 (1953); *Chem. Abstr., 48:*8923 (1954).

29. DAVEY, C. L.: *Nature,* London, *183:*995 (1959).
30. YEFIMOCHKINA, E. F., and BRAUNSTEIN, A. E.: *Arch. Biochem. Biophys., 83:*350 (1959).
31. SODD, M. A., and WEIL-MALHERBE, H.: Unpublished.
32. KREBS, H. A.: *Biochem. J., 29:*1951 (1935).
33. WEIL-MALHERBE, H.: *Biochem. J., 30:*665 (1936).
34. STRECKER, H. J.: *Arch. Biochem. Biophys., 46:*128 (1953).
35. FAULKNER, P., and QUASTEL, J. H.: *Nature,* London, *177:*1216 (1956).
36. LELOIR, L. F., and CARDINI, C. E.: *Biochem. Biophys. Acta, 20:*33 (1956).
37. WAKABAYASI, Y.: *J. Biochem. (Japan), 28:*185 (1938).
38. JORDAN, W. K., MARCH, R., HOUCHIN, O. B., and POPP, E.: *J. Neurochem., 4:*170 (1959).
39. PUGH, C. E. M., and QUASTEL, J. H.: *Biochem. J., 31:*286, 2306 (1937).
40. WEIL-MALHERBE, H., and DRYSDALE, A. C.: *J. Neurochem., 1:*250 (1957).
41. GEIGER, A., DOBKIN, J., and MAGNES, J.: *Science, 118:*655 (1953).
42. VRBA, R.: *Nature,* London, *176:*117 (1955).
43. MYCEK, M. J., and WAELSCH, H.: *Federation Proc., 19:*336 (1960).
44. VRBA, R., FOLBERGR, J., and KANTUREK, V.: *J. Neurochem., 2:*187 (1958).
45. WARBURG, O., POSENER, K., and NEGELEIN, E.: *Biochem. Ztschr., 152:*309 (1924).
46. LOEBEL, R. O.: *Biochem. Ztschr., 161:*219 (1925).
47. BELOFF-CHAIN, A., CATANZARO, R., CHAIN, E. B., MASI, I., and POCCHIARI, F.: *Proc. Roy. Soc., B., 144:*22 (1955).
48. TOWER, D. B.: In *Biochemistry of the Central Nervous System.* Proc. 4th Internat. Cong. Biochem., Vol. 3, p. 213. London, Pergamon Press (1959).
49. BUSCH, H., GOLDBERG, M. H., and ANDERSON, D. C.: *Cancer Res., 16:*175 (1956).
50. VRBA, R.: *Nature,* London, *176:*1258 (1955).
51. SCHWERIN, P., BESSMAN, S. P., and WAELSCH, H.: *J. Biol. Chem., 184:*37 (1950).
52. AWAPARA, J., and SEALE, B.: *J. Biol. Chem., 194:*497 (1952).
53. SOLLMAN, T.: A Manual of Pharmacology, 7th Ed., p. 776ff. Philadelphia Saunders (1948).
54. KARR, N. W., and HENDRICKS, E. L.: *Am. J. M. Sc., 218:*302 (1949).
55. AJMONE-MARSAN, C., FUORTES, M. G. F., and MAROSSERO, F.: *EEG Clin. Neurophysiol., 1:*291 (1949).
56. CLARK, G. M., and EISEMAN, B.: *New England J. Med., 259:*178 (1958).
57. HANDFORD, S. W.: *Gastroenterology, 36:*770 (1959).
58. DuRUISSEAU, J., GREENSTEIN, J. P., WINITZ, M., and BIRNBAUM, S. M.: *Arch. Biochem. Biophys., 68:*161 (1957).
59. FLOCK, E. V., BLOCK, M. A., GRINDLAY, J. H., MANN, F. C., and BOLLMAN, J. L.: *J. Biol. Chem., 200:*529 (1953).
60. BESSMAN, S. P.: Inorganic Nitrogen Metabolism, p. 408 W. D. McElroy and Bentley Glass, Eds. Baltimore, Johns Hopkins Press (1956).
61. BESSMAN, S. P., and BESSMAN, A. N.: *J. Clin. Invest., 34:*622 (1955).
62. WEBSTER, L. T., JR., and GABUZDA, G. J.: *J. Clin. Invest., 37:*414 (1958).
63. WARREN, K. S., and NATHAN, D. G.: *J. Clin. Invest., 37:*1725 (1958).
64. NAJARIAN, J. S., HARPER, H. A., and McCORKLE, H. J.: *Surgery, 44:*11 (1958).
65. ELLIOTT, W. H.: *Nature,* London, *161:*128 (1948).
66. RYBOVÁ, R.: *J. Neurochem., 4:*304 (1959).
67. GUHA, S. R., and GHOSH, J. J.: *Ann. Biochem. & Exper. Med., 19:*67 (1959).
68. WEIL-MALHERBE, H.: *Biochem. J., 32:*2257 (1938).
69. FINDLAY, M., MAGEE, W. L., and ROSSITER, R. J.: *Biochem. J., 58:*236 (1954).

70. BRAGANCA, B. M., FAULKNER, P., and QUASTEL, J. H.: *Biochem. Biophys. Acta,* *10*:83 (1953).
71. CRANE, R. K., and BALL, E. G.: *J. Biol. Chem., 188*:819 (1951).
72. GORE, M. B. R., and MCILWAIN, H.: *J. Physiol., 117*:471 (1952).
73. MCILWAIN, H.: *J. Ment. Sc., 97*:674 (1951).
74. MCILWAIN, H.: *Biochem. J., 52*:289 (1952).
75. RECKNAGEL, R. O., and POTTER, V. R.: *J. Biol. Chem., 191*:263 (1951).
76. KINI, M. M. and QUASTEL, J. H.: *Nature,* London *184*:252 (1959).

XVI

CYTOPHYSIOLOGICAL ASPECTS OF THE NUCLEIC ACIDS AND PROTEINS OF NERVOUS TISSUE

Holger Hydén

Among the somatic cells of the organism, the large nerve cells are characterized by the highest load of ribonucleic acids (RNA) and are probably among the most active producers of nucleo-proteins and as such comparable to pancreatic exocrine cells. The main part of the RNA of the nerve cell seems to constitute the chemical correlate of the Nissl substance in the form of liponucleoproteins. During the past twenty years a large amount of cytological data and an increasing number of biochemical observations have accumulated which relate the RNA to the synthesis of proteins in the cell.

The central nervous system is composed of the neuroglia and the neurons, the glia outnumbering the neurons by a factor of perhaps ten. A bulk analysis of the nervous system will therefore not reflect the conditions of the nerve cells. Neither is the preparative technique using differential centrifugation so advanced that pure fractions can be obtained from the nervous tissue. Therefore, observations obtained with biochemical and ultra-microchemical methods and by optical analysis have to be integrated to give a picture of the nucleic acids and the proteins of the nervous tissue.

QUANTITATIVE METHODS FOR THE DETERMINATION OF NUCLEIC ACIDS AND PROTEINS IN NERVE CELLS AND GLIA CELLS

In this laboratory individual nerve cells have been isolated by micro-dissection from the fresh or the fixed nerve tissue for further analysis Fig. 1. The RNA per isolated nerve cell is determined according to the method of Dr. Edström.[69,73] The cells are precipitated with Carnoy's solution or with cold $HClO_4$ and treated with ethanol and chloroform. The RNA from each nerve cell is depolymerized and extracted by a

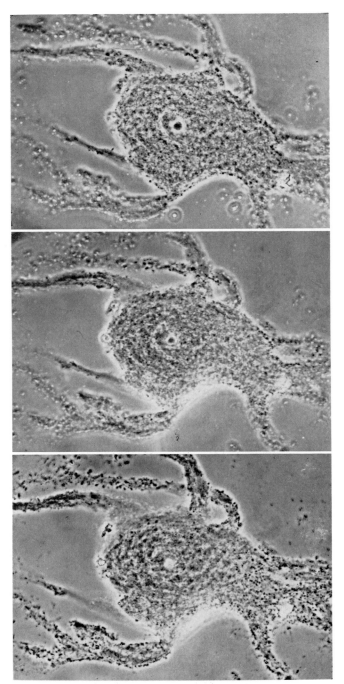

Fig. 1. Giant nerve cell from the Deiters' nucleus. Shown above an example of such a cell dissected out by hand, photographed in the phase contrast microscope at three different levels of focus. Slightly stained by methylene blue to show the density of the synapses as small knobs on the surface.

buffered solution of ribonuclease, sucked up in a micropipette and placed on a quartz glass. This is done in a paraffin oil chamber. It is then dissolved in a small volume of a glycerol-containing buffer. The amount of RNA per cell is determined photometrically by photographing the optically homogenous, round spots on the quartz glass near 2600 Å together with a reference system. The standard error is ±5% for amounts down to 25 $\mu\mu$g. of RNA.

The RNA contains the purine bases adenine and guanine, and the pyrimidine bases uracil and cytosine. The quantitative determination of these constituents can be performed by electrophoresis on the microscale according to the procedure of Edström.[69-71] The ribonuclease extract from each nerve cell undergoes acid hydrolysis, is dried, dissolved in sodium hydroxide and finally placed on a microscopic cellulose thread, soaked with a buffer of a very high viscosity. An emf. of about 5000 V/cm. is applied by microelectrodes for half an hour. At pH 3.2 the electrophoresis gives the purine bases and the pyrimine nucleotides and at pH 1 the bases. If the starting value of RNA amounts to 200 $\mu\mu$g. per cell, the RNA constitutents can be determined quantitatively with a standard error of ±10% by photometry of the bands on the cellulose thread at 2600 Å.

Another quantitative method, which can be used for determination of RNA per surface unit of a section through a nerve cell, is the microspectrographic procedure developed by Caspersson.[41,42] The purine and pyrimidine bases give the nucleic acids a high selective absorption at 2600 Å. The absorption of the polynucleotides is about 50 times higher than that of an equal concentration of protein and thus dominates that of the cell protein. If optical conditions are ideal, an analysis of the absorption spectrum, in the range of 2400 to 3000 Å, of a cell area containing nucleic acids, is stated to permit a determination of 1 to 10 $\mu\mu$g. of nucleic acids per square micron. Ideal optical conditions are, however, nearly impossible to obtain.

The advantage and limitation of ultraviolet microspectrography from a methodological aspect has been dealt with repeatedly in the current literature (see, for example, refs. 48, 251, 6, 43, 267). As a semi-quantitative method the ultraviolet microspectrography demonstrates gradients and differences in nucleic acid concentrations and has been of a great pioneering value in biology.

If optical measurements are performed on sections of nervous tissue to determine absolute amounts of a substance, two sources of errors cannot be overlooked. One is the optical inhomogeneity of the tissue irrespective of treatment.[48,169,231] The other is the thickness determination of a microscopic section from a topographical point of view. An accurate and rapid method for this purpose has been developed by Dr. Hallén at this laboratory.[111] Interference microscopy can be used for determination of weight, mass and thickness of free cells.[50,49,11,12] The evaluation of the optical density over a free-lying, compressed, and highly irregular spheroid like a large nerve cell soma, however, is not easy. The result will at present be an approximate one. Two other sources of error must also be pointed out. The cytological procedure using chemical fixation and including embedding, cutting, and mounting, causes a high degree of volume shrinkage of the nerve tissue components. Hydén[144] and Brattgård et al.[38] found that Carnoy's solution gives a volume shrinkage of 80 and 60% for nerve cells from fish and rabbit, respectively. Robins et al.[229] found that formaldehyde fixation causes a volume shrinkage of 80% in rabbit material. In cases where fixed material must be used, a correction may be made, provided the fixation effect on the particular cell material has been studied.

A much more serious error than that resulting from shrinkage is also introduced by the histochemical procedure.[35] X-ray microradiography has shown that the nerve cell cytoplasm loses around 50% of its organic material during this procedure (fixation by Carnoy's solution, embedding in paraffin, and removal from the section by benzene). The nerve cell nucleus loses 80% or more of its material.[149,150] This is the most serious error so far encountered in histo- and cyto-chemical work, including electron microscopy. This type of error has also been discussed for biochemical work on cell suspensions.[6] The use of frozen and dried material is a good way to avoid this problem. It must be pointed out, however, that the freezing of material in liquid nitrogen, followed by embedding, is subject to the same type of error, when ethanol solutions or other solutions are used.

Few methods are available for the determination of proteins on the cytoscale. Interference microscopy has already been mentioned. Quantitative x-ray microradiography has been used to determine the dry weight of isolated, fresh and dried nerve cells and for the division of the mass of the cell into lipid and protein fractions. Fig. 2. The sources of error in this procedure have been thoroughly dealt with.[35,36,173,112] The x-radiograms are quantitatively evaluated with an electronic scanner povided with a function transformer.[157,158]

There exists by now a vast literature on the use of staining methods for the identification and localization of RNA in nerve cells. Brachet[29,30] developed the well-known reaction using staining with pyronine after digestion of the cell section with ribonuclease. Einarson[78-80] developed the staining method with gallocyanine-chrome alum and has presented evidence to show that this staining reaction is a quantitative and stoichiometrical reaction for nucleic acids. For reviews see Scholz,[237] Einarson.[81]

QUANTITATIVE ASPECTS

The neurons vary greatly with respect to volume and size. A large motor neuron (cell and processes) can be estimated to have a volume of 0.001 mm.^{3} or $10^6\mu^3$. It may be noted that the volume of the nerve cell easily undergoes considerable changes *in vivo* due to physiological

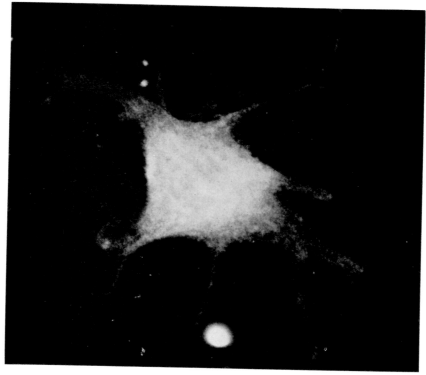

Fig. 2. Giant nerve cell from the Deiters' nucleus. Dissected out by hand from the fresh tissue, exposed at 8 to 10 Å. White denotes high mass. Magnification 400×.

factors. Furthermore, volume values obtained on fixed and stained samples are heavily influenced by the cytological procedure as is seen from Table I. The perikaryon of a cortical cell only accounts for 10% of the total neuronal surface,[236] and the shape of the neuron is dominated by the ramifications of the dendrites. Taking the Purkinje cells as an example, Fox and Barnard[93] estimated that within the ramifications of the dendrites belonging to one Purkinje cell, passed approximately 270,000 axons from the underlying granular layer.

The dry weight of the nerve cell, reflecting its organic mass, varies correspondingly as seen from examples in Table I. A Deiters' giant nerve cell with a dry weight of 21,000 $\mu\mu$g. would have a wet weight of 0.00083 mg.

A pertinent question is the ratio between the relative volume of nerve cell and processes and that of the neuroglia. Pope[217] estimated that, in the cortex, the nerve cell plus dendrites should occupy 30%

of the cortical volume, myelin, neuroglia and vessels 35%, and the extra-cellular fluid space 35%. With accumulating data from high resolution optics new aspects of this problem have arisen. All interstices in the neuropil are found to be filled with the multifolded processes of the astrocytes and of the oligodendrocytes. All nerve cell structures seem to be closely surrounded by such delicate processes. The only visible extracellular space seems to be the 100 to 200 Å. wide "clefts" which separate the different membranes.[210,58,84,238]

TABLE I

VOLUME AND DRY WEIGHT OF SOME NERVE CELLS

Cell Type	Volume of Fixed and Embedded Cells	Volume of Fresh Cells	Dry Weight ($\mu\mu g./cell$)
Nucleus XII[38]	5,600 μ^3	13,000 μ^3	2,770
Anterior horn cells*	22,000 μ^3 (range 5000–40000 μ^3)		8–9,000
Spinal ganglion cells[77]		25000–500000 μ^3 (median 180000 μ^3)	5,000–75,000*
Nucleus supra-[74,75] opticus (several subgroups)	2,740 μ^3 (1000–5000 μ^3)		
Deiters' nerve cells[154]		87,000 μ^3	20,100
Lat. vest. cells,* medium sized		49,000 μ^3	10,000

*Hydén, unpublished.

In evaluating these findings it should be remembered that the pictures are taken from a fixed and embedded tissue. This cytological procedure has most certainly caused an osmotic transfer of water and influenced the distance between the different surfaces as well as the whole volume of the tissue.[234,153,155] Thus, the intermembrane distances *in vivo* may or may not present a system of aqueous pathways.

Based on the estimation of Pope, my own x-ray data[153,154] and the distribution of gangliosides within the nervous tissue, as far as it has been determined,[250] it is the author's view that the nerve cell plus dendrites occupies around 40% of the gray matter and the neuroglia, myelin (and vessels) 60%.

NUCLEIC ACIDS AND PROTEINS OF THE NERVE CELL NUCLEUS

It was early pointed out that in a given cell species there is a constant relation between the volume of the nucleus and that of the protoplasm.[127] This relation was not found in the neuron. Heidenhain[122] estimated the volume of the cytoplasm and processes to be about 125 times that of the nucleus. He therefore considered the Nissl substance to be a nucleus-supporting material which could restore the normal nucleus-plasma relation if changed.

According to Bok,[27] the surface of the nerve cell body varies with the volume of the nucleus. The nuclear membrane is easy to observe in nerve cell cultures or in living, free-dissected cells. In stained preparation it appears as a thin, linear structure which in the electron micrographs appears to be a double-contoured membrane, the inner component of which is 130 Å. and smooth. The outer osmophilic component is 75 Å. thick and presents fine undulations and tubular extensions.[211,119,59,60,52] Polarization studies indicate that the nuclear membrane is composed of protein lamellae with their long axis parallel to the surface of the nucleus.[44] At intervals collections of dense particles around 100 Å. in diameter are situated adjacent to the nuclear membrane of both sides.[59,60] There are also found several thin lines forming the nuclear membrane.[119] The nuclear membrane of different types of nerve cells may appear folded, but even if substances which absorb strongly at 2600 Å. surround the membrane on both sides it still appears as an unbroken line in the ultra-violet micrograph.[145] Special interest has been focused on the submicroscopic structure of such nuclear membranes and the possible occurrence of pores in the nuclear membrane and a nucleocytoplasm at the macromolecular level. In pyramidal cells, nuclear protrusions are described through what seem to be gaps in the membrane, and also vesicles in the cytoplasm which communicate with the nucleoplasm.[119]

THE NUCLEOLUS

In a large nerve cell, the nucleolus is a highly characteristic structure, amphophilic in its staining properties and often possessing a basophilic cortical layer, an acidophilic center, and one or more vacuoles. There are one or more nucleoli even in the small types of nerve cells.[206,17] A survey of the nucleolus problems of the nerve cell is given by Hertl[126] and one of the problem in general by Vincent.[257] From a physiological point of view, an increasing body of data places the nucleolus in a central position of the cellular activity in general, especialy when protein production is concerned.

The volume of the nucleolus of the large-type neurons in man varies from 2 to 60 μ^3; it may be twice as large in adult specimens as in young nerve cells of the same type in mammals. In fishes there are nerve cell nucleoli of about 6000 μ^3.[145,146] There is no definite relation between the volume of the nucleus and that of the nucleolus. The state of functional activity seems to be a factor of importance.[110] In fact, motor activity can more than double the volume of the nucleoli in the motor nerve cells (see Edström[72]).

The nucleolus has a high dry weight per unit volume. Hydén and Larsson[157] found 0.40 $\mu\mu$g./μ^3 for fixed spinal ganglion cells, using a computer for the evaluation of the x-radiographs. Assuming a specific weight of close to 1, this means a 40% concentration of organic material. Even higher values are reported, 50%[35] and 70%.[203] Since the material was lipid-extracted, the protein concentration equals the values for the mass concentration. The basic character of the nucleolar protein is shown by its high amount of free amino groups.[146] All these values are found on fixed material and can be criticized.

The RNA concentration in frozen dried material is found to be around 0.5% in nucleoli of fish ganglion cells, 1% for mammalian spinal ganglion cells,[145,146] and 2% for anterior horn cells.[203] These figures were the result of microspectrographic measurements. Edström and Eichner[75] have analyzed nucleoli from cells of the supraoptical nucleus and found 1.7 $\mu\mu$g. RNA per nucleolus, i.e., around 20% RNA by weight or volume. These authors also found that the RNA content per cell body was proportional to the volume of the nucleolus.[74]

Three other structures associated with the especially well developed nucleolus in the nerve cell can be mentioned. On the surface of the nucleolus appear small, DNA-rich granules or rods (Fig. 3).[146,207] By analogy with the nucleolus organizer in other organisms (plants) it has been designated "nucleolus-associated chromatin" and part of the heterochromatin. At a distance from the nucleolus are one or several areas of the same size as the nucleolus and of irregular form, which x-ray and UV analysis have shown to have a greater protein and RNA concentration than the rest of the nucleoplasm and a large number of free basic groups (Fig. 4). It lacks measurable amounts of DNA. Judging from its composition, behavior, and distribution, this substance was concluded to be a heterochromatic derivative and closely related to the nucleolus. In nerve cells from male rabbits it is more developed and frequent than in the female cells. It was therefore though to be correlated with the Y chromosome.[146] The area can increase its substance in virus infection, after stimulation, and during anoxia.[147,149,150,133,72] Cytologic description of this irregular area is given in the early literature.[170,226,232] Its relation to the paranucleolar structures is discussed by Hertl.[126]

Of special interest is the occurrence of a small DNA-containing particle near the nucleolus or near the nuclear membrane. It is a particle with a diameter of 0.5 to 1 μ, which is shown for many types of cells to be quantitatively more developed and significantly more frequent in the female cells of various species.[15,14,191,222] In a series of investigations this particle, the sex chromatin, has been used for sex determination with success. This sex difference also exists in neuroglia cells.[20] It is thought to be a derivative of the heterochromatic regions of the X chromosomes, which combine to form the particle, thus explaining

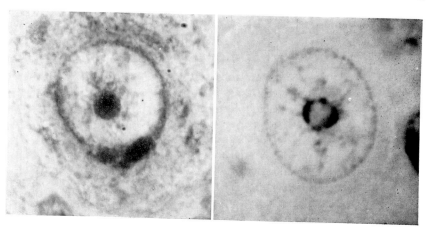

Fig. 3. (a) Purkinje cell photographed at 2570 Å, the nucleolus and a part of the cytoplasm near the nuclear membrane containing RNA. The rest of the cytoplasm poor in RNA. Objective 2.5 mm. monochromate. N.A. 0,85. Ocular 10×.
(b) Feulgen's nucleal reaction performed on a Purkinje cell of the type shown in (a) DNA-rich particles enclosing the nucleolus and representing the nucleolar-associated chromatin. The rest of the cell gives no positive reaction.

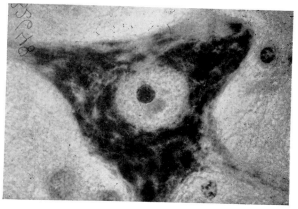

Fig. 4. Anterior horn cell from the ventro-lateral nucleus within C_5 of a rabbit. Photographed at 2570 Å.

the difference in its development in the two sexes. After electric stimulation it could be seen to move from the nerve cell nucleolus toward the nuclear membrane and return again. The sex chromatin was therefore thought to be involved in protein production, like the nucleolus.[14]

THE NUCLEOPLASM

Very little can be said with certainty at present about the structure and composition of the nucleoplasm, and the main constituent of the nucleus. One reason is that the nucleus is the region of the nerve cell that loses most material during the usual cytological procedure. Freeze-drying followed by embedding constitutes no improved method from that point of view. The nucleoplasm in Carnoy-fixed cells, for example, has lost more than 80% of its organic material.[149,150] The old description of the nerve cell nucleus as empty, seems thus to be fitting.

The mass concentrations in the nucleus and in the cytoplasm of fresh, merely frozen and dried, motor nerve cells do not differ significantly and average 0.20 $\mu\mu g./\mu^3$. It must therefore be concluded that structural studies of the nerve cell nucleus at high resolution cannot at present be expected to reflect much of the conditions *in vivo*.

Interphase nuclei of oöcytes and other cells have been successfully investigated at high resolution. It seems that in such material, as well as during mitosis, the basic unit composing the chromosomes are fibrils approximately 200 Å. thick.[227] No such systematic study has been made on the nerve cell nucleus although granules and thin fibrils have been described.[119,278,141] It is an old observation that the nerve cell nucleus seems poor in chromatin.[122] The fact that the heterochromatic chromocenters containing DNA seem scanty and far apart can be explained by a dilution effect in this large nucleus, and does not naturally reflect a smaller content of DNA than is present in more stainable cells. It can be recalled that Geitler[102] in studies on insects found that the nerve cells remained diploid in contrast to other somatic cells during growth.

From determinations on homogenates, Heller and Elliott[125] concluded that each nerve cell nucleus contains 7.1 $\mu\mu g.$ DNA on an average.

No reliable value of the RNA content of the nerve cell nucleus is available at present. Microspectrographic measurements indicate the presence of about 20 $\mu\mu g.$ RNA in a nucleus having a dry weight of 800 $\mu\mu g.$ It is to be noted that the RNA concentration varies greatly in different, and also in the same, types of nerve cell.[146-148]

The nucleus has a total lipid content of 20 to 30%, determined chemically and by x-ray microradiography, in terms of the dry weight.[253,35] Debuch and Stammler[53] found 5 to 10% lipids. Considerable amounts of cerebrosides have been found in isolated cell nuclei from the cortex. The concentration of dry organic substance after chloroform extraction of the fresh, freeze-dried nucleus (= protein content) lies around 20% and varies according to the type of nerve cell. In general, it seems that the protein and lipid content of the nucleus is the same as or just a little lower than that of the nerve cell body.[157] Yet the solubility of the substance building up the nucleus must differ considerably from that of the cytoplasm since as much as 80% of the nuclear substance may be dissolved by the solution during a cytological or preparative procedure. Measurements on fixed nerve cell material can, however, lead to the paradoxical result of a mass concentration similar to that of the fresh material as a result of cell shrinkage.

NUCLEIC ACIDS AND PROTEINS OF THE NERVE CELL CYTOPLASM

Structural Aspects.—In most nerve cell bodies in vertebrates and invertebrates there is present a substance which is easily stainable with basic aniline dyes and takes the form of large granules, thin plates, or a diffuse fine granular form. It is present far out in the dendrites, but not in the area of origin of the axon, the so-called axon hillock, or in the outermost periphery of the perikaryon, or in a thin perinuclear zone or in the axoplasm. The substance was originally described by Key and Retzius[163] and by Flemming;[90] it was, however, Nissl[198-202] who devised a special staining method and in a systematic study divided the nerve cells, with respect to the pattern and staining intensity of the basophile substance, into two main groups with several subgroups. Finally, he tried, in several experimental studies, to reveal its physiological importance.

The Nissl substance in fresh cells is readily stained with methylene blue[224,225,68] and is rendered visible by the action of acetic acid solution. Chemically the studies by Held[123,124] and by Scott[239] indicated that the Nissl substance had all the properties of a nucleoprotein that were then known. During recent years several papers have dealt with the structure of the Nissl substance as seen in the electron microscope. The following description follows mainly that of Palay and Palade.[211]

In the electron micrograph the Nissl substance has been correlated with the so-called endoplasmic reticulum, cyto-membranes forming flat channels, tubules, and vesicles limited by membranes, and of small granules. The *first* component appears in a section as parallel, straight or curved, 60 Å.-thick membranes which are regularly spaced at intervals of 800 to 2000 Å. The lumina limited by these membranes are 300 to 500 Å. wide with dilatations up to 2500 Å. This continuous system of membrane-bound cavities is arranged in broad sheets in the areas taken up by the Nissl substance and piled one upon the other in a regular way. The cavities of this channel system anastomose with the more loosely arranged tubules and cisternae of the endoplasmic reticulum in the rest of the perikaryon and the processes. In section, highly oriented profiles occur in motor neurons, but disordered ones are seen in Purkinje cells and in small nerve cells in general. Sensory and sympathetic ganglion cells represent an intermediate type.

The *second* component consists of granules, 100 to 300 Å. in diameter, or short, dense rods. These particles are situated in rows, close to the outer surfaces of the membranes, sometimes arranged in loops, spirals, or as rosettes of five to seven granules. These granules of the Nissl substance have been thought to be responsible for the basophilia and shown to contain RNA. The Nissl substance should thus consist of dense areas of granular-rich membranes, also designated as a reticulum. A debate has once more arisen as to whether or not the Nissl substance exists *in vivo*. Deitch and Murray[55] and Deitch and Moses[54] found indications that it does. The writer's view is that a correlation has been found between the basophile substance, the RNA absorbing at 2600 Å., the "endoplasmic reticulum" and the areas of higher optical density in the cytoplasm. The observations are unequivocal. But how the nucleoprotein-containing structures exist *in vivo* is quite another question.

These discrete particles near the membranes are observed in fixed, alcohol-treated, and embedded material. The pertinent question, therefore, is whether they really exist and have their counterpart in the living cell. Sjöstrand[243] has produced convincing evidence that these small particles near the membranes in glandular cells are artifacts or precipitation products caused by the cytological treatment. The Nissl substance has generally been associated with the basophilic substance, the ergastoplasm—the name coined by Garnier[97] and Bouin and Bouin[28]—present in other protein-producing cells, e.g., albuminous glandular cells and liver cells. The two components of the Nissl substance are found also in these cells, and the granules, the "microsomes," have been found to contain RNA.[45,244,221,209] Most of the protein and phospholipids are associated with the membrane.

Chemical Composition.—The chemical correlate of the Nissl substance is a ribonucleoprotein probably present as *liponucleoprotein*.[149,150,35] As has already been mentioned, Held[123,124] and Scott[239] had already concluded that the Nissl substance contained nucleoproteins, and van Herverden[256] succeeded in removing the Nissl substance by a nuclease. Einarson[79] also came to the conclusion that the

Nissl substance contained a "nuclein" compound. Iron and phosphorus were found in the substance by Mackenzie,[186] Macallum,[185] Scott,[240] and Nicholson.[195]

The conclusive demonstration that the Nissl substance contains a ribonucleic acid with the four mononucleotides that characterize this acid was made by Edström and Hydén.[76] From dissected-out anterior horn cells the RNA was extracted and hydrolyzed from each nerve cell separately, after which the mononucleotides formed were separated by ionophoresis on a microscopic thread and identified.

Digestion with ribonuclease and ultraviolet microspectrophotometry has also been used for better identification.[105,114,115] Hild[129] made the interesting observation that ribonuclease removed the capacity of the nucleolus in the living nerve cell to bind basic dyes but left the Nissl substance unaffected. After return to normal nutrient medium for a few days, the nucleolar basophilla was restored.

The amount of RNA per nerve cell varies according to the type of cell. In general the values lie between 50 and 1000 $\mu\mu$g. For the determination of such minute amounts per cell with sufficient accuracy, only one type of technique has so far proved to be satisfactory.[69] The cell is isolated and the sample consists of cell body and the first part of the dendrites. The RNA is extracted, the extract photographed at 2570 Å. and the amount of RNA determined photometrically.

TABLE II

RNA CONTENT IN DIFFERENT TYPES OF NERVE CELLS

Type of Nerve Cell	RNA ($\mu\mu$g./cell)	Concentration in Weight/Volume	
		Carnoy Fixed Cells (%)	Fresh Cells (%)
Retinal gangl. cells, rabbit[280]	45	1.6	
Nerve cells of the supraopt. nucl., rabbit[74,75]	70	2.4	
Spinal gangl. cells, rabbit[77]	1070		0.5
Hypoglossal cells, rabbit[38]	200	3.5	1.5
Ant. horn cells, rabbit[70,71]	530	2.5	
Ant. horn cells, man* 40–50 years	670		
Ant. horn cells, man* 60–70 years	540		
Deiters' giant cells, rabbit[154]	1550	3.1	1.7
Deiters' nucleus, medium sized cells*	885		1.8

*Hydén, unpublished.

Table II gives some values for RNA obtained in different types of nerve cells, freshly fixed in Carnoy's solution. From these values it is evident that the large nerve cell is the RNA-containing cell par préférence in the organism. The only cell that can compete seems to be the pancreatic exocrine cell from small animals.

There is no difference in the quantitative result if the nerve cells are fixed directly in the Carnoy's solution or if fixation is by freezing and drying.[70] But it is clearly seen that the volume shrinkage, caused by the cytological procedure, falsely increases the concentration values, e.g., in the case of the hypoglossal cells from 1.5 to 3.5%.

It may be of value to compare the concentration values obtained with the microchemical technique and with ultraviolet microphotometry. For material fixed according to the freeze-drying method, values of 1% RNA in spinal ganglion cells, 0.1 to 2% for the different types of Purkinje cells in the cerebellum, and 2 to 3% in anterior horn cells have been obtained with the ultraviolet technique.[168,145] For Carnoy-fixed anterior horn cells 1.7%,[156,203] 2% for spinal ganglion cells,[113] and 1.5 to 2% for vestibular ganglion cells have been reported.[114,115] Summarizing, it can be said that, irrespective of the technique used, fixed nerve cell material tends to give considerably higher RNA concentration values, owing to the error caused by the fixation, than if fresh or frozen and dried material is used.

Some analyses have been carried out on the composition of the RNA in Deiters' giant nerve cells, hypoglossal cells, trigeminal ganglion cells and neurosecretory cells from hypothalamus. The molar proportions which were similar in all cases were: adenine 19%, quanine 33%, cytosine 27%, and uracil 21% (Brattgård, Edström, Eichner, Hydén, unpublished).

In a study on brain microsomes, Toschi[252] and Hanzon and Toschi[117] found the particles of 100-175 Å. in diameter, attached to the membrane structures or occurring free in the cytoplasm, to be the site of RNA. The membrane structures were found to be rich in cholinesterase.

The RNA is found not only in the perikaryon of the nerve cell but also in the dendrites. An approximate value of the amount of RNA in the dendrites has been obtained for Deiters' cells and lies at 100 $\mu\mu$g., which is around 10% of the total amount of RNA in such a large nerve cell (Edström and Hydén, unpublished). Edström and Pigón[77] found a proportionality between the area of the cell body surface and the content of RNA for the spinal ganglion cells. It was supposed that the membrane area was a factor determining the level of RNA.

It is important to determine the *dry weight* of frozen and fresh nerve cells as a basis for further analyses. Lowry *et al.*[178-180] weigh the dry specimen directly with a quartz fishpole balance. Brattgård and Hydén[35,36] use x-ray microradiography under carefully controlled conditions. The results of the two methods agree well. Table I gives some examples of the total dry weight of nerve cells. In general the values lie in the range 0.15 to 0.25 $\mu\mu g./\mu^3$ for various cell types.

Whole-brain analysis gives very litle information about the protein composition of the nerve cells. The proteins of the whole brain are for the most part globulins.[56] The amino acid composition seems to remain constant during life.[22] Histidine, however, is present in higher concentrations in the brain protein of adult than in young animals. In Table III some values are given from fresh, isolated Deiters' cells, treated for 20 seconds with 1 N cold perchloric acid and dried in high-vacuum (Hydén, unpublished). The treatment with perchloric acid probably does not introduce an error in the weighing of the cell, if anything, small amounts of small molecular substances may be dissolved, but this can probably be overlooked. The protein concentration in dry weight per volume in these nerve cells is about 20%, and about 80% of the dry weight of the cell. This agrees well with the calculation of Lowry et al.[178] and also with the values of Robins et al.[229] It is naturally difficult to compare results obtained with cytochemical methods with those of histochemical methods which analyze layers within, e.g., cortex. If, however, 50% of the layer is supposed to be composed of nerve cell bodies and dendrites and 50% composed of myelin-rich axons, then the values given by those two types of methods agree well.

TABLE III

Dry Weight, Protein, and Lipid Content of Isolated Deiters' Cells (Rabbit) Treated with 1 N Cold Perchloric Acid

Number of Cells	Mean Dry Weight ($\mu\mu g.$)	Volume (μ^3)	Protein ($\mu\mu g.$)	Total Lipids Extr. by $CHCl_3$ ($\mu\mu g.$)
16	10,540	42,160	8,440	2100
44	20,800	83,230	16,700	4100

A gradient of 25% in the protein content of the cell has been found to extend from the nucleus to the cell periphery in Deiters' cells.[157] Fixed and embedded material gave false values.

The *lipids* make up around 65% of the dry weight of the "white matter" and 35 to 40% of the "grey matter."[32] As to the localization of the various types of lipid substances, the conclusions from histochemical data are still uncertain with respect to the nerve cells.

The free lipids of the nerve cell bodies (extractable by pure chloroform from fresh dry material) constitute about 20% of the dry weight

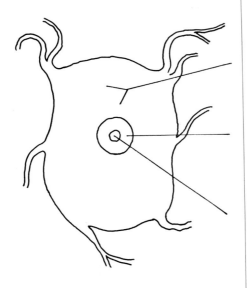

Component	Nucleolus	Nucleoplasm	Cytoplasm	Dendrites	Nuclear Cell Membrane
Total weight/volume	100 μμg.	800 μμg.	20.800 μμg.	—	—
Dry weight/volume	0.38 μμg./μ³	0.21 μμg./μ³	0.23 μμg./μ³	0.20-0.10 μμg./μ³	Concentric
RNA total	1.5%	—0.5%	1.545 μμg.	—100 μμg.	Proteins
RNA conc. weight/volume	—	—	1.2-1.5%	—	Radial lipids
RNA con. (% of dry protein)	—	—	9%	—	(Cerebrosides)
Proteins (total)	—	650 μμg.	16,600 μμg.	—	—
Proteins (conc., weight/volume)	—	16%	20%	—	—
Proteins (weight/cell weight)	—	—	75%	—	—
Lipid fraction	—	200 μμg.	4.200 μμg.	—	—
Lipids (conc., weight/volume)	—	5%	5%	—	—

Fig. 5. Deiters' nerve cell, rabbit: Dry weight, total: 23.200 μμg. Volume: 94.000 μ³.

for many types of nerve cells.[35,36,154] Lowry et al.[178] concluded by inference that the total lipids amounted to 2.8% on a wet weight basis,
which would mean around 13% of the dry weight. They concluded
also that the lipids consisted in equal parts of lecithin and cephalins.
Lowry et al.[178] found 20% total lipids in the pyramidal layer of the
Ammon's horn. Robins et al.[229] found 25 to 31% lipids in the molecular and granular layer of the cerebellum. Nonphosphorus-contain-
ing sphingolipids (probably gangliosides) dominated in the granular
layer. Brante[32] calculated that the chief lipids of the nerve cell cytoplasm were lecithin and phosphatidyl ethanolamine in equal parts
(approximately 5% of the dry weight). He also found small amounts
of gangliosides, a glycolipid containing sialic acid, and hexosamine.
The gangliosides and their localization in the nerve cells have been
more closely investigated by Klenk,[164,165] and by Svennerholm.[248-250]
The latter concluded that the gangliosides are present also in the
dendrites and axons. Using a staining reaction based on metachromasy
and correlated with a chemical analysis, Diezel[65] has found that gangliosides react positively inside the nerve cells, and Brante[33] has discussed
the so-called false metachromasy given by gangliosides.

Figure 5 summarizes data obtained at this laboratory on Deiters'
nerve cells of rabbit.

To return to the question of Nissl substance, it seems probable that
the condensed part of the cytoplasm containing the submicroscopic
system of channels and granules and giving the basophilic staining, is
the remaining structure of a highly organized liponucleoprotein. In
this connection it is relevant to note the finding of Folch and Uzman[92]
of a birefringent liponucleoprotein from the CNS showing a high degree of organization and containing a phospholipid and a carbohy-
drate-rich lipid.

In connection with studies on brain mitochrondria, the localization of enzyme activities in nerve structures has been described. The
work referred to was mostly performed with quantitative histochemical
methods. For observations obtained with specific staining reactions,
see review articles by, e.g., Dixon,[66] Scholz,[237] and Feigin and Wolf.[85]

Few determinations of enzyme activities have been made on individual nerve cells. The examples in Table IV are taken from motor and
sensory nerve cells. It is surprising that the activity of the glycolytic
enzyme phosphoglucoisomerase is in such great excess compared with
that of the respiratory enzymes per cell.

In discussing the relative distribution of the enzyme activity within
layers of the cortex Lowry et al.,[178-180,176,177] Pope,[215,216,218,220] and
Robins,[228,229] among others, have come to the following conclusions.
Respiratory enzymes, including DPN and components of the cyto-

TABLE IV

ENZYME ACTIVITY IN INDIVIDUAL NERVE CELLS*

Cell Type	Enzyme	Activity (moles/kg./hr.)	Activity (μl. O_2/cell/hr. $\times 10^{-4}$)	Metabolic System
Anterior horn cell (8)[176,177]	Alkaline phosphates	0.08	—	Phosphoesterase
Anterior horn cell (8)[176,177]	Phosphoglucoisomerase	24	—	Glycolysis
Anterior horn cell (10)[179,180]	Glutamic-aspartic transaminase	26	—	Amino acid metabolism
Anterior horn cell (6)[179,180]	Glutamic dehydrogenase	2.9	—	Amino acid metabolism
Spinal ganglion cells[176,177]				
Large type (11)	Phosphoglucoisomerase	39	—	Glycolysis
Small type (10)	Phosphoglucoisomerase	29	—	Glycolysis
Large type (12)[162]	Succinoxidase	15	—	Cellular respiration
Large type (13)[162]	Succinic dehydrogenase	7	3.4	Citric acid cycle
Large type (13)[162]	Cytochrome oxidase	20	1.6	Cellular respiration
Large type (7)[179,180]	Glutamic-aspartic transaminase	27.9	4.5	Amino acid metabolism
Small type (4)[179,180]	Glutamic-aspartic transaminase	31.3	—	Amino acid metabolism
Large type (6)[179,180]	Glutamic dehydrogenase	2	—	Amino acid metabolism
Small type (5)[179,180]	Glutamic dehydrogenase	3	4.4	Amino acid metabolism
Deiters' cells (13)[160]	Cytochrome oxidase	20	1.8	Cellular respiration
Deiters' cells (17)[160]	Succinoxidase	8	2–10 μl. (O_2/cell/hr.)	Cellular respiration
Symp. ganglion cell (18)[281,106]	Cholinesterase	9–45	—	Acetylcholine turnover

*In terms of dry weight per living cell. The table gives for comparison the values per cell recalculated as moles per kilogram per hour based on the dry weight of these types of cells. Figures within parentheses denote number of experiments.
Lowry (176, 177)
Hydén et al. (162)
Hydén and Pigón (160)
Giacobini (281), Giacobini and Holmstedt (106)
Lowry et al. (179, 180)

chrome system, are mainly localized in the mitochondria in the nerve cell bodies and dendrites. This recalls earlier observations on indophenol oxidase activity in nerve cell bodies and dendrites.[187,143,230]

Robins et al.[229] found that the glutamic dehydrogenase activity seemed to be high in the area of cortical cell dendrites but low in the Purkinje cell dendrites. Lactic dehydrogenase was high in both areas. Nerve cell bodies and dendrites seem to have the greatest capacity for glucose metabolism. Lowry et al.[178] and Pope et al.[220] localize in general the greatest enzyme activity in the dendrites and speak of a "dendrite metabolism." Proteolytic activity, reflected in a dipeptidase hydrolysing alanylglycin, was localized both to the nerve cell and to the glia.[219,216]

DATA ON THE COMPOSITION OF THE AXON

Leaving aside the composition of the myelin sheath (see e.g., refs. 82, 86) we will concern ourselves here only with some observations made on extruded axoplasm.

By x-ray diffraction technique Cohen and Geren-Uzman (1958, quoted by Schmitt[233]) have obtained from squid axoplasm an oriented pattern resembling the α-pattern of fibrous proteins of the KMEF class. The results indicate a definite polypeptide chain configuration of this protein. The amino acid composition of squid axoplasm is given by Schmitt and Gerschwind.[235]

Experiments on extruded axoplasm from the squid have supported the idea that the viscosity is caused by presence of the long protein filaments (Hodge and Jakus, quoted by Schmitt.[233]) The protein may amount to about 2.6% of the dry weight. Its isoelectric point is at pH 6.0. Maxfield[189] showed that the axon filaments are composed of highly charged protein with a particle weight of about 10^8, they behave in solution as flexible rods and constitute about 10% of the protein of the nerve axoplasm. As the pH and ionic strength are increased the filaments probably decompose into globules of about 70,000 molecular weight. Maxfield and Hartley[190] found that the axon filament diameter is greater at pH 6.0 than at pH 7.7.

The effect of pH is reversible and, according to Schmitt,[233] may involve a splitting of the filaments into two components. This change may prove to be of physiological importance.

The visible change in viscosity in teased vertebrate nerve fibers was studied by Lubinska.[181,182] The greatest structural instability was found to occur at the nodes. Deuticke et al.[64] have isolated from nerves of the cow two protein components which probably represent those of the nerve fibers. According to Bear and Schmitt[16] the protein content of the squid axon amounts to 3 to 4%, which is 30 to 40% of the dry substance; the water content is over 90%. These authors also isolated a nucleoprotein and a lipid complex. Edström[70,71] could not find any measurable amount of RNA in the axoplasm of the rabbit. Engström and Lüthy[83] determined the amount of dry substance in mammal nerve axoplasm to lie at 8 to 9% and Brattgård and Hydén[35] at 6%. Lipids constitute 33% of the dry substance, and Brante[32] concluded the composition to be lecithin 1.1% of the wet weight, colamine-cephalin 1.1%, cerebrosides 0.35%, and gangliosides 0.5%.

RNA AND PROTEIN METABOLISM

Macrochemical Studies.—The results of macro- and microchemical bulk analyses show unequivocally a high turnover rate of these substances in the brain and indicate protein synthesis. On the whole, they confirm the conclusions drawn from earlier cytochemical results that there is in the nerve cells a high RNA and protein production and metabolism that increases with increasing functional demands.[145,151,152]

From the cerebrospinal fluid P^{32} is rapidly incorporated into the pentose nucleic acids.[247] In *in vitro* experiments this was shown to be a phenomenon depending upon the aerobic metabolism.[88] The most direct studies showing nucleic acid (and lipid) metabolism during activity are those of Geiger *et al.*[99,98] Electric stimulation of the brain cortex for 20 seconds was found to cause a decrease of nitrogen compounds in the hot perchloric acid from a small cortical area, but an increase of the amino nitrogen content. There was also an increase of the nonprotein nitrogen content. All changes were reversible at rest after 5 minutes. They were approximately proportional to the number of stimuli. The split products from the nitrogenous components of the lipids and nucleic acids became water soluable. The authors assumed that these were bases and capable of changing the acid-base balance. By the use of specific-activity ratios Dawson and Richter[51] showed a considerable metabolic activity in the nucleoprotein fraction of the brain. Geiger *et al.*[99] found that stimulation for 30 seconds changed the composition of RNA in the cortex. The cytidine and adenine content of the nucleic acids increased, that of uridine and guanine remaining constant. Geiger concluded that these changes indicated synthesis of polynucleotides which, in turn, would induce a change in protein synthesis. Palladin,[212] in a review on findings of Russian investigators, also emphasizes the high metabolism and specific functions of RNA in brain.

Isotope studies have shown that the brain protein on the whole is characterized by a high metabolism which, judged from these data, can be assumed to be an intracellular protein metabolism. The probability seems less to favor synthetic processes for replacement of nerve tissue cells. Cohn et al.,[46] using S^{35}-methionine, found a higher incorporation in regions rich in nerve cell bodies than in the white substance. They could correlate this finding with a localization of the labeled amino acid to the cells. Niklas and Oehlert[197] found also an incorporation of S^{35}-methionine into the nerve cells. Gaitonde and Richter[94,95] concluded that the incorporation of S^{35} into the brain proteins is attributable to protein formation in the brain and that the free labeled amino acid, once through the blood-brain barrier, is rapidly incorporated into the protein. Lajtha et al.,[167] Waelsch,[266] concluded on the basis of isotope studies using C^{14}-lysine that there is most likely a dynamic state of the brain proteins. There are proteins with a high and a low turnover rate, as can be expected in such as inhomogenous tissue. The shortest value for the half-life of the protein was 2.2 days for the whole brain. The highest rate of incorporation was found in the corpus callosum. A comment here would be that the glia cells might be suspected to account for the latter result. The authors found further that the microsomal fractions incorporated at the highest rate. Half the free lysine was replaced in 45 minutes and the authors discuss the possibility that the movements of lysine and potassium may be interdependent. In this connection, the finding of basic, water-soluble split products of lipids and nucleic acids after stimulation is relevant.[99]

Geiger found further that during Metrazol convulsions and glucose-free perfusion, the rate of oxygen consumption of the brain tissue doubled. Lactic acid production accounted for the whole amount of glucose disappearing during these conditions. This indicated that the substrates for the increased oxygen consumption were derived from non-carbohydrate sources, probably proteins and lipids. Gerard[103] also concluded that the nervous tissue can utilize substances other than glucose.

Geiger et al.[100] found that, in control animals, the rates of incorporation of glucose C^{14} into the brain proteins was considerably slower than into amino acids. During convulsive activity the incorporation rate increased. The specific activity of microsomal protein was the highest and that of the mitochondria the lowest. In another series of similar experiments[13] the role of amino acids in relation to the metabolism of glucose was studied. The results indicated that endogenous carbon sources were contributing to form glycolytic and tricarboxylic acid intermediates at a rate which was almost as great as that by which they were being formed from exogenous sources.

Ungar et al.[254,255] found that stimulation seemed to cause a reversible change in the configuration of protein in the direction of a denaturation. Prolonged stimulation caused a breakdown of proteins and the appearance of proteolytic activity. On the other hand, Abood et al.[1] found a significant decrease of free amino acids on stimulating frog nerves. Abood et al. found no decrease in any of the nucleotide components, but an inhibition in the turnover of the phospholipids and in a phosphopeptide complex.

Shapot[241] studied changes of ATP and the incorporation of S^{35}-methionine into brain proteins of rats which had been teased and irritated. The incorporation into the proteins of the experimental animals was found to be lower than that of the control rats. After half an hour's sleep, the incorporation of S^{35} was considerably increased. The author interpreted the results to show that during the sleep energy became available for the resynthesis of structural protein components which in their turn restored the functional capacity of the nerve cells.

Ungar et al.[254,255] (see also Winterstein[275]) studied the nitrogen production, especially the formation of ammonia, using frog spinal cord, and found the ammonia to increase approximately threefold after electrical stimulation. Gerard[104] found that the total ammonia formation was threefold greater than reported, since two-thirds is retained by combination with glutamic acid. Weil-Malherbe and Green[270] suggested that the formation of ammonia was linked with proteolysis. Vrba[261-263] studied glutamic acid changes in the brain after intense motor activity and found a decrease of the free glutamic acid and the Kjeldahl nitrogen concentration of the protein fraction, formation of ammonia which was bound as glutamine, and consequently an increase of free glutamine. As an indication of degradation of nitrogen-containing components in the proteins during activity, a decreased concentration of amide groups was found. The author concluded that there is an increased protein metabolism in the brain during activity and that the free glutamine serves also as a basis for resynthetic processes.

In a later paper, Vrba and Folbergrova[264,265] described the fractionation of nitrogen compounds in fresh and incubated brain cortex slices. The decrease of the nitrogen in the protein and nucleoprotein fractions during incubation could be accounted for by an increase of ammonia of non-protein nitrogen and of lipid nitrogen. They assumed that these degradation processes were accompanied by utilization of endogenous bound pentose. It also indicated that the break-down of nucleoproteins, the utilization of substrates other than glucose, and the ammonia formation were interdependent processes in vitro and may be also in vivo.

Concluding, some highly important data for the further discussion of metabolism at the cytoscale have arisen from the macrochemical studies cited above. Lipids, RNA and proteins of the CNS are characterized by a high metabolism, which is further increased during increased activity. It is interesting to note that substances, previously regarded as "structure-forming" materials, have considerable metabolism in the CNS. At a certain point in increased neuronal activity there seems to occur a change in the substrate for the metabolism. This phenomenon has not so far been clarified. The studies cited cannot, however, tell the site within the nervous tissue of these various activities. Are the substances metabolized in the nerve cells, their dendrites and neurites, or in the glia cells which dominate numerically? Is it a nutrient metabolism or an expression of a specific functional synthesis, and if so, what is the intraneuronal mechanism for the synthesis?

Cytochemical Studies.—Recent studies of nerve cells during regeneration have given results of interest for the RNA and protein production in nerve cells in general. After crushing of a nerve, new thin axons begin to grow out almost immediately, and with a high velocity. During this stage the cell bodies are increased in volume and show chromatolysis. When the contact with the effector organ is reached, the new axons continue to grow in thickness. The chromatolysis persists for a considerable time. During the first of these stages Brattgård et al.[38] found a doubling of the amount of proteins and lipids in hypoglossal nerve cells in spite of a concentration decrease. The amount of RNA per cell did not at first increase, but the state of aggregation changed toward smaller particles. This was interpreted as a change from an active to a more active state. Using C^{14}-orotic acid, Brattgård et al.[39,40] found that the chromatolytic regenerating nerve cells at this stage incorporated considerably more of the orotic acid than did the control cells; this indicated an increased turnover rate of RNA. During the continued regeneration, the amount of RNA per cell increased tremendously, as did the proteins and lipids. Fisher et al.[89] found that regenerating nerve cells incorporated more S^{35}-methionine per unit area than the control cells, indicating an increased protein synthesis. The examples cited show an increased *synthetic metabolism* which can be correlated with the retrograde reaction of the nerve cells.

Using C^{14}-adenine and C^{14}-orotic acid, Koenig[166] found radioactivity over the nucleus 4 hours after the injection. The blackening gradually increased over the cytoplasm, with the exception of the axon hillock, and still remained 50 days after the injection. The specificity of the blackening was controlled with ribonuclease and deoxyribonuclease. When S-labeled methionine was used, the radioactivity over the nerve cells could be shown within 1 hour and began to decrease 4 hours after the injection. The author concludes that a rapid turnover of ribonucleoproteins takes place in nerve cells.

These and other recent investigations support the conclusions from studies with UV microspectrography by the writer and associates (1941-1957). These results indicated a production of RNA, proteins, and lipids in the nerve cell accompanying increased neuronal activity. Adequate stimulation for a short time may increase the concentration of RNA in proteins. Prolonged or very intense stimulation may lead to a reversible decrease in the amount of these substances. Large differences in the RNA, proteins, and lipids of the individual nerve cells may reflect differences in the functional state. RNA concentration changes occur rapidly in the nerve cells with increasing functional demands, no doubt following rapid volume changes.

A technical comment may be made in connection with determinations with UV microspectrography; it concerns the absolute values of nucleic acids inferred from the absorption spectra. When a cell undergoes rapid volume changes the amount of nucleic acids may well increase although absorption spectra indicate a concentration decrease. Absolute values of RNA or protein per cell can at present be determined accurately only on isolated individual cells.

The following findings may be referred to: Increased *motor activity* (running until exhaustion) was found to cause a marked decrease in RNA and protein concentration in the motor root cells. It was therefore concluded that the functional activity of the nerve cell was accompanied by increased nucleotide and protein metabolism.[145] Using x-ray microradiography, Gomirato[108,109] found motor exhaustion to produce a marked decrease of the total dry mass, including the RNA-containing fraction, per unit area in the motor root cells. Attardi[9] found a significant decrease of the RNA content of the Purkinje cells after muscular exhaustion.

Moderate *sensory stimulation,* by rotation, caused an increase of about 40% in the RNA concentration in the vestibular ganglion cells and also an increase of the amino acid absorption.[114] The same effect was found in the Deiters' cells; there also the results showed an increased nuclear concentration of nucleotides.[115] The frequency distribution of the different types of nerve cells in the Deiters' nucleus showed a significant shift toward the groups with a higher RNA concentration. Prolonged, intense rotatory stimulation (8 minutes each day for 6 days) caused a decrease in the RNA concentration in the vestibular ganglion cells.

A significant increase in the amount of RNA and proteins per isolated nerve cell could be shown in isolated Deiters' giant nerve cells from rabbits which were subjected to moderate vestibular stimulation for 25 minutes per day for 7 days.[160] (See further under the section on the glial cells.)

The dry weight of the Purkinje cells in the flocculus was found also to increase considerably after rotatory stimulation.[149] Acoustic stimulation caused a decrease in the nucleoprotein concentration in the spinal ganglion cells. The whole cycle of changes took 3 weeks under the conditions used.[113] The importance of adequate stimulation for postnatal chemical development has been shown by Brattgård,[34] studying the retinal ganglion cells. When the animals received normal light stimulation the mass, i.e., the total amount of organic substance, increased 100% during the early postnatal period. This development did not occur if the stimulation was excluded.

Edström and Eichner[74,75] have studied the ganglion cells of the supraoptic nucleus after stimulation by giving sodium chloride intravenously. The amount of RNA in the cytoplasm and the nucleolus increased by 80% and 35%, respectively. The RNA concentration of the nucleolus decreased significantly. There was a volume increase of the cell body, nucleus, and nucleolus. The findings indicated intensified RNA, and thus protein, production caused by the stimulation.

Among nerve cells of a given type, e.g., Purkinje cells, anterior horn cells, Deiters' cells, spinal ganglion cells, two or more subgroups have been found differing with respect to RNA, lipids, and proteins, or enzyme activity.[144-146,115,35,109,70,71,106] The conclusion was that these differences may depend upon the functional states of the subgroups.[145,146,153]

Alternatively, quantitative or qualitative differences in the composition may reflect an existing biochemical specificity in the nerve cells.[116] (See also Bodan,[24] Weiss,[271] and Gerard.[104]) Polio-virus attacks specifically motor neurons. In thiamin deficiency there is a degeneration of vestibular nuclei. Streptomycin attacks the same nuceli and causes changes in the RNA concentration.[91] Various examples can be referred to. This is another cytogenetic problem for further investigation.

A large body of information can be obtained from morphological studies on what Scholz[237] terms "Stoffwechselmorphologie"—cellular changes following stimulation or due to other external factors. Some of them have been clarified by the above-cited studies. Einarson[80] found, as have other workers, that chromophobia of the nerve cells is the structural correlate of increased activity.

Thus, the experiments referred to above on the cytoscale and also, by inference, on the macro- and microscale, have demonstrated that RNA, proteins, and lipids are synthesized in the nerve cells at a rate that follows the neuronal activity. The metabolic rate of these substances seems to be high. It seems not far fetched to visualize the neuron as an enormous, glandlike cell, fulfilling its function under steady and rapidly changing production of proteins and lipoproteins, with the mediation of RNA as an activator and governing molecule.

THE NERVE CELL MECHANISM FOR PROTEIN SYNTHESIS; THE NUCLEOCYTOPLASMIC RELATIONSHIP

Cytochemical observations have indicated that RNA plays an important role in protein synthesis in cells[42,30] This has now been shown also biochemically by blocking the RNA and by isotope studies. The present view encompasses the following points. DNA is necessary for protein synthesis in the nucleus, and even indirectly in the cytoplasm.[7] The nucleus has an energy-yielding system and one function of polynucleotides, whether DNA or RNA, seem to be to mediate the synthesis of ATP.[7] The activation of the nucleus to synthesize protein seems to require a preliminary synthesis of RNA so that it incorporates amino acids into its proteins[3,4]

A DNA with a high molecular weight, approximately 40×10^6 and metabolically active, and another DNA fraction with lower activity and weight have been isolated from different nuclei.[171] Likewise, there are two or more types of RNA in the nucleus. One fraction probably represents RNA of the nucleolus and is metabolically the more active; the other ribonucleoprotein complex is also very active.[4,258] Using autoradiography, Ficq[87] could show that the nucleolus especially has a high RNA metabolism.

Goldstein and Plaut,[107] using amoebas, indicated that labeled RNA probably passed from the nucleus into the cytoplasm. Plaut and Rustad[214] found that this organism incorporated RNA in the cytoplasm even in the absence of the nucleus, indicating an independently working system. Besides the production of the nuclear protein, ultimately governed by a specific DNA and dependent upon the RNA, there is also a cytoplasmic protein production. This seems to be located to the so-called microsome fraction rich in RNA[5] (for a review see Brachet[31]). As is pointed out on above the small particles rich in RNA, the microsomes, may well be precipitation products, the RNA actually existing *in vivo* in more diffuse aggregates.

Be that as it may, the fraction of the cytoplasm rich in ribonucleoproteins is also the site of the protein production. The production of a specific protein requires a specific RNA. By analogy with the model of the DNA molecule, according to Watson and Crick,[268,269] the RNA should serve as a template for the protein. The sequence of the bases should determine the physicochemical and enzymatic properties of the protein formed, by determining the nature and position of the polar groups. An important fact is that the synthesis of proteins proceeds from free amino acids. They undergo condensation into polypeptide chains without the intermediate formation of complex peptides. The free amino acids are activated by reaction with ATP and enzymes.[130,57] These activated amino acids are transferred to protein in an incorporation process which, according to Gale,[96] may be an exchange reaction between the activated amino acids and the amino acids already present in the protein associated with the RNA. Within a few minutes amino acids can be collected and assembled into a single molecule and released into the cytoplasm as a specific protein (see Loftfield[174] who has also suggested an operating mechanism for this process). The results and conclusions cited are based on studies on various types of material. A generalization may be hazardous, but the resulting picture is appealing.

The nerve cell offers unique possibilities to study changes of the

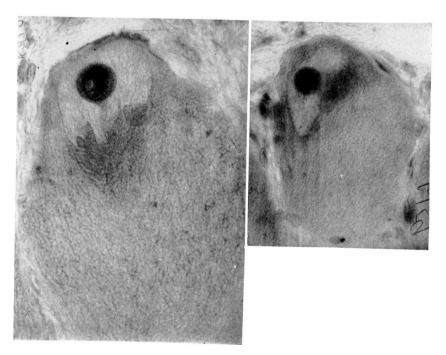

Fig. 6. Spinal ganglion cells from Lophius piscatorius. The nucleus is eccentrically situated and the nuclear membrane is folded within the part facing the center of the cell. In that area RNA is present in high concentrations. From the enlarged nucleolus toward this part of the nuclear membrane a gradient in the protein concentration has been observed, indicating a migration.[145]

nucleolus and nucleus and signs of chemical interaction between the nucleus and the cytoplasm. The following results have been obtained with quantitative cytochemical methods. They can be supported by many previous cytological findings on living and fixed cells. Detailed analyses have been made with UV microspectrography and x-ray microradiography of the large spinal ganglion cells of the angler fish *Lophius piscatorius* and other fish species[146,149,150] (Fig. 6). These cells differ in size and content of RNA and proteins. The nucleolus of the large cells contain approximately three times as much RNA as do the smaller and they contain relatively more proteins. Edström and Eichner[75] found a significant increase (80%) of the absolute amounts of RNA in nucleoli of supra optical nerve cells after stimulation compared with that in the control cell nucleoli. Hydén (unpublished) has observed that P^{32} is incorporated first in the nucleus of the nerve cell.

In nerve cells of *Lophius* containing large amounts of proteins, the measurements showed a gradient in the nucleoprotein content from the nucleolus onto the folded part of the nuclear membrane. X-ray analyses showed this gradient to amount to around 30%, computed on the mass near the nucelolar edge. On the outside of the nuclear membrane RNA and proteins were found in high concentrations. The nuclear membrane seemed to be unperforated. Since the small-type nerve cell seemed to be transformed successively to the larger type, characterized by an increased protein content, the production of RNA near the nuclear membrane was associated with the production of cytoplasmic proteins. The tentative conclusion was drawn that these nerve cells were characterized by a lively protein production. It was assumed that protein substances migrated from the nucleus to the folded part of the nuclear membrane, on the outside of which formation of nucleoproteins took place. It was also concluded that previous nerve cell changes interpreted as "Chromatin-Austritt"[134] could be explained by this activity of the nucleolus.

An increase in the RNA concentration in the nucleus, especially in the chromocenter regions near the nucleolus, and the formation of RNA and proteins in high concentrations near the nuclear membrane, have been found after stimulation in other types of nerve cells in connection with an increase of RNA concentration in the cell.[145,147,114,115,133] Confirmation that such findings indicate that the protein formation in the nerve cell is more active, comes from a study of nerve regeneration. The finding of nuclear membrane nucleoproteins is frequent in the stage when the amount of RNA has increased by around 100% and the protein content has doubled.[38]

In nerve cell cultures, R. S. Geiger[101] has observed particles detaching from the nucleolus and moving toward the nuclear membrane. They were seen to merge with the membrane. Lewis[172] coined the term pinocytosis for the process whereby cells engulf substances as droplets from the surrounding medium and transport them to another part of the cell. Holter and Marshall[140] have studied pinocytosis in amoebas. Palade[208] discussed pinocytosis in endothelial cells, and Bennet[19] considered this phenomenon to be a method of transport through cell membranes. It seems to the writer that the chemical observations in the nerve cells of *Lophius* may well be explained as signs in pinocytosis, whereby the nucleus exchanges larger complexes of substances with the cytoplasmic liponucleoproteins as well as with other substances. This interrelationship between nucleus and cytoplasm is no doubt mutual. Biochemical and biophysical, as well as cytological, evidence stress the nucleolus and attached regions in the nucleus as important centers for the intracellular nucleoprotein production.

An independent protein production in the nerve cell cytoplasm can of course not be excluded[105,148] and is probably steadily going on. This is rendered probable by the results of regeneration studies.[38] It may therefore be concluded that in the nerve cell body RNA, probably of both nuclear and cytoplasmic origin, is present.

A correlation between structural changes and functional activity in the nerve cells, indicating production of the Nissl substance by the nucleus, has been frequently noticed in important cytological studies (for review see refs. 246, 79, 80, 145, 146, 260, 237). In frog sympathetic ganglion cells, DeRobertis[60] has described a rich accumulation of electron-dense particles within folds of the nuclear membrane and also the occurrence of holes in this double-lined membrane. The opinion of the present author is that such defects in a membrane at this high resolution might equally well be due to disruption caused by the cytological procedure.

The findings of a high nucleoprotein production in nerve cells have been correlated especially with the results of Weiss and Hiscoe[273] indicating a movement peripheral to the axoplasm. These authors conclude that there is a perpetual growth of the neuron with a steady replacement of catabolized proteins in the periphery. This production of new protoplasm would occur solely in the nerve cell body, and the finding of a high cellular protein production supports this view. For further discussion, see Weiss[272] and the section on regeneration of peripheral neurons.

THE INTERACTION BETWEEN NERVE CELLS AND
GLIA CELLS

The glia cells outnumber the nerve cells in grey matter by a factor of around 10. There are many morphological and a few chemical data that indicate a functional relationship between glia and nerve cells.

Wilke and Kircher[274] and Bairati and Bartoli[10] have studied the birefringent glia protein components and Bairati identified the glia protein as an α-keratin.

The following discussion centers on the view that glia cells may furnish nerve cells with energy-rich substances advanced by the author and associates[162,160,154] and based on a study of the RNA and protein and on the relative activity of respiratory enzymes in nerve cells and glia cells. Since pinocytosis has been described to occur frequently both in nerve cells and in glia cells[101] that may be the mechanism by which substances are transferred from the glia to the nerve cell.

The Mass of Glia Cells.—The bodies of the glia cells are hard to stain. At high resolution they appear empty, especially the astrocytes. This can no doubt be explained by the destructive effect of cytological procedures, fixation, embedding, and staining, which remove, it seems, a large part of the organic substances in these cells. Determined per volume unit, the weight of fresh, frozen, and dried hypoglossal and Deiters' cells is around 0.20 $\mu\mu g./\mu^3$ The mass of the glia cells was the same, 0.20 $\mu\mu g./\mu^3$ (Hydén, unpublished).

Extraction with pure chloroform gave a larger loss for the glia cells than for the nerve cell bodies, indicating that glia cells contain more free lipids.

Submicroscopical Structure.—This problem has lately been dealt with by Palay and Dempsey in *The Biology of Neuroglia* (1958). (See also refs. 276, 183, 184, 84, 238, 196.) The astrocyte has a uniformly granular nucleus and nucleoli may be present. Luse[184] and Dempsey[58] described the astrocyte cytoplasm as scanty but elaborated in complexly folded processes containing meager amounts of cytoplasmic structures. Schultz et al.[238] emphasize the "empty" impression made by astrocytes, with only traces of content left after the fixation. The oligodendrocytes resemble rather the nerve cells, according to Schultz et al. Glia cells of both types have fewer mitochondria than have nerve cells.

All interstices in the neuropil are filled with the multifolded processes of the astrocytes and by the oligodendrocytes. The nerve cell bodies, dendrites, neurites, and oligodendrocytes, seem to be surrounded with the delicate processes of the astrocytes. They frequently establish contact with the neurons on the one hand and with capillary walls on the other and are closely applied to the capillary basement membrane. The capillaries are ensheathed by glial processes. Thus the nerve cell is clearly isolated from the immediate blood supply by the glia. As was emphasized earlier, the only extracellular space seems to be the 100 to 200 Å.-wide "spaces" which separate the protoplasmic membranes. Wyckoff and Young,[276,277] Farquhar and Hartmann,[84] and Schultz et al.,[238] like Holmgren[136-139] point out that the morphological relations suggest that the astrocytes may serve as the principal transport system to the nerve cells.

Hess found that the processes of the glia cells form a thin sheath around the nerve cells consisting of several overlapping layers. The inner layer of the sheath penetrates into the neuron as invaginations to which the appearance of the trophospongium of Holmgren would seem to be attributable. The glial cytoplasm is, however, always separated from the neuronal cytoplasm by two "membranes."

Enzyme Activity.—Using the microdiver technique, Hydén *et al.*[162] studied the activity of cytochrome oxidase and succinoxidase in spinal ganglion cells and their capsules containing the glial satellites, as indicators of the respiratory rate. Determined per unit volume, the relative activity of cytochrome oxidase was 0.9 for the nerve cells as compared with 1.6 for the glia cells. Corresponding figures for succinoxidase were 0.7 for the nerve cells and 5.1 for the glia cells. Thus, both enzymes exhibit higher activities per unit volume of glia cells. The glia cell:nerve cell ratio for succinoxidase activity was 7, as compared with approximately 2 for cytochrome oxidase.

If the findings of Lowry *et al.*[179,180] on the enzyme activity in spinal ganglion cells and their capsules containing glia cells are computed on the same basis, assuming that the volume of the spinal ganglion cell is approximately five times greater than that of the glia cells, the following is found: The activity of phosphoglucoisomerase is five times higher in the glia cells per unit volume; that of glutamic-aspartic transaminase, five times, and that of glutamic dehydrogenase, four times higher than these activities in the nerve cells. The results of Pope[218] indicate that proteolytic activity in the glial cells is of the same order as that in neurons.

Thus, these experiments may indicate a higher respiratory rate and amino acid metabolism per unit volume in the oligodendroglia cells than in the nerve cells. They may further indicate a certain specialization, i.e., a division of labor between the nerve cells and their satellites. Either the glia cells consume a large amount of energy, or they may be concerned with supply of energy to the nerve cells. It seems important that such comparative studies be performed on nerve cells and isolated glia cells which actually surround these nerve cells. Marginal glia cells or these from cauda equina may well have different functions.

Some Cytophysiological Data.—Microchemical analyses were performed on fresh, isolated Deiters' giant cells from the lateral vestibular nucleus and on the same volumes having the same dry weight of the

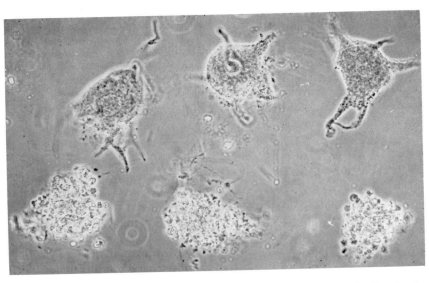

Fig. 7. Fresh Deiters' nerve cells with the neuroglial cells originally closely surrounding each cell dissected free and trimmed to the same volume as that of their nerve cell and placed in a row below the nerve cells. Photographed in the phase contrast microscope.[154]

oligodendrocytes closely surrounding these nerve cells (Fig. 7). The samples were dissected out by hand from a section through the fresh brain.[154,160] The diagrams in Figure 8 summarize the results.

The oligodendrocytes of the control animals contained on an average 120$\mu\mu$g. RNA compared with 1545 $\mu\mu$g. in the nerve cells they surrounded. The respiratory enzyme activities were twice as high in the oligodendrocytes as in the nerve cells. The same type of analyses were performed on samples from animals that had been subjected to moderate vestibular rotatory stimulation for 25 minutes per day for 7 days. This stimulation was followed by a significant increase of the amount of RNA and proteins of the nerve cells. There was also a change in the absorption at 2600 Å of the collections of RNA in the cells toward

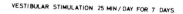

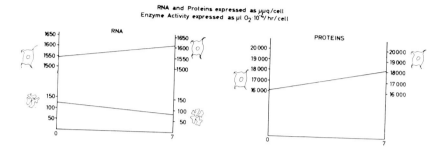

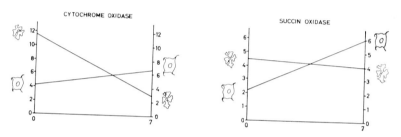

Fig. 8. Diagram showing the quantitative changes in the RNA and protein content and respiratory enzyme activities in the nerve cells and neuroglial cells after vestibular rotatory stimulation.[160]

smaller aggregates. The cytochrome oxidase and the succinoxidase activities per nerve cell also increased, showing that the stimulation caused a real increase of the enzyme concentration. On the other hand, a significant decrease of the RNA of the glial cells and their enzyme activities was found.

The conclusion was drawn that the nerve cell and its surrounding oligodendroglial cells represent two interdependent functional systems which together form a functional unit in the nervous tissue. As a working hypothesis it was assumed that the nerve cells are given priority to the energy yield of the electron transporting system of the oligodendroglial cells at increased functional demands.

REGENERATION OF PERIPHERAL NEURONS

Regeneration is an inherent characteristic of peripheral neurons and comprises the morphological and functional reconstitution which can be repeated over and over again during a life cycle.

Cytochemical Observations.—Chemical determinations have shown that great production of RNA, proteins, and lipids occurs during regeneration.[38] The changes are different during the outgrowth and the maturation period and can be correlated with morphological changes. During regeneration the nerve cell replaces fifty to a hundred times the organic material contained in the cell body. That means for a large nerve cell approximately 2 μg. and for a smaller cell about 0.1 μg. Since data indicate also increased protein and RNA metabolism in the nerve cell during regeneration,[89,37] the total production of nucleoproteins is certainly large.

The Latent and the Outgrowth Period.—During this stage the thin axons slowly traverse the scar tissue and rapidly grow out to the ef-

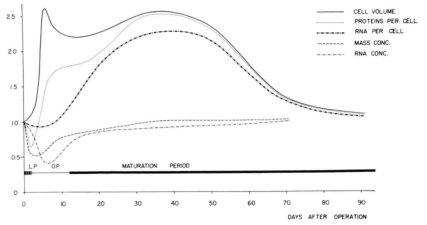

Fig. 9. Diagram of the quantitative hypoglossal nerve cell changes occurring during the 1st-ninetieth day after the crushing of N.XII.[39]

fector organs. The chromatolytic reaction rapidly develops. After the first day, the concentration of nucleoproteins decreases within a sector of the cytoplasm (Fig. 9). After a week, when the thin—0.5 μ-thick—axons grow at a rate of around 3 mm. per day, the RNA concentration is very low in the cytoplasm. The UV microspectrographic studies cited are those of Hydén,[144,145,151,152] Gersh and Bodian,[105] and Bodian.[23] The quantitative results quoted are taken from Brattgård *et al.*[38] In some nerve cells RNA appears as a crescent around the part of the nucleus facing the largest cytoplasmic mass.

The central part of the nerve cell, weakly absorbing at 2600 Å., was characterized by a strong positive reaction for acid phosphatase.[26,18] Howe and Mellors[142] found decreased cytochrome oxidase activity in such cells. The nucleolar satellite moves slowly away from the nucleolus toward the nuclear membrane during the "retrograde" changes. it was found to return later. The nucleolus was found to enlarge during the regeneration.[47] Outgrowing nerve fibers showed a strong cholinesterase reaction according to Koelle's method.[245] The protein-bound phosphorus and other phosphorus-containing fractions in regenerating nerves were increased and showed increased specific activity.[175,25]

The quantitative results of a study of regenerated hypoglossal nerve cells showed a decrease in the amount of proteins per cell of $\sim 30\%$ during the latent period. During the outgrowth of the axons there were several striking changes. There was a decrease in the RNA concentration per cell, confirming the results of the ultraviolet studies; but the amount of RNA per cell, 200 $\mu\mu g.$, remained unchanged. This was explained by a 260% volume increase of the nerve cell body due to uptake of water. In spite of the decrease in protein concentration in the cell, an increase of 100% in total protein was found during the first two days, and the amount was again doubled later. The amounts of lipids also increased, paralleling the proteins. Although the RNA remained quantitatively the same, there is a change in the aggregation of RNA toward a finely dispersed condition. This was assumed to mean a change of the RNA from a less active to a more active form in this stage of protein increase during dilution of the cell material. It explains the stained picture of the chromatolytic cell.

It is logical to assume that a major part of the RNA in this protein-producing nerve cell with increased water content, should be soluble RNA. As shown by Hoagland et al.[131] amino acids easily become bound to a soluble RNA, now called transfer RNA, if the fraction containing amino acid-activating enzymes of the cell sap of liver is incubated with ATP. The working hypothesis at present is that transfer RNA serves as an intermediate in the process whereby amino acids become synthesized to proteins and bound to the "ribosome" RNA as nucleoproteins.[132] The typical displacement of the nucleus may be explained by the changes in viscosity in connection with the concentration decrease and a speeded-up protein production directed toward and down the axon. The similarity with a glandular cell seems striking. A day after trauma, the synaptic endings were found to be swollen and the vesicles and mitochondria had degenerated or disappeared.[61]

The finding of a nearly 100% increase of the mitochondria in regenerating hypoglossal cells and electron microscopic changes is relevant.[118,120,121] It may mean that the oxidative process in these nerve cells has been speeded up. There are also observations indicating an increased metabolism of proteins and RNA in regenerating nerve cells during the outgrowth period. Fischer *et al.*[89] found that regenerating cells incorporated per unit area more S^{35}-methionine than did the control cells. Brattgård and Hydén[37] used C^{14}-orotic acid injected intracisternally and found that the regenerating hypoglossal cells incorporated per cell more of the labeled nucleic acid precursor than did the control cells. This confirms the conclusion that there is a high production and an increased metabolism of RNA and proteins in the nerve cells during the outgrowth of the axons. There seems to be no conduction impairment during chromatolysis, but a reduction of the action potential.[188]

Thus, the first changes are quite dramatic during the time when it is urgent for the nerve cell to spin out the thin axon to re-establish the functional contact with the periphery.

The Maturation Period.—When the connection with the periphery has been re-established it can be assumed that the stimulus from the effector organ back to the cell which follows with the re-establishment of the functional contact changes the course of the chemical processes. Aitken[2] found that the maturation of regenerating nerves is much more complete if the fibers make contact with the denervated muscle fibers. The RNA concentration has increased and the cells with the broad rings of RNA around the nuclei are most conspicuous. Quantitatively there begins now a second period of volume increase which will become maximal about one month after the nerve crush. This cell growth is not, however, due to water uptake, but to a real increase in the amounts per cell of RNA, proteins, and lipids, which will be more than doubled. The RNA reaches values of 470 $\mu\mu$g. per cell compared with 200 $\mu\mu$g. for the control cell. The mass concentration has been restored by one month after the crush.

At that time the Schwann cells undergo changes which by analogy with other cells indicate a protein production. The nucleus increases enormously, the nucleolus enlarges, and RNA can be detected in the increased cytoplasm.[161]

Conclusion.—It may be said that the characteristic changes during the short outgrowth period may be regarded as the activation of an emergency reaction which results in a rapid production of the new axon and its membrane. To determine whether other types of chromatolytic reaction also reflect a rapid production of proteins and an increased RNA metabolism with uptake of water, seems urgent.

The maturation period, characterized by an increase in volume of the nerve cell due to a large production of nucleoproteins and lipids, is initiated by the re-establishment of a functional relationship with the periphery.

AGING PROCESSES IN THE NEURON

Though somatic cells may reconstitute tissue by mitosis neurons do not have this potentiality. There are many data on changes in the CNS with age. A conspicuous change is in the yellow pigment, lipofuscin.

In nerve cells in man there emerge early in the postnatal period refracting granules in the cytoplasm that are stainable with osmium tetroxide. During the first decade these granules are faintly yellow and increase in amount. They are first detectable in anterior horn cells, in which they increase in amount and in color during the second decade so that they may fill up a part of, and even deform, the cell body. The pigment can be seen both in sensory and motor cells, but is scanty in the Purkinje cells, even at advanced ages. It varies in amount in different parts of the CNS and has been found in man, primates, old cattle, and guinea pigs.

The pigment usually takes up a large and well-defined part of the cytoplasm, which may bulge and cause the nerve cell to appear pear-shaped. In earlier cytological studies, the pigment was described as being composed of a fraction stainable with lipid dyes which seems to be more abundant at earlier ages. With increases in age, this fraction changes in color from light yellow to darker yellow. The pigment can be stained at pH greater than 5.5, where the Nissl substance does not stain. The isoelectric point has been determined to lie at pH 4.5. The pigment is very stable against organic solvents and acids.[213,192,193,205,204,259,279,21,8] On the basis of these cytological observations, a general conception was that the lipofuscin represented a "wear and tear" substance. Altschul,[8] however, concluded that the pigment represented a supporting substance for nerve cells with decreasing capacity.

Dixon and Herbertson[67] found glycolipids in this pigment which they considered to be aggregates derived from a more dispersed form of glycolipids resulting from cell traumata. Nageotte[194] considered that the yellow pigment was a derivative from the mitochondria, as did Hess.[128] The latter observed pictures in electron micrographs that indicated that the yellow pigment developed in relation to swollen and degenerated mitochondria.

Cytochemical studies have indicated the possibility that the yellow pigment is a pteridine.[159] Some new data have accumulated since then (Hydén, unpublished). In the region 2600 to 3000 Å., the area containing pigment absorbs heavily and evenly in Carnoy-fixed nerve cell section. After removal of the RNA, strongly absorbing granules appear which were embedded in the RNA. The absorption spectrum before digestion of the RNA shows maxima at 2600 and 2800 Å.; after removal of RNA there is a rather broad maximum at 2900 to 2950 Å. The earlier report that treatment with ribonuclease did not remove the 2600 Å. band[159] most certainly resulted from the inefficiency of the enzyme used. The fluorescence has been measured with a sensitive microfluorimeter. The emitted radiation has a sharp intensity maximum at 5000 Å. and a small band at 4600 Å. The presence of flavines can be excluded. The concentration of organic material including lipids is about 60% higher in the pigment than in the remainder of the cytoplasm. On microincineration the ash residue seems denser than in the remainder of the cell and is bluish-white in color in the dark field, compared with the yellow ash of the less pigmented parts. Valid determinations of iron in the pigment have not been carried out.

Judged by the cytological data and the UV spectrographic data on sections, it looks as if the amount of RNA decreases with increasing age when the amount of pigment increases. In microchemical RNA analyses on human anterior horn cells the amount of RNA per nerve cell was found to increase from age 3 to age 40. It remained rather constant up to age 55 to 60 and decreased significantly at higher ages. The amount of yellow pigment, determined by x-ray microradiography, increased up to age 40 to 50, although it varied in amount in the anterior horn cells and in different persons. But it did not decrease in amount at higher ages. Thus, there seems not to be an inverse correlation between the amount of RNA and yellow pigment per nerve cell.

Siebert *et al.*[242] made a chemical elementary analysis of a purified suspension of lipofuscin granules and concluded that they contain insoluble, inactive proteins.

In conclusion, it can be said that the yellow pigment contains a lipoprotein with a complex chromophore, and nothing so far contradicts the working hypothesis that it belongs to the group of pteridines. The pigment occurs physiologically and increases early with age in a type of cell which does not reconstitute itself chemically through mitosis. The lipofuscin accumulation may reflect a continuously occurring chemical reconstitution of the nerve cell. It may take part actively in the cell metabolism.

REFERENCES

1. ABOOD, L. G., GOLDMAN, E., and LIPMAN, V.: *J. Neurochem.,* 2:318 (1958).
2. AITKEN, J. T.: *J. Anat., 83:*32 (1949).
3. ALLFREY, V. G., and MIRSKY, A. E.: *Proc. Nat. Acad. Sc.,* 43:589 (1957a).
4. ALLFREY, V. G., and MIRSKY, A. E.: *Proc. Nat. Acad. Sc., 43:*821 (1957b).

5. ALLFREY, V. G., DALY, M. M., and MIRSKY, A. E.: *J. Gen. Physiol., 37:*157 (1953).

6. ALLFREY, V. G., MIRSKY, A. E., and STERN, H.: *Advances Enzymol., 16:*411, (1955).

7. ALLFREY, V. G., MIRSKY, A. E., and OSAWA, S.: *J. Gen. Physiol., 40:*451 (1957).

8. ALTSCHUL, R.: *Virchow's Arch. path. Anat. u. Physiol., 301:*273 (1938).

9. ATTARDI, G.: *Experientia, 9:*422 (1953).

10. BAIRATI, A., and BARTOLI, E.: *Ztschr. Zellforsch., 42:*278 (1955).

11. BARER, R.: *Nature, 169:*366 (1952).

12. BARER, R., ROSS, K. F. A., and TKACZYK, S.: *Nature, 171:*720 (1953).

13. BARKULIS, S. S., GEIGER, A., KAWAKITA, Y., and AGUILAR, V.: *J. Neurochem.,* in press (1960).

14. BARR, M. L., and BERTRAM, E. G.: *J. Anat., 85:*171 (1951).

15. BARR, M. L., BERTRAM, L. F., and LINDSAY, H. A.: *Anat. Rec., 107:*283 (1950).

16. BEAR, R. S., and SCHMITT, F. O.: *J. Cell. & Comp. Physiol., 14:*205 (1939).

17. BEHEIM-SCHWARZBACH, D.: *J. Hirnforsch., 2:*1 (1955).

18. BEJDL, W.: *Wien Ztschr. Nervenheilk. u. Grenzg., 10:*168 (1954).

19. BENNETT, H. S.: *Proc. 1st Regional Conf. on Electron Microscopy in Asia and Oceania,* p. 88. (1958).

20. BERTRAND, I., and GIRARD, C.: *Rev. neurol., 97:*321 (1957).

21. BETHE, A., and FLUCK, M.: *Ztschr. Zellforsch., 27:*211 (1937).

22. BLOCK, R. J.: *J. Biol. Chem., 120:*467 (1937).

23. BODIAN, D.: *Symp. Soc. Exper. Biol. 1:*163 (1947).

24. BODIAN, D.: In *Genetic Neurology,* p. 174. P. Weiss, Ed. Chicago, Univ. Chicago Press, (1950).

25. BODIAN, D., and DZIEWIATKOWSKI, D.: *J. Cell. & Comp. Physiol., 35:*155 (1950).

26. BODIAN, D., and MELLORS, R. C.: *J. Biol. Chem., 167:*655 (1947).

27. BOK, S. T.: *Proc. Acad. Sc. Amst. 35:*1; *39:*1209 (1936).

28. BOUIN, M., and BOUIN, P.: *Bibliographia anat., 6:*53 (1898).

29. BRACHET, J.: *Compt. rend. Soc. biol., 133:*88 (1940).

30. BRACHET, J.: *Arch. biol. (Liége), 53:*207 (1942).

31. BRACHET, J.: *Biochemical Cytology.* New York, Acad. Press (1957).

32. BRANTE, G.: *Acta physiol. scand.,* Suppl. 63 (1949).

33. BRANTE, G.: In Biochemistry of the Developing Nervous System, p. 153. H. Waelsch, Ed. New York, Acad. Press (1955).

34. BRATTGÅRD, S.-O.: *Acta radiol.,* Suppl. 96 (1952).

35. BRATTGÅRD, S.-O., and HYDÉN, H.: *Acta radiol.,* Suppl. 94 (1952).

36. BRATTGÅRD, S.-O., and HYDÉN, H.: *Internat. Rev. Cytol. 3:*455 (1954).

37. BRATTGÅRD, S.-O., and HYDÉN, H.: To be published (1960).

38. BRATTGÅRD, S.-O., EDSTRÖM, J.-E., and HYDÉN, H.: *J. Neurochem., 1:*316 (1957).

39. BRATTGÅRD, S.-O., EDSTRÖM, J.-E., and HYDÉN, H.: *Exper. Cell. Res.,* Suppl. 5. 185 (1958).

40. BRATTGÅRD, S.-O., HYDÉN, H., and SJOSTRAND, F.: *Nature, 182:*801 (1958).

41. CASPERSSON, T.: *Scandinav. Arch. Physiol., 73:*Suppl. 8 (1936).

42. CASPERSSON, T.: *Naturwissenschaften, 29:*33 (1941).

43. CASPERSSON, T.: *Experientia, 11:*45 (1955).

44. CHINN, P.: *J. Cell. & Comp. Physiol., 12:*1 (1938).

45. CLAUDE, A.: *J. Exper. Med., 84:*61 (1946).

46. COHN, P., GAITONDE, M. K., and RICHTER, D.: *J. Physiol.* (London) *126:*7 (1954).

47. CROUCH, Y. F., and BARR, M. L.: *J. Neuropath. & Exper. Neurol., 13:*353 (1954).

48. DAVIES, H. G., and WALKER, P. M. B.: *Progr. Biophys. & Biophys. Chem.*, *3*:195 (1953).
49. DAVIES, H. G., and WILKINS, M. H. F.: *Nature, 169*:541 (1952).
50. DAVIES, H. G., WILKINS, M. H. F., CHAYEN, J., and LA COUR, L. F.: *Quart. J. micr. Sc., 95*:271 (1954).
51. DAWSON, R. M. C., and RICHTER, D.: *Proc. Roy. micr. Soc., B 137*:252 (1950).
52. DAWSON, I. M., and WYBURN, G. M.: 2nd Intern. Congr. Neuropathol, London. In *Excerpta med., Sect. VIII, 8*:869 (1955).
53. DEBUCH, H., and STAMMLER, A.: *Ztschr. physiol. Chem., 305*:111 (1956).
54. DEITCH, A. D., and MOSES, M. J.: *J. Biophys. Biochem. Cytol., 3*:449 (1957).
55. DEITCH, A. D., and MURRAY, M. R.: *J. Biophys. Biochem. Cytol., 2*:433 (1956).
56. DEMLING, L., KINZLMEIER, H., and HENNING, N.: *Ztschr. ges. exper. Med., 122*:416 (1953-1954).
57. DE MOSS, J. A., and NOVELLI, G. D.: *Biochem. Biophys. Acta, 18*:592 (1955).
58. DEMPSEY, E. W., and LUSE, S.: In Symposium on the Biology of Neuroglia, p. 99. W. F. Windle, Ed. Springfield, Ill., Thomas (1958).
59. DEROBERTIS, E.: *J. Histochem. & Cytochem., 2*:341 (1954a).
60. DEROBERTIS, E.: *Gaz. méd. port., 7*:253 (1954b).
61. DEROBERTIS, E.: *J. Biophys. Biochem. Cytol., 2*:503 (1956).
62. DEROBERTIS, E., and BENNETT, H. S.: *Federation Proc., 13*:35 (1954a).
63. DEROBERTIS, E., and BENNETT, H. S.: *Exper. Cell Res., 6*:543 (1954b).
64. DEUTICKE, H. J., HÖVELS, O., and LAUENSTEIN, K.: *Pflüger's Arch. ges. Physiol., 255*:46 (1952).
65. DIEZEL, P. B.: *Deutsch. Ztschr. Nervenheilk., 171*:344 (1954).
66. DIXON, K. C.: *Quart. J. Exper. Physiol., 39*:129 (1954).
67. DIXON, K. C., and HERBERTSON, B. M.: *J. Path. & Bact., 63*:175 (1951).
68. DOGIEL, A. S.: *Int. Mschr. Anat. Physiol., 14*:73 (1897).
69. EDSTRÖM, J.-E.: *Biochim. Biophys. Acta, 12*:361 (1953).
70. EDSTRÖM, J.-E.: *J. Neurochem., 1*:159 (1956a).
71. EDSTRÖM, J.-E.: *Biochim. Biophys. Acta, 22*:378 (1956b).
72. EDSTRÖM, J.-E.: *J. Comp. Neurol., 107*:295 (1957).
73. EDSTRÖM, J.-E.: *Microchem. J., 2*:71 (1958).
74. EDSTRÖM, J.-E., and EICHNER, D.: *Nature, 181*:619 (1958a).
75. EDSTRÖM, J.-E., and EICHNER, D.: *Ztschr. Zellforsch., 48*:187 (1958b).
76. EDSTRÖM, J.-E., and HYDÉN, H.: *Nature, 174*:128 (1954).
77. EDSTRÖM, J.-E., and PIGÓN, A.: *J. Neurochem., 3*:95 (1958).
78. EINARSON, L.: *Am. J. Anat., 53*:141 (1933).
79. EINARSON, L.: *J. Comp. Neurol., 61*:101 (1935).
80. EINARSON, L.: *Acta Jutlandica, 17*:1 (1945).
81. EINARSON, L.: In *Metabolism of the Nervous System*, p. 403. D. Richter, Ed. New York, Pergamon Press (1957).
82. ENGSTRÖM, A., and FINEAN, J. B.: *Biological Ultrastructure*. New York, Acad. Press (1958).
83. ENGSTRÖM, A., and LÜTHY, H.: *Exper. Cell Res., 1*:81 (1950).
84. FARQUHAR, M. G., and HARTMANN, J. F.: *J. Neuropath. & Exper. Neurol., 16*:18 (1957).
85. FEIGIN, J., and WOLF, A.: *J. Neuropath. & Exper. Neurol., 14*:11 (1955).
86. FERNANDEZ-MORÁN, H., and FINEAN, J. B.: *J. Biophys. Biochem. Cytol., 3*:725 (1957).
87. FICQ, A.: *Arch. biol. (Liège), 66*:509 (1955).
88. FINDLAY, M., ROSSITER, R. J., and STRICKLAND, K. P.: *Biochem. J., 55*:200 (1953).

89. FISCHER, J., LODIN, Z., and KOLOUSÉK, J.: *Nature, 181*:341 (1958).
90. FLEMMING, W.: *Zellsubstanz, Kern und Zellteilung.* Leipzig, F. C. W. Vogel (1882).
91. FLOBERG, L.-E., HAMBERGER, C.-A., and HYDÉN, H.: *Acta oto-laryng.*, Suppl. 75:36 (1949).
92. FOLCH, J., and UZMAN, L. L.: *Federation Proc., 7*:155 (1948).
93. FOX, C. A., and BARNARD, J. W.: *J. Anat., 91*:299 (1957).
94. GAITONDE, M. K., and RICHTER, D.: *Biochem. J., 59*:690 (1955).
95. GAITONDE, M. K., and RICHTER, D.: *Proc. Roy. Soc., B 145*:83 (1956).
96. GALE, E. F.: *Harvey Lect., 51*:25 (1957).
97. GARNIER, C.: *J. Physiol. Path. gén., 2*:481 (1899).
98. GEIGER, A.: In *Metabolism of the Nervous System*, p. 245. D. Richter, Ed. New York, Pergamon Press (1957).
99. GEIGER, A., YAMASAKI, S., and LYONS, R.: *Am. J. Physiol., 184*:239 (1956).
100. GEIGER, A., HORVATH, N., and KAWAKITA, Y.: *J. Neurochem., 5*:311 (1960).
101. GEIGER, R. S.: *Prog. Neurobiol., II*:83 (1957).
102. GEITLER, L.: *Chromosoma, 1*:1 (1939).
103. GERARD, R. W.: *Physiol. Rev., 12*:469 (1932).
104. GERARD, R. W.: In *Neurochemistry*, p. 458. K. A. C. Elliott, I. H. Page, and J. H. Quastel, Eds. Springfield, Ill., Thomas (1955).
105. GERSH, I., and BODIAN, D.: *J. Cell. & Comp. Physiol., 21*:253 (1943).
106. GIACOBINI, E., and HOLMSTEDT, B.: *Acta physiol. scandinav., 42*:12 (1958).
107. GOLDSTEIN, L., and PLAUT, W.: *Proc. Nat. Acad. Sc., 41*:874 (1955).
108. GOMIRATO, G.: *Minerva med., 43*:N.23 (1952).
109. GOMIRATO, G.: *J. Neuropath. & Exper. Neurol., 13*:359 (1954).
110. GRIMM, U.: Über die Grössenbeziehung zwischen Kern und Nucleolus menschlicher Ganglienzellen. Dissertation, Bern (1949).
111. HALLÉN, O.: *Acta anat. Suppl.* 25 (1956).
112. HALLÉN, O., and HYDÉN, H.: *Exper. Cell Res.*, Suppl. 4, 197 (1957).
113. HAMBERGER, C.-A., and HYDÉN, H.: *Acta oto-laryng.*, Suppl. 1, 61 (1945).
114. HAMBERGER, C.-A., and HYDÉN, H.: *Acta oto-laryng.*, Suppl. 75, 53 (1949a).
115. HAMBERGER, C.-A., and HYDÉN, H.: *Acta oto-laryng.*, Suppl. 75, 82 (1949b).
116. HAMBERGER, C.-A., and HYDÉN, H.: *Mschr. Ohrenheilk. u. Laryngol.-Rhinol., 87*:253 (1953).
117. HANZON, V., and TOSCHI, G.: *Exper. Cell Res., 16*:256 (1959).
118. HARTMANN, J. F.: *Anat. Rec., 97*:390 (1947).
119. HARTMANN, J. F.: *J. Comp. Neurol., 99*:201 (1953).
120. HARTMANN, J. F.: *Anat. Rec., 118*:19 (1954).
121. HARTMANN, J. F.: *J. Biophys. Biochem. Cytol.*, Suppl. 2, 375 (1956).
122. HEIDENHEIN, M.: In *Handbuch der Anatomie des Menschen*, Plasma und Zelle, Vol. 2, p. 687. Fischer, Jena (1911).
123. HELD, H.: Beiträge zur Struktur der Nervenzellen und ihrer Fortsätze. *Arch. Anat. Physiol.*, Anat. Abt., p. 396 (1895).
124. HELD, H.: Zweite Abhandl., *Ibid.*, p. 204 (1897).
125. HELLER, I. H., and ELLIOTT, K. A.: *Canad. J. Biochem., 32*:584 (1954).
126. HERTL, M.: *Ztschr. Zellforsch., 46*:18 (1957).
127. HERTWIG, R.: *Biol. Zentralbl., 23*:49, 108 (1903).
128. HESS, A.: *Anat. Rec., 123*:399 (1955).
129. HILD, W.: *Anat. Rec., 127*:308 (1957).
130. HOAGLAND, M. B., KELLER, E. B., and ZAMECNIK, P. C.: *J. Biol. Chem., 218*:345 (1956).

131. HOAGLAND, M. B., ZAMECNIK, P. C., and STEPHENSON, M. L.: *Biochim. Biophys. Acta, 24:*215 (1957).
132. HOAGLAND, M. B., STEPHENSON, M. L., SCOTT, J. F., HECHT, L. J., and ZAMECNIK, P. C.: *J. Biol. Chem., 231:*241 (1958).
133. HOCHBERG, I., and HYDÉN, H.: *Acta physiol. scandinav.*, Suppl. 60 (1949).
134. HOLMGREN, E.: Zur Kenntnis der Spinalganglienzellen von Lophius Pisc. Lin. *Ergebn. allg. Path. path. Anat.* (1899a).
135. HOLMGREN, E.: *Anat. Anz., 16:*161 (1899b).
136. HOLMGREN, E.: *Anat. Hefte Abt. I, 18:*269 (1901).
137. HOLMGREN, E.: *Arch. Anat. u. Physiol. Anat., Abt. 15* (1904a).
138. HOLMGREN, E.: *Anat. Anz., 24:*225 (1904b).
139. HOLMGREN, E.: *Anat. Anz., 46:*127 (1914).
140. HOLTER, H., and MARSHALL, J. M.: *Compt. rend. Lab. Carlsberg, 29:*7 (1954).
141. HORSTMANN, E., and KNOOP, A.: *Ztschr. Zellforsch., 46:*100 (1957).
142. HOWE, H. A., and MELLORS, R. C.: *J. Exper. Med., 81:*489 (1945).
143. HUSZAK, S.: *Biochem. Ztschr., 298:*137 (1935).
144. HYDÉN, H.: *Nord. Med., 13:*144 (1942).
145. HYDÉN, H.: *Acta physiol. scandinav.*, Suppl. 17 (1943a).
146. HYDÉN, H.: *Ztschr. mikr.-anat. Forsch., 54:*96 (1943b).
147. HYDÉN, H.: *Symp. Soc. Exper. Biol., 1:*152 (1947).
148. HYDÉN, H.: In *Genetic Neurology*, p. 177. P. Weiss, Ed. Chicago, Univ. Chicago Press (1950).
149. HYDÉN, H.: *3rd Colloq. Ges. physiol. Chem., Mosbach/Baden,* 1 (1952a).
150. HYDÉN, H.: *Proc. I. Int. Congr. of Neuropathol., III:*570 (1952b).
151. HYDÉN, H.: In *Neurochemistry*, p. 204. K. A. C. Elliott, I. H. Page, and J. H. Quastel, Eds. Springfield, Ill., Thomas (1955a).
152. HYDÉN, H.: *In Biochemistry of the Developing Nervous System*, p. 358. H. Waelsch, Ed. New York, Acad. Press (1955b).
153. HYDÉN, H.: *Proc. 4th Int. Congr. Biochem. Vienna 1958, Symp. III*, p. 64. F. Brücke, Ed. London, Pergamon Press (1958).
154. HYDÉN, H.: *Nature, 183:*433 (1959).
155. HYDÉN, H.: In *The Cell*, Vol. IV. J. Brachet and A. Mirsky, Eds. New York, Acad. Press (1960) Chapter 5, p. 215.
156. HYDÉN, H., and HARTELIUS, H.: *Acta psychiat. scandinav.* Suppl. 48 (1948).
157. HYDÉN, H., and LARSSON, S.: *J. Neurochem., 1:*134 (1956).
158. HYDÉN, H., and LARSSON, S.: *Proc. Int. Congr. X-ray Microscopy.* Stockholm 1959 (1960).
159. HYDÉN, H., and LINDSTRÖM, B.: *Discussions Faraday Soc., 9:*436 (1950).
160. HYDÉN, H. and PIGÓN, A.: *J. Neurochem., 6:*57 (1960).
161. HYDÉN, H., and REXED, B.: *Ztschr. mikr.-anat. Forsch., 54:*352 (1943).
162. HYDÉN, H., LØVTRUP, S., and PIGÓN, A.: *J. Neurochem., 2:*304 (1958).
163. KEY, E. A. H., and RETZIUS, G.: *Studien in Anatomie des Nervensystems und des Bindegewebes.* Stockholm (1876).
164. KLENK, E.: *Hoppe-Seylers Ztschr. physiol. Chem., 273:*76 (1942).
165. KLENK, E.: *3rd Colloq. Ges. physiol. Chem., Mosbach/Baden.* Berlin (1952).
166. KOENIG, H.: *J. Biophys. Biochem. Cytol., 4:*785 (1958).
167. LAJTHA, A., FURST, S., GERSTEIN, A., and WAELSCH, H.: *J. Neurochem., 1:*289 (1957).
168. LANDSTRÖM-HYDÉN, H., CASPERSSON, T., and WOHLFART, G.: *Ztschr. mikr.-anat. Forsch., 49:*534 (1941).
169. LANGE, P. W.: *Svenska Träforskningen, Med. No. 69, Dissertation* (1954).

170. LEVI, G.: *Riv. Pat. nerv. ment., 1:*141 (1896).
171. LEVINTHAL, C.: In *The Chemical Basis of Heredity*, p. 737. W. D. McElroy, and B. Glass, Eds. Baltimore, Johns Hopkins Press (1957).
172. LEWIS, W. H.: *Bull. Johns Hopkins Hosp., 49:*17 (1931).
173. LINDSTRÖM, B.: *Acta radiol.*, Suppl. 125 (1955).
174. LOFTFIELD, R. B.: *Progr. Biophys. & Biophys. Chem., 8:*348 (1957).
175. LOGAN, J. E.: *Canad. J. M. Sc., 30:*457 (1952).
176. LOWRY, O. H.: *Progr. Neurobiol., II:*53 (1957a).
177. LOWRY, O. H.: In *Metabolism of the Nervous System*, p. 323. D. Richter, Ed. New York, Pergamon Press (1957b).
178. LOWRY, O. H., ROBERTS, N. R., LEINER, K. Y., WU, M. L., and FARR, A. L.: *J. Biol. Chem., 207:*1, 19, 39 (1954).
179. LOWRY, O. H., ROBERTS, N. R., CHANG, M. L.: *J. Biol. Chem., 222:*97 (1956a).
180. LOWRY, O. H., ROBERTS, N. R., and LEWIS, C.: *J. Biol. Chem., 220:*879 (1956b).
181. LUBINSKA, L.: *Exper. Cell Res., 10:*40 (1956a).
182. LUBINSKA, L.: *Acta biol. exper. (Lodz), 17:*135 (1956b).
183. LUSE, S. A. (1956a) *Anat. Rec. 124,* 329
184. LUSE, S. A.: *J. Biophys. Biochem. Cytol., 2:*531 (1956b).
185. MACALLUM, A. B.: *Brit. M. J., II:*778 (1898).
186. MACKENZIE, J. H.: *Rep. Brit. A. A. S. Toronto*, p. 822 (1897).
187. MARINESCO, G.: *Compt. rend. Soc. Biol., 82:*98 (1919).
188. MARK, V. H.: *Am. J. Physiol., 159:*233 (1949).
189. MAXFIELD, M.: *J. Gen. Physiol., 37:*201 (1953).
190. MAXFIELD, M., and HARTLEY, R. W.: *Biochim. Biophys. Acta, 24:*83 (1957).
191. MOORE, K. L., and BARR, M. L.: *J. Comp. Neurol., 98:*213 (1953).
192. MÜHLMANN, M.: *Verhandl deutsch. Ges. Path., 3:*148 (1900).
193. MÜHLMANN, M.: *Arch. mikr. Anat., 58:*231 (1901).
194. NAGEOTTE, J.: *Anat. Anz., 31:*225 (1907).
195. NICHOLSON, F. M.: *J. Comp. Neurol., 36:*37 (1923).
196. NIESSING, K., and VOGELL, W.: *Ztschr. Naturforsch., 12:*641 (1957).
197. NIKLAS, A., and OEHLERT, W.: *Beitr. path. Anat., 116:*92 (1956).
198. NISSL, F.: *Allg. Ztschr. Psychiat., 48:*197, 675 (1892).
199. NISSL, F.: *Allg. Ztschr. Psychiat., 50:*370 (1894a).
200. NISSL, F.: *Neurol. Zentralbl., 13:*676, 781, 810 (1894b).
201. NISSL, F.: *Zentralbl. Nervenheilk. u. Psychiat., 17:*337 (1894c).
202. NISSL, F.: *Allg. Ztschr. Psychiat., 52:*1147 (1896).
203. NURNBERGER, J. A., ENGSTRÖM, A., and LINDSTRÖM, B.: *J. Cell & Comp. Physiol., 39:*215 (1952).
204. OBERNDORFER, M.: *Ztschr. ges. Neurol. u. Psychiat., 72:*105 (1921).
205. OBERSTEINER, H.: *Arb. Neurol. Inst. Wien Univ., 10:*245 (1903).
206. OLSZEWSKI, J.: *Biol. Zentralbl., 66:*265 (1947).
207. OLSZEWSKI, J.: *J. Hirnforsch., 1:*206 (1954).
208. PALADE, G. E.: *J. Biophys. Biochem. Cytol.*, Suppl. 2, 85 (1956).
209. PALADE, G. E., and SIEKEVITZ, P.: *J. Biophys. Biochem. Cytol., 2:*171 (1956).
210. PALAY, S. L.: *Exper. Cell Res.*, Suppl. 5, 275 (1958).
211. PALAY, S. L., and PALADE, G. E.: *J. Biophys. Biochem. Cytol., 1:*69 (1955).
212. PALLADIN, A. V.: In *Biochemistry of the Developing Nervous System*, p. 177. H. Waelsch, Ed. New York Acad. Press (1955).
213. PILCZ, J.: *Arb. Neurol. Inst. Wien Univ., 3:* (1895).
214. PLAUT, W., and RUSTAD, R. C.: *J. Biophys. Biochem. Cytol., 3:*625 (1957).
215. POPE, A.: *J. Neurophysiol., 15:*115 (1952).

216. Pope, A., Caveness, W., and Livingston, K. E.: *A.M.A. Arch. Neurol. & Psychiat.*, *68:*425 (1952).
217. Pope, A.: *J. Neuropath. & Exper. Neurol.*, *14:*39 (1955).
218. Pope, A.: In *Symposia on the Biology of Neuroglia*, p. 211. W. F. Windle, Ed. Springfield, Ill., Thomas (1958).
219. Pope, A., and Anfinsen, C. B.: *J. Biol. Chem.*, *173:*305 (1948).
220. Pope, A., Hess, H. H., Ware, J. R., Thomson, R. H.: *J. Neurophysiol.*, *19:*259 (1956).
221. Porter, K. R.: *J. Histochem. Cytochem.*, *2:*346 (1954).
222. Prince, R. H., Graham, M. A., and Barr, M. L.: *Anat. Rec.*, *122:*153 (1955).
223. Ramon y Cajal, S.: *Textura del sistema nervioso del hombre y de los vertebrados*, Vol. 2. Madrid, Imprenta y libreria de Nicolás Moya. (1890).
224. Ramon y Cajal, S.: *Anat. Anz.*, *5:* (1890).
225. Ramon y Cajal, S.: *Trabajos de Laboratorio de investigaciones biologicas de la Universidad de Madrid*, T 3 (1904).
226. Ramon y Cajal, S.: *Histologie du système nerveux de l'homme et des vertébrés.* Paris, Maloine (1909).
227. Ris, H.: In *The Chemical Basis of Heredity*, p. 23. W. D. McElroy and B. Glass, Eds. Baltimore, Johns Hopkins Press (1957).
228. Robins, E., and Smith, D. E.: *A. Nerv. & Ment. Dis., Proc.*, *32:*305 (1953).
229. Robins, E., Smith, D. E., and Eydt, K. M.: *J. Neurochem.*, *1:*54 (1956).
230. Roizin, L.: *J. Neuropath. & Exper. Neurol.*, *14:*47 (1955).
231. Rudkin, G. T., and Corlette, S. L.: *J. Biophys. Biochem. Cytol.*, *3:*821 (1957).
232. Saguchi, S.: *Zytol. Studien*, Kanazawa, H 4 (1930).
233. Schmitt, F. O.: In *Metabolism of the Nervous System* p. 36. D. Richter, Ed. New York, Pergamon Press (1957).
234. Schmitt, F. O.: *Rev. Modern Phys.*, *31:*455 (1959).
235. Schmitt, F. O., and Gerschwind, N.: *Progr. Biophys. Biophys. Chem.*, *8:*165 (1957).
236. Scholl, D. A.: *The Organization of the Cerebral Cortex.* New York, Wiley (1956).
237. Scholz, W.: In *Handbuch der speziellen pathologischen Anatomie und Histologie*, Vol. 13, Pt. la, p. 42. Rössle, Ed. Berlin, Springer (1957).
238. Schultz, R. L., Maynard, E. A., and Pease, D. C.: *Am. J. Anat.*, *100:*369 (1957).
239. Scott, F. H.: *Tr. Roy. Canad. Inst.*, *5:* (1898).
240. Scott, F. H.: *Tr. Roy. Canad. Inst.*, *6:*405 (1899).
241. Shapot, V. S.: In *Metabolism of the Brain*, p. 257. D. Richter, Ed. New York, Pergamon Press (1957).
242. Siebert, G., Heidenreich, O., Böhmig, R., and Lang, K.: *Naturwissenschaften*, *42:*156 (1955).
243. Sjöstrand, F.: To be published (1958).
244. Slautterback, D. B.: *Exper. Cell Res.*, *5:*173 (1953).
245. Snell, R. S.: *Nature, 180:*378 (1957).
246. Spielmeyer, W.: *Histopathologie des Nervensystems*, Vol. 1. Berlin, Springer (1922).
247. Strickland, K. P.: *Canad. J. M. Sc.*, *30:*484 (1952).
248. Svennerholm, L.: *Nature, 177:*524 (1956a).
249. Svennerholm, L.: *Acta Soc. Med. upsalien.*, *61:*75 (1956b).
250. Svennerholm, L.: *Acta Soc. Med. upsalien.*, *62:*1 (1957).
251. Thorell, B., and Ruch, F.: *Nature, 167:*815 (1951).
252. Toschi, G.: *Exper. Cell Res. 16:*232 (1959).

253. TYRELL, L. W., and RICHTER, D.: *Biochem. J., 49*:li (1951).
254. UNGAR, G., ASCHHEIM, E., PSYCHOYOS, S.: *Internat. Physiol. Congr., 20*:904 (1956a).
255. UNGAR, G., ASCHHEIM, E., PSYCHOYOS, S., and ROMANO, D. V.: *J. Gen. Physiol., 40*:635 (1956b).
256. VAN HERWERDEN, M. A.: *Arch. Zellforsch., 10*:431 (1913).
257. VINCENT, W. S.: *Int. Rev. Cytol., 4*:269 (1955).
258. VINCENT, W. S.: *Science, 126*:306 (1957).
259. VOLKMANN, R. V.: *Ztschr. wiss. Mikr., 49*:457 (1932).
260. VRAA-JENSEN, G.: *Acta psychiat. scandinav.*, Suppl. 109 (1956).
261. VRBA, R.: *Nature, 176*:117 (1955a).
262. VRBA, R.: *Nature, 176*:1258 (1955b).
263. VRBA, R.: *J. Neurochem., 1*:12 (1956).
264. VRBA, R., and FOLBERGROVÁ, J.: *Nature, 182*:237 (1958).
265. VRBA, R., and FOLBERGROVÁ, J.: *J. Neurochem., 4*:338 (1959).
266. WAELSCH, H.: In *Metabolism of the Nervous System*, p. 431. D. Richter, Ed. New York, Pergamon (1957).
267. WALKER, P. M. B., and RICHARDS, B. M.: *The Cell*, Vol. I, p. 91. J. Brachet, and A. Mirsky, Eds. New York, Acad. Press (1959).
268. WATSON, J. D., and CRICK, F. H. C.: *Nature, 171*:737 (1953).
269. WATSON, J. D., and CRICK, F. H. C.: *Proc. Roy. Soc., A223*:80 (1954).
270. WEIL-MALHERBE, H., and GREEN, R. H.: *Biochem. J., 61*:210 (1955).
271. WEISS, P.: In *Genetic Neurology*, p. 1. P. Weiss, Ed. Chicago Univ. Chicago Press (1950).
272. WEISS, P.: In *Analysis of Development*, p. 346. B. H. Williger, Ed. Philadelphia, Saunders (1956).
273. WEISS, P., and HISCOE, H. B.: *J. Exper. Zool., 107*:315 (1948).
274. WILKE, G., and KIRCHER, H.: *Deutsch. Ztschr. Nervenheilk., 167*:529 (1952).
275. WINTERSTEIN, H.: In *Handbuch der normalen und pathologischen Physiologie*, Vol. 9, p. 515. A. Bethe, G. von Bergmann, G. Embden, and A. Ellinger, Eds. Berlin, Springer (1929).
276. WYCKOFF, W. G., and YOUNG, J. Z.: *J. Anat. London, 88*:568 (1954).
277. WYCKOFF, W. G., and YOUNG, J. Z.: *Proc. Roy. Soc., B 144*:440 (1956).
278. YOUNG, J. Z.: *J. Exper. Biol., 33*:709 (1956).
279. ZEGLIO, P.: *Arch. ital. Anat., 35*:371 (1935).
280. EDSTROM, J.-E., and EICHNER, D.: *Ztschr mikr.-anat. Forsch., 63*:413 (1957).
281. GIACOBINI, E.: *Acta physiol. scandinav.*, Suppl. 145, p. 49 (1957).

XVII

TRANSPORT PHENOMENA IN BRAIN

Rose M. Johnstone and P. G. Scholefield

The body fluids, in their passage through the various organs of the body, bring with them the essential nutrients for the maintenance of these organs and may, on leaving the organs, carry away the end products of metabolism. The emphasis in studies of the mechanisms involved in these processes has usually been on the passage of such nutrients from the blood or other body fluids into the organs concerned. The term "blood-brain barrier" implies that, in studies of the distribution of nutrients between the blood and the brain, emphasis has largely been placed not on the entry but on the prevention of entry of nutrients into the brain. The role of the blood-brain barrier in regulating the passage of nutrients into the brain is dealt with in detail in another chapter. It is important, however, to consider here some of the factors involved in the final appearance of various molecules in the brain cells. It is also important to define clearly the meaning of such terms as entry, penetration, accumulation, concentration, transport and exchange as they seem to apply in brain.

The term "entry" is used to cover any and all mechanisms by which a molecule can get into the brain or a brain slice. The term "penetration" is used to cover the same wide range of mechanisms but carries with it the connotation that a molecule has successfully overcome a permeability barrier. "Accumulation," indicates a cumulative entry of a molecular species with no reference to relative concentrations in the tissue and in the medium. When the concentration of the substance is caused for any reason to be greater in brain than in the blood or the incubation medium, the substance is said to be "concentrated" by the brain. The entry of any compound into the brain by means of a biological rather than a physico-chemical process may be designated "transport." Such a process is usually energy-dependent, may lead to concentration of the substrate by the tissue, often against a diffusion gradient, and is frequently referred to by the more general term of "uptake." Finally, there are the processes known by the general name of "exchange" reactions. In these, there is no net transfer of a material across the cell membrane but a given molecule enters the cell at the same rate as that at which a similar or identical molecule is lost from within the cell. The special case of "exchange diffusion" is characterized by the fact that the entry and the loss are brought about by a common mechanism so that the rates bear a strict mole-to-mole relationship to each other.

Many compounds are known to enter the brain. Among them are potential substrates, metabolic inhibitors and also compounds which apparently have no influence on the metabolic pattern of the brain. Few, if any, however, of the compounds studied have been shown to be transported into the brain by a biological carrier system. Consideration will, therefore, be given first to those compounds which enter the brain but whose mode of entry has not been fully established.

OXYGEN

There seems to be no direct evidence bearing on the mode of entry of oxygen into the brain. The extensive investigations of Kety and his colleagues have, however, yielded information concerning the rate of utilization of oxygen by the brain *in vivo*. Kety and Schmidt[1] showed in 1948 that the rate of oxygen consumption of a normal adult human brain is approximately 3.3 ml./100 gm. brain/minute or 50 ml./brain/minute, that is, about 20% of the basal oxygen requirement of the adult human body. These figures indicate that the entry of oxygen into the brain is sufficiently rapid to support a $-Q_{o_2}$ value of 10. It is unlikely that the rate of passage of oxygen into the brain controls the metabolic rate of that organ since increase in the oxygen tension of the blood by exposure to an environment of 3.5 atmospheres of oxygen does not significantly increase the rate of oxygen utilization by the brain.[2] On the other hand, there is certainly no great reservoir of oxygen in the brain since elimination of the cerebral blood supply is known to produce loss of consciousness in six to eight seconds. Recovery in an equally short period of time indicates a rapid re-entry of oxygen into the brain. The quick onset of the symptoms of anesthesia after the administration of nitrous oxide indicates that it is also able to enter the brain quite rapidly.

GLUCOSE

As with oxygen, no figures are available for the rate of entry of glucose into the brain and no suggestions have been made concerning the means by which it enters the brain. Nevertheless, a considerable

body of related evidence is available which suggests that the availability of glucose to the cerebral tissues may well control their metabolic activities. Decrease in the arterial blood content of glucose leads
to a marked decrease in the cerebral oxygen consumption.[4-6] Similar
effects may be demonstrated *in vitro* with rat brain cortex slices where
a decrease in the glucose content of the medium from 5 to 0.5 mM
(90 to 9 mg.%) leads to 50% inhibition of the extra oxygen uptake
due to added glucose.[7] This is in excellent agreement with the report
by Kety[8] that, in 142 cases of deep coma in man, the blood sugar
averaged 10 mg.%

There is available indirect evidence concerning the rate of entry
of glucose into the brain. It is well known that intravenous injection
of glucose into patients in hypoglycemic coma leads to almost immediate recovery, which suggests a very rapid entry of glucose into the
brain. This suggestion is supported by the rapidity with which insulin
shock occurs after administration of the hormone.

The presence of 10 mM glucose leads to 99% inhibition of the oxidation of 10 mM fructose-1-C^{14} to $C^{14}O_2$ in rat brain cortex slices.
It has been suggested[9,10] that this effect may be due in part to competition for a common carrier system since competition for hexokinase
and isotopic dilution would be unlikely to cause such an extensive
inhibition.

There is some evidence that the carbohydrate-like compound, ascorbic acid, is actively transported into brain slices.[11] The results obtained
after prompt sampling of rat cerebral cortex tissue indicate a normal
level of ascorbic acid of approximately 2.3 μmoles/gm. fresh tissue.
This value decreases rapidly when slices are incubated aerobically
in a glucose-containing medium but may be prevented, and the level
actually increased, by addition of 1 mM ascorbate to the medium. The
maintenance of the ascorbic acid level does not occur anaerobically
nor does it occur in the absence of glucose. The requirements for
conditions which supply an adequate source of energy suggest a transport mechanism.

DRUGS

The penetration of neurotropic drugs into the central nervous system has been the subject of much discussion but rather less experimentation. The high concentration of lipids in brain has long been
correlated with penetration of neurotropic drugs, particularly those
with anesthetic activity.[12,13] These agents are presumed to be selectively removed from the blood stream by the lipids of the brain cell
membranes and then to pass inside the cell where their metabolic

effects may be exerted. Such a formulation is quite consistent with the earlier observations of Ehrlich[14] and Lewandowsky[15] that the water-soluble aniline dyes and sodium ferricyanide do not penetrate into the brain parenchyma, facts which had helped to establish the concept of a blood brain barrier. This suggestion is also in harmony with the observations of Nicloux and Yovanovitch[16] and McCollum[17] that during chloroform anesthesia this agent reaches a higher concentration in the brain than in the blood. The chloroform is probably retained by its association with the brain lipids. The distribution of many drugs, including antibiotics, have since been studied but the mechanisms involved in the attainment of the steady state levels have usually escaped attention.

Recent work by Mayer, Markel and Brodie,[18] however, has shown that several drugs enter rabbit brain *in vivo* and appear in the cerebrospinal fluid (CSF) as the result of simple diffusion. It was also shown that the kinetics of this process may be described in terms of Fick's law of diffusion. The concentration of antipyrine in the water of rabbit brain or the CSF relative to that in the plasma reaches a value of unity within five minutes of its injection into the femoral vein. Similarly, the fast acting narcotic, thiopental, reaches a steady state level in the CSF within 5 minutes. The concentration of salicylate in brain, after intravenous injection, reaches a level which is only one-quarter of that present in the plasma and 2 to 3 hours are required for this value to be attained. On the other hand, salicylic acid reaches a steady state level in the liver in an hour, after which time the concentration in the liver is 60% of that in the plasma.

Mayer *et al.*[18] also showed that intravenous administration of antipyrine or of 4-aminoantipyrine into rabbits leads to equal concentrations of these drugs in the brain stem, medulla, cerebellum and the left and right cortex. The level of aminopyrine reached in these various parts of the nervous system is approximately one-half of that initially produced in the plasma by injection and is equal to the concentration finally present in the plasma water after due allowance is made for protein binding of the drug.

Such binding of drugs is an important factor to be considered in attempting to determine the role of an active transport system in the penetration of brain slices by a drug and in attempting to assay the effective concentration of a drug present in the brain. The work of Bell[19] has shown that analgesic *p*-cyclohexyloxy-d-phenylethylamine (CHP) may apparently be concentrated by rat cerebral cortex slices to the extent of nearly 80-fold. However, it was also shown by this author that concentration of CHP occurs to an equal extent by both

slices and *"suspensions"* and that neither anaerobic conditions nor the
absence of glucose leads to a decrease in this apparent concentration
of the drug in the tissue. Such firm binding of CHP by the brain provides a ready explanation for the fact that the inhibitory effect of
this drug is not easily reversible on washing of the cortex slices.[18] On
the other hand, the rapid entry of thiopental into the brain as the
result of simple diffusion, as shown by Mayer *et al.*,[18] is in agreement
with the earlier observations of Quastel and Wheatley[20] that the actions of several neurotropic agents on the respiratory activity of cortex slices may be reversed by washing of the slices in a saline medium.

WATER

There seems to be no doubt that water may easily enter most parts
of the central nervous system. It has been shown[21] that the steady
state level of deuterated water is attained within 20 minutes of intravenous injection of deuterated water in the following areas of the
central nervous system: the superior sagittal sinus blood, cerebral
grey matter, cerebral white matter, cerebellum, spinal cord, ventricular CSF, cisterna magna CSF, and lumbar CSF. The work of Sweet,
Selverstone, Soloway and Stetten[22] indicated that, after injection of
deuterated water, the times required for its concentration in various
tissues to reach one-half that present in the blood are 1.5 minutes for
the cisterna magna, 8 to 11 minutes for the ventricles and 18 to 26
minutes for the lumbar sac. Such results indicate that water may
appear in the fluids of the central nervous system more rapidly than
it appears in, or exchanges with, most other fluids present in the
body. The results of Bering[21] show that the "half time of D_2O appearance" in cerebral grey and white matter *(in the dog)* may be of
the order of 10 to 20 seconds after intravenous injection.

Such rapid movement of water may be the result of a simple diffusion of water which "thus permits maintenance of isotonicity of intracranial fluids with other body fluids at all times."[23] However, the
passage of water into the nervous tissues may also be a consequence of
ion transport, particularly during periods of stimulation. On the other
hand, it is well known[22] that equilibration of Na^{24} between the blood
and the various parts of the nervous system is much slower than the
rapid equilibration of D_2O. It may be pointed out in this connection
that movement of greatly hydrated forms of cations may account for
some of the disparity between the rates of movement of electrolytes
and that of water. Nevertheless, Holmes and Tower (ref. 23, p. 271)
are of the opinion that "Since it (the central nervous system) is inca-

pable of rapid solute transfer, isotonicity is maintained by transfer of water."

For other aspects of *in vivo* transport of water, such as in hydrocephalus and cerebral edema in general, the reader is referred to some of the standard texts on changes in the intracranial fluids and their clinical significance.

The accumulation of water by brain under *in vitro* conditions is a process which has been the subject of more precise investigation. It was shown by Elliott[24] that incubation of rat brain slices in Ringer's solution or in cerebrospinal fluid leads to an increase of approximately 50% in the original tissue water. The corresponding increases found for slices of rat liver and rat kidney cortex are less than 5 and 15% respectively, again emphasizing the importance of movement of water into the brain. Such movement of water into rat brain cortex slices is not always accompanied by non-specific entry of solutes into this tissue. The extensive accumulation of water by brain slices was confirmed by Stern, Eggleston, Hems and Krebs[25] and later by Allen.[26] The latter also suggested that the swelling must be largely intracellular. Subsequent work by Pappius and Elliott[27] indicated, however, that the amount of extra fluid may be correlated with the size of such "spaces" as the thiocyanate space. According to the latter results the accumulated fluid must either be extracellular or associated only with those cells which are permeable to thiocyanate. Studies with the electron microscope (see, for example, ref. 28) suggests the latter alternative since they provide no evidence of any extracellular fluids in such preparations.

ELECTROLYTES

The transport of electrolytes into the brain has been extensively studied in connection with certain aspects of brain metabolism. From such studies several important points have emerged. Thus, the ubiquitously high intracellular potassium concentration in brain despite the much lower level in the blood and the cerebrospinal fluid emphasizes that potassium may enter the brain cells quite readily. The variability in the rates of D_2O and P_i[32] uptake by different areas of the brain emphasize that in brain we are dealing with many different types of cells, each of which may have its own permeability characteristics. The role of glutamate in potassium transport[29,30] indicates the possibility of the involvement of organic anions in the transport of inorganic cations. The demonstration by Ussing and Zerahn[31] that chloride entry into frog skin is purely a passive process dependent upon the size of a bioelectric potential, and the demonstration by Hogben[32] that, in gastric mucosa, chloride is actively transferred from serosa to mucosa, indicate that quite different results may be obtained in studies of electrolyte transport in various tissues. Finally, it has become apparent that cationic fluxes, particularly those of sodium and potassium, are an integral part of the responses of the nervous system to stimuli.

Detailed descriptions of electrolyte transport into brain will be found elsewhere in this book.

CREATINE

The concentration of free creatine normally present in guinea pig brain cortex *in vivo* is approximately 10 mM.[33] The concentration of creatine in normal human plasma is of the order of 0.1 mM.[34] It seems reasonable to suppose that creatine may be actively transported into the brain and there concentrated. Alternative explanations may be offered, e.g., a very rapid synthesis of this compound by the brain itself and a relatively slow loss or an extensive binding of creatine by the brain tissue. In fact, it has been shown that loss of creatine from brain cortex slices is quite rapid and incubation of such slices in a medium devoid of creatine may cause the concentration to fall from 10 mM to 2 mM. Under anaerobic conditions, the concentration may reach a level as low as 0.2 mM.[33] Further, it has been shown by Thomas[33] that creatine will accumulate against a diffusion gradient if oxygen and glucose are present during the incubation, which provides some support for the suggestion that an active transport of creatine into brain occurs.

AMINO ACIDS

It has been known since the early work of Van Slyke and his associates[35] that the concentrations of free amino acids are higher in the tissues than in the blood. Brain is no exception, the concentrations of certain amino acids in the brain of the cat and the rat greatly exceeding those in the plasma.[36-41] As pointed out by Waelsch,[42] the essential amino acids are, in general, not concentrated by the brain and are, therefore, present only at concentrations which are approximately equal to or less than those in plasma. Among the non-essential amino acids which are well concentrated are aspartic, glutamic and gamma aminobutyric acids (GABA). The question arises as to whether the high concentrations are due to the fact that, once formed in the brain, these amino acids cannot leave the brain, or whether they are transported into the brain and there concentrated.

In Vivo Experiments with Radioactive Amino Acids

(a) Glutamate

Some years ago, Schwerin, Bessman and Waelsch[43] and Kamin and Handler[44] showed that the glutamate concentration in brain cannot be increased either by intravenous injection of the amino acid or by radial vein infusion. Injection of glutamine, methionine, histidine, lysine or arginine, but not aspartate or glutamate, causes small increases in the brain concentrations of the respective amino acids.

However, more recent experiments by Lajtha, Berl and Waelsch[45] have shown that when glutamic acid, uniformly labelled with C^{14} is injected intravenously into a rat or a mouse, the glutamate present in brain becomes radioactive. Five minutes after injection, the total amount of radioactivity present in the plasma represents at most 7% of the injected dose, the remaining activity being mainly present in the organs such as liver, kidney and muscle. The total radioactivity in brain after 5 minutes is approximately 12% of that found in plasma at that time. The specific activity (cpm./μmole) of brain glutamate is less than 1% of that of the plasma glutamate but it must be borne in mind that the concentration of glutamate in brain is about 100 times that in plasma.[42]

The results indicate that plasma glutamate does at least enter the brain and that neither the blood-brain barrier nor the brain cell membrane is completely impermeable to glutamate. It has been pointed out by Lajtha *et al.*[45] that the uptake of radioactivity is probably due to an exchange process since there is no net uptake of glutamate even when the plasma concentration is raised 30- to 50-fold. In these experiments[45] only small quantities of glutamate were injected, and the quantities were insufficient to alter the plasma concentration.

Exchange of plasma glutamate with brain cell glutamate may occur by three separate means:

(1) Equal rates of passive diffusion into and out of the brain.

(2) An active transport into the brain balanced by an equal rate of diffusion out.

(3) A process of exchange-diffusion as defined by Ussing[46] and Heinz and Walsh[47] whereby a molecule of glutamate in the plasma may replace a molecule of glutamate, or other amino acid, in the brain as the result of the action of a transport or carrier system.

The results obtained by Lajtha *et al.*[45] do not allow any conclusions to be drawn as to the possible mechanism of the exchange. However, it seems rather unlikely that glutamate enters by simple diffusion since, as pointed out before, the radioactive glutamate appears in the brain minutes after the injection of the isotope and the glutamate concentration in the brain is apparently higher than that of the plasma. Either of the other two mechanisms could account for the exchange of plasma glutamate with brain glutamate.

(b) Lysine

One of the major difficulties in studying the concentration and specific activity of glutamate in brain is the continuous oxidation and resynthesis of this amino acid. Similar experiments with other amino acids, that are less readily metabolized and synthesized, would give a better indication of the ability of brain *in vivo* to take up amino acids. It has been shown by Kamin and Handler[44] that perfusion of anesthetized dogs with lysine causes an increase in brain lysine. The experiments of Lajtha, Furst, Gerstein and Waelsch,[48] using uniformly labelled lysine-C^{14}, have shown that, after intravenous injection of this amino acid, the specific activity of the plasma lysine drops quickly while that of the brain increases (Table I). Two minutes after the injection, the specific activity of the brain lysine attains a value which

TABLE I

SPECIFIC ACTIVITY OF FREE LYSINE IN PLASMA AND BRAIN OF THE MOUSE
AFTER ADMINISTRATION OF UNIFORMLY LABELLED LYSINE-C^{14}

Time after Administration (mins.)	Counts min./μg. Lysine	
	Plasma	Brain
2	2570	280
5	1200	420
10	870	430
20	280	360
30	170	250
45	120	240
60	76	250

The lysine content of mouse plasma is 63 μg./ml. and of mouse brain is 37 μg./gm. fresh tissue.
For details, see ref. 48.

is 70% of the maximum observed. Twenty minutes after the injection, the specific activity of brain lysine actually exceeds that of plasma lysine. Such an effect is not observed with glutamate.

These results do not indicate that the lysine concentration in the brain has increased, since the specific activities and not the lysine concentration have been measured. Moreover, insufficient lysine was given to alter the plasma concentration. The results do show that lysine penetrates the brain very quickly and that, once the amino acid is in the brain, it leaves very slowly. It would be tempting to speculate that two separate areas of the brain are involved in this phenomenon, one whose lysine content rapidly exchanges with the amino acid of the plasma and a second area which receives the amino acid, not from the plasma but from the area which becomes labelled rapidly. In this way, brain lysine with a specific activity higher than plasma lysine could be obtained. Such an interpretation would be consistent with the results obtained by Furst, Lajtha and Waelsch[49] which indicate that the free amino acids of the white matter become labelled to a smaller extent than all other parts of the brain. However, the specific activity of lysine in the white matter remains constant for the duration of the experiment (45 minutes) while that in the other parts of the brain drops considerably (30 to 40%) during the experimental period.

(c) Leucine

Lajtha[50] has shown that injection of leucine uniformly labelled with C^{14} into mice causes a very rapid rise in the specific activity of brain leucine. The rate of uptake is sufficiently rapid that within five minutes the specific activity of leucine in the brain is equal to that in the plasma. Such is not the case with either glutamate or lysine. Moreover, the specific activity of brain leucine exceeds that of liver by a factor of at least 2 for the duration of the experiment (2 hours). Lajtha[50] concluded that the free amino acids of the brain are not in a homogenous pool. Unfortunately, data for the uptake of leucine by different parts of the brain are not available for comparison with the data obtained with lysine.

(d) Alpha-Aminoisobutyric Acid

Recently Kuttner, Sims and Gordon[83] have shown that the unnatural amino acid, α-aminoisobutyric acid, is taken up by rat brain after intraperitoneal injection. The maximum concentration of this amino acid in the brain occurs twenty hours after injection. This is in marked contrast to the results obtained by Lajtha et al.[48] with lysine and Lajtha[50] with leucine which showed that these amino acids enter the brain rapidly. However, 20 hours after injection, the concentration of α-aminoisobutyric acid in the brain was twice that present in the plasma. The loss of α-aminoisobutyrate from the brain is also slow, since 40 hours after injection, the level in the brain was approximately two thirds of the level observed after 20 hours.

Uptake of Amino Acids in Relation to Lipid Solubility

The experiments described indicate that quantitatively the brain behaves differently towards leucine than towards glutamate and lysine. This difference in uptake of the different amino acids may be related to the lipid solubility of the amino acids. Dingman and Sporn,[51] using proline derivatives, have shown that N-acetylproline ethyl ester, the most lipid soluble of the derivatives tested, was taken up by rat brain *in vivo* more quickly than less lipid soluble derivatives, such as proline or N-acetylproline. Proline ethyl ester was also taken up rapidly, although at a lower rate than N-acetylproline ethyl ester. Comparative rates of uptake of proline and its derivatives and their lipid solubilities are given in Table II.

Chirigos, Greengard and Udenfriend,[52] however, have recently shown that lipid solubility plays little part in the uptake of tyrosine and tyrosine derivatives in the brain. For example, α-methyl DL-tyrosine is 50% more lipid soluble than tyrosine itself, yet ten times

TABLE II
LIPID SOLUBILITY AND MEAN RELATIVE PENETRATION RATIOS OF
PROLINE AND PROLINE DERIVATIVES

Compound	Lipid Solubility*	Mean $C_B/C_P \times 100$
Proline	0	1.9
N-acetylproline	9	2.1
Proline ethyl ester	15	70.1
N-acetylproline ethyl ester	50	78.3

*Percentage of compound extracted from aqueous phase by lipid solvents. Three lipid solvents were used:
(a) Highly purified peanut oil.
(b) Petroleum ether.
(c) Carbon tetrachloride.
C_B/C_P = ratio of increase in concentration in brain over the increase in concentration in plasma.
For details, see ref. 51.

more tyrosine than the α-methyl derivative appears in the brain 30 minutes after intraperitoneal injection. No attempt has been made by these authors[52] to determine whether the tyrosine derivatives are rapidly removed from the blood stream and excreted, a possibility which could significantly affect the interpretation of the results. It cannot, therefore, be stated with any certainty that lipid solubility plays a definite role in the uptake of amino acids by brain *in vivo*.

Elevation of Amino Acid Concentration in the Brain by Injection of Amino Acids and Their Derivatives

In contrast to the results obtained earlier[43,44,53] with other amino acids, the intraperitoneal injection of L-tyrosine results in an elevated concentration of this amino acid in the brain.[52] The elevated concentration may be five times greater than that found under normal circumstances. D-tyrosine is also taken up but to a lesser extent and at a lower rate than the natural enantiomorph. The uptake of L-tyrosine may be inhibited by a number of amino acids such as leucine, isoleucine, valine, histidine, cysteine, tryptophane and fluorophenylalanine.[52] The other amino acids examined do not affect the uptake of tyrosine (Table III). These results provide evidence that the uptake of amino acids by brain *in vivo* is the result of a specific mechanism rather than simple diffusion.

Dingman and Sporn[51] showed that it is possible to elevate the brain concentration of proline by intravenous injection of proline ethyl ester. This compound appears to be completely hydrolyzed to free

TABLE III

EFFECT OF OTHER AMINO ACIDS ON THE BRAIN TO PLASMA DISTRIBUTION OF TYROSINE

Amino Acid	Amount Administered (mmoles)	Brain: Plasma Ratio 60 Minutes after Administration of Tyrosine
Control	—	1.04
L tryptophane	0.81	0.31
L tryptophane	0.26	0.67
D tryptophane	0.81	0.71
p fluorophenyl DL alanine	0.81	0.31
L leucine	1.14	0.41
L isoleucine	1.14	0.39
L valine	0.78	0.47
L cysteine	0.81	0.65
L histidine	0.96	0.62
L alanine	1.69	0.87
L serine	1.42	1.22
L threonine	1.26	0.81
L arginine	0.86	1.49
L lysine	1.02	1.04
L glutamate	1.02	1.08
L glutamine	1.02	1.36

Amino acids were injected 5 minutes before administration of 0.55 mmoles L-tyrosine. For details, see ref. 52.

proline in the brain since the authors could obtain no evidence for the presence of the ester in brain. Injection of proline, N-acetylproline and N-acetylproline ethyl ester do not significantly alter the free proline content of the brain, but a significant concentration of N-acetylproline ethyl ester (78% of that in the plasma) appears in the brain.

Administration of proline intracisternally rather than intravenously also increases the proline concentration in the brain. Sporn, Dingman and Defalco[53] showed that 1 hour after intracisternal injection of uniformly labelled proline-C^{14}, 20% of the activity originally injected remains in the brain in an acid soluble form. One hour after intravenous injection, only 0.1% of the total dose of radioactivity is present in the brain in an acid soluble form.

Gaitonde and Richter[54] found that intracisternal or subarachnoid injection of methionine-S^{35} results in a four-fold increase in the extent of labelling of the proteins of the brain in one hour as compared with the labelling occurring after injection by the intravenous route. In four other tissues examined, the route of administration did not significantly change the degree of labelling. These authors concluded, as did Friedberg, Tarver and Greenberg[55] that the blood-brain barrier prevents the uptake of methionine by the brain.

Structural factors play an important role in determining the rate and extent of uptake of amino acids by the brain. In many cases, there is a significant exchange of brain and blood amino acids without a net increase in amino acid concentration in the brain.[48-50] However, the experiments of Chirigos *et al.*,[52] Dingman and Sporn,[51] and Sporn, Dingman and Defalco[53] show that with certain amino acids, or their derivatives, elevated amino acid concentrations can be obtained in the brain. These results are in agreement with the hypothesis that the brain *in vivo* is capable of removing amino acids from the surrounding medium.

Uptake of Amino Acids In Vitro

(a) Glutamate

The investigations described so far have dealt with the uptake of amino acid by whole brain *in vivo*. These results provide little information concerning the factors involved in the transport system, and the operation of the blood-brain barrier may give misleading results about the ability of the brain cells themselves to transport amino acids. In recent years, *in vitro* experiments with brain slice preparations have shown that brain cells are capable of concentrating amino acids and some information on the factors involved in amino acid transport has been obtained.

Stern, Eggleston, Hems and Krebs[25] first observed that brain cortex slices from guinea pigs can accumulate L-glutamate against a concentration gradient. When L-glutamate is added to the medium in which a brain slice is incubated, the L-glutamate concentration in the slice increases at the expense of the medium glutamate, in spite of the fact that initially the glutamate concentration in the brain is higher than that of the medium. Transfer of the amino acid ceases when the difference between external and internal concentration is about 20 mM, the difference being more or less independent of the external level. For example, raising the external L-glutamate concentration from 2.5 mM to approximately 10 mM does not change the difference between the cell concentration of glutamate and that of the medium which remains constant at approximately 20 mM. The transport of glutamate by guinea pig brain slices against a concentration gradient is largely dependent on the presence of glucose. In the absence of glucose, pyruvate and lactate cause some stimulation of glutamate uptake but the uptake is considerably less than that observed in the presence of glucose, although the oxygen uptake in presence of glucose, pyruvate or lactate is approximately the same (Table IV).

It is apparent that all the substrates which support active transport of glutamate are oxidizable. However, it is also obvious that oxidizability of the substrate is not sufficient to cause accumulation. Succinate, fumarate, glutamate and α-glycerophosphate do not cause an increase of the intracellular glutamate nor even maintain it at its original concentration.

Stern et al.[25] have shown that under anaerobic conditions the glutamate concentration in the brain is maintained but not increased in

TABLE IV

THE INCREASE IN THE LEVEL OF L-GLUTAMATE IN GUINEA PIG BRAIN CORTEX SLICES
DURING INCUBATION WITH VARIOUS SUBSTRATES

Experiment	Additions	Glutamate Increase (μmoles/gm. wet weight)
1	Glucose	29.8
	Fructose	13.7
	Pyruvate	11.5
	Lactate	12.5
2	Glucose	25.4
	Succinate	−3.3
	Fumarate	−2.6
	Citrate	−6.3

Glutamate added, 10 mM; other additions, 20 mM.
Guinea pig brain cortex slices were incubated for 40 minutes.
Data calculated from the figures quoted by Stern et al.[25]

the presence of glucose and glutamate in the medium. Furthermore, such agents as 2,4 dinitrophenol and iodoacetate prevent the accumulation of glutamate by the brain. The results indicate that brain tissue is capable of active transport of glutamate and that the energy for transport is derived from the oxidation of glucose, other oxidizable substances being considerably less effective. The reasons for this are still not known.

In a further study of the factors controlling the uptake of D- and L-glutamate by guinea pig brain slices. Takagaki, Hirano and Nagata[56] showed that after incubation for 1 hour, in presence of glucose and 10 mM L-glutamate, the concentration of free L-glutamate in brain is 40 μmoles/gm. wet weight of brain. Stern et al.,[25] using a different method of analysis, had obtained values in good agreement with this figure.

The results of Takagaki et al.[56] show further that D-glutamate is concentrated in the brain to an extent comparable with L-glutamate. These results, however, do not indicate to what extent D-glutamate had been converted to L-glutamate by the tissue, although Stern et al.[25] have shown this conversion to be rather small in brain tissue, the addition of 40 μmoles D-glutamate yielding 2 μmoles L-glutamate per 155 mg. slice in 40 minutes. It is obvious, therefore, that the concentration gradient obtained with D-glutamate cannot be due solely to the conversion of the D amino acid to the L form, and must be due largely to concentration of the D isomer by the brain. Takagaki et al.[56] showed that potassium ions are required to obtain high concentrations of D or L glutamate in the brain. Thus, in the complete absence of potassium ions in the medium, the concentrative uptake of both D and L glutamate drops by approximately 50%. A higher potassium ion concentration (70 mM K$^+$ decreases the D glutamate concentration in the brain by approximately 25%. Data for the effects of high potassium ion concentrations on L glutamate uptake are not given.[56]

The dependence of glutamate uptake on sodium ions is also very clearly shown by the experiments of Takagaki et al.[56] Thus, replacement of sodium chloride by choline chloride in a medium which contains 10 mM L-glutamate leads to a decrease in the uptake of L-glutamate from 43.5 μmoles/gm. wet tissue to 8 μmoles/gm. and of D-glutamate from 40.6 μmoles/gm. to 8 μmoles/gm. Since the glutamate concentration in the brain in the absence of added glutamate is quoted as 5 μmoles/gm., these results indicate a complete inhibition of glutamate transport in the absence of sodium ions. Sodium ions are apparently also required together with L-glutamate to obtain high levels of potassium ions in the brain.[29,30] No attempt has been made by Takagaki et al.[56] to assess the effects of choline chloride on glutamate transport by brain slices and the decreased uptake in absence of sodium ions may be due, in part, to an inhibition of transport by choline ions. Calcium ions influence the uptake of Both D and L glutamate. The absence of calcium ions results in an increased uptake of the two isomers of glutamate as well as an increased oxygen uptake in the presence of the amino acids.

The results obtained by Takagaki et al.[56] and by Stern et al.[25] do not agree with respect to the effects obtained with 2,4 dinitrophenol. In the former case, it is reported that 2,4 dinitrophenol (0.05 mM) has no effect on the accumulation of D-glutamate whereas, in the latter, L-glutamate uptake was completely suppressed by 2,4 dinitrophenol (1 mM). It seems likely that the differences observed by the two groups of workers is due to the differences between the concentrations of 2,4 dinitrophenol which were used. Although 0.05 mM

dinitrophenol is sufficient to cause an extensive inhibition of oxidative phosphorylation, experiments on transport phenomena with other tissues have suggested that transport reactions are less sensitive to the action of uncouplers and respiratory inhibitors than are other energy dependent reactions.[57] For example, with the Ehrlich ascites tumour cells, concentrations of 2,4 dinitrophenol, which completely inhibit the incorporation of glycine-1-C^{14} into the proteins of the tissue, have considerably less effect on the transport of glycine into the cells.[57] The same interpretation can account for the quantitative differences between the results of Stern et al.[25] and of Takagaki et al.[56] on the effects of other metabolic inhibitors (iodoacetate, azide) on glutamate uptake by brain slices.

The date given by Quastel[58,82] on the uptake of L-glutamate by rat brain slices are in good agreement with the data given by Stern et al.[25] and Takagaki et al.[56] with guinea pig slices. The brain concentrations of glutamate were calculated from the results given in the report by Quastel[58] and show that there is approximately five times more glutamate-1-C^{14} (or radioactivity from glutamate-1-C^{14}) present in the slices than in the medium if corrections are applied from the data

TABLE V

EFFECT OF LEAD TETRAETHYL ON UPTAKE OF GLUTAMATE-1-C^{14} AND GLYCINE-1-C^{14} BY RAT BRAIN CORTEX SLICES

Additions	Slice/Medium Ratio of Radioactive Amino Acid after 60 Minutes Incubation	Q_{O_2}
Glutamate-1-C^{14}	4.6	10.6
Glutamate-1-C^{14} + lead tetraethyl 0.03 mM	1.3	9.3
Glycine-1-C^{14}	11.4	—
Glycine-1-C^{14} + lead tetraethyl 0.03 mM	2.7	—

Figures quoted are calculated from the data given by Quastel.[58]

given for the amount of glutamate oxidized. With glycine-1-C^{14} [58] similar calculations show that the uptake is such that the glycine concentration in the brain slice is ten to twelve times that of the medium (Table V). The work of Vardanis and Quastel[58,82] has also shown that lead tetraethyl and, to a smaller extent, tin tetraethyl have a pronounced effect on the uptake of glutamate and glycine (Table V) without affecting the respiratory activity. Although the formation of $C^{14}O_2$ from glutamate is decreased by the presence of both tetraethyl derivatives, the decrease in CO_2 production is considerably less than the decrease in uptake of glutamate. The formation of $C^{14}O_2$ from glucose, however, is not affected. It would appear, therefore, that the decreased $C^{14}O_2$ production from glutamate in presence of the tetra-ethyl compounds is the result of a decreased glutamate concentration in the cell and not of a direct effect on the oxidations. Lead tetraethyl also has a pronounced effect on the uptake of glycine-1-C^{14}, a concentration of 0.03 mM leading to approximately 75% inhibition of the glycine uptake by brain slices from a medium containing 2 mM glycine. The results suggest that these organo metallic compounds interfere with the transport of amino acids. It is, of course, possible that tin tetraethyl and lead tetraethyl may act as uncoupling agents. Aldridge and Cremer[59] have shown that tin triethyl can uncouple oxidation from phosphorylation in mitochondrial preparations. Cremer,[60] however, has shown that tin tetraethyl is not converted to the triethyl derivatives *in vitro* by brain preparations and that tin tetra-ethyl has no effect on the respiratory activity when added *in vitro*. It is possible that the triethyl and tetraethyl derivatives have different inhibitory effects, the tetraethyl compound affecting the transport mechanism, and the triethyl compounds affecting the respiratory and phosphorylating mechanisms. Since there is a relationship between glutamate transport and ion transport in brain tissue (Stern *et al.*;[25] Terner *et al.*;[29,30] and Takagaki *et al.*[56]) it would be of interest to compare the effects of lead tetraethyl and tin tetraethyl on amino acid transport with their effects on ion transport. Unfortunately, such data are not yet available.

Glutamine is also readily taken up by brain slices *in vitro*.[25] Although the initial rate of uptake of glutamine is greater than that of glutamate, the sum of glutamate and glutamine in the brain slice is the same with both amino acids, after 30 minutes incubation.

(b) γ-Aminobutyric Acid

GABA, like glutamate, is present in the brain at concentrations which are considerably greater than those found in the plasma.[42] The results obtained by Elliott and Van Gelder[61] show that after aerobic incubation of 2 mM GABA with rat brain slices for 60 minutes, in a medium containing glucose, the tissue contains GABA at ten times the concentration at which it is present in the medium. Similarly, with 5 mM GABA initially present in the medium, the tissue concentration is about five times that of the medium. Concentration differences of the same order were obtained by Tsukada *et al.*[62] (Table VI) These data are in excellent agreement, particularly since the two methods used for estimating GABA are quite different, one being a biological assay[61] and the other a chemical assay.[62] The results of Tsukada *et al.*[62] and Elliott and Van Gelder[61] show that glucose is required under aerobic conditions to obtain high concentrations of GABA in brain

TABLE VI

EFFECTS OF GLUCOSE ON THE UPTAKE OF GABA BY RAT BRAIN CORTEX SLICES

Experiment	Additions	Slice/Medium Ratio of GABA
1	2 mM GABA 2 mM GABA + glucose 5 mM GABA + glucose	4.0 11.0 5.4
2	5 mM GABA 5 mM GABA + glucose	2.3 3.6

Data quoted for Experiment 1 compiled from Elliott and Van Gelder,[51] and for Experiment 2 from Tsukada et al.[62]

cells. Anaerobiosis[61] or the addition of 2,4 dinitrophenol[62] results in a marked diminution of uptake of GABA by the slice; in fact, under anaerobic conditions, in absence of added GABA, the concentration of GABA in the slice decreases.

Elliott and Van Gelder,[61,63] on the basis of their biological estimations of GABA, have concluded that at least 60% of the GABA in the brain is bound by the tissue. Moreover, they have suggested that intact cells are required for the binding since homogenates are unable to bind GABA. The results obtained by Bell,[19] however, show that brain homogenates are capable of binding certain drugs and that this simple binding is independent of respiration or of the integrity of the brain cells. If binding does occur, and if, as suggested,[61,63] the 60% binding is a minimum value, the high concentration ratio between cell and medium is the result of an energy dependent binding process and not an active transport process. Little is known about the nature of this binding except that the GABA can be released under very mild conditions.[63]

Tsukada et al.[62] concluded on the basis of their findings that GABA is actively transported by brain in vitro. The uptake of GABA is stimulated in Ca++ free media, which is in agreement with the results obtained by Takagaki et al.[56] on glutamate uptake in brain slices. Pyridoxal, which stimulates amino acid uptake in Ehrlich ascites cells,[64] also stimulates the uptake of GABA by brain slices. These data are consistent with an active transport of GABA rather than an energy dependent binding process. Tsukada et al.[62] have also tried to correlate the transport of GABA with the incorporation of P[32] into phospholipid components of the cytoplasmic particles of brain. The results obtained appear to indicate that conditions which stimulate transport also increase the specific activity of the phospholipids, especially phosphatidic acid and phosphatidyl choline. However, it is uncertain from the data of Tsukada *et al.*[62] whether the stimulations of P[32] incorporation are dependent on the presence of GABA, or whether conditions that stimulate uptake of GABA independently stimulate P[32] incorporation. It would therefore be premature to conclude that phospholipid components are involved in the transport of GABA or other amino acids by brain slices.

(c) Other Amino Acids

Since, in the past ten years, the uptake of only a limited number of amino acids by brain slices *in vitro* has been examined, it is conceivable that a large number of amino acids and other substances may be taken up by the brain by energy dependent processes and may be concentrated in the brain cells. For example, it has been shown[42] that threonine is present in the brain at a concentration considerably greater than that in the plasma. Since threonine is not known to be synthesized in the animal body, it is probable that this amino acid is actively transported and concentrated by the brain.

Recent work by Schanberg and Giarman[65] has shown that when 5 hydroxy tryptophane-1-C[14] is incubated with rat brain slices, the amino acid appears in the brain at a concentration which is several times that of the medium, e.g., when the extracellular concentration is approximately 2 mM, the slice/medium ratio is four. The results show that the uptake of 5, hydroxy-tryptophane is dependent on phosphorylation since the presence of 2,4 dinitrophenol reduces the uptake considerably. It should be pointed out that at the concentration of 2,4 dinitrophenol used (0.1 mM) the uptake is not completely abolished. At 0°C little 5, hydroxytryptophane is taken up.

Brain, *in vivo,* contains relatively high concentrations of serotonin.[66] This substance, however, is not taken up from the medium by rat brain slices.[65]

The results presented by Schanberg and Giarman,[65] therefore, suggest that the brain may obtain its serotonin by the following mechanism: tryptophane is converted to 5, hydroxy-tryptophane by the extra-cerebral organs,[67] 5, hydroxy-tryptophane is transported to, and concentrated by, the brain, and some of the 5, hydroxy-tryptophane is converted in the brain to serotonin which is then retained by the tissue.

It must be borne in mind that measurement of the extent of concentration of 5, hydroxy-tryptophane by the brain may not be entirely accurate. Only the appearance of radioisotope in the slice was measured and no attempt was made to determine the extent of conversion of 5, hydroxy-tryptophane to other compounds. However, it is unlikely that any of the activity measured was due to serotonin in the brain, since the serotonin formed from 5, hydroxy-tryptophane-1-C^{14} would not be radioactive.

Neame[84,85] has recently shown that a number of amino acids, including proline, histidine, arginine, ornithine and tyrosine, are transported by mouse and rat brain slices and in the case of histidine the level attained in the mouse brain slice after 90 minutes incubation may reach twelve times that of the medium. Phenylalanine caused appreciable inhibition of the uptake by rat brain slices of a number of amino acids, particularly tyrosine.

Scholefield and Abadom[86] have shown that the uptake of glycine-1-C^{14} by rat brain cortex slices is proportional to the adenosine triphosphate level in the brain slice.

MISCELLANEOUS

The penetration of brain slices by urea, which is commonly used to measure body fluids, has been studied by Coxon.[68] The results obtained confirmed the *in vivo* observation that the steady state level in the brain-water is the same as that of the surrounding medium. Preliminary experiments discussed by Coxon in the same article[68] suggest that the same conclusion is to be made when pyruvate distribution is considered provided due allowance is made for the rapid intracellular metabolism of pyruvate. On the other hand it appears[69] that citrate and isocitrate enter pigeon-brain slices only with some difficulty. Lactate transfer from the blood to the brain is claimed to be too slow to influence the level of lactate in the brain significantly. The latter is found to bear no relation to the amount in the blood despite great changes in the blood level produced by such methods as injection of lactate or of adrenaline, by exercise, fasting, glucose administration, pancreatectomy or adrenal inactivation.[70-76]

Geiger, Magnes, Taylor and Veralli[77] have shown that the liver may play a role in maintaining normal cerebral metabolism and functions. These workers also showed that the presence of the liver is unnecessary when cytidine and uridine are added to the perfusion medium. Presumably, therefore, the nucleosides are able to penetrate the brain under the perfusion conditions employed. The dinucleotide, cozymase, is readily lost from guinea pig brain cortex slices on incubation under anaerobic conditions.[11] Incubation under aerobic conditions retards this loss, suggesting that a mechanism may exist for the retention of the coenzyme.

As a result of studies on the mechanism of production of respiratory paralysis by certain hemicholiniums, MacIntosh, Birks and Sastry[78] have made the interesting suggestion that these compounds may act by competing with choline for transport into the neurone.

Finally, it is well to recall that injection of thiamin to pigeons suffering from a B_1-avitaminosis leads to a prompt increase in the ability of the pigeon-brain homogenate to oxidise pyruvate.[79] It is also of interest to recall that thiamin is more active in brain brei than is the pyrophosphate[80] despite the demonstration by Lohmann and Schuster[81] that the active principle, cocarboxylase, is thiamin pyrophosphate. Presumably the vitamin is able to penetrate into the brain cells whereas the pyrophosphate form is unable to do so.

REFERENCES

1. KETY, S. S. and SCHMIDT, C. F.: *J. Clin. Invest., 27:*476 (1948).
2. LAMBERTSEN, C. J., KOUGH, R. H., COOPER, D. Y., EMMEL, G. L., LOESCHKE, H. H. and SCHMIDT, C. F.: *J. Appl. Physiol., 5:*471 (1953).
3. DUNCUM, B. M.: *The Development of Inhalation Anesthesia.* London, Oxford Univ. Press (1947).
4. KETY, S. S., WOODFORD, R. B., HARMEL, M. H., FREYHAN, F. A., APPEL, K. E. and SCHMIDT, C. F.: *Am. J. Psychiat., 104:*765 (1948).
5. HIMWICH, H. E., BOWMAN, K. M., DALY, C., FAZEKAS, J. F., WORTIS, J. and GOLDFARB, W.: *Am. J. Physiol., 132:*640 (1941).
6. KETY, S. S., LUKENS, F. D. W., WOODFORD, R. B., HARMEL, M. H., FREYHAN, F. A. and SCHMIDT, C. F.: *Federation Proc., 7:*64 (1948).
7. McILWAIN, H.: *Biochemistry and the Central Nervous System,* p. 50. London, Churchill (1959).
8. KETY, S. S.: In *Metabolism of the Nervous System,* p. 221. D. Richter, Ed. New York, Pergamon Press (1957).
9. PARMAR, S. S.: Ph.D. Thesis, McGill University, Montreal (1955).
10. PARMAR, S. S. and QUASTEL, J. H.: See QUASTEL, J. H. *Proc. Intern. Symp. Eng. Chem.* p. 510, Tokyo (1957).
11. McILWAIN, H., THOMAS, J. and BELL, J. L.: *Biochem. J., 64:*332 (1956).
12. OVERTON, E.: *Studien über Narkose.* Jena (1901).
13. MEYER, H. H.: *Arch. exper. Path. u. Pharmakol., 42:*109 (1899).
14. EHRLICH, P.: *Das Sauerstoffbedürfnis des Organismus. Eine farbenanalytische Studie.* Berlin (1885).
15. LEWANDOWSKY, M.: *Ztschr. Klin. Med., 40:*480 (1900).
16. NICLOUX, M. and YOVANOVITCH, A.: *Compt. rend. Soc. biol., 93:*272 (1925).
17. McCOLLUM, J. L.: *J. Pharmacol. & Exper. Therap., 40:*305 (1930).
18. MAYER, S., MARKEL, R. P. and BRODIE, B. B.: *J. Pharmacol. & Exper. Therap., 127:*205 (1959).
19. BELL, J. L.: *J. Neurochem., 2:*265 (1958).
20. QUASTEL, J. H. and WHEATLEY, A. H. M.: *Biochem. J., 28:*1521 (1934).
21. BERING, E. A.: *J. Neurosurg., 9:*275 (1952).
22. SWEET, W. H., SELVERSTONE, B., SOLOWAY, S. and STETTEN, D.: *Surgical Forum, American College of Surgeons,* p. 376. Philadelphia, Saunders (1951).
23. HOLMES, J. H. and TOWER, D. B.: *Neurochemistry,* p. 276. Springfield, Ill., Thomas (1955).
24. ELLIOTT, K. A. C.: *Proc. Soc. Exper. Biol. & Med., 63:*234 (1946).

25. STERN, J. R., EGGLESTON, L. V., HEMS, R. and KREBS, H. A.: *Biochem. J.*, *44*:410 (1949).
26. ALLEN, J. N.: *Arch. Neurol. & Psychiat.*, 73:241 (1955).
27. PAPPIUS, H. M. and ELLIOTT, K. A. C.: *Canad. J. Biochem. Physiol.*, *34*:1007 (1956).
28. SCHULTZ, R. L., MAYNARD, E. and PEASE, D. C.: *Am. J. Anat.* 100:369 (1957).
29. TERNER, C., EGGLESTON, L. V. and KREBS, H. A.: *Biochem. J.*, *47*:139 (1950).
30. KREBS, H. A., EGGLESTON, L. V. and TERNER, C.: *Biochem. J.*, *48*:530 (1951).
31. USSING, H. H. and ZERAHN, K.: *Acta physiol. scandinav.*, 23:110 (1951).
32. HOGBEN, C. A. M.: *Am. J. Physiol.*, 180:641 (1955).
33. THOMAS, J.: *Biochem. J.*, 64:335 (1956).
34. ALLINSON, M. J. C.: *J. Biol. Chem.*, 157:169 (1953).
35. VAN SLYKE, D. D. and MEYER, G. M.: *J. Biol. Chem.*, 16:197 (1913).
36. TALLAN, H. H., MOORE, S. and STEIN, W. H.: *J. Biol. Chem.*, 211:927, (1954).
37. SCHURR, P. E., THOMPSON, H. T., HENDERSON, L.M., WILLIAMS, J. H., JR. and ELVEHJEM, C. A.: *J. Biol. Chem.*, 182:39 (1950).
38. ANSELL, G. B. and RICHTER, D.: *Biochem. J.*, 57:70 (1954).
39. SILBER, R. H.: *J. Cell. & Comp. Physiol.*, 18:21 (1941).
40. LEWIS, P. R.: *Biochem. J.*, 52:330 (1952).
41. KOECHLIN, B. A.: *J. Biophys. Biochem. Cytol.*, 1:511 (1956).
42. WAELSCH, H.: *Advances Protein Chem.*, 6:301 (1951).
43. SCHWERIN, P., BESSMAN, S. P. and WAELSCH, H.: *J. Biol. Chem.*, 187:37 (1950).
44. KAMIN, H. and HANDLER, P.: *J. Biol. Chem.*, 188:193 (1951).
45. LAJTHA, A., BERL, S. and WAELSCH, H.: *J. Neurochem.*, 3:322 (1959).
46. USSING, H. H.: *Advances Enzymol.*, 13:21 (1952).
47. HEINZ, E. and WALSH, P. M.: *J. Biol. Chem.*, 233:1488 (1960).
48. LAJTHA, A., FURST, S., GERSTEIN, A. and WAELSCH, H.: *J. Neurochem.*, *1*:289 (1957).
49. FURST, S., LAJTHA, A. and WAELSCH, H.: *J. Neurochem.*, 2:216 (1958).
50. LAJTHA, A.: *J. Neurochem.*, 3:358 (1959).
51. DINGMAN, W. and SPORN, M. B.: *J. Neurochem.*, 4:148 (1959).
52. CHIRIGOS, P., GREENGARD, P. and UDENFRIEND, S.: *J. Biol. Chem.*, 235:2075 (1960).
53. SPORN, M. B., DINGMAN, W. and DEFALCO, A.: *J. Neurochem.*, 4:141 (1959).
54. GAITONDE, M. K. and RICHTER, D.: *Proc. Roy. Soc., London*, Series B *145*:83 (1956).
55. FREIDBERG, F., TARVER, H. and GREENBERG, D. M.: *J. Biol. Chem.*, 173:355 (1948).
56. TAKAGAKI, G., HIRANO, S. and NAGATA, Y.: *J. Neurochem.*, 4:124 (1959).
57. JOHNSTONE, R. M. and SCHOLEFIELD, P. G.: *Cancer Res.*, 19:1149 (1959).
58. QUASTEL, J. H.: *IVth International Congress of Biochemistry*, Vol. III, Biochemistry of the Central Nervous System. Vienna, Sept., 1958.
59. ALDRIDGE, W. H. and CREMER, J. E.: *Biochem. J.*, 61:406 (1955).
60. CREMER, J. E.: *Biochem. J.*, 68:685 (1958).
61. ELLIOTT, K. A. C. and VAN GELDER, N. N.: *J. Neurochem.*, 3:28 (1958).
62. TSUKADA, Y., NAGATA, Y. and HIRANO, S.: *Nature*, 186:474 (1960).
63. ELLIOTT, K. A. C. and VAN GELDER, N. N.: *J. Physiol.*, 153:423 (1960).
64. CHRISTENSEN, H. N., RIGGS, T. R. and COYNE, B. A.: *J. Biol. Chem.*, 209:413 (1954).
65. SHANBERG, S. and GIARMAN, N. J.: *Biochim. et Biophys. Acta*, 41:556 (1960).
66. ERSPAMER, V.: *Rend. Sc. Farmitalia*, 1:1 (1954).
67. DALGLIESH, C. E.: *Advances Clin. Chem.*, 5:1 (1958).

68. Coxon, R. V.: *Metabolism of the Nervous System*, p. 153. London, Pergamon Press (1957).
69. Coxon, R. V.: *Bull. Soc. chim. belg.*, *65*:68 (1956).
70. Gurdjian, E. S., Stone, W. E. and Webster, J. E.: *Arch. Neurol. & Psychiat.*, *51*:472 (1944).
71. Stone, W. E., Webster, J. E. and Gurdjian, E. S.: *A. Nerv. & Ment. Dis., Proc.* *24*:226 (1945).
72. Klein, J. R. and Olsen, N. S.: *J. Biol. Chem.*, *167*:1 (1947).
73. Kerr, S. E. and Ghantus, M.: *J. Biol. Chem.*, *116*:9 (1936).
74. Kerr, S. E., Hampel, C. W. and Ghantus, M.: *J. Biol. Chem.*, *119*:405 (1937).
75. Richter, D. and Dawson, R. M. C.: *Am. J. Physiol.*, *154*:73 (1948).
76. Stone, W. E.: *Biochem. J.*, *32*:1908 (1938).
77. Geiger, A., Magnes, J., Taylor, R. M. and Veralli, M.: *Am. J. Physiol.*, *177*:138 (1954).
78. MacIntosh, F. C., Birks, R. I. and Sastry, P. B.: *Nature*, London, *178*:1181 (1956).
79. Meiklejohn, A. P., Passmore, R. and Peters, R. A.: *Proc. Roy. Soc. London*, Series B, *111*:391 (1932).
80. Peters, R. A.: *Biochem. J.*, *31*:2240 (1938).
81. Lohmann, K. and Schuster, P.: *Biochem. Ztschr.*, *294*:188 (1937).
82. Vardanis, A. and Quastel, J. H.: *Canad. J. Biochem. Physiol.*, *39*:1811 (1961).
83. Kuttner, R., Sims, J. A. and Gordon, M. W.: *J. Neurochem.* *6*:311 (1961).
84. Neame, K. D.: *J. Neurochem.*, *6*:358 (1961).
85. Neame, K. D.: *Nature, London*, *192*:173 (1961).
86. Scholefield, P. G. and Abadom, P. N.: *Proc. Can. Fed. Biol. Soc.*, *4*:56 (1961).

XVIII

THE "BRAIN BARRIER SYSTEM"

Abel Lajtha

THE RESTRICTION of the penetration of substances into the brain was first recognized about 75 years ago.[55,114] A great number of observations have been made in the intervening years covering many aspects of this problem, but the mechanism of passage of substances into and out of the brain and the factors controlling passage still have to be clarified.

Organ and cellular permeability are general problems in biochemistry and pharmacology. Barriers and transport processes are not unique for the brain, but are present in other organs as well. Some analogous properties of retina and brain[134] and of cerebrospinal fluid (CSF) and aqueous humor,[44] for instance, have been described. It is likely that at least some, and possibly most, of the factors responsible for the permeability behavior of the brain are operative to some extent in other organs as well. It has yet to be decided if the difference between the brain and the rest of the organism is only a quantitative one, or if processes active in the brain are particular to this organ alone.

The term blood-brain barrier, implying a permeability barrier between the circulating blood and the brain, is not a fortunate choice mainly because the term is poorly defined and is used in the literature to cover different concepts. As we know more about the many factors in the complex system governing the passage and the level of substances in the brain, terms that are more precise and better understood will be used to describe individual components of the system. If after intravenous administration of a substance, in one case brain content is measured five minutes later and, in another case, CSF levels are measured after several hours, the two sets of data will not necessarily measure the same aspect of blood-brain barrier. Similarly, the staining of the brain by systemically administered trypan blue does not measure the same blood-brain barrier as that found by the determination of exchange rates of sodium between blood and brain,[34] since

399

K and Na, unlike dyes, play a part in transmission. The need exists for clear distinctions to be made in experimental procedures measuring: (a) the time to reach final equilibrium, (b) the initial rate of passage, or (c) the final equilibrium distribution ratios, since these three parameters are likely to be governed by different factors. For a meaningful comparison of the work of one experimenter with that of another, well defined data are necessary, expressed in units of uptake, exchange, and transport if possible. Concentration ratios between blood and brain, for example, are not too well defined, since the value of these ratios in many instances is dependent on absolute blood levels. It also has to be realized that, since there are basic differences between the entry of various substances into the brain, influencing the entry of one substance is not necessarily followed by an altered blood-brain barrier for other substances.

For these reasons the term "brain barrier system" will be used in the present discussion to cover all the factors that determine or play a role in the passage of substances in and out of the brain; it denotes a complex system rather than one real barrier. In this system all factors are not necessarily interconnected.

Although the role of the "brain barrier system" in brain function is not clear, it is obvious that it is very important in influencing the composition of and the availability of substrates, thereby indirectly influencing the metabolism of this organ. "Brain barrier system" has been described in all animals investigated, for example, sharks,[156] fresh water teleosts,[117] fishes, reptiles, and birds,[9] but only dyes were used in these experiments. The phylogenetic development of the "brain barrier system" in terms of exchange rates and the mechanisms and extent of active transport processes with other test substances are presently being investigated in this laboratory.

It is impossible to cover a subject so complex and widely investigated within a brief space; the discussion, therefore, will be limited to only some of the aspects of the whole problem and the reader is referred to the many reviews on the subject discussing aspects such as: determining factors,[64] pathological aspects,[33] structural aspects,[30] dynamic aspects,[11] CSF,[71,159] capillary permeability,[135] local differences,[101] (for more general reviews see refs. 51, 96, 170, 170A). References were chosen to illustrate a point rather than to try to cover the existing literature comprehensively.

LOCALIZATION OF THE BARRIER SYSTEM

It becomes increasingly clear that the permeability properties of the brain cannot be defined as the properties of a single membrane or a definite anatomical structure. Certain substances are stopped beyond the outer wall of the capillary endothelium at the glial plasma membrane,[49,120,170] some at the endothelial linings as well as at neuroglial cell membranes;[28] however, the great differences in behavior between various substances show conclusively the decisive importance of a number of factors rather than one single property such as the lack of extracellular space[53] or presence of ground substance.[81] As will be shown later, some substances enter the brain directly from the blood while others enter mainly through the CSF, and so barriers between the blood and the CSF[46,85] as well as between CSF and brain[80,172] have to be considered. Intravenous administration and subsequent detection in the brain does not exclude the possibility of the entry of the test substance through the CSF or the influence of the so called CSF–brain barrier. It is likely that the permeability properties of the

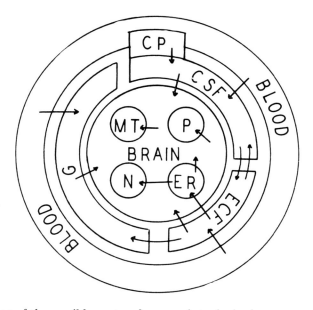

Fig. 1. Some of the possible routes of passage into the brain.

Brain = Intracellular space of brain including neuronal and glial elements.
CP   = Choroid plexuses.
CSF = Cerebrospinal fluid.
ECF = Extracellular fluid.
G   = Glia.
ER   = Endoplasmic reticulum.
MT   = Mitochondria.
N   = Nuclei.
P   = Other particulate elements (e.g., lysosomes).

membranes surrounding the cells and of the particulates within the cells such as nuclear and mitochondrial membranes influence the uptake and distribution of substances in the brain. Important and not necessarily indirect influences are metabolic rates, blood flow, intracellular binding, and many more. While all the above membranes have some similar characteristics, it is likely that many differences exist between them. At present there is no experimental evidence describing the behavior of these membranes in the living organ. Some of the above factors cannot be considered independently since the passage of a substance is concurrently influenced by several of them, although one element of the system may be of decisive influence with a particular substance.

These facts make it unlikely that the "brain barrier system" will be localized in the future as being a single histological entity or a single biochemical mechanism. Figure 1 is a representation of the barriers that may exist in the brain, the arrows showing some of the possible routes of passage into the brain. Some of the arrows may denote active, some passive penetration.

REGIONAL DIFFERENCES

In an organ which is morphologically as heterogeneous as the brain, heterogeneity in distribution of substances is expected as well. Since the penetration of substances is governed by several factors rather than one, variations in their relative influence from one brain area to another may result in differences in the "brain barrier system" in these areas.

After their administration some substances, among them codeine, methadone,[126] aminopyrine, and N-acetylaminoantipyrine,[121] were equally distributed throughout the brain; others like morphine,[126] chlorpromazine,[181] acetazol amide,[148] and adrenaline[183] were localized in particular areas to a greater extent. Differences can be shown in accumulation rates as well as in the final degree of distribution. Phenobarbital initially penetrates grey matter more than white in adults, myelin perhaps offering the hindrance;[52] in longer experiments the distribution is uniform.[124] In newborn, initially it is the reverse and white contains more phenobarbital.[52] Na^{24} distribution was uniform in embryonic but inhomogeneous in adult brains.[13] Unequal distribution of ions has also been observed with Na,[39,42] Br,[27,180] Fe and I^{187} and K.[39]

Although differences have been found in the penetration rates to anatomical or histological areas, very few, if any, substances are restricted to a single area. Some areas of the brain that showed increased permeability with several test substances (trypan blue, silver nitrate, P^{32}, Br^{82}) include the pineal gland, hypophysis, area postrema, choroid plexuses, and tuber cinereum; in the quantitative sense, these areas are beyond the "brain barrier system."

In our laboratory differences were found in the exchange rates and also in the degree of net uptake of amino acids from one brain part to another.[101,107] When the appearance of the label from intravenously administered tracer doses of C^{14}-amino acid in the brain was measured (exchange), the rate of exchange was found to be influenced by the level of amino acid in the brain (Table I).

TABLE I

THE DEPENDENCE OF EXCHANGE RATE ON THE LEVEL OF AMINO ACID IN THE BRAIN[107]

	Relative Exchange Rate (control = 100)
Leucine exchange at control levels	100
when brain lysine is elevated	100
when brain leucine is elevated	130
Lysine exchange at control levels	100
when brain lysine is elevated	150
when brain leucine is elevated	130

Exchange was measured as the appearance of label in the brain 5 minutes after intravenous administration to rats of C^{14} leucine or C^{14} lysine.

The variations occurring under physiological circumstances in amino acid levels from one brain area to another can be expected to result in differences in exchange rates. Somewhat unequal endogenous levels in brain areas have been found in glutamic acid and its derivatives,[24] lysine,[66,174] tryptophan,[139] and others.[130]

When the exchange and distribution of lysine were measured (Table II),[107] endogenous lysine distribution showed some inhomogeneity (column 1) and similar distribution was shown by the exchange estimated by the appearance of label in the brain after intravenous injection of tracer doses of C^{14}-L-lysine (column 2). It is of interest that after subarachnoid administration of L- or D-lysine, brain lysine levels are elevated, but the relative distribution shows inhomogeneity similar to that of the amino acid at physiological levels; also, exchange rates at elevated cerebral lysine levels show inhomogeneity similar to the rates at control levels. Repeating these experiments with leucine it was found that the distribution of leucine in the brain parts is more homogeneous than that of lysine and that no significant differences of exchange rates could be shown between these parts of the rat brain.

TABLE II

HETEROGENEITY OF LYSINE LEVELS AND LYSINE EXCHANGE RATES IN VARIOUS BRAIN
PARTS[101]

Brain Area	Distribution*	Exchange†
Cerebellum—Pons—Medulla	150	140
Posterior half of cerebrum	98	99
Anterior half of cerebrum	73	79

*Distribution: μg lysine/g tissue, whole brain = 100 in control animals.
†Exchange: counts/min./g tissue, whole brain = 100, determined 5 minutes after intravenous C^{14} lysine injection to rats.

Both net uptake and rate of exchange (and probably other elements of the brain barrier system) thus can vary from one brain area to another and the pattern can vary with the substance used for measurement.

The reasons for this inhomogeneity are manifold. In addition to local variations in membranes, active transport, vascularization, and binding, the superimposition of rates of entry from blood on that from CSF may play a role. It is to be expected, for example, that a substance entering the brain mainly from the CSF shows a higher initial inhomogeneity of distribution than a substance entering mainly from the circulating blood. The superimposition of varying routes of passage of metabolites to the various brain areas has to be kept in mind when changes and influences of the "brain barrier system" are investigated. The existence of compartments in the brain must play a further important role. It was found in our laboratory[25,105,177,177A] that glutamic acid administered into the CSF was in rapid equilibrium with a small portion (2% or less) of the total brain glutamic acid, and this small pool was more active metabolically than the larger glutamic acid pool. One of the possibilities is that the endoplasmic reticulum is in a more rapid equilibrium with the outside of the cell. Cellular compartmentation thus might contribute to the heterogeneity of the "brain barrier system" which extends into cell parts.

ROUTE OF ENTRY

The barrier system is often divided into the blood-brain and spinal fluid-brain barriers. At present these two barriers cannot be always definitely separated but should be considered as members of the supply system of the brain acting interdependently in the living organism.

Blood to Brain.—No histological difference has been established between the cerebral capillaries and those of other organs[30] and there is no reason to believe that the main supply route of metabolites for the brain is not the blood. Capillary permeabilities in units of flow rate per driving force across units of capillary areas have been measured in very few instances[135] and no such well-defined comparisons have been made between the brain and other organs; therefore, the role of capillary permeability in the regulation of cerebral metabolism is yet to be established.

Indirect evidence (uniform distribution in brain after intravenous administration) points to the entrance of drugs or other foreign substances from the blood directly into brain without passage through the CSF. While drug entry to brain is largely governed by the lipid solubility (see section on properties of substances), entry of such drugs from CSF to brain is not limited by lipid solubility.[121,122] The initial concentration of substances after their intravenous administration is usually higher in brain extracellular fluid than in the CSF, the difference usually being greater, the more lipid-soluble the substance. This is also evidence that they diffuse from the brain to the CSF rather than in the reverse direction (ref. 46, p. 121).

Glucose taken up from the blood is normally sufficient for function of the brain; subarachnoidally administered glucose does not restore changes due to lowered blood glucose levels.[2] Apparently bromide and iodide enter the brain from the blood rather than the CSF.[27,179,180] Triiodothyronine (T_3) enters the brain from blood but not when administered through the CSF. The flow of T_3 is plasma $\longrightarrow$ brain $\longrightarrow$ CSF $\longrightarrow$ plasma because of the unidirectional passage between brain and CSF.[62] The compound can enter the CSF either from the brain or from the plasma and leaves the CSF through the plasma. The major part of the T_3 leaves the brain through the CSF, not through the plasma.

Since most substances are impeded in penetration of brain and few (such as some gases perhaps) are limited by blood flow only, the local blood flow is not of great influence. Relative vascularity does not determine the local exchange of P^{32} (10) or the distribution of C^{14} isoniazide.[16]

Brain to CSF.—Ions enter the CSF by secretion rather than diffusion.[72,153,159,166] Ion exchange in the CSF occurs throughout the brain as well as through the choroid plexuses since choroid plexotomy affects the exchange of Na,[24] K,[42] D_2O and I^{131} albumin only to a small extent.[22,23] For bromide the choroid plexus is not the main route to the CSF, as the lumbar fluid contains more initially than does fluid from the lateral ventricle.[86,161] Some of these observations, especially the experiments with T_3, raise the possibility that some compounds leave the brain through the CSF. The formation of the CSF has been presented in detail elsewhere[46,47,159] and will not be discussed here.

CSF to Brain.—The reason for considering the CSF beyond the blood-brain barrier is that the increase of cerebral levels is greater after intraspinal than intravenous administration of similar doses of a substance. For proper comparisons, however, it has to be realized that administered substances leave the plasma rapidly (through liver or kidney) while the local concentrations after intraspinal administration can remain high in a part of the CSF; also, plasma volumes are much greater than CSF volumes. If identical levels in the two fluids are compared, the available surface for passage has to be considered as well. For P^{32} to produce identical levels in CSF and plasma, about 1/300 had to be administered intraspinally.[159]

The entrance of P^{32} into the brain was studied in detail (for the limitations of P^{32} as a tracer see section on ions). The levels of P^{32} in the brain are higher after intracisternal than after intravenous administration, the rates of entry being higher from the CSF than from blood even after corrections for volume and concentration differences.[11,12] P^{32} concentration in the various cortical layers is mainly determined by the diffusion from the CSF,[12] and occlusion of one lateral ventricle by injection of paraffin into it results in a decrease in that hemisphere as compared to the contralateral side. These data lead to the conclusion that the main route of entry of P^{32} to the brain is through the CSF and that entry from the blood, though present, is only of secondary importance especially in the initial stages of an experiment.[9,152]

In repeating some of the above experiments with Na^{24} this ion behaved similarly to P^{32} in that its absorption was faster from the CSF than from plasma when levels were similar in the two fluids.[13] Therefore, though transcapillary exchange is superimposed, the diffusion of Na^{24} from the CSF is the more significant event initially. The penetration of Na^{24} into the brain on one hand and into the CSF on the other, however, have to be considered as two independent processes. Diamox slowed down the entry of Na^{24} into the CSF but not into the brain, probably because diamox does not penetrate the brain.[47] I^{131} bovine albumin penetrated the brain from the CSF from the subarachnoid space and perivascularly along the blood vessels.[111]

Measuring of the uptake of amino acids from the CSF by the brain showed that the passage of lysine, leucine or phenylalanine was not greatly inhibited by other amino acids, thereby not supporting evidence for the participation of common carriers in this passage.[103] These processes, however, do not have to operate between the CSF and brain but could be active within the brain only after the diffusion of the test substance into the tissue proper, thereby influencing the CSF-brain passage only indirectly.

EXCHANGE

A distinction has to be made between the two-directional process of exchange and unidirectional transport leading to net uptake but the two processes are not necessarily independent. Exchange is usually measured in the steady state, meaning that influx equals efflux, or that any movement in one direction is compensated by a movement of the same size in the opposite direction. Unidirectional movement cannot be called exchange. It has to be realized, however, that exchange can exist (and most often does) even when concomitant unidirectional net transport occurs. The rate of exchange is different from transport rate; most likely it is greater.[79,176] The exchange of ions, probably governed by diffusion, can be at several times the rate at which the ions are brought to the organs by the circulating plasma.[135] The rate of exchange of a substance can vary from one brain area to another[101] (Table II) and can be different in different parts of the CSF. The exchange of sodium, potassium, and phosphate after intravenous administration was most rapid in the ventricles and decreased in the following order: cisterna magna, lumbar space, subarachnoid space over the cerebral hemispheres.[159] This variation in local exchange rate in the CSF should not be taken as evidence for the local production of the CSF, nor that this mechanism serves to alter the local composition of the fluid—only unidirectional transport is capable of doing that.

All of the content of the brain is not necessarily exchangeable; all brain potassium was found to be exchangeable in young rats but not all in adult animals.[89] The exchangeable part of a substrate in the brain may be in heterogenous pools and the rate of exchange of the various pools may be different.

Although exchange means two-directional flow, high exchange rate can mask net unidirectional flow of low rate in an experimental procedure. The exchange rate of lysine is high, although a restriction exists to net uptake[99,106] and the exchange is considerably greater than the rate at which the amino acid is metabolized. A fractional increase of the influx rate over the efflux rate thus is capable of supplying the brain with the necessary amount of lysine without possible detection in the usual experimental procedure. Lack of finding a net increase or decrease in brain levels when rapid exchange occurs thus cannot be taken to mean the complete absence of net uptake or exit from the brain if the compound is utilized or metabolized slowly as com-

TABLE III

Restrictions of Uptake of Amino Acids by the Brain

Amino Acid	Plasma Increase over Control ($\mu g./gm.$)	Brain at Control Levels ($\mu g./gm.$)	Time (min.)	Animal	Plasma/Brain Ratio Increase over Control	Reference
Glutamine	300		20		1.1	158
	350	570	30	rat	1.1	
	230		30		1.2	
	60	720	45	mouse	1.2	
			120–240	dog	1.9	88
Tyrosine	67		15		3.0	38
	63	17	60	rat	1.0	
	46		120		0.7	
Phenylalanine	310	23	20	mouse	5.6	108
	270		45		4.0	
Methionine			120–240	dog	6.0	88
Histidine			120–240	dog	8.5	88
Leucine	38		20		4.8	108
	690	12	20	adult mouse	18	
	370		60	mouse	13	
	100	19	20	newborn mouse	2.4	
	860		20	mouse	6.6	
Lysine	130		20	adult mouse	67	99
	480		20	mouse	16	
	90		20	newborn mouse	2.2	
	710		20	mouse	14	
			120–240	dog	15	88
Arginine			120–240	dog	17	88
Glutamic Acid	820	1520	20	rat	> 300	158
	650		30		> 300	
	410	1690	30	mouse	> 200	
	350		45		> 200	

pared to its exchange rate. High rate of exchange has been found for most ions studied and for a number of amino acids, such as lysine,[106] leucine,[100] glutamic acid,[61,104,175] methionine,[6] and tyrosine,[38] with the average half-life of free lysine and leucine in the brain under an hour and of methionine under ten minutes. The restriction of uptake varies from one amino acid to another. Some of the results are summarized in Table III. It can be shown that the restrictions of glutamine and tyrosine seem to be less than those of other amino acids tried, and that of glutamic acid more. Glutamic acid levels in the brain are much higher than those of the other amino acids and even with greatly increased plasma levels the physiological brain levels are higher than the elevated plasma levels. D-tyrosine enters the brain slower and to a lesser degree than the L-isomer[38] and the uptake of the α-amino isobutyric acid is also strongly restricted.[97] The rate of exchange of a substance can be changed as shown by the increased exchange of amino acids when brain amino acids were elevated (Table I). It is of interest, in Table I, that elevated lysine levels in the brain increased lysine exchange more than leucine exchange, and, conversely, elevated leucine levels influenced leucine exchange mainly and not lysine exchange, pointing to the possibility of influencing the exchange of one substance without changing the exchange rates of other substances. The factors controlling exchange are not known, but the participation of active processes beyond passive diffusion cannot be excluded at the present time.

ACTIVE TRANSPORT

Active or mediated transport processes form part of the "brain barrier system" and at least a part of the metabolites utilized by the organ are transported by such processes. At present it is not clear where such processes are localized, but it is quite possible that a major part of active transport occurs inside cells and at cell membranes rather than at or near the capillary endothelium or between the CSF and the brain. The present experimental evidence points to the participation of active transport processes in the entry of amino acids into the brain from the blood,[38] in the exit of amino acids from the brain,[101,108] and in the uptake of amino acids by brain slices.[94,129,155,164,168,171]

The first evidence for the presence of active transport processes in brain tissue was the dependence, in cortex slices, of the accumulation of L-glutamate, against a concentration gradient, on a source of energy.[164] Respiratory inhibition decreased the rate of entry of aspartic acid, though glycine was unaffected.[94] Brain slices but not liver or kidney slices also actively accumulate gamma-aminobutyrate; this process is inhibited by dinitrophenol.[56A,171] That the active uptake by brain slices is not restricted to naturally occurring amino acids is shown by the uptake of D-glutamate to approximately five times its concentration in the medium.[168] Against a concentration gradient, brain slices took up histidine, proline, lysine, ornithine, methionine and arginine, all the amino acids that were tried. Histidine uptake was inhibited by anaerobic conditions and cyanide.[129] The facilitated transport of 5-hydroxytryptophane is indicated by the enhancement of uptake by glucose and O_2 and the inhibition of uptake by dinitrophenol; serotonin is not taken up this way.[155] Thus, brain slices as was proposed originally,[164] retain a number of their permeability characteristics and can serve for the further clarification of the mechanism of transport in the brain. Although some properties of the whole brain are not reflected by the behavior of the slices,[77A] certain properties do contribute to the difference in permeability characteristics of brain contrasted with other tissues.

The complexity of the processes operating in the intact brain was indicated by such observations as the increased glucose uptake by the perfused brain if the perfusate contained liver extract,[68] and the interference of SH inhibitors with the CSF-brain barrier as measured with P^{32}.[80] Indications from our laboratory for active transport of amino acids to the brain of the living organism were in the finding of a rapid

TABLE IV

TRANSPORT OF LEUCINE FROM BRAIN[108]

	μg. Leucine/gm. Fresh Tissue Increase over Control		
Time, minutes	20	30	45
Plasma	280	180	250
Brain	110	56	24

Brain levels were elevated by subarachnoid leucine administration, plasma levels were kept high by repeated intraperitoneal administration of leucine to rats.

exchange in spite of a barrier to a net uptake with lysine,[99,106] leucine[100,108] and glutamic acid;[104,158] it is difficult to explain the inhibition of the net uptake while a rapid exchange, that is, simultaneous influx and efflux, of this substrate occurs by invoking a passive semipermeable membrane.

More direct evidence is the finding of competitive inhibition of tyrosine uptake from the blood by amino acids such as tryptophane, leucine, isoleucine, valine, cysteine, and histidine, while other amino acids such as alanine, serine, threonine, arginine, lysine, glutamate and glutamine are inactive.[38] This raises the possibility of several carrier mechanisms, some of which are common for some of the amino acids. The decrease in the endogenous levels of tyrosine after tryptophane, leucine or β-fluorophenyl DL-alanine administration[38] would indicate that these processes play a role not only when amino acid levels in plasma or CSF are unphysiologically high.

Active transport processes play a role in the exit of amino acids from the brain as well as in their entrance. A more rapid rate for the L than the D isomer of several amino acids has been found[102] and, as more direct evidence, a transport of amino acids from the brain against a concentration gradient[108] (Table IV). While leucine and lysine were shown to be transported against a concentration gradient and though such transport with phenylalanine could not be shown, the possibility of the participation of active processes in the exit of all amino acids, as well as other compounds, cannot be excluded at the present time. The fact that with varying plasma potassium levels the potassium influx to brain did not change was interpreted as suggesting a carrier-limited system.[112] Active transport of diodrast and phenolsulfonphtalein occurs from CSF to blood. The site of the transport which is inhibited by p-aminohippurate is perhaps in the fourth ventricle.[135A]

The recognition of the participation of active or mediated transport processes in the "brain barrier system" opens a whole new approach to such questions as the mechanism of the transport processes, the controlling factors of these processes, and also the contribution of these processes to brain function. It is likely that qualitative or quantitative differences in active processes between the brain and other organs add their contribution for distinguishing the "brain barrier system" from other permeability barriers in the body.

EXIT OF SUBSTANCES FROM THE BRAIN

While the entry of substances into the brain and the CSF has been studied with numerous compounds, only in few instances has the rate of exit been studied as well. It should be realized that, to study net exit of metabolites present in brain under normal circumstances, cerebral levels must be raised above physiological levels or labeled substances must be administered intracerebrally; in both areas the mixing with the physiological pools needs to be better understood. If, following intracerebral or intracisternal administration of labeled amino acids, the brain is sectioned into several parts, the label can be found fairly evenly distributed in each part, and also incorporated into proteins.[107] This shows that the amino acids spread throughout the brain rapidly and are not restricted to the areas adjacent to the site of injection or to the surface areas of the brain, but does not prove that the administered dose is mixed with, or shows the same behavior as the amino acid present in the brain.

Exit from CSF.—Comparing the disappearance rate from the CSF of intracisternally injected substances to that of sodium, a number such as inulin, sucrose, and p-aminohippurate were slower, others like thiocyanate, iodide and ethylthiourea were faster.[44] The rate of exit was higher from CSF to blood than it was in the reverse direction with bromide, thiocyanate, iodide,[44,180] methionine,[67] and sulfate[143] and was equal with others such as Na[24] and Br,[82] which had a turnover time of 170 minutes.[131] After subarachnoidal administration, amino acids reached their maximum level in brain rapidly (leucine in 5, phenylalanine in 10, proline in 20, lysine in 40 minutes) and thereafter cerebral levels decreased; CSF levels seemed to fall faster.[102] Similarly lipid-soluble drugs disappear in less than one hour from the CSF; the lipid insoluble ones more slowly, although 90% of these compounds leaves the CSF in 80 minutes. The drugs reach their peak concentration in the brain in 5 to 10 minutes (usually about 10% of the injected dose penetrates the brain).[122]

Some of the above results seem to indicate that the net influx into the CSF is governed by factors different from those governing net efflux. As a rule substances leave the CSF rapidly. It is possible that little or no restriction to efflux from the CSF to blood exists for many substances. However, active processes also might operate in exit from CSF to plasma. Sulfate reaches a CSF to plasma ratio of 0.2 even if it is initially injected into the CSF, showing in this case, a secretion from CSF to plasma against a concentration gradient.[143] Active transport of diodrast and phenolsulfonphthalein from CSF to blood has also been shown.[135A]

Exit from Brain.—The exit of methionine[41,67] and gamma-aminobutyric acid[144] from the brain is rapid, that of α-aminoisobutyric acid slow.[97] In our laboratory[101,102] the exit of intracerebrally injected lysine, leucine, phenylalanine and proline from the brain was compared. The speed of exit varied, the times needed for brain levels to decrease to half being the following: lysine 140, phenylalanine 27, proline 23, leucine 14 minutes. Variations were found in uptake rates as well; that of α-amino-isobutyric acid[97] was considerably lower than that of lysine,[99] leucine or phenylalanine.[108]

Studying the exit of the D isomers of the above amino acids, it was found that the rate of exit of D-leucine from the brain was higher than that of D-lysine, as the exit rate of L-leucine was higher than that of L-lysine. In each case, the exit rate of the D-isomer was lower than that of the L-isomer (L-lysine average half-life time 140 minutes, D-lysine 200 minutes).[102]

The difference in exit rates between the L and D isomers pointed to the possibility of stereospecific transport in amino acid efflux from brain. For a test of participation of active transport processes in the exit, brain amino acid levels were increased by subarachnoid administration while plasma concentrations were kept elevated by intraperitoneal injections. With time brain leucine and lysine levels decreased against a concentration gradient while the levels of phenylalanine remained constant[108] (Table IV). This was interpreted as active transport of lysine and leucine from the brain. If plasma levels were kept elevated, brain levels, though decreased, did not return to physiological levels. Plasma to brain concentration ratio was about 5.6 with lysine; with leucine it was about 16 at two different plasma leucine levels. The rate of leucine was higher than that of lysine in these experiments also.

The cerebral levels of an amino acid are governed by the processes of influx and efflux, at equilibrium the two rates being equal. Presumably after an increase in plasma levels influx to brain is increased, resulting in an increased brain level followed by the extablishment of a new equilibrium. This equilibrium may depend only on the ratio of concentrations in plasma and brain or depend also on the absolute level of the amino acid in the brain or in the plasma. Thus threshold levels may exist above which uptake occurs. The equilibrium ratio is different with different amino acids; it appears to be lower with tyrosine[38] than with lysine or leucine,[108] although for strict evaluation experiments with identical absolute plasma levels will have to be compared. The lack of decrease in phenylalanine levels against a concentration gradient[108] does not necessarily indicate the absence of active transport of this amino acid from the brain, it may only mean a less efficient "phenylalanine pump." It is interesting to note that rapid exchange between blood and brain continues while there is a net exit of amino acids from the brain.[107]

The difference in the exit rates of various amino acids and between the rate of exit of the D and L isomer, the relatively slow exit of some other substances, and the possibility of transport of some amino acids against a concentration gradient show that aspects of the "brain barrier system" are operative in efflux. At present it cannot be stated whether similar restrictions exist on the exit of substances from the brain as exist on the uptake—but the processes of transport out of the brain may play a role which is equally as important as the processes of uptake in regulating the level of substances in this organ.

EXTRACELLULAR SPACE

A discussion of the arguments for and against the existence of extracellular space in the brain is outside the scope of this paper; some relationship between the extracellular space and the "brain barrier system" has to be discussed, however, especially since it has been claimed recently[53,123] that the blood-brain barrier is but an expression of the lack of extracellular space in the brain. Brain thus would differ from other tissues in that substances entering the organ have to cross simultaneously not only the capillary wall but also a cell membrane.

Considerable evidence could be cited against the view that the lack of the extracellular space is responsible for the permeability behavior of the brain; one example is the finding that the entry of a compound is changed without an apparent change in extracellular space (e.g., the finding of inhibitors in the active transport of amino acids that themselves do not enter the brain[38]). More direct argument is that substances such as p-amino hippurate, sucrose and I^{131}, which do not penetrate the brain but penetrate muscle *in vivo,* penetrate into pieces of these two tissues *in vitro* at about equal rates; that is, the difference between the two tissues is not due to the lack of extracellular space in one of them.[48]

According to electron microscopic evidence no extracellular space can be distinguished in brain as opposed to other tissues, at least nothing quantitatively comparable.[57,123,157,185,186] It is of interest that the electron microscopic evidence[157,186] is also against the general presence of ground substance, which is, according to some investigators, responsible for the blood-brain barrier. The parallel increase of penetration of drugs with increased lipid solubility, likewise, argues against the extracellular ground substance as the main reason for the "brain barrier system" (for a discussion of the existence of the cerebral ground substance see ref. 30).

While the histological evidence differentiates the brain from other tissues in respect to the extracellular space, most of the chemical evidence does not support the existence of significant differences between the brain and other tissues in this respect. Some substances such as inulin that are used for measuring the extracellular space in other organs do not penetrate the brain at all,[128] although when measured in brain slices[4] they define a space in the expected range. The size of the space is also dependent somewhat on the substance it is measured with, being much larger with chloride[119] than with sulfate. The sulfate space in adult brains was recently found to be 4%,[15] a size which may be undetectable electronmicroscopically. It is of interest that during development sodium, chloride[60] and sulfate[15] spaces decrease as they do in other organs.

The most likely reason for the existence of chemical evidence for extracellular space in the brain though histological evidence is lacking, is that the ions measuring this space can penetrate some cells in the brain. Movement of chloride from intercellular spaces into neuronal elements in the cerebral cortex under various experimental conditions has been reported.[154,171A]

Some cells in the brain thus would be permeable to the ions which in other organs, do not usually penetrate cells. This in turn would mean that chloride space—that is a compartment in rapid equilibrium with the plasma chloride—is partly extra-, partly intracellular, being in effect composed of two compartments; it could also mean that the chloride space is not necessarily the same "space" measured by other substances, such as sulfate or thiocyanate.

The present experimental evidence is not sufficient to decide if the living brain has a significant amount of extracellular space, perhaps more than can be seen in the electronmicroscope, or if glial cells constitute this space.[71A] It has been suggested that astroglia[68A] or clear glial cytoplasm[196A-B] instead of extracellular space function as the water and ion compartment. Some evidence pointing to the presence of a large portion of the cerebral Na in glia has been discussed.[88A]

The possibility of the presence in pathologic conditions of an extracellular "third" space not in continuum with normal extracellular space has also been discussed.[136] Part or all of an edema or swelling in brain may be intracellular too.[165,196A-B] It is likely that, on closer kinetic analysis of the penetration of substances, the existence of a number of spaces and compartments in the brain will be established; knowledge of the size of the true extracellular space or available extracellular space is, nevertheless, still important.

It does not seem too likely the extracellular space is completely absent from the central nervous system, although it may be considerably smaller than in other organs. Changes in this tissue upon preparation for histological examination will have to be elucidated before this question can be decided. This quantitative difference may be of importance in comparing the permeability properties of the brain with other organs, but it is unlikely to be the only influence in the "brain barrier system." The better histological and chemical definition of the various spaces and compartments and their possible alterations in pathological conditions remains an important goal of the research in this field.

IONS

Ions, as well as other substances, penetrate the central nervous system with more difficulty than they do other organs (for a discussion see ref. 119). There is a barrier to the penetration of sulfate,[5] iodide, thiocyanate, bromide,[178,184] Na,[24] and Cl,[38,119A-B] for example. The penetration into brain is more rapid from the CSF than from blood, and it has been suggested that the CSF is in the same relationship to the extracellular space of the brain as the plasma is to the extracellular space of other organs.[47,178] Such relationship can exist even if we give a different meaning to the cerebral extracellular space, since most likely, at least a part of this space is intracellular in the brain (glial?).

Some of the halogen ions that are extracellular in other organs are intracellular in the brain.[5,26] Perhaps this is the reason that brain chloride cannot be replaced by other ions such as sulfate[5] and bromide[184] as can the chloride content of other organs. Although the CSF and the brain "extracellular space" are in close relation, the entry of substances into these two spaces are distinct processes. The distribution rate of Na^{24} between plasma and CSF is about the same as between plasma and brain "extracellular fluid," while creatinine, thiourea and its derivatives enter the cerebral extracellular fluid faster.[45] The passage of Na into the CSF and the cerebral "extracellular fluid" comprises two independent processes.[47] These results show the need for the further elucidation of the intimate relation between CSF and brain spaces.

The ions enter the CSF from cerebral capillaries as well as from the choroid plexus[119,180] and the CSF-serum ratio depends on the ion concentration in the serum; the threshold at which ions are taken up into the CSF varies with the ion.[179] The delay of entrance to CSF from blood varies with different ions and is in this increasing order: $K < Na < Br < Ru < Sr < P < I$.[72] It has to be kept in mind that the exit of ions can be restricted too.[138]

The substance whose penetration was investigated in greatest detail was P^{32}. This ion is not a very fortunate choice. Very soon after entry, a major portion of P^{32} in brain is in organic linkage as ATP, as creatine phosphate,[115] part of it in lipids,[43] nucleic acids and a host of other substances; therefore, the total P^{32} of the tissue cannot be considered as a single compound. This way penetration, as well as a number of other reactions, is measured and the distribution might be a reflection of metabolic rates rather than of permeability barriers. The measurement of the kinetics of the passage of a substance into or out of the brain is made difficult by the existence of a number of compartments in the CSF (ventricular, cisternal, subarachnoid, lumbar) and especially in the brain (cellular, particular, metabolic pools), as well as by transport processes. The disappearance curve of a not-too-reactive and extracellular ion, sulfate, from the CSF showed at least three components with three or more rate constants.[143] If to these and other multiple factors are added the variety of compounds into which P^{32} is incorporated and the incorporation rates, a meaningful quantitative evaluation becomes for the present impossible. A detailed kinetic study of other ions might, however, measure the size and the number of these compartments.

Ions (especially the labeled isotopes) that are not involved in metabolic pathways and which are restricted to a particular compartment offer advantages for the measurement of exchange rates and mechanisms that have not been fully utilized up to the present.

CHANGES DURING DEVELOPMENT

The possibility of changes in the "brain barrier system" during development was recognized early,[20,169] but such changes do not affect the entry of all substances into the brain.[70,77] A higher exchange rate of chloride[98,173] and greater permeability of young than adult brains to glutamic acid,[83] lysine,[99] leucine,[108] P32,[7,65] alpha aminoisobutyric acid[97] and thiocyanate[98] were found. (Compare adult and newborn plasma-brain ratios of lysine and leucine in Table III.) A greater lability of the young barrier to gamma-aminobutyric acid has also been demonstrated.[140] Unlike the flux of chloride, that of glutamic acid was ten times greater into adult brains than into newborns, although in both ages glucose supplied, by synthesis, at least ten times as much glutamic acid as did glutamic acid flux.[145] Not enough substances have been tested to make it a general rule, but the conclusion of the above studies was that the "brain barrier system" in the early stages of development is not as restrictive for many substances as it is in adults, although restrictions are present in any developmental stage.

The reasons for the changes in the "brain barrier system" during development may be manifold, and caution has to be exercised in our present stage of knowledge in attributing the changes to any single cause such as changes in the ground substance.[81] During development a number of changes occur in the brain, such as increases in proteins, enzymes, and lipids and decreases in chloride space, water content, and blood circulation, any one of which is likely to influence permeability characteristics; but evidence that parallel changes occur between any of the above factors and permeability properties is not sufficient proof of a causal relationship. The distribution of P32 in newborn and adult brains will be greatly influenced by the metabolic activity in the organ as was discussed above and thus changes in metabolic activity could result in apparent permeability changes as measured with this marker. Exchange rates are likely to be influenced by distribution; a more uniform distribution of Na24 in embryonic than adult brains has been found.[13] All brain potassium was found to be exchangeable in young brains but not all in adults,[89] a fact which would result in measurements of an apparent altered "brain barrier system."

That increased permeability in young is not the only possible explanation for the findings was shown by recent experiments in which newborn and adult mice were compared.[108] The injected doses were chosen so that at the beginning of the experiment brain leucine levels,

and during the experimental time the average blood leucine levels
were similar in newborns and adults, and so that blood levels were
well above brain levels. Starting from the same level, newborn brain
concentrations increased while those of adults decreased against the
concentration gradient of higher blood levels. Thus newborn brain
levels were above adult at the termination of the experiment (Fig. 2).

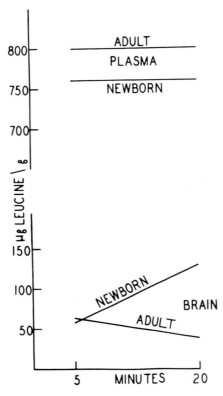

Fig. 2. Changes in leucine levels with time in newborn and adult brains
when plasma leucine levels are elevated.[108]

The possible explanation for this finding is the existence of stronger
transport mechanisms (in this case transporting substances out of the
brain against a concentration gradient) capable of restoring physiological levels faster or to a greater degree in adult than in newborn
brain. Again it has to be emphasized that this is only one of the many
possible explanations.

It is likely that changes in the "brain barrier system" during development are the result of not one but of several factors. Changes in

the structure and composition of the various membranes play a role as do changes in the availability of transport processes.

PROPERTIES OF SUBSTANCES

The importance of the different factors comprising the "brain barrier system" varies with the substances investigated and at present no general rule can be drawn that would be valid for ions, sugars, amino acid drugs and dyes equally. One important principle becomes somewhat easier to discern if the substances that are present under physiological conditions are excluded from consideration, since with a great number of other substances the penetration into the brain was roughly parallel with lipid solubility.

The importance of lipid solubility in anesthetic action was recognized early.[35] Since cell membranes contain lipids and since substances entering the brain have to pass through these membranes, it was proposed that the blood-brain barrier is a reflection of the behavior of cell membranes.[96] Collodion membrane containing lecithin and cephalin did show similar permeability properties to that of brain.[182] Lipid solubility is not the only determinant;[36] dissociation constant is important as well.[58,69] Since pK is important, the pH of the blood and CSF by influencing the dissociation will influence blood-CSF distribution ratios.[142] The true determinant is the lipid solubility of the undissociated molecule and the dissociation constant is important only as it determines the concentration of the undissociated molecules.[31,32] A number of studies with many series of substances established a parallelism between lipid solubility and penetration into brain or CSF.[32,45,121,162,163] This was true for proline and proline derivatives,[50] but tyrosine penetrated the brain more than its more lipid soluble derivatives.[38]

Studying the exit of a number of compounds from the CSF, it was found that the lipid soluble ones disappear from the CSF somewhat faster than the lipid insoluble ions, but in these experiments the lipid insoluble compounds penetrated the brain to a greater extent from the CSF[122] (possibly by staying longer in the CSF). A more detailed study of the penetration of the same compound into the brain from the blood on one hand and from the CSF on the other will be able to determine the influence of the cell membranes within the brain on the rate of entry and on the distribution of these compounds. The dependence on lipid solubility of the entry from blood as opposed to the lack of correlation in the entry from CSF would point to the presence of the "lipidlike barrier" between blood and brain and blood and CSF but not between CSF and brain.

It is to be expected that lipid solubility would determine initial rates of passage to a greater extent than the final equilibrium. It has to be emphasized that lipid solubility as the main determinant has been established for only some classes of compounds, although it might be true for all foreign organic compounds. Substances normally present in the brain and also compounds of related structure will be influenced by other factors, one of which might be electrostatic charge structure.[78] Lipid solubility is not a well defined term at present; the solvents vary from one study to another. At present it is not known to what extent the measured organic solvent-water partition coefficients reflect solubility in the constituents of the cell wall or in the brain lipids. It is likely that the fine structure of the cell wall will further influence the passage of substances into and out of the brain; the above studies, however, make it clear that the solubility of the penetrating substance in the components of membranes is of decisive influence at least with foreign organic compounds.

ALTERATIONS IN THE SYSTEM

Perhaps the largest volume of literature deals not with the mechanisms of entry, exit or distribution, but with the modification of the passage of substances into the brain. The obvious clinical and therapeutic significance of the possibility of influencing the metabolite levels in the brain, and thereby metabolism, and increasing cerebral drug content when necessary, does not have to be emphasized here.

Test Substance.—It is unfortunate that it has not been generally recognized that no one test substance represents all the complex behavior of the "brain barrier system"; any particular agent can influence the entrance of several substances without having effect on a host of others. In the use of dyes, for example, it is claimed that Geigy blue indicates some fine differences that trypan blue does not,[17] also that damage caused by shock results in increased penetration of P^{32} into the brain although no effect can be seen with stain techniques;[132] thus conclusions arrived at with a single test substance at present cannot be generalized. Substances whose penetration is partially limited by blood flow will be influenced by factors altering cerebral blood flow, while other substances limited by lipoprotein membranes will remain unaffected. It is likely that some test substances will be limited by only a single factor in the "brain barrier system," and thereby will be suitable for the study of single aspects. The fact that the dyes penetrate the brain from the subarachnoid space or from the surface of the organ better than they do from the blood can be interpreted as indicating that they are not much affected by the glial membranes[34,170] or other membranes throughout the brain. The passage of the amino acids on the other hand, seems to be governed more by active transport processes, although they might also be influenced by membrane permeabilities. Dyes thus are more suitable for the measurement of cerebrovascular permeability or of the permeability of the perivascular membranes, and amino acids are more suitable for the measurements of active transport processes.

Added to this already complex situation are the differences among the various species in the degree of restriction of the "brain barrier system" and in the responses to attempts to influence it. Responses might vary with developmental stages and in various tissues. Hyperbilirubinemia induced no changes in newborn rabbits but some in newborn puppies and kittens.[150] It is of interest that while insulin influences the transport of several hexoses and pentoses in muscle, it has no such effects in brain[137] *in vivo*, although a small effect could be shown *in vitro*.[141A]

Decrease in Penetration.—Most alterations result in an increased penetration into the central nervous system but some resulting in a decrease of penetration have also been observed. Trypan red decreased entrance of cocaine into cortex by 31% and into CSF by 40%.[3] Sulfapyridine and sulfanilamide penetration was decreased by a number of agents (sodium bicarbonate, sodium nitrite, sodium salicylate and physostigmine) and increased by others (ammonium chloride, adrenaline, aminophylline, traumatic trypan red staining, acetylcholine and dehydration), moderate measures producing only minor changes.[19] Note the opposite effects of trypan red, decreasing cocaine[3] but increasing sulfonamide[19] entrance. The presence in serum of a thermolabile factor which decreases the rate of appearance of C^{14}-glucose in mouse brain was claimed. Schizophrenic sera also contained this factor which increased with the age of the patient.[84] A number of psychotomimetic drugs and chlorpromazine and physostigmine decreased the entrance of C^{14} from glucose, while a number of other tranquilizers had no effect.[75] Chlorpromazine also decreased the transport of Na^{22} and K^{42} in each brain area studied, and the uptake by the brain of S^{35}-sulfate, S^{35}-methionine, I^{131}-thyroxine and Rb^{86}.[39]

Exchange.—K^{42} exchange was decreased while Na^{24} exchange and Br^{82} uptake was increased by venostasin.[141] The exchange of Na between the serum and CSF, although not influenced by a number of factors such as cortisone, hypertension and hypoglycemia, was increased by vasopressin and decreased by acetazolamide.[59] The influx of K was not altered by adrenalectomy, but all brain K became exchangeable; cortisone restored the non-exchangeable compartment.[112] Amino acid exchange rates are influenced by cerebral amino acid levels[107] (Tables I and II). These results show that rates of exchange, as well as net uptake, might be influenced by various elements. The most intriguing question in this respect is in what way the "brain barrier system" responds to the changing metabolic and functional needs of the brain.

Factors Possibly Present under Physiological Conditions.—While alterations in brain permeability under normal conditions have not been observed, a number of factors might have some influence under physiological circumstances. The passage of albumin from serum to CSF was increased by hypoxia;[160] 25 minutes or longer of ischemia allowed increased P^{32} penetration into the spinal cord.[133] There was an increase of staining with trypan blue in hypothermia with no change shown with methylene blue.[116] Glucose uptake was increased after fasting, and this uptake was independent of plasma glucose levels.[149] Net uptake of glutamic acid by the brain after cerebral glutamic acid levels had been depressed by insulin hypoglycemia was shown,[82] indicating a tendency to restore normal levels while impeding a net increase of the physiological levels. A large portion of hypoglycemic rabbits showed staining with trypan blue[1] but it is not clear if this is partly due to lesions. Penicillin entrance to brain and CSF was increased by adrenalin, probably partly through vasodilation, increased CSF pressure, and increased penicillin levels in blood.[90] Histamine and CO_2 inhalation increased P^{32} entry,[29] and histamine increased the penetration of antibiotics.[91] Intraspinal tuberculin administration to a sensitized subject (sterile meningitis) increased Br and penicillin entrance into the CSF, but the maximal effect for the two substances was found at different stages of the reaction.[161]

Enzyme Inhibitors.—Greig and her collaborators found that inhibition of cholinesterase increased the penetration of substances into brain. Physostigmine (an inhibitor of this enzyme) and acetylcholine increased the penetration of acid fuchsin[74] and physostigmine increased the entrance of barbital into the brain of living mice[76] and guinea pig brain slices.[73] Acetylcholine and physostigmine also increased penicillin and streptomycin entry.[92] Physostigmine, along with other drugs (a number of psychotomimetic drugs and chlorpromazine), decreased the entrance of C^{14} from glucose into brain, the inhibition of transport probably being related to the inhibition of pseudocholinesterase. Atropine and amphetamine reversed the inhibitory effects of physostigmine but not of the other drugs.[75] It is not known at the present time if the inhibited enzymes (cholinesterase and pseudocholinesterase) take part directly in the "brain barrier system" or if the effects of the inhibitors are indirectly mediated.

Effects of Enzymes.—The reports of enzymatic influence of permeability are largely controversial because of the different experimental techniques and the failure to establish the activity and localization of the administered enzyme in the experimental animal. It is likely that enzymes causing tissue or capillary damage will increase the penetration of a variety of substances. No effect[95] and increased penetration[91] of antibiotics by hyaluronidase have been reported. This enzyme does not seem to affect P^{32} [9,151] entry. Proteolytic enzymes and lecithinase were reported to increase barbiturate penetration into brain;[21] they also increased P^{32} penetration from the CSF but not from the blood.[80] Further clarification of the controversial results must await the repetition of some of the experiments under more carefully controlled conditions and with several test substances.

Tissue Damage.—The large body of literature dealing with changes in brain permeability after wounds and hemorrhages and in other pathological conditions and dealing with localization of brain tumors is outside the scope of this discussion. This subject has been reviewed often.[9,77,118,125,127] Among the injuries most recently investigated were stab injuries,[8] ionizing[40,146] and ultrasonic radiation,[14] air embolism,[110] heat coagulation[13,109] and temporary concussion.[37]

In general, tissue damage of any kind, including relatively small damage, causes a greater permeability of the injured area including increased penetration of dyes and P^{32} and increased exchange of Na^{24}. The changes can be seen immediately after the damage and reach their maximum shortly afterwards. Scar formation and autolytic changes might serve to prolong the changes with effects of small damage like pressure or exposure lasting only for minutes and of intense laceration lasting for weeks. The effects seen will again depend on the test substance used; P^{32}, which partly measures metabolism, showing a somewhat different time curve than does Na^{24} exchange.

Drug Effects.—The lack of well defined experimental procedures makes a number of studies in this field inconclusive. The need for caution is shown for example, by the finding with physostigmine, bromodiphenhydramine and acetazolamide that each decreased the latent period of barbital—the first by reducing the threshold, the second by increasing the blood levels, and the third by increasing penetration—and that secondarily all three resulted in increased brain barbital levels.[93] Reserpine and iproniazide or electroshock increased the passage of noradrenaline into the CSF. Both treatments increased blood levels and it is not clear if the "brain barrier system" itself was influenced, or if increased CSF levels reflected only the elevated blood levels caused by decreased binding and metabolism.[147] Histamine was reported to increase antibiotic entrance into CSF and the effect was not prevented by pyribenzamine;[63] histamine did not affect the entrance of trypan blue[56] or that of a host of other drugs.[87] Prolonged metrazol or electroshock increased albumin penetration into CSF in young puppies[113] and cardiazol shock, the penetration of Geigy blue.[18] Chlorpromazine decreased the entrance of the six test substances tried.[39]

CONCLUSIONS

With increasing investigation and knowledge, the "brain barrier system" emerges not as a passive membrane but as a complex of morphological and metabolic compartments, a system of membranes and of transport processes.

Although some of the properties of permeability and of transport processes have not been shown in other tissues, the differences between brain and other organs in this respect are not clear and it is not established if the central nervous system is different only in a quantitative sense or if qualitatively also it possesses properties not present in the rest of the organism.

Aspects of the system are operative in the efflux as well as in the influx of substances in the brain, including in the direction of CSF to blood.

The system is not static but reacts to many influences. Aspects of the system show variations from one brain area to another and there are differences in development, with the restriction to net increase usually being less in newborn than in adults. The flux of substances into and out of the brain can also be influenced by a number of other factors, some of which may be operative under physiological conditions.

Further investigation will establish the role of the "BBS" in brain function. Its role is undoubtedly important in cerebral homeostasis and in the regulation of the available metabolites. By responding to changes and needs it might also have an important role in the regulation of metabolic pathways and metabolic needs in the brain.

REFERENCES

1. ABNEY, R. L., HAUSER, C. W., and BRUNSON, J. G.: *Federation Proc., 19*:105 (1960).
2. ABOOD, L. G., GERARD, R. W., and TSCHIRGI, R. D.: In *Phosphorus Metabolism*, Vol. 2, p. 798. W. D. McElroy and B. Glass, Eds. Baltimore, John Hopkins Press (1952).
3. AIRD, R. B., and STRAIT, L.: *Arch. Neurol. & Psychiat., 51*:54 (1944).
4. ALLEN, J. N.: *Arch. Neurol. & Psychiat., 73*:241 (1955).
5. AMBERSON, W. R., NASH, T. P., MULDER, A. G., and BINNS, D.: *Am. J. Physiol., 122*:224 (1938).
6. APPEL, K. R., APPEL, E., and MAURER, W.: *Biochem. Ztschr., 332*:293 (1960).

7. BAKAY, L.: *Arch. Neurol. & Psychiat.*, 70:30 (1953).

8. BAKAY, L.: *Arch. Neurol. & Psychiat.*, 73:2 (1955).

9. BAKAY, L.: In *The Blood Brain Barrier.* Springfield, Ill., Thomas (1956).

10. BAKAY, L.: *Arch. Neurol. & Psychiat.*, 78:29 (1957).

11. BAKAY, L.: In *Metabolism of the Nervous System*, p. 136. D. Richter, Ed. London, Pergamon Press (1957).

12. BAKAY, L.: *Neurology*, 9:18 (1959).

13. BAKAY, L.: *Neurology*, 10:564 (1960).

14. BAKAY, L., BALLATINE, JR., H. T., and BELL, E.: *Arch. Neurol. & Psychiat.*, 1:59 (1959).

15. BARLOW, C. F., DOMEK, N. S., GOLDBERG, M. A., and RICHTER, R. B.: *Proc. Am. Neurol. A.* (Boston), p. 9 (1960).

16. BARLOW, C. F., SCHOOLAR, J. C., and ROTH, L. J.: *Neurology*, 7:820 (1957).

17. BAUER, K. F., and LEONHARDT, H.: *Arch. Psychiat. u. Neurol.* 193:68 (1955).

18. BAUER, K. F., and LEONHARDT, H.: *J. Comp. Neurol.*, 106:363 (1956).

19. BECKER, R. A., and AIRD, R. B.: *J. Cell. & Comp. Physiol.*, 46:127 (1955).

20. BEHNSEN, G.: *Ztschr. Zellforsch. u. mikroskop. Anat.*, 4:515 (1926).

21. BEILER, J. M., BRENDEL, R., and MARTIN, G. J.: *J. Pharmacol. & Exper. Therap.*, 118:415 (1956).

22. BERING, E. A., JR.: *J. Neurosurg.*, 12:385 (1955).

23. BERING, E. A., JR.: *Am. J. Physiol.*, 197:825 (1959).

24. BERL, S., and WAELSCH, H.: *J. Neurochem.*, 3:161 (1958).

25. BERL, S., LAJTHA, A., and WAELSCH, H.: *J. Neurochem.*, 7:186 (1961).

26. BRATTGARD, S., and LINDQUIST, T.: *J. Neurol., Neurosurg. & Psychiat.*, 17:11 (1954).

27. BRATTGARD, S., and LINDQUIST, T.: *Acta psychiat. et neurol. scandinav.*, 30:423 (1955).

28. BREEMAN, V. L., and CLEMENTE, C. D.: *J. Biophys. Biochem. Cytol.*, 1:161 (1955).

29. BRIERLEY, J. B.: *J. Physiol.*, 116:24P (1952).

30. BRIERLEY, J. B.: In *Metabolism of the Nervous System*, p. 121. D. Richter, Ed. London, Pergamon Press (1957).

31. BRODIE, B. B., and HOGBEN, C. A. M.: *J. Pharm. & Pharmacol.*, 9:345 (1957).

32. BRODIE, B. B., KURZ, H., and SCHANKER, L. S.: *J. Pharmacol. & Exper. Therap.*, 130:20 (1960).

33. BROMAN, T.: In *The Permeability of the Cerebral Vessels in Normal and Pathological Conditions.* Copenhagen, Munksgaard (1949).

34. BROMAN, T.: *Acta psychiat. et neurol. scandinav.*, 30:8 (1955).

35. BUTLER, T. C.: *J. Pharmacol. & Exper. Therap.*, 74:118 (1942).

36. BUTLER, T. C.: *J. Pharmacol. & Exper. Therap.*, 100:219 (1950).

37. CASSEN, B., and NEFF, R.: *Am. J. Physiol.*, 198:1296 (1960).

38. CHIRIGOS, M. A., GREENGARD, P., and UDENFRIEND, S.: *J. Biol. Chem.*, 235:2075 (1960).

39. CHRISTENSEN, J., FENG, Y. S. L., POLLEY, E., and WASE, A. W.: *Federation Proc.*, 17:358 (1958).

40. CLEMENTE, C. D., and HOLST, E. A.: *Arch. Neurol. & Psychiat.* 71:66 (1954).

41. CLOUET, D. H., and RICHTER, D.: *J. Neurochem.*, 3:219 (1959).

42. CROW, H. J.: *J. Neurol., Neurosurg. & Psychiat.*, 21:66 (1950).

43. DAVISON, A. N., and DOBBING, J.: *Biochem. J.*, 73:701 (1959).

44. DAVSON, H.: *J. Physiol.*, 128:52P (1955).

45. DAVSON, H.: *J. Physiol.*, 129:111 (1955).

46. DAVSON, H.: In *Physiology of the Ocular and Cerebrospinal Fluids*. London, Churchill, Ltd. (1956).
47. DAVSON, H.: In *The Cerebrospinal Fluid*, Ciba Foundation Symposium, p. 189. Wolstenholme, G. E. W., and O'Connor, C. M., Eds. Boston, Little, Brown (1958).
48. DAVSON, H., and SPAZIANI, E.: *J. Physiol., 149*:135 (1959).
49. DEMPSEY, E. W., and WISLOCKI, G. B.: *J. Biophys. Biochem. Cytol., 1*:245 (1955).
50. DINGMAN, W., and SPORN, M. B.: *J. Neurochem., 4*:148 (1959).
51. DOBBING, J.: *Guy's Hosp. Rep., 105*:27 (1956); *Physiol. Rev., 41*:130 (1961).
52. DOMEK, N. S., BARLOW, C. F., and ROTH, L. J.: *J. Pharmacol. & Exper. Therap., 130*:285 (1960).
53. EDSTRÖM, R.: *Acta psychiat. et neurol. scandinav., 33*:403 (1958).
54. EDSTRÖM, R.: *Acta psychiat. et neurol. scandinav., 35*:27 (1960).
55. EHRLICH, P.: In *Das Sauerstoff-Bedurfnis Des Organismus*. Berlin, Farben Analytische Studie (1885).
56. EICH, J.: *Deutsch. Ztschr. Nervenheilk., 164*:537 (1950).
56A. ELLIOTT, K. A. C., and VAN GELDER, N. M.: *J. Neurochem., 3*:28 (1958).
57. FARQUHAR, M. G., and HARTMANN, J. F.: *J. Neuropathol., 16*:18 (1957).
58. FISCHER, S. H., TROAST, L., WATERHOUSE, A., and SHANNON, J. A.: *J. Pharmacol. & Exper. Therap., 79*:373 (1943).
59. FISHMAN, R. A.: *J. Clin. Invest., 38*:1698 (1959).
60. FLEXNER, L. B.: In *Biochemistry of the Developing Nervous System*, p. 281. H. Waelsch, Ed. New York, Acad. Press (1955).
61. FLEXNER, L. B., FLEXNER, J. B., and ROBERTS, R. B.: *J. Cell. & Comp. Physiol., 51*:385 (1958).
62. FORD, D. D.: *J. Nerv. & Ment. Dis., 129*:530 (1959).
63. FÖLDES, I., and KELENTEL, B.: *Acta physiol. hung., 5*:149 (1954).
64. FRIEDEMANN, U.: *Physiol. Rev., 22*:125 (1942).
65. FRIES, B. A., and CHAIKOFF, I. L.: *J. Biol. Chem., 141*:479 (1941).
66. FURST, S., LAJTHA, A., and WAELSCH, H.: *J. Neurochem., 2*:216 (1958).
67. GAITONDE, M. K., and RICHTER, D.: *Proc. Roy. Soc.* (London), B, *145*:83 (1956).
68. GEIGER, A., MAGNES, J., TAYLOR, R. M., and VERALLI, M.: *Am. J. Physiol., 177*:138 (1954).
68A. GERSHENFELD, H. M., WALD, F., ZADUNAISKY, J. A., and DE ROBERTIS, E. D. P.: *Neurology, 9*:412 (1959).
69. GOLDSWORTHY, P. D., AIRD, R. B., and BECKER, R. A.: *J. Cell. & Comp. Physiol., 44*:519 (1954).
70. GRAZER, F. M., and CLEMENTE, C. D.: *Proc. Soc. Exper. Biol. & Med., 94*:758 (1957).
71. GREEN, J. B.: *J. Nerv. & Ment. Dis., 127*:359 (1958).
72. GREENBERG, D. M., AIRD, R. B., BOELTER, M. D., CAMPBELL, W. W., COHN, W. E., and MURAYAMA, M. M.: *Am. J. Physiol., 140*:47 (1943).
73. GREIG, M. E., and CARTER, M. K.: *Arch. Biochem. Biophys., 52*:175 (1954).
74. GREIG, M. E., and HOLLAND, W. C.: *Science, 110*:237 (1949).
75. GREIG, M. E., and GIBBONS, A. J.: *Am. J. Physiol., 196*:803 (1959).
76. GREIG, M. E., and MAYBERRY, T. C.: *J. Pharmacol. & Exper. Therap., 102*:1 (1951).
77 GRONTOFT, O.: *Acta path. et microbiol. scandinav.*, Suppl. 100, 1-109 (1954).
77A. GUROFF, G., and UDENFRIEND, S.: *J. Biol. Chem., 235*:3518 (1960).
78. HARDY, S. M.: *Nature, 185*:245 (1960).
79. HEINZ, E., and MARIANI, H. A.: *J. Biol. Chem., 228*:97 (1957).

80. HERLIN, L.: In *The Cerebrospinal Fluid,* p. 209. Wolstenholme, G. E. W., and O'Connor, C. M., Eds. Boston, Little, Brown (1958).

81. HESS, A.: *Arch. Neurol. & Psychiat., 73:*380 (1955).

82. HIMWICH, W. A., and PETERSEN, J. C.: *Dis. Nerv. System, 19:*104 (1958).

83. HIMWICH, W. A., PETERSEN, J. C., and ALLEN, M. L.: *Neurology, 7:*705 (1957).

84. HOLMBERG, G. K., GREIG, M. E., and GIBBONS, A. J.: *J. Neuropsychiat., 2:*15 (1960).

85. HUNTER, G., and SMITH, H. V.: *Nature, 186:*161 (1960).

86. HUNTER, G., SMITH, H. V., and TAYLOR, L. M.: *Biochem. J., 56:*588 (1954).

87. HURST, E. W., DAVIES, O. L.: *Brit. J. Pharmacol., 5:*147 (1950).

88. KAMIN, H., and HANDLER, P.: *J. Biol. Chem., 188:*193 (1951).

88A. KATZMAN, R.: *Neurology, 11:*27 (1961).

89. KATZMAN, R., and LEIDERMAN, H. P.: *Am. J. Physiol., 175:*263 (1953).

90. KELENTEI, B.: *Acta Physiol. Hung., 8:*165 (1955).

91. KELENTEI, B., and FÖLDES, I.: *Acta Physiol. Hung., 5:*139 (1954).

92. KELENTEI, B., and FÖLDES, I.: *Acta Physiol. Hung., 7:*433 (1955).

93. KERLEY, T. L., YIM, G. K. W., and CARR, C. J.: *Federation Proc., 17:*383 (1958).

94. KOREY, S. R., and MITCHELL, R.: *Biochim. Biophys. Acta, 7:*507 (1951).

95. KRAUTWALD, A., and KOLMAR, D.: *Ztschr. ges. inn. Med. u. ihre Grenzgebiete, 8:*1126 (1953).

96. KROGH, A.: *Proc. Royal Soc.,* B, *133:*140 (1946).

97. KUTTNER, R., SIMS, J. A., and GORDON, M. W.: *J. Neurochem., 6:*311 (1961).

98. LAJTHA, A.: *J. Neurochem., 1:*216 (1957).

99. LAJTHA, A.: *J. Neurochem., 2:*209 (1958).

100. LAJTHA, A.: *J. Neurochem., 3:*358 (1959).

101. LAJTHA, A.: In *Regional Neurochemistry,* p. 19. S. Kety and Elkes, J. Ed. New York, Pergamon Press (1961).

102. LAJTHA, A. and TOTH, J.: *J. Neurochem.,* in press.

103. LAJTHA, A.: Unpublished.

104. LAJTHA, A., BERL, S., and WAELSCH, H.: *J. Neurochem., 3:*322 (1959).

105. LAJTHA, A., BERL, S., and WAELSCH, H.: In *Inhibition in the Nervous System and Gamma-Aminobutyric Acid,* p. 460. E. Roberts *et al.,* Eds. New York, Pergamon Press (1960).

106. LAJTHA, A., FURST, S., GERSTEIN, A., and WAELSCH, H.: *J. Neurochem., 1:*289 (1957).

107. LAJTHA, A., and MELA, P.: *J. Neurochem., 7:*210 (1961).

108. LAJTHA, A., and TOTH, J.: *J. Neurochem., 8:*216 (1961).

109. LEE, J., and OLSZEWSKI, J.: *Neurology, 9:*7 (1959).

110. LEE, J. C., and OLSZEWSKI, J.: *Neurology, 9:*619 (1959).

111. LEE, J. C., and OLSZEWSKI, J.: *Neurology, 10:*814 (1960).

112. LEIDERMAN, H. P., and KATZMAN, R.: *Am. J. Physiol., 175:*271 (1953).

113. LENDING, M., SLOBODY, L. B., and MESTERN, J.: *Am. J. Physiol., 197:*465 (1959).

114. LEWANDOWSKY, M.: *Ztschr. Klin. Med., 40:*480 (1900).

115. LINDBERG, O., and ERNSTER, L.: *Biochem. J., 46:*43 (1950).

116. LOURIE, H., WEINSTEIN, W. J., and O'LEARY, J. L.: *J. Nerv. & Ment. Dis., 130:*1 (1960).

117. LUNDQUIST, F.: *Acta physiol. scandinav., 4:*201 (1942).

118. MACKLIN, C. A., and MACKLIN, M. T.: *Arch. Neurol. & Psychiat., 3:*353 (1920).

119. MANERY, J. F.: *Physiol. Rev., 34:*334 (1954).

119A. MANERY, J. F., and BALE, W. F.: *Am. J. Physiol., 132:*215 (1941).

119B. MANERY, J. F., and HAEGE, L. F.: *Am. J. Physiol., 134:*83 (1941).

120. MAYER, S. E., and BAIN, J. A.: *J. Pharmacol. & Exper. Therap., 118:*17 (1956).
121. MAYER, S., MAICKEL, R. P., and BRODIE, B. B.: *J. Pharmacol. & Exper. Therap., 127:*205 (1959).
122. MAYER, S. E., MAICKEL, R. P., and BRODIE, B. B.: *J. Pharmacol. & Exper. Therap., 128:*40 (1960).
123. MAYNARD, E. A., SCHULTZ, R. L., and PEASE, D. C.: *Am. J. Anat., 100:*409 (1957).
124. MAYNERT, E. W., and VAN DYKE, H. B.: *J. Pharmacol. & Exper. Therap., 98:*184 (1950).
125. MILLEN, J. W., and HESS, A.: *Brain, 81:*248 (1958).
126. MILLER, J. W., and ELLIOTT, H. W.: *J. Pharmacol. & Exper. Therap., 113:*283 (1955).
127. MOORE, G. E.: In *Diagnosis and Localization of Brain Tumors.* Springfield, Thomas (1953).
128. MORRISON, A. B.: *J. Clin. Invest., 38:*1769 (1959).
129. NEAME, K. D.: *J. Neurochem., 6:*358 (1961).
130. OKUMURA, N., OTSUKI, S., and FUKAI, N.: *Acta Med. Okayama, 13:*27 (1959).
131. OLSEN, N. S., and RUDOLPH, G. G.: *Am. J. Physiol., 183:*427 (1955).
132. OTOMO, E., and MICHAELIS, M.: *Proc. Soc. Exper. Biol. & Med., 104:*259 (1960).
133. OTOMO, E., VAN BUSKIRK, C., and WORKMAN, J. B.: *Neurology, 10:*112 (1960).
134. PALM, E.: *Acta ophth., 25:*29 (1947).
135. PAPPENHEIMER, J. R.: *Physiol. Rev., 33:*387 (1953).
135A. PAPPENHEIMER, J. R., HEISEY, S. R., and JORDAN, E. F.: *Am. J. Physiol., 200:*1 (1961).
136. PAPPIUS, H. M., and ELLIOTT, K. A. C.: *Canad. J. Biochem. Physiol., 34:*1007 (1956).
137. PARK, C. R., JOHNSON, L. H., WRIGHT, JR., J. H., and BATSEL, H.: *Am. J. Physiol., 191:*13 (1957).
138. PERLMAN, I., CHAIKOFF, I. L., and NORTON, M. E.: *J. Biol. Chem., 139:*433 (1941).
139. PRICE, S. A. P., and WEST, G. B.: *Nature, 185:*470 (1960).
140. PURPURA, D. P., and CARMICHAEL, M. W.: *Science, 131:*410 (1960).
141. QUADBECK, G., and HELMCHEN, H.: *Deutsch. med. Wchschr., 82:*1377 (1957).
141A. RAFAELSEN, D. J.: *J. Neurochem., 7:*45 (1961).
142. RALL, D. P., STABENAU, J. R., and ZUBROD, C. G.: *J. Pharmacol. & Exper. Therap., 125:*185 (1959).
143. RICHMOND, J. E., and HASTINGS, A. B.: *Am. J. Physiol., 199:*814 (1960).
144. ROBERTS, E., ROTHSTEIN, M., and BAXTER, C. E.: *Proc. Soc. Exper. Biol. & Med., 97:*796 (1958).
145. ROBERTS, R. B., FLEXNER, J. B., and FLEXNER, L. B.: *J. Neurochem., 4:*78 (1959).
146. ROSE, R. G.: *Internat. J. Appl. Radiation & Isotopes 4:*50 (1958).
147. ROSENBLATT, S., CHANLEY, J., SOBOTKA, H., and KAUFMAN, M. R.: *J. Neurochem., 5:*172 (1960).
148. ROTH, L. J., SCHOOLAR, J. C., and BARLOW, C. F.: *J. Pharmacol. & Exper. Therap., 125:*128 (1959).
149. ROWE, G. G., MAXWELL, G. M., CASTILLO, C. A., FREEMAN, D. J., and CRUMPTON, C. W.: *J. Clin. Invest., 38:*2154 (1959).
150. ROZDILSKY, B., and OLSZEWSKI, J.: *Neurology, 10:*631 (1960).
151. RUCKES, J., and DIEMER, K.: *Klin. Wchschr., 34:*919 (1956).
152. SACKS, J., and CULBRETH, G. G.: *Am. J. Physiol., 165:*251 (1951).
153. SAMACHSON, J., KABAKOW, B., SPENCER, H., and LASZLO, D.: *Proc. Soc. Exper. Biol. & Med., 102:*287 (1959).

154. SCHADE, J. P., and VAN HARREVELD, A.: *Anat. Rec., 133:*333 (1959).
155. SCHANBERG, S., and GIARMAN, N. J.: *Biochim. et Biophys. Acta, 41:*556 (1960).
156. SCHMID, H.: *Arch. Psychiat. Nervenkrankh., 95:*303 (1931).
157. SCHULTZ, R. L., MAYNARD, E. A., and PEASE, D. C.: *Am. J. Anat., 100:*369 (1957).
158. SCHWERIN, P., BESSMAN, S. P., and WAELSCH, H.: *J. Biol. Chem., 184:*37 (1950).
159. SELVERSTONE, B.: In *The Cerebrospinal Fluid, Ciba Foundation Symposium,* p. 147. Wolstenholme, G. E. W., and O'Connor, C. M., Eds. Boston, Little, Brown (1958).
160. SLOBODY, L. B., LANG, D., LENDING, M., BORRELLI, F. J., and TYREE, M.: *Am. J. Physiol., 190:*365 (1957).
161. SMITH, H. V., TAYLOR, L. M., and HUNTER, G.: *J. Neurol., Neurosurg. & Psychiat., 18:*237 (1955).
162. SOLOWAY, A. H.: *Science, 128:*1572 (1958).
163. SOLOWAY, A. H., WHITMAN, B., and MESSER, J. R.: *J. Pharmacol. & Exper. Therap., 129:*310 (1960).
164. STERN, J. R., EGGLESTON, L. V., HEMS, R., and KREBS, H. A.: *Biochem. J., 44:*410 (1949).
165. STREICHER, E., and PRESS, G. D.: *Federation Proc., 19:*285 (1960).
166. SWEET, W. H., BROWNELL, G. L., SCHOLL, J. A., BOWSHER, D. R., BENDA, P., and STICKLEY, E. E.: *A. Res. Nerv. & Ment. Dis. Proc., 34:*101 (1954).
167. SWEET, W. H., and LOCKSLEY, H. B.: *Proc. Soc. Exper. Biol. & Med., 84:*397 (1953).
168. TAKAGAKI, G., HIRANO, S., and NAGATA, Y.: *J. Neurochem., 4:*124 (1959).
169. THEILER, M.: *Ann. Trop. Med., 24:*249 (1930).
169A. TORACK, R. M., TERRY, R. D., and ZIMMERMAN, H. M.: *Am. J. Path., 35:*1135 (1959).
169B. TORACK, R. M., TERRY, R. D., and ZIMMERMAN, H. M.: *Am. J. Path., 36:*273 (1960).
170. TSCHIRGI, R. D.: In *The Biology of Mental Health and Disease,* p. 34. New York, Hoeber (1952).
170A. TSCHIRGI, R. D.: In *Handbook of Physiology,* Vol. 3, Neurophysiology, p. 1865. Field, J. Ed. Washington Am. Physiol. Soc. (1960).
171. TSUKADA, Y., NAGATA, Y., and HIRANO, S.: *Nature, 186:*474 (1960).
171A. VAN HARREVELD, A., and SCHADE, J. P.: In *Structure and Function of the Cerebral Cortex,* p. 239. Tower, D. B., and Schade, J. P., Eds. Amsterdam, Elsevier (1960).
172. VEITH, G., and WAGNER, H.: *Beitr. Path. Anat. u. allgem. Path., 115:*237 (1955).
173. WAELSCH, H.: In *Biochemistry of the Developing Nervous System,* p. 187. H. Waelsch, Ed. New York, Acad. Press (1955).
174. WAELSCH, H.: In *Metabolism of the Nervous System,* p. 431. D. Richter, Ed. London, Pergamon Press (1957).
175. WAELSCH, H.: *J. Nerv. & Ment. Dis., 126:*33 (1958).
176. WAELSCH, H.: In *Biochemistry of the Central Nervous System,* p. 36. F. Brucke, Ed. London, Pergamon Press (1959).
177. WAELSCH, H.: In *Structure and Function of Cerebral Cortex,* p. 313. D. B. Tower and J. P. Schade, Eds. Amsterdam, Elsevier (1960).
177A. WAELSCH, H., and LAJTHA, A.: *Physiol. Rev., 41:*709 (1961).
178. WALLACE, G. B., and BRODIE, D. B.: *J. Pharmacol. & Exper. Therap., 65:*220 (1939).
179. WALLACE, G. B., and BRODIE, B. B.: *J. Pharmacol. & Exper. Therap., 68:*50 (1940).

180. WALLACE, G. B., and BRODIE, B. B.: *J. Pharmacol. & Exper. Therap., 70:*418 (1940).
181. WASE, A. W., CHRISTENSEN, J., and POLLEY, E.: *Arch. Neurol. & Psychiat., 75:*54 (1956).
182. WEATHERBY, J. H.: *J. Lab. & Clin. Med., 28:*1817 (1943).
183. WEIL-MALHERBE, H., AXELROD, J., and TOMCHICK, R.: *Science, 129:*1226 (1959).
184. WEIR, E. G., and HASTINGS, A. B.: *J. Biol. Chem., 129:*547 (1939).
185. WOOLLAM, D. H. M., and MILLEN, J. W.: *Biol. Rev., 29:*251 (1954).
186. WYCKOFF, R. W. G., and YOUNG, J. Z.: *Proc. Roy. Soc.* (London), B, *144:*440 (1956).
187. YAMAMOTO, T.: *J. Neuropath. & Exper. Neurol., 18:*418 (1959).

XIX

ACETYLCHOLINE DISTRIBUTION AND SYNTHESIS IN THE CENTRAL NERVOUS SYSTEM

J. H. QUASTEL

DISTRIBUTION OF ACETYLCHOLINE IN BRAIN

V<small>ARIOUS ESTIMATIONS</small> of acetylcholine content of different parts of the mammalian central nervous system have been made (Barsoum,[1] Dikshit,[2] MacIntosh,[3] Welsh and Hyde,[4] Feldberg and Vogt[5]). The results indicate that, on the whole, the cerebellum has the least acetylcholine of any part of the brain, the greatest quantity being found in the region of the brain stem. Welsh and Hyde[4] have made estimates of the free acetylcholine in various parts of the brains of rats of different ages, and their results (given as averages) are quoted in Table I. They conclude that different parts of the nervous system of the rat have widely different levels of free acetylcholine, that the relative values of the different parts of the brain change with age, and that there is an increase in the free acetylcholine per unit weight of the entire brain with age. Elliott and Henderson[6] think, however, that the free acetylcholine found in brain is largely an artefact, most of it being liberated in the process of extraction in amounts varying with the amount of bound acetylcholine present and varying with the conditions of homogenization. Nevertheless, traces of acetylcholine are found in the cerebrospinal fluid for periods up to 48 hours after head injury in cats and dogs (Bornstein[7]). It is also found in the cerebrospinal fluid in human patients after head injury, the concentrations being roughly proportional to the extent of clinical and electroencephalographic abnormalities, and in the cerebrospinal fluid of epileptics (though not, or seldom, in that of non epileptics) (Tower and McEachern[8]).

Stone[9] quotes values of approximately 1 γ/gm. total acetylcholine in frozen brain cortical tissue which is considerably increased after tetra-

TABLE I[4]

DISTRIBUTION OF FREE ACETYLCHOLINE IN BRAINS OF RATS

(*Free acetylcholine µg./gm. tissue*)

Age of Rats	Brain Stem	Medulla	Pallium	Cerebellum	Whole Brain
Infant	0.28	0.60	0.16	0.26	0.1
25 days	0.70	0.80	0.20	0.13	0.2
Adult	0.58	0.37	0.20	0.10	0.4

ethylpyrophosphate injection to the animals. Bennett *et al.*,[10] using brains (excluding cerebellum, medulla and pons) of various strains of rats frozen in liquid oxygen, and using improved methods of extraction, quote values of acetylcholine of about 4 γ/gm. They suggest from their analyses of acetylcholine concentrations in the brain and of cholinesterase activities that the genetic mechanisms controlling these values are independent.

The total acetylcholine of brain is usually one and one-half to four times the apparently free acetylcholine (Corteggiani,[11] Mann, Tennenbaum and Quastel,[12] Welsh,[13] Welsh and Hyde[4]). MacIntosh[3] found, with the cat, that the total acetylcholine was least in the cerebellum (0.18 μg./gm.) and greatest in the autonomic nerves and ganglia (15-40 μg./gm.). The basal ganglia were richest in total acetylcholine (7.0 μg./gm.) among several parts of the brain examined. Szepsenwol and Caretti[14] have found, with the developing chick, results similar to those with the rat. It has been pointed out[4] that, except for the cerebral cortex or pallium, the changes in acetylcholine level of the various parts of the brain with age are paralleled by changes in respiration, glucose utilization and glycogen storage. Thus Himwich, Baker and Fazekas[15] have found that the excised cerebral tissue of rats 1 to 25 days old has a lower respiratory activity than the adult tissue, a fact confirmed by Tyler and van Harreveld[16] who also demonstrated an increased glucose utilization per unit weight with age. Crossland[17] notes that the acetylcholine content of whole brain is lower in infant rats than in the adults and that[18] the increase during development takes place in cerebral hemispheres, cerebellum and upper brain stem but a decrease occurs in the pons and medulla. Welsh and Hyde[4] point out that the order of increasing resistance of the parts of the nervous system to anoxia and to hypoglycemia is similar to the order of these parts arranged to show increasing amounts of acetylcholine per unit weight. The parts (cerebellum and cortex) least resistant to anoxia have the lowest contents of acetylcholine, the parts that are most resistant (spinal nerves, autonomic ganglia) are richest in acetylcholine.

The distribution of acetylcholine throughout the nervous system is apparently roughly parallel to that of choline acetylase.[19] It is (in the rat) greatest in the upper brain stem, least in the cerebellum and intermediate in the cerebral hemispheres and in the division including the pons and medulla.[18]

ACETYLCHOLINE AND FUNCTIONAL STATE

Richter and Crossland[20] have pointed out that the (total) acetylcholine content of the rat brain depends on the physiological state of the animal. It seems to vary inversely with the activity of the animal, being increased during barbiturate anaesthesia and sleep and being reduced in emotional states or after electrical stimulations or in convulsions. Electrical stimulation of the animals (by passage of the electric current through scalp electrodes for 1 to 3 seconds) caused a loss of over 50% of the whole brain acetylcholine. The level was raised about 40% in anaesthesia and was three times the value found after convulsions. Both the loss of brain acetylcholine and its resynthesis *in vivo* were rapidly reversible. The rate of resynthesis *in vivo* after electric stimulation is about 7 μg. acetylcholine per gram (five times the normal brain content) per minute.

Further studies[18,21] on rabbits and mice, as well as on rats, confirmed the fact that brain acetylcholine is raised in anaesthesia and that the acetylcholine level is reduced below the normal during seizures induced by pentylenetetrazol or picrotoxin. Stone[9] has also shown that there is lowering of cerebral acetylcholine after seizures in dogs due to administration of pentylenetetrazol or picrotoxin or methylfluoracetate. A lowering due to pentylenetrazol administration also occurs even if seizures are blocked as in deep pentobarbital anaesthesia.[9]

Hypoxia leads to a lowering of brain acetylcholine, due either to the hypoxia itself or to the excitement caused thereby[22] but oxygen lack also counteracts the increase due to anaesthesia.[21] Acetylcholine is decreased in rat brain during insulin hypoglycemia,[23] the effect being probably due to a decreased rate of acetylcholine synthesis (owing to diminished availability of acetyl groups[9]).

In interpreting the results of anaesthesia or of excitement on acetylcholine levels in the brain, two factors have to be borne in mind: (1) the diminished stimulation in the nervous system due to paralysis of certain nerve centres by anaesthetics and hence the rise in the ratio ATP/ADP, (which falls during electrical stimulation or increased K^+/Ca^{++}) with resulting increased acetylcholine level partly due to increased ATP; (2) the release of free acetylcholine from bound acetylcholine, following nerve stimulation (e.g., electrical or by increased K+), destruction of the free acetylcholine by cholinesterase and hence a fall in total acetylcholine.

BIOLOGICAL SYNTHESIS OF ACETYLCHOLINE

Intact cells

Observations had been made by Beznak[24] that acetylcholine is formed in minced frog heart muscle when sufficient eserine is present to prevent its destruction by choline esterase. Chang[25] stated that it is formed in placenta. The fact, however, that acetylcholine is synthesized by the brain, under conditions aproximating the physiological, was first shown by Quastel, Tennenbaum and Wheatley.[26] They demonstrated that when brain cortex slices are allowed to respire in a medium containing eserine, acetylcholine is formed, this being synthesized as a result of metabolic processes taking place in the tissue. The rate of synthesis is greatly suppressed by anaerobic conditions or by the presence of sodium cyanide. The presence of glucose, sodium lactate, sodium pyruvate, sodium α-glycerophosphate or sodium glutamate increases the rate of synthesis of acetylcholine by brain cortex slices, the effect of glucose being the greatest. The presence of sodium succinate, while increasing the rate of oxygen uptake of the brain cortex slices, does not result in increased acetylcholine synthesis. Neither is the presence of sodium fluoride or of acetate effective in raising the rate of synthesis of the ester. It was suggested as a result of consideration of the effects of potassium and calcium ions on the rates of acetylcholine synthsis in presence of glucose, in phosphate or bicarbonate media, that the synthesis is intimately connected with glucose metabolism in intact brain tissue. It was also concluded from investigations of the relative activities of brain, liver, kidney, spleen, testis and defibrinated blood that there is no correlation between the choline esterase of an organ and its power of synthesizing acetylcholine *in vitro*.

Bound and Free Acetylcholine

Mann *et al.*[12,27] pursuing these enquiries found that there exists in brain a substance, not pharmacologically active so far as the eserinized leech is concerned, that breaks down under a variety of conditions to form acetylcholine. This is known as bound acetylcholine and it may be broken down at once to form free acetylcholine by the presence of denaturing agents, e.g., excess chloroform, or acids. At pH 3.0 free acetylcholine is liberated from the bound form at room temperature, and at pH 6.0 or 6.5 at 37°C. The bound form is synthesized in brain tissue reaching a limiting value when the latter is allowed to respire in the presence of glucose, sodium lactate or sodium pyruvate;

under anaerobic conditions little or no synthesis takes place. The presence of eserine has no measurable effect on the synthesis or breakdown of the bound acetylcholine (but see also Elliott and Henderson[6]).

The existence of a substance in the brain, which on heating forms free acetylcholine was noted by Corteggiani et al.[28] (see also Loewi[29]). Pinotti[30] found that much acetylcholine is present in an inactive state in cholinergic fibres, the vagus in particular, and Chang[31] noted a similar phenomenon in connection with placenta. Kahane and Levy[32] have discussed the effects of extraction procedures on the appearance of free and bound acetylcholine. Trethwie[33] concluded that bound acetylcholine is an association of acetylcholine with cell debris, etc., but it is clear that since acetylcholine is not freely diffusible in the cell it must be held in the cell in some fairly well defined manner.[12,34,38]

Stedman and Stedman[35] showed that macerated brain suspended in saline-chloroform, or saline-ether mixtures, liberates free acetylcholine. Such acetylcholine is for the most part derived from preformed bound acetylcholine[36,37] and its appearance, under these conditions, is not evidence of de novo synthesis of the ester.

There is little doubt that the bound acetylcholine described by Mann et al.[12] is identical with the complex in brain tissue described by Corteggiani et al.[28] which on heating to 70°C. for 3 minutes gives rise to acetylcholine. The action of alcohol, or of acid alcohol, in liberating free acetylcholine described by Loewi[29] is probably due to a denaturing action on bound acetylcholine. Mann et al.[12] found (1) that the formation of the bound form is not appreciably higher in the presence of eserine, which prevents the destruction of free acetylcholine, than in its absence; (2) that the initial rate of formation of bound acetylcholine in brain tissue exceeds that of free acetylcholine. The amount of bound acetylcholine rapidly reaches a limiting value, whilst that of the free increases more slowly with time. This result would also occur if free acetylcholine were formed first with subsequent rapid adsorption to form the complex, but experiments[12] showed no such rapid formation of the complex from brain tissue and added acetylcholine. That some formation of the complex takes place when acetylcholine is added to brain tissue, initially devoid of it, is apparent.[12,47] Elliott et al.[6,46] have given further evidence of this reversibility. Schallek[41] failed to find any binding of acetylcholine by albumin or globulin, and Corteggiani[47] could find none with casein. Schallek[41] found that the addition of acetylcholine to ground lobster nerve cord, previously freed from acetylcholine by treatment with 0.5 M KCl and then placed in a potassium free medium, resulted in the formation of some bound acetylcholine. Hobbiger and Werner[48] have adduced evidence in favour of an equilibrium in the central nervous system between free and bound acetylcholine. They suggest also the existence of a third unknown form in the brains of warm blooded animals.

Corteggiani *et al.*[49,50] have found that the lecithinase of cobra venom releases free acetylcholine from brain tissue. Braganca and Quastel[38] have suggested that bound acetylcholine may simply be free acetylcholine held within the cell mitochondria, the structure of which is broken down by venom lecithinase as well as by a variety of other agents.

The presence of either ether or chloroform brings about a rapid breakdown of bound into free acetylcholine in brain suspensions in aqueous media. Ether, it should be noted, is highly inhibitory to acetylcholine synthesis in intact brain tissue bathed in phosphate or bicarbonate media.[37]

Other subcellular particles might act similarly to mitochondria in binding acetylcholine.[52] There is, in fact, a suggestion that "synaptic vesicles" which are small subcellular particles found in the presynaptic axoplasm in a wide variety of synapses may be the sites in which acetylcholine is stored pending discharge into the intermembranal space of the synapse. These vesicles may represent quantal units of the transmitter substance.[53]

ACTION OF POTASSIUM AND OTHER IONS ON SYNTHESIS OF BOUND AND FREE ACETYLCHOLINE IN BRAIN TISSUE

Mann, Tennenbaum and Quastel[27] found that the addition of potassium chloride (0.027 M) to a medium containing eserine, and in which intact rat brain slices are respiring, brings about a large increase in the rate of formation of acetylcholine. In bicarbonate media containing pyruvate or glucose the total acetylcholine formed may reach a value of 40 γ/gm. wet weight of tissue. The large increase in acetylcholine formation effected by potassium seems to lie entirely with the free acetylcholine, for the amount of bound acetylcholine is either unchanged or diminished. Rubidium, and to a smaller extent caesium ions, have effects similar to potassium. The accelerating action of potassium ions is neutralized by the addition of calcium or magnesium ions. Under conditions where no synthesis of acetylcholine is taking place in either minced brain, or in intact brain slices, the effect of potassium is to break down the bound acetylcholine and to release the free ester, this phenomenon occurring both aerobically and anaerobically. These results were interpreted[27] as being due to an effect of potassium ions on the permeability of the cell whereby acetylcholine diffuses through the cell membrane at an increased rate. It is possible, however, that stimulation of the citric acid cycle in brain *in vitro* by added potassium ions (Kini and Quastel[120]) may increase acetylcholine synthesis by increasing the availability of acetyl-CoA. Sodium ions must play an important role in the process of acetylcholine formation or liberation in brain slices for if they are replaced by potassium ions acetylcholine synthesis ceases.[27] Ammonium ions act similarly to potassium in bringing about a conversion of bound acetylcholine into free acetylcholine. They have, however, a highly inhibitory action on acetylcholine synthesis in brain slices. This may be partly due to the fact[54] that, in presence of respiring brain slices, the presence of extra ammonium ions increases the rate of formation of glutamine, thereby diminishing the available adenosine triphosphate and therefore the rate of synthesis of acetylcholine.

Similar findings to those found by Mann *et al.* were obtained by Welsh and Hyde[39] who used the bivalve mollusc *Venus mercenaria* for their bio-assay of acetylcholine (see also Welsh and Taub[40]). Schallek[41] found that acetylcholine in arthropod nerve is present in both the free and bound forms, the latter being converted to the former by the presence of potassium ions by a process of cation exchange, and not by a permeability change. Renshaw, Green and Ziff[34] had already suggested that the effects of injection of a series of choline derivatives were due to release of acetylcholine by "exchange adsorption;" such ionic exchange was also indicated by the experiments of Ziff, Jahn and Renshaw[42] on the inhibition of choline esterase by ethoxycholine. Duliére and Loewi[43] showed that the application of acetylcholine to the central nervous system of the frog results in the release of potassium, pointing to the possibility of cationic exchange. Schallek[41] could find no effect of calcium ions in releasing free acetylcholine from the bound form. Brown and Feldberg[44] had shown some years earlier that acetylcholine could only be released from perfused sympathetic ganglia by potassium and not by calcium ions.

McLennan and Elliott,[45] and Elliott and Henderson[6] have also studied the accelerating action of potassium ions on acetylcholine synthesis in intact brain tissue *in vitro,* and on the relations between free and bound acetylcholine. The former find that the synthesis of acetylcholine is highly sensitive to the calcium ion concentration of the medium, the optimum being 0.0013 M. The smaller rate of synthesis of acetylcholine in phosphate media as compared with that in a medium containing bicarbonate, as found by Mann *et al.*,[27] is due according to McLennan and Elliott to the inactivation by phosphate of the small quantity of calcium ions required for the synthesis and also to the requirement of the synthesizing reactions in brain slices for the bicarbonate-CO_2 system. The optimal bicarbonate cencentration is 0.025 M.

The relation between free and bound acetylcholine in brain tissue is greatly affected, as already pointed out, by the presence of ammonium, potassium, rubidium and caesium ions. The increased rate of synthesis of acetylcholine found with potassium ions has been held to be due to the action of the latter in accelerating the process of release in brain tissue of free acethylcholine from the bound, which is a rate-limiting step. Experiments by Braganca and Quastel[38] have shown that addition of cobra venom, which has been heated to inactivate all enzymes except lecithinase, has a marked effect in breaking down bound to free acetylcholine and in increasing by nearly 100% the rate of acetylcholine synthesis in brain homogenates in presence of glucose or sodium pyruvate. The effect seems to be similar to that of potassium. It is concluded that venom lecithinase affects acetylcholine synthesis by accelerating the rate- limiting step involved in the formation of free from bound acetylcholine, but it may act by changing the permeability of mitochondria for substances such as adenosine triphosphate which may profoundly affect acetylcholine synthesis.

Application of electrical impulses to brain slices respiring in a glucose medium also causes a loss of bound acetylcholine and, with eserine present, an increase in the free form (Rowsell[55]). Thus such application resembles the effects of the presence of increased potassium ions.

In the absence of aqueous media, the presence of small quantities of ether accelerates acetylcholine formation in minced brain. The increase is entirely due to free acetylcholine formation, the amount of bound acetylcholine being diminished. This accelerating action of ether is diminished or removed by the addition to the tissue of 0.02 M calcium ions or by carrying out the experiments anaerobically. The effect of ether, under such circumstances, resemble those due to potassium on acetylcholine formation in brain slices. The suggestion made by Mann et al.[37] is that both potassium ions, and ether in relatively small concentration, react in a similar manner on the rate limiting step controlling acetylcholine formation in brain tissue, i.e., on the conversion of bound to free acetylcholine. Feldberg[51] has found an accelerating effect of ether on acetylcholine formation using guinea pig brain homogenates.

SYNTHESIS OF ACETYLCHOLINE IN CELL FREE EXTRACTS

The discovery of acetylcholine synthesis by enzymatic means[26] had considerable consequences in the field of biochemistry for it was the first demonstration *in vitro* of an enzyme controlled acetylation.

The subject was materially advanced by the finding of Nachmansohn and Machado[56] who showed that extracts of brain and nervous tissue will synthesize acetylcholine in the presence of choline, under anaerobic conditions and in the absence of glucose, so long as adenosine triphosphate is supplied and if fluoride is added to prevent the breakdown of adenosine triphosphate (ATP) by adenosine triphosphatase. It thus became obvious that ATP derived from carbohydrate metabolism in brain may be available for brain acetylations. Homogenizing the brain tissue apparently brought the enzyme system into solution, for the extracts were not diminished in activity when the solid particles were removed by centrifuging.[71] The enzyme system was termed choline acetylase. It is now realized that the system is a complex one and the term choline acetylase is reserved for the enzyme apparently specifically concerned with the transfer of acetate to choline.[72]

Nachmansohn and John[57] and Feldberg and Mann[73] have shown that the enzyme system can be extracted from acetone dried brain tissue and that this procedure yields more active preparations than homogenates. The later also found[65] that adenosine triphosphate cannot be replaced by creatine phosphate unless muscle adenylic acid is still present. The synthesis of acetylcholine under these conditions is accelerated by potassium ions and inhibited by calcium ions, so that it is clear that these ions may exert effects independently of permeability changes. The synthesis is inhibited by certain naphthoquinones[32] and by α-keto acids.[58] Doubtless this inhibition is due to combination with the thiol groups of the acetylating enzyme. Reagents such as p-chloromercuribenzoate and iodosobenzoate that react with thiol groups inhibit acetylcholine synthesis.[75] Feldberg and Mann[73] showed that the presence of cysteine or glutathionine in the medium secures optimal anaerobic synthesis, and synthesis under aerobic conditions, possibly by maintaining the integrity of the thiol groups of the choline acetylase system. These groups seem to be well protected, in the intact cell, for Stadie, Riggs and Haugaard[74] have found no inhibitory effect of a high oxygen tension on the synthesis of acetylcholine in brain slices, whereas cell free extracts under these conditions are rapidly inactivated.

COMPONENTS OF THE SYSTEM, IN BRAIN, SYNTHESIZING ACETYLCHOLINE

Feldberg and Mann[65] reported that a heat stable, dialyzable substance normally present in extracts prepared from fresh acetone dried tissue is required for optimal synthesis of acetylcholine. Similar observations were made independently by Lipton,[76] Lipmann and Kaplan[77] and Nachmansohn and Berman.[68] The substance was called the coenzyme of acetylation or coenzyme A (Lipmann). It is essential for many metabolic steps and its constitution is now well established (see Novelli et al.,[78] Snell et al.,[79] Lynen and Reichert[80]). Acetyl-CoA is essential for the formation of acetylcholine, and together with choline it is the substrate of choline acetylase, the enzyme that controls the rate of synthesis of acetylcholine.[82]

It is formed during the oxidative breakdown of fatty acids, amino acids and sugars. Pyruvate[83,84] is often the immediate precursor of acetyl-CoA, the reaction involved being as follows:

$$\text{Pyruvate} + \text{DPN} + \text{CoA} \rightarrow \text{Acetyl-CoA} + CO_2 + \text{DPNH}_2$$

Thus oxidative metabolism of glucose via pyruvate is a principal source of acetyl-CoA in the brain cell and hence of acetylcholine.

In brain cell extracts, in which pyruvate oxidation does not proceed, acetate is a source of acetyl-CoA so long as ATP, CoA and the necessary activating enzyme (acetyl kinase) is present.

The reactions involved seem to be as follows (Berg[84a]):

1. ATP + acetate $\rightleftharpoons$ adenylacetate + pyrophosphate
2. Adenylacetate + CoA $\rightleftharpoons$ acetyl-CoA + adenylic acid

Other donors of acetyl-CoA may be acetylphosphate (in presence of phosphotransacetylase[85]) or citrate by operation of the condensing enzyme.[86]

Intrathoracic injections of acetate-2-C[14] into the adult house fly Musca domestica gives rise to acetyl-C[14]-choline;[103] the labelled acetylcholine arises from labelled acetyl-CoA either directly from labelled acetate or from labelled pyruvate arising during metabolism.

Measurements of choline acetylase activities in tissue extracts require the presence of some excess of acetyl-CoA, so that the amount of the latter is not rate-limiting. Considerable advances in the methods of estimation of choline acetylase have been made by Hebb,[87] and Hebb and Smallman,[88] and these are summarized in a recent review by Hebb[89] of the properties and distribution of choline acetylase. Smallman[90] has shown that the rate of synthesis of acetylcholine is dependent on the availability of acetyl-CoA, and Milton,[91] in a study of acetylcholine synthesis in rabbit atria (acetone powders), to which an acetylphosphate-CoA system was added, has shown that an optimal rate of acetylcholine synthesis takes place with a limiting quantity of CoA, increase of which does not increase the rate of acetylcholine formation. Moreover, with less than optimal quantities of CoA present, the addition of acetylcholine suppresses synthesis of acetylcholine (see also Mann et al.[27]).

CHOLINE ACETYLASE

This enzyme which controls the reaction:

Choline + Acetyl-CoA → Acetylcholine + CoA

is measured in tissue extracts under conditions where there is an adequate supply of acetyl-CoA present. This may be accomplished by addition of acetyl-CoA (care being taken, however, to assess the activities

TABLE II[89]

CHOLINE ACETYLASE CONCENTRATIONS IN VARIOUS PARTS OF THE NERVOUS SYSTEM

(Concentrations given as mg. acetylcholine formed per gm. acetone dried brain per hour at 37°)

Cerebral cortex	Man	0.1– 0.29	(New cortex); 0.58 (Allocortex)
	Pig	0.5– 1.1	(New cortex); 1.8–2.6 (Allocortex)
	Cat	0.8– 1.3	(New cortex); 2.1–4.5 (Allocortex)
	Sheep	1.0– 1.7	(New cortex); 1.6–5.2 (Allocortex)
	Dog	1.2– 3.0	(New cortex); 2.6–4.2 (Allocortex)
	Rabbit	4 – 4.8	(New cortex); 3.5–4.5 (Allocortex)
	Guinea pig	4.0	(New cortex); 3.7–5.0 (Allocortex)
Basal ganglia	Caudate nucleus		
	Man	10–13.5	
	other mammals	7–15.0	
	(given above)		
Amygdaloid nucleus	Man	2.6	
	other mammals	2.5–11.0	
	(given above)		
Thalamus	Man	0.3	
	other mammals	1.7– 3.5	
	(given above)		
Optic lobes	Domestic fowl	10.8–12.0	
	Pigeon	7.0–11.3	
Cerebellar cortex	Man	0.01– 0.2	
	Sheep	0.07	
	Dog	0.09	
	Cat	0.25	
Retina	Domestic fowl	22–32	
	Pigeon	18–22	
	Sheep	15–17	
	Guinea pig	10.4	
	Pig	10.5–12	
	Horse	3 – 3.3	
	Dog	0.54	
	Cat	0.4	
Optic nerve	Man, cat, ox	0	
	Dog	0 – 0.01	
	Pigeon	0.3– 0.4	
Ventral spinal roots	Dog	10.8–12	
	Cat	8.8–10	
Dorsal spinal roots	Dog	0 – 0.02	
	Cat	0.02	

of deacylases present that may hydrolyze the acetyl-CoA) or by the addition of an enzyme system generating acetyl-CoA.[89]

It is a thiol enzyme, relatively stable and can be kept at low temperatures as an acetone powder for lengthy periods. Its activity is not affected by ether, or by anticholinesterases, or by narcotics.[92] Anaesthetics that strongly inhibit acetylcholine synthesis in respiring brain slices have little or no effect on the extracted enzyme. This is due to their suppression of ATP or acetyl-CoA formation which may represent a rate limiting step. Similarly the inhibition of acetylcholine formation in respiring brain slices by 2 mM cocaine is not due to inhibition of choline acetylase.[93,94] Continuous cyclopropane anesthesia lowers the rate of formation of labelled acetylcholine from labelled acetate in the adult house fly, probably by its effect on acetate metabolism.[103]

Distribution of Choline Acetylase

The richest sources of choline acetylase, so far observed, are the squid head ganglian and the brain of the blowfly (Smallman[95]). Many details concerning the distribution of choline acetylase in the animal kingdom in organisms without a nervous system and in non-nervous tissue of metazoa are given by Hebb.[89] It is concluded that some cells and tissues other than the nervous system synthesize acetylcholine "but the number of instances in which a non-nervous origin of acetylcholine has been unequivocally demonstrated are few." Both *L. plantarum* and the human placenta contain an enzyme, synthesizing acetylcholine, which seems to be identical with the enzyme of nervous origin.

Values of concentrations of choline acetylase in different parts of the nervous system are given by Hebb[89] and some of these are given in Table II. Feldberg and Vogt,[96] as a result of their studies on the distribution of choline acetylase, conclude that cholinergic neurones are present in the central nervous system and form only a fraction of the total population of nerve cells. The variation of choline acetylase from one region to another is related to the number of cholinergic neurones, or parts of neurones, in the different regions (see Hebb[89]).

Specificity of Choline Acetylase

The existence of esters of choline, other than acetylcholine, in mammalian and invertebrate tissues has now been demonstrated e.g., propionylcholine,[97] butyrylcholine,[98] imidazole-acetylcholine[99] in mammalian tissue and other choline esters (e.g., the urocanic ester) in invertebrate tissue.[100] Berry and Whittaker[101] studying the acyl-group specificity of sheep, pigeon and rat brain choline acetylase, by coupling the enzyme with a preparation from pigeon liver capable of activating various fatty acids, have shown that the enzyme is able to synthesis all the n-acyllcholines up to C_6 and also palmitoylcholine. The physiological significance of the synthesis of the homologues of acetylcholine by brain tissue is not clear. It is doubtful whether such homologues actually occur in brain tissue; if they are synthesized *in vivo* they must be broken down rapidly to account for their lack of accumulation even in small quantities.

Choline Acetylase and Choline Esterase

The formation of choline acetylase in the developing nervous system seems to parallel that of true choline esterase.[102] It is just detectable in the rabbit cerebrum at 18 to 20 days and in the guinea pig cerebrum at 33 days of gestation. A further 90 days growth is required before the enzyme reaches the adult level. The significance of the relation of the cholinesterases to choline acetylase has been examined in detail by Hebb.[89] Results given in Table III, collected from the values of Hebb and Silver[104] and of Burgen and Chipman[105] show the preponderance of choline acetylase and of choline esterase in the caudate nucleus. Experiments have been carried out recently on the

TABLE III

ACETYLCHOLINE SYNTHESIS AND HYDROLYSIS IN DOG BRAIN

Part of Brain	Acetylcholine Synthesis $\mu moles/gm./hr.$ Formed	Acetylcholine Esterase $\mu moles/gm./hr.$ Decomposed	Acetylcholine Hydrolyzed by Pseudocholine Esterase $\mu moles/gm./hr.$ Decomposed
Cerebral cortex	1.3–3.7	60–100	2–4
Cerebellar cortex	0.09	460	0.5
Caudate nucleus	13	1900	2
Thalamus	3.1	220–310	5
Hypothalamus	2	190	11

gradients of choline esterase and choline acetylase, in sectioned nerves (these enzymes increasing above the site of the lesion). The results[106] support the view that transport of the enzyme depends on movement of the structural framework of the axon, perhaps growth of the whole axon, axonal choline acetylase being firmly bound to structural elements.[107]

Site of Choline Acetylase in the Cell

About 50 to 70% of the choline acetylase of the nerve cell is located in the mitochondria.[89] Little or none is associated with the cell membrane or the nuclei, and little is found in the microsomes.

INHIBITION OF ACETYLCHOLINE FORMATION

MacIntosh, Birks and Sastry[117] have shown that the toxicity of a 'hemicholinium' compound (Schueller[118]) is due to an inhibition of acetylcholine synthesis. Its effect is due to its competition with choline entering the cell, or the mitochondria, and is not due to inhibition of choline acetylase itself. This conclusion is supported by the observation of Gardiner,[119] using the substance HC3 (Schueller[118]) which at $10^{-4}M$ greatly reduces (75 to 90%) the production of acetylcholine by the superior cervical ganglion of the cat or by minced mouse brain. The inhibition is reversed by the addition of choline. The inhibitory effect is abolished by treatments that disorganize the mitochondria.

ACETYLCHOLINE CYCLE IN BRAIN TISSUE

The following scheme (Fig. 1) represents the cycle of events resulting in acetylcholine synthesis in the brain cell.

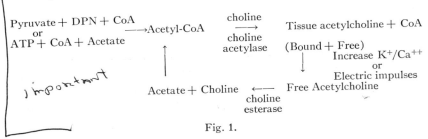

Fig. 1.

EFFECTS OF SUGARS ON ACETYLCHOLINE SYNTHESIS

Quastel et al.[26] showed that synthesis of acetylcholine in intact brain slices is closely associated with the aerobic breakdown of glucose and it was then suggested[12] that the synthesis may depend on the availability of energy supplied by oxidative reactions taking place during the combustion of glucose, or of its breakdown products, lactate or pyruvate, or upon the production from these substances of a specific metabolite necessary for synthesis to occur. Later these authors[37] found that fructose, which aids aerobic respiration of brain, cannot effectively replace glucose in the synthesis of acetylcholine with intact brain slices. The conclusion that glucose, or a breakdown product of this sugar, is important for the synthesis of acetylcholine under physiological conditions was confirmed by the experiments of MacIntosh[69] on the perfusion of the superior cervical ganglion of the cat. Moreover, Kahlson and MacIntosh[70] found that fructose does not enhance acetylcholine formation in perfused ganglia.

Results obtained by Mann *et al.*[37] on the effects of the presence of sugars on the rate of acetylcholine synthesis in presence of rat brain show that glucose and mannose are the most active in establishing synthesis, whereas fructose and galactose have small and perhaps questionable effects.

The combustion of glucose under aerobic conditions in intact brain slices provides a sufficiently high concentration of acetyl-CoA for acetylcholine synthesis. Since the anaerobic conversion of glucose to lactate provides only a small fraction of the energy released by the complete aerobic breakdown of the glucose and little or no acetyl-CoA, it is evident that the finding of Quastel *et al.*[33] that acetylcholine is not synthesized by brain slices under anaerobic conditions is satisfactorily explained by the assumption that the amount of acetyl-CoA available is inadequate.

In contrast to the virtual necessity of glucose for the synthesis of acetylcholine by brain slices, Feldberg and Mann[73] found that the presence of glucose, at concentrations similar to those in the blood, and also of fructose, strongly inhibits the synthesis of acetylcholine by extracts of acetone brain powders. As the inhibition was associated with a decrease in seven minute-hydrolyzable phosphate, they suggested that it might be due to loss of adenosine triphosphate from the system owing to phosphorylation of the sugar. Harpur and Quastel[108] found that glucose and fructose were phosphorylated by adenosine triphosphate in presence of acetone dried beef brain extracts and that the fall in adenosine triphosphate concentration would account for the fall in acetylcholine synthesis. They confirmed this conclusion by showing that the presence of d-glucosamine, which they found was phosphorylated by adenosine triphosphate in presence of brain hexokinase, would also bring about a drop in acetylcholine synthesis in brain extracts. They obtained the additional information that the presence of N-acetylglucosamine, which is not phosphorylated by brain hexokinase, and which by competitive inhibition prevents phosphorylation of d-glucosamine and fructose, diminishes the inhibitive action of d-glucosamine and fructose on acetylcholine synthesis.

The inhibitory effect of glucose on acetylcholine synthesis in a brain extract in presence of adenosine triphosphate does not take place if the extract is made in the presence of nicotinamide (Harpur and Quastel[108]). In fact, in the presence of a nicotinamide, or preferably a nicotinamide-cysteine, extract of acetone dried brain, the addition of either glucose or fructose secures a high rate of acetylcholine synthesis which is found to be correlated with a high rate of glycolysis. The effect of nicotinamide is not difficult to explain. Phosphorylation of glucose to hexosediphosphate takes place, but further metabolism, past the

triosephosphate stage, will only occur in presence of diphosphopyridinenucleotide (DPN). Brain extracts contain an active DPN-ase which
is inhibited by nicotinamide.[109] Thus the accelerating action of nicotinamide is due to its ability to preserve DPN, which by enabling
glycolysis to take place at a high rate in the brain extract, causes
adenosine triphosphate to be resynthesized at a rate at least comparable
with the rate of its breakdown. Sufficient adenosine triphosphate is,
therefore, formed to enable acetylcholine synthesis to take place. It
follows from these facts that the synthesis of acetylcholine, dependent
upon an optimal concentration of adenosine triphosphate, requires
in the cell an optimal rate of formation of diphosphopyridine nucleotide to compensate for those activities which might result in the loss
of the nucleotide from the cell. It also follows that any circumstances,
physical or chemical, which interfere adversely with the activity of the
diphosphopyridine nucleotide carrier system or with the synthesis of
adenosine triphosphate in the cell, will also have an adverse effect on
the synthesis of acetylcholine.

PYRUVIC ACID AND ACETYLCHOLINE SYNTHESIS

The presence of sodium pyruvate and salts of other α-ketonic acids,
brings about a definite inhibition of acetylcholine synthesis by extracts of acetone powders of brain in presence of adenosine triphosphate. They also inhibit the synthesis of acetylcholine by brain slices
in presence of glucose (McLennan and Elliott[45]). The inhibition may
be due to a condensation of the α-ketonic acid with thiol groups of
the acetylating enzyme, or with free thiol groups in the medium, such
as those presented by cysteine or glutathione, which are often included to ensure a maximum rate of acetylcholine synthesis. Schubert[110] has shown that pyruvate forms an addition compound with
cysteine.

Another explanation of pyruvate inhibition is, however, possible.
It is noteworthy that for maximum acetylcholine synthesis a high
concentration of potassium ions is desirable or necessary. Lardy and
Ziegler[111] have shown that in presence of high potassium ion concentrations a reversible reaction between adenosine triphosphate and
pyruvate may take place, thus:

Phosphopyruvate + adenosine diphosphate $\rightleftharpoons$ pyruvate + adenosine triphosphate

The kinetics of this reaction have been studied by Meyerhof and
Oesper[112] and recently by Kachmar and Boyer[113] who have concluded
that the presence of potassium ions is essential for the reaction to take
place. It is, therefore, conceivable that pyruvate inhibition of acetylcholine synthesis, in presence of high potassium ion concentrations,

is due partly to removal of adenosine triphosphate from the system.

If, however, brain extracts are made in the presence of nicotinamide, an entirely different situation develops. In presence of a brain extract, in which the diphosphopyridinenucleotide carrier system is intact, and in presence of phosphate and potassium ions, pyruvate undergoes a rapid dismutation and under these circumstances acetylcholine is synthesized (Johnson and Quastel[92]). Thus, pyruvate, alone, will ensure acetylcholine synthesis in presence of a brain extract. The phenomenon is analogous to that taking place with glucose. The addition of pyruvate to a brain extract in presence of glucose, where both glycolysis and acetylcholine synthesis are proceeding, does not inhibit the rate of synthesis.

VITAMIN B₁ AND ACETYLCHOLINE SYNTHESIS

The fact that vitamin B_1 plays a part in the synthesis of acetylcholine in intact brain was shown by the results of Mann and Quastel[114] in their work on polyneuritic pigeon brain. These authors showed that the rate of acetylcholine synthesis in polyneuritic pigeon brain slices, metabolising in a pyruvate-bicarbonate medium, containing a high concentration of potassium ions (0.03 M), is considerably less than that in normal pigeon brain slices examined under the same conditions. The addition of vitamin B_1 to the brain slices restored the rate of synthesis of acetylcholine to normal. These results confirm the conclusion that pyruvate metabolism in intact brain plays an important part in acetylcholine synthesis.

CITRATE AND ACETYLCHOLINE SYNTHESIS

The presence of sodium citrate ensures a high rate of acetylcholine synthesis in brain extracts[66] though not in a highly purified choline acetylase system prepared from the squid. In fact citrate, in common with a variety of other organic anions, brings about some inhibition of acetylcholine synthesis by the choline acetylating system obtained from the head ganglia of the squid.[72]

Feldberg and Hebb[64] showed that citrate activiation of acetylcholine synthesis in brain extracts is dependent on the presence of magnesium ions. It is likely that the effect of citrate is due to its ability to act as an acetate donor. Lipton and Barron[61] reported that an extract of an acetone dried powder brings about a synthesis of acetylcholine in presence of citrate and adenosine triphosphate. Persky and Barron[115] claim that in this synthesis two reactions take place, first a split of citrate into oxalacetate and "active" acetate, and second, a reaction between "active acetate" and choline to form acetylcholine. It has been shown by Ochoa and his colleagues[116] that citrate may act as an acetyl donor to orthophosphate, to sulphanilamide, and to choline, in presence of the appropriate enzymes and acetyl acceptor systems. Whether this is the whole explanation of citrate activation still remains to be seen.

REFERENCES

1. BARSOUM, G. S.: *J. Physiol., 84:*259 (1935).
2. DIKSHIT, B. B.: *J. Physiol., 80:*409 (1934); *Quart. J. Exper. Physiol., 28:*243 (1938).
3. MacINTOSH, F. C.: *J. Physiol., 99:*436 (1941).
4. WELSH, J. H. and HYDE, J. E.: *J. Neurophysiol., 7:*41 (1944).
5. FELDBERG, W. and VOGT, M.: *J. Physiol., 107:*372 (1948).
6. ELLIOTT, K. A. C. and HENDERSON, N.: *Am. J. Physiol., 165:*365 (1951).
7. BORNSTEIN, M. B.: *J. Neurophysiol., 9:*349 (1946).
8. TOWER, D. B. and McEACHERN, D.: *Canad. J. Res. E., 27:*105, 120 (1949).
9. STONE, W. E.: *Am. J. Phys. Med., 36:*222 (1957).
10. BENNETT, E. L., CROSSLAND, J., KRECH, D., and ROSENZWEIG, M. R.: *Nature, 187:*787 (1960).
11. CORTEGGIANI, E.: *Compt. rend. Soc. biol., 125:*949 (1937).
12. MANN, P. J. G., TENNENBAUM, M., and QUASTEL, J. H.: *Biochem. J., 32:*243 (1938).
13. WELSH, J. H.: *J. Neurophysiol., 6:*329 (1943).
14. SZEPSENWOL, J. and CARETTI, J. A.: *Rev. Soc. argent. biol., 18:*532 (1942).
15. HIMWICH, H. E., BAKER, Z. and FAZEKAS, J. F.: *Am. J. Physiol., 125:*601 (1939).
16. TYLER, D. B. and HARREVELD, A. VAN: *Am. J. Physiol., 136:*600 (1942).
17. CROSSLAND, J.: *J. Physiol., 114:*318 (1951).
18. CROSSLAND, J. and MERRICK, A. J.: *J. Physiol., 125:*56 (1954).
19. BURGEN, A. S. V. and MacINTOSH, F. C.: In *Neurochemistry*, Elliott, Page and Quastel, Eds. 1st Ed. Springfield, Ill., Thomas (1955).
20. RICHTER, D. and CROSSLAND, J.: *Am. J. Physiol., 159:*247 (1949).
21. CROSSLAND, J.: *J. Ment. Sc., 99:*247 (1953).
22. RICHTER, D.: *Biochem. Soc. Symp., 8:*62 (1952).
23. CROSSLAND, J., ELLIOTT, K. A. C. and PAPPIUS, H. M.: *Am. J. Physiol., 183:*32 (1955).
24. BEZNAK, A. B. L.: *J. Physiol., 82:*129 (1934).
25. CHANG, H. C.: *Proc. Soc. Exper. Biol. & Med., 32:*1001 (1935).
26. QUASTEL, J. H., TENNENBAUM, M. and WHEATLEY, A. H. M.: *Biochem. J., 30:*1668 (1936).
27. MANN, J. P. G., TENNENBAUM, M. and QUASTEL, J. H.: *Biochem. J., 33:*822 (1939).
28. CORTEGGIANI, E.: *Compt. rend. Soc. biol., 124:*1197 (1937); *125:*944, 945, 949; and CORTEGGIANI, E., GAUTRELET, J., KASWIN, A. and MENTZER, C.: *Compt. rend Soc. biol., 123:*667 (1936).
29. LOEWI, O.: *Naturwissenschaften, 25:*461 (1937).
30. PINOTTI, O.: *Boll. Soc. ital. biol. sper., 12:*765 (1937).
31. CHANG, H. C.: *Chinese J. Physiol., 13:*145, 153 (1938).
32. KAHANE, E. and LEVY, J.: *Ann Physiol., 14:*575 (1938).
33. TRETHEWIE, E. R.: *Australian J. Exper. Biol. & Med. Sc., 16:*225 (1938).
34. RENSHAW, R. R., GREEN, D. and ZIFF, M.: *J. Pharmacol. & Exper. Therap., 62:*430 (1938).

35. STEDMAN, E. and STEDMAN, E.: *Biochem. J., 33:*811 (1939).
36. MANN, P. J. G., TENNENBAUM, M. and QUASTEL, J. H.: *Nature,* London, *141:*374 (1938).
37. MANN, P. J. G., TENNENBAUM, M. and QUASTEL, J. H.: *Biochem. J., 33:*1506 (1939).
38. BRAGANCA, B. M. and QUASTEL, J. H.: *Nature,* London, *169:*695, (1952).
39. WELSH, J. H. and HYDE, J. E.: *Am. J. Physiol., 142:*512 (1944).
40. WELSH, J. H. and TAUB, R.: *Biol. Bull., 95:*346 (1948).
41. SCHALLEK, W.: *J. Cell. & Comp. Physiol., 26:*15 (1945).
42. ZIFF, M., JAHN, F. P., and RENSHAW, R. R.: *J. Am. Chem. Soc., 60:*178 (1938).
43. DULIÉRE, W. and LOEWI, O.: *Nature,* London, *144:*244 (1939).
44. BROWN, G. L. and FELDBERG, W.: *J. Physiol., 86:*290 (1936).
45. McLENNAN, H. and ELLIOTT, K. A. C.: *Am. J. Physiol., 163:*605 (1950).
46. BRODKIN, E. and ELLIOTT, K. A. C.: *Am. J. Physiol., 173:*437 (1953).
47. CORTEGGIANI, E.: *Contribution a l'etude de l'acetyl-choline libre et dissimilée sous forme d'un complexe dans le cerveau.* Doullens (1938).
48. HOBBIGER, F. and WERNER, G.: *Ztschr. Vitaminforsch., 2:*234 (1948/49).
49. CORTEGGIANI, E., CARAYON-GENTIL, A., GAUTRELET, J. and KASWIN, A.: *J. physiol.. et path. gen., 37:*5 (1939).
50. GAUTRELET, J., CORTEGGIANI, E., and CARAYON-GENTIL, A.: *Compt. rend. Soc. biol., 135:*832 (1941).
51. FELDBERG, W.: *J. Physiol., 103:*367 (1945).
52. WHITTAKER, V. P.: *Biochem. J., 68:*21P (1958).
53. DE ROBERTIS, E.: *Exper. Cell Res.,* Suppl. 5:347 (1958); DEL CASTILLO, J. and KATZ, B.: *Progr. Biophys. & Biophys. Chem., 6:*122 (1956); WHITTAKER, V. P.: *Biochem. J., 72:*694 (1959).
54. BRAGANCA, B. M., FAULKNER, P. and QUASTEL, J. H.: *Biochem. et Biophys. Acta, 10:*83 (1953).
55. ROWSELL, E. V.: *Biochem. J., 57:*666 (1954).
56. NACHMANSOHN, D. and MACHADO, A. L.: *J. Neurophysiol., 6:*397 (1943).
57. NACHMANSOHN, D. and JOHN, H. M.: *Proc. Soc. Exper. Biol. & Med., 57:*361 (1944).
58. NACHMANSOHN, D. and JOHN, H. M.: *J. Biol. Chem., 158:*157 (1945).
59. TORDA, C. and WOLFF, H. G.: *J. Biol. Chem., 162:*149 (1946).
60. NACHMANSOHN, D. and WEISS, M. S.: *J. Biol. Chem., 172:*677 (1948).
61. LIPTON, M. A. and BARRON, E. S. G.: *J. Biol. Chem., 166:*367 (1946).
62. EMMELIN, N. and FELDBERG, W.: *J. Physiol., 106:*27 (1946).
63. TORDA, C. and WOLFF, H. G.: *Proc. Soc. Exper. Biol. & Med., 57:*234 (1944).
64. FELDBERG, W. and HEBB, C.: *J. Physiol., 105:*8 (1946); *J. Physiol., 104:*42 (1945).
65. FELDBERG, W. and MANN, T.: *J. Physiol., 104:*411 (1946).
66. NACHMANSOHN, D., JOHN, H. M., and WAELSCH, H.: *J. Biol. Chem., 150:*485 (1943).
67. FELDBERG, W. and HEBB, C.: *J. Physiol., 106:*8 (1947).
68. NACHMANSOHN, D. and BERMAN, M.: *J. Biol. Chem., 165:*551 (1946).
69. MacINTOSH, F. C.: *J. Physiol., 93:*46 (1938).
70. KAHLSON, G. and MacINTOSH, F. C.: *J. Physiol., 96:*277 (1939).
71. NACHMANSOHN, D. and ROTHENBERG, M.: *J. Biol. Chem., 158:*653 (1945).
72. KOREY, S. R., DE BRAGANCA, B. and NACHMANSOHN, D.: *J. Biol. Chem., 189:*705 (1951).
73. FELDBERG, W. and MANN, T.: *J. Physiol., 104:*8 (1945).
74. STADIE, W. C., RIGGS, B. C. and HAUGAARD, N.: *J. Biol. Chem., 161:*189 (1945).

75. BERMAN-REISBERG, R.: *Biochim. et Biophys. Acta, 14:*442 (1954).
76. LIPTON, M. A.: *Federation Proc., 5:*145 (1946).
77. LIPMANN, F. and KAPLAN, N. O.: *J. Biol. Chem., 162:*743 (1946).
78. NOVELLI, G. D., GREGORY, J. D., FLYNN, R. M. and SCHMETZ, F. J.: *Federation Proc., 10:*229 (1951).
79. SNELL, E. E., BROWN, G. M., PETERS, V. J., CRAIG, J. A., WITTLE, E. L., MOORE, J. A., McGLOHON, V. M. and BIRD, O. D.: *J. Am. Chem. Soc., 72:*5349 (1950).
80. LYNEN, F. and REICHERT, E.: *Angew. Chem., 63:*47 (1951).
81. NOVELLI, G. D., SCHMETZ, F. J., and KAPLAN, N. O.: *J. Biol. Chem., 206:*533 (1954).
82. KORKES, S., CAMPILLO, A. DEL., KOREY, S. R., STERN, J. R., NACHMANSOHN, D. and OCHOA, S.: *J. Biol. Chem., 198:*215 (1952).
83. KORKES, S., CAMPILLO, A. DEL., GUNSALUS, I. C., and OCHOA, S.: *J. Biol. Chem., 193:*721 (1951).
84. KORKES, S., CAMPILLO, A. DEL. and OCHOA, S.: *J. Biol. Chem., 195:*541 (1952).
84a. BERG, P.: *J. Biol. Chem., 222:*991, 1015 (1956).
85. STADTMANN, E. R., NOVELLI, G. D., and LIPMANN, F.: *J. Biol. Chem., 191:*365 (1951).
86. STERN, J. R. and OCHOA, S.: *J. Biol. Chem., 179:*491 (1949); *191:*161 (1951).
87. HEBB, C. O.: *Quart. J. Exper. Physiol., 40:*176 (1959).
88. HEBB, C. O. and SMALLMAN, B. N.: *J. Physiol., 134:*385 (1956).
89. HEBB, C. O.: *Physiol. Rev., 37:*196 (1957).
90. SMALLMAN, B. N.: *J. Neurochem., 2:*119 (1958).
91. MILTON, A. S.: *J. Physiol., 149:*462 (1959).
92. JOHNSON, W. J. and QUASTEL, J. H.: *Nature, 171:*602 (1953).
93. RYMAN, B. and WALSH, E.: *Biochem. J., 58:*111 (1954).
94. KUMAGAI, H., EBASHI, S. and TAKEDA, F.: *Japan J. Pharm. 4:*24 (1954).
95. SMALLMAN, B. N.: *J. Physiol., 132:*343 (1956).
96. FELDBERG, W. and VOGT, M.: *J. Physiol., 107:*372 (1948).
97. BANISTER, J., WHITTAKER, J. P., and WIJESUNDRAS, J.: *J. Physiol., 121:*55 (1953). HENSCHLER, D.: *Naturwissenschaften, 43:*522 (1956).
98. HOLTZ, P. and SCHUEMANN, H. J.: *Naturwissenschaften, 41:*306 (1954).
99. GRUNER, G. and KEWITZ, H.: *Naturwissenschaften, 42:*628 (1955).
100. KEYL, M. J., MICHAELSON, I. A., and WHITTAKER, V. P.: *J. Physiol., 139:*434 (1957).
WHITTAKER, V. P.: *Biochem. J., 71:*32 (1959).
ERSPAMER, V., and GLAESSER, A.: *Brit. J. Pharmacol., 12:*176 (1957).
101. BERRY, J. F. and WHITTAKER, V. P.: *Biochem. J., 73:*447 (1959).
102. HEBB, C. O.: *J. Physiol., 133:*566 (1956).
103. WINTERINGHAM, F. P. W. and HARRISON, A.: *Biochem. J., 78:*22P (1961).
104. WEBB, C. O. and SILVER, A.: *J. Physiol., 134:*718 (1956).
105. BURGEN, A. S. V. and CHIPMAN, L. M.: *J. Physiol., 114:*296 (1951).
106. LUBINSKA, L., NIEMIERKO, S. and OBERFELD, B.: *Nature, 189:*122 (1961). HEBB, C. O. and SILVER, A.: *Nature, 189:*123 (1961).
107. HEBB, C. O., KRAUSE, M. and SILVER, A.: *J. Physiol., 148:*69P (1959).
108. HARPUR, R. P. and QUASTEL, J. H.: *Nature, 164:*779 (1949).
109. MANN, P. J. G. and QUASTEL, J. H.: *Biochem. J., 35:*502 (1941).
110. SCHUBERT, M. P.: *J. Biol. Chem., 114:*341 (1936).
111. LARDY, H. A. and ZIEGLER, J. A.: *J. Biol. Chem., 159:*343 (1945).
112. MEYERHOF, O. and OESPER, P.: *J. Biol. Chem., 179:*1371 (1949).
113. KACHMAR, J. F. and BOYER, P. D.: *Federation Proc., 10:*204 (1951).

114. MANN, P. J. G. and QUASTEL, J. H.: *Nature, 145:*856 (1940).
115. PERSKY, H. and BARRON, E. S. G.: *Biochim. et Biophys. Acta, 5:*66 (1950).
116. STERN, J. R., SHAPIRO, B., STADTMAN, E. R. and OCHOA, S.: *Federation Proc.,*
      *10:*253 (1951).
117. MACINTOSH, F. C., BIRKS, R. I. and SASTRY, P. B.: *Nature, 178:*1181 (1956).
118. SCHUELLER, F. W.: *J. Pharmacol., 115:*127 (1955).
119. GARDINER, J. E.: *J. Physiol., 138:*13P (1957).
120. KINI, M. M. and QUASTEL, J. H.: *Nature, 184:*252 (1959).

XX

THE PHYSIOLOGICAL SIGNIFICANCE
OF ACETYLCHOLINE

Catherine O. Hebb and Krešimir Krnjević

I. INTRODUCTION

THE MAJORITY of those who have studied the role of acetylcholine (ACh) consider that our present knowledge limits the physiological functions of ACh mainly to that of chemical mediator in the transmission of nerve impulses at certain types of synapse, including among other structures the neuromuscular junction. There are indications, such as its presence in non-nervous tissue, to suggest that it has other functions but these are still matter for speculation and cannot as yet be evaluated with any certainty. On the other hand, acceptance of the role of ACh in nervous tissue raises a number of other questions. It is not the universal excitatory transmitter and it is therefore of some importance to discover in which parts of the mammalian nervous system it is found and also what is its comparative distribution. In addition it is equally important to know more about the mechanisms governing its activity; how, on the one hand, the presynaptic impulse acts as the required stimulus for its release and, on the other, by what means the transmitter once released can in its turn excite (or inhibit) the receptor or postsynaptic structure.

In this chapter we shall consider first of all the history of the theory of chemical transmission, including collateral lines of evidence about the enzymes concerned in the metabolism of ACh, and then go on to discuss more recent evidence about the distribution of the ester and our present knowledge of the mechanisms involved in its synaptic action.

II. HISTORICAL SURVEY

Although it was suggested as early as 1877 by Du Bois-Reymond (see Dale[89]) that when somatic motor nerves excite muscles to contract they do so by the liberation of some chemical agent, the suggestion was not followed up for more than fifty years afterward and the real impetus for discovery of the principle of chemical transmission came instead from studies on the autonomic nervous system.

The proposal that adrenaline was liberated from sympathetic endings was made in 1904 by Elliott[141,142] who was impressed by the close correspondence between its effects on various organs and those produced by stimulation of their sympathetic nerve supply. Gaskell[183] writing in 1916 suggested that adrenaline found in certain ganglion cells of the leech might normally reach the innervated organ by passage along the nerve belonging to these cells; it may be that in this he was influenced to some extent by Elliott's earlier papers. Direct support for the idea of a chemical mediator of sympathetic nerve impulses was first provided in the course of Loewi's experiments on the frog heart in 1921 when he demonstrated the release not only of "Vagusstoff" but of an "accelerator" principle on stimulation of the cardiac nerves and by Cannon's demonstration of the release of an adrenaline-like substance from mammalian nerves (for references see Cannon and Rosenblueth[64]) the active principle of which has since been identified in certain sympathetic nerves as consisting mostly of noradrenaline.[150]

The first suggestion that parasympathetic nerve impulses were mediated chemically seems to have been made by Dixon[119] in 1906 (see also Dixon and Hamill[120]) who claimed to have shown that vagal stimulation liberated a muscarine-like substance from the dog's heart. These results did not attract much interest, however, and the idea was not pursued further at that time. Then in 1914 Dale published an important paper on the properties of certain choline esters among which was acetylcholine. He identified this compound as a natural, although occasional, constituent of ergot extract and found it to have actions on many organs which closely corresponded to those of their parasympathetic nerve supply. Further, in this paper he drew a distinction between the 'nicotinic' and 'muscarinic' properties of ACh, and made the important suggestion that the brevity of its action might be due to its destruction by a tissue esterase.

Crucial evidence for the theory of chemical transmission was provided by Loewi's now classical experiments[282,283] demonstrating the release of 'Vagusstoff' from the frog's heart. In these and in subsequent experiments with his colleagues he showed that 'Vagusstoff' and ACh had similar properties; both were blocked by atropine and both enhanced by eserine, eserine preventing the destruction of the mediator after its release from the nerves. The evidence that the parasympathetic agent might be ACh became more convincing when ACh was itself identified for the first time in animal tissues by Dale and Dudley[91] who were able to show by chemical methods that it was present in the ungulate spleen. In general, however, the amounts of ACh present in tissues were found to be so small that they were below the limits of accurate chemical detection; so in order to obtain quantitative information from small samples of tissue or tissue fluids some other approach was necessary.

Bioassay met this need. One such method was based on an earlier observation of Führner[178] that the eserinized leech muscle is extremely sensitive to ACh, approximately one million times more so than the uneserinized leech muscle. First used for the assay of ACh by Minz[313] this preparation was introduced into Dale's laboratory by Feldberg (see Dale[90]). Subsequently Chang and Gaddum[70] published an account of the properties of a number of preparations which are specially sensitive to ACh and showed how these might be used in combination to distinguish ACh from other bioactive substances, including other choline esters.

ACh was now identified as the active substance liberated not only at parasympathetic nerve endings but also at preganglionic sympathetic endings (for a further account of this work see Dale[90]). An important aid in these latter experiments was the method described by Kibjakow[245] for the perfusion of the superior cervical ganglion *in situ* in isolation from the rest of the body; it was thus possible to collect in a relatively small volume of solution any substance liberated from the presynaptic endings.

Dale[88] now suggested a new terminology to describe nerve fibres in the autonomic nervous system. He proposed that all fibres which act by the liberation of ACh should be called *cholinergic* and those which act by the liberation of the adrenaline-like substance ("sympathin") *adrenergic*. On this criterion all preganglionic fibres, both sympathetic and parasympathetic were cholinergic; so too were all parasympathetic postganglionic fibres and some exceptional fibres anatomically classed as sympathetic postganglionic, such as those innervating the sweat glands in the cat, that were known however to have parasympathetic-like properties and also transmitted their effects by the release of an acetylcholine-like substance. Otherwise all postganglionic sympathetic fibres were adrenergic. Subsequently the term cholinergic was also applied to the somatic motor fibres when these too were shown to liberate ACh at their endings. Furthermore, whereas the effect of postganglionic parasympathetic stimulation could be mimicked by drugs with muscarine-like actions and were more or less blocked by atropine, the effects of stimulating preganglionic fibres and somatic motor nerves were not. On the contrary in these transmissions ACh had a nicotine-like action—nicotine first stimulates then paralyzes ganglia—and was blocked by curare, which was without effect on the muscarinic actions of ACh. Because of these differences, a distinction was made between cholinergic fibres concerned in muscarinic responses and those concerned in nicotinic responses (see also Dale[87]).

The first clear evidence of the release of ACh by somatic motor fibres and of its action on muscle was obtained by Dale and Feldberg[92] in 1934 and was subsequently amplified by Dale, Feldberg and Vogt[94] and by Brown, Dale and Feldberg.[47] In brief their evidence showed that ACh was released by stimulation of the motor nerve in amounts to be expected from previous experiments on ganglia; that ACh mimicked the effect of an asynchronous discharge of the motor nerve; and that certain pharmacological agents, in particular curare, modified the response to motor nerve stimulation in the same way as they modified the action of ACh. Their conclusions were received rather critically by many neurophysiologists and largely because of technical difficulties the experiments were less convincing than the previous ones demonstrating the transmitter role of ACh in the autonomic nervous system. As Dale[89] later pointed out it was necessary to perfuse the muscles with eserinized Locke solution and this rapidly led to oedema of the tissue; even with the technique of 'close arterial' injection ACh had to be introduced at a considerable distance from the receptors so that the amount required for stimulation was relatively large and the receptors could not be fired synchronously.

These criticisms were later met by improved technical methods which provided further evidence in support of the theory of chemical transmission particularly at the neuromuscular junction. Undoubtedly, however, early criticism had great value in stimulating a more exact and critical analysis of the evidence on which the theory was founded and the result in the end has been to give it a firm experimental basis. Fuller accounts of the events outlined in this section are to be found in Dale,[90] Rosenblueth[356] and Minz.[314] (See note at end of reference list.)

Metabolism of ACh in Relation to Neural Function

Cholinesterases.—In 1914 Dale[87] suggested that the rapid disappearance of ACh from blood and tissue is due to the action of an esterase. Further support for this idea was obtained by Fühner[178] who showed that in the presence of eserine ACh becomes far more effective in causing a contraction of leech muscle, while choline, which also stimulates the muscle but only in relatively large amounts, is not affected by eserine. This suggested that the potentiating action of eserine was due to an inhibitory effect on the tissue hydrolysis of ACh. Subsequently a similar conclusion was reached by Loewi and his coworkers.[148] In 1930, Engelhart and Loewi[148] and Matthes[299] independently demonstrated the enzymic nature of the tissue hydrolysis.

Two years later, Stedman, Stedman and Easson[378] prepared from horse serum an eserine-sensitive enzyme which hydrolysed ACh and could show that it differed from other esterases in its ability to hydrolyse choline esters. Because of its specificity they proposed the name 'choline-esterase,' now written *cholinesterase* (here abbreviated to ChE). The Stedmans[379] later demonstrated the widespread occurrence of ChE and at the same time reached the conclusion that its specificity is relative rather than absolute since it can hydrolyse some non-choline esters, a result which has since received confirmation from other authors who have emphasized that the specificity of ChE relates to the shape of the alcoholic group rather than to the choline molecule as such (see ref. 404).

The first indications that there are two classes of ChE were obtained by Alles and Hawes[3] and were subsequently fully explored by Mendel and his co-workers[303-305] who concluded that the serum ChE isolated by the Stedmans was not the true ChE normally responsible for ACh hydrolysis in the body; this was instead to be found chiefly in the nervous system (and in the red blood corpuscles of many species as well). One of their reasons for regarding the enzyme in nervous tissue as the true enzyme was that it destroyed ACh at a much lower concentration than did the serum ChE; while on the other hand serum ChE hydrolyzed benzylcholine and true ChE did not. Because of these and other substrate preferences they called the serum ChE pseudocholinesterase and the other ChE true cholinesterase. This nomenclature has not in general received the approval of biochemists (see ref. 404) or of some physiologists (see the first edition of this book) for many reasons. It is worth noting too that the substrate preferences of the two types of enzyme are quite variable from one species to another. In ruminants for example butyrylcholine but not benzoylcholine is hydrolyzed by pseudocholinesterase; while true and pseudo-ChE of certain avian species both hydrolyze propionylcholine in preference to either ACh or BuCh, although they can be distinguished from each other by the fact that true ChE does not apparently hydrolyze BuCh.[318] Another point is that both are in fact found in nervous tissue although pseudo ChE distribution is apparently limited to cell nuclei and glial tissue (cf. refs. 204, 214). Nevertheless, the terms true and pseudo ChE have fulfilled a useful purpose in drawing attention to their location and hence to their probable function. And if as now seems possible it should be found that in some situations pseudo ChE rather than true ChE is responsible for *in vivo* hydrolysis of ACh the terminology may still be useful in distinguishing between the physiological behaviour of ACh in some tissues as compared with others.

A more recent development in the study of ChE has been the elaboration of histochemical techniques to display the tissue and cellular distribution of pseudo and true ChE. Of the methods devised those described by Koelle and his colleagues[246,247] which employ acetyl- and butyrylthiocholine (recently propionylthiocholine has been employed with some success in this laboratory in the study of chicken ChE) are the most satisfactory since they come the nearest by the use of appropriate substrates and inhibitors to a selective identification of the type of enzyme involved. The drawbacks of the method are nevertheless numerous. Even under optimal conditions the enzyme activity in the required substrate mixture is about 50% of normal; the fixation of the tissues interferes further, while in fresh sections there is evidence of diffusion possibly of both enzyme[247] and of the reaction product.[55] Attempts to precipitate the enzyme *in situ* are of doubtful benefit in overcoming diffusion and may cause further loss of enzyme activity. For these reasons the method has little quantitative value. On the other hand, it has undoubtedly been of great use in displaying qualitative differences in the distribution of BuChE (butyrylcholinesterase) and AChE (acetylcholinesterase or true ChE), in pinpointing sites of ACh activity in tissues such as skeletal muscle where the overall activity is low, in revealing certain unsuspected sites of ChE activity, e.g., pseudo ChE in Pacinian corpuscles[207] neuronal nuclei[213] and true ChE in parts of the muscle other than the end-plate (see 188) and in confirming some earlier guesses such as the suggestion that glial tissue contains pseudo ChE (cf. ref. 57). (For further information consult Feldberg,[155] Hebb,[204] Augustinsson's[10] comprehensive review up to 1948, Whittaker's[404] valuable account of the biochemistry of ChE, and Couteaux's[78] critical discussion of the histochemical detection of ChE).

Anticholinesterases.—As already indicated eserine (physostigmine) was the first anticholinesterase agent to be recognized as such. While many other natural alkaloids have some antiChE action, eserine is by far the most active and is fairly specific, still serving to distinguish between cholinesterases which it inhibits almost completely in a concentration of 10^{-5}M and ali-esterases which with few exceptions (see Holmstedt[223]) are resistant to it. Prostigmine (neostigmine) is a synthetic anti-ChE, in structure similar to eserine, but because it is a quaternary nitrogen compound, it simulates to some extent the actions of ACh and does not penetrate tissues as effectively as eserine. For these reasons its effects *in vivo* cannot always be equated solely with its anti-ChE action and need to be interpreted with caution.

A different class of inhibitors, the organophosphorus compounds, of which there are a large number, is exemplified by DFP (diisopropyl-phosphoro fluoridate) and TEPP (tetraethylpyrophosphate). The anticholinesterase action of DFP, discovered during and after the Second World War (see refs. 148, 222, 223) has been shown to depend on a slow but nearly irreversible combination of enzyme and inhibitor, a process in which the enzyme is phosphorylated. The esteratic rather than the anionic site of attachment of ACh to the enzyme is apparently the point at which AChE (acetylcholinesterase, i.e., true ChE) is attacked; BuChE (butyrylcholinesterase) lacks the anionic site and is about ten times more susceptible to DFP. Although a more active anti-ChE than DFP, TEPP is less generally used in experiments since its action is slowly reversible, it is less stable in aqueous solution, does not distinguish so clearly between types of ChE and does not penetrate all cells with equal rapidity.

The use of DFP both for *in vivo* and *in vitro* experiments has emphasized the distinction made first on the basis of substrate preference between two types of ChE since it was usually found in all species tested that pseudo ChE was 10 or more times more susceptible to the inhibiting action of DFP than was true ChE. This difference is now generally made use of in identification of cholinesterases. However, in spite of early claims to the contrary DFP cannot be regarded as specific for the ChE enzymes. It also inhibits chymotrypsin and other enzymes of the carboxylesterase group as well as a quite unrelated enzyme phosphoglucomutase[244] although in higher concentrations. What does appear is the probability that it is specific for certain amino-acid groupings which in all of these enzymes are important for their activity but do not necessarily determine their substrate specificity nor the type of reaction in which they can take part. (The most comprehensive accounts of the chemistry, pharmacological and biochemical properties of the anticholinesterases are given by Koelle and Gilman[248] and by Holmstedt.[223])

Choline Acetylase.—The fact that ACh is being continuously produced in some tissues was first demonstrated in 1936 by Brown and Feldberg[48] who showed that the total amount of ACh released by a perfused ganglion during intermittent stimulation over a period of some hours far exceeds the quantity present in unstimulated ganglia. In the same year Quastel and his colleagues[345] published the first account of synthesis of ACh by brain slices; while in the next year the Stedmans[380] demonstrated the formation of ACh by incubation of saline-chloroform suspensions of homogenized brain tissue. Later they showed that ether-saline was also a suitable medium for incubation.[381]

Important progress in the elucidation of the synthetic process was made by Nachmansohn and Machado[320] in 1943 when they demonstrated that its acceleration was dependent on ATP. From further experiments by Nachmansohn and his colleagues and by Feldberg and Mann (see Feldberg[155]) the enzymic basis of synthesis was fairly established and its *in vitro* requirements of choline, ATP, certain inorganic ions (K and Mg), and of coenzyme A for activation were determined. It was not clear however, what substrate was the source of the acetyl groups or what part the coenzyme played; in fact it appeared that there might be more than one source of acetyl groups and that these had different coenzyme requirements (see Balfour and Hebb[14]). However, these problems were soon solved after the discovery by Lipmann (see Lipmann[278]) of the role of coenzyme A in biological acetylations. It then became evident that the synthesis of ACh like other acetylations, was a two-stage process; first, with energy supplied by high-energy phosphate, acetate and coenzyme A combine to form acetyl-coenzyme A, a reaction which may be brought about by more than one enzyme depending upon the substrate acting as acetyl donor, which can for example be acetate itself, or citrate or some other intermediate (see Korkes *et al.*[250]); and second, the acetyl-CoA so formed combines with choline to form ACh. This last reaction is catalyzed by *choline acetylase,* the enzyme specifically concerned in the synthesis of ACh and so called by Nachmansohn and Machado[320] in their original paper.

The discovery of the two stages of acetylation was important practically as well as theoretically. Until 1952 measurements of the choline acetylase concentration of various tissues were done with an incomplete system which relied on each tissue to produce sufficient acetyl-CoA for maximal activity of the choline acetylase present, regardless of the substrate supplied. In fact, as later measurements[203] showed, the full choline acetylase activity of almost all tissues (the dog's retina is an exception) can only be realized if the incubation system provides for the independent generation of acetyl-CoA. This is conveniently achieved by adding acetyl phosphate and phosphotransacetylase as well as CoA to the system; but other methods may be used (see Hebb[204]). By such means it is possible to measure the choline acetylase activity with a high degree of accuracy. It should be noted however that it was not until after 1955 that methods of this kind were generally used; and figures for tissue concentrations of choline acetylase given in papers published before that date are usually much too low and unreliable for comparative purposes.

Although an understanding of the acetylation process and accurate measurement of choline acetylase activity have thus only recently been achieved, some important ideas were developed during the earlier periods in which synthesis of ACh was studied. Thus Feldberg[155] was the first to emphasize the close spatial relation that exists between ACh and the synthesizing enzyme, not only at tissue but at subcellular levels. An important consequence of this, appreciated as early as 1936 by Brown and Feldberg[48] is that it is not necessary to assume a transport system for ACh to maintain supplies at the nerve endings. Because too of the close association of the enzyme and ester it is probably safe to assume that determination of the enzyme alone (which, of the two, is the more easily and accurately measured) will show in which tissues or cells ACh may have a function. Earlier workers[16] also showed in experiments since amply confirmed[215,22] that ACh and choline acetylase both disappear, and at the same rate, from degenerating cholinergic nerves; this again emphasizes their close relation to one another.

Another idea which is of some importance in the analysis of the role of ACh in the central nervous system is the proposal, put forward by Feldberg and Vogt,[167] on the basis of choline acetylase concentrations in the CNS, that in the sensory and motor pathways of the brain cholinergic and noncholinergic neurons alternate. Although this idea requires considerable modification it has been partially confirmed.[211] It is perhaps more important that their evidence, as well as the earlier evidence obtained by Feldberg, showed that ACh and choline acetylase are absent from a proportion of central and peripheral neurons. (For best review of this subject to 1945, see Feldberg;[155] for later work see Hebb.[204,206])

III. SOME CHEMICAL AND PHYSICO-CHEMICAL PROPERTIES OF ACh

ACh (β-acetoxyethyl trimethylammonium) is a relatively simple ester with a molecular weight of 146.2, easily obtained by heating the base choline with acetic anhydride. Its formula is given below

$$CH_3 - \overset{\overset{\displaystyle O}{\|}}{C} - O - CH_2 - CH_2 - \overset{\overset{\displaystyle CH_3}{|}}{\underset{\underset{\displaystyle CH_3}{|}}{N^+}} - CH_3$$

ACh is strongly ionized and readily forms salts, the halides being most commonly used. The chloride and the bromide are highly soluble in water, but they have the disadvantage of being very hygroscopic, unlike the iodide. ACh perchlorate is also not hygroscopic, and, being very stable, can be kept as a convenient standard.

Solutions of ACh tend to become acid because the ester is hydrolyzed in the presence of hydrogen or hydroxyl ions. The rate of hydrolysis depends very much on the pH. It is slowest at a pH of about 4 but it increases very rapidly on either side.[62,386] From the rate constants of hydrolysis given by Tammelin[386] one can calculate the expected half-time of hydrolysis (i.e., the time required for the ACh concentration to fall to one half) at different levels of pH. In a solution at 25°C. with an ionic strength of 0.1 (roughly similar to that of biological fluids), the approximate half time would be 14 years at pH 5, 50 days at pH 7, 5 days at pH 8, 1 hour at pH 10 and 40 seconds at pH 12. The rate of hydrolysis is also a function of the absolute temperature, as given by the Arrhenius equation. It is halved at 15°C. and almost doubled at 37°C.; at 50°C. it is increased by a factor of 5, at 100°C. by a factor of 60. The boiling of extracts or solutions in alkali (at pH 12) for a few minutes has been a standard experimental procedure for the elimination of ACh.

The hydrolysis of ACh is catalyzed by various inorganic and organic agents, the most important being the cholinesterases of living tissues. The reaction between the ester and the enzyme, involving the formation of an intermediate acylated enzyme, has been studied very extensively (for recent reviews see Davies and Green[96] and Nachmansohn[319]). The cholinesterase present at the neuromuscular junction is capable of hydrolyzing some 10^9 molecules of ACh in one millisecond.[296]

The diffusion coefficient of ACh in an 0.15 M saline-agar gel is 9.8 x 10^{-6} cm.²/sec. at 20°C., and 14.8 x 10^{-6} cm.²/sec. at 37°C. (Krnjević and Mitchell,[258] see also Brecht[39a]). Calculations based on the limiting equivalent conductance of ACh solutions give a somewhat lower value of 8 x 10^{-6} cm.²/sec. at 18°C. (Fatt[152]). The surface tension of water is slightly reduced by ACh. For instance 0.04 M ACh chloride causes a change in surface tension of −2 dyn/cm. at 25°C. (Bangham[15]). At the interface between an oil and water, ACh in quite low concentrations can have a pronounced electrogenic effect (Beutner and Barnes[23]). It has been suggested that ACh may play a part in the movement of ions in tissues because it stimulates the formation of phosphatidic acid which may be concerned in the active transport of Na+ (Hokin and Hokin[220a]) and also because, in an artificial system, cephalin in its presence can accumulate Na+ or K+ (Schulman[370a]).

IV. DISTRIBUTION OF ACETYLCHOLINE AND THE ENZYMES CONCERNED IN ITS METABOLISM

Non-nervous Tissues and Cells.—Acetylcholine is not confined to animal tissues. As mentioned earlier it was first described as a naturally-occurring substance in extracts of ergot (see Dale[87]) although it had been synthesized much earlier. As shown in Table 1 it also occurs in other plants and is produced in relatively large quantities by *Lactobacillus plantarum,* the activity of which accounts for its presence in fermenting cabbage and cucumber juice. No reason for the production of ACh by this organism is known. *Lactobacillus* grows equally well without the addition of choline in which case no ACh is found, so it is evidently not necessary for the economy of the cell. When choline is present, however, the rate of ACh formation is in exact proportion to the rate of glucose fermentation and the production of organic acid. Both the growth of the organism and the synthesis of ACh are CoA dependent and it would appear that the mechanisms of acetylation are the same as those responsible for acetylation of choline by animal tissues. Unlike most animal tissues, however, cultures of *Lactobacillus* have no cholinesterase; consequently the ACh concentration may be rather high. A rather remote possibility, suggested by these observations is that the formation of ACh is a detoxication process, analogous to some acetylations carried out by the mammalian liver, which prevents choline from accumulating in the culture and possibly interfering with other metabolic reactions. Another possibility is that the bacterial enzyme is a non-specific acetylase normally utilizing substrates other than choline.

It seems probable that the high concentration of ACh in the nettle hair fluid in association with histamine contributes to the painful actions of the hairs when they penetrate the skin of animals. Its presence in hornet venom may have a similar meaning. Whether this is the whole significance of ACh in nettles is doubtful, however, since it is present in many other parts of the plant including the roots; moreover, as Lin[276] has pointed out, its presence in similar concentrations in the seeds of the Jackfruit plant evidently has some quite different meaning. It will be noted that both in the nettle hair and in the venom sac of the hornet no choline acetylase could be detected. This makes it probable that in both cases the ACh is synthesized in some other tissue.

It has been suggested that the ACh produced by *Paramoecium* and *Trypanasoma Rh.* (Table I) plays a part in controlling their motility, although this suggestion relies so far only on the negative evidence that ACh is not present in other, non-motile, protozoa.[54] There is better evidence for the suggestion that the ACh produced in the gill-plate of *Mytilus* controls movement of its cilia. Unlike the organisms and tissues already discussed, the gill-plate contains ChE and it has been shown that the rate at which the cilia beat is increased by the external application of either ACh or eserine.[53] Together with other pharmacological evidence this strongly suggests that the rhythm of ciliary movement is dependent upon the alternate release and removal of ACh.

The two last entries in Table I are mammalian tissues. The amount of ACh in the placenta is higher than is generally found in nervous

TABLE I

ACh in Various Plants and Organisms Without a Nervous System and in Non-nervous Tissues of Animals With a Nervous System

	Organism or Tissue	ACh Concentration Reported	ChE	Evidence about Enzymes Present Choline Acetylase	Reference
Bacteria	Lactobacillus plantarum	40 μg./ml. of culture	Absent	Present in high concentration	381
Plants	Claviceps purpura (ergot)	up to 200 μg./ml. of extract	No evidence	No evidence	87
	Urtica urens (nettle plant) hair fluid	10-15 mg./ml.*	Absent	Tests negative	143, 144
	Artocarpus integra (Malayan jackfruit) seed	0.3–1 mg./gm. tissue	Absent	Not investigated	276
Animals	Paramoecium	5 x 10^{-7} μg./cell	Probably absent	Not investigated	20
	Trypanosome Rh.	10^{-9} μg./cell (= 10.3 μg./gm. of cells)	No evidence	Evidence incomplete: synthesis demonstrated	54
	Mytilus edulis gill-plate	0-12 μg./gm. tissue	Present	Present	53, 312
	Vespa crabro (hornet) venom sac	18-50 mg./gm. dried sac	Probably absent	Tests negative	26, 206a
	Human placenta	28 μg./gm. fresh tissue	Present	Activity higher than rabbit brain	70, 204, 55a
	Ungulate spleen	4-30 μg./gm. fresh tissue	Present	Activity present equiv. to 5% of rabbit brain	91, 17, 206a

*Indicates that ACh is thought to be concerned in producing sting. It is likely that the concentration of ACh in the fresh venom is about the same as in the nettle hair fluid.

tissue and the choline acetylase activity is also higher[55a]. True ChE is
present in the organ not only in the blood but in the tissue as well.
However, its concentration is low. The rate of hydrolysis of acetyl-β-
methylcholine is between 2 and 6 μmoles/hr. per gm. of tissue (see
Table II for comparison with the nervous system). The high concentration of ACh reported for the ungulate spleen may not be correct.
In extracts of this tissue both ACh and propionylcholine are present,
and when assayed on the frog rectus for ACh, falsely high values might
be obtained.[17] A difference between the placenta and spleen is that
the choline acetylase concentration in the spleen is less than 10% of
that in the placenta.

The claim that ACh is normally present in the milk of certain
mammals cannot be confirmed in this laboratory. In repeated tests
carried out in the last few years by Linzell and Hebb[277] on fresh
milk of cows and goats, no ACh was found (see also ref. 405). The
material present in the milk which stimulated contraction of the frog
rectus abdominis was not alkali-labile, and from other tests and analyses it was identified as potassium. Similarly, the potassium present in
human red cells accounts for most if not all of the activity simulating
ACh; and it is certain that extracts of such cells cannot synthesize
physiologically significant amounts of ACh (see Hebb[204] for other
evidence).

Recent discoveries of other naturally-occurring choline esters places
the problem of ACh in non-nervous tissue in a somewhat different
perspective since they have shown that it is only one, although perhaps
the most important, of a class of compounds which, while still limited
in number, are widely distributed through the animal kingdom. Propionylcholine in extracts of ungulate spleen,[17] urocanylcholine or
murexine in the hypobranchial glands of certain Mediterranean whelks
(see ref. 149) senecioylcholine in a related marine species[242] have all
been identified by chemical and chromatographic analysis; while in
addition a choline ester found in the cervical 'defensive' glands of the
Tiger Moth has been identified by similar means as a compound
closely related to senecioylcholine.[29]

All of these esters appear to be derived from non-nervous tissue.
Various functions have been proposed for them. For example, Erspamer[149] has suggested that murexine may be a weapon to paralyze
muscles of animals on which whelks prey—a sort of underwater arrow
poison; Keyl *et al.*[242] have suggested however, that the choline esters
of the hypobranchial glands may control ciliary movement in the same
way that ACh is thought to control ciliary movement in *Mytilus*. It is
possible that the choline ester secreted by the Tiger Moth behaves
like ACh in hornet venom and the nettle sting.

None of these suggestions rests on any more secure evidence than the explanations previously discussed for the presence of ACh in non-nervous tissue. It is perhaps worth pointing out, however, that in its occurrence in non-nervous tissue ACh may be regarded as one of a group of similar compounds whereas it is the only choline ester that has so far been recovered from nervous tissue and shown to participate in nervous processes, although other choline esters can be synthesized by brain tissue under certain circumstances. It may be therefore that ACh is the only member of the group that is of the right molecular structure to act as a transmitter, although its evolution into this role may have been determined by the whole pattern of metabolism in the neuron where the synthesis of a choline ester could be limited by the supply of the appropriate acyl-groups from contiguous metabolic systems.

It should be noted that the cholinesterases are far more widely distributed than ACh or its choline analogues. For example in mammals pseudo ChE is present in plasma, liver and smooth muscle (see Koelle[246]) none of which contain ACh or choline acetylase. There are also some cells, e.g., the red blood corpuscles, which contain true ChE but no ACh, although these seem to be the exception rather than the rule. Nevertheless it should be emphasized that the presence of true ChE in a tissue does not imply that it is concerned in the hydrolysis of ACh and by implication that ACh has a function in such a tissue. Like pseudo ChE, true ChE can also hydrolyze some non-choline esters[404,318] and its presence in certain tissues may have no significance for ACh metabolism.

Nervous System of Mammals

Peripheral and Autonomic Systems.—Among peripheral nervous structures those having the highest concentrations of ACh are autonomic ganglia, preganglionic nerve trunks and the motor spinal roots. In all of these, the choline acetylase content is also high. True ChE is present in the motor roots but the amount is small in comparison with choline acetylase. It is probable that nearly all of the ACh in mixed nerves such as the sciatic is contributed by the motor fibres since spinal sensory roots contain little or no ACh and insignificant amounts of the synthetic enzyme. The ChE present includes both true and pseudo ChE.

A very small proportion of peripheral sensory fibres may possibly be cholinergic (for discussion see Hebb[206]) but the evidence is as yet only suggestive. In this connexion it may be noted that spinal ganglia contain a small but significant amount of choline acetylase. This may belong to some of the ganglion cells but since it is impossible to sep-

arate the ganglia cleanly from the motor fibres it may represent an
artifact. When the vagus trunk is cut central to the nodose ganglion
all choline acetylase disappears from the ganglion.[16]

Quantitative values, obtained by bioassay and by biochemical analysis, for ACh, choline acetylase and ChE in representative peripheral
tissues are given in Table II.

It is not yet possible to measure ACh or choline acetylase in single
cells and this has handicapped a detailed analysis of their distribution
in the nervous system. The distribution of the two types of ChE can, on
the other hand, be studied by means of a fairly sensitive and specific
histochemical method developed by Koelle.[246,247] Giacobini and
Zajicek[190] have also described a technique for the quantitative measurement of ChE in single cells.

Details of the distribution of ChE in the nervous system may be
obtained from publications by Koelle[246,247] and other workers who
have used either Koelle's method or modifications of it.[175,213,373,159] The
results of such investigations are in general agreement with those obtained by biochemical analysis and have given support for the chemical
transmission theory as it applies to the peripheral and autonomic systems. One example of this kind is that histochemistry provided the
first convincing demonstration that most of the true ChE of somatic
muscles is concentrated in the motor end-plate[80] although there is some
true ChE in the muscle fibres themselves (see Giacobini[188]).

There are certain other conclusions which can be drawn from the
histochemical data that are of general interest. In the first place Mendel's distinction between true and pseudo ChE gains new significance
from the distribution of the two types of enzyme in the nervous system.
Except for its presence in the nuclei of some nerve cells pseudo ChE is
absent from true nervous tissue and in association with nerves only
in blood vessels, connective tissue, Schwann cells and neuroglia. In
contrast to this distribution, true ChE, also found in some glial cells,
is a more prominent constituent of the cytoplasm of known cholinergic
neurons, as well as being in many neurons of the CNS which have not
been identified so certainly, and it also forms part of the post-synaptic
structures where cholinergic neurons have their endings. In the cell
bodies of motor neurons, such as the anterior horn cells, or the hypoglossal nucleus, the enzyme is heavily concentrated in the perikaryon
and distributed in a manner reminiscent of the Nissl bodies except for
its presence in the axon hillock. The clear definition of intracellular
structures by the stain derived from the end products of hydrolysis by
true ChE, shows that the enzyme is itself intracellular. On the other
hand, as pointed out elsewhere[205] synapses at which the afferent neuron is cholinergic, e.g., in autonomic ganglia, details of cell structure

TABLE II

ACh, CHOLINE ACETYLASE AND TRUE ChE IN THE MAMMALIAN NERVOUS SYSTEM

(a)

SOME PERIPHERAL AND AUTONOMIC STRUCTURES

Tissue	ACh Content (μg./gm. Tissue)	Choline Acetylase (μg./ACh Synthesized/gm. Tissue/hr.)	True ChE (μM Acetyl-β-Methyl Choline Hydrolysed/gm./hr.)
Ventral spinal roots	9–18 (d and c)	2,500–5,000 (g, r and d)	23–48 (d)
Dorsal spinal roots	10.4 (o) 0–0.25 (d and c)	2,200, 4,700 (o and d) 0–6 (c, d and o)	8.2–9.2 (o) 3–13
Dorsal spinal ganglia	—	5–30 (d)	8.0–8.1 (o)
Mixed spinal roots	6 (c)	480–950, 2,080 (g, r)	36–44 (c)
Sciatic N	4–6 (c)	300–680, 1120 (g, r)	
Vagus N	6–9 (c)		14 (c)
Cervical sympathetic N	18–30 (c)	1,120 (s)	59 (c)
Superior cervical ganglion	18–44 (c)	1,600–2,000 (s)	136 (c) 440 (c) 528 (g. p.)

(b)

IN SOME PARTS OF THE CENTRAL NERVOUS SYSTEM

Tissue	ACh Content	Choline Acetylase	True ChE
Spinal grey matter	1.5–2.6 (c)	500 (g)	143 (d)
Cerebellar cortex	0.1–0.3 (c)	0–60 (d, r, c, s)	251 (d)
Cerebellar peduncles	—	200–250 (s)	41–102 (d)
Superior colliculus	1.7 (c)	220, 460 (c, d)	172–264 (d)
Caudate nucleus	3.0 (c)	2,750, 4,000 (d, g)	921 (d)
Olfactory bulb	1.3 (c)	440 (c)	46 (d)
Retina	5–6 (o, s)	1,020, 3,000–3,500 (o, s)	—
Optic N	0–0.3 (o, c)	0–6 (o, c, r)	2.6 (d)
Cerebral cortex area 51	—	900, 750 (c, d)	109 (d)
Cerebral cortex area 17	2.2 (c)	175, 260 (c, d)	25 (d)
Cerebral cortex area 4	4.5 (c)	270, 600 (c, d)	42 (d)

Notes: (1) The initials in brackets indicate species: c, cat; d, dog; g, goat; g.p., guinea-pig; o, ox; r, rabbit; s, sheep.
(2) The values in the table for ACh are from MacIntosh,[292] Feldberg[155] and Wolfram;[410] for choline acetylase from Hebb and Silver,[211] Hebb and Mitchell;[210] and Cohen;[74] and for true ChE from Sawyer and Hollinshead,[364] Burgen and Chipman,[57] and Wolfgram.[410]

are not defined by the stain which, instead of being intracellular, is distributed over the surface of the cholinoceptive cell.

A second conclusion which can be drawn from histochemical studies is that at all synapses where cholinergic fibres end in apposition to other nerve cells or their processes, e.g., the ganglia of the autonomic nervous system, only true ChE is present in the synaptic region. It is also present together with some pseudo ChE at the motor end-plate of most somatic muscles but in visceral structures such as the smooth muscle and glands of the intestine and lungs innervated by post-glanglionic fibres, there is an abundance of pseudo ChE (butyryl ChE) instead. Moreover, Häggqvist[200] has recently reported that in some somatic muscle fibres BuChE and not AChE is to be found. He has suggested that these are tonic or slow muscle fibres as distinct from phasic or twitch fibres, in which AChE is the enzyme present.

It is possible therefore that in situations in which the required response to ACh has a relatively long time-course BuChE is the enzyme responsible for its destruction. This idea is derived from the biochemical evidence that the optimal concentration for the hydrolysis of ACh by pseudo ChE is higher than that for true ChE. That is ACh would have no chance to accumulate at synapses or neuro-effector junctions where AChE is present; but at junctions containing BuChE, it would accumulate to some extent before being destroyed.

The recent studies by Schild[368] indicating that there are two types of ACh receptor in the guinea-pig ileum may be relevant here. It may be imagined that at the preganglionic endings at which true ChE can be demonstrated, the enzyme is associated with a receptor molecule having comparable active groups for interaction with ACh, the whole system being one designed for a rapid and shortlasting action of ACh on the innervated cell; but when released at the postganglionic terminals it may come in contact with a different type of receptor which reacts maximally, as does BuChE, only as the concentration of ACh reaches a relatively high level in its vicinity. Thus the response of the smooth muscle would be both gradual in onset and long lasting.

Effects of Cutting Cholinergic Nerves.—(1) *Distal to Sections:* After section the degenerating distal portion of a cholinergic nerve such as the cervical sympathetic rapidly loses ACh,[290] choline acetylase[215] and true Che.[365] Pseudo ChE may also diminish but it is much less affected by the section than the concentration of true ChE which falls to between 20 and 40% of its original value during the first 5 to 7 days after section and remains at this level until regenerating fibres have begun to appear.

ACh and choline acetylase fall more abruptly to between 15 and 40% of their original concentrations at the end of 3 days. Subsequently, choline acetylase continues to fall, although more slowly than at first, and is between 10 and 15% at 5 days, 2 to 4% at 12 days, 1 to 2% at 21 days, and then remains virtually at zero until regenerating fibres have effectively invaded the distal portion of nerve.[215]

True ChE does not disappear completely from a degenerating nerve trunk presumably owing to the circumstance that some of the enzyme in a nerve trunk is derived from extraneuronal elements, such as the sheath and cells of Schwann; some of the scavenger cells which aid in the process of degeneration may also contain true ChE. The rate and extent of disappearance of the enzyme are about the same for the denervated superior cervical ganglion as they are for the degenerating preganglionic trunk[364] so it is unlikely that retention of post-synaptic ChE in the denervated ganglion contributes significantly to the persisting fraction of enzyme.

The reduction of ChE and choline acetylase[208] in degenerating somatic nerves occurs at about the same rate as in the denervated superior cervical ganglion. The recent brief report by Bhatnagar & MacIntosh[24] that some ACh persists in somatic muscle for long periods after denervation (up to 60 days) is therefore of interest. In recent experiments conducted in this laboratory it has been found that all levels of the distal portion of the nerve lose choline acetylase at approximately the same rate. The intramuscular nerve terminals were not examined, however, and it may be that the enzyme within them is in some way protected from total destruction. It is of course not always possible to be sure of the total denervation of mammalian muscle since there is the possibility of the growth of collaterals from other nerves and until a fuller account of the experiments by Bhatnagar and MacIntosh is forthcoming, some doubt must remain as to the meaning of the results they have reported.

(2) Proximal to the Section. In the proximal part of the nerve true ChE[364] and choline acetylase[215] both increase much above their normal level during the first 5 to 7 days. The rise in both of the enzymes is entirely confined to the terminal 2 to 3 cm. of the nerve[212,288] and is apparently related to the growth and multiplication of fibres associated with regeneration in this part of it. During the first 7 days morphological changes in the tip of the nerve include considerable branching of existing fibres as well as ballooning and spiralling, all of which suggest a damming-up of forward growth and at this time the concentration of choline acetylase per unit length of nerve becomes about double the usual value; but it then starts to return to normal as forward growth begins. It is possible that the concentration of enzyme remains high in the region of the advancing tips of new nerve fibres but this has not yet been examined. It would be of interest to

know whether this is the case since recent evidence suggests that in many respects the morphology of the regenerating nerve terminals is similar to that of normal nerve endings.

Experiments of this kind are of interest in another way. It has long been known that cholinergic nerve fibres contain ACh, true ChE and choline acetylase throughout their length; the behaviour of the enzymes after nerve section, increasing in the proximal and diminishing in the distal portions, suggests that the enzymes are synthesized in the perikaryon and are present in the axon because they are being slowly transported to the nerve terminals where they have their function. If this is so, then it may also be that ChE is secreted from the endings to form part of the post-synaptic enzyme.

Central Nervous System.—Values for ACh content, choline acetylase and true ChE for representative parts of the CNS are given in Table II (b). The highest concentrations of the two enzymes are found in the head of the caudate nucleus, while the lowest (less than significant in the case of choline acetylase) are in the optic nerve (but not the tract). It is generally true that white matter contains less ACh and enzyme than does the grey matter, but the cerebellum provides an exception, at least so far as choline acetylase is concerned. The cerebellar peduncles, particularly the superior and inferior, all have quite high concentrations of enzyme but in the cerebellar cortex choline acetylase and ACh are absent or present only in low concentrations. The cerebellum is of interest for another reason. It is the only part of the CNS where true ChE is high and both ACh and choline acetylase are very low. It appears that much of the true ChE is in glial cells of the organ but the highest concentrations are in the granular layer (innermost cortical layer of nerve cells) where second order afferents end; these fibres enter the cerebellum by way of the peduncles and are probably cholinergic. Fibres of this group may well account for all the choline acetylase of the organ.

Interspecies differences in the concentrations of choline acetylase and of true ChE in the neocortex may be large. Tower and Elliott[397] have shown that there is an inverse relation between the weight of the brain and the concentration of ACh and ChE in the neocortex and its production in the free state by cortical slices. Since there is also a similar relation between cell density and brain weight they have concluded that the evolutionary enlargement of the neocortex has not been associated with any diminution in the relative numbers of cholinergic neurons. However, data available in this laboratory (partly published by Hebb and Silver[211]) for choline acetylase concentrations of various areas of the neocortex, especially area 17, suggest that this conclusion requires some modification. Thus the cortical choline acetylase concentration in the dog is higher than in the cat which has the smaller brain and in the grey squirrel is much below values in the rat, guinea-pig and rabbit; and that observed in man is considerably below what is to be expected from the relation between cell density and brain size unless cholinergic neurons are relatively fewer than in some nonprimate mammalian species.

The choline acetylase concentration of the retina also varies greatly from one species to another.[205] In the cat and dog, the activity is equivalent to 400 to 600 μg. ACh/gm. dried tissue/hr., but in other species, e.g., the sheep, it is 30 to 40 times higher. In general this variation can be related to the thickness of the bipolar layer, the cells of which appear to be cholinergic; the activity is highest in eyes in which high visual acuity depends upon retinal grain rather than on the size of the eye, as it does in the horse which has a rather low concentration of the enzyme in its retina.

Intracellular Distribution.—Early evidence reviewed in some detail by Feldberg in 1945 made it clear that ACh can exist in tissues either in comparatively free solution (although it is then only recoverable if some anti-ChE is present), or physically bound to some tissue component in which condition it is resistant to the action of ChE. There were also indications that ACh enters the bound state as it is formed. The complete release of bound ACh could be brought about by treatment with organic solvents such as ether, or with acids, but otherwise there was no evidence to show to what type of tissue particle ACh was attached or what was the nature of the binding forces.

Evidence on these points was later obtained in experiments in which the intracellular distribution in brain tissue of both choline acetylase and ACh were studied by the method of differential centrifugation.[214,216] These showed that the largest proportion of choline acetylase is associated with the mitochondrial or large granule fraction; that ACh is present in this fraction in the same proportions; and that particles with which both ACh and choline acetylase are associated can be separated from the bulk of the mitochondria by centrifuging the large granule fraction in a density gradient provided by 0.8 to 1.6 M sucrose solution. Most of the choline acetylase in the particulate is inactive and its close association with ACh is emphasized by the fact that procedures which activate the enzyme also release ACh. Ether is the most effective activating agent and it also releases all of the ACh. Other treatments which only partially activate the enzyme, such as freezing and thawing, also release only part of the ACh.

Since morphological evidence (see later) suggests that neurohumors such as ACh may be contained in the so-called synaptic vesicles the question arises whether the particles containing the enzyme and ester that are separated by centrifuging are in fact synaptic vesicles. One difficulty in accepting their identification as synaptic vesicles is that the latter are of microsomal proportions 0.02 to 0.06 μ and should not be precipitated by the relatively low centrifugal force required for precipitation of the large granule fraction. However, it is possible that the brain particles containing ACh and the enzyme are microsomal in size but are precipitated in clusters, since electron microscopy indicates that this is how they are grouped in the nerve terminals.[332] Moreover, it has recently been shown by Gray and Whittaker[195] that whole end-feet tend to be sedimented as single structures in the fraction from which ACh and choline acetylase are recovered. This does not help to identify the precise location of the enzyme and ester but it removes the earlier difficulty in reconciling the results of centrifugal analysis with the concept of synaptic vesicles as carriers of neurohumors such as ACh.

It has recently been found that 40 to 60% of the choline acetylase present in motor spinal roots is in the small granule or microsomal fractions.[208] Although not fully active unless treated with ether, the enzyme in this fraction is relatively more active before treatment than is the enzyme in untreated brain particulates. It is also much less stable after activation. There may be some temptation to identify particles to which the enzyme is attached in the microsomal fraction of the motor roots with the synaptic vesicles; there is little evidence, however, to show that these vesicles exist anywhere in the neuron except at the nerve endings where they are thought by some to be formed by budding off from the endoplasmic reticulum[332] (but see also ref. 400a). If as seems probable choline acetylase is also associated with this system of membranes then presumably its binding will undergo some change with the formation of the vesicles at the terminals, and so the particles to which it is attached in the microsomal fraction of the motor axons may be their precursors rather than identical with them.

There is evidence that true ChE in nervous tissue is divided between at least two particulate fractions,[325] one microsomal and the other a heavier (or more readily sedimentable) fraction. According to Toschi[395] the distribution of ChE in the microsomal fraction, although this also contains many granules and has a high RNA content, is correlated with the presence of vesicles with thin membranes. Part of the ChE in the RNA-containing fraction may represent enzyme derived from the perikaryon, where as already mentioned a high concentration of true ChE can be demonstrated by histochemistry. The remainder may be post-synaptic enzyme associated with cell membranes. It would be of interest to know in which fraction the true ChE of the axons is found; but this has not yet been analyzed separately.

Before closing this discussion is should be emphasized that as yet all attempts to relate the distribution of either ACh or of its associated enzymes as determined by centrifugal analysis to the structural components of the nerve cell observed by electron microscopy involves more speculation than fact. It is unlikely that the electron microscope gives a wholly accurate picture of the nerve cell: some structures will be highlighted while others may be overlooked, or distorted, owing to the methods of fixation and mounting; while, complete homogenizing of the cell leaves only a few structures such as the nucleus and mitochondria which are still recognizable. Much of the identification then is a matter of guesswork and consequently the arguments set forth in the preceding paragraphs are to be regarded as interpretative and speculative rather than in any way conclusive.

Comparative Evidence

Vertebrates.—The distribution of ACh in the nervous system has only been investigated systematically in mammals; and for some vertebrates, reptiles and fish, there are almost no data for comparison with other species. One remarkable figure is that given by Feldberg and Fessard[159] for the electric organ of *Torpedo marmorata* which they estimate contains a concentration of between 40 and 100 μg.ACh/gm., figures which are higher than for any other vertebrate tissue.

Choline acetylase activity of the brain has been estimated for a number of vertebrate species in this laboratory. The investigation is still in its preliminary stage and the figures obtained are therefore to be regarded as provisional only. Among the vertebrates investigated *Labrus bergylta,* a teleost fish, was found to have the highest choline acetylase activity for whole brain amounting to a rate of synthesis of 5000 μg.ACh/gm. tissue/hr. Next highest is the brain of chickens and pigeons; and mammals come in third place with values for the rat brain of 1200 to 1600 μg./gm./hr.

At the other end of the scale the rate of ACh synthesis by the dogfish brain is only just measurable (less than 25 μg./gm./hr.). Rather low values (300-350 μg./gm./hr.) are given by the snake *(Natrix natrix)* and frog *(Rana temporaria)* brains. Some of the findings on frog brain suggest that the enzyme in this species is easily inactivated and it is possible therefore that in all of these species the capacity of the tissue to acetylate choline is in fact greater than we have observed. This seems more likely in view of the finding that the concentration of ACh in the frog brain is between 5 and 10 μg./gm. which is of the same order as that found in mammals.

The results from the dogfish and *Labrus* suggest that cholinergic neurons are poorly represented in the brain of the one species and well-represented in the brain of the other. A somewhat similar conclusion might be drawn from Augustinsson's figures[10] for the rates of ACh and MeCh (acetyl-β-methylcholine) hydrolysis by *Labrus* brain and by the brains of two elasmobranchs, *Scyllium* and *Squalus*. The rates of hydrolysis by *Labrus* were the highest for the vertebrate brains examined while those for the other two species were the lowest.

As in mammals, the concentration of the enzymes controlling ACh metabolism may vary in different parts of the nervous system. In *Raja*, for example, the concentration of choline acetylase is lower in the medulla than in the optic lobes and lower still in the cerebellum. In birds and mammals, it is lower in the hind brain than in the forebrain; but in relation to cerebral levels it is higher in the cerebellum of birds (equivalent to 400 to 600 μg./gm./hr.) than in the cerebellum of mammals (see Table IIb). Similarly, in the brains of birds and mammals there are large regional variations in true ChE. In addition, Shen et al.[372] have found that the concentration of true ChE (as measured by hydrolysis of acetyl-β-methylcholine) is about ten times higher in the optic lobe and fourteen to fifteen times higher in the hindbrain than it is in the cerebrum of the frog.

Augustinsson's[10] figures show that both elasmobranch and teleost fishes have higher concentrations of true ChE in their somatic muscles (rate of hydrolysis of MeCh: 16 to 20 μmole/gm./hr.) than has the dog (rate of hydrolysis of MeCh: 7 μmole/gm./hr.). He suggests that the difference is related to the greater speed of locomotion of fish.

Invertebrates.—Values for ACh concentration in the nervous system of many invertebrates species are listed by Prosser.[344] The highest concentrations are those found in the CNS of insects and molluscs; the concentrations in crustacea are somewhat lower. Of the various invertebrates in which ACh is present so far only the insect has been systematically investigated to determine the distribution of ACh and of the enzymes metabolizing it. ACh values given recently by Colhoun[75] for the brain of the cockroach, *Periplaneta americana,* 139 to 149 μg./gm. are the highest yet observed for nervous tissue in any animal. In the peripheral nerves of the same species ACh is present in lower concentration while it is absent altogether from the muscles. Similarly the choline acetylase activity is greatest in the brain (50 to 53 mg ACh/gm./hr.; about ten times higher than the highest values observed in vertebrate brains) less in connective and peripheral nerves, and absent from muscle. ChE is high in all parts of the nervous system but it is also absent from muscle.

There is as yet little evidence about the function of ACh in the nervous system of insects although it has been extensively investigated.[374] It is thought to be concerned in intercellular transmission but this in fact has not been proved. One of the recognized difficulties of studying the action of ACh is that the whole nervous system is enclosed in a sheath which is impermeable to ACh and to many other ions (see ref. 326). Another is that complete *in vivo* inhibition of ChE by anti-ChE agents such as DFP may be delayed or prevented by substrate protection of the enzyme. DFP may also produce other effects such as indirect inhibition of ACh synthesis (see ref. 409). Furthermore in insects poisoned by DFP there may be translocation of ACh from one part of the nervous system (i.e., within the protecting sheath) to another.[375] The ester will leak out of the system only very slowly so long as the protective sheath is intact. It therefore tends to accumulate in inhibitory concentrations in the neighborhood of nerve cells which are thought to be normally responsive to it.

The question of how ACh acts in insects is of some practical importance for the understanding of the mode of action of some insecticides which have strong anti-Ch E properties. According to Smallman[374] the most reasonable hypothesis on present evidence is that their insecticidal action depends upon their anticholinesterase properties. This perhaps is most clearly suggested by the evidence that insect eggs (from the housefly) when treated with anti-ChE at an early stage of development continue to grow normally until just before hatching, when their ACh content normally increases very rapidly, and they then die.

Winteringham *et al.*,[409] however, have found evidence that DFP reduces *in vivo* synthesis of ACh. Since this agent has no direct inhibiting effect on choline acetylase, the result suggests that the effect is indirect though the accumulation of ACh or that it is due to an action on the enzyme system ultimately responsible for the production of acetyl-CoA. If so, the anti-ChE action of DFP and of other insecticides with similar properties is the incidental rather than the primary cause of their toxicity.

Choline acetylase extracted from the squid head ganglion has been studied extensively by Nachmansohn and his colleagues (see refs. 321, 346). This work is important chiefly because of the information obtained about the properties of the enzyme, its substrate specificity and the optimal conditions for its activity. Like the enzyme obtained from cold-blooded vertebrates the temperature optimum is near 30°C. (see ref. 204). Otherwise the properties of the squid enzyme seem to be similar to the properties of the mammalian enzyme.

V. TRANSMITTER FUNCTION OF ACETYLCHOLINE

Introductory Survey. —Cholinergic neurons are probably present in both the peripheral and central nervous systems, but the evidence demonstrating the cholinergic nature of some central neurons as well as some in the autonomic system is less complete than it is in the case of preganglionic sympathetic and somatic motor axons. In general there are three kinds of evidence on which the identification of any nerve as cholinergic depends:— (1) Pharmacological evidence showing whether injected ACh mimicks the effect of stimulation of the nerve. The activity produced by both types of stimuli should be modified by appropriate drugs, including anticholinesterases which enhance and prolong the action of ACh, and agents such as atropine, which blocks the muscarinic actions of ACh, or nicotine and curare, which block its nicotinic actions. (2) Demonstration of the release of ACh from the endings of the nerve. (3) Biochemical and histochemical evidence showing whether ChE and choline acetylase are present in the nerve and whether ChE is concentrated at the receptor sites of the cells innervated, that is whether the cell innervated is likely to be *cholinoceptive*.

It will be appropriate to consider in this survey how far these criteria can be met in attempts to classify neurons of the vertebrate, more particularly the mammalian, nervous system. In the case of certain nerves, e.g., the somatic motor neurons, the evidence will be considered in much greater detail in the text following this introductory survey when we come to examine the mechanisms of transmission.

Somatic Motor Neurons.—All three types of evidence are available on which to base the identification of the motor nerves to skeletal muscle as cholinergic. As already indicated in Section II the effect of nerve stimulation can be imitated by injections of ACh, and the ester can be recovered from eserinized nerve muscle preparations after stimulation of the nerve. Moreover it can be shown that the motor nerves contain true ChE and choline acetylase and that ChE is concentrated at the endplate (see Section III).

Sympathetic Preganglionic Neurons.—Evidence that preganglionic nerves are cholinergic is similar in kind to the evidence for the motor nerves.

Postganglionic Sympathetic Nerves Innervating the Sweat Glands of the Cat.—The muscarinic action of ACh on the sweat glands of the cat was demonstrated by Dale.[87] Subsequently Dale and Feldberg[93] showed that the nerves to the sweat glands release ACh. Generally, pharmacological evidence supports the view that the nerves to these glands are cholinergic in most mammalian species, but not in the horse and sheep in which they are adrenergic. Evidence of other postganglionic sympathetic cholinergic fibres to the blood vessels of certain muscles[89] is suggestive but by no means complete.

Parasympathetic Pre-and post-ganglionic Neurons.—It is convenient to consider these together since in many cases the pre- and post-gang-lionic fibres end within the innervated organ and it is difficult to determine from which endings the ACh released by stimulation of the parasympathetic nerve supply is derived.

This applies particularly to organs innervated by the vagus and the pelvic nerves, such as the lungs, the heart and the gastro-intestinal tract. In all of these tissues the preganglionic fibres are distributed rather diffusely to numerous ganglia of microscopic dimensions lying within each organ. In most it is possible to demonstrate the release of ACh when the parasympathetic supply is stimulated and on the basis of pharmacological tests it is generally accepted that both pre- and post-ganglionic vagal fibres are responsible for the release. There are certain gaps in the evidence, however, and it may be as well to consider these cases first.

The pharmacological tests of chief importance are to determine separately the effects of nicotine which has a stimulating followed by a ganglion-blocking action, atropine which blocks the effect of ACh on the effector cell (smooth muscle or gland) and eserine which enhances its effects on both ganglia and effector cells. In Dale's earliest paper on ACh[93] he had shown that atropine antagonizes all of the parasympathomimetic actions of ACh. In the heart and stomach it can be shown that both nicotine and atropine block, whereas eserine enhances, the effects of vagal stimulation. Similarly, the action of ACh is abolished by atropine and enhanced by eserine; while after nicotine ACh still produces an effect. By analogy with its effect on sympathetic ganglia it is assumed that nicotine blocks solely by causing failure of ganglionic transmission and since atropine does not block at ganglia, except in unspecifically high concentrations it must prevent the action of ACh on the effector cells; thus the intrinsic muscles of the eyes can be shown to become insensitive to ACh and to stimulation of the post-ganglionic fibres of the third cranial nerve after atropine (see below).

However, the responses to parasympathetic stimulation and the responses to small doses of nicotine (which stimulate the ganglia) are not always prevented by atropine, even when this is given in doses that wholly suppress the action of muscarine and ACh itself. This is true in certain species of contraction of the bladder and large intestine induced by stimulation of the pelvic nerves, contraction of the small intestine induced by vagal stimulation or stimulation by nicotine (see ref. 4). Vagal bronchoconstriction in the guinea-pig is also strongly resistant to atropine.[76] Two reasons that have been suggested for the resistance of the intestine and bladder are: (1) that the ACh liberated by the nerve endings may be inaccessible to injected atropine, the 'proximity' theory (see Ambache[4]) and (2) that a proportion of the

postganglionic neurons are not cholinergic. An additional possibility
is that the muscle receptors of these viscera may have become modified (see Part III) so that under certain conditions, say when the
concentration rises above a certain level, ACh can displace atropine
from a proportion of the receptors. The point to be made here, however, is that the pharmacological evidence is not unequivocally in
favour of the view that the postganglionic fibres in these situations
are cholinergic. In the case of the secretory fibres of the vagus (to
pancreas, stomach, etc.) and the 7th and 9th nerve the evidence is less
equivocal. In all of these cases atropine blocks parasympathetically
induced secretion. Furthermore, the liberation of ACh from the submaxillary gland on stimulation of the chorda tympani has been demonstrated;[12] while it has been shown by Emmelin and Muren[146] that
when ganglionic transmission is prevented by d-tubocurarine, and
postganglionic excitation in this way eliminated, stimulation of the
nerve still releases about one-third of the amount of ACh usually
liberated.

Schmiedeberg according to Ambache[4] probably succeeded in his
very early experiments (1870) on the frog heart in demonstrating that
the postganglionic fibres arising within the heart were atropine-sensi-
tive. He obtained vagal inhibition that was antagonized by atropine
when he stimulated in the region of the sinus venosus and in that
position he was probably stimulating all of the postganglionic fibres.
Similarly Adamück's experiments of about the same date, also quoted
by Ambache, demonstrated that the mydriatic action of atropine
depends upon block of the stimulus set up in the postganglionic fibres
of the short ciliary nerves.

Release of ACh (identified by slowing action on the toad heart) into
the aqueous humour of the eye occurs on stimulation of the oculo-
motor nerve;[147] this constitutes more direct evidence that the postganglionic fibres are cholinergic. In agreement with this conclusion
it has also been shown[302] that injection of pseudo ChE into the eye
can reduce or prevent reflex pupil constriction.

Evidence that the preganglionic ciliary fibres are cholinergic has
also been obtained by Perry and Talesnik[341] who found that the ciliary
ganglion cells are depolarized by ACh and that this effect, as well as
the response of the eye muscle to preganglionic stimulation, is modified by nicotine and hexamethonium in the same way as is transmission through the superior cervical ganglion. Release of ACh from the
preganglionic fibres in this pathway has not been demonstrated. An
experiment done by Anderson[5] in 1905 is of interest here. He showed
that after removal of the ciliary ganglion, re-innervation enabled the
intrinsic eye muscles to regain their normal responses. Presumably

this was re-innervation by the preganglionic fibres and they could only be effective if they transmit stimuli by the release of ACh. (For further information about the problems discussed here the article by Ambache[4] is recommended.)

Role of ACh in Neuromuscular Transmission

On the basis of a large amount of experimental evidence the following general picture has evolved of the function of ACh in neuromuscular transmission is vertebrates (for recent reviews see Fatt;[152] del Castillo and Katz;[109] Katz;[239] Shanes,[371a] Eccles[127a]). ACh is synthesized and stored in the endings of the motor nerves, probably in discrete packets or quanta; when a nerve impulse reaches the motor terminals, many such quanta of ACh are released almost simultaneously in the immediate vicinity of the muscle end-plate. The end-plate is a specialized region of the surface membrane of the muscle fibre highly sensitive to ACh, which produces a marked but rather unspecific increase in its permeability to ions. The sudden change in permeability causes ionic currents to flow through the end-plate and tends to depolarize the membrane by allowing its resting charge to leak away. If the membrane depolarization reaches a critical voltage, an all-or-none impulse is started that travels over all parts of the muscle fibre, initiating its contraction. The effect of ACh is quite transient and the permeability change disappears very rapidly as the ACh diffuses away and is destroyed by the cholinesterase present in large amounts at the end-plate.

(1) Synthesis and Storage of ACh in Motor Nerves

Evidence has already been presented that extracts of motor nerves are capable of synthesizing large quantities of ACh (Table Ia). There is no direct evidence that ACh is present in large amounts in the motor nerve endings in muscle, but it is known that the ventral root fibres contain much ACh (see Table IIa), and when the part of the muscle which contains the terminal nerve branches is compared with a nerve-free part, a substantial excess of ACh is found in the former (Hebb and Krnjević[209]). Although the excess is probably ACh held within the nerve terminals there is no direct proof of this, and the additional ACh can only indicate the maximum possible amount stored presynaptically.

The suggestion has been made that ACh is bound within the submicroscopic vesicles that are abundant in motor nerve endings as in other presynaptic terminals.[101,109,355,27] The quantal release of ACh at the end-plate (see below) is consistent with this attractive idea, which nevertheless remains largely speculative, lacking in any direct

supporting evidence. For instance, it has not been possible to demonstrate convincingly depletion of vesicles in motor nerve endings after
prolonged maximal activity (Birks, Huxley and Katz;[27] cf. de Robertis[99,100]). Initial studies with the electron microscope of fractions
of brain homogenates separated by centrifuging (Whittaker[405]) suggested that most of the recoverable ACh was associated with particles
similar in dimensions to synaptic vesicles, but more recent work
has shown that fractions similarly prepared contain whole nerve endings (Gray and Whittaker[195]). Whatever the manner in which ACh
is bound it is clear that free ACh would not be stored in the nerve
terminals, since these contain a large quantity of cholinesterase (Koelle
and Koelle[249]).

(2) Release of ACh by Motor Nerve Endings

Early experiments had shown that ACh (or an ACh-like compound)
was released in muscles during nerve stimulation, e.g., Hess,[217]
Shimidzu,[373] but they did not exclude the possibility that autonomic
or sensory nerve fibres, or the muscles themselves, were the source of
ACh. In the study already referred to, Dale, Feldberg and Vogt[94] found
that ACh was released from mammalian tongue and leg muscles perfused with a Tyrode solution containing an anticholinesterase agent,
during activity of only the motor nerve endings, produced by stimulating the appropriate ventral roots (after sympathectomy). Direct
stimulation of the muscle was not effective, except in so far as intramuscular nerve branches were excited. Contraction of the muscle was
not important since the release continued after paralysis by curare.

The principal objection subsequently raised against this study was
that the release of ACh could only be demonstrated under 'unphysiological' conditions, i.e., during perfusion with Tyrode which rapidly
leads to oedema and loss of function.[173] However, Emmelin and Mac-
Intosh[145] have since shown that perfusion with plasma, or even blood,
maintains the muscle in a sound condition, and yet the release of ACh
can be demonstrated if one uses a sufficient concentration of anticholinesterase. These results are not dependent upon the action of one
particular anticholinesterase, and if no anticholinesterase is used
choline can be recovered from the effluent in the expected amount. So
is does not seem that anticholinesterases are themselves responsible
for the release of ACh. It has been claimed that ACh is liberated by
the muscle rather than the nerve terminal, on the ground that ACh
can be collected from denervated muscle excited by direct stimulation.[300] However, as these experiments were only performed 5 to 10
days after cutting the motor nerves this does not seem very strong

evidence that the ACh could not originate in the degenerating nerve terminals (see Part III). On the other hand, it is likely that a small amount of ACh is liberated continuously in denervated muscle, possibly from Schwann cells which remain at the end-plate. Spontaneous miniature end-plate potentials, though much reduced in amplitude and especially frequency, can still be recorded many weeks after denervation (Fig. 1), (Birks, Katz and Miledi;[28] Miledi[308]).

Amount of ACh Released.—To calculate the mean amount of ACh released per impulse at a nerve ending one must know the number of nerve endings in the muscle. In the original articles by Dale *et al.*,[94] and Emmelin and MacIntosh,[145] no attempt was made to calculate the mean release per ending, but approximate calculations based on these experiments were given later by Dale,[89] Acheson[2] and MacIntosh.[293] The amounts estimated ranged from 0.5 to 7×10^{-18} mole. In recent experiments with the isolated rat and guinea-pig diaphragm (Brooks,[42] Straughan;[384] Krnjević and Mitchell[259,260]) relatively high yields of ACh have been obtained, between 2 and 10×10^{-18} mole per nerve ending per impulse, the higher values being associated with stimulation for short periods at particularly low rates (2 to 5/sec.)

Spontaneous Release of ACh.—It is possible to detect the spontaneous liberation of small amounts of ACh from isolated muscle in the absence of any evident stimulation.[42,123,384,260] This is consistent with the spontaneous subthreshold activity at the muscle end-plate first seen in frogs by Fatt and Katz,[154] later observed by Boyd and Martin[35] and Liley[273] in mammals, and by Ginsborg[192] in birds. A comprehensive study of this phenomenon led Fatt and Katz[154] to the suggestion that ACh is present in the nerve endings in discrete quanta, some of which tend to leak out in a random manner causing the spontaneous electrical activity of the end-plate membrane which can be observed with intracellular microelectrodes (Fig. 1).

Factors Which Influence the Release of ACh from Nerve Endings.— Since it is difficult to obtain adequate amounts of ACh for assay from muscle, there have been comparatively few direct studies of the release of ACh in muscle under different conditions. Hence much of our information concerning the presynaptic release of ACh is somewhat indirect, being based upon the interpretation of electrical changes within the framework of the ACh hypothesis. This demonstrates the internal logic of the hypothesis and its wide applicability without adding as much independent support as might be desirable.

The release of ACh as seen by its effect on the end-plate membrane probably always occurs in quanta or multiples of quanta. The amount of ACh in a quantum is approximately fixed, and changes in the overall rate of release are determined by variations in the number of quanta released (del Castillo and Katz[109]). The spontaneous discharge is quite sensitive to conditions such as the temperature and the osmotic pressure of the medium[154,179,109,273,35,271] although it seems that more than one factor may be involved in the complex response to cooling.[273] The spontaneous leak can be markedly increased by depolarizing, or reduced by hyperpolarizing, the presynaptic nerve terminals, by pass-

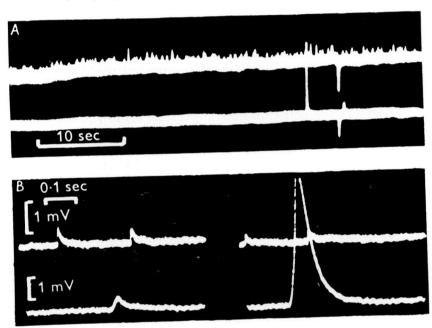

Fig. 1. Simultaneous intracellular records of miniature end-plate potentials at an innervated (upper trace) and a denervated (lower trace) end-plate in the *same* muscle fibre from a frog sartorius. Traces show that spontaneous potentials still occur after denervation, though much less frequently. The downward stroke appearing simultaneously in both traces in *A* corresponds to a hyperpolarizing pulse applied through a third intracellular micro-electrode located 7 mm. from the innervated end-plate. Voltage calibrations in *A* same as in *B* where miniature potentials are shown on faster time scale. The pelvic branches of the nerve were cut 15 days earlier (Miledi[308]).

ing a current through the nerve as close to the ending as possible (del Castillo and Katz,[105] Liley[274]). The effect of the polarizing current clearly must reach the junctional region where ACh is released, yet no electrotonic potentials can be detected across the muscle end-plate membrane; this is powerful evidence against the previously held view that transmission is mediated by the direct spread of electrical current from the nerve to the muscle (for other evidence against the "electrical" hypothesis, see Kuffler, 1948; but note that electrical transmission may occur normally at certain crustacean synapses[180]). The action of depolarizing currents on the motor nerve terminals can be reproduced by solutions containing an excess of K+, which, of course, would also be expected to depolarize the nerve endings. The relation between the calculated change in membrane potential at the nerve terminals and the change in the rate of "spontaneous" activity recorded at the end-plate in the rat diaphragm is extremely steep; Liley[274] therefore postulated that an action potential in the nerve terminals would produce a sufficient amount of depolarization (even though lasting less than a millisecond) to release the 100 to 300 quanta of ACh estimated to be associated with normal transmission.[103,297,36]

The amount of ACh liberated by a nerve impulse depends very much on the ratio of Ca:Mg in the medium, the number of quanta being low if the ratio is reduced and vice versa; a muscle can be paralysed by either lack of Ca or excess Mg (del Castillo and Engbaek;[102] del Castillo and Katz[103]). The release of ACh is also apparently increased by stretch (Hutter and Trautwein[231]) and in the presence of adrenaline (Krnjević and Miledi[256]).

Previous activity usually causes a mixture of depression and facilitation, the predominant effect depending upon the experimental conditions and the type of animal.[367,168,131,289,104] During prolonged repetitive activity the output of ACh diminishes rapidly.[94,359,357,169,104,384,260] The amount released changes with the frequency of the stimulation. According to Straughan,[384] the output of ACh per impulse in the rat diaphragm diminishes with increasing frequency, the total output over 20 minutes period reaching a maximum at a frequency of 25/sec.

Short periods of repetitive excitation at high frequencies (>100/sec.) are followed by a condition of post-tetanic potentiation during which transmission is enhanced, probably by the release of larger amounts of ACh (cf. Boyd;[37] Hutter;[228] Liley and North;[275] Johns, Grob and Harvey[236]). There is some evidence that the nerve terminals are hyperpolarized after a tetanus and that the nerve action potenial is temporarily larger than normal (Lloyd;[281] Eccles and Krnjević[133]). These larger spikes are likely to be more effective in liberating the junctional transmitter although it is possible that the transmitter is somehow more readily available for release during the post-tetanic phase, because the rate of spontaneous release is also greater than normal (Liley;[273] Hubbard;[226] however, del Castillo and Katz[105] found that the rate of spontaneous activity and the height of the e.p.p. are sometimes inversely related after repetitive stimulation).

It is of some interest that there are at least two types of paralyzing drug whose principal action is said to be to prevent the release of ACh: Botulinum toxin (Guyton and MacDonald;[199] Burgen, Dickens and Zatman;[58] Brooks[42,43]) and the hemicholiniums (Schueler;[370] Longo;[284] Reitzel and Long;[347] Wilson and Long[407]); the latter probably interfere with the synthesis of ACh *in situ* (MacIntosh[293]). However, there is now also good evidence that hemicholiniums block neuromuscular transmission by interference with the action of ACh.[393a,297a]

(3) ACh Has a Powerful Action on Muscle

Vertebrate skeletal muscle responds to ACh applied in a suitable manner. Amphibian, reptilian and avian muscle contracts readily in the presence of ACh (Riesser and Neuschlosz;[352] Buchthal and Lindhard;[51] Gasser and Dale[184]), but mammalian muscle only proved to be normally and regularly responsive with a special technique of close arterial injection (Brown, Dale and Feldberg;[47] Brown[46]) which made possible the sudden appearance of a relatively high concentration of ACh within the muscle. (Fish muscle also reacts to a local application of ACh[254a]) The commonest response is a brief twitch, associated with propagated electrical impulses, but in certain muscle fibres there is a slower kind of contraction, known as a contracture, which is usually not accompanied by propagated electrical disturbances. This type of response does not normally occur in mammalian muscle where it is only seen after denervation.

The end-plate of the muscle fibre is the circumscribed region where the motor nerve ending and the muscle membrane come into close contact, in a manner so intimate and complex that until recently it was suggested that there is cellular continuity between these two elements. However, it has now been made clear by means of the electron microscope that the axon and the muscle fibre preserve their individual surface membranes, which remain separated by a space several hundred Å wide, even though the branching nerve terminals may be deeply embedded within grooves in the surface of the muscle fibre (for full details of the morphology reviews by Couteaux[77,79] should be consulted).

The End-plate Potentials.—The end-plate region, varying in size from some 10-50 μ in mammalian muscle to 0.5 mm. in the frog, is differentiated from the remainder of the muscle fibre by its functional properties. Unpropagated potential changes, which do not behave in an all-or-none manner, can be recorded from this region of the muscle fibre under certain conditions. Such end-plate potentials (e.p.ps) were first recorded with external electrodes (Göpfert and Schaeffer;[193] Eccles and O'Connor;[135] Feng;[168] Eccles, Katz and Kuffler[132]). Their properties were later analysed in great detail with intracellular micro-electrodes by Fatt and Katz[153] in frog muscle (see also Nastuk[323]), most of their observations being confirmed in studies of mammalian muscle (Boyd and Martin[36]). During normal neuromuscular transmis-

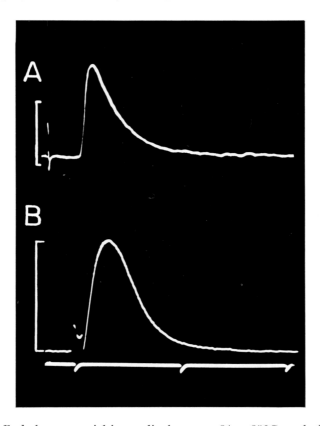

Fig. 2. *A* End-plate potential in rat diaphgram at 24 to 25 °C. evoked by stimulation of phrenic nerve at 2 c./s. The muscle was paralysed by 15.0 m*M* magnesium. *B*, Acetylcholine potential evoked in another diaphragm at same temperature, by a 1 msec. pulse of current (3.5 x 10^-8 amp.) through an ACh containing pipette whose tip was very close to the end-plate. The potentials were recorded with intracellular electrodes. Voltage scale: 5mV in *A* and 10 mV in *B*. Common time scale: 10 msec. (Krnjević and Miledi[257]).

sion there may be little obvious difference between electrical events at the end-plate and elsewhere but the e.p.p. is revealed if transmission is blocked by factors which prevent the full release of transmitter (e.g., fatigue or excess Mg [cf. Fig. 2A], or which interfere with its post-synaptic action, e.g., curare). The e.p.p. rises to its peak in a time of the order of 1 msec., but the subsequent rate of fall is much slower, being very much like the rate of passive decay observed when the membrane potential is altered momentarily by an electrical pulse. The amplitude of the e.p.p. diminishes rapidly with distance as the recording electrode is moved to other points further along the fibre. The total amount of charge displaced from the membrane during the e.p.p. decays with time at a rate which is a simple exponential, as would be expected in a passive system. Hence, Fatt and Katz[153] suggested that the transmitter (ACh) liberated by the nerve ending produces an almost instantaneous depolarization of the end-plate membrane and that the *status quo* is restored by a passive redistribution of charge along the capacitive-resistive electrical system represented by the muscle fibre membrane (see also Kuffler[262]). More recent experiments in which the end-plate membrane was clamped electrically at a fixed voltage by a feedback system using two micro-electrodes, have shown directly that the flow of current through the end-plate membrane caused by action of the transmitter lasts only a few msec (Takeuchi and Takeuchi[385]).

If the voltage change during the e.p.p. reaches a certain level, the surrounding part of the muscle membrane is sufficiently depolarized for the initiation of a self-regenerative process leading to a propagated action potential which travels over the whole muscle fibre. Under optimal conditions (i.e., during activity at a low frequency and in the absence of blocking agents) the maximal possible height of the e.p.p. in mammalian muscle is several times greater than the threshold voltage for all-or-none impulses, giving a substantial safety factor for transmission (Boyd and Martin[36]).

Extent of Area Sensitive to ACh.—Topical application of strong solutions of ACh with small pipettes or loops first made it possible to explore the most sensitive area of the surface membrane (Buchthal and Lindhard;[51] Kuffler;[263] Ginetsinskii and Shamarina[191]). It was thus found that, under normal conditions, most muscle fibres only respond to ACh applied in the immediate vicinity of the nerve terminals (Fig. 3) in agreement with the observations made by Langley[268] using nicotine, although recent studies with a more delicate method show that the sensitive area extends some distance beyond the junctional region (Miledi[309]). However, 'slow' muscle fibres (Kuffler and Vaughan Williams[266,267]) which have been found in amphibians, reptiles and birds, but so far not in mammals, tend to react to ACh applied at any point on their surface (cf. ref. 191) mainly because each fibre is supplied by many nerve endings scattered over its surface. Slow muscle fibres characteristically respond to ACh or a steady electrical current with a graded and maintained contracture instead of the brief contraction typical of the more common "twitch" fibres. Slow muscle fibres are therefore much better quantitative indicators for the assay of ACh; hence the frequent use of the frog *rectus abdominis,* which is relatively rich in slow fibres (no frog muscle is made up exclusively of slow fibres). It is generally considered that the slow type of fibre represents a more primitive stage in the development of muscle (Krüger[261]; Kuffler and Vaughan Williams[266,267]), that reappears to some extent when twitch fibres are denervated.

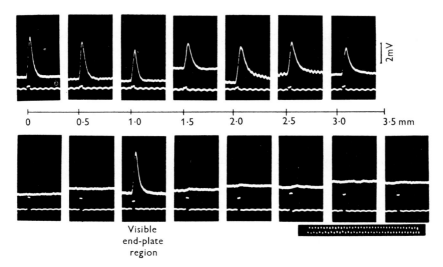

Fig. 3. The sensitivity of a cat's tenuissimus muscle fibre to locally applied ACh was tested by moving the tip of an ACh pipette close to the muscle membrane at points separated by distances of about 0.5 mm. In an innervated fibre (lower records) only the end-plate region is sensitive to ACh. In a 14 days denervated fibre (upper records) a constant pulse of ACh produced at each point of the membrane a potential change. Timer marker, 100 c./s. (Axelsson and Thesleff[11]).

Loss of nerve supply leads to a great increase in sensitivity to ACh[176,45,358]; for a comprehensive review see Cannon and Rosenbleuth.[65] This is particularly marked in mammalian muscle, normally showing little if any reaction to intravenous injections of ACh; after denervation it gradually develops typical contractures in response to ACh, even when only minute amounts are given into a vein. The principal change in the membrane properties after denervation (Fig. 3) is a progressive increase in the area of the surface responsive to ACh (Ginetsinskii and Shamarina;[191] Axelsson and Thesleff;[11] Miledi,[308]

Thesleff[393]). An analogous process is seen in reverse in the newborn animal, whose muscle fibres are initially sensitive to ACh all over; soon after birth there is a rapid progressive limitation of the sensitive region which approximates that found in the adult within 2 weeks (Ginetsinskii and Shamarina;[191] Diamond and Miledi[117]). Permanent paralysis with Botulinum toxin, which blocks the activity of the nerve endings without causing any gross morphological changes, also causes supersensitivity (Thesleff[392]). The motor nerve evidently plays a significant role in limiting ACh sensitivity to the end-plate region presumably by the topical release of some chemical agent, but there is evidence that the responsible factor is not ACh (Miledi[308,310]).

ACh Potentials.—The remarkably transient character of transmitter action explains why it is so difficult to demonstrate excitation of muscle by ACh. Clearly even close arterial injection cannot imitate a process which reaches its peak and is over within a few msec. The most successful method developed so far for applying ACh to muscle in a manner approximating to the normal release is the iontophoretic delivery of small "pulses" of ACh from micro-pipettes (Nastuk;[324] del Castillo and Katz[106]). The magnitude and time course of potentials obtained in this way, with a given amount of ACh, depends very much upon the distance between the end-plate and the point of release;[106] with an instantaneous point source the peak concentration attained at any point in the medium by diffusion varies inversely as the cube of the distance from the source, while the time to the peak is proportional to the square of this distance (Carslaw and Jaeger[67]). As a rule, ACh potentials are therefore much slower than e.p.ps. and require rather large pulses of ACh; nevertheless this method is extremely convenient for analysing in detail the reaction between ACh and its receptors at the end-plate; and when multiple pipettes are used, it is possible to study the interaction of ACh and various drugs at a single end-plate on a micro-scale (del Castillo and Katz[110-113]). Fig. 4 illustrates an ingenious experiment in which a double pipette was used to show that tubocurarine depresses the depolarizing action of carbachol (a close derivative of ACh) without changing the electrical properties of the end-plate membrane.

The tip of the ACh-containing micropipette can sometimes be brought so close to a sensitive spot that ACh potentials are elicited which differ very little from e.p.ps (Fig. 2). Only minute pulses of ACh+ (lasting about 0.1 msec) are needed to produce potentials under these conditions, the total amount actually released being of the order of 10^{-16} to 10^{-17} mole (Krnjević and Miledi[257]). This method of application (from a point source) is not as efficient as the normal release from nerve endings distributed over most of the sensi-

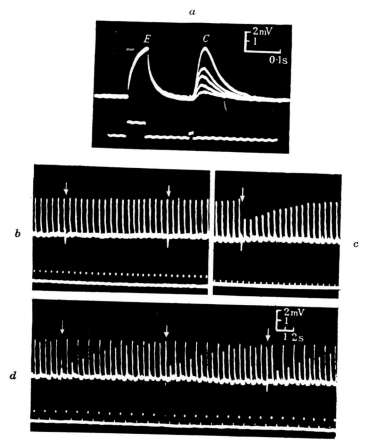

Fig. 4. Tubocurarine (TC) has no action on the electrical properties of the frog muscle membrane. *a* several superimposed traces, during which a single *TC* pulse was applied iontophoretically from a micropipette; *E* electrontonic potentials produced by outward current pulses across fibre membrane (monitored in lower trace) are not changed by *TC;* C potential changes produced by external iontophoretic application of carbachol (successive potentials show depression and subsequent recovery after the *TC* pulse). *b-d* the same as above recorded on slow film: *b* electrotonic potentials; *c* carbachol potentials; *d* alternate electrotonic and carbachol potentials. *TC* pulses were applied at instants indicated by arrows. Calibration of monitor trace: 1 scale div. = 1.1 x 10⁻⁸ A. Note that 4 electrodes were used: 2 were inserted inside the fibre to record the membrane potentials and to apply electrotonic pulses; 2 were parts of an extracellular double-barrelled pipette, one barrel containing carbachol the other tubocurarine (del Castillo and Katz[110]).

tive area; nevertheless, these amounts of ACh are of the same order of magnitude as the amounts liberated under optimal conditions in similar nerve-muscle preparations while stimulating the motor nerve (Krnjević and Mitchell,[259] see above). It is clear that ACh must play an important part in neuromuscular transmission.

Desensitization by Excess ACh.—A characteristic feature of the action of ACh is that prolonged or too frequent application rapidly leads to desensitization.[184,47,357,151,197,240,393] A similar desensitization is also seen with other agents which depolarize the muscle end-plate such as succinylcholine and decamethonium (Paton and Zaimis[337]), and it was thought at one time that the prolonged blocking action was caused by maintained depolarization resulting in a catelectrotonic block of transmission (Burns and Paton[61]). However, the desensitization cannot be ascribed to such a mechanism since the membrane progressively returns to its resting voltage in the continued presence of ACh (Thesleff[388-390]). It has therefore been suggested that ACh forms a relatively stable compound with the receptor, which causes a competitive block and is only slowly reversible (Katz and Thesleff[240]). There is evidence that desensitization may be one of the factors involved in the causation of neuromuscular failure during prolonged repetitive activity (Rosenblueth et al.;[357] Krnjević and Miledi;[255] Thesleff[391]).

ACh Receptors in the End-plate Membrane.—Although little is known at present about the identity of the ACh receptor, it is possible to demonstrate the presence at the end-plate of large molecules with some of the required properties, such as binding of labelled curare (Waser;[402] cf. also Chagas;[68] Ehrenpreis[139]). According to Waser[402] autoradiography of end-plates labelled with radio-active curare shows that there are about 8 million receptor sites available at one end-plate, a number suprisingly similar to the mean number of molecules of ACh released by one impulse. It has been suggested (e.g., Županćić[412]) that acetylcholinesterase, so abundant in the folds of the end-plate membrane[247,80,79] may combine at different sites on one molecule the receptor and esteroclastic functions; this would seem difficult to prove or disprove. Whatever their exact nature, the ACh receptors must be situated on the external surface of the membrane. As shown in Figure 5, iontophoretic pulses of ACh fail to produce the expected depolarization when the tip of the pipette is pushed through into the cell (del Castillo and Katz[106]). Even large quantities of ACh injected intracellularly are ineffective, showing that ACh cannot readily diffuse through the cell membrane. In agreement with this, it is found that the rate of diffusion of ACh and its distribution inside muscle are such as would be expected if ACh remained almost exclusively in the extracellular space (Krnjević and Mitchell[258]).

Change Produced in the Membrane by ACh.—It is now established beyond doubt that the reaction with ACh causes a very pronounced increase in the permeability of the surface membrane (Katz;[238] Fatt and Katz;[153] del Castillo and Katz;[107] Takeuchi and Takeuchi[385]) which can still be detected when the membrane is fully depolarized

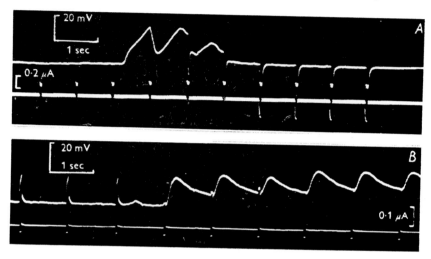

Fig. 5. Action of ACh applied iontophoretically on the outside and the inside of the end-plate membrane. *A:* approach and penetration of an end-plate with ACh pipette, using inward pulses of current. Lower trace shows current pulses. Note progressive depolarization (slow upward deflection) caused by ACh diffusing from approaching electrode, with interruptions due to inward pulses; then, as electrode penetrates membrane (at the 6th pulse) the depolarizing action of ACh disappears, and only anelectrotonic pulses remain. *B:* at another end-plate, showing the withdrawal of the ACh pipette from the cell. Outward pulses are used, producing at first brief catelectrotonic, then—after withdrawal—slow ACh potentials (del Castillo and Katz[106]).

(Fig. 6) (del Castillo and Katz[107]). Unlike the very specific increase of permeability to Na+ which is observed in the remainder of the muscle fibre during activity, the permeability change at the end-plate allows the free movement of all diffusible ions, so that the equilibrium potential is near zero (allowing for diffusion potentials between the cytoplasm and the exterior fluid). A rapid flow of current results from this short-circuit of the high resting membrane resistance, which discharges the membrane until the point is reached where all-or-none activity begins. A similar unspecific increase in permeability takes place at the junctional region in frog slow muscle fibres, without however initiating propagated electrical responses (Kuffler and Vaughan Williams;[266] Burke and Ginsborg[60]). In denervated mammalian muscle ACh causes a similar change in permeability[245a] which initiates contractures even when the fibre membrane is totally depolarized by isotonic K_2SO_4 (Jenkinson and Nicholls[234]). This action depends upon the presence of Ca^{++}. It may explain the apparent dissociation between the effects of repeated applications of ACh and electrical currents previously observed in denervated muscle by Gasser and Dale.[184]

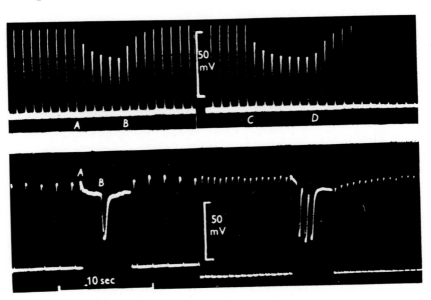

Fig. 6. ACh reduces membrane resistance at end-plate fully depolarized with K_2SO_4. The records show electrotonic potentials built up by outward currents across the fibre membrane, and the reduction of these potentials by ACh. In the upper picture ACh was allowed to diffuse from the external pipette, during the interval AB, and again during CD. In the lower picture, a prolonged electrotonic potential was set up at A, and a brief ACh-pulse applied at B; this was then repeated with three ACh-pulses (del Casstillo and Katz[107]).

Removal of ACh from the End-plate

Great stress has often been laid upon the importance of the rapid removal of a transmitter agent from the synaptic region. If the transmitter remains attached to the receptors it will be necessary to provide some mechanism for its active removal. But when the reaction between the transmitter and receptor is quite transient, as is the case at the motor end-plate (cf. del Castillo and Katz[112]), the duration of the reaction should depend upon the rate at which the transmitter is removed by diffusion. Since the distances involved are very small the concentration of active agents should drop extremely rapidly; whether one considers the simplest theoretical model, i.e., an instantaneous point source[152] a small sphere or cylinder,[328] or a model trying to reproduce the geometry of the end-plate,[130] it is clear that diffusion ought to

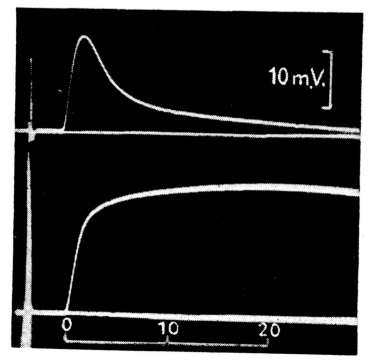

Fig. 7. Effect of prostigmine on end-plate potential in frog muscle when external sodium is reduced. Upper record: E.p.p. in sodium-deficient muscle (4/5 of Na replaced by sucrose). Lower record: after addition of prostigmine bromide (10⁻⁶). Time, msec. (Fatt and Katz[153]).

remove most of the ACh from the end-plate within a few msec (although during repetitive activity some ACh may be expected to accumulate). In practice, it is found that slow ACh potentials are remarkably similar in shape to simple theoretical diffusion curves (del Castillo and Katz[106]). Nevertheless, like e.p.ps. they are appreciably prolonged in the presence of anticholinesterases (Feng and Li;[171] Eccles, Katz and Kuffler;[132] Eccles and MacFarlane;[134] Fatt and Katz[153]). This effect is seen particularly clearly when the external Na concentration is reduced (Fig. 7). The hydrolysis of ACh by cholinesterase concentrated in the synaptic folds[296,172,247,80] is therefore an important factor in the removal of ACh from the end-plate. It would seem that the simple diffusion models fail because ACh remains temporarily attached in the vicinity of the receptors, or because free diffusion is impeded by certain barriers. When ACh is added to a muscle, it can all diffuse out quite quickly, except for a small fraction which may have gone into the fibres, or may be bound to some tissue component.[258] An alternative explanation is that the anticholinesterases prevent not only the hydrolysis of ACh but also, to some extent, its immediate removal by diffusion. Some anticholinesterases, such as DFP, sensitize the receptors to the action not only of ACh but even of compounds that cannot be hydrolyzed by the esterase, such as choline, or succinylcholine (Cohen and Posthumus[73]). Eserine on the other hand, when in a relatively high concentration, may have a depressant action resembling the competitive inhibition seen with curare.[134,151]

Transmission in Autonomic Ganglia

Studies on transmission in autonomic ganglia have principally been done either on the superior cervical ganglion of the cat which is readily accessible, has a very convenient effector organ, the nictitating membrane, and can be perfused comparatively easily (Kibjakow[245]); or on the stellate ganglion, which is more convenient for analysing various electrophysiological aspects of synaptic function (Bronk[41]). The parallel between properties of the neuromuscular junction and the sympathetic ganglion was first drawn by Elliott.[142] It can be said at the outset that the subsequent observations have confirmed the basic similarity of the mechanism of transmission at these two sites. However, a somewhat different but to some extent complementary experimental approach has distinguished studies on ganglia from those on muscle. The synaptic elements in the latter are comparatively few and far apart, but are more readily accessible for a detailed analysis of the electrical changes associated with activity. The relatively small number of synapses per unit weight of tissue makes conditions unfavorable for the collection of ACh released by the motor nerve endings. In the ganglion, by contrast, a large number of synaptic elements are contained within a very small volume (for details of the morphology see de Castro[98]). There are some 100,000 cells in the superior cervical ganglion of the cat which only weighs about 20 mg. The number of synapses is even greater because there are several synapses on each cell; hence it is comparatively easy to collect by perfusion substantial amounts of ACh. On the other hand, electrical recording of the activity of single cells has not been possible except on a relatively small scale, because tough connective tissue makes the introduction of microelectrodes very difficult and the small cells do not survive penetration long enough to allow an extensive analysis (Pascoe;[333] R. M. Eccles[138] but cf. Nishi and Koketsu[325a]).

Electrical Activity.—Various aspects of transmission through sympathetic ganglia have been studied by electrical methods of recording (cf. refs. 124, 125, 41, 269, 287, 136, 137, 235, 325a). As in muscle, a localized post-synaptic depolarizing potential can be demonstrated when transmission is blocked by curare, the slow potential (lasting over 100 msec.) can be interpreted as the result of a brief release of transmitter, followed by a comparatively prolonged residual action (Eccles[125]). However, the situation here is much more complex than at the muscle end-plate. Large doses of tubocurarine not only depress further the local depolarization but actually reverse the changes to give a hyperpolarization (Lorente de Nó and Laporte;[287] R. M. Eccles[137]). Various explanations have been offered for this puzzling phenomenon, such as that tubocurarine may alter the depolarizing action of ACh into a hyperpolarizing one (this does not happen when ACh is applied to the ganglion[334]) or that the curare block reveals a hyperpolarization produced by inhibitory fibres, normally hidden by the predominating depolarization.

The ganglion differs from muscle in another respect; it shows a less powerful action of eserine. Nevertheless definite effects are seen (Feldberg and Vartiainen;[166] Rosenblueth and Simeone;[360] R. M. Eccles[137]) especially during repetitive stimulation. Cholinesterase in sympathetic ganglia is associated particularly with the presynaptic endings (von Brücke;[401] Koelle;[247] Snell[376]) and may be therefore less well situated to destroy the ACh released by transmission, most of which is likely to be removed by diffusion. In the ganglion as in muscle, large doses of anticholinesterase may reduce the sensitivity to ACh by a kind of competitive blocking action (cf. Feldberg and Vartiainen;[166] Paton and Perry[336]).

The ganglion shows postsynaptic facilitation (temporal and spatial) and occlusion, as might be expected in view of its structure; and also a potentiation of transmission after activity, which can be ascribed to presynaptic changes as in muscle.[269,235,136]

Action of ACh on Ganglion Cells.—The cells in the superior cervical ganglion are excited by small doses of ACh injected into its blood supply or into a perfusate (Feldberg and Vartiainen;[166] Bronk;[41] Paton and Perry[336]). It is a direct effect upon the cells since, as shown in Figure 8, they fire without any obvious activity in the preganglionic fibres (Bronk[41]). Actual depolarization of the cells in the ganglion has been demonstrated by recording from the ganglion *in situ* (Paton and Perry[336]) or *in vitro* (Pascoe[334]). The action of ACh is reproduced initially by nicotine, and blocked by curarine and hexamethonium, although the effects of these two antagonists differ in some respects (Pascoe[334]). It is rather curious that the cells' sensitivity to ACh is very much reduced after section of the *postganglionic* trunk, so that transmission ceases and cannot be restored even by the strongest potentiating procedures (Brown and Pascoe[49]).

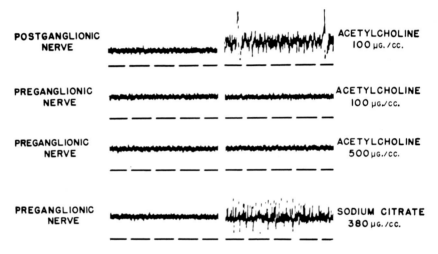

Fig. 8. Preganglionic and postganglionic response to ACh and sodium citrate in cat's superior cervical ganglion. Controls with Ringer's fluid in left hand column. Time: 0.1 sec. (Bronk[41]).

Release of ACh in the Ganglia.—Kibjakow[245] had demonstrated the presence of an active agent in the perfusate from a stimulated superior cervical ganglion; its identity as ACh was established by Feldberg and Gaddum[160] using the criteria previously laid down by Chang and Gaddum.[70] Feldberg and Vartiainen[166] showed that the release of ACh did not occur during antidromic stimulation and that ACh appeared in the venous effluent even in the presence of blood (cf. Emmelin and MacIntosh[145]); Lorente de Nó[285] claimed later that ACh could only be detected when there was obvious evidence of injury to the tissues but MacIntosh,[291] in a careful re-investigation, could not confirm his observations.

The output of ACh from a ganglion during a period of repetitive stimulation is substantially greater than the amount of ACh normally present in the ganglion (cf. Brown and Feldberg[48]); in fact, the ACh content does not normally diminish appreciably as a result of prolonged activity. Clearly, ACh must be synthesized continuously to replenish what is lost at the nerve terminals but as long as sufficient glucose and choline are available the rate of release is not limited by inadequate synthesis (Kahlson and MacIntosh[237]; MacIntosh[293]). Yet it is found that the release of ACh in perfused ganglia diminishes very rapidly during prolonged stimulation.[48,339] The rate and the extent of the reduction is approximately proportional to the frequency of stimulation, so that the total amount released in a given time is about the same whether one stimulates at a high or a low frequency (Perry[339]).

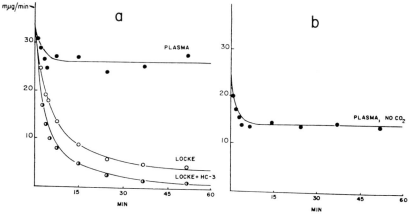

Fig. 9. (a) ACh output from eserinized superior cervical ganglia during 1 hour's preganglionic stimulation at 20/sec (each curve gives the mean values for five experiments). Perfusion fluids from above downwards: heparinized cat plasma equilibrated with 5% CO_2 in O_2, oxygenated Locke's solution, oxygenated Locke's solution containing hemicholinium ($2 \times 10^{-5}M$). (b) ACh output from ganglia similarly stimulated, during perfusion with eserinized plasma equilibrated with CO_2-free oxygen (mean of five experiments) (MacIntosh[293]).

However, the rapid diminution in release is characteristic of perfusion with a Locke solution and is not seen when the ganglion is perfused with plasma (Fig. 9). Under these conditions, and particularly if the perfusate is not deprived of CO_2, the rate of liberation is maintained at a level only slightly less than the initial maximum (MacIntosh[293,29]). The factor responsible for optimum release can be dialysed from plasma, but it has not yet been identified. The ionic composition of the perfusate is also known to be of some importance; the concentration of Ca^{++} in particular plays a significant role, as in muscle. If

Ca++ is reduced, less ACh is liberated (lack of Ca++ leads to block of transmission, Bronk[41]), and an increase in Ca++ is associated with more ACh (Harvey and MacIntosh;[202] Hutter and Kostial[229,230]). Magnesium on the other hand, has an opposite effect, the actual amount of ACh liberated depending upon the ratio of Ca to Mg (Hutter and Kostial[229]).

The release of ACh is independent of Na over a wide range of concentrations (Hutter and Kostial[230]); this is not consistent with the hypothesis that the release is determined by the amplitude of the action potential in the nerve endings (cf. Liley[274]), which should be quite sensitive to variations in external Na (cf. Hodgkin;[218] Desmedt[114]). But if the K concentration is raised, the spontaneous leak of ACh becomes markedly greater,[48,230] presumably because of depolarization of the nerve endings, in a manner analogous to the acceleration of miniature e.p.ps. observed in muscle when the K concentration is raised (cf. Liley[274]).

The release of ACh is not very sensitive to changes in temperature as long as the ganglion is stimulated at a low frequency (Kostial and Vouk[251,252]). There is little difference between the rate of release at 40 and 20°C. (at 2/sec.). The temperature dependence which can be seen at lower temperatures and higher rates of stimulation is likely to be caused by failure of synthesis of ACh, or by failure of nerve conduction.

ACh Action on the Heart

The release of ACh into the heart during vagal stimulation had the distinction of being the first mechanism of neurohumoral transmission to be demonstrated, in the classical experiments of Loewi[282] and Loewi and Navratil.[283] Vagal stimulation which inhibited an isolated frog heart also caused the release of a substance into fluid perfusing this heart, so that the same fluid now had an inhibitory effect upon a second heart. The inhibitory substance (Vagusstoff) was in time identified as ACh, and further experiments showed that vagal stimulation also releases ACh in the mammalian heart (Feldberg and Krayer[161]). The situation was somewhat complicated by repeated observations that vagal stimulation also causes K to be liberated from the heart (Howell and Duke;[225] Lehnhartz;[270] Holland et al.[221]). There was clearly a possibility that K+ might be responsible for the vagal effects (Howell[224]). However, it could be shown that the effects of ACh on the heart resemble very much those of vagal stimulation, whereas the effects of K + differ in most respects (Garcia-Ramoz and Rosenblueth[181]) and it was therefore much more likely that the release of K was somehow a result of the action of ACh. The exact mechanism by which this takes place has been elucidated to a great extent in recent years. The inhibition caused by both vagal stimulation and ACh causes the heart beat to become slower ("chronotropic effect") and weaker ("inotropic effect").

Studies of action potentials in atrial muscle *in vitro* or *in situ* with intracellular microelectrodes were begun by Burgen and Terroux[59] and Hoffman and Suckling,[220] who confirmed an observation first made by Samojloff[363] that vagal stimulation, or parasympathetic drugs, shorten the duration of the heart's action potential. Burgen and Terroux found a correlation between the strength of the heart beat and the duration of the action potential (in the presence of ACh) and suggested that contractile elements in the cardiac fibre were only activated by membrane depolarization after an appreciable time, so that very short action potentials could only excite a small fraction of the available elements. Although such a simple relation does hold as a rule, there are certain exceptions when, under the influence of ACh, a heart may give a powerful beat associated with a short action potential (Vaughan Williams[400]). Burgen and Terroux[59] also noted that ACh tended to raise the membrane potential by making the inside of the fibre more negative (Fig. 10). This observation was an indirect

Fig. 10. Membrane potential in dog's auricle recorded with an intracellular electrode. Anodal pulses were applied through a second electrode at rate of 5/sec., the amplitude of the recorded electrotonic potentials indicating the membrane resistance. At the break in the trace, 100 μg. ACh were applied, causing an increase in membrane negative potential and a reduction in its resistance. Time calibration 2 sec. (Trautwein and Dudel[398]).

confirmation of Gaskell's[182] finding that vagal stimulation augments the demarcation current which can be recorded from the auricle in the tortoise. Later experiments with intracellular electrodes inserted in the region of the pacemaker repeated and extended the earlier observations and showed that hyperpolarization and a slower rate of depolarization were responsible for the chronotropic effect of vagal stimulation (Hutter and Trautwein;[231] del Castillo and Katz;[108] West et al.[403]). In further studies (Fig. 10) it was found that the change in membrane potential was associated with a pronounced reduction in the electrical resistance of the membrane (Trautwein, Kuffler and

Edwards;[399] Trautwein and Dudel[398]). This effect of ACh on the membrane resistance, although reminiscent of its action on the end-plate of skeletal muscle, clearly differs in one important respect. The associated change in membrane potential is a hyperpolarization, not a depolarization, and it is evident that ACh here does not produce an unspecific increase in permeability. If electrical pulses are applied to the membrane, it is possible to show that under the influence of ACh the membrane potential tends to an equilibrium level of about 102 mV; if the external K^+ concentration is varied over a wide range, the equilibrium level changes accordingly (Trautwein and Dudel[398]). In other words the membrane potential is fixed at a level corresponding to the expected K^+ equilibrium potential because it is made very much more permeable to K^+ by the action of ACh. Accordingly, Harris and Hutter[201] found that ACh causes faster movement of ^{42}K into or out of cardiac fibres. This temporary change in the properties of the membrane tends to neutralize the depolarizing influence of the pacemaker, and, if large enough, may stop the heart completely. It is therefore comparable with other post-synaptic inhibitory mechanisms, such as those studied in crustacean muscle (Boistel and Fatt[31]) and stretch receptors (Kuffler and Eyzaguirre[265]), and in mammalian motor neurones (Eccles[127]); but there is good reason to believe that ACh is not the inhibitory transmitter at these other sites. It is interesting to find that ACh can act in the same animal both as an excitatory transmitter, at the neuromuscular junction, and as an inhibitory transmitter in the heart.

Action of ACh on Nerve Endings

(A) Motor Nerve Endings.—During stimulation of a nerve-muscle preparation in the presence of anticholinesterases, recurrent impulses can be recorded in ventral root fibres (Masland and Wigton;[298] Feng and Li;[171] Eccles, Katz and Kuffler[132]). Feng and Li[171] showed that this phenomenon can arise even in the absence of any anticholinesterase, after preliminary tetanic stimulation. A recurrent discharge can also be recorded in motor fibres if acetylcholine is applied to the motor nerve endings by intra-arterial injection.[298] Masland and Wigton therefore suggested that the presynaptic terminals in the muscle could be excited by an excess of ACh (see also Werner[402a]). However, it is known that active muscle fibres can excite the motor nerve terminals directly (Lloyd[280]); since agents such as curare or physostigmine, which block or facilitate the effects of injected ACh, have corresponding effects upon neuromuscular transmission, there is no real evidence at present that ACh ever causes direct excitation of the motor nerve endings in muscle. Recent experiments with regenerating nerves have

shown that the growing ends of the motor nerve fibres are not particularly sensitive to ACh (Diamond[116]).

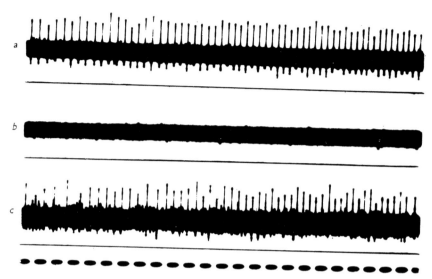

Fig. 11. Impulses in single sensory unit from cat's carotid sinus excited by ACh. Intrasinusal pressure in *A, B* and *C*, 60 mm. Hg. In *B* perfusion fluid contained hexamethonium 10^{-6} gm./ml. Flow 10 ml/min. *A* 9 sec. after injection of 1.0 ml 10^{-4} gm./ml. acetylcholine solution; *B* 9 sec. after injection of 1.0 ml 10^{-3} gm./ml. acetylcholine solution; *C* 9 sec. after injection of 1.0 ml 10^{-4} gm./ml. acetylcholine solution, after recovery from block by hexamethonium; time: 1/10 sec. (Diamond[116]).

(B) Sensory Nerve Endings.—Unlike motor endings, sensory endings have been found by many observers to respond very readily to injected ACh. Quite a wide variety of receptors have been studied (e.g., Fig. 11) and they include receptors which normally record changes in tension, temperature or the chemical composition of blood (see reviews by Gray and Diamond;[196] Witzleb[410]). Even crustacean stretch-receptors are excited by ACh, yet ACh has no stimulating effect on crustacean muscle (Florey[174]); this action of ACh would seem to be even more universal in its distribution than is its use in neuromuscular transmission. It is probable that excitation by ACh is not normally an essential step in the generation of impulses in the sensory endings because drugs like curare and hexamethonium, which block the action of applied ACh, do not interfere with the excitatory effect of the physiological stimulus (e.g., touch or pressure); the response of sensory endings to ACh would seem to be only one aspect of a somewhat unspecific sensitivity to pharmacological agents (including serotonin,[172a,-][185]).

ACh in Nerve Conduction

It is not necessary to present in detail arguments put forward in support of the hypothesis that ACh is essential for the initiation of the complex changes in permeability underlying the action potential. A particularly full account has been published again recently by its principal supporter (Nachmansohn[319]). The hypothesis has been modified on several occasions, to accommodate various objections, but no really convincing evidence has yet appeared. As already stated, ACh, choline acetylase and cholinesterase can all be found in peripheral nerves, and several authors have reported the liberation of ACh from nerve trunks during repetitive stimulation (Calabro;[63] Bergami;[21] Lissak[279]); even sensory nerves may release ACh (Brecht and Corsten[39]). However, there is good reason to believe that the enzyme for the synthesis of ACh originates in the motoneurone (Hebb[205,206]) whence it migrates to the periphery along the axon. It is therefore not surprising that some ACh should leak out of motor nerves during prolonged activity. On the other hand, the amount released from sensory nerves is exceedingly small, being less that 1/10,000 of that released from motor nerves; this would be difficult to understand if ACh were essential for the conduction of impulses in all fibres.

High concentrations of anticholinesterases block nervous conduction; this was considered as compelling evidence, since at first sight an accumulation of ACh might be expected to block further activity (Bullock et al.[56]). However, other authors have shown that the concentrations which cause block are much greater than are needed to inhibit cholinesterase activity (Cantoni and Loewi;[66] Crescitelli et al.[81]). As already pointed out in Section II anticholinesterases in adequate concentrations are known to inhibit somewhat unspecifically a variety of enzymatic reactions (Brooks et al.;[44] Michaelis et al.;[307] Kennedy and Koshland;[244] Paulet and André[338]). Moreover, when anticholinesterases stop the conduction of impulses, it is not by depolarizing the nerve membrane.[394] It has been claimed recently that eserine in low concentration depolarizes isolated frog nerve fibres (Dettbarn[115]), but it is not clear why eserine should be much less effective when applied to intact nerves, since it is a tertiary amine which is said to penetrate lipid barriers readily (Nachmansohn[319]). In any case, this kind of evidence cannot be conclusive; complete inhibition of cholinesterase activity at the muscle end-plate does not cause a block of neuromuscular transmission, except during stimulation at a high frequency (e.g., Barnes and Duff;[18] Meer and Meeter;[301] Barstad[19]).

It has been argued that quaternary ammonium compounds such as ACh and curare fail to penetrate nerve or muscle fibres, except at the muscle end-plate, hence the lack of any observed action on nerve trunks when they are applied externally (a weak excitatory action of ACh in relatively high concentrations on non-myelinated mammalian nerve fibres has been reported recently by Douglas and Ritchie[121] and Armett and Ritchie;[9] cf. also Lorente de Nó[286]). This particular difficulty has been overcome by micro-injection of ACh and curare directly into muscle or nerve fibres (Graham, quoted by Gerard;[186] del Castillo and Katz;[106] Hodgkin and Keynes[219]). The suggestion has now been made that a lipid barrier prevents the access of such compounds both on the inside and on the outside of the membrane (Nachmansohn[319]). If this is indeed the case, the postulated ACh mechanism is so effectively sealed off within the membrane that it is difficult to see how it can ever be investigated satisfactorily.

ACh in the Function of the Central Nervous System

All the components of the ACh system, i.e., choline acetylase, acetylcholine itself, and cholinesterase are found in the CNS (Table IIb); yet in spite of numerous attempts to demonstrate a significant role for ACh in central nervous activity, very few definite statements can be made at present in this respect. Transmission by ACh is extremely likely at the endings of recurrent collaterals of motoneurones on Renshaw cells in the spinal cord, and quite likely in the supraoptic nucleus of the hypothalamus; but these synapses only make up a very small fraction of the synapses in the CNS. The subject of ACh in relation to central nervous function has been reviewed repeatedly; references should therefore be made to the various reviews for detailed lists of relevant experiments (Feldberg;[155-158] Perry;[340] Stone;[383a] Paton;[335] Crossland[82]).

Presence of ACh, Choline Acetylase and Cholinesterase in the CNS. —A description has already been given of the distribution of these substances in the CNS (Part IV). The most interesting features from the point of view of synaptic functions are: (a) there is much variation in the amounts found at different sites (e.g., Feldberg and Vogt;[167] Hebb[204]), suggesting that cholinergic nerves, if they are present, are limited to certain groups of fibres (which in longer chains of sensory neurones tend to alternate); (b) there is a reasonable correlation between relative amounts of ACh, choline acetylase and cholinesterase found at any point (Burgen and Chipman[57]) although cholinesterase is distributed much more widely and plentifully than the others; (c) according to the latest information nerve endings provide the richest source of ACh (Gray and Whittaker[195]), possibly in association with intracellular synaptic vesicles (Hebb and Whittaker;[216] Whittaker[406]), and (d) the ACh content of the brain apparently is not fixed; it can be shown to vary with the functional state of the tissue. For instance, Richter and Crossland[350] and Elliott et al.[140] found substantially more ACh in rat brains during sleep or deep anaesthesia than during periods of convulsive activity. There is always a danger in such experiments that the apparent ACh content may depend upon very rapid synthesis or hydrolysis occurring in the tissues when the animal is killed; whether synthesis or hydrolysis predominates could be determined by metabolic factors influenced by previous rest or activity. This should not be surprising since the brain ACh seems to be extremely labile; the maximal changes seen by Richter and Crossland for example, were complete within a time of the order of 10 seconds. If these results are taken at their face value, one must conclude that ACh synthesis in the brain is very much less efficient than in peripheral nerves where depletion of ACh cannot be demonstrated even after prolonged excitation (cf. MacIntosh[293]). It has been stated recently that there is a correlation between brain cholinesterase activity and the learning ability of rats (Rosenzweig et al.[361]). These claims must be treated with caution since many other factors are also likely to be involved (cf. Tower[396]).

Release of ACh in the CNS.—There are several reports that ACh can be found in fluids (usually eserinized) which have been in contact with the CNS: these include blood from the dog's and cat's head;[69,72] Ringer perfused through the dog's spinal cord;[52] cerebro-spinal fluid (e.g., refs. 164, 33, 243); Ringer solution flowing over the frog's spinal cord;[272,6] perfusate from the cerebral ventricles,[25] and fluid in small cups held against the surface of the cortex in cats and sheep.[140,295,315] All these observations cannot be considered entirely conclusive because it was not always possible to exclude all extraneous sources of ACh; and it is difficult to be certain that injury to the tissues resulting from unphysiological conditions did not release ACh by an abnormal process. There is, for example, evidence that ACh only appears in the cerebrospinal fluid after cerebral injury (Bornstein[33]). Even the most sensitive methods of assay may give negative results under normal conditions (e.g., ref. 227).

The most impressive results are those obtained with cups on the cortex, which can be placed in position with a minimum of surgical interference. If the cerebro-spinal fluid pressure is in equilibrium with the pressure in the cups, the fluid inside the cup (which is stirred) takes up ACh from the brain by diffusion without change in volume, presumably until the concentrations in the cup and in the free ACh space of the brain are equal. In accordance with this interpretation, the final concentration of ACh in the cup is the same whether one starts off with fluid free of ACh or with fluid containing large amounts, in which case ACh diffuses into the tissues (MacIntosh[294]). Judging by this evidence, in the presence of eserine the concentration of ACh in the cortex can be astonishingly high, being regularly as much as 10^{-6}M. It does not depend upon cholinergic vasodilator fibres and it can be altered by various procedures which influence cortical activity, such as undercutting the cortex, the injection of convulsant drugs and changes in the level of anaesthesia (Fig. 12); atropine often causes

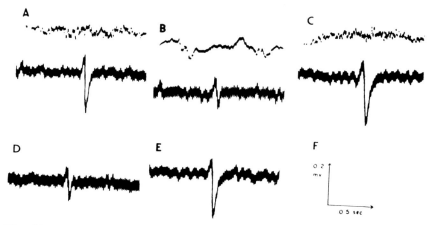

Fig. 12. Release of acetylcholine by cerebral cortex of cat. A, B and C: *ABOVE* electrical activity recorded by electrodes touching the cortex beneath a pool of eserinized saline (0.5 ml. of fluid, overlying about 1.5 cm.² of cortex); *BELOW* arterial pressure of another cat, used for estimation of acetylcholine that diffused into the pool over a 10 minute period, during which the record above was made. A, very light ether anaesthesia; B, 20 minutes later deep anaesthesia (corneal reflex lost but still breathing spontaneously); C, 20 minutes later, return to a very light anaesthesia. Acetylcholine output is correlated with high-frequency activity in the electrocorticogram. D and E, response of assay cat to 0.003 and 0.012 μg respectively of acetylcholine. F, time and voltage calibration for electrical record (Burns and MacIntosh, in *Neurochemistry*, 1st Ed., p. 377, 1955).

a large increase in the amount which can be collected (MacIntosh;[294] Mitchell[315]). In spite of the high concentration of ACh in the surrounding tissues, no ACh can be detected in fully eserinized blood collected from veins on the surface of the cortex (Mitchell[315]). This would suggest that the blood-brain barrier, here as elsewhere in the CNS (Curtis and Eccles[85]), slows very much the exchange of ACh between tissue fluid and blood, and, by preventing its removal, allows ACh to accumulate in the tissues.

Effects Produced by ACh on Neurones of the CNS

Spinal Cord.—Although many suggestions have been made that ACh excites motoneurones (cf. Feldberg[155,156]) it is now quite certain that motoneurones are very insensitive to ACh,[86a] and that any effect observed can only be attributed to an indirect activation, either by excitation of afferent fibres from the periphery (through a direct action, or as a result of muscular contraction) or by excitation of interneurones. Technical developments have made possible experiments in which individual neurones in the spinal cord can be identified with some certainty and their responses analysed in great detail, often by recording inside the soma the electrical changes associated with excitation or inhibition (Eccles[126,127]). The chemical sensitivity of the neuronal membrane can then be studied if various drugs are applied directly on to the cell from micropipettes[84-86] (cf. Fig. 13), as in the experiments performed at the muscle end-plate by del Castillo and Katz.[110-113]

So far the only spinal neurones to have proved particularly sensitive to ACh are the so-called Renshaw cells. These interneurones are excited by collateral branches of motor axons and they exert an inhibitory action on motoneurones (Renshaw;[348,349] Eccles, Fatt and Koketsu;[129] Granit, Pascoe and Steg[194]). The functional significance of this closed loop system is not entirely clear, but it is likely to have a general stabilizing influence on motoneuronal activity and there is evidence that it exerts a more selective control over 'tonic' motoneurones, which are particularly responsible for the maintenance of postural tone.

Since motor axons liberate ACh at the periphery, it seems likely that ACh will also be released by their collateral branches in the spinal cord. Although this has not been demonstrated directly it is now clear that the Renshaw cells can be activated by ACh (Eccles, Fatt and Koketsu;[129] Eccles, Eccles and Fatt;[128] Curtis, Eccles and Eccles;[83] Curtis and Eccles[84,85]). Thus injections of ACh into the blood supply of the spinal cord usually cause some inhibition of the reflex discharge of motoneurones, after total de-afferentation to exclude any peripheral actions of ACh; however, the effects are rather variable and seldom very pronounced (Curtis *et al.*[83]) whereas nicotine regularly gives a clear-cut inhibition, even when injected in much smaller doses (e.g., Schweitzer and Wright;[371] Bülbring and Burn;[52] Taugner and Culp;[387] Curtis *et al.*[83]). When the electrical activity of Renshaw cells is recorded directly, ACh and other quaternary derivatives injected intraarterially are found to be much less effective than tertiary compounds like nicotine (Eccles *et al.*[128]). On the other hand, when the various drugs are applied directly onto Renshaw cells with a micropipette, most of the discrepancies disappear; the Renshaw cells then behave pharmacologically very much like other cells sensitive to ACh, showing the same potentiating effects of anticholinesterases (Fig. 13) and the competitive block of curare-like compounds, with only relatively

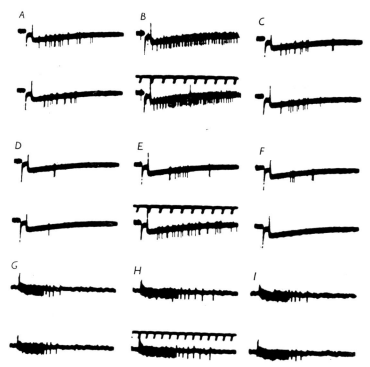

Fig. 13. Discharges evoked from a single Renshaw cell in cat's spinal cord. *A-C*, current pulse of 12 x 10⁻⁹ amp. flowing for 5 msec. through an acetylcholine electrode. D-F, as for A-C but for a current of 4 x 10⁻⁹ amp. G-L synaptic stimulation by a volley in a segmental ventral root. Two successive records are illustrated for each type of stimulus. After the control records *A, D* and *G*, the anticholinesterase agent edrophonium was ejected from another barrel of the electrode by a current of 10⁻⁷ amp.; B, E. and H were recorded during this; C, F and L 20 seconds after the edrophonium current ceased; time marker 10 msec. (Curtis and Eccles[85]).

minor peculiarities (Curtis and Eccles[84,85]). The relative ineffectiveness of quaternary compounds (including ACh itself) injected into the blood stream can therefore be ascribed to slow penetration into the tissues presumably because of the "blood-brain barrier" (cf. refs. 383, 241, 177, 13, 97). Accordingly prostigmine and ACh are quite effective in depressing reflex activity of the spinal cord when injected intrathecally in man (Kremer[253]).

Although the predominant effect of activity in the motor axon collaterals is inhibition of reflex discharge, it is also possible to show certain excitatory actions (Renshaw;[348] Wilson and Talbot[408]) which may be explained either by inhibition of background excitation or by activation of excitatory interneurones; ACh may therefore also have some indirect excitatory effects on motoneurones.

Brain.—Experiments on the spinal cord illustrate some of the difficulties inherent in pharmacological studies of the central nervous system. Most parts of the brain, like the spinal cord, are to some extent isolated from the blood stream by the "blood-brain barrier." ACh and many other related compounds can probably only pass this barrier very slowly; if an adequate concentration of ACh can be produced sufficiently quickly by intracarotid injection to excite sensitive cells, the effect is likely to be transient, for the ACh is rapidly removed by dilution, diffusion and hydrolysis. The interpretation of any observed changes is complicated by the fact that the blood stream carries ACh to other parts of the organism where it may have various actions reflected in changes in cerebral activity (e.g., alterations in blood pressure, or excitation of sensory nerve endings cf. Nakao et al.[322]). Finally, it must be remembered that cerebral blood vessels are sensitive to ACh (see review by Sokoloff[377]) and that local vasodilatation might alter sufficiently the blood O_2 or CO_2 content, or the local metabolism, to affect the electrical activity (cf. Darrow et al.;[95] Schlag[369]). One cannot therefore consider as very strong evidence for the presence of cholinergic pathways in the brain such observations as those made by Bonnet and Bremer,[32] Moruzzi[317] and Bremer and Chatonnet,[40] who found that 0.1-1 μg. of ACh injected into the carotid artery had a stimulating effect on the cat's cortex lasting several minutes. By contrast, ACh applied directly to the cortex as a rule only causes marked excitation if in very strong solutions (1% or more). The effects are potentiated by eserine or prostigmine and may take the form of epileptiform convulsions (Miller et al.;[311] Chatfield and Dempsey;[71] Hyde et al.;[233] Arduini and Machne[8]). The action of ACh can be prevented by atropine, but atropine does not prevent similar convulsions elicited by electrical stimulation (Arduini and Machne[8]) suggesting that a cholinergic mechanism is not responsible for the convulsive activity. Very weak solutions of ACh have been found effective when applied to the cortex by some authors (e.g., Bornstein[33]) but not by others (Elliott et al.[140]).

More recent observations of the effects of ACh injected into the blood stream in small doses (see review by Bovet and Longo[34]) have tended to suggest that the electrical changes in the cortex are identical with the arousal reaction, during which the electrical activity of the neocortex is "desynchronized," changing from large slow waves to fast, irregular and rather small deflections (in the rhinencephalon opposite electrical changes are seen, Brücke et al.[50]). The arousal reaction can be elicited by peripheral excitation or by appropriate stimulation of the brainstem reticular formation and it is usually associated with a corresponding alteration in the behavior of the animal. A systematic study by Rinaldi and Himwich[353,354] suggested that ACh injected into the carotid artery has no direct effect on the cortex and that its action is probably mediated via the midbrain reticular formation, because ACh had its usual action when injected in the "cerveau isolé" preparation, in which the brain is cut at the level of the midbrain but had no effect on the isolated hemisphere. These results are suggestive without really proving that ACh acts directly on neurones in the brain stem. The visual and olfactory pathways remain intact in an animal with the "cerveau isolé" and they could be activated by ACh. The activity of single reticular cells can apparently be altered by intracarotid injections of ACh (Bradley and Mollica[38a]), but not when ACh is applied directly by iontophoresis (Curtis and Koizumi[85a]). The reticular formation in any case has a rather unspecific sensitivity to various drugs, and is, moreover, quite likely to be affected by vasomotor changes (Rossi and Zanchetti;[362] Bovet and Longo[34]). Further evidence of a possible cholinergic mechanism is the fact that atropine neutralizes the electrical phenomena associated with the arousal reaction, whether elicited by an electrical or a pharmacological stimulus (Rinaldi and Himwich[354]); but it is important to remember that even moderate doses of atropine can have an unspecific depressant action on nerve cells.[85b,260a]

A puzzling feature of studies of arousal is the possibility of an apparent dissociation between the electrical activity of the brain and the animal's behavior. In conscious animals, anticholinesterases like eserine produce the typical electrical changes associated with arousal (i.e., desynchronization of the electrical record) and atropine reverses the process to give large slow waves; but these electrical changes are not reflected in the behavior of the animals, which remain throughout drowsy or lively as the case may be (Bradley and Elkes;[38] but cf. Monnier[316]). Bradley and Elkes therefore concluded that only a part of the complex arousal mechanism could be cholinergic.

On the whole it seems that ACh and synergic drugs stimulate the activity of the cortex, while atropine and other "cholinolytic" drugs (cf. Anichkov[7]) have a depressant effect, probably through a direct action on cortical neurones (many cortical units are readily excited by ACh applied iontophoretically,[260a] see fig. 14), and also via diffuse activating mechanisms which may include a cholinergic component. Evidence based upon experiments with anticholinesterases (reviewed by Holmsted[223]) is particularly difficult to evaluate because these drugs inhibit tissue respiration independently of their action on cholinesterase.[44,307,338] According to Ostow and Garcia,[331] Chang,[68a] Grundfest,[198] Feldberg *et al.*[163] and Morlock and Ward[316a] curare has an exciting action on the cortex (though large doses depress activity), but some of the authors used such strong solutions that at least part of the effects observed could have been caused by local or general vascular changes (cf. Schlag;[369] Ochs[327]). Tubocurarine may also produce convulsive activity when introduced into the cerebral ventricles by some action on midbrain structures (Feldberg and Sherwood;[165] Feldberg and Malcolm[162]).

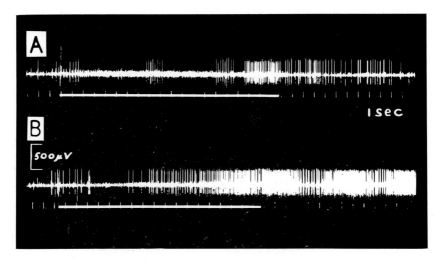

Fig. 14. Impulses recorded with multiple micropipette from a Betz cell in the cerebral cortex of a cat. During white line L-glutamate (A) or ACh (B) were applied by iontophoretic currents of 0.05 and 0.06µA respectively. Most neurones are easily depolarized by L-glutamate, but in this case ACh was clearly more effective, and, as usual, it had a more prolonged action. (Krnjević and Phillis, unpublished observations).

ACh and related drugs are said to have a significant effect on function in various other parts of the brain; perhaps the best substantiated is a postulated cholinergic mechanism in the supraoptic nucleus of the hypothalamus. ACh and anticholinesterases given by intracarotid injection, or applied directly, trigger the activity of cells in the supraoptic nucleus causing the release of antidiuretic and oxytocic hormones from the posterior pituitary with corresponding changes in urinary secretion and uterine activity (Pickford;[342] Duke et al.;[122] Pickford and Watt;[343] Abrahams and Pickford[1]). Evidence that the respiratory centre functions by a cholinergic mechanism (Dikshit;[118] Gesell et al.;[187] Krivoy et al.;[254] Metz[306]) seems somewhat less satisfactory.*

REFERENCES

1. ABRAHAMS, V. C. and PICKFORD, M.: J. Physiol., 133:330 (1956).
2. ACHESON, G. H.: Federation Proc., 7:447 (1948).
3. ALLES, G. A. and HAWES, R. C.: J. Biol. Chem., 133:375 (1940).
4. AMBACHE, N.: Pharmacol. Rev., 7:467 (1955).
5. ANDERSON, H. K.: J. Physiol., 33:414 (1905).
6. ANGELUCCI, L.: Brit. J. Pharmacol., 11:161 (1956).
7. ANICHKOV, S. V.: Abstr. Symp. XXI int. physiol. Congr., 23 (1959).
8. ARDUINI, A. and MACHNE, X.: Arch. Fisiol., 48:152 (1949).
9. ARMETT, C. J. and RITCHIE, J. M.: J. Physiol., 152:141 (1960).
10. AUGUSTINSSON, K.-B.: Acta physiol. scandinav., 15:suppl. 52 (1948).
11. AXELSSON, J. and THESLEFF, S.: Acta physiol. scandinav., 43:15 (1958).
12. BABKIN, B. P., ALLEY, A. and STAVRAKY, G.: Tr. Roy. Soc. Canad. Sect., V:89 (1932).
13. BAKAY, L.: The Blood-brain Barrier with Special Reference to the Use of Radioactive Isotopes. Springfield, Thomas (1956).
14. BALFOUR, W. E. and HEBB, C. O.: J. Physiol., 118:94 (1952).
15. BANGHAM, A. D.: Personal communication (1960).
16. BANISTER, R. J. and SCRASE, M.: J. Physiol., 111:437 (1950).
17. BANISTER, J., WHITTAKER, V. P. and WIJESUNDERA, S.: J. Physiol., 121:51 (1953).
18. BARNES, J. M. and DUFF, J. I.: Brit. J. Pharmacol., 8:334 (1953).
19. BARSTAD, J. A. B.: Arch. internat. Pharmacodyn., 107:21 (1956).
20. BAYER, G. and WENSE, T.: Pflüger's Arch. ges. Physiol., 237:417 (1936).
21. BERGAMI, G.: Klin. Wchnschr., 15:1030 (1936).
22. BERRY, J. F. and ROSSITER, R. J.: J. Neurochem., 3:59 (1958).
23. BEUTNER, R. and BARNES, T. C.: Science, 94:241 (1941).
24. BHATNAGAR, S. P. and MACINTOSH, F. C.: Proc. Canad. Fed., 3:12 (1960).
25. BHATTACHARYA, B. K. and FELDBERG, W.: Brit. J. Pharmacol., 13:163 (1958).
26. BHOOLA, K. D., CALLE, J. D. and SCHACHTER, M.: J. Physiol., 152:75 (1960).
27. BIRKS, R., HUXLEY, H. E. and KATZ, B.: J. Physiol., 150:134 (1960).
28. BIRKS, R., KATZ, B. and MILEDI, R.: J. Physiol., 150:145 (1960).
29. BIRKS, R. and MACINTOSH, F. C.: Canad. J. Biochem. Physiol., 39:787 (1961).
30. BISSET, G. W., FRAZER, J. F. D., ROTHSCHILD, M. and SCHACHTER, M.: Proc. Roy. Soc. B., 152:255 (1960).
31. BOISTEL, J. and FATT, P.: J. Physiol., 144:176 (1958).
32. BONNET, V. and BREMER, F.: Compt. rend. Soc. biol., Paris, 126:1271 (1937).
33. BORNSTEIN, M. B.: J. Neurophysiol., 9:347 (1946).
34. BOVET, D. and LONGO, V. G.: Abstr. Rev. XX int. physiol. Congr., p. 306 (1956).
35. BOYD, I. A. and MARTIN, A. R.: J. Physiol., 132:61 (1956).
36. BOYD, I. A. and MARTIN, A. R.: J. Physiol., 132:74 (1956).

*We should like to acknowledge with thanks the assistance of Mrs. T. E. Hartridge in the preparation of the manuscript.

37. BOYD, T. E.: *Am. J. Physiol., 100:*569 (1932).
38. BRADLEY, P. B. and ELKES, J.: *Brain, 80:*77 (1957).
38a. BRADLEY, P. B. and MOLLICA, A.: *Arch. ital. Biol., 96:*168 (1958).
39. BRECHT, K. and CORSTEN, M.: *Pflüger's Arch. ges. Physiol., 245:*160 (1941).
39a. BRECHT, K.: *Arch. exp. Path. Pharmakol., 214:*292 (1952).
40. BREMER, F. and CHATONNET, J.: *Arch. internat. Physiol., 57:*106 (1949).
41. BRONK, D. W.: *J. Neurophysiol., 2:*380 (1939).
42. BROOKS, V. B.: *J. Physiol., 123:*501 (1954).
43. BROOKS, V. B.: *J. Physiol., 134:*264 (1956).
44. BROOKS, V. B., RANSMEIER, R. E. and GERARD, R. W.: *Am. J. Physiol., 157:*299 (1949).
45. BROWN, G. L.: *J. Physiol., 89:*438 (1937).
46. BROWN, G. L.: *Physiol. Rev., 17:*485 (1937).
47. BROWN, G. L., DALE, H. H. and FELDBERG, W.: *J. Physiol., 87:*394 (1936).
48. BROWN, G. L. and FELDBERG, W.: *J. Physiol., 88:*265 (1936).
49. BROWN, G. L. and PASCOE, J. E.: *J. Physiol., 123:*565 (1954).
50. BRÜCKE, F., SAILERS, S. and STUMPF, C.: *Arch. exper. Path. u. Pharmacol., 232:*433 (1958).
51. BUCHTHAL, F. and LINDHARDT, J.: *J. Physiol., 90:*82P (1937).
52. BÜLBRING, E. and BURN, J. H.: *J. Physiol., 100:*337 (1941).
53. BÜLBRING, E., BURN, J. H. and SHELLEY, H. J.: *Proc. Roy. Soc. B., 141:*445 (1953).
54. BÜLBRING, E., LOURIE, E. M. and PARDOE, U.: *Brit. J. Pharmacol., 4:*290 (1949).
55. BULL, G., LAWES, M. and LEONARD, M.: *Stain Technól., 32:*59 (1957).
55a. BULL, G., HEBB, C. O. and RATKOVIC, D.: *Nature, Lond. 190:*1202 (1961).
56. BULLOCK, T. H., GRUNDFEST, H., NACHMANSOHN, D., ROTHENBERG, M. A. and STERLING, K.: *J. Neurophysiol., 9:*253 (1946).
57. BURGEN, A. S. V. and CHIPMAN, L. M.: *J. Physiol., 114:*296 (1951).
58. BURGEN, A. S. V., DICKENS, F. and ZATMAN, L. J.: *J. Physiol., 109:*10 (1949).
59. BURGEN, A. S. V. and TERROUX, K. G.: *J. Physiol., 120:*449 (1953).
60. BURKE, W. and GINSBORG, B. L.: *J. Physiol., 132:*599 (1956).
61. BURNS, B. D. and PATON, W. D. M.: *J. Physiol., 115:*41 (1951).
62. BUTTERWORTH, J., ELEY, D. D. and STONE, G. S.: *Biochem. J., 53:*30 (1953).
63. CALABRO, Q.: *Riv. Biol., 15:*299 (1933).
64. CANNON, W. B. and ROSENBLUETH, A.: *Autonomic Neuro-effector Systems.* New York, Macmillan (1937).
65. CANNON, W. and ROSENBLUETH, A.: *The Supersensitivity of Denervated Structures.* New York, Macmillan (1949).
66. CANTONI, G. L. and LOEWI, O.: *J. Pharmacol., 81:*67 (1944).
67. CARSLAW, H. S. and JAEGER, J. C.: *Conduction of Heat in Solids.* Oxford, Clarendon Press (1947).
68. CHAGAS, C.: In *Curare and Curare-like Agents,* p. 327 Bovet *et al.,* Eds. Amsterdam, Elsevier (1959).
68a. CHANG, H. C.: *J. Neurophysiol., 16:*221 (1953).
69. CHANG, H. C., CHIA, K. F., HSU, C. H. and LIM, R. K. S.: *Chin. J. Physiol., 12:*1 (1937).
70. CHANG, H. C. and GADDUM, J. H.: *J. Physiol., 79:*255 (1933).
71. CHATFIELD, P. O. and DEMPSEY, E. W.: *Am. J. Physiol., 135:*633 (1942).
72. CHUTE, A. L., FELDBERG, W. and SMYTH, D. H.: *Quart. J. Exper. Physiol., 30:*65 (1946).

73. COHEN, J. A. and POSTHUMUS, C. H.: *Acta physiol. pharmacol. Neerl.*, *5*:385 (1957).
74. COHEN, M.: *Arch. Biochem. Biophys.*, *60*:284 (1956).
75. COLHOUN, E. H.: *Canad. J. Biochem. & Physiol.*, *37*:1127 (1959).
76. CORDIER, D. and MAYNE, H.: *Ann. Physiol. Physicochim. biol.*, *3*:486 (1927).
77. COUTEAUX, R.: *Rev. Canad. Biol.*, *6*:563 (1947).
78. COUTEAUX, R.: *Internat. Rev. Cytol.*, *4*:335 (1955).
79. COUTEAUX, R.: In *The Structure and Function of Muscle.* G. H. Bourne, Ed. New York, Acad. Press (1960).
80. COUTEAUX, R. and TAXI, J.: *Arch. Anat. Micr.*, *41*:352 (1952).
81. CRESCITELLI, F., KOELLE, G. B. and GILMAN, A.: *J. Neurophysiol.*, *9*:241 (1946).
82. CROSSLAND, J.: *J. Pharm. Lond. 12*:1 (1960).
83. CURTIS, D. R., ECCLES, J. C. and ECCLES, R. M.: *J. Physiol.*, *136*:420 (1957).
84. CURTIS, D. R. and ECCLES, R. M.: *J. Physiol.*, *141*:435 (1958).
85. CURTIS, D. R. and ECCLES, R. M.: *J. Physiol.*, *141*:446 (1958).
85a. CURTIS, D. R. and KOIZUMI, K.: *J. Neurophysiol.*, *24*:80 (1961).
85b. CURTIS, D. R. and PHILLIS, J. W.: *J. Physiol.*, *153*:117 (1960).
86. CURTIS, D. R., PHILLIS, J. W. and WATKINS, J. C.: *J. Physiol.*, *150*:656 (1960).
86a. CURTIS, D. R., PHILLIS, J. W. and WATKINS, J. C.: *J. Physiol.*, *158*:296 (1961).
87. DALE, H. H.: *J. Pharmacol.*, *6*:147 (1914).
88. DALE, H. H.: *J. Physiol.*, *80*:10P (1933).
89. DALE, H. H.: *J. Mt. Sinai Hosp.*, *4*:401 (1938).
90. DALE, H. H.: *Adventures in Physiology.* London, Pergamon Press (1953).
91. DALE, H. H. and DUDLEY, H. W.: *J. Physiol.*, *68*:97 (1929).
92. DALE, H. H. and FELDBERG, W.: *J. Physiol.*, *81*:39P (1934).
93. DALE, H. H. and FELDBERG, W.: *J. Physiol.*, *82*:121 (1934).
94. DALE, H. H., FELDBERG, W. and VOGT, M.: *J. Physiol.*, *86*:353 (1936).
95. DARROW, C. W., McCULLOCH, W. S., GREEN, R., DAVIS, E. W. and GAROL, H. W.: *Arch. Neurol. & Psychiat.*, *52*:337 (1944).
96. DAVIES, D. R. and GREEN, A. L.: *Advances Enzymol.*, *20*:283 (1958).
97. DAVSON, H.: *Physiology of the Ocular and Cerebrospinal Fluids.* London, Churchill (1957).
98. DE CASTRO, F.: *Arch. internat. Physiol.*, *59*:479 (1951).
99. DE ROBERTIS, E.: *Internat. Rev. Cytol.*, *8*:61 (1959).
100. DE ROBERTIS, E.: *Abstr. Symp. XXI int. physiol. Congr.*, p. 213 (1959).
101. DE ROBERTIS, E. and BENNETT, H. S.: *Federation Proc.*, *13*:35 (1954).
102. DEL CASTILLO, J. and ENGBAEK, L.: *J. Physiol.*, *124*:370 (1954).
103. DEL CASTILLO, J. and KATZ, B.: *J. Physiol.*, *124*:560 (1954).
104. DEL CASTILLO, J. and KATZ, B.: *J. Physiol.*, *124*:574 (1954).
105. DEL CASTILLO, J. and KATZ, B.: *J. Physiol.*, *124*:586 (1954).
106. DEL CASTILLO, J. and KATZ, B.: *J. Physiol.*, *128*:157 (1955).
107. DEL CASTILLO, J. and KATZ, B.: *J. Physiol.*, *128*:396 (1955).
108. DEL CASTILLO, J. and KATZ, B.: *Nature*, London, *175*:1035 (1955).
109. DEL CASTILLO, J. and KATZ, B.: *Progr. Biophys.*, *6*:122 (1956).
110. DEL CASTILLO, J. and KATZ, B.: *Proc. Roy. Soc. B.*, *146*:339 (1957).
111. DEL CASTILLO, J. and KATZ, B.: *Proc. Roy. Soc. B.*, *146*:357 (1957).
112. DEL CASTILLO, J. and KATZ, B.: *Proc. Roy. Soc. B.*, *146*:362 (1957).
113. DEL CASTILLO, J. and KATZ, B.: *Proc. Roy. Soc. B.*, *146*:369 (1957).
114. DESMEDT, J. E.: *J. Physiol.*, *121*:191 (1953).
115. DETTBARN, W. D.: *Federation Proc.*, *18*:36 (1959).
116. DIAMOND, J.: *J. Physiol.*, *145*:611 (1959).

117. DIAMOND, J. and MILEDI, R.: *J. Physiol., 149:*50P (1959).
118. DIKSHIT, B. B.: *J. Physiol., 80:*409 (1934).
119. DIXON, W. E.: *Brit. M. J.,* p. 1807 (1906).
120. DIXON, W. E. and HAMILL, P.: *J. Physiol., 38:*314 (1909).
121. DOUGLAS, W. W. and RITCHIE, J. M.: *J. Physiol., 150:*501 (1960).
122. DUKE, H. N., PICKFORD, M. and WATT, J. A.: *J. Physiol., 111:*81 (1950).
123. DUN, F. T.: *Abstr. XXI int. physiol. Congr.,* p. 79 (1959).
124. ECCLES, J. C.: *J. Physiol., 85:*179 (1935).
125. ECCLES, J. C.: *J. Physiol., 101:*465 (1943).
126. ECCLES, J. C.: *The Neurophysiological Basis of Mind.* Oxford, Clarendon Press (1953).
127. ECCLES, J. C.: *The Physiology of Nerve Cells.* Baltimore, Johns Hopkins Press (1957).
127a. ECCLES, J. C.: *Ergebn. Physiol., 51:*299 (1961).
128. ECCLES, J. C., ECCLES, R. M. and FATT, P.: *J. Physiol., 131:*154 (1956).
129. ECCLES, J. C., FATT, P. and KOKETSU, K.: *J. Physiol., 126:*524 (1954).
130. ECCLES, J. C. and JAEGER, J. C.: *Proc. Roy. Soc., B., 148:*38 (1957).
131. ECCLES, J. C., KATZ, B. and KUFFLER, S. W.: *J. Neurophysiol., 4:*362 (1941).
132. ECCLES, J. C., KATZ, B. and KUFFLER, S. W.: *J. Neurophysiol., 5:*211 (1942).
133. ECCLES, J. C. and KRNJEVIĆ, K.: *J. Physiol., 149:*274 (1959).
134. ECCLES, J. C. and MACFARLANE, W. V.: *J. Neurophysiol., 12:*59 (1949).
135. ECCLES, J. C. and O'CONNOR, W. J.: *J. Physiol., 97:*44 (1939).
136. ECCLES, R. M.: *J. Physiol., 117:*181 (1952).
137. ECCLES, R. M.: *J. Physiol., 117:*196 (1952).
138. ECCLES, R. M.: *J. Physiol., 130:*572 (1955).
139. EHRENPREIS, S.: *Biochem. Biophys. Acta., 44:*561 (1960).
140. ELLIOTT, K. A. C., SWANK, R. L. and HENDERSON, N.: *Am. J. Physiol., 162:*469 (1950).
141. ELLIOTT, T. R.: *J. Physiol., 31:*20P (1904).
142. ELLIOTT, T. R.: *J. Physiol., 32:*401 (1905).
142a. ELLIOTT, T. R.: *J. Physiol., 35:*367 (1907).
143. EMMELIN, N. and FELDBERG, W.: *J. Physiol., 106:*14P (1947).
144. EMMELIN, N. and FELDBERG, W.: *New Phytol., 48:*143 (1949).
145. EMMELIN, N. and MACINTOSH, F. C.: *J. Physiol., 131:*477 (1956).
146. EMMELIN, N. and MUREN, A.: *Acta physiol. scandinav., 20:*13 (1950).
147. ENGLEHART, E.: *Pflüger's Arch. ges. Physiol., 227:*220 (1931).
148. ENGLEHART, E. and LOEWI, O.: *Arch. exper. Path. u. Pharmakol., 150:*1 (1930).
149. ERSPAMER, V.: *Arch. exper. Path. u. Pharmakol., 218:*142 (1953).
150. VON EULER, U. S.: *Acta physiol. scandinav., 11:*168 (1946).
151. FATT, P.: *J. Physiol., 111:*408 (1950).
152. FATT, P.: *Physiol. Rev., 34:*674 (1954).
153. FATT, P. and KATZ, B.: *J. Physiol., 115:*320 (1951).
154. FATT, P. and KATZ, B.: *J. Physiol., 117:*109 (1952).
155. FELDBERG, W.: *Physiol. Rev., 25:*596 (1945).
156. FELDBERG, W.: *Brit. M. Bull., 6:*312 (1950).
157. FELDBERG, W.: *Pharmacol. Rev., 6:*85 (1954).
158. FELDBERG, W.: In *Metabolism of the Nervous System,* p. 493. Richter, Ed. London, Pergamon Press (1957).
159. FELDBERG, W. and FESSARD, A.: *J. Physiol., 101:*200 (1942).
160. FELDBERG, W. and GADDUM, J. H.: *J. Physiol., 81:*305 (1934).
161. FELDBERG, W. and KRAYER, O.: *Arch. exper. Path. u. Pharmakol., 172:*170 (1933).

162. FELDBERG, W. and MALCOLM, J. L.: *J. Physiol., 149:*58 (1959).
163. FELDBERG, W., MALCOLM, J. L. and DARIAN SMITH, I.: *J. Physiol., 138:*178 (1957).
164. FELDBERG, W. and SCHRIEVER, H.: *J. Physiol., 86:*277 (1936).
165. FELDBERG, W. and SHERWOOD, S. L.: *J. Physiol., 123:*148 (1954).
166. FELDBERG, W. and VARTIAINEN, A.: *J. Physiol., 83:*103 (1934).
167. FELDBERG, W. and VOGT, M.: *J. Physiol., 107:*372 (1948).
168. FENG, T. P.: *Chin. J. Physiol., 15:*367 (1940).
169. FENG, T. P.: *Chin. J. Physiol., 16:*341 (1941).
170. FENG, T. P.: *Biol. Symp., 3:*121 (1941).
171. FENG, T. P. and LI, T. H.: *Chin. J. Physiol., 16:*37 (1941).
172. FENG, T. P. and TING, Y. C.: *Chin. J. Physiol., 13:*141 (1938).
172a. FJÄLLBRANT, N. I. and IGGO, A.: *J. Physiol., 156:*578 (1961).
173. FLEISCH, A., SIBUL, T. and KAELIN, M.: *Arch. internat. Physiol., 44:*24 (1938).
174. FLOREY, E.: *J. Gen. Physiol., 40:*533 (1957).
175. FRANCIS, C. M.: *J. Physiol., 120:*435 (1953).
176. FRANK, E., NOTHMANN, M. and HIRSCH-KAUFFMANN, H.: *Pflüger's Arch. ges. Physiol., 197:*270 (1922).
177. FRIEDEMANN, U.: *Physiol. Rev., 22:*125 (1942).
178. FÜHNER, H.: *Arch. exper. Path. u. Pharmakol., 82:*51, 81 (1917).
179. FURSHPAN, E. J.: *J. Physiol., 134:*689 (1956).
180. FURSHPAN, E. J. and POTTER, D. D.: *J. Physiol., 145:*289 (1959).
181. GARCIA RAMOS, J. and ROSENBLUETH, A.: *Arch. Inst. Cardiol. Mex., 17:*384 (1947).
182. GASKELL, W. H.: *J. Physiol., 8:*404 (1887).
183. GASKELL, W. H.: *The Involuntary Nervous System,* p. 146. London, Longmans Green & Co. (1916).
184. GASSER, H. S. and DALE, H. H.: *J. Pharmacol., 28:*287 (1926).
185. GELDER, N. VAN: Unpublished observations (1961).
186. GERARD, R. W.: *Ann. New York Acad. Sc., 47:*575 (1946).
187. GESELL, R., HANSEN, E. T. and WARZNIAK, J. J.: *Am. J. Physiol., 138:*776 (1943).
188. GIACOBINI, E.: *Acta physiol. scandinav., 45:*suppl. 156 (1959).
189. GIACOBINI, E. and HOLMSTEDT, B.: *Acta physiol. scandinav., 42:*12 (1958).
190. GIACOBINI, E. and ZAJICEK, J.: *Nature,* London, *177:*185 (1956).
191. GINETSINSKII, A. G. and SHAMARINA, I. M.: *Uspehi sovremennoi biologii, 15:*283 (1942).
192. GINSBORG, B. L.: *J. Physiol., 150:*707 (1960).
193. GÖPFERT, H. and SCHAEFER, H.: *Pflüger's Arch. ges. Physiol., 239:*597 (1938).
194. GRANIT, R., PASCOE, J. E. and STEG, G.: *J. Physiol., 138:*381 (1957).
195. GRAY, E. G. and WHITTAKER, V. P.: *J. Physiol., 153:*35P (1960).
196. GRAY, J. A. B. and DIAMOND, J.: *Brit. M. Bull., 13:*185 (1957).
197. GROB, D., JOHNS, R. J. and HARVEY, A. M.: *Johns Hopkins Hosp. Bull., 99:*136 (1956).
198. GRUNDFEST, H.: *Ann. New York Acad. Sc., 66:*537 (1957).
199. GUYTON, A. C. and MacDONALD, M. A.: *Arch. Neurol. & Psychiat., 57:*578 (1947).
200. HÄGGQVIST, G.: *Acta physiol. scandinav., 48:*63 (1960).
201. HARRIS, E. J. and HUTTER, O. F.: *J. Physiol., 133:*58P (1956).
202. HARVEY, A. M. and MacINTOSH, F. C.: *J. Physiol., 97:*408 (1940).
203. HEBB, C. O.: *Quart. J. Exper. Physiol., 40:*176 (1955).
204. HEBB, C. O.: *Physiol. Rev., 37:*196 (1957).
205. HEBB, C. O.: *Acta physiol. et pharmacol. neerl. 6:*621 (1957).

206. HEBB, C. O.: *Synthesis, Storage and Release of Acetylcholine.* Heffter Heubner Handbook (in press) (1962).

206a. HEBB, C. O.: Unpublished observations (1960).

207. HEBB, C. O. and HILL, K. J.: *Nature,* London, *175*:597 (1955).

208. HEBB, C. O., KRAUSE, M. and SILVER, A.: *J. Physiol., 148*:69P (1959).

209. HEBB, C. O. and KRNJEVIĆ, K.: Unpublished observations (1960).

210. HEBB, C. O. and MITCHELL, J. M.: Unpublished observations.

211. HEBB, C. O. and SILVER, A.: *J. Physiol., 134*:718 (1956).

212. HEBB, C. O. and SILVER, A.: Unpublished observations (1960).

213. HEBB, C. O., SILVER, A., SWAN, A. B. and WALSH, E. G.: *Quart. J. Exper. Physiol., 38*:185 (1953).

214. HEBB, C. O. and SMALLMAN, B. N.: *J. Physiol., 134*:385 (1956).

215. HEBB, C. O. and WAITES, G. M. H.: *J. Physiol., 132*:667 (1956).

216. HEBB, C. O. and WHITTAKER, V. P.: *J. Physiol., 142*:187 (1958).

217. HESS, W. R.: *Quart. J. exper. Physiol.,* (Suppl.) p. 144 (1923).

218. HODGKIN, A. L.: *Biol. Rev., 26*:339 (1951).

219. HODGKIN, A. L. and KEYNES, R. D.: *J. Physiol., 131*:592 (1956).

220. HOFFMAN, B. F. and SUCKLING, E. E.: *Am. J. Physiol., 173*:312 (1953).

220a. HOKIN, L. E. and HOKIN, M. R.: *J. Biol. Chem., 234*:1387 (1959); *Nature, Lond. 184,* 1068. *Int. Rev. Neurobiol., 2*:99 (1960).

221. HOLLAND, W. C., DUNN, F. C. and GREIG, M. E.: *Am. J. Physiol., 168*:546 (1952).

222. HOLMSTEDT, B.: *Acta physiol. scandinav., 25*:suppl. 90 (1951).

223. HOLMSTEDT, B.: *Pharmacol. Rev., 11*:567 (1959).

224. HOWELL, W. H.: *Am. J. Physiol., 15*:280 (1905).

225. HOWELL, W. H. and DUKE, W. W.: *Am. J. Physiol., 21*:51 (1908).

226. HUBBARD, J. I.: *Nature,* London, *184*:1945 (1959).

227. HUGHES, B.: *Brit. J. Pharmacol., 10*:36 (1955).

228. HUTTER, O. F.: *J. Physiol., 118*:216 (1952).

229. HUTTER, O. F. and KOSTIAL, G.: *J. Physiol., 124*:234 (1954).

230. HUTTER, O. F. and KOSTIAL, K.: *J. Physiol., 129*:159 (1955).

231. HUTTER, O. F. and TRAUTWEIN, W.: *J. Physiol., 129*:48P (1955).

232. HUTTER, O. F. and TRAUTWEIN, W.: *J. Physiol., 133*:610 (1956).

233. HYDE, J., BECKETT, S. and GELLHORN, E.: *J. Neurophysiol., 12*:17 (1949).

234. JENKINSON, D. H. and NICHOLLS, J. G.: *J. Physiol., 152*:12P (1960).

235. JOB, C. and LUNDBERG, A.: *Acta physiol. scandinav., 28*:14 (1953).

236. JOHNS, R. J., GROB, D. and HARVEY, A. M.: *Johns Hopkins Hosp. Bull., 99*:125 (1956).

237. KAHLSON, G. and MACINTOSH, F. C.: *J. Physiol., 96*:277 (1939).

238. KATZ, B.: *J. Neurophysiol., 5*:169 (1942).

239. KATZ, B.: *Johns Hopkins Hosp. Bull., 102*:275 (1958).

240. KATZ, B. and THESLEFF, S.: *J. Physiol., 138*:63 (1957).

241. KATZENELBOGEN, S.: *The Cerebro-spinal Fluid and Its Relation to the Blood.* Baltimore, Johns Hopkins Press (1935).

242. KEYL, M. J., MICHAELSON, I. A. and WHITTAKER, V. P.: *J. Physiol., 139*:434 (1957).

243. KELEN, A. and MCEACHERN, D.: *Canad. J. Res., 27*:46 (1949).

244. KENNEDY, E. P. and KOSHLAND, D. E.: *J. Biol. Chem., 228*:419 (1957).

245. KIBJAKOW, A. W.: *Pflüger's Arch. ges. Physiol., 232*:432 (1933).

245a. KLAUS, W., LÜLLMAN, H. and MUSCHOLL, E.: *Arch. exp. Path. Pharmak., 241*:281 (1961).

246. KOELLE, G. B.: *J. Pharmacol., 100*:158 (1950).

247. KOELLE, G. B.: *J. Pharmacol., 103*:153 (1951).
248. KOELLE, G. B. and GILMAN, A.: *Pharmacol. Rev., 1*:166 (1949).
249. KOELLE, W. A. and KOELLE, G. B.: *Federation Proc., 17*:384 (1958).
250. KORKES, S., DEL CAMPILLO, A., KOREY, S. R., STERN, J. R., NACHMANSOHN, D. and OCHOA, S.: *J. Biol. Chem., 198*:215 (1952).
251. KOSTIAL, K. and VOUK, V. B.: *J. Physiol., 132*:239 (1956).
252. KOSTIAL, K. and VOUK, V. B.: *Experientia, 14*:103 (1958).
253. KREMER, M.: *Quart. J. Exper. Physiol., 31*:337 (1942).
254. KRIVOY, W. A., HART, E. R. and MARRAZZI, S.: *J. Pharmacol., 103*:351 (1951).
254a. KRNJEVIĆ, K.: *Nature, Lond., 191*:1403 (1961).
255. KRNJEVIĆ, K. and MILEDI, R.: *J. Physiol., 140*:440 (1958).
256. KRNJEVIĆ, K. and MILEDI, R.: *J. Physiol., 141*:291 (1958).
257. KRNJEVIĆ, K. and MILEDI, R.: *Nature,* London, *182*:805 (1958).
258. KRNJEVIĆ, K. and MITCHELL, J. F.: *J. Physiol., 153*:562 (1960).
259. KRNJEVIĆ, K. and MITCHELL, J. F.: *Nature,* London, *186*:241 (1960).
260. KRNJEVIĆ, K. and MITCHELL, J. F.: *J. Physiol., 155*:246 (1961).
260a. KRNJEVIĆ, K. and PHILLIS, J. W.: *Experientia, 17*:469 (1961).
261. KRÜGER, P.: *Tetanus und Tonus der quergestreiften Skelettmuskeln der Wirbeltiere und des Menschen.* Leipzig, Akad. Verlag (1952).
262. KUFFLER, S. W.: *J. Neurophysiol., 5*:309 (1942).
263. KUFFLER, S. W.: *J. Neurophysiol., 6*:99 (1943).
264. KUFFLER, S. W.: *Federation Proc., 7*:437 (1948).
265. KUFFLER, S. W. and EYZAGUIRRIE, C.: *J. Gen. Physiol., 39*:155 (1955).
266. KUFFLER, S. W. and VAUGHAN WILLIAMS, E. M.: *J. Physiol., 121*:289 (1953).
267. KUFFLER, S. W. and VAUGHAN WILLIAMS, E. M.: *J. Physiol. 121*:318 (1953).
268. LANGLEY, J. N.: *J. Physiol. 36*:347 (1907).
269. LARRABEE, M. G. and BRONK, D. W.: *J. Neurphysiol., 10*:139 (1947).
270. LEHNARTZ, E.: *J. Physiol., 86*:37P (1936).
271. LI, C. L.: *Am. J. Physiol., 194*:200 (1958).
272. LI, T. H.: *Chin. J. Physiol., 13*:173 (1938).
273. LILEY, A. W.: *J. Physiol., 132*:650 (1956).
274. LILEY, A. W.: *J. Physiol., 134*:427 (1956).
275. LILEY, A. W. and NORTH, K. A. K.: *J. Neurophysiol., 16*:509 (1953).
276. LIN, R. C. Y.: *Brit. J. Pharmacol., 12*:265 (1957).
277. LINZELL, J. L. and HEBB, C. O.: Unpublished observations (1956).
278. LIPMANN, F.: *Science, 120*:855 (1954).
279. LISSAK, K.: *Am. J. Physiol., 127*:263 (1939).
280. LLOYD, D. P. C.: *J. Neurophysiol., 5*:153 (1942).
281. LLOYD, D. P. C.: *J. Gen. Physiol., 33*:147 (1949).
282. LOEWI, O.: *Pflüger's Arch. ges. physiol., 189*:239 (1921); *Ibid., 193*:201 (1922); *Ibid., 203*:408 (1924); *Ibid., 204*:629 (1924).
283. LOEWI, O. and NAVRATIL, E.: *Pflüger's Arch. ges. physiol., 206*:123 (1924); *Ibid., 206*:135 (1924); *Ibid., 214*:678 (1926); *Ibid., 214*:689 (1926).
284. LONGO, V. G.: *Arch. internat. pharmacodyn., 119*:1 (1959).
285. LORENTE DE NÓ, R.: *Am. J. Physiol., 121*:331 (1938).
286. LORENTE DE NÓ, R.: *Johns Hopkins Hosp. Bull., 83*:497 (1948).
287. LORENTE DE NÓ, R. and LAPORTE, Y.: *J. Cell. & Comp. Physiol., 35*:Suppl. 2 (1950).
288. LUBIŃSKA, L.: Personal communication (1960).

289. LUNDBERG, A. and QUILISH, H.: *Acta physiol. scandinav., 30:*Suppl. 111, p. 111 (1953).
290. MacINTOSH, F. C.: *Arch. internat. physiol., 47:*321 (1938).
291. MacINTOSH, F. C.: *J. Physiol., 94:*155 (1938).
292. MacINTOSH, F. C.: *J. Physiol., 99:*436 (1941).
293. MacINTOSH, F. C.: *Canad. J. Biochem. & Physiol., 37:*343 (1959).
294. MacINTOSH, F. C.: Personal communication (1960).
295. MacINTOSH, F. C. and OBORIN, P. E.: *Abstr. XIX int. Physiol. Congr.,* p. 580 (1953).
296. MARNAY, A. and NACHMANSOHN, D.: *J. Physiol., 92:*37 (1938).
297. MARTIN, A. R.: *J. Physiol., 130:*114 (1955).
297a. MARTIN, A. R. and ORKAND, R. K.: *Fed. Proc., 20:*579 (1961).
298. MASLAND, R. L. and WIGTON, R. S.: *J. Neurophysiol., 3:*269 (1940).
299. MATTHES, K.: *J. Physiol., 70:*338 (1930).
300. McINTYRE, A. R.: In *Curare and Curare-like Agents,* p. 210. Bovet *et al,* Ed. Amsterdam, Elsevier (1959).
301. MEER, C. VAN DER and MEETER, E.: *Acta physiol. et pharmacol. neerl., 4:*454 (1956).
302. MENDEL, B. and HAWKINS, R. D.: *J. Neurophysiol., 6:*431 (1943).
303. MENDEL, B. and RUDNEY, H.: *Biochem. J., 37:*59 (1943).
304. MENDEL, B. and MUNDEL, D. B.: *Biochem. J., 37:*64 (1943).
305. MENDEL, B., MUNDELL, D. B. and RUDNEY, H.: *Biochem. J., 37:*473 (1943).
306. METZ, B.: *Am. J. Physiol., 192:*100 (1958).
307. MICHAELIS, M., ARANGO, N. I. and GERARD, R. W.: *Am. J. Physiol., 157:*463 (1949).
308. MILEDI, R.: *J. Physiol., 151:*1 (1960).
309. MILEDI, R.: *J. Physiol., 151:*24 (1960).
310. MILEDI, R.: *J. Physiol., 154:*190 (1960).
311. MILLER, F. R. STAVRAKY, G. W. and WOONTON, G. A.: *J. Neurophysiol., 3:*131 (1940).
312. MILTON, A. S.: *J. Physiol., 145:*33P (1959).
313. MINZ, B.: *Arch. Exper. Path. u. Pharmakol., 168:*292 (1932).
314. MINZ, B.: *The Role of Humoral Agents in Nervous Activity.* Springfield, Ill., Thomas (1955).
315. MITCHELL, J. F.: *J. Physiol., 155:*22P (1960).
316. MONNIER, M.: *Abstr. Symp. XXI int. Physiol. Congr.,* p. 149 (1959).
316a. MORLOCK, N. and WARD, A. A.: *Electroenceph. Clin. Neurophysiol., 13:*60 (1961).
317. MORUZZI, G.: *Arch. internat. physiol., 49:*33 (1939).
318. MYERS, D. K.: *Biochem. J., 55:*67 (1953).
319. NACHMANSOHN, D.: *Chemical and Molecular Basis of Nerve Activity.* New York & London, Acad. Press (1959).
320. NACHMANSOHN, D. and MACHADO, A. L.: *J. Neurophysiol., 6:*397 (1943).
321. NACHMANSOHN, D. and WEISS, M. S.: *J. Biol. Chem., 172:*677 (1948).
322. NAKAO, H., BALLIN, H. M. and GELLHORN, E.: *EEG. & Clin. Neurophysiol., 8:*413 (1956).
323. NASTUK, W. L.: *J. Cell. & Comp. Physiol., 42:*249 (1953).
324. NASTUK, W. L.: *Federation Proc., 12:*102 (1953).
325. NATHAN, P. and APRISON, M. H.: *Federation Proc., 14:*106 (1955).
325a. NISHI, S. and KOKETSU, K.: *J. cell. comp. Physiol., 55:*15 (1960).
326. O'BRIEN, R. D.: *Ann. ent. Soc. Am., 50:*223 (1957).

327. Ochs, S.: *Am. J. Physiol., 197:*1136 (1959).

328. Ogston, A. G.: *J. Physiol., 128:*222 (1955).

329. Ord, M. G. and Thompson, R. H. S.: *Nature,* London, *165:*927 (1950).

330. Ord, M. G. and Thompson, R. H. S.: *Biochem. J., 46:*346 (1950).

331. Ostow, M. and Garcia, F.: *J. Neurophysiol., 12:*225 (1949).

332. Palay, S. L.: *Exper. Cell Res.,* Suppl. 5, 275 (1958).

333. Pascoe, J. E.: *J. Physiol., 128:*26P (1955).

334. Pascoe, J. E.: *J. Physiol., 132:*242 (1956).

335. Paton, W. D. M.: *Ann. Rev. Physiol., 20:*431 (1958).

336. Paton, W. D. M. and Perry, W. L. M.: *J. Physiol., 119:*43 (1953).

337. Paton, W. D. M. and Zaimis, E. J.: *Pharmacol. Rev., 4:*219 (1952).

338. Paulet, G. and André, P.: *J. Physiol.* (Paris), *49:*335 (1957).

339. Perry, W. L. M.: *J. Physiol., 119:*439 (1953).

340. Perry, W. L. M.: *Ann. Rev. Physiol., 18:*279 (1956).

341. Perry, W. L. M. and Talesnik, J.: *J. Physiol., 119:*455 (1953).

342. Pickford, M.: *J. Physiol., 106:*264 (1947).

343. Pickford, M. and Watt, J. A.: *J. Physiol., 114:*333 (1951).

344. Prosser, L.: *Physiol. Rev., 26:*337 (1946).

345. Quastel, J. H., Tennenbaum, M. and Wheatley, A. H.: *Biochem. J., 30:*1668 (1936).

346. Reisberg, R. B.: *Yale J. Biol. & Med., 29:*403 (1957).

347. Reitzel, N. L. and Long, J. P.: *Arch. internat. pharmacodyn., 119:*20 (1959).

348. Renshaw, B.: *J. Neurophysiol., 4:*167 (1941).

349. Renshaw, B.: *J. Neurophysiol., 9:*191 (1946).

350. Richter, D. and Crossland, J.: *Am. J. Physiol., 159:*247 (1949).

351. Richter, D. and Hullin, R. P.: *Biochem. J., 48:*406 (1951).

352. Riesser, O. and Neuschlosz, S. M.: *Arch. exper. Path. u. Pharmakol., 91:*342 (1921).

353. Rinaldi, F. and Himwich, H. E.: *Arch. Neurol. & Psychiat., 73:*387 (1955).

354. Rinaldi, F. and Himwich, H. E.: *Arch. Neurol. & Psychiat., 73:*396 (1955).

355. Robertson, J. D.: *J. Biophys. Biochem. Cytol., 2:*381 (1956).

356. Rosenblueth, A.: *The Transmission of Nerve Impulses at Neuro-effector Junctions and Peripheral Synapses.* New York, John Wiley & Sons (1950).

357. Rosenblueth, A., Lissak, K. and Lanari, A.: *Am. J. Physiol., 128:*31 (1939).

358. Rosenblueth, A. and Luco, J. V.: *Am. J. Physiol., 120:*781 (1937).

359. Rosenblueth, A. and Morison, R. S.: *Am. J. Physiol., 119:*236 (1937).

360. Rosenblueth, A. and Simeone, F. A.: *Am. J. Physiol., 122:*708 (1938).

361. Rosenzweig, M. R., Krech, D. and Bennett, E. L.: In *Biological and Biochemical Bases of Behavior,* p. 367. Harlow, H. F. and Woolsey, C. N., Eds. Madison, Wis., Univ. Wisconsin Press (1958).

362. Rossi, G. F. and Zanchetti, A.: *Arch. ital. biol., 95:*199 (1957).

363. Samojloff, A.: *Pflüger's Arch. ges. Physiol., 155:*471 (1914).

364. Sawyer, C. H.: *Am. J. Physiol., 146:*246 (1946).

365. Sawyer, C. H. and Hollinshead, W. H.: *J. Neurophysiol., 8:*137 (1945).

366. Schachter, M. and Thain, E. M.: *Brit. J. Pharmacol., 9:*352 (1954).

367. Schaefer, H. and Haass, P.: *Pflüger's Arch. ges. physiol., 242:*364 (1939).

368. Schild, H. O.: *J. Physiol., 153:*26P (1960).

369. Schlag, J. D. A.: *EEG & Clin. Neurophysiol., 8:*421 (1956).

370. Schueler, F. W.: *J. Pharmacol., 115:*127 (1955); *Internat. Rev. Neurobiol., 2:*77 (1960).

370a. SCHULMAN, J. H. and ROSANO, H. L.: III Internationaler Kongress für Grenz-flächenaktive Stoffe, Sektion B, Vol. II, 112. (1960).
371. SCHWEITZER, A. and WRIGHT, S.: *J. Physiol., 94:*136 (1938).
371a. SHANES, A. M.: *Pharmacol. Rev., 10:*59 (1958).
372. SHEN, S. C., GREENFIELD, P. and BOELL, E. J.: *J. Comp. Neurol., 102:*717 (1955).
373. SHIMIDZU, K.: *Pflüger's Arch. ges. physiol., 211:*403 (1926).
374. SMALLMAN, B. N.: *Canad. J. Biochem. & Physiol., 37:*1123 (1959).
375. SMALLMAN, B. N. and FISHER, R. W.: *Canad. J. Biochem. & Physiol. 36:*575 (1958).
376. SNELL, R. S.: *J. Anat.,* London, *92:*409 (1958).
377. SOKOLOFF, L.: *Pharmacol. Rev., 11:*1 (1959).
378. STEDMAN, E., STEDMAN, E. and EASSON, L. H.: *Biochem. J., 26:*2056 (1932).
379. STEDMAN, E., STEDMAN, E. and WHITE, A. C.: *Biochem. J., 27:*1053 (1933).
380. STEDMAN, E. and STEDMAN, E.: *Biochem. J., 31:*817 (1937).
381. STEDMAN, E. and STEDMAN, E.: *Biochem. J., 33:*811 (1939).
382. STEPHENSON, M. and ROWATT, E.: *J. Gen. Microbiol., 1:*280 (1947).
383. STERN, L. and GAUTIER, R.: *Arch. internat. physiol., 17:*391 (1922).
383a. STONE, W. E.: *Am. J. Med. 36:*222 (1957).
384. STRAUGHAN, D. W.: *Brit. J. Pharmacol., 15:*417 (1960).
385. TAKEUCHI, A. and TAKEUCHI, N.: *J. Neurophysiol., 22:*395 (1959).
386. TAMMELIN, L. E.: *Svensk. Kem. Tidskr., 70:*157 (1958).
387. TAUGNER, R. and CULP, W.: *Arch. exper. Path. u. Pharmakol. 220:*423 (1953).
388. THESLEFF, S.: *Acta physiol. scandinav., 34:*218 (1955).
389. THESLEFF, S.: *Acta physiol. scandinav. 34:*386 (1955).
390. THESLEFF, S.: *Acta physiol. scandinav., 37:*330 (1956).
391. THESLEFF, S.: *J. Physiol., 148:*659 (1959).
392. THESLEFF, S.: *J. Physiol., 151:*598 (1960).
393. THESLEFF, S.: *Physiol. Rev., 40:*734-752 (1960).
394. TOMAN, J. E. P., WOODBURY, J. W. and WOODBURY, L. E.: *J. Neurophysiol., 10:*429 (1947).
395. TOSCHI, G. W.: *Exper. Cell Res., 16:*232 (1959).
396. TOWER, D. B.: In *Biological and Biochemical Bases of Behavior,* p. 285. Harlow, H. F. and Woolsey, C. N., Eds. Madison, Wisc., Univ. Wisconsin Press (1958).
397. TOWER, D. and ELLIOTT, K. A. C.: *Am. J. Physiol., 168:*747 (1952).
398. TRAUTWEIN, W. and DUDEL, J.: *Pflüger's Arch. ges. Physiol., 266:*324 (1958).
399. TRAUTWEIN, W., KUFFLER, S. W. and EDWARDS, C.: *J. Gen. Physiol., 40:*135 (1956).
400. VAUGHAN WILLIAMS, E. M.: *J. Physiol., 147:*325 (1959).
400a. VAN BREEMEN, C. L., ANDERSON, E. and REGER, J. F.: *Exper. Cell Res.,* Suppl. 5, p. 193 (1958).
401. VON BRÜCKE, F. T.: *J. Physiol., 89:*429 (1937).
402. WASER, P. G.: In *Curare and Curare-like Agents,* p. 218. Bovet *et al.,* Eds. Amsterdam, Elsevier (1959).
402a. WERNER, G. J.: *J. Neurophysiol., 23:*453 (1960).
403. WEST, T. C., FALK, G. and CERVONI, P.: *J. Pharmacol., 117:*245 (1956).
404. WHITTAKER, V. P.: *Physiol. Rev., 31:*312 (1951).
405. WHITTAKER, V. P.: *Nature* London, *181:*856 (1958).
406. WHITTAKER, V. P.: *Biochem., J., 72:*694 (1959).
407. WILSON, H. and LONG, J. P.: *Arch. internat. pharmacodyn., 120:*343 (1959).
408. WILSON, V. J. and TALBOT, W. H.: *J. Gen. Physiol., 43:*495 (1960).

409. WINTERINGHAM, F. P. W., HARRISON, A., McKAY, M. A. and WEATHERLEY, A.:
      Biochem. J., *66*:49P (1957).
410. WITZLEB, E.: *Pflüger's Arch. ges. Physiol.*, *269*:439 (1959).
411. WOLFGRAM, F. J.: *Am. J. Physiol.*, *176*:505 (1954).
412. ŽUPANČIĆ, A. O.: *Acta physiol. scandinav.*, *29*:63 (1953).
      Note: All the papers by H. H. Dale which are quoted here are reprinted in
      his *Adventures in Physiology* (see ref. 90 in the list).

XXI

CHEMICAL AND MOLECULAR BASIS OF NERVE ACTIVITY*

David Nachmansohn

A. NECESSITY OF CHEMICAL REACTIONS FOR THE GENERATION OF BIOELECTRIC CURRENTS

(1) Ion Movements.—A characteristic feature of living cells is the unequal distribution of ions between the interior and the outer environment. K ions are present in high concentrations inside cells, usually ten to twenty times as high as in the surrounding fluid; the reverse is true for the Na ion concentration. Conducting cells are endowed with special ability to use these ionic concentrations gradients for generating electric currents. In a fluid medium ions must be the carriers of these currents.

Bernstein's 'membrane theory' assumed that nerve fibers are surrounded by a semipermeable membrane, selectively permeable to K.[1] The resting membrane is charged positively on the outside and negatively on the inside. The active region of the membrane becomes permeable to all ions and is thereby depolarized: currents are generated and stimulate adjacent points; the same process takes place there. In this way successive parts of the membrane are activated and the impulse is propagated along the axon. Measurements of the membrane potential, carried out with electrodes inserted into Squid giant axons, revealed, however, that at the activated point there is not merely a depolarization, but a reversal of polarity.[2,3] During activity the membrane resistance is greatly decreased.[4]

The availability of radioactive ions after the Second World War made it possible to measure quantitatively ion movements in rest and during activity. Rothenberg,[5,6] using the Squid giant axon, found that 4 $\mu\mu$moles of Na per cm.[2] surface per impulse enter the interior. These figures were confirmed by Hodgkin and his associates.[7] An equivalent

*This work was supported in part by the National Science Foundation Grant No. G-12901, and by the Division of Research Grants and Fellowships of the National Institutes of Health, Grant No. B-400 U.S. Public Health Service.

amount of K moves to the outside.[8,9] The analysis of ion movements have been extended by the Cambridge group by the use of the so-called 'voltage clamp' method, worked out by Cole.[10,11] There is at first a strong, rapid and transitory increase of Na conductance, coinciding with the rising phase of the action current. Subsequently, there is a much smaller increase of K conductance; K moves to the outside during the falling phase.[12]

Recently, Whittam and Guinnebault,[13] in experiments on the isolated single electroplax of *Electrophorus electricus* found an efflux of 5 to 8 $\mu\mu$moles K per cm.[2] per impulse. This figure is very close to that obtained with the Squid giant axon. The results suggest that the ion movements underlying electric currents, which so far had been demonstrated only on special types of invertebrate axons, may be a process similar in all excitable membranes.

We may then consider as reasonably well established that during activity ions move across the conducting membrane and that the membrane conductance changes in a specific way during activity. This immediately raises the question as to the mechanism which is responsible for the changes and which controls these special ion movements across conducting membranes. Some special events must take place in the conducting membrane by which the ionic concentration gradients are used for the generation of electric currents. Two views confront each other: (1) conduction is a purely physical process[7,12,14] and (2) specific chemical reactions change Na conductance and control the ion movements.[15-20]

(2) The Initial Heat.—The view of a purely physical process has become untenable by the recent measurements of A. V. Hill and his associates on the initial heat production. In the early measurements of A. V. Hill and his associates the initial heat production was found to be rather small. Hodgkin[7] attributed this small effect to the mixing of Na and K. Recently, however, Hill and his associates[21] using faster recording instruments than previously available, found that the initial heat production, in *Maja* nerve at 0°C., takes place in two successive phases. In the first phase positive heat is produced averaging in a single impulse about 9 x 10[-6] cal./gm. nerve, or after some necessary corrections, about 14 x 10[-6] cal. This phase coincides roughly with electrical activity. The positive heat is followed by a negative heat produced within 100 to 300 milliseconds, averaging about –7 x 10[-6] cal./gm. nerve or, after correction, about –12 x 10[-6] cal. With the previous method only the difference between the two processes was recorded. The ions are assumed to move across a membrane of about 50 Å thickness; the observed permeability change must take place in this layer and so should chemical events associated with this change. If

the positive initial heat is referred to 1 gm. active material instead of 1 gm. nerve, the value is remarkably high, 2.8 x 10^{-3} cal./gm./impulse, which is the same order of magnitude as the heat produced per g muscle during a single twitch.

The observations on heat production in *Maja* nerve are supported by measurements on the heat released by the discharge of the electric organ of *Torpedo marmorata* (Abbott, Aubert and Fessard[22]); these results are in contradiction to those of Bernstein and Tschermak[23] and are incompatible with their simple explanation and the fundamentally similar views of Hodgkin.[7]

(3) Temperature Coefficient.—Hodgkin and Katz[24] found high temperature coefficients, but this finding was not considered as relevant for the problem of the nature of the conducting process. Recently, Schoffeniels[25,26] has evaluated the Q_{10} and the energy of activation of bioelectric potentials over a wide range of temperature, using an isolated single electroplax of *Electrophorus*. The duration of the spike is a good measure of the change in conductance and pertinent for the question whether or not chemical reactions are required for this process. The logarithm of the reciprocal of the half width of the spike was plotted against the reciprocal of the temperature according to the principle of Arrhenius. The Q_{10} of the action current was found to be around 3.6 and the energy of activation to be 21000 cal./mole.

(4) Integration of Physical and Chemical Events.—Even the physical recordings contradict the assumption of conduction being purely a physical process. During the last two decades chemical reactions have been linked with the elementary processes of conduction. A large amount of evidence has accumulated in favor of an essential role of acetylcholine (ACh) in the generation of bioelectric potentials. This ester has been assumed to be a 'neurohumoral transmitter.' It was believed by many that ACh is secreted from nerve endings, crosses the intercellular space and acts as a mediator of the nerve impulse from the nerve ending to the effector cell, nerve or muscle. This hypothesis, based on data obtained with classical pharmacological methods, appeared, however, unsatisfactory in many respects and in contradiction with electrophysiological results (see e.g. refs. 27, 28). It was necessary to explain the pharmacological observations and to find an interpretation which reconciled the opposing views. A biochemical approach was applied. The sequence of energy transformations associated with nerve activity has been established, the hydrolysis and formation of ACh have been integrated into the metabolic pathways of the nerve cell; the enzymes and proteins of the system have been isolated and their reaction mechanisms analyzed; many relationships have been established between chemical reactions and molecular forces in pro-

teins studied *in vitro* and the physical and electrical events occurring in the intact cell.[15-20] According to the concept which emerged, the release and the action of ACh are *intra*, not *inter*-cellular processes which take place within the axonal and synaptic membranes and which control ion movements. The reaction of the ester with a receptor protein is essential for the conductance changes during activity. A presentation of the development, its various experimental and theoretical aspects, may be found in a recent monograph.[17] The present article summarizes the most essential data and includes more recent facts.

B. ASSOCIATION OF ELECTRICAL WITH ACH-ESTERASE ACTIVITY

(1) Physiologically Significant Features of the Enzyme.—There is a special type of esterase referred to as acetylcholinesterase (ACh-esterase)[29] which has various features different from other esterases and has a relatively high affinity to ACh. Certain properties of the enzyme are of interest to the biochemist, but quite a few features are pertinent for the evaluation and the understanding of the function of ACh in nerve activity. The enzyme is present in high concentrations in conducting tissue throughout the animal kingdom without any exception in all types of nerve: motor and sensory, sympathetic and parasympathetic (co-called "cholinergic" and "adrenergic"), peripheral and central, vertebrate and invertebrate; its presence has also been demonstrated in various types of muscle and in monocellular organisms provided with cilia for movement.[30] No ACh-esterase is present in non-conducting tissue, such as liver or kidney. On the average 5 to 50 mg. of ACh may be split/gm. fiber (fresh weight)/hour.[14,17] However, the actual concentration per g active material is several orders of magnitude higher than these figures indicate. The enzyme is localized essentially in or near the surface membranes, as has been demonstrated in experiments with Squid giant axons. No enzyme is present in the axoplasm, whereas all the enzyme is found in the envelope in which the active membrane must be localized.[31,32] The Ach-esterase is one of the fastest acting enzymes known. One molecule of enzyme may split one molecule of ester in about 40 μseconds.[33] A chemical reaction which plays an essential role in the generation of bioelectric potentials must take place with a speed comparable to that of the electrical process. If the action of ACh on a protein is responsible for the increased Na conductance and the hydrolysis of the ester for the return to the resting state, theory required the hydrolytic process to be very rapid since the increase of Na conductance reaches its peak in about 0.1 millisecond and then starts to decrease. The speed of the enzymatic action satisfies this pertinent prerequisite.

(2) Inseparability of Electrical and Enzyme Activity.—The features described are consistent with the assumption that the activity of the enzyme plays an essential role in conduction. A conclusive evidence requires the demonstration of a direct relationship between enzyme and electrical activity. If the proposed concept is correct, it should be impossible to separate the two activities. It has been shown, with a great variety of procedures applied to a great number of different preparations, that conduction is impossible without ACh-esterase activity. Eserine, a potent, specific and reversible inhibitor of cholinesterase, blocks conduction reversibly.[34] During the second world war a powerful and irreversible type of inhibitors of ACh-esterase became known, the organophosphorus compounds. For many reasons these compounds are particularly useful tools for testing the problem of inseparability of electrical and enzyme activity, mainly due to the irreversible nature of the reaction and the availability of a great variety of compounds of different properties. There are, however, many pitfalls in the use of these compounds. It first seemed possible to destroy the enzyme completely without affecting conduction. Extensive further investigations with alkylphosphates have, however, shown conclusively that it is impossible, under any condition, to separate electrical and enzyme activity. A striking parallelism was established between irreversible block of conduction and decrease of enzyme activity as a function of time and of temperature. Electrical activity in axons ceases when the enzyme activity falls to about 20% of the initial concentration. The five-fold excess of this enzyme above the functional minimum required is in the usual range of excess of many enzyme concentrations. The inseparability of electrical and chemical activity was shown with many types of nerve fibres, motor and sensory, sympathetic and parasympathetic, central and peripheral, vertebrate and invertebrate, and with muscles.[16,17] When enzyme and electrical activity were measured on intact nerve fibers of crab, various factors such as the concentration of the inhibitor, its chemical structure and other properties were found to affect only the speed with which the 20% level is obtained, but not the level itself.[35]

The evidence for the inseparability of the enzyme activity from axonal conduction has been questioned because the concentration of inhibitor applied is several orders of magnitude higher than that used at synaptic junctions.[36] It has, however, been experimentally ascertained that the concentration of compounds found in the interior of the axon at the time at which electrical activity ceases is only a fraction of that applied externally. Structural barriers prevent the penetration of an inhibitor completely or reduce the rate of diffusion to such a degree that only an extremely small fraction of the amount applied outside reaches the active site. This applies even to highly lipid soluble compounds such as DFP. At the time of block of conduction less than 1 μg./gm. axoplasm was found in the interior, whereas the outside concentration was several hundred or a thousand times as high. The experiments show the irrelevance of the outside concentration. The pertinent fact is the demonstration of the interdependence of the two processes, i.e., the disappearance of electrical activity when the enzyme activity, measured in the intact nerve, falls to 20% of the initial value. Recently, a new and striking confirmation has been obtained by Dettbarn[37-39] in experiments on Ranvier nodes of a single frog sciatic nerve fiber. Electron microscope studies show that the conducting membrane at these nodes is covered only by a very thin and apparently porous structure.[40] On exposure to 300 μg./ml. of eserine conduction is blocked in about 30 seconds; using the whole frog sciatic nerve block occurs in 30 minutes at a concentration of 5 mg./ml. By removing inactive material, fat, connective tissue, etc. the potency has increased by a factor of 1000. With 30 to 40 μg./ml. of eserine block of conduction is achieved within minutes.

If the action of ACh increases Na conductance and the return to the resting state is due to hydrolysis of the ester, a decrease in the rate of removal should increase the spike height and amplitude before blocking conduction. Several factors, however, complicate the picture. The postulated effect will take place only at a certain level of enzyme activity. Below the minimum compatible with electrical activity, conduction fails; in presence of an excess no change of the spike potential would be expected. The appropriate level of enzyme activity may be in a narrow range and the period of time during which this level is maintained may be short. In preparations where the spike is the resultant of the electrical activity of many fibers the effect may be masked. Some inhibitors of the enzyme have a high affinity also to the receptor protein and this factor may modify the picture. However, on applying 1.5 to 10 μg./ml. of eserine to Ranvier nodes of single frog sciatic fibers, Dettbarn did indeed observe a marked increase of spike height and amplitude.[38,39] Paraoxon produced similar and sometimes even stronger effects.[39] A markedly increased spike height and amplitude was also observed in strips of frog sartorius muscle on exposure to either eserine or Paraxon.[41]

(3) Electrical Activity Restored by a Specific Chemical Reaction.— Recently, a new type of evidence has been obtained for the essentiality of ACh-esterase in electrical activity. If the irreversible inhibition of the enzyme by organophosphorus compounds is responsible for the irreversible block of electrical activity in conducting membranes, as proposed by the author in 1946, then electrical activity should reap-

pear if the enzyme activity is restored by a chemical reaction. A potent and highly specific compound has been developed, pyridine-2-aldoxime methiodide (PAM), which reactivates ACh-esterase inhibited by certain organophosphorus compounds by displacing the phosphoryl group from the enzyme (see section D, 2). PAM is a quaternary ammonium ion and lipid insoluble. It will therefore not reach the conducting membrane, as will be discussed later. However, benzoyl-pyridine oxime methiodide is somewhat lipid soluble and nearly as potent as PAM.

Strips of frog sartorius muscle were exposed to Paraoxon until irreversible block was achieved. When the strips were bathed in a solution containing the benzoyl derivative a restoration of electrical activity was obtained.[41] The experiments were in some respects not yet fully satisfactory, but the essential principle was established: electrical activity of a conducting membrane, abolished by potent inhibitors of ACh-esterase which phosphorylate the enzyme, was restored by a compound which specifically reactivates phosphorylated ACh-esterase.

C. SEQUENCE OF ENERGY TRANSFORMATIONS. INTEGRATION OF ACH INTO METABOLIC PATHWAYS

(1) ACh-esterase in Electric Organs.—Knowledge of the sequence of energy transformations is essential for the understanding of the biochemistry of cellular function.[42] However, the chemical reactions controlling ion movements across conducting membranes during activity take place on a scale which in ordinary nerves is not readily measurable. A unique tool for studying chemical mechanisms underlying electrical activity are the electric organs of fish. These organs, the most powerful bioelectric generators created by nature, are highly specialized in their function. Here the magnitude of the energy transformations, of chemical reactions linked to electrical activity, are in the range of measurement. The electrical characteristics of the cellular unit, the electroplax, are similar to those in nerve and muscle cells; it is only their arrangement in series by which the discharge becomes so powerful. The so-called "electric eel" *Electrophorus electricus,* has the most powerful organs with a discharge of about 600 volts and is for many reasons a most suitable material for many studies. The electroplax of this species has both synaptic and conducting membranes. The response to neural and direct stimulation can be readily distinguished. The use of these fish for the study of the chemical basis of bioelectric currents, initiated by the writer in 1937, proved to be invaluable for the development of the field.

The strong electric organs of *Torpedo* and *Electrophorus* contain a strikingly high concentration of ACh-esterase: They are capable of hydrolyzing 2 to 4 gm. of ACh per gm. tissue (fresh weight) per hour. This is particularly remarkable in view of the high water and low protein content of the tissue, 93 and 2%, respectively. The actual concentration is actually several orders of magnitude higher since the enzyme again is localized in an extremely small fraction of the tissue. Such an extraordinary concentration of a specific enzyme in an organ highly specialized for generating electric currents at once suggests the possibility of a direct relationship with the primary function. The electric organ of *Electrophorus* has unique structural features which permit the correlation of function (electrical activity) with enzyme activity.[17] A direct proportionality was found to exist in this organ between voltage per cm and enzyme concentration.[43,44] The organs offer an exceptionally favorable material for preparing highly active and purified enzyme solutions.[45,46] These preparations permitted the study of the properties of the enzyme protein and the analysis of the molecular forces in the active site.

(2) Discovery of Choline Acetylase.—The release of energy by the breakdown of phosphocreatine during the discharge of *Electrophorus* is more than adequate to account for the total electrical energy released.[47,48] It was assumed, on the basis of analogy with events known to take place in muscular contraction, that ATP hydrolysis would precede that of phosphocreatine. But it appeared unlikely for many reasons that ATP would be directly associated with the elementary process as in muscular contraction. If the action of ACh and its hydrolysis are responsible for the primary event, then the free energy of ATP hydrolysis should be used, at least partly, for the resynthesis for ACh, i.e., for the acetylation of choline; another part may be used for the restoration of the ionic concentration gradients.

The assumption proved to be correct. An enzyme system, choline acetylase, was extracted in 1943, from brain and electric tissue which in the presence of ATP was capable of synthesizing ACh in solution.[49] Previously Quastel and his associates had shown the synthesis of ACh in respiring brain slices.[50,51] By the discovery of choline acetylase the first enzymatic acetylation was achieved in solution and the first demonstration that the energy of ATP hydrolysis may be used for acylation reactions; it suggested that the energy of ATP, until then linked only with glycolysis, may be used for biosynthesis in general. It was also found, in the same year, that the system requires a coenzyme, since it became rapidly inactivated on dialysis.[52] These observations opened the way for the study of acetylating mechanisms in general and during the following decade this became one of the most active fields in biochemistry.

The coenzyme contains pantothenic acid and is used for acylation reactions in general.[53] It has, therefore, been referred to by Lipmann as coenzyme A (CoA). Its functional group is an SH group.[54] The acetylation reaction proceeds in at least two enzymatic steps. First, acetate is activated by ATP, in an S_N2 reaction, and forms acetyl adenylate (or acetylphosphate in bacterial cells). The acyl group is then transferred in an enzymatic substitution reaction to CoA. These two steps are presumably catalyzed by the same enzyme. The acetyl group is then transferred from CoA to a receptor by an enzyme specific for the latter. Choline acetylase has been redefined as the enzyme transferring the acetyl group from CoA to choline.[55] The enzyme has been found to be present in a great variety of conducting tissue, motor and sensory axons, vertebrate and invertebrate, central and peripheral nerve tissue, and in muscle. Reports about its absence in sensory fibers (dorsal roots) were due to inadequate techniques.[16,17]

(3) *Depolarizing Action of ACh.*—The significance of the fact, that ATP is used for ACh synthesis, for understanding the chemical basis of nerve activity is the evidence that in the sequence of energy transformations the hydrolysis of ACh precedes the other chemical reactions. It could be argued that theoretically another chemical reaction may precede that of ACh with the receptor. Such an assumption is contradicted by the fact that ACh has a depolarizing action. This was first proposed by Monnier and Dubuisson[56] and Cowan[57] and experimentally demonstrated on Torpedo in 1939.[58] ACh is the only substance so far known which has the prerequisites to be associated with the conductance changes in a conducting membrane during activity.

(4) *Sensory Receptors.*—Both cholinesterase and choline acetylase are present in sensory fibers; inhibitors of cholinesterase block conduction in dorsal roots[59] and other sensory fibers in the same way as in motor fibers and thus show the functional necessity of the enzyme for conduction in both types of fibers. ACh and analogue compounds activate sensory receptor endings just as well as effector cells at synaptic junctions.[60-62] Recently, Loewenstein and Molins[63] determined the cholinesterase distribution in Pacinian corpuscles obtained from the mesentery and pancreas of cat. By far the largest fraction of the enzyme is localized in the axon, the nerve ending and in the thin hull of core structure which surrounds the ending, precisely where the generation of electrical activity of this receptor organ has been shown to take place. Per ending 0.7×10^9 molecules of ACh per millisecond may be hydrolyzed. This activity is remarkably close to the figure obtained for a single motor end plate of frog sartorius muscle, which is 1.6×10^9 molecules per millisecond.[63] Thus, ACh may have the same physiological role in the generation of bioelectric potentials

in sensory receptors as in motor end plates. In the former there is no synaptic junction which makes it difficult to picture the release and the action of the ester other than intracellularly.

(5) *The Elementary Process.*—The picture of the role of the ACh system in the elementary process which has emerged from the data accumulated may be described as follows (Fig. 1): In the resting condition ACh (o−) is in a bound and inactive form. It may be tentatively called the storage form (S). Excitation of the membrane, by current or any other stimulus, leads to a dissociation of the complex; ACh is released. The free ester acts upon a receptor protein (R) and this action upon the receptor is essential for the change of ionic conductance of the membrane and thus the generation of the bioelectric currents. Some facts to be discussed later suggest that ACh may act by changing the configuration of the receptor protein.

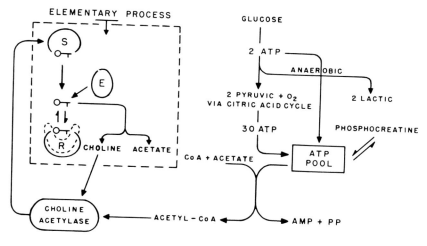

Fig. 1. Schematic presentation of the sequence of energy transformations associated with conduction, and integration of the acetylcholine system into the metabolic pathways of the nerve cell. The tentative picture of the elementary process is described in the text.

The complex between ACh and the receptor is in a dynamic equilibrium with the free ester and the receptor. The free ester is susceptible to attack by ACh-esterase (E). The enzymatic hydrolysis of ACh will permit the receptor to return to its resting condition. Na conductance returns to its original level. Thus the action of the enzyme leads to the immediate recovery and ends the cycle of the elementary process. It is the speed of this inactivation process which makes rapid restoration of the membrane conductance possible and permits the nerve to respond to the next stimulus within a millisecond or less. All these events, which control the ion movements during activity, must take place within the structure which functions as a barrier for these ions in rest. The further recovery leads to the resynthesis of ACh by choline acetylase and the other components of the acetylating system. At this point, the cyclic processes known for other cells enter the picture.

The evidence summarized support the view that ACh is the 'specific operative substance' in the elementary process of conduction of nerve impulses in the sense applied by Meyerhof to the role of ATP in muscular contraction. Just as the latter is inseparably associated with motility, ACh is essential for the primary events generating bioelectric currents in conducting membranes throughout the animal kingdom. Obviously many additional factors and membrane constituents must be important, about which at present virtually nothing is known. Suggestions as to the precise mechanism of action must, therefore, clearly be only tentative. This, of course, cannot be construed as an argument against the essential role proposed.

D. MOLECULAR FORCES IN ACH-ESTERASE AND THEIR RELATION TO FUNCTION

During the last decade pertinent information has been obtained about the molecular forces acting in the proteins of the ACh system. In several instances it was possible to establish relationships between the reactions of the proteins in solution and the function of the intact cell. Four proteins, as we have seen, are directly tied to the function of ACh. Three of them, the two enzymes and, recently, the receptor protein[65-67] have been isolated and are available for analysis in purified form in solution. A molecule such as ACh has only a limited number of possibilities of reacting with a protein; the molecular forces acting between the small molecule and the macromolecules of the system must, therefore, be similar. Relatively small modifications in the surface of the protein may lead to important changes in function. Information obtained by the analysis of molecular forces in one protein will, therefore provide valuable information for an understanding of the reactions with other proteins. ACh-esterase is for many reasons the most suitable protein of the system for such an analysis.

(1) Active Surface of ACh-esterase; Mechanism of the Hydrolytic Process.—The enzymatic process is usually formulated as follows:

$$E + S \rightleftharpoons ES \rightarrow E + \text{products}$$

where E is the enzyme, S the substrate, ES the enzyme-substrate (Michaelis-Menten) complex. Analysis of the molecular forces acting in the active surface of the enzyme was carried out with a great variety of substrates and inhibitors; it has revealed that the surface has two functionally and spatially separated subsites: an "anionic" site and an "esteratic" site. The former attracts the cationic group of the substrates by Coulombic and van der Waals' forces. The esteratic site has an acidic and a basic or nucleophilic group, symbolized by H and G. The nucleophilic group forms a covalent bond with the electrophilic carbon of the carbonyl group.[68]

ANIONIC SITE   ESTERATIC SITE

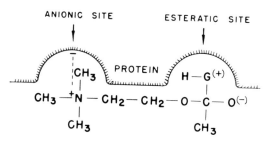

Fig. 2. Schematic presentation of interaction between the active groups of acetylcholinesterase and its substrate (the Michaelis-Menten complex).

The following mechanism have been proposed for the hydrolytic process:[69]

$$H\text{—}G + R'O\text{—}C\text{=}O \rightleftharpoons R'O\text{—}\underset{R}{\overset{H\text{—}G^{(+)}}{C}}\text{—}O^{(-)} \rightleftharpoons \underset{R}{\overset{G^{(+)}}{C}}\text{—}O^{(-)} + R'OH$$

$$(A) \qquad (B)$$

$$H\text{—}\underset{\cdot\cdot}{O}: + \underset{R}{\overset{G^{(+)}}{C}}\text{—}O^{(-)} \rightleftharpoons HO\text{—}\underset{R}{\overset{H\text{—}G^{(+)}}{C}}\text{—}O^{(-)} \rightleftharpoons H\text{—}G + HO\text{—}\underset{R}{C}\text{=}O$$

$$(B) \qquad (C)$$

The alcohol is eliminated from the enzyme-substrate complex by an electronic shift and as a result of the first phase an acetylated enzyme is formed. This reacts with H_2O to form acetate thus regenerating the enzyme. Experimental evidence in support of this mechanism has been offered in many ways. Detailed discussions may be found in several reviews.[16,17,19,70]

(2) Mechanism of "Nerve Gas" Action and Development of a Powerful Antidote.—Knowledge of the molecular forces has greatly helped

the understanding of various aspects of nerve function. An illustration is the analysis of the mechanism of the action of nerve gas and the development of an extremely potent antidote. Certain organophosphorus compounds are widely used as insecticides. Some of them are volatile and are extremely toxic. To this group belong the famous nerve gases such as DFP, sarin, tabun etc., the most powerful chemical warfare agents ever developed. The compounds have the general for-

mula $\begin{array}{c}RO \\ RO\end{array} \!\!\diagdown\!\!{P}\!\!\diagup\!\!\begin{array}{c} O \\ X \end{array},$ where X is an acidic group. P-X can be readily

split by esterases. All esterases are irreversibly inhibited by the action of these compounds. Their lethal action, however, is due to the inhibition of ACh-esterase, i.e., to a specific chemical lesion.[71] The mechanism of alkylphosphate action was explained as a nucleophilic attack of the enzyme on the phosphorus atom in an $S_N 2$ reaction.[72] Instead of an acetylated enzyme, the physiological intermediary, a phosphorylated enzyme is formed. But whereas the acylated form reacts extremely fast, within a fraction of a millisecond, with water to form acetate and restored enzyme, the phosphorylated enzyme does not react with water at all or extremely slowly, requiring days or weeks. The enzyme is inactivated and because loss of vital function death ensues.

Once the mechanism of alkylphosphate poisoning was recognized, it seemed possible to reverse the inhibition of the enzyme by a nucleophilic group which would attack the phosphorus atom and remove the phosphoryl group from the enzyme in a displacement reaction. Several nucleophilic agents were found to reactivate the enzyme. With hydroxylamine for example, in 0.7 M concentration, it is possible to restore around 50% of the enzyme activity inhibited by tetraethylpyrophosphate in about 5 hours.[73] By attaching the active nucleophilic group to a cationic quaternary nitrogen group at a proper atomic distance the attack on the P atom should be greatly promoted. The cationic group of the molecule would be attracted to the anionic site and the nucleophilic atom would thus be directed towards the P atom. This would be analogous to the fact that ACh is a greatly superior substrate for ACh-esterase compared to ethyl acetate, since the presence of the cationic group increases the force of binding by more than 1000-fold, and thus helps the compound to be attracted and oriented on the protein surface. The first compound of this type, nicotinohydroxamic acid methiodide, was many times better as a reactivator of alkylphosphate inhibited ACh-esterase than hydroxylamine.[74,75] With the hydroxamic acid group in the 2-position (picolinohydroxamic acid methiodide) the reactivating power increased further by a factor of

10.[76] By far the most potent reactivator, however, turned out to be pyridine-2-aldoxime methiodide (PAM). When this compound was tested, its ability to reactivate alkylphosphate inhibited ACh-esterase *in vitro* was found to be about 1 million times as high as that of hydroxylamine.[77] The active molecule has the following structure:

$$\text{I}^-\ \underset{\overset{|}{CH_3}}{\overset{+}{N}}\ \ C\overset{H}{\diagup}\ N\ O^-$$

It may be mentioned that shortly after the description of PAM in this laboratory, a series of oximes was described which had been synthesized independently.[78] One of them was PAM. The authors recognized the improvement of the oximes over the hydroxamic acids, but they did not recognize the extraordinary reactivating power of this particular oxime compared with that of other active oximes.

When PAM was applied to animals, it proved to be an extremely potent antidote.[79] In the first experiment, 20 mice were exposed to a 100% sure lethal dose (LD_{100}) of alkylphosphate. Ten were treated with PAM, all survived, all other were dead within half an hour. In combination with atropine, which protects the receptor protein, animals survived ten- to twenty-fold lethal doses of nerve gas.[80]

It is generally agreed that respiratory failure is the principal cause of death in alkylphosphate poisoning. In most cases the action is predominantly peripheral, although with some alkylphosphates there are also marked central effects. An outstanding early symptom is the paralysis of the diaphragm. It appeared, therefore, logical to test the cholinesterase activity in the diaphragm of PAM treated animals. A marked reactivation of the cholinesterase in this tissue has been demonstrated in animals exposed to alkylphosphate and treated with PAM.[81] In brain the first experiments on the reactivation of cholinesterase by PAM were inconclusive.[82] Studies on the effect of PAM on the electroencephalogram of rabbits exposed to sarin suggested some action on the brain.[83] Recently, Rosenberg,[84] using chloroform extraction procedures in which some earlier inadequacies were eliminated, found a significant reactivation of cholinesterase by PAM in various brain centers of the rabbit. Reactivation was not equally strong in all parts but seemed most marked in the pons, the region of area postrema and the remainder of the medulla. The observations show that the principal action of PAM is due to the reactivation of the enzyme activity. A direct reaction with some of the alkylphosphate does also occur and this factor may in some cases contribute to the antidotal action. However, the reaction is very slow, especially with some of the alkylphosphates such as paraoxon, and therefore inefficient so that this cannot be the principal factor of the antidotal power of PAM.

A wide variety of alkylphosphates are known; the properties of the phosphoryl group attached to the enzyme vary greatly. The ability of PAM to reactivate the enzyme attacking the phosphoryl group depends naturally on the structure and properties of the latter. Some will be readily detached by PAM, others only poorly and some not at all. The phosphorylated enzyme formed after the reaction with tabun or octomethylpyrophosphoramide (OMPA) (when the latter has been transformed in the organism into an active form) is not reactivated by PAM at all. Consequently, it should be expected, if the theory proposed is correct, that in those cases PAM is not an antidote. This is indeed the case. PAM has only a very small protective effect after poisoning by tabun and none against OMPA (81). The slight protection against tabun must be attributed to a direct reaction in the blood between drug and PAM, since this reaction is relatively fast, in any case faster than with some other alkylphosphates tested. These negative results support the view that the antidotal properties of PAM must be attributed to the reactivation of the phosphoryl enzyme and not to a direct reaction with alkylphosphate.

In order to explain the extraordinary power of PAM to reactivate alkylphosphate inhibited enzyme, Wilson and his associates undertook a systematic study of the "geometry" of the enzyme. They prepared a series of derivatives of phenyltrimethyl ammonium ions to obtain information about the degree of binding in terms of the respective positions of various atoms of the inhibitor and of the enzyme. It turned out that PAM has a perfect complementary conformation to the phosphorylated enzyme.[85-87] When the quaternary nitrogen is attached, through Coulombic forces, to the anionic site of the enzyme, the nucleophilic oxygen atom of the oxime is exactly one bond length away from the P atom. If the oxime groups is in the 4-position, the compound is still a very good reactivator, although about 40 times poorer; but in the 3-position, it is virtually inactive. Both results are in agreement with theory derived from these studies.

In view of the molecular complementariness of PAM to the phosphorylated ACh-esterase it is to be expected that this compound exerts the extraordinary power of reactivation only in the case of this particular enzyme. This proved to be correct. The reactivation of phosphorylated serum esterase by PAM is much less efficient. For phosphorylated chymotrypsin PAM is a very poor reactivator. Moreover, there is no difference between a 2-, 3-, and 4-position of the oxime. These facts are additional evidence that the reactivating power of PAM is not due to an especially high intrinsic power of the oxygen atom to attack the P atom, but to molecular complementariness and to the special promotion of the reaction by the cationic nitrogen located in the most favorable atomic distance.

PAM was tested on a large scale by Namba and Hiraki[88] on humans suffering from acute alkylphosphate poisoning in Japan where insecticides (parathion) are widely used. The antidotal power was striking. Many lives were saved. Other dramatic recoveries in severe poisoning of humans have been described elsewhere (e.g., ref. 89).

In view of the molecular complementariness of PAM to phosphorylated ACh-esterase, the principal features of the antidote can hardly be changed without impairing the antidotal power. However, some increase of effectiveness may be achieved by additional binding forces. Bisquaternary derivatives of 4-PAM for instance, were found to be more active in the test tube for the reactivation of phosphorylated enzyme in vitro and as an antidote.[90,91]

The development of PAM is the outcome of the systematic studies of the proteins and enzymes of the ACh system. It illustrates the value of the biochemical approach for the understanding of the physiology and pharmacology of nerve function. A more detailed discussion may be found in a recent monograph.[17] The results described formed the basis of much interesting work in many laboratories during the last few years and a huge literature already exists about this problem.

E. THE ACh RECEPTOR

(1) Demonstration of its Existence as a Distinct Cell Constituent.— The analysis of the molecular forces acting in the proteins of the ACh system has been helpful in the interpretation of problems of conduction, particularly concerning the interaction between ACh and the receptor. During the analysis of the role of van der Waals' forces acting in the enzyme-substrate complex formation a remarkable fact was observed: if one substitutes the protons of an ammonium ion by methyl groups, each of the first three methyl groups increase the *binding* by a factor of about 7. The fourth methyl group is without effect. Similar results were obtained with hydroxyethyl ammonium ion: the fourth alkyl (third methyl) group does not increase the binding.[92]

In striking contrast the difference in *enzymatic activity* is extremely marked between tertiary and quaternary nitrogen derivatives; the rate of formation of acetyl enzyme by ACh was found to be about ten times as high with ACh as substrate as with its tertiary analogue, dimethylaminoethyl acetate. A similar difference was observed in the activity of choline acetylase towards choline and its tertiary analogue, dimethylethanolamine. The latter compound is acetylated at a rate only 8% of that of the former.[93,94]

The question arises as to the significance of these striking differences of enzyme activity due to the presence of one extra methyl group. The binding forces, as we have seen, are not increased. The quaternary nitrogen is a saturated group and is less reactive than a tertiary nitrogen because at neutral pH the latter is in equilibrium with a small concentration of conjugated base which has a free pair of electrons. Chemical reactivity then cannot be the answer and another explanation must be found. A clue may be the tetrahedral structure of the quaternary nitrogen group. Such a structure is more or less spherical. If a molecule like this is attracted to a protein surface, the fourth alkyl will not be able to have direct contact since it is oriented in a direction away from the protein. One way in which the protein could be simultaneously in contact with all the methyl groups would be by enveloping the molecule. possibly the configuration of the protein changes during the active state in the enzymatic process.

This possibility has found experimental support in studies on the enthalpies and entropies of activation, $\triangle S^*$ and $\triangle H^*$, of the ester of ethanolamine and its methylated derivatives.[95] Substitution of the first two protons by methyl groups did not greatly change the activation energies. But the third additional methyl group has a very pronounced effect. The $\triangle H^*$, of the hydrolysis of ACh is about $-14,000$ cal. as compared with about -8000 cal. of that of the tertiary analogue. This would be less favorable for the hydrolysis of the quaternary ester. But the $\triangle S^*$, is extremely favorable for the quaternary compared to that of the tertiary compound. The value for the tertiary is -7 to -9 entropy units, whereas it is strongly positive with the quaternary, about $+15$ to $+25$ e. u. This extraordinary difference of the entropy of activation produced by the presence of the extra methyl group can be explained in terms of rearrangement of the protein molecule, i.e., a change in configuration.

A change of configuration of proteins was proposed by Meyer[96] as a possible basis of the change of permeability to ions during conduction by a rearrangement of acidic and basic groups. Does ACh produce such an effect when reacting with the receptor? A receptor has long been postulated. Its existence as a cell constituent distinct from ACh-esterase has been experimentally demonstrated by a combination of two methods, which permitted a distinction to be made between compounds acting predominantly on the receptor and those acting on the enzyme or on both.[97] Segments of electric tissue, containing one to three rows of electroplax, were isolated. The effects upon the electrical activity of compounds acting on the ACh system were measured with microelectrodes inserted into the interior of a cell. At the same time the ACh activity was determined on the row of intact cells. Some compounds, such as ACh, carbamylcholine, procaine, and d-tubocurarine block conduction without affecting the esterase. The enzyme activity remains at a high level in the presence of these compounds, even at a 200-fold concentration above that producing block. Consequently, the blocking action cannot be explained by the esterase but must be attributed to the effect upon a different but similar cell constituent. With other compounds the enzyme activity is at quite a low level when electrical activity stops. In these cases the blocking action on conduction may be attributed, either partly or entirely, to the decrease of enzyme activity to a level incompatible with electrical activity.[16,17]

   (2) Receptor Activators and Inhibitors.—The compounds acting on the receptor may be divided into two distinctly different types according to the way in which they affect electrical activity. One type blocks conduction without depolarization, the other blocks and simultaneously depolarizes the membrane. In one case the barrier to ion movements evidently remains unchanged when activity stops, in the other case it is reduced. Quaternary compounds, such as ACh, carbamyl-

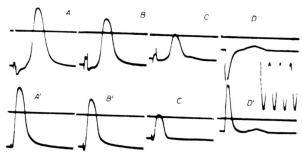

Fig. 3. Effect of Prostigmine on the electrical activity of the electroplax of *Electrophorus electricus* to stimulation. Experimental arrangement in this and the next figure: The tip of one microelectrode is fixed on the outside of the electroplax as close as possible to the innervated membrane; the other electrode is inserted through the non-innervated face and fixed just opposite the first electrode. The upper horizontal line appearing in the oscilloscope corresponds to the potential difference between the two electrodes as long as both are outside the cell, i.e., the difference is zero. As soon as the second electrode is inserted, the lower line appears. The distance between the two lines indicates the potential difference in rest between the inside and outside, usually about 80 mv. A′ to D′ direct stimulation. A,A′ control. B,B′ 1 minute, C,C′ 2 minutes, D,D′ 9 minutes after addition of Prostigmine. At the block of conduction resting potential is strongly decreased. Stimulation: 25/second. Calibration: 1000 cycles and 100 mv.

choline, decamethonium and others, usually belong to the latter category. Most tertiary analogues, as for example procaine and tetracaine, block but do not depolarize. An interesting example of how the presence of the extra methyl group profoundly changes the effect on electrical activity is the striking difference between the effect of Prostigmine and that of its tertiary analogue: the quaternary compound blocks with depolarization, the same molecular structure minus the extra group blocks, but does not depolarize (Figs. 3 and 4).

If one associates the transient change of permeability in conducting tissues with the reaction between ACh and the receptor, one must assume that ACh not only combines with the receptor but produces a simultaneous change. This was postulated by Clark.[98] We have therefore introduced the distinction between receptor activators which ef-

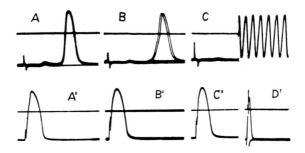

Fig. 4. Effect of the tertiary analogue of Prostigmine. All arrangements as in Fig. 3. A-C neural, A'-D' direct stimulation. A,A' control B,B' 2 minutes, C,C' 7½ minutes, D'176 minutes after addition of compound (1 mg./ml.). Potential difference between inside and outside remains the same. 124 minutes before the last recording 10 μg./ml. of carbamylcholine were added, but had no effect.

fect this change, and receptor inhibitors which combine with the receptor but do not produce a change. The latter apparently block the access of ACh to the active surface. These two different types of interaction are analogous to those in enzyme chemistry where it is possible to distinguish between enzyme substrates and inhibitors.

One may visualize that the receptor protein in the active state undergoes a change in configuration comparable to that suggested to occur in the enzyme during activity. Such an action may be associated with the change of conductance taking place in the active membrane. One possible picture would be that positively charged amino groups may form an obstacle for the rapid passage of Na+. A small, even very limited change in a long protein chain may remove a strategically located positive charge by a few A, thereby greatly increasing the rate of flow. Folding or unfolding of a small section of a helical or non-helical portion of a protein may be enough for such a process and thus act as a trigger. The data available indicate that the action of one molecule of ACh may permit the passage of about 1000 Na ions. This is a relationship of an order of magnitude consistent with that which is expected for a trigger process in which the controlling energy required must be small.

Since the receptor inhibitor must react with the same receptor site as a receptor activator, it follows that if an inhibitor is applied first at the proper concentration it should prevent the activation of the receptor by the subsequent addition of an activator. It has been found that depolarization by the receptor activator carbamylcholine is antagonized by either procaine or d-tubocurarine or the tertiary analogue of Prostigmine. Since the receptor inhibitors and activators are competitive, the effect of one should be overcome by increased concentrations of the other and this proved indeed to be the case.[99,100]

The features required for a molecule to be a receptor activator are still poorly understood. This is analogous to the situation with enzyme inhibitors and substrates. A great variety of compounds may be inhibitors, but only a few have the specifications for being a substrate. The cationic nitrogen group seems to be an important factor in promoting activation, the carbonyl group another although less essential one.[16,17]

(3) Isolated Single Electroplax Preparation.—In the last three years Schoffeniels developed a method in which a single isolated electroplax is used to study factors involved in electrical activity.[99-101,26] A single electroplax is dissected and kept between a nylon sheet with a window adjusted to the dimensions of the cell and a grid consisting of nylon threads. The cell is placed between two chambers in such a way that it separates two pools of fluid. Only one face is innervated and has a conducting membrane, which has a rectangular shape and is, therefore, uniquely suitable for the study of ion movements between the two chambers across the membrane. The rates of flux across the two types of membranes can be measured separately by the use of radioactive material. The preparation eliminates many disturbing factors, especially various structural barriers which were an obstacle to the study of ion flux and of physical and chemical effects on electrical manifestations.

With the new preparation the effects of ACh and related compounds are obtained at low concentrations and are readily reversible.[102-104] ACh and decamethonium act in concentrations of less than 0.5 μg./ml., carbamylcholine in about 3-5 μg./ml. (Fig. 5). Investigations have been initiated on the flux rates of Na and K ions under different conditions across innervated and non-innervated membranes. The data on the rate of K efflux/cm.^{2}/impulse have been mentioned before.[13]

(4) Isolation and Identification of the ACh Receptor Protein.—The experimental evidence for the existence of a receptor as a distinct cell constituent raised the question of whether it is a separate protein and whether its isolation is possible. Chagas and his co-workers have initiated the isolation of curare receptors.[105-107] They injected a radioactive curare-like substance into the electric organ of *Electrophorus*

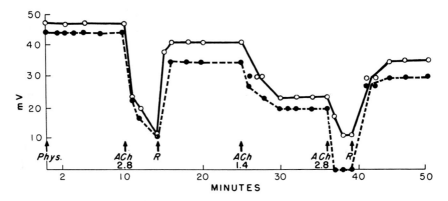

Fig. 5. Reversible action of ACh on the electrical activity of an isolated single electroplax.

The compound was added to the pool bathing the innervated membrane. The response (in mV) to direct (•---•) and in direct (○——○) stimulation was recorded with an oscilloscope using extracellular electrodes. Physostigmine (Phys.), 10 μg./ml., was added 10 minutes prior to ACh and was always present when the cell was exposed to the ester. The figures below ACh indicate its concentration in mμmoles/ml. (2.8 = 0.5 μg./ml.).

and then prepared extracts which were dialyzed against distilled water. The radioactive compound was bound to a component or components present in the extract. However, complex formation was markedly reduced by very dilute salt solutions (.02 M). This and various other facts raised the question of whether the macromolecules responsible for binding are the physiological ACh receptor. Since curare has two cationic nitrogens, it is possible that Coulombic and van der Waals' forces led to complex formation with a number of unspecific macromolecules of the extract, not identical with the ACh receptor. The problem has been investigated by Ehrenpreis[65-67] with a different procedure. Tissue extracts of electric organ have been subjected to ammonium sulfate fractionation. This procedure eliminated other components which were found to react with curare such as nucleic acids and chondroitin sulfuric acid.[108] One of the proteins in the fractions obtained is precipitated by curare. This complex is not solubilized by prolonged dialysis even at high ionic strength contrary to the other macromolecules. Curare has two phenolic hydroxyl groups which apparently form hydrogen bonds with this particular protein. At pH 9, at which these groups are dissociated, the complex is solublized. The complex may also be dissociated by urea. The protein has been obtained essentially as a single component according to electrophoretic analysis and in analytical ultracentrifugation. Its molecular weight is about 100,000.

The identification of the protein with the receptor protein offered a crucial and challenging problem which does not exist in enzyme purification. Instrumental for this identification was the monocellular electroplax preparation: its sensitivity towards various compounds reacting with the ACh system is high and small variations of the chemical structure may greatly modify the effect on the electrical response. The reaction offers, therefore, a good indication as to the effectiveness of closely related structures to react with the receptor. A large series of tertiary, mono- and diquaternary nitrogen derivatives related to ACh were tested as to their affinity to this protein by equilibrium dialysis according to Klotz,[109] under strict control of pH and ionic strength. Great variations of affinity were found. When the affinity of a compound to the protein was compared with its effectiveness to block electrical activity of the monocellular electroplax preparation, a striking parallelism was obtained.[102,103] No other protein had similar affinities, if any, to these compounds. Other nonprotein macromolecules have been excluded by a variety of procedures.[66,67] It thus became apparent that the isolated protein was indeed the ACh receptor protein. There is, however, a marked difference between receptor activators and inhibitors as to binding in relation to the strength of action. The binding of activators is weaker than that of inhibitors. This is not surprising and comparable to the situation prevailing in the interaction of enzymes with substrates and inhibitors. Strong inhibitors have usually very much higher affinities than substrates. For a rapid interaction a high binding strength may be detrimental.

(5) Inseparable Association of Electrical Activity with Receptor Protein.—A striking and pertinent demonstration for the inseparable association of electrical activity with the action of ACh is the recent finding of Ehrenpreis and Kellock[110] of the relatively high specificity of the reaction of local anesthetics with the receptor protein. The structure of procaine, tetracaine, and other local anesthetics is analogous to that of ACh (Fig. 6). However, the local anesthetics are

tertiary derivatives. The neutral form is lipid soluble. Presence of the aniline ring increases the lipid solubility. Due to the absence of the quaternary nitrogen group these compounds, as discussed before, are receptor inhibitors. The competitive nature of the action of ACh and receptor inhibitors had been shown in the experiments on the electroplax.[99,104] The effectiveness of the action of different local anesthetics in abolishing electrical activity again closely parallels the binding strength to the receptor protein.[103,110,111] Recently, a competition between ACh and tetracaine has been demonstrated on the electroplax by Higman and Bartels[104] in a new and particularly convincing way.

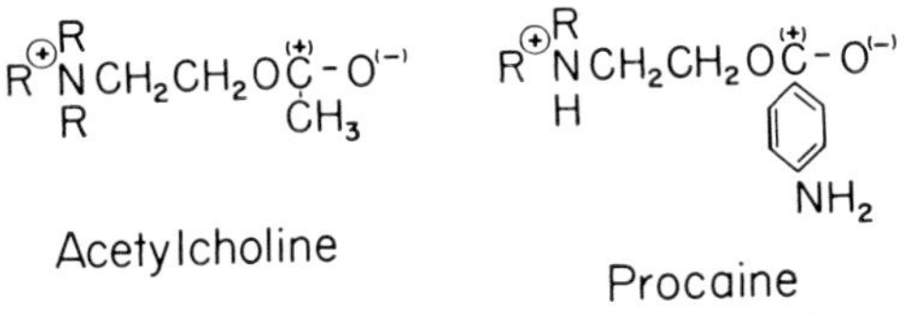

$$R \overset{\oplus}{\underset{R}{N}} CH_2CH_2O\overset{(+)}{C} - O^{(-)} \qquad R \overset{\oplus}{\underset{H}{N}} CH_2CH_2O\overset{(+)}{C} - O^{(-)}$$
$$\qquad\qquad CH_3 \qquad\qquad\qquad NH_2$$

Acetylcholine   Procaine

Fig. 6. Analogy of structure of ACh and procaine.

The demonstration of the specific reaction of local anesthetics offers not only a chemical explanation for their effect on axons, but provides a new and, in the opinion of the writer, particularly strong evidence for the proposed role of ACh in conduction. In view of the well known generality of the action of local anesthetics on electrical activity in all types of nerves, motor, sensory, adrenergic, cholinergic, etc., and the high specificity of the reaction, it is difficult to envisage an alternative explanation. The data supplement the evidence of the inseparability of conduction from the activity of ACh-esterase.

F. EFFECTS OF QUATERNARY AMMONIUM IONS ON CONDUCTION

(1) Structural Barriers for Lipid-insoluble Quaternary Ammonium Ions.—The powerful action of ACh is limited to synaptic junctions. Applied to axons, ACh has no effect even in very high concentrations. This failure of ACh to affect electrical activity in axons has been for many years, and still is, one of the main objections to the theory of an essential role of the ester in conduction.

Axons are surrounded by structural barriers impervious to lipid-insoluble compounds. ACh, a methylated quaternary ammonium salt, is lipid-insoluble, and therefore unable to reach the active site in the membrane. It has been demonstrated in many ways that ACh and other compounds of this type do not enter the axon. When the nerve fiber was exposed to a solution containing ACh (0.1 M) labeled with N^{15}, the isotopic nitrogen was not found in the interior of the axon,[112] whereas tertiary nitrogen compounds entered. Powerful inhibitors of ACh-esterase which are quaternary nitrogen derivatives, as for example Prostigmine, do not block either chemical or electrical activity of nerve fibers, even when applied in extremely high concentrations to Squid giant axons. These so-called unmyelinated fibers have an equivalent lipid-containing membrane, only it is thin. No trace of inhibitor was found in the interior of the axon exposed for several hours to 10^{-2} M Prostigmine, although one millionth of this concentration would have been detectable.[34] Tertiary nitrogen drivatives, on the other hand, such as eserine, block conduction and enzyme activity and their penetration into the interior has been demonstrated. In contrast to Prostigmine, its tertiary analogue, although a hundred times weaker as an inhibitor of cholinesterase than the quaternary form, blocks electrical and enzyme activity.[35]

(2) Action of Lipid-soluble Quaternary Ammonium Ions.—Recently, a series of lipid-soluble quaternary ammonium ions has been prepared by substituting a dodecyl group for a methyl on the nitrogen. These lipid-soluble quaternary ammonium ions block axonal conduction. In experiments on Ranvier nodes electrical activity was affected by 10^{-7} M concentration.[38] This is equivalent to 0.02 μg./ml. of ACh. The conducting membrane of electroplax of *Electrophorus* was found to be depolarized even after complete block of the synaptic junction by d-tubocurarine; this indicates that the compounds affect the conducting membrane directly.[113,104] They produce muscular contractions of both frog's rectus and sartorius muscle. Some of the effects are reversible and may be repeated many times. As in the electroplax the action is not blocked by curare in contrast to that of the lipid-insoluble nitrogen derivatives. The effects on the muscle emphasize the significance of the action of these lipid soluble quaternary ammonium ions because they are able to reproduce the biological action postulated for the physiological role of ACh.[114-116]

The question arises, whether or not the compounds act specifically upon the ACh system. Evidence in this direction has been obtained by tests for the competitive action with eserine.[117] This compound inhibits the enzyme and is also a receptor inhibitor. When eserine is added to the desheathed frog tibialis nerve, subsequent addition of one of the compounds, pyridine aldoxime dodeciodide, in otherwise effective concentration, had no effect. Higher concentrations did overcome the protective action of eserine. The antagonism found between the two compounds is typical for a competitive action.

In high concentrations the lipid-soluble quaternary ammonium ions may have an unspecific and 'detergent' action. The relatively low concentrations used and the various biological effects described suggest, however, a more specific type of action on the ACh system. Whether the compounds act primarily on the receptor or on the esterase or on a storage protein apparently may depend on their structural features and on the concentrations used and may, therefore, vary according to experimental conditions, type of preparation, etc.

(3) Action of Curare on Axonal Conduction.—The classical observations of Claude Bernard that curare acts on the neuromuscular junction only and does not affect nerve and muscle fibers, was the basis of all modern concepts of a special mechanism of synaptic transmission including the hypothesis of neurohumoral transmission. It has been suspected for a long time, and has now been shown *in vitro,*[65-67] that curare forms a complex with the ACh receptor protein, thereby apparently protecting it against the action of ACh. The limitation of the curare action to the junction was considered by the theory of neurohumoral transmission as a decisive indication that ACh acts only at the junction. In the new concept, the absence of an effect on axons was explained by the existence of structural barriers impervious to quaternary ammonium ions.

However, applied to Ranvier nodes of a single frog sciatic fiber, d-tubocurarine blocks electrical activity rapidly and reversibly.[119] Within 1 to 2 minutes the spike disappears. The concentration required is usually 10^{-3} M, although in a few cases slightly higher. Prostigmine blocks in about the same concentration which is about ten times higher than that required for eserine. Evidentally charged molecules penetrate poorly even at the nodes compared with uncharged ones.

Walsh and Deal[120] attempted to reduce the barriers for lipid soluble quaternary ammonium ions. They found indeed that after pretreatment with the cationic detergent cetyltrimethylammonium bromide conduction in frog sciatic nerve bundles was reversibly affected by curare.

Still more recently, Rosenberg and Ehrenpreis[121,122] applied a series of enzymes to Squid giant axons to test whether the structural barriers could be reduced to a degree that compounds not acting on the intact fiber would produce effects. Several enzymes tested did not change the response. But with cobra venom the effect was striking: curare, inactive in 10^{-2} M concentration before the treatment, blocked electrical activity rapidly and reversibly. The concentrations required were about 10^{-3} M, in some cases 5×10^{-4} M. The experiments to remove the barriers are still in an early stage. The specific enzyme (or enzymes) in the cobra venom producing this action have not yet been identified.

But the evidence for an action of curare on the conducting membrane of axons removes one of the outstanding facts upon which the assumption of a special mechanism of transmission across the neuromuscular junction was based. The limitation of the effect of curare to the junction has profoundly influenced the thinking of physiologists since the classical experiments of Claude Bernard. Clearly, these observations were correct, but the interpretation must be modified. It is not the difference of the mechanism which limits the curare action in a nerve muscle preparation to the junction, but the inaccessibility of the conducting membrane in the fibers. What has long been apparent on the basis of biochemical and physicochemical data, has now been clearly and unequivocally demonstrated on the intact cell, by a type of experiment which is a "direct" evidence according to the physiological way of thinking.

Of interest in this connection are recent observations of Armett and Ritchie.[123] The unmyelinated C fibers of the cat vagus react to ACh after the removal of the sheath: the ester depolarizes the axons, reduces the spike height, slows conduction. The greater the concentration of ACh the stronger the action. The concentrations required are about ten times as high as those acting at nerve endings. The effects are reversible. Although the observations require considerable amplification for the interpretation of certain aspects, they demonstrate that ACh affects the electrical activity of axons. The structural barriers in this type of fibers are apparently unable to prevent penetration when high concentrations are used. Recently, W. D. Dettbarn and F. Davis have found a reversible effect of ACh on axonal activity of crustacean nerve fibers without pre-treatment (unpublished data).

G. NEUROMUSCULAR AND SYNAPTIC TRANSMISSION

We have discussed so far the evidence for the concept that the release and the action of ACh are intracellular (or intramembranous) processes inseparably associated with the conductance changes in axonal membranes during the generation of bioelectric currents. The question naturally occurs whether it is still justified, in view of the new information, to maintain the hypothesis of neurohumoral transmission in its original form. Do the experimental facts support an *inter*cellular role of ACh at synaptic junctions in contrast to the *intra*cellular one in the axon? The reader interested in this complex problem is referred to the recent monograph of the author.[17] Here only a few aspects may be briefly discussed.

(1) The Original Basis of the Hypothesis.—Originally the hypothesis of neurohumoral transmission was based essentially on two facts: (1)

ACh has a powerful action on synaptic junctions. It does not affect, even in high concentration, axonal conduction. (2) When the nerve is stimulated, ACh appears in the perfusion fluid of synaptic junctions, although only in the presence of eserine. These two observations were taken as evidence that the physiological function of ACh is limited to the synaptic junction and that the ester, released from the nerve terminal, acts on the effector cell.

The failure of ACh and other lipid-insoluble quaternary ammonium ions to affect conduction when applied externally has found an experimentally well documented explanation in the existence of structural barriers. As to the appearance of ACh in the perfusion fluid, this observation does not reveal its mode of action. As was emphatically and repeatedly stressed by Dale and his collaborators, ACh appears only if eserine is present in the perfusion fluid. Obviously, if one interferes with the rapid physiological removal of ACh by the esterase, ACh, when released, would be expected to diffuse from the pre- and post-synaptic membranes into the surrounding medium. This would occur only at synaptic junctions where apparently no strong structural barrier exists for ACh. No such leakage would be expected from the intact fiber. If, however, the nerve fiber is cut and stimulated, ACh is released from the cut surface where the barrier is no longer an obstacle.[124,125]

It is commonly accepted as an established fact that ACh is released exclusively from the nerve ending. There exists, however, only one experimental observation in support of this view: when the nerve fiber is cut and the ending has degenerated, no ACh is detectable in the perfusion fluid after direct stimulation of the muscle fiber.[126] However, this observation has been challenged by McIntyre.[127,128] He finds that ACh is released from active muscle even after complete degeneration of the nerve endings. He has provided an explanation for the apparently negative results of the previous experiments.

(2) The Concentration of Cholinesterase at Synaptic Junction.—Of particular interest is the problem of the concentration of cholinesterase at synaptic junctions in relation to that in fibers. A considerable amount of confusion exists about this problem. The author admits to share the responsibility for this situation. Some clarification appears necessary. The theory of neurohumoral transmission required the removal of ACh by cholinesterase within the brief period of one or a few milliseconds (depending on the type of preparation). Determinations of the concentration and distribution of cholinesterase in frog sartorius muscle, have revealed that in the part containing motor end plates the concentration of the enzyme was about three to four times as high as in the pelvic end which is free of motor endplates.[129,130]

Since the number of end plates in the muscle is known, it is possible to calculate that per motor end plate about 1.6×10^9 molecules may be split per millisecond,[14] an amount which indeed permits the assumption of an active role of ACh in the process of synaptic transmission, although obviously it does not indicate what this role may be.

However, at that time, the writer assumed that cholinesterase is evenly distributed in nerve and muscle fibers outside the end plate and only more concentrated at the junction. If one refers the concentrations in the fibers and at the end plates to the corresponding volumes, the data seem to indicate that the actual concentration at the motor end plates is several thousand times higher than in the fibers, since the end plates form an extremely small fraction of the volume of the fiber, probably less than one thousandth. Later, however, it was found that the enzyme is not evenly distributed in fibers, but localized in the region of the surface membrane. This was first suggested in experiments on the superior cervical ganglion of cat. The enzyme activity of this tissue amounts to about 600 mg. of ester split/gm./hour whereas in the preganlionic fibers only 50 mg. are split/gm./hour. After section of the fibers, the activity falls within a week to 240 mg./gm./hour and then remains constant.[131] The temporal coincidence of the two processes suggests that this decrease is due to the degeneration of the terminals. The strong decrease of concentration indicates a higher enzyme concentration in the fibers inside the ganglion than that at the outside. The nerve terminals branch many times in the ganlion and form an extremely extensive endarborization. One possibility to explain this increased concentration inside the ganglion is a high concentration of the enzyme near the surface membrane. The large increase in surface area due to the endarborization would then explain the high concentration in the fibers inside the ganglion and the strong decrease of enzyme activity within the ganglia when the terminals degenerate. This assumption was born out by the experiments on the Squid giant axon, showing the complete absence of cholinesterase in the axoplasm and its exclusive localization in the sheath.[31,32] The experiments on the superior cervical ganglion showed, moreover, that the enzyme must be present in high concentrations in pre- and postsynaptic membranes.

Investigations of the concentration and distribution of cholinesterase in mammalian muscle gave similar results. In the guinea pig gastrocnemius the nerve fibers with all their branches including the motor end plates are localized in a well defined zone. When sections of the frozen muscle are prepared with the microtome in an appropriate way, most sections are virtually free of motor end plates; only a few are extremely rich in nerve fibers and end plates. In these sections the concentration of cholinesterase is three to five times higher than in the sections free of nerve fibers and end plates.[131,132] For the interpretation of this increase the information about the structure as revealed by the studies with light and electron microscope is essenial.[133,134] The nerve terminals lie in gutters. These gutters are formed by complex folds of the muscular membrane whereby the surface area is greatly increased, although estimates of the increase are not available at present. But it is apparent that a three- to five-fold increase of enzyme concentration in sections rich in end plates may be due either entirely or at least to a large extent to the increase of active surface area. It is still possible that per unit surface area the enzyme concentration is higher at the junction, but if so the difference can be only minor. Although the early data about the concentration of cholinesterase in muscle and the absolute values for the activity per motor end plate are correct, the interpretation assuming an unusually high concentration at motor end plates in contrast to the low concentration in fibers, must be abandoned. Thus, there is no justification, on the basis of enzyme activity to attribute to the substrate a role at the junction which differs from that in the fiber.

When Koelle and Friedenwald[135] introduced their well known histochemical staining technique, they noticed at once the strong staining of motor end plates in contrast to the rest of the muscle fiber. This seemed to support the original interpretation of an extraordinary concentration of the enzyme at the junction. However, in the following decade Koelle himself, as other investigators in the field, became aware of the many pitfalls inherent in this as in many other staining techniques for localizing enzyme activity in the cell. The great value of the method and its many potentialities are not questioned and much interesting information has been obtained. But it is necessary to recognize the limitations and to avoid the pitfalls. The method can supplement chemical data and provide additional information which the chemical methods cannot do. But it cannot possibly contradict unequivocal results of chemical determinations.

(3) Presence of the ACh System on the Two Sides of the Junction.—For the understanding of the ACh at the junction it is of interest to know exactly where the various proteins of the ACh system are located. If the action of ACh is intracellular or intramembraneous, then they should be present on both sides of the junction, i.e., in the pre- and postsynaptic membranes. If this is the case it would render difficult the idea of neurohumoral transmission: besides many other difficulties, the fact that all the proteins of the system are present in the two synaptic and axonal membranes, would force us to assume that some of them are without any function and useless on one side,

others on the opposite side; this is obviously an unsatisfactory and an unconvincing ad hoc interpretation. The presence of the complete system on both sides makes more likely the assumption that the mode of action is similar to that in the axon, namely that it is essential for changing the conductance to ions in pre- and postsynaptic membranes without being the transmitting agent. On the other hand, an incomplete system on either side, as for instance the absence of the receptor at the terminal or the absence of choline acetylase in the effector cell, would make difficult the theory of intramembranous action at the junction.

The experiments on the superior cervical ganglion of cat discussed before have clearly shown that high concentrations of cholinesterase are present in nerve terminals as well as in the effector cell. Chemical determinations with other biological preparations have similarly shown the presence of the enzyme on both sides.[136-138,131-133] Attempts at precise localization with histochemical staining methods at first encountered considerable technical difficulties. Recently, however, Koelle found definite evidence for the localization of ACh-esterase in axon terminals of various ganglia of the cat by applying new procedures in which staining techniques were used in combination with reversible and irreversible enzyme inhibitors and by comparing the ganglia before and after denervation.[139,140] In some terminals the enzyme appeared to be absent. However, once again it appears questionable whether failure of histochemical techniques to find the enzyme can be used as evidence for its absence. It appears to the writer most significant that, by designing experiments in which a resourceful combination of methods has been applied, the demonstration of the presence of cholinesterase in nerve terminals has been achieved, at least in some of them, although only a few years earlier this problem seemed to have encountered nearly insurmountable technical difficulties.[133]

Choline acetylase is present in nerve and muscle fibers and, as discussed before, ACh appears in the perfusion fluid of active muscle after complete degeneration of nerve terminals. This indicates that ACh may be formed on both sides of the junction.

ACh receptors are also present on both side, i.e., in the terminal as well as in the postsynaptic membrane. For many years it was assumed that ACh applied externally acts only on the synaptic membrane. However, 20 years ago, Masland and Wigton[141] reported that Prostigmine applied to the motor end plate produced rapid bursts of electrical activity in the motor roots in addition to its action upon the muscle fiber. Curare blocked both muscle and nerve response. The authors concluded that their observations provide evidence that ACh and Prostigmine stimulate the motor nerve terminal as well as the muscle; the concept of a specific local effect of ACh on the muscle at the myoneural junction is, in the view of the authors, unable to explain the findings. Recently, Riker and his associates fully confirmed these results and concluded that ACh receptors must be present in nerve terminals.[142] In this connection the response to ACh demonstrated with several sensory nerve terminals may also be recalled.

(4) Present State.—We have briefly discussed the biochemical data concerning the proteins of the ACh system at junctions. The allotted space does not permit any discussion of electrical data. Nobody denies differences of electrical manifestations compared with those of the axon. Several observations have at present no satisfactory explanation. However, the complex structure of the junction compared with the simplicity of the axon may be responsible for many unexplained deviations. Eccles has emphasized the importance of "geometry" even in studies of electrical events in axons.[143] This factor must play an even more important role in the electrical events at junctions, although at present very little is known in this respect. Physical and chemical data concerning the events at junctions are based on indirect methods and on analogy. At best they permit speculations as to the precise mechanism of ACh action at synapses. However, electrical data alone cannot provide the final answer. They must be supplemented by chemical analyses. The classical pharmacological techniques are too crude for the analysis of events taking place in microseconds in membranes of less than 100 Å. An illustration for the weakness of such speculations are the three hypotheses proposed during the last decade by Katz and his associates.[36] First, they suggested that at nerve terminals Na is exchanged for ACh, in contrast to the axon where Na and K are exchanged. The authors realized themselves that this idea is untenable. The second hypothesis is based on the finding of vesicles near terminals.[144] Katz and his associates proposed that the vesicles are containers of ACh, that they discharge, during the collision with the membrane, "quanta" of ACh, etc.[36] Further developments have discredited these speculations. Vesicles are found in many places of the nervous system. Some postsynaptic regions are particularly rich in vesicles. The third hypothesis was based on the observation of "miniature" end plate potentials during rest. This was considered as evidence of quantal release of ACh from nerve terminals. No alternative interpretation was even considered. Recently, this hypothesis was invalidated by the finding that after complete degeneration of the nerve terminals the miniature potentials persist.[145]

It is interesting to compare the categorical and dogmatic statements of some of the adherents of neurohumoral transmission with the remarks of Dale, one of the great pioneers in the field, in his Harvey

Lecture.[146] Dale envisaged the possibility of a role of acetylcholine in conduction eliminating thereby the difficulty of assuming fundamentally different mechanisms in conduction and transmission. This assumption would imply, as he stated, profound changes in the then current concept of conduction. It is perhaps even more remarkable that Dale repeated that statement at a symposium in 1953 and warned his followers not to consider the neurohumoral transmitter story as a final answer.[147]

Methods of approach greatly influence our thinking. The remarkable unity of biochemical principles and systems throughout the great diversity of living cells must influence the reasoning of the investigator attacking the problem primarily by chemical analysis. Physiology and pharmacology study manifestations of intact cells characterized by a nearly infinite variety as to organization and structure. A great number of facts have accumulated in favor of the primary role of ACh in axonal conduction. The objections raised have been answered. The original facts on which the neurohumoral transmitter theory was based have found an explanation compatible with the unified theory proposed. New and more conclusive data must be provided for admitting a fundamentally different chemical mechanism at the junction. At present it appears to the writer preferable to follow a fundamental rule of scientific thinking, *viz.*, not to assume without necessity two different mechanisms.

REFERENCES

1. BERNSTEIN, J.: *Pflüger's Arch. ges. Physiol.*, 92:521 (1902).
2. CURTIS, H. J., and COLE, K. S.: *J. Cell. & Comp. Physiol.*, 19:135 (1942).
3. HODGKIN, A. L., and HUXLEY, A. F.: *J. Physiol.*, 104:176 (1945).
4. COLE, K. S., and CURTIS, H. J.: *J. Gen. Physiol.*, 22:649 (1939).
5. ROTHENBERG, M. A.: *Tr. Am. Neurol. A.*, 230 (1949).
6. ROTHENBERG, M. A.: *Biochem. et biophys. acta*, 4:96 (1950).
7. HODGKIN, A. L.: *Biol. Rev.*, 26:338 (1951).
8. KEYNES, R. D., and LEWIS, P. R.: *J. Physiol.*, 113:99 (1951).
9. KEYNES, R. D., and LEWIS, P. R.: *J. Physiol.*, 114:151 (1951).
10. COLE, K. S.: *Arch. sc. physiol.*, 3:253 (1949).
11. COLE, K. S.: *Electrochemistry in Biology and Medicine*, p. 121. T. Shedlovsky, Ed. New York, John Wiley and Sons (1955).
12. HODGKIN, A. L.: *Proc. Roy. Soc.*, B, 148:1 (1957).
13. WHITTAM, R., and GUINNEBAULT, M.: *J. Gen. Physiol.*, 43:1171 (1960).
14. KEYNES, R. D.: *IV. Intern. Congress of Biochemistry*, Vienna Symps. III, p. 18 (1958).
15. NACHMANSOHN, D.: *Harvey Lectures 1953/1954*, p. 57. New York Acad. Press (1955).
16. NACHMANSOHN, D. ASHER-SPIRO: *Ergebn. Physiol.*, 48:575 (1955).
17. NACHMANSOHN, D.: *Chemical and Molecular Basis of Nerve Activity*. New York, Acad. Press (1959).

18. NACHMANSOHN, D.: In *Structure and Function of Muscle*, Vol. II, p. 199. G. Bourne, Ed. New York, Acad. Press (1960).
19. NACHMANSOHN, D., and WILSON, I. B.: *Advances Enzymol., 12:*259 (1951).
20. NACHMANSOHN, D., and WILSON, I. B.: *Currents in Biochemical Research,* p. 628. D. E. Green, Ed. New York, Interscience (1956).
21. ABBOTT, B. C., HILL, A. V., and HOWARTH, J. V.: *Proc. Roy. Soc., B, 148:*149 (1958).
22. ABBOTT, B. C., AUBERT, X., and FESSARD, A.: *J. Physiol., 50:*99 (1958).
23. BERNSTEIN, J., and TSCHERMAK, A.: *Pflüger's Arch., 112:*439 (1906).
24. HODGKIN, A. L., and KATZ, B.: *J. Physiol., 108:*33 (1950).
25. SCHOFFENIELS, E.: *Science, 127:*1117 (1958).
26. SCHOFFENIELS, E.: *Thèse degrégation. Université de Liège* (1959).
27. FULTON, J. F.: New York, Oxford Univ. Press (1938; 1943; 1949).
28. ERLANGER, J. J.: *Neurophysiol., 2:*370 (1939).
29. AUGUSTINSSON, K. B., and NACHMANSOHN, D.: *Science, 110:*98 (1949).
30. SEAMAN, G. R., and HOULIHAN, R. K.: *J. Cell. & Comp. Physiol., 37:*309 (1951).
31. BOELL, E. J., and NACHMANSOHN, D.: *Science, 92:*513 (1940).
32. NACHMANSOHN, D., and MEYERHOF, B.: *J. Neurophysiol., 4:*348 (1941).
33. LAWLER, C.: *J. Biol. Chem., 236:*2296 (1961).
34. BULLOCK, T. H., NACHMANSOHN, D., and ROTHENBERG, M. A.: *J. Neurophysiol., 9:*9 (1946).
35. WILSON, I. B., and COHEN, M.: *Biochim. et biophys. acta, 11:*147 (1953).
36. DEL CASTILLO, J., and KATZ, B.: *Progress in Biophysics,* p. 121. J. A. V. Butler, Ed. London and New York, Pergamon Press (1956).
37. DETTBARN, W. D.: *Federation Proc., 18:*36 (1959).
38. DETTBARN, W. D.: *Biochim. et biophys. acta, 41:*377 (1960).
39. DETTBARN, W. D.: *Bioelectrogenesis,* p. 262. C. Chagas and A. Paes de Carvalho, Eds. Amsterdam, Elsevier (1961).
40. ROBERTSON, J. D.: In *Molecular Biology,* p. 87. D. Nachmansohn, Ed. New York, Acad. Press (1960).
41. HINTERBUCHNER, L. P., and NACHMANSOHN, D.: *Biochim. et biophys. acta, 44:*554 (1960).
42. MEYERHOF, O.: *Zur Energetik der Zellvorgaenge.* Vandenhoeck und Ruprecht (1913).
43. NACHMANSOHN, D., COATES, C. W., and COX, R. T.: *J. Gen. Physiol., 25:*75 (1941).
44. NACHMANSOHN, D., COATES, C. W., and ROTHENBERG, M. A.: *J. Biol. Chem., 163:*39 (1946).
45. NACHMANSOHN, D., and LEDERER, E.: *Bull. Soc. chim. biol. Paris, 21:*797 (1939).
46. ROTHENBERG, M. A., and NACHMANSOHN, D.: *J. Biol. Chem., 168:*223 (1947).
47. NACHMANSOHN, D., COX, R. T., COATES, C. W., and MACHADO, A. L.: *J. Neurophysiol., 6:*383 (1943).
48. NACHMANSOHN, D., COATES, C. W., ROTHENBERG, M. A., and BROWN, M. V.: *J. Biol. Chem., 165:*223 (1946).
49. NACHMANSOHN, D., and MACHADO, A. L.: *J. Neurophysiol., 6:*397 (1943).
50. QUASTEL, J. H., TENNENBAUM, M., and WHEATLEY, A. H. M.: *Biochem. J., 30:*1668 (1936).
51. MANN, P. J. G., TENNENBAUM, M., and QUASTEL, J. H.: *Biochem. J., 32:*243 (1938).
52. NACHMANSOHN, D., JOHN, H. M., and WAELSCH, H.: *J. Biol. Chem., 150:*485 (1943).

53. LIPMANN, F.: *Harvey Lectures 1948/1949*, Vol. 44, p. 99. (1950).
54. LYNEN, F., REICHERT, E., and RUEFF, L.: *Liebigs Ann., 574:*1 (1951).
55. KOREY, S. R., DE BRAGANZA, B., and NACHMANSOHN, D.: *J. Biol. Chem., 189:*705 (1951).
56. MONNIER, A. M., and DUBUISSON, M.: *Arch. internat. physiol., 38:*180 (1934).
57. COWAN, S. L.: *J. Physiol., 88:*4 (1936).
58. FELDBERG, W., FESSARD, A., and NACHMANSOHN, D.: *J. Physiol., 97:*3P (1940).
59. COHEN, M.: *Arch. Biochem. & Biophys., 60:*284 (1956).
60. SKOUBY, A. P.: *Acta physiol. scandinav. 24:*174 (1951).
61. ZOTTERMAN, Y.: Tr. of the 4th Conference on *Nerve Impulse.* D. Nachmansohn, Ed. New York, Josiah Macy, Jr. Foundation (1953).
62. BUCHTHAL, F.: *Pharmacol. Rev., 6:*97 (1954).
63. LOEWENSTEIN, W. R. and MOLINS, D.: *Science, 128:*1284 (1958).
64. NACHMANSOHN, D.: *J. Physiol., 95:*29 (1939).
65. EHRENPREIS, S.: *Science, 129:*1913 (1959).
66. EHRENPREIS, E.: *Biochim. et biophys. acta, 44:*561 (1960).
67. EHRENPREIS, S.: *Bioelectrogenesis,* p. 379. C. Chagas and A. Paes de Carvalho, Eds. Elsevier, Amsterdam (1961).
68. BERGMANN, F., WILSON, I. B., and NACHMANSOHN, D.: *J. Biol. Chem., 186:*693 (1950).
69. WILSON, I. B., BERGMANN, F., and NACHMANSOHN, D.: *J. Biol. Chem., 186:*781 (1950c).
70. WILSON, I. B.: *The Mechanism of Enzyme Action,* p. 642. W. D. McElroy and B. Glass, Eds. Baltimore, Johns Hopkins Press (1954).
71. NACHMANSOHN, D., and FELD, E. A.: *J. Biol. Chem., 171:*715 (1947).
72. WILSON, I. B., and BERGMANN, F.: *J. Biol. Chem., 185:*479 (1950).
73. WILSON, I. B.: *J. Biol. Chem., 190:*111 (1951).
74. WILSON, I. B., and MEISLICH, E. K.: *J. Am. Chem. Soc., 75:*4628 (1953).
75. WILSON, I. B.: *Faraday Society Discussions, 20:*119 (1955).
76. WILSON, I. B., and GINSBURG, S.: *Arch. Biochem. & Bophys., 54:*569 (1955).
77. WILSON, I. B., and GINSBURG, S.: *Biochim. et biophys. acta, 18:*168 (1955).
78. CHILDS, A. F., DAVIES, D. R., GREEN, A. L., and RUTLAND, J. P.: *Brit. J. Pharmacol., 10:*462 (1955).
79. KEWITZ, H., and WILSON, I. B.: *Arch. Biochem. & Biophys., 60:*261 (1955).
80. KEWITZ, H., WILSON, I. B., and NACHMANSOHN, D.: *Arch. Biochem. & Biophys., 64:*456 (1956).
81. KEWITZ, H.: *Arch. Biochem. & Biophys., 66:*263 (1957).
82. KEWITZ, H., and NACHMANSOHN, D.: *Arch. Biochem. & Biophys., 66:*271 (1957).
83. LONGO, V. G., NACHMANSOHN, D., and BOVET, D.: *Arch. internat. pharmacodyn., 123:*No. 3-4, 282 (1960).
84. ROSENBERG, P.: *J. Biochem. Pharmacol., 3:*312 (1960).
85. WILSON, I. B., and QUAN, C.: *Arch. Biochem. & Biophys., 73:*131 (1958).
86. WILSON, I. B., GINSBURG, S., and QUAN, C.: *Arch. Biochem. & Biophys., 77:*286 (1958).
87. WILSON, I. B.: Second Conference on Physicochemical Mechanism of Nerve Activity. *Ann. New York Acad. Sc., 81:*307 (1959).
88. NAMBA, T., and HIRAKI, K.: *J. A. M. A., 166:*1834 (1958).
89. ERDMANN, W. D., SAKAI, F., and SCHELER, F.: *Deutsch. med. Wchnschr., 32:*1359 (1958).
90. POZIOMEK, E. J., MACKLEY, B. E., and STEINBERG, G. M.: *J. Org. Chem., 23:*714 (1958).

91. WILSON, I. B., and GINSBURG, S.: *J. Biochem. Pharmacol., 1*:200 (1959).
92. WILSON, I. B.: *J. Biol. Chem., 197*:215 (1952).
93. BERMAN, R., WILSON, I. B., and NACHMANSOHN, D.: *Biochim. et biophys. acta, 12*:315 (1953).
94. BERMAN-REISBERG, R.: *Yale J. Biol. & Med., 29*:403 (1957).
95. WILSON, I. B., and CABIB, E.: *J. A. C. S., 78*:202 (1956).
96. MEYER, K. H.: *Helvet. chim. acta, 20*:634 (1937).
97. ALTAMIRANO, M., SCHLEYER, W. L., COATES, C. W., and NACHMANSOHN, D.: *Biochim. et biophys. acta, 16*:268 (1955).
98. CLARK, A. J.: *Handb. Experiment. Pharmacol.* IV W. Heubner and J. Schuel ler, Eds. Berlin, Springer (1937).
99. SCHOFFENIELS, E., and NACHMANSOHN, D.: *Biochim. et biophys. acta, 26*:1 (1957).
100. SCHOFFENIELS, E.: *Biochim. et biophys. acta, 26*:585 (1957).
101. SCHOFFENIELS, E.: *Ann. New York Acad. Sc., 81*:Article 2, 285 (1959).
102. ROSENBERG, P., HIGMAN, H., and NACHMANSOHN, D.: *Biochim. et biophys. acta, 44*:151 (1960).
103. ROSENBERG, P., and HIGMAN, H.: *Biochim. et biophys. acta, 45*:348 (1960).
104. HIGMAN, H. and BARTELS, E.: *Biochim. et biophys. acta,* in press.
105. CHAGAS, C., PENNA-FRANCA, E., NISHIE, K., and GARCIA, E. J.: *Arch. biochem. et biophys., 75*:251, 1958.
106. CHAGAS, C.: *Curare and Curare-like Agents,* p. 327. D. Bovet, F. Bovet-Nitti and G. B. Marini-Bettolo, Eds. Amsterdam, Elsevier (1959).
107. CHAGAS, C.: *Ann. New York Acad. Sc., 81*:345 (1959).
108. EHRENPREIS, S., and FISHMAN, M. M.: *Biochim. et biophys. acta, 44*:577 (1960).
109. KLOTZ, I. M., WALKER, F. M., and PIVAN, R. B.: *J. Am. Chem. Soc., 68*:1486 (1960).
110. EHRENPREIS, S., and KELLOCK, M. G.: *Biochem. & Biophys. Res. Comm., 2*:311 (1960).
111. BARTELS, E., DETTBARN, W. D., HIGMAN, H., and ROSENBERG, P.: *Biochem. & Biophys. Res. Comm., 2*:316 (1960).
112. ROTHENBERG, M. A., SPRINSON, D. B., and NACHMANSOHN, D.: *J. Neurophysiol., 11*:111 (1948).
113. SCHOFFENIELS, E., WILSON, I. B., and NACHMANSOHN, D.: *Biochim. et biophys. acta, 27*:629 (1958).
114. HINTERBUCHNER, L. P., WILSON, I. B., and SCHOFFENIELS, E.: *Federation Proc., 17*:71 (1958).
115. HINTERBUCHNER, L. P., and WILSON, I. B.: *Biochim. et biophys. acta, 31*:323 (1959).
116. HINTERBUCHNER, L. P., and WILSON, I. B.: *Biochim. et biophys. acta, 32*:375 (1959).
117. DETTBARN, W. D.: *Biochim. et biophys. acta, 32*:381 (1959).
118. DETTBARN, W. D.: *Nature, 183*:465 (1959).
119. DETTBARN, W. D.: *Nature, 186*:891 (1960).
120. WALSH, R. R., and DEAL, S. E.: *Am. J. Physiol., 197*:547 (1960).
121. ROSENBERG, P., and EHRENPREIS, S.: *Nature,* London, *190*:728 (1961).
122. ROSENBERG, P., and EHRENPREIS, S.: *Biochem. Pharm., 8*:192 (1961).
123. ARMETT, CH.J., and RITCHIE, J. M.: *J. Physiol., 152*:141 (1960).
124. CALABRO, Q.: *Riv. biol., 15*:299 (1933).
125. BERGAMI, G., CANTONI, G., and GUALTIEROTTI, T.: *Arch. 1st Biochim. ital., 8*:267 (1936).

126. DALE, H. H., FELDBERG, W., and VOGT, M.: *J. Physiol., 86:*353 (1936).
127. MCINTYRE, A. R., DOWNING, F. M., BENNETT, A. L., and DUNN, A. L.: *Proc. Soc. Exper. Biol. & Med., 74:*180 (1950).
128. MCINTYRE, A. R.: *Curare and Curare-like Agents,* p. 211. D. Bovet, F. Bovet-Nitti and G. B. Marini-Bettolo, Eds. Amsterdam, Elsevier (1959).
129. MARNAY, A., and NACHMANSOHN, D.: *Compt. rend. Soc. biol. Paris, 125:*41 (1937).
130. MARNAY, A., and NACHMANSOHN, D.: *J. Physiol., 92:*37 (1938).
131. COUTEAUX, R., and NACHMANSOHN, D.: *Proc. Soc. Exper. Biol. & Med., 43:*177 (1940).
132. COUTEAUX, R.: *Bull. biol. France Belg., 76:*14 (1942).
133. COUTEAUX, R.: *Internat. Rev. Cytol., 4:*335 (1955).
134. ROBERTSON, J. D.: *J. Biophys. & Biochem. Cytol., 2:*381 (1956).
135. KOELLE, G. B., and FRIEDENWALD, J. S.: *Proc. Soc. Exper. Biol. & Med., 70:*617 (1949).
136. FENG, T. P., and TING, V. C.: *Chinese J. Physiol., 13:*141 (1938).
137. NACHMANSOHN, D., and HOFF, E. C.: *J. Neurophysiol., 7:*27 (1944).
138. STOERK, H. C., and MORPETH, E.: *Proc. Soc. Exper. Biol. & Med., 57:*154 (1944).
139. KOELLE, W. A., and KOELLE, G. B.: *Federation Proc., 17:*384 (1958).
140. KOELLE, G. B.: *J. Pharmacol. & Exper. Therap., 120:*488 (1957).
141. MASLAND, R. L., and WIGTON, R. S.: *J. Neurophysiol., 3:*269 (1940).
142. RIKER, W. F., WERNER, G., ROBERTS, J., and KUPERMAN, A.: *J. Pharmacol. & Exper. Therap., 125:*150 (1959).
143. ECCLES, J. C.: *Ann. New York Acad. Sc., 47:*429 (1946).
144. DE ROBERTIS, E. D. P., and BENNETT, H. S.: *J. Biophys. Biochem. Cytol., 1:*47 (1955).
145. KATZ, B., and MILEDI, R.: *J. Physiol., 146:*44P (1959).
146. DALE, H. H.: *Harvey Lectures, 32:*229 (1937).
147. DALE, H. H.: *Pharmacol. Rev., 6:*7 (1954).

XXII

ELECTROLYTES AND THE FUNCTION AND PHARMACOLOGY OF NERVE

ABRAHAM M. SHANES

T HE PAST decade has seen a substantial revival of interest and a great refinement in the concepts of the role of ions in bio-electrical phenomena—refinements which were beginning to be introduced shortly before the article by Keynes and Lewis[1] dealing with this subject in the earlier edition was written. The basic principles have since been greatly clarified with respect to peripheral nerve and extended to other excitable systems; moreover, these principles now appear to offer a satisfactory approach to the mechanism of action of a number of physiological and pharmacological agents.[2,3]

The relatively steady difference of potential between the interior and exterior of excitable and other cells—generally referred to as the "resting potential"—and the rapid and slow transitory changes in this potential that constitute the "action potential", have certain properties in common. But they are also sufficiently different to merit separate consideration.

The reappraisals of data that led to a fuller appreciation of the role of electrolytes in resting and action potentials occurred quite independently. Thus, the ionic hypothesis for resting potentials was strengthened with the recognition by Shanes[4] and Shanes and Hopkins[5] that the changes in this potential with the metabolic state of vertebrate and invertebrate nerve, observed in earlier studies, were attributable to relatively small shifts in the potassium level surrounding the fibers—a conclusion soon verified by measurements establishing the predicted potassium movements under a wide variety of experimental conditions.[6-13] The same principle was found to account, under certain conditions, for the slow fluctuations in membrane potential following excitation known as "after-potentials,"[14] a conclusion since supported and extended.[15-17]

The experiments on metabolism and membrane potential also served to establish that one class of compounds—known as "stabilizers" and represented by local anesthetics—reduced the interchanges of intra-cellular potassium for extracellular sodium during metabolic inhibi-tion, whereas another group of compounds—classified as "unstabilizers" or "labilizers" and represented by veratrine and pure veratrum alka-loids such as veratridine and cevadine—had the opposite effect.[2,11,12] Since these studies, much more detail in terms of permeability changes brought about by these drugs has been revealed through the applica-tion of isotope techniques.[18-20]

An important improvement in the ionic hypothesis for the action potential—more specifically for the initial large, rapid transitory change in membrane potential known as the spike—may be said to date from the recognition by Hodgkin and Katz[21] that the reversal of membrane potential during the spike[22,23] is attributable to a temporary large in-crease in permeability to sodium ions, the gradient of which therefore determines the direction as well as the magnitude of the reversal. The subsequent application of radioisotope techniques, and especially of the voltage clamp method by Hodgkin and Huxley,[24] originally de-veloped by Marmont[25] and Cole,[26] has added substantially to our knowledge of the sequence of and controlling factors in the sodium and potassium permeability changes during the spike[3,24,27] and of the role of physiological and pharmacological agents in this and related phenomena.[28-30]

Thus, current research on the resting and action potential has re-focused attention on (a) the ionic gradients, particularly with respect to cations, and (b) the relative permeability of the cells to specific ionic species. Both the gradients and permeabilities are susceptable to change and thereby govern the functional activity. This view has also proven useful for an understanding of the mechanisms controlling the operation of myoneural and synaptic junctions.[2,3]

THE RESTING POTENTIAL

The basic view of the resting potential as a diffusion potential is now so well known as hardly to require reiteration. As pointed out by Keynes and Lewis[1] and in numerous reviews since,[2,24] there appear to be no exceptions among excitable cells with respect to the high intra-cellular concentration of potassium ions relative to that outside (i.e., $[K]_i/[K]_o > 1$); the reverse is generally true of sodium and chloride (i.e., $[Na]_i/[Na]_o < 1$ and $[Cl]_i/[Cl]_o < 1$). Because of their high concentration in either the interior or exterior of the cells, sodium, potassium, and chloride are normally of greatest significance as the basis of diffusion potentials. Calcium cannot be ignored as an important factor however—perhaps in the regulation of permeability.[2,3] Because it is largely bound in axoplasm[31-33] and myoplasm,[34-36] its concentration (or activity) gradient is directed inward.

Recent investigations lead to the view that the distribution of ions is a dynamic one, being primarily the result of a balance between (a) the *leakage* of sodium into and potassium out of the cell and (b) the *active transport* of potassium into the cell, either by exchange with sodium extruded from the interior or with sodium excluded by rejection of the sodium tending to enter from the exterior. The exclusion mechanism appears to be predominant in fibers which have not gained excessive sodium through activity or through metabolic deficiency. It was proposed by Shanes[2] as a result of the finding that, upon cessation of active transport in vertebrate nerve, sodium outflux is unchanged but its influx increases concomitantly with a decrease in potassium influx;[18] this has also been noted in muscle.[37,38] Thus, it appears that metabolism can reduce the leakage of sodium into the fibers by ejecting it in exchange for potassium before it actually traverses the membrane. The more familiar extrusion process, seen in many other types of cells, is evident in previously stimulated invertebrate nerve as a decline in sodium outflux and potassium influx with metabolic inhibition;[39] in vertebrate nerve it is apparent as an increase in sodium outflux upon return to oxygen following anoxia.[18]

Extrusion of sodium occurs largely by exchange with potassium but also apparently by transport with an anion, perhaps as an ion pair; it does not contribute appreciably to membrane potential nor is it affected by the potential.[2,39] Exclusion, on the other hand, does contribute to the potential, but only to the extent that it reduces the depolarizing inward leak of sodium and thereby brings the membrane potential closer to that of the potassium equilibrium potential,[2] soon to be described.

The present view, then, is that active transport does not contribute to the membrane potentials in a direct manner, either by oxidation-reduction potentials or by unidirectional transport of ions. Rather, the simplest explanation of the resting potential appears to be that the concentration (actually, the activity) gradients, maintained by the electrically inert, active Na-K transport process, cause the continuous back-diffusion of these ions through the membrane, the selective permeability characteristics of which determine the magnitude and orientation of potential.

Were the cell membrane permeable to only one ion species, say sodium, then the transmembrane potential, E_m, would be given in millivolts and at 25°C. by the Nernst equilibrium equation

$$E_m = E_{Na} = 59 \log ([Na]_i/[Na]_o).$$

In this case, because $[Na]_i < [Na]_o$, E_{Na}, the sodium equilibrium potential, would be negative, i.e., the outside of the cell negative to the interior. This follows from the tendency of sodium to diffuse from the more concentrated to the less concentrated solution carrying its positive change with it. Conversely, the potassium equilibrium potential, $E_K = 59 \log ([K]_i/[K]_o)$, would be oriented in the opposite direction because $[K]_i > [K]_o$; the equilibrium potential for chloride would be oriented as for potassium, for although the ionic gradient is the reverse of potassium, the ions are oppositely charged. Since the resting potential is normally positive, as expected from E_K and E_{Cl}, either of these (or both) could be the primary basis of the resting potential. Actually, E_K is normally the major source of the resting potential. Even in skeletal muscle, where $P_{Cl} > P_K$, the anions eventually distribute themselves according to the potential set by potassium, rather than the potential according to the anionic gradient.[40]

The Nernst equation represents an ideal never quite reached in real membrane systems. This is because some "leak" exists to ions to which the "selective" membrane is considered to be "impermeable." For example, with sodium and potassium ions on both sides of a living membrane that has a low permeability to sodium and a high permeability to potassium, E_m will be less than E_K by an amount depending on (a) the magnitude of E_{Na} and on (b) the permeability to sodium, P_{Na}, relative to that to potassium, P_K. As a rough approximation, E_{Na} may be thought of as an oppositely oriented generator (i.e., tending to make the outside less positive to the inside) in parallel with E_K, each with an internal resistance inversely proportional to the permeabilities. Diffusion equations, in which the mobility and concentration terms for the membrane are lumped as "permeability," provide a better but still approximate representation of events. Despite the oversimplifications inherent in the Hodgkin-Katz derivation of the Goldman equations,[21] they have remained useful for quantitative estimates of membrane potential and conductance, and of cationic (and anionic) outflux and influx. In terms of only the physiological cations

$$E_m = 59 \log \frac{P_K[K]_i + P_{Na}[Na]_i}{P_K[K]_o + P_{Na}[Na]_o}.$$

Outflux is the rate of transfer of a given ion species outward and influx its rate in the opposite direction. Estimates of each can be determined by putting radioisotopes first on one side, then on the other side of the membrane. That radioisotopes can be used to estimate the behavior of the non-radioactive isotopes is amply justified by (a) the success with which *net transfer*, i.e., the actual shift of the non-radioactive species, can be predicted from the difference of individual fluxes, and (b) by the identity of the distribution of radio-active and nonradioactive isotopes that is attained.

Either the electrical analogue or the diffusion equation readily shows that when the permeability to sodium increases relative to potassium, or when potassium permeability decreases relative to sodium, the membrane potential decreases (i.e., moves from E_K towards E_{Na}); conversely, when these permeabilities change in the opposite directions, E_m increases (i.e., approaches E_K) if it is initially smaller than the potassium equilibrium potential.

In general, a small change in P_K can be detected as a resistance change because P_K is a large or major part of the total permeability. A small alteration in P_{Na} will not be seen as a change in resistance because the permeability to this ion is small compared to that to potassium. Measurements of ionic flux provide a check on this as well as on changes in other permeabilities. Thus, the modern physiologist and pharmacologist has at his disposal three related variables susceptible to evaluation—membrane potential, membrane resistance, and ionic flux—and which therefore can rather clearly indicate the presence of permeability effects by physiological and pharmacological agents and also contribute to determining the role of active transport processes.

The principles which have been presented permit a more refined analysis of relative permeability or of changes in permeability by the classical method of potential measurement. Thus, a reduction by local anesthetics of the ability of sodium and potassium to depolarize nerve fibers[41] confirmed the demonstration by earlier ionic studies of a reduced permeability to the cations.[11,12] Conversely, the enhancement by veratrum alkaloids[42] and by low calcium levels of the medium[43] of the depolarizability of nerve fibers by sodium and potassium has corroborated the increase in ion permeability indicated by measurements of ion transfer.[11,12] More recently, the elegant studies of Hodgkin and Horowicz[40] of the rapid and slow potential changes induced in single skeletal muscle fibers by changes in the concentrations of the ions in the milieu have been shown to predict permeabilities in good agreement with the ionic studies. When account is taken of data on calcium fluxes,[31,44] and more recent findings on P_{Cl} of squid axon,[135] the relative permeabilities in muscle are $P_{Cl}:P_K:P_{Na}:P_{Ca} = 200:100:1:0.1$ and in the squid axon are $20:100:2.5:0.1$.

An important development of the past decade has been an increased recognition of the complexity of the membrane property designated permeability. On the one hand, it is a highly labile feature, susceptible to change not only with potential but by physiological and pharmacological agents as well.[2,3] On the other hand, the transfer of ions involves a mechanism substantially more complicated than passage through aqueous holes in a rigid framework or displacement of molecules in a liquid film.[2] For this reason, the flux measurements do not agree exactly with fluxes predicted from simple membrane theory.[40,45]

Neither a liquid nor a solid model can ordinarily account for the penetration of alkali metal ions in living membranes; for example, instead of permeation increasing continually with decreasing hydrated diameter, e.g., according to the series Li < Na < K < Rb < Cs, more usually there is an optimum with K.[46-49] This has led to the proposal that it is the *unhydrated* ion which enters.[2] Thus, interaction with certain sites in the membrane, e.g., by chelation or by solvation, would increase with the ease that water of hydration can be displaced from the ions, as occurs as one goes from lithium to cesium; however, since the diameter of the ions also increases in this order, the entry of the larger ions would be limited by the fewer number of large channels— channels that are probably of the dimensions of molecular spaces.[2] The small size of the channels demanded by this proposal has the additional merit of being consistent with the evidence obtained in the squid giant axon,[45] and more recently in muscle fibers,[40] that passive transport of ions in one direction interferes with their transport in the opposite direction. Hodgkin and Keynes[45] point out that this lack of independence between outflux and influx is accounted for by "single-file" transfer, which leads to membrane conductances larger than would be predicted from the fluxes or, conversely, to smaller fluxes than would be estimated from the conductances. Mullins[50] has sought to explain these and other observations in terms of small pores that must exactly fit ions with one water molecule of hydration; aside from the question of the significance of a single diameter assigned to such hydrated ions, it remains to be demonstrated that the proposed critical fit can indeed determine the passage of ions in physico-chemical systems.

The concept of the transport of ions in the unhydrated form receives further support from electrical studies on vertebrate nerve which indicate that calcium interferes more markedly with sodium transfer and barium more with potassium transport.[2] Attention has been called to the closeness of the *unhydrated* diameters of the divalent ions to those of the monovalent ions they antagonize.[2] It remains to be seen whether the relatively large channel diameters (8 Å) estimated from studies of water transport[51] in invertebrate fibers are correct and hence inconsistent with the ionic studies, or whether they are in error because of oversimplifying assumptions inherent in the derivation of the mathematical theory that was applied.

Changes of ionic permeability were so generally and uncritically proposed during the classical period of physiology as the basis of function and of the action of a wide variety of experimental agents, that in more recent years there has been a natural reluctance to accept this idea as valid. However, the variety of colligated parameters (potential, resistance, and ion flux) now susceptible to direct, precise measurement eliminates many of the uncertainties that plagued the earlier work and appears to justify to some extent many of the old speculations. Of course, these measurements provide much more detail and hence additional complexities to be resolved, but the more general aspects appear quite clear.

The "voltage-clamp" technique has provided ample evidence in several excitable systems for rapid permeability changes during excitation that are governed by membrane potential.[3] These will soon be discussed. Rectification—the greater maintained flow of current outward than inward for the same potential changes in opposite directions—was recognized in the squid axon rather early[52] and very recently studied in great detail in vertebrate fibers.[53] It reflects the sustained increase in potassium permeability often obtained after some delay with depolarization, and the decrease in permeability with hyperpolarization.[45]

In addition to interfering at low concentrations with the increase in permeabilities during depolarization and excitation,[29,30] local anesthetics and other "stabilizers" at somewhat higher concentrations reduce ion permeability in unexcited fibers;[11,12,41] this effect is primarily on passive transport, active transport being relatively little affected.[18,20] Moreover, an analysis of the kinetics of the modification of fluxes upon application of a stabilizer to frog nerve suggests that the permeability change occurs primarily at the outermost interface,[19] in keeping with Truant's findings that procaine taken up by a squid giant axon cannot block unless it is allowed to leak out around the fiber.[54] Conversely, another class of compounds, designated "labilizers" or "unstabilizers," which includes veratrine and certain pure veratrum alkaloids, increases ionic permeability.[11,12,42] The labilizers are antagonized by stabilizers,[11,12,55] calcium, and low pH.[42] Indeed, so far as the resting properties of nerve and muscle are concerned, calcium and low pH may be included in the category of stabilizers since they lower ionic permeability and excitability.[2,56,57] However, it will be pointed out later that the effect of calcium is so different from local anesthetics once excitation has begun[3,29] that it is probably best considered separately.

The permeability changes induced by pharmacological and physiological agents and the various antagonisms that have been demonstrated represent criteria that must be satisfied by any model or hypothesis proposed to account for the nature and the properties of excitable membranes. An important clue to a suitable model was provided by Skou[58-61] with his demonstration that the potency of a wide variety of agents that block nerve conduction closely parallels their ability to interact with monomolecular films of stearic acid and especially of myelin extracts. This interaction causes them to add their own bulk to the films, thereby increasing molecular packing and hence the surface pressure as measured with a Langmuir film balance. These observations led to the proposal[2] that a similar process of increased packing and surface pressure develops among natural membrane molecules and this interferes with passage of ions. The interactions were visualized as occurring with membrane molecules that *surround* ionic sites or channels rather than *with* the sites of penetration themselves, since this makes it possible to explain why stabilizers more readily affect the *increase* in ion permeability—such as might occur through opening of channels during excitation—than the ion permeabilities of unstimulated fibers.

The significance of this model of the membrane has been appreciably increased by the finding by Shanes and Gershfeld[62,63] that labilizers, at the same concentrations that increase the permeabilities of natural membranes, have the opposite effect from stabilizers on monomolecular films of stearic acid, namely, they reduce packing and surface pressure by gradually removing the film molecules; moreover, the antagonisms of stabilizers, calcium, and low pH are also demonstrable on this "dissolution" process. The opposite effects of labilizers and stabilizers in terms of surface pressure require that the packing of film molecules be between that of a liquid and a solid; in other words, the state of organization must be "mesomorphic,"[64] in keeping with other indications of such organization for the living membrane.[2] Less tight packing of film molecules causes labilizers to exhibit primarily the effects of stabilization, *viz.,* increased surface pressure—a result of interest in view of early and recent evidence that, under carefully controlled conditions, labilizers can exhibit stabilizer effects as well.[55,65]

In summary, then, the resting potential appears to be a consequence of the ionic gradients sustained by active transport which, in the process of tending to run down passively through a membrane of labile selective properties, give rise to the potential. Active transport can be depressed by general metabolic inhibition, more specifically by cardiac glycosides (which seem to act on a coupling mechanism in the outermost layer of the membrane[2,66,67]), and by a deficiency of extracellular potassium (which is needed for the exclusion or extrusion type of sodium transport). Passive transfer can be altered by changes in membrane potential directly or by changes in membrane permeability, such as are induced electrically or by physiological and pharmacological agents. The interference of flux in one direction by that in the opposite direction, apparently due to single-file passage of a single ion species, has already been noted. More recently, an opposite effect, namely, a facilitation of sodium outflux by its influx in skeletal muscle, has been observed;[68] this "exchange diffusion", predicted by Levi and Ussing[69] on the basis of energy requirements for transfer, may be the consequence of the inability of sodium to be displaced from certain binding sites by any other physiological ion, as appears to be the case for calcium.[70] Most recently, interference of potassium outflux by sodium influx has been seen in heart fibers,[71] a phenomenon predicted by Shanes[3] from the properties of the action potential in this tissue.

Consequently, although much progress has been made in delineating the properties of the membrane, much remains to be resolved with respect to both passive and active transfer characteristics. The concept of the membrane, or of limited regions in it, as mesomorphic in structure, and of passive transport requiring interactions of unhydrated ions with the molecules in these mesomorphic regions, shows promise as a basis for determining the physico-chemical factors involved.

ACTION POTENTIAL

Spike.—Cole and Curtis's demonstration over 20 years ago of the large decrease in membrane resistance accompanying the action potential in the squid giant axon[72] represented strong evidence for the classical view of an underlying increase in permeability to ions. Had the technique developed for this observation been used to show the dependence of this resistance change as well as of the spike amplitude on extracellular ions, especially on sodium—as was done only recently by Grundfest *et al.*[73]—the role of sodium in the generation of the impulse might have been recognized much sooner. But it was not until 10 years later that Hodgkin and Katz[21] demonstrated the importance of sodium in the squid axon for the production of the initial part of the action potential known as the spike. They pointed out that a large increase in permeability to this ion would produce a reversal in transmembrane potential that approached the sodium equilibrium potential in magnitude, as actually found.

Many other excitable systems have since been shown to require sodium for spike generation.[3] In several situations it appears from electrical measurements that other ions can serve as well or better—for example, multivalent ions in invertebrate muscles and in C-fibers,[74,75] guanidinium in vertebrate nerve,[76] hydrazinium in muscle,[77] and even potassium in invertebrate and vertebrate nerve.[78,79] These findings serve to focus attention on the change in physical state of the membrane, reflected by an increase in permeability to cations, rather than on the transport of a specific cation. Failure to recognize this led in a few instances to premature dismissal of diffusion potentials as the basis of spikes in nerve.[80,81] In certain heart fibers[82] and in spinal ganglia[83] it is still not definite how spike amplitude is preserved in low sodium media, but since a decrease in resistance during the impulse has been found in the one instance where such measurement was made,[84] enhanced ion transport, perhaps of calcium, still remains a possibility.

In the systems where careful measurements of unidirectional transport have been made, the possible contribution of calcium to the currents during excitation has been found to be small compared to that of sodium. Thus, in the squid giant axon this is only $1/1000$ of the sodium[31] and in skeletal muscle fibers $1/50$.[44] The possibility remains to be examined that in some cells, especially in the heart, where competition between sodium and calcium in contractile phenomena is recognized,[85] calcium may contribute appreciably to the action potential when the level of sodium is reduced; this merits exploration in smooth muscle as well.

The voltage-clamp technique, as applied by Hodgkin and Huxley to the squid giant axon[3] and more recently by Tasaki and Bak[86] and Dodge and Frankenhaeuser[27] to the node of Ranvier, has shown that a sudden, sustained depolarization applied to the excitable membrane produces an initial inwardly directed current which subsides and is eventually replaced by an outward current. On the basis of a variety of experimental procedures and theoretical deductions Hodgkin and Huxley and their associates conclude that a large increase in sodium permeability is normally the first event; this is secondarily depressed by a process designated "inactivation," which is accompanied by or followed by an increase in potassium permeability.[3,87,88] The three processes are functions solely of membrane potential, for on the basis of this principle remarkable success has been achieved in predicting subthreshold excitation phenomena, the spike, the accompanying changes in resistance, the ionic transfer, and the bioelectrical behavior of the squid giant axon under a wide variety of experimental conditions.[3,89-91]

Tasaki and Bak,[86,92] on the basis of oscillations of potential seen by them and others under voltage clamp conditons, both with the giant axon and single nodes of Ranvier, have sought to reject these important conclusions about the sequence of permeability changes during depolarization and during the spike. However, inadequate clamping, through high resistance of internal electrodes and inhomogeneities in squid axons[93] or because of network peculiarities inherent in the internodes of vertebrate single fibers,[27] appears to be the more likely cause of the oscillations. Other observations, such as prolonged action potentials or the existence of "two stable states," one of polarization and the other of depolarization, that were considered to render the ion diffusion approach untenable,[94] have since been noted to be predictable from the Hodgkin-Huxley scheme or to involve ionic membrane properties peculiar to low currents that remain to be clarified.[3,91,136] Consideration may ultimately have to be given to certain passive properties of the membrane not yet fully defined—for example, interaction between sodium and potassium fluxes or the reversal of normal rectification properties (anomalous rectification).[3,40,71] Under the circumstances, observations that appear not to conform to the principles that have been elucidated to date must be carefully evaluated before permeability is rejected as a factor.

The initial rise in permeability, usually to sodium, and the succeeding inactivation—the decrease in this sodium permeability—appear to be relatively general phenomena; the increase in potassium permeability which contributes to a recharging of the membrane may be much delayed or even absent, thereby contributing to prolongation of the action potential.[3] The tetraethylammonium ion (TEA), barium and probably other heavy metals, and hyperpolarization all share the property of interfering with the increase in potassium permeability and thereby prolong the action potential; they also probably reduce the permeability to potassium in the unexcited membrane.[3,95,96] The calcium ion also reduces the permeability of the unexcited membrane to ions, an effect possibly due to occupation of the sites—probably negative ones—required by sodium and potassium for transport through the membrane.[3] Many observations of the past point to an increase in P_K and P_{Na} when the calcium level of the medium is lowered.[3,43,97] This has made it appear likely that calcium is displaced from the sites it occupies by excitation or depolarization.[3,97] Such displacement provides a basis for the observation that elevation of the calcium in the medium increases the spike.[98,99] The greater spike has been shown to be associated with larger permeability changes to both sodium and potassium.[29] In the case of sodium this is related in part to the ability of calcium to reduce the inactivation normally present in squid axons.[28] However, the reduction of the leakiness to sodium and potassium could itself play a part in the improved magnitudes of the permeability changes; for example, if calcium were to leave the additional occupied sites during excitation, there would be correspondingly more available for ion transport.

REGULATION OF FUNCTION

Alterations in the ability of excitable cells to function appear to be basically due to physico-chemical factors even when metabolism is most directly affected. It has already been pointed out that, with respect to the resting potential, continuous energy turnover plays its part in maintaining the ionic gradients and, through sodium exclusion, in reducing the depolarizing influence of inward leaking sodium. In the systems studied so far, the membrane permeability characteristics appear to be remarkably stable for long periods despite low or negligible energy turnover.

In the generation of the spike there is no substantial evidence of an involvement of metabolism other than indirectly through its regulation of ionic gradients and membrane potential.[3] Thus, one may regard the gradients as a store of potential energy, built up through metabolism during an earlier period, to be rapidly released in small amounts per impulse during a cyclic series of events that themselves appear to require very little energy other than that derived from the ionic gradients and the associated electric field. Earlier thermal measurements had indicated an initial heat liberation too small to account even for the current flow of conduction.[100] The recent studies of Abbott et al.[101] with improved methods have revealed that the heat output is actually ten times larger but quickly followed by an endothermic process of unknown nature that absorbs 90% of the heat produced. The initial heat is regarded as probably largely accounted for by the physico-chemical processes, for example, the heat of ionic mixing, rather than by an energy yielding reaction such as the splitting of adenosine triphosphate.

During metabolic derangement the spike will be depressed by an increase in the intracellular sodium level, by depolarization, or both. The first follows from the dependence of the reversal of potential on the sodium equilibrium potential, the second from the dependence of the kinetics and magnitude of the increase of sodium permeability on membrane potential. The condition of inactivation, which weakens the increase in sodium permeability, increases rapidly with depolarization, so that changes in membrane potential of only 20 to 30 millivolts can suffice to block excitability.

Metabolic disturbance can cause depolarization either through accumulation of potassium around the fibers if diffusion is a limiting factor, through depletion of intracellular potassium, or through increased inward leak of sodium. In the squid giant axon, although the active sodium and potassium fluxes are greatly depressed by metabolic inhibitors, the membrane potential is essentially unaltered and the impulses and the associate ionic interchanges are also normal for long periods.[39] Even when many inhibitors are present simultaneously to block metabolism, which in vertebrate nerve *in vitro* depolarizes partly by potassium accumulation around the fibers,[3] repolarization by passage of an electric current suffices to restore impulse production.[102] Conduction continues for many hours in vertebrate nerve even when the increase in oxygen consumption associated with activity is prevented,[103,104] presumably because resting metabolism is adequate in these fibers for the restoration of ions lost during activity.[105] It has been pointed out that the ionic interchanges of activity, expressed per unit area, are about the same for large and small fibers; since the surface to volume ratio in the latter is larger, the decline of the ionic gradients will be faster.[106] From an evolutionary standpoint, this provides a basis for the greater activity metabolism of smaller fibers in invertebrates[107,108] and vertebrates;[109] this greater metabolism in small fibers is reflected in its ability to cause potassium reabsorption following activity.[106]

Occasional suggestions of metabolic effects by other than the mechanisms outlined require careful evaluation before they can be seriously considered. In such cases it often appears that the consequences of the use of metabolic inhibitors may arise from interactions (e.g., stabilization) which have nothing to do with metabolic inhibition.[3]

In addition to the effects induced by metabolic change, functional activity may be altered (a) by agents which affect the membrane potential through modification of the ion permeabilities at rest, and (b) by agents which modify the mechanism of permeability change during excitation more directly.[3] It has already been mentioned that (b) is achieved by lower concentrations of the same drugs that can cause (a), a situation that may be explained by interaction with molecules that surround the sites of ion passage. Such interaction is visualized as altering the surface pressure and so modifying the ease with which membrane molecules are displaced to facilitate ion transport during excitation. For example, suppose negative charges on adjacent molecules in the membrane normally are neutralized by calcium in the medium. If, during depolarization, this calcium is removed, the exposed negative charges will cause the membrane molecules to move apart and also provide additional sites for sodium or potassium entry. The presence of a stabilizer among the molecules would raise the surface pressure, thereby hampering separation of the molecules. This view is consistent with voltage-clamp studies.[3,29,30] The idea of a separation of molecules around sites of ion passage also provides a qualitative basis for the phenomenon that the permeability increase in low concentrations of veratrum alkaloids is accentuated temporarily by passage of the impulse and so causes a negative afterpotential.[3] Thus, an increase in surface pressure in lipoidal (stearate) monomolecular films enhances the removal of the lipid molecules by these alkaloids.[62,63] The postulated separation of membrane molecules by mutual repulsion during the spike would raise the surface pressure around the ion channels and so remove more membrane molecules and increase the leakiness to ions. The internal reserves of surface active lipid would have to restore the membrane molecules to terminate the negative afterpotential. It remains to be seen whether the expected release of lipid during activity can be induced by veratrum alkaloids.

Of probable significance for the different sensitivities of various types of neurons to blocking agents is the finding, with monomolecular films, that the interactions are a function of the specific lipoidal molecules composing the film as well as of the structure of the drugs.[59,60] The corresponding veratrum studies[62,63] also serve to emphasize the degree of packing of the molecules in the film. One emerges, then, with the view that an understanding of the selective aspects of drug action in the central nervous system will ultimately require knowledge not only of the composition but of the organization of the molecular components at interfaces, especially those of the membranes. The art of electron and other forms of microscopy has opened up new possibilities in the visualization of detail in membranes and other ultrastructure;[110,111] but one cannot dare to guess when it will be able to contribute with certainty to the problem of organization. Until then, extraction procedures, combined with film studies of the interactions of the extracted materials with physiological and pharmacological agents whose effects have been well defined in living systems, may serve to provide clues to these problems.

Afterpotentials.—The slower variations in membrane potential that often follow the spike or repetitive activity—the residual delayed repolarization known as the negative afterpotential and the succeeding hyperpolarization, the positive afterpotential, that gradually subsides—appear explicable in terms of the passive and active transport characteristics already discussed.[3] Thus, the negative afterpotential in nerve can be the consequence (a) of a transitory accumulation of potassium around the fibers resulting from release during excitation, as in invertebrate[15,112,113] and C-fibers,[16,113] and (b) of a delay in the return of sodium permeability to its low resting value, as in myelinated nerve and in veratrinized fibers.[3,114] The positive afterpotential has been clearly correlated with depletion of extracellular potassium by active transport in crab nerve.[112,113,137] A similar proposal for C-fibers[16,115] has been questioned.[3,17] Connelly[17] presents indirect evidence for active transport contributing to the positive afterpotential independently of potassium depletion in vertebrate nerve. He suggests that the outward transport of sodium generates the afterpositivity, a view inherent in undirectional sodium transport as once proposed for frog skin;[116] however, the operation of an augmented sodium exclusion mechanism would account for the results as well and has the advantage of not being based on a process that has had to be rejected as non-existent in frog skin[117] and for which there is now no clear evidence. Meves[138] presents evidence for the positive afterpotential in frog nerve being due to a sustained increase in potassium permeability. More detailed analysis of the positive afterpotential, especially of its dependence on external ions, may be helpful in delineating the associated events in different biological systems.

JUNCTIONS

An understanding of the properties of the central nervous system must ultimately involve an appreciation not only of the peculiarities of the individual neuronal elements but of their interactions with each other as well. This must include, therefore, familiarity with the characteristics of synapses.

With one exception in invertebrates,[118] it appears that junctional transmission involves release of a chemical agent—a transmitter—by prejunctional fibers, and this transmitter, by increasing the ionic permeability of the junctional membrane of the postjunctional fibers, induces a change in potential or an increase in membrane conductance which accounts for the transmitter's effects.[2] These permeability changes are even more susceptible to modification by physiological and pharmacological agents than are the nerve and muscle membranes discussed previously.[2]

At the myoneural junction, the release of acetylcholine by afferent fibers causes a localized excitatory depolarization due to an increase in permeability of the junction to sodium and potassium, and perhaps to chloride; this increase in permeability produces a localized short-circuit of the muscle membrane, thereby causing adjacent regions to discharge into it and to become excited.[119] Impairment of this mechanism can occur at many more points than in the individual cells. Thus, in addition to the active and passive transport processes and the excitability mechanisms in nerve and muscle already discussed, alterations can conceivably occur with respect to (a) synthesis of the transmitter, (b) the mechanism of transmitter release, (c) the interaction of transmitter with the junction, (d) the changes in permeability of the junctional membrane, and (e) destruction of the transmitter by an esterase.

The effects of cholinesterase inhibitors on (e) and of curariform agents on (c) are too well-known to require comment. It might be noted, however, that curarization may involve not only competition with the transmitter for "receptors" but a stabilization similar to that discussed for nerve.[2] Jenkinson[139] presents data favoring competition as the basis for tubocurarine action. Axelsson and Thesleff[120] have demonstrated that the transmitter itself may secondarily exhibit curariform action. Calcium is essential for the release of acetylcholine by the nerve terminals,[121] an action antagonized by magnesium, which also augments cholinesterase activity.[122] One is inclined to wonder to what extent the familiar phenomenon of "magnesium narcosis," so readily neutralized by an injection of calcium, is due to the interaction of these ions at the myoneural junctions or to a similar action at central synapses.

Recent evidence indicates that, in addition to calcium, organic cations such as tetraethylammonium[123] and guanidinium[124] enhance the release of acetylcholine by stimulated prejunctional fibers.

Inhibitory transmitter action, as evident in the action of acetylcholine on sino-auricular fibers[2] and of stimulated inhibitory fibers on crustacean stretch receptors[125,126] and muscle,[127] differs from the excitatory type in that the increase in permeability to sodium is small or negligible compared to that to other ions, (either chloride, potassium, or both), consequently there is a large increase in conductance, usually with no depolarization or with a hyperpolarization. The similarity of the effects of certain γ-amino acids to those of inhibitory transmitters has stimulated much research and controversy.[128,129]

The careful studies of Fatt, Eccles and their collaborators on single motoneurons[130] reveal essentially the same differences between the permeability changes at excitatory (depolarizing)[131] and at inhibitory (hyperpolarizing synapses[132] observed in corresponding peripheral structures.

The dependence of transmitter release on calcium and the negligible amount of free calcium in the protoplasm of cells where this has been carefully examined[31,32] provides a basis for the postulate that a transitory rise in intracellular ionized calcium by virtue of entry of calcium into nerve terminals causes release of the transmitter. Hodgkin and Keynes[31] point out this possibility for the myoneural junction and Shanes[3] (p.263) has called attention to the likelihood of its importance for the release of other humoral agents. Studies similar to those which have established a relationship between calcium entry and muscle contraction[44,140,141] should be useful as a test of the proposed role of calcium in transmission.

CONCLUSION

It has been possible to touch on only some of the highlights and some of the possibilities in the recent developments in our concepts of the role of electrolytes in nerve function. The application of precise, new techniques for the study of rapid and slow changes in potential, resistance, and ion distribution has established interrelationships among these properties which, on the one hand, provide strong evidence for the electrochemical basis of resting and action potentials and, on the other hand, demonstrate that the "passive" transport characteristics of the excited and unexcited living membrane are far more complex than originally appreciated. The nature of "permeability" and of the mechanisms whereby the permeability changes occur pose challenging problems for the future. Physico-chemical methods, combined with the use of physiological and pharmacological agents with well-defined actions on living membranes, seem promising as an approach to these problems.

Modern methods have also clarified our understanding of the role of metabolism, which is less direct than often postulated. As recognized by McIlwain[133] and Kini and Quastel,[134] it is important to distinguish in experimental studies between metabolic changes which are a *consequence* of functional changes brought about by direct physico-chemical interactions from those that *cause* the functional changes. The former may be far more common than is usually assumed.

In any case, it is clear that these methods, and the concepts to which they have led, cannot be neglected if nerve function is ultimately to be understood fully.

REFERENCES

1. KEYNES, R. D., and LEWIS, P. R.: In *Neurochemistry*, 1st Ed. K. A. C. Elliott, I. H. Page, J. H. Quastel, Eds. Springfield, Ill., Thomas (1955).
2. SHANES, A. M.: *Pharmacol. Rev., 10*:59 (1958).
3. SHANES, A. M.: *Pharmacol. Rev., 22*:165 (1958).
4. SHANES, A. M.: *Am. J. Physiol., 153*:93 (1948).
5. SHANES, A. M., and HOPKINS, H. S.: *J. Neurophysiol., 11*:331 (1948).
6. SHANES, A. M.: *Biol. Bull., 95*:245 (1948).
7. SHANES, A. M.: *Biol. Bull., 97*:247 (1949).
8. SHANES, A. M.: *J. Gen. Physiol., 33*:643 (1950).
9. FENN, W. O., and GERSHMAN, R.: *J. Gen. Physiol., 33*:195 (1950).
10. FENG, T. P., HAU, C. H., and LIU, Y.: *Chin. J. Physiol., 17*:281 (1950).
11. SHANES, A. M.: *Federation Proc., 10*:611 (1951).
12. SHANES, A. M.: *Ann. New York Acad. Sc., 55*:1 (1952).
13. HURLBUT, W. P.: *J. Gen. Physiol., 41*:959 (1957).
14. SHANES, A. M.: *J. Gen. Physiol., 34*:795 (1951).
15. FRANKENHAEUSER, B., and HODGKIN, A. L.: *J. Physiol., 131*:341 (1957).
16. RITCHIE, J. M., and STRAUB, R. W.: *J. Physiol., 136*:80 (1957).

17. CONNELLY, C. M.: *Rev. Mod. Phys., 31:*475 (1959).
18. SHANES, A. M.: In *Metabolic Aspects of Transport Across Cell Membranes.* Q. R. Murphy, Ed. Madison, Univ. of Wisconsin Press (1957).
19. SHANES, A. M., and BERMAN, M. D.: *J. Pharmacol. & Exper. Therap., 125:*316 (1959).
20. SHANES, A. M.: *Science, 124:*724 (1956).
21. HODGKIN, A. L., and KATZ, B.: *J. Physiol., 108:*37 (1949).
22. HODGKIN, A. L., and HUXLEY, A. F.: *Nature, 144:*710 (1939).
23. CURTIS, H. J., and COLE, K. S.: *J. Cell. & Comp. Physiol., 19:*135 (1942).
24. HODGKIN, A. L.: *Proc. Roy. Soc. London,* B, *148:*1 (1957).
25. MARMONT, G.: *J. Cell. & Comp. Physiol., 34:*351 (1949).
26. COLE, K. S.: *Arch. sc. physiol., 3:*253 (1949).
27. DODGE, F. A., and FRANKENHAEUSER, B.: *J. Physiol., 143:*76 (1958).
28. FRANKENHAEUSER, B., and HODGKIN, A. L.: *J. Physiol., 137:*218 (1957).
29. SHANES, A. M., FREYGANG, W. H., GRUNDFEST, H., and AMATNIEK, E.: *J. Gen. Physiol., 42:*793 (1959).
30. TAYLOR, R. E.: *Am. J. Physiol., 196:*1071 (1959).
31. HODGKIN, A. L., and KEYNES, R. D.: *J. Physiol., 138:*253 (1957).
32. CHAMBERS, R., and KAO, C.-Y.: *Exper. Cell Res., 3:*564 (1952).
33. SOLOMON, S., and TOBIAS, J. M.: *Biol. Bull., 101:*198 (1951).
34. NIEDERGERKE, R.: *J. Physiol., 128:*12P (1955).
35. HARRIS, E. J.: *Biochim. et biophys. acta, 23:*80 (1957).
36. GILBERT, D. L., and FENN, W. O.: *J. Gen. Physiol., 40:*393 (1957).
37. CALKINS, E., TAYLOR, I. M., and HASTINGS, A. B.: *Am. J. Physiol., 177:*211 (1954).
38. FRAZIER, H. S., and KEYNES, R. D.: *J. Physiol., 148:*362 (1959).
39. HODGKIN, A. L., and KEYNES, R. D.: *J. Physiol., 128:*28 (1955).
40. HODGKIN, A. L., and HOROWICZ, P.: *J. Physiol., 148:*127 (1959).
41. STRAUB, R.: *Arch. internat. pharmacodyn., 57:*414 (1956).
42. STRAUB, R.: *Helvet. physiol. acta, 14:*1 (1956).
43. SCHMIDT, H., and STÄMPFLI, R.: *Helvet. physiol. acta, 16:*379 (1958).
44. BIANCHI, C. P., and SHANES, A. M.: *J. Gen. Physiol., 42:*803 (1959).
45. HODGKIN, A. L., and KEYNES, R. D.: *J. Physiol., 128:*61 (1955).
46. HOEBER, R.: *Physical Chemistry of Cells and Tissues.* Philadelphia, Blakeston (1945).
47. COWAN, S. L.: *Proc. Roy. Soc. London,* B, *115:*216 (1934).
48. FENG, T. P., and LIU, Y. M.: *J. Cell. & Comp. Physiol., 34:*33 (1949).
49. MULLINS, L. J.: *J. Gen. Physiol., 42:*817 (1959).
50. MULLINS, L. J.: In *Molecular Structure and Functional Activity of Nerve Cells.* Washington, D. C., Am. Inst. Biol. Sc. (1956).
51. VILLEGAS, R., and BARNOLA, F. V.: *J. Gen. Physiol., 44:*963 (1961).
52. COLE, K. S., and BAKER, R. F.: *J. Gen. Physiol., 22:*649 (1939).
53. STÄMPFLI, R.: *Helvet. physiol. acta, 16:*127 (1958).
54. TRUANT, A. P.: *Federation Proc., 9:*321 (1950).
55. SHANES, A. M.: *J. Cell. & Comp. Physiol., 38:*17 (1951).
56. DETTBARN, W. D., and STÄMPFLI, R.: *Helvet. physiol. acta. 15:*16C (1957).
57. MEVES, H.: In *Medizin, Theorie und Klinik in Einzeldarstellungen,* Vol. 5. Heidelberg, Alfred Hüthig Publishers (1958).
58. SKOU, J. C.: *Acta pharmacol. et toxicol., 10:*281 (1954).
59. SKOU, J. C.: *Acta pharmacol. et toxicol., 10:*317 (1954).
60. SKOU, J. C.: *Acta pharmacol. et toxicol., 10:*325 (1954).

61. SKOU, J. C.: *Biochim. et biophys. acta, 30:*625 (1958).
62. GERSHFELD, N. L., and SHANES, A. M.: *Science, 129:*1427 (1959).
63. SHANES, A. M., and GERSHELD, N. L.: *J. Gen. Physiol., 44:*345 (1960).
64. BROWN, G. H., and SHAW, W. G.: *Chem. Rev., 57:*1049 (1957).
65. HERR, F., and AKCASU, A.: *J. Pharmacol. & Exper. Therap. 130:*328 (1960).
66. CALDWELL, P. C., and KEYNES, R. D.: *J. Physiol., 148:*8P (1959).
67. POST, R. L.: *Federation Proc., 18:*121 (1959).
68. KEYNES, R. D., and SWAN, R. C.: *J. Physiol., 147:*591 (1959).
69. LEVI, H., and USSING, H. H.: *Acta physiol. scandinav., 16:*232 (1948).
70. SHANES, A. M., and BIANCHI, C. P.: *J. Gen. Physiol., 42:*1123 (1959).
71. CARMELIET, E.: *Helvet. physiol. acta, 18:*C15 (1960).
72. COLE, K. S., and CURTIS, H. J.: *J. Gen. Physiol., 22:*649 (1939).
73. GRUNDFEST, H., SHANES, A. M., and FREYGANG, W.: *J. Gen. Physiol., 37:*25 (1953).
74. FATT, P., and GINSBORG, B. L.: *J. Physiol., 142:*516 (1958).
75. GREENGARD, P., and STRAUB, R. W.: *J. Physiol., 145:*562 (1959).
76. LÜTTGAU, H.-C.: *Pflüger's Arch. ges. Physiol., 267:*331 (1958).
77. KOKETSU, K., and NISHI, S.: *J. Physiol., 150:*440 (1960).
78. LÜTTGAU, H.-C.: *Nature, 184:*1494 (1959).
79. MOORE, J. W.: *Nature, 183:*265 (1959).
80. LORENTE, DE NÓ, R., VIDAL, R., and LARRAMANDI, L. M. H.: *Nature, 179:*737 (1957).
81. MÜLLER, P.: *J. Gen. Physiol., 42:*137 (1958).
82. DÉLÈZE, J.: *Circulation Res., 7:*461 (1959).
83. KOKETSU, K., CERF, J. A., and NISHI, S.: *J. Neurophysiol., 22:*693 (1959).
84. KOKETSU, K., CERF, J. A., and NISHI, S.: *J. Neurophysiol., 22:*177 (1959).
85. LÜTTGAU, H.-C., and NIEDERGERKE, R.: *J. Physiol., 143:*486 (1958).
86. TASAKI, I., and BAK, A. F.: *J. Neurophysiol., 21:*124 (1958).
87. DODGE, F. A., and FRANKENHAEUSER, B.: *J. Physiol., 148:*188 (1959).
88. FRANKENHAEUSER, B.: *J. Physiol., 148:*671 (1959).
89. HODGKIN, A. L., and HUXLEY, A. F.: *J. Physiol., 117:*500 (1952).
90. COLE, K. S., ANTOSIEWICZ, H. A., and RABINOWITZ, P.: *J. Soc. Indust. Appl. Math., 3:*153 (1955).
91. HUXLEY, A. F.: *Ann. New York Acad. Sc., 81:*221 (1959).
92. TASAKI, I., and BAK, A. F.: *Am. J. Physiol., 193:*301 (1958).
93. TAYLOR, R. E., MOORE, J. W., and COLE, K. S.: Personal communication.
94. TASAKI, I., and HAGIWARA, S.: *J. Gen. Physiol., 40:*859 (1957).
95. WERMAN, R., and GRUNDFEST, H.: *Federation Proc., 19:*298 (1960).
96. WERMAN, R., and GRUNDFEST, H.: *J. Gen. Physiol., 44:*997 (1961).
97. BRINK, F.: *Pharmacol. Rev., 6:*243 (1954).
98. SHANES, A. M.: *J. Gen. Physiol., 33:*57 (1949).
99. ADELMAN, W. J., and DALTON, J. C.: *J. Gen. Physiol., 43:*609 (1960).
100. HODGKIN, A. L.: *Biol. Rev., 26:*23 (1951).
101. ABBOTT, B. C., HILL, A. V., and HOWARTH, J. V.: *Proc. Roy. Soc.* London, B, *148:*149 (1958).
102. LORENTE, DE NÓ, R.: *Harvey Lect., 42:*43 (1946).
103. DOTY, R. W., and GERARD, R. W.: *Am. J. Physiol., 162:*458 (1950).
104. BRINK, F., BRONK, D. W., CARLSON, F. D., and CONNELLY, C. M.: *Cold Spr. Harb. Symp. Quant. Biol., 17:*53 (1952).
105. ASANO, T., and HURLBUT, W. P.: *J. Gen. Physiol., 41:*1187 (1958).
106. SHANES, A. M.: *Am. J. Physiol., 177:*377 (1954).

107. CONNELLY, C. M., and CRANEFIELD, C. F.: *Abstr. Comm. Internat. Physiol. Cong. Montreal, 19:*276 (1953).
108. FENG, T. P.: *Ergebn. Physiol., 38:*73 (1936).
109. LARRABEE, M. G., and BRONK, D. W.: *Cold Spr. Harb. Symp. Quant. Biol., 17:*245 (1952).
110. ROBERTSON, J. D.: *J. Physiol., 140:*58P (1957).
111. FINEAN, J. B., and ROBERTSON, J. D.: *Brit. M. Bull., 14:*267 (1958).
112. SHANES, A. M.: *J. Gen. Physiol., 33:*75 (1949).
113. SHANES, A. M.: *J. Gen. Physiol., 34:*795 (1951).
114. MEVES, H.: *Pflüger's Arch. ges. Physiol., 271:*655 (1960).
115. GREENGARD, P., and STRAUB, R. W.: *J. Physiol., 145:*562 (1959).
116. USSING, H. H.: In *Ion Transport Across Membranes.* H. T. Clarke, Ed. New York, Academic Press (1954).
117. KOEFOED-JOHNSEN, V., and USSING, H. H.: *Acta physiol. scandinav., 42:*298 (1958).
118. FURSHPAN, E. J., and POTTER, D. D.: *J. Physiol., 145:*289 (1959).
119. DEL CASTILLO, J., and KATZ, B.: *Progr. Biophys., 6:*122 (1956).
120. AXELSSON, J., and THESLEFF, S.: *Acta physiol. scandinav., 43:*15 (1958).
121. DEL CASTILLO, J., and STARK, L.: *J. Physiol., 116:*507 (1952).
122. DEL CASTILLO, J., and ENGBAEK, L.: *J. Physiol., 124:*370 (1954).
123. STOVNER, J.: *Acta pharmacol. et toxicol., 15:*55 (1958).
124. OTSUKA, M., and ENDO, M.: *J. Pharmacol. & Exper. Therap., 128:*273 (1960).
125. KUFFLER, S. W., and EYZAGUIRRE, C.: *J. Gen. Physiol., 39:*155 (1955).
126. EDWARDS, C., and HAGIWARA, S.: *J. Gen. Physiol., 43:*315 (1959).
127. BOISTEL, J., and FATT, P.: *J. Physiol., 144:*176 (1958).
128. KUFFLER, S. W., and EDWARDS, C.: *J. Neurophysiol., 21:*589 (1958).
129. GRUNDFEST, H.: *J. Nerv. & Ment. Dis., 128:*473 (1959).
130. ECCLES, J. C.: *Pflüger's Arch. ges. Physiol., 260:*385 (1955).
131. COOMBS, J. S., ECCLES, J. C., and FATT, P.: *J. Physiol., 130:*374 (1955).
132. COOMBS, J. S., ECCLES, J. C., and FATT, P.: *J. Physiol., 130:*396 (1955).
133. McILWAIN, H.: *Biochemistry and the Central Nervous System.* London, J. & A. Churchill, Ltd. (1959).
134. KINI, M. M., and QUASTEL, J. H.: *Science, 131:*412 (1960).
135. CALDWELL, P. C., and KEYNES, R. D.: *J. Physiol., 154:*177 (1960).
136. JOHNSON, E. A., and GEORGE, E. P.: In *Biophysics of Physiological and Pharmacological Actions.* A. M. Shanes, Ed. Washington, D. C. Amer. Assoc. Adv. Science (1961).
137. NARAHASHI, T., and YAMASAKI, T.: *J. Physiol., 151:*75 (1960).
138. MEVES, H.: *Pflüger's Arch. ges. Physiol., 272:*336 (1961).
139. JENKINSON, O. H.: *J. Physiol., 152:*309 (1960).
140. SHANES, A. M.: *J. Cell. Comp. Physiol., 57:*193 (1961).
141. WINEGRAD, S., and SHANES, A. M.: *J. Gen. Physiol., 45:* In press (1962).

XXIII

PHYSIOLOGY OF CATECHOLAMINES

U. S. von Euler

Of the most important new developments in the physiology of the catecholamines since the previous edition of this volume may be mentioned the demonstration of specific storage granules in chromaffin cells and in adrenergic neurons, the effect of drugs and various factors on the release and storage of amines, the relationships between stimulus rate and uptake by receptors, the elaboration of new and sensitive methods for the estimation of catecholamines in plasma, urine and organs, and the demonstration of specific dopamine-storing cells. Recent discoveries in the biochemistry of catecholamines, such as O-methylation, relationships between storage granules and ATP are treated in a separate chaper.

DISTRIBUTION AND PHYSIOLOGICAL SIGNIFICANCE OF NORADRENALINE AND ADRENALINE

The presence of noradrenaline in adrenergic neurons and in certain chromaffin cells and consequently in all organs and tissues containing such structures, and its role as adrenergic nerve transmitter, is now well established. For details the reader is referred to recent reviews on the subject.[1-6] On the other hand, the role of the noradrenaline present in the adrenal gland seems to be subsidiary only, since no important disturbances have been noted after adrenalectomy in human subjects maintained on cortisol and the urinary excretion of noradrenaline is mainly unchanged.[7] The importance of the noradrenaline released from the adrenergic nerve system is, however, amply demonstrated by the severe disturbances occurring in postural hypotension and after large doses of ganglionic blockers, conditions which are accompanied by a marked reduction of the noradrenaline excretion in urine.[8,9]

The noradrenaline present in organs usually occurs in amounts which are characteristic for each one organ and are directly related to the supply of adrenergic fibers, which contain the transmitter, particularly in the terminal part (nerve endings). The finding of noradrenaline in the vascular wall is but one example of this general rule and depends obviously on the presence of vasomotor adrenergic nerves in the vessels. A definite quantitative correlation between fibre supply and noradrenaline content was demonstrated in the vascular wall by Schmiterlöw.[10] The role of the noradrenaline present in the vascular wall is clearly to regulate the vascular tone through the vasomotor nerves. On the other hand there is no evidence that the adrenergic transmitter should leave the neurons and collect in the tissue[11] where it would presumably soon be inactivated and removed.

After section of the adrenergic nerves noradrenaline almost completely disappears from the organ and reappears on regeneration.[12,13] The ability of the tissues to store noradrenaline in the absence of adrenergic nerves is very small, as evidenced by the failure of injection of large doses of this amine to increase markedly the content in a denervated organ for any length of time.[14]

Except in the organ of Zuckerkandl in fetal organisms there is little evidence of the presence of noradrenaline in chromaffin cells outside the adrenal medulla. The relatively large amounts (5 to 7 μg./gm.) of noradrenaline in the vesicular gland of the adult bull[15] suggest, however, that this amine may be present in extraadrenal chromaffin cells which have been shown to occur in this gland.

No evidence has been presented to show that adrenaline is involved in adrenergic nerve transmission. Although adrenaline mainly acts as a hormone of the adrenal medulla there is increasing evidence that it also plays a physiological role as a secretory product from extraadrenal chromaffin cells. A special type of such cells have been described by Adams-Ray and Nordenstam[16] and has later been shown to be widely distributed in the body and to occur in most organs. The evidence for the presence of adrenaline in chromaffin extraadrenal cells is chiefly based on the finding that after section of the postganglionic sympathetic nerves to an organ the adrenaline, which is usually present in amounts of 2 to 20% of the total catecholamines, remains more or less unchanged.[12,13,17] This seems to be most adequately explained by assuming that while the noradrenaline is contained in the postsynaptic sympathetic fibres and disappears on degeneration of these, adrenaline must be present in a system which is not affected by degeneration of postsynaptic fibres. It is known that the chromaffin cells, for instance in the adrenal medulla, do not lose their contents on degeneration of the presynaptic fibres. Postsynaptic sympathetic neurons likewise maintain their noradrenaline after decentralization.[18] Since, however, chromaffin cells are present in most organs the conclusion appears justified that adrenaline is bound to such cells in the organs and tissues.

The adrenaline excretion in urine after total adrenalectomy in man is greatly reduced, but about one fifth of the resting excretion remains. Indications of increased secretion from extraadrenal chromaffin cells have been obtained during various conditions such as muscular work[19] and during insulin hypoglycemia,[20,21] suggesting that at least some of these cells are innervated. They are different from those described by Falck, Hillarp and Torp[22] in certain tissues of ruminants which contain dopamine.

In this connection the relatively large amounts of adrenaline in the frog's heart are notable. As demonstrated by Loewi[23] the frog's heart is rich in adrenaline. More recent analyses[15] have shown that the frog's ventricle (Rana temporaria) contains 5 to 6 μg. adrenaline per g but only insignificant amounts of noradrenaline, if any. Since the frog's ventricle is not or very sparsely innervated, the adrenaline is presumably bound to chromaffin cells.

Still higher amounts of adrenaline are found in the heart ventricle of the hagfish, Myxine glutinosa (up to 50 μg./gm.) and in the auricle of the lamprey, Petromyzon fluviatilis (up to 140 μg./gm.) Noradrenaline has been found in amounts of about 50 μg./gm. in the auricle and in the portal heart of Myxine. These amounts can not be accounted for by nerves, especially since it has been reported that Petromyzon lacks cardiac nerves.[24] It is therefore assumed that these catecholamines (dopamine is only present in traces in these hearts) occur in chromaffin cells, which have been demonstrated in great abundance.[25]

Although the anatomical localization of adrenaline and noradrenaline in brain has been well established[26,27,33] the kind of cell containing these amines is still not known. While it may be assumed, by analogy, that the adrenaline is present in chromaffin cells, it is still an open question whether the noradrenaline occurs in postsynaptic adrenergic neurons or in chromaffin cells. Degeneration of the postsynaptic fibres from the superior ganglia does not deplete the noradrenaline, however.[28]

Catecholamines can be partly sedimented in granules from homogenates of brain.[29] From their observations on chromaffin cell reactions Falck and Hillarp[30] conclude, however, that the catecholamines present in the brain are not stored in chromaffin cells.

Burn and Rand[31] have offered the hypothesis that the extractable noradrenaline is present around the sympathetic nerve endings forming a store from which noradrenaline can be released by sympathetic impulses. These stores are thought to take up noradrenaline from the blood.

DOPAMINE

Dopamine was discovered in extracts of suprarenal glands of the sheep by Goodall.[12] He also showed its presence in sheep's heart. Montagu[32] reported its presence in brain, and Bertler and Rosengren[33] found that it occurred mainly in corpus striatum. Particularly large amounts have been found in the lung and preparations of bronchi from the cow.[34] Schümann[35] showed that it was present in extract of splenic nerves. The large variations in proportions between noradrenaline and dopamine, which can hardly be explained solely by the role of dopamine as precursor to noradrenaline, became more clear as it was shown[22] that dopamine was present in special cells. The role of these dopamine cells is as yet not known, nor has it been ascertained whether or not they are innervated and how their contents are released. The characteristic distribution of dopamine in the brain[27,33] and observations on the alerting effect of dopa on the reserpine-treated animal[36] suggests, however, a central nervous function.

RELEASE OF ADRENERGIC NERVE TRANSMITTER BY NERVE STIMULATION IN RELATION TO "OVER-FLOW" AND UPTAKE BY RECEPTORS

Brown and Gillespie[37] have shown that the amount of noradrenaline released by a given number of stimuli applied to the splenic nerve of the cat depends on the stimulus frequency. Thus at low frequencies the amount of noradrenaline recovered in the venous blood from the spleen is small and increases as the stimulation frequency increases up to 30 stimuli per second, whereafter it falls again. Iproniazid did not alter these results. In a preparation pretreated with dibenzyline, however, the amount found in the venous blood from the spleen is increased at low frequencies and similar to that found at higher frequencies up to 30 per second. The findings are interpreted as indicating that normally at low stimulation frequencies a large part of the released transmitter is taken up by the receptors and does not enter into the circulation. At higher frequencies the uptake is less complete and a larger fraction appears in the venous blood. After blocking the receptors with dibenzyline the uptake is likewise inhibited and the "overflow" is large even at low stimulation frequencies.

After neuronal rest the amount recovered per stimulus in the splenic vein blood was invariably lower, about 0.3 ng. per stimulus, than after repeated series of 200 stimuli or after 1000 conditioning stimuli, when the output was about 1 ng. per stimulus.[38] It is suggested that in the rested preparation the number of vacant receptors available for combination with the transmitter is increased.

STORAGE AND RELEASE FROM INTRACELLULAR
GRANULES

The presence of catecholamines in intracellular granules from adrenal medullary cells was shown independently by Hillarp et al.[39] and by Blaschko and Welch.[40] The granules have a diameter of 0.1 to 0.6 μ and are covered by a membrane which can be broken up by freezing and thawing, by hypotonic solutions, acids, detergents and other surface active compounds.[41]

By gradient centrifugation a partial separation of noradrenaline and adrenaline containing granules can be achieved[42] but otherwise they seem to have very similar structure and properties.

The assumption that the postsynaptic adrenergic neurons contain the transmitter substance in similar granular structures was experimentally proven by Euler and Hillarp.[43] By high g centrifugation a granular sediment rich in noradrenaline could be isolated from homogenates of spleen and splenic nerves. Granules have later been prepared by squeezing splenic nerves and centrifugation of the press juice.[44] As washing fluid cold isotonic sucrose or various electrolyte solutions have been used. The yield with these techniques is approximately 25% of the total noradrenaline present in the fresh nerve preparation.

The stability of the granules has been studied by exposing the granule suspension to varying temperatures, acidity, tonicity, ions and a variety of drugs.[15] Like the adrenal medullary granules the nerve granules show a considerable stability at pH 6 to 8 in isotonic solution at temperatures just over the freezing point. At room temperature the granules lose their noradrenaline in a few hours, and at pH-values below 5 the release is rapid even at low temperatures. In hypo- or hypertonic solutions the stability is diminished, although the granules from nerves seem to be less sensitive than adrenal medullary granules. Detergents cause an immediate and complete release of the transmitter.

The action of a variety of drugs has been tested on granules from nerves after sedimentation and resuspension in isotonic K-phosphate, followed by incubation at 20°C. for 30 minutes. During these conditions about 30 to 40% of the noradrenaline is released "spontaneously." Of the drugs tested, reserpine,[45] tyramine,[46] promethazine, lidocaine and others have a releasing action. In low concentrations, 10^{-6}-10^{-8} M, reserpine strongly inhibits the spontaneous release of noradrenaline from nerve granules.[45a]

The largest proportion of noradrenaline isolated from granules has been 37% of the total amount present, using the methods of homogenization or squeezing. This percentage is rather smaller than that obtained from adrenal medulla,[41] suggesting that the larger part of the nerve transmitter either occurs in free form in the neuron or in a loosely bound form.

Adrenaline and noradrenaline-containing granules have recently been prepared from the heart tissue of two cyclostomes, Myxine glutinosa (hagfish) and Petromyzon fluviatilis (lamprey). The maximal yields of catecholamines in the granules were obtained by using neutral K-phosphate (0.3 and 0.075 M respectively), and amounted to 40 to 60% of the total quantity. The catecholamines were released by the same factors as in the case of the adrenal or nerve granules.[25] Since the large amounts of catecholamines in the cyclostome hearts cannot be accounted for by adrenergic nerves it is assumed that they are present in chromaffin cells. Histological evidence has been presented for the occurrence of such cells and of storing granules of similar types as those found in the adrenal chromaffin cell and in adrenergic nerves.[25]

Strongly osmiophilic granules have recently been demonstrated in cardiac nerves of the guinea-pig by electron microscopic technique.[47]

No precise information is available as regards the mechanism of release of the transmitter from chromaffin cells or from adrenergic nerves. If a large part of the nerve transmitter occurs in a free or in a loosely bound form as suggested by the findings referred to above, the nerve impulse may be assumed to allow the transmitter to escape through the nerve membranes and reach the target cell by diffusion. Alternatively the nerve impulse may exert a releasing action on the transmitter granules thereby increasing the amount of transmitter available in free form or permitting it to pass from the granule via the membrane of the Schwann cell to the target cell. Hillarp[48] has recently suggested that the small but definite amount occurring in free form in chromaffin cells is in equilibrium with the larger amount (about 90% of the total) present in the granular stores.

EFFECTS OF DRUGS ON STORAGE AND RELEASE OF CATECHOLAMINES

Important observations have been made during recent years concerning the actions of a variety of drugs on the storage and release of adrenaline and noradrenaline from the adrenal medulla, from adrenergic nerves and from tissues containing such nerves and chromaffin cells. The finding that reserpine causes a depletion not only of 5-HT in the brain[49] but also of catecholamines in the brain[50] and in the adrenal medulla and in the heart[51,52] has induced extensive studies in this field. Similarly the discovery of the actions of certain choline phenyl ethers and other more or less closely related substances has widened the interest in these phenomena. Finally tyramine shows some peculiarities of action which have led to certain assumptions as to its mode of action.

Reserpine.—A large number of investigations have confirmed the releasing action of reserpine on the catecholamines from the stores in the adrenal medulla as well as in adrenergic nerves and in chromaffin cells in various tissues. Of particular interest is also the finding that the releasing effect on adrenaline and noradrenaline does not go parallel in certain animals.[53]

The effect of reserpine is partly central and partly peripheral.[54] A releasing effect of reserpine on transmitter granules isolated from adrenergic nerves has also been shown.[45]

The slow repletion of the catecholamine stores in the adrenal medulla and in the adrenergic nerves after reserpine suggests either that the resynthesis mechanism is impaired or that the storing capacity is reduced or less efficient. According to Hillarp[48] the uptake mechanism is disturbed, although the same effect would probably be seen if the storage capacity is diminished. It has been reported[11] that reserpine also depletes the contents of the chromaffin cells in the rabbit's ear. Prolonged treatment with reserpine in small doses also causes depletion of the special kinds of storing cells present in the heart of Petromyzon and Myxine.[25] The catecholamine-releasing effect of reserpine on the storage granules suggests a disturbance of the membrane functions, possibly by interference with metabolic processes serving to maintain the homeostatic mechanisms of the membrane.

It has been shown that tissues can take up small amounts of catecholamines after depletion with reserpine if the amines are administered in large quantities intravenously. Part of the amines so fixed can even be released by subsequent nerve stimulation,[31] suggesting that the amines are in some way attached to the nerves. This, however, does not indicate that the storage granules take up the amines, which possibly may adhere temporarily in small amounts to the nerves in an unspecific way.

The supersensitivity of reserpine-treated cats towards the effect of adrenaline on the blood pressure[55] has been interpreted as due to diminished quantities of the normal transmitter at receptor levels.[56]

Xylocholine (choline 2,6-xylyl ether bromide, T.M.10).—Hey and Willey[57] showed that xylocholine blocked the responses of the nictitating membrane to sympathetic nerve stimulation in the cat. Exley[58] further demonstrated that noradrenaline was not released from the adrenergic nerve endings on stimulation after xylocholine. It is possible that xylocholine interferes with the formation of noradrenaline from dopamine, since it has been reported that this reaction is inhibited in homogenates of human chromaffin cell tumours.[59] The effect of xylocholine can be blocked by cocaine intravenously.[60]

Bretylium (Darenthin, N-o-bromobenzyl-N-ethyl: N : N-dimethylammonium p-toluenesulphonate) like T.M.10 prevents the effects of sympathetic nerve stimulation. It does not deplete the suprarenals or the tissues of catecholamines.[61] Its action is thought to depend on a blocking of the postsynaptic sympathetic neurone, particularly the endings, after selective accumulation in these parts. It has no or little action on the adrenal medulla which might indicate that it does not affect the release from chromaffin cells. The observation that no radioactive bretylium could be found in brain after i.v. administration suggests that the catecholamines do not occur in postsynaptic neurons in the brain, or else that bretylium cannot enter into the brain.

The effect of injected adrenaline and noradrenaline is increased as after sympathectomy.

Guanethidine (SU-5864 ; [2(octahydro-1-azocinyl)-ethyl]-guanidine sulfate).—The main action of guanethidine is to make sympathetically innervated organs unresponsive to stimulation of adrenergic nerves for periods ranging from 4 days to 3 weeks. This effect is preceded by a brief period of sympathetic stimulation and a transient diminution of nerve conduction and ganglionic transmission. During the period of lowered or abolished responsiveness to sympathetic stimulation the organs are hyperresponsive to injected noradrenaline. From these observations it is concluded that guanethidine chronically interferes with the release and/or distribution of noradrenaline at the adrenergic nerve endings.[62] In accordance herewith the response to carotid occlusion is abolished.[63] Analyses of catecholamines in organs of rats after administration of guanethidine showed no effect after 24 hours. In the heart and spleen catecholamines (estimated by a modification of the method of Weil-Malherbe and Bone) were reduced almost 50% two hours after administration of the drug.[64]

Tyramine.—According to Fleckenstein[65] tyramine belongs to a group of drugs which act by releasing noradrenaline and adrenaline from adrenergic nerve endings and from chromaffin cell stores. In this respect it has similar actions to those of phenylethylamine but differs from its m-hydroxylated analogue dopamine. Accordingly tyramine loses its action after pretreatment of an animal with reserpine[66,56] and after sympathetic denervation. In recent experiments[67,46] it has been shown that tyramine, in concentrations of 3 to 300 μg. per ml, causes an increased release of granules isolated from the adrenal medulla or from adrenergic nerves when incubated at 20° to 37°.

An actual release of noradrenaline from the cat's spleen after injection of tyramine has recently been demonstrated.[68] On the other hand no release of catecholamines was found from the adrenal medulla.

5-Hydroxytryptamine.—A liberating action of 5-HT on the catecholamines of the adrenal medulla in the cat after pretreatment of the animal with iproniazid has been demonstrated.[69]

QUANTITATIVE METHODS FOR THE ESTIMATION OF CATECHOLAMINES

As a result of the elaboration of sensitive convenient and accurate chemical methods, generally based on fluorimetry, the biological assay technique though sometimes useful, has lost ground. The fluorimetric techniques are based on the formation of lutins[70] or on fluorescing condensates of catechol compounds with ethylene diamine.[71] The former or trihydroxy indole (THI) method has proved to be particularly useful since it combines sensitivity with a high degree of specificity. By using two filter sets and oxidation at pH 6-6.5[72,73] the technique has been further improved and can be used for quantitative estimation of adrenaline and noradrenaline in plasma. It has also been adopted for urine and organ extracts.[74,75]

Purification of extracts is achieved either by adsorption on alumina and subsequent elution or by the use of ion exchange resins.

The ethylene diamine condensation method (EDA) which is even more sensitive than the THI method may be used with advantage when pure catechol compounds are available. In the presence of a mixture of catechol compounds its specificity is less satisfactory, however. Thus dihydroxyphenylacetic acid which is present in plasma, urine and tissues and reacts in a way indistinguishable from noradrenaline, may cause too high values. A method for the estimation of adrenaline and noradrenaline in plasma using the THI method has recently been reported by Vendsalu.[76] The adrenaline level in plasma is about 0.1 ng./ml. in venous antecubital blood and 0.3 ng./ml. in arterial blood, while the noradrenaline concentrations are about 0.4 ng./ml. in venous blood and 0.3 ng./ml. in arterial blood in man. Generally the estimations are made with fixed filter sets in a fluorimeter, although some authors use the spectrophotofluorimeter which allows increased specificity by selection of suitable activation and fluorescence wave lengths.

A method for the estimation of dopamine has been described.[77]

REFERENCES

1. EULER, U. S. VON: *Noradrenaline*. Springfield, Ill., Thomas (1956).
2. EULER, U. S. VON: *Handbook of Physiology*—Neurophysiology I, Chapter VII, p. 215 (1959).
3. EULER, U. S. VON: Harvey Lecture, New York (1960).
4. Symposium on Catecholamines. National Institutes of Health, Bethesda, Md., October 16-18 (1958).
5. Colloques Nationaux du Centre National de la Recherche Scientifique, Lyon (1957). L'adrénaline et la noradrénaline dans la régulation des fonctions homéostasiques.
6. Symposium on Adrenergic Mechanisms. London, March 28-29 (1960).
7. EULER, U. S. VON, FRANKSSON, C., and HELLSTRÖM, J.: *Acta physiol. scandinav.*, *31*:1 (1954).
8. LUFT, R., and EULER, U. S. VON: *J. Clin. Invest.*, *32*:1065 (1953).
9. SUNDIN, T.: *Acta med. scandinav.*, *161*:Suppl. 336 (1958).
10. SCHMITERLÖW, C. G.: *Acta physiol. scandinav.*, *16*:Suppl. 56 (1948).
11. BURN, J. H., and RAND, M. J.: *Brit. M. J.*, April *19*:903 (1958).
12. GOODALL, McC.: *Acta physiol. scandinav.*, *24*:Suppl. 85 (1951).
13. EULER, U. S. VON, and PURKHOLD, A.: *Acta physiol. scandinav.*, *24*:212 (1951).
14. EULER, U. S. VON: *Circulation Res.*, *4*:647 (1956).
15. EULER, U. S. VON, and LISHAJKO, F.: Unpublished observations.
16. ADAMS-RAY, J., and NORDENSTAM, H.: *Lyon chir.*, *52*:125 (1956).
17. GOODALL, McC., and KIRSHNER, N.: *J. Clin. Invest.*, *35*:649 (1956).
18. REHN, N. O.: *Acta physiol. scandinav.*, *42*:309 (1958).
19. BIRKE, G., EULER, U. S. VON, and STRÖM, G.: *Acta med. scandinav.*, *164*:219 (1959).
20. EULER, U. S. VON, and LUFT, R.: Unpublished observations.
21. ARMIN, J., and GRANT, R. T.: *J. Physiol.* (London), *149*:228 (1959).
22. FALCK, B., HILLARP, N.-Å., and TORP, A.: *J. Histochem. Cytochem.*, 7:323 (1959).
23. LOEWI, O.: *Pflüger's Arch. ges. Physiol.*, *237*:504 (1936).
24. AUGUSTINSSON, K.-B., FÄNGE, R., JOHNELS, A., and ÖSTLUND, E.: *J. Physiol.* (London), *131*:257 (1956).
25. ÖSTLUND, E., BLOOM, G., ADAMS-RAY, J., RITZÉN, M., SIEGMAN, M., NORDENSTAM, H., LISHAJKO, F., and EULER, U. S. VON: *Nature*, *188*:324 (1960).
26. VOGT, M.: *J. Physiol.* (London), *123*:451 (1954).
27. SANO, I., GAMO, T., KAKIMOTO, Y., TANIGUCHI, K., TAKESADA, M., and NISHINUMA, K.: *Biochim. et biophys. acta*, *32*:586 (1959).
28. BERTLER, Å., and ROSENGREN, E.: *Acta physiol. scandinav.*, *47*:362 (1959).
29. WEIL-MALHERBE, H., and BONE, A. D.: *Nature* (London), *180*:1050 (1957).
30. FALCK, B., and HILLARP, N.-Å.: *Acta anat.* (Basel), *38*:277 (1959).
31. BURN, J. H., and RAND, M. J.: *J. Physiol.* (London), *150*:295 (1960).
32. MONTAGU, K. A.: *Nature* (London), *180*:244 (1957).
33. BERTLER, Å., and ROSENGREN, E.: *Acta physiol. scandinav.*, *47*:350 (1959).
34. EULER, U. S. VON, and LISHAJKO, F.: *Acta physiol. pharmacol. neerl.*, *6*:295 (1957).
35. SCHÜMANN, H. J.: *Arch. exper. Path. u. Pharmakol.*, *234*:17 (1958).
36. CARLSSON, A., LINDQVIST, M., and MAGNUSSON, T.: *Nature* (London), *180*:1200 (1957).
37. BROWN, G. L., and GILLESPIE, J. S.: *J. Physiol.* (London), *138*:81 (1957).

38. BROWN, G. L., DAVIES, B. N., and FERRY, C. B.: *J. Physiol.* (London), *147*:13P (1959).

39. HILLARP, N.-Å., LAGERSTEDT, S., and NILSON, B.: *Acta physiol. scandinav.,* *29*:251 (1953).

40. BLASCHKO, H., and WELCH, A. D.: *Arch. exper. Path. u. Pharmakol.,* *219*:17 (1953).

41. HILLARP, N.-Å., and NILSON, B.: *Acta physiol. scandinav.,* *31*:Suppl. 113, 79 (1954).

42. EADE, N. R.: *J. Physiol.* (London), *141*:183 (1958).

43. EULER, U. S. VON, and HILLARP, N.-Å.: *Nature* (London), *177*:44 (1956).

44. EULER, U. S. VON: *Acta physiol. scandinav.,* *43*:155 (1958).

45. EULER, U. S. VON, and LISHAJKO, F.: *Science, 132*:351 (1960).

46. EULER, U. S. VON, and LISHAJKO, F.: *Experientia* (Basel), *16*:376 (1960).

47. KISCH, B.: *Electron Microscopy of the Cardiovascular System,* Figs. 87 and 88, pp. 141, 143. Springfield, Ill., Thomas (1960).

48. HILLARP, N.-Å.: First internat. Congr. Endocrinol. Copenhagen, July 18-23, 1960.

49. BRODIE, B. B., TOMICH, E. G., KUNTZMAN, R., and SHORE, P. A.: *J. Pharmacol. & Exper. Therap., 119*:461 (1957).

50. HOLZBAUER, M., and VOGT, M.: *J. Neurochem., 1*:8 (1956).

51. CARLSSON, A., and HILLARP, N.-Å.: *Kungl. Fysiograf. Sällsk. Lund förhandl., 26*:nr. 8 (1956).

52. BERTLER, Å., CARLSSON, A., and ROSENGREN, E.: *Naturwissenschaften, 43*:521 (1956).

53. KRONEBERG, G., and SCHÜMANN, H. J.: *Arch. exper. Path. u. Pharmakol., 231*:349 (1957).

54. BRODIE, B. B., OLIN, J. S., KUNTZMAN, R. G., and SHORE, P. A.: *Science, 125*:1293 (1957).

55. BEIN, H. J., GROSS, F., TRIPOD, J., and MEIER, R.: *Schweiz. med. Wchnschr., 83*:1007 (1953).

56. BURN, J. H., and RAND, M. J.: *J. Physiol.* (London), *144*:314 (1958).

57. HEY, P., and WILLEY, G. L.: *Brit. J. Pharmacol., 9*:471 (1954).

58. EXLEY, K. A.: *Brit. J. Pharmacol., 12*:297 (1957).

59. BAIN, W. A., and FIELDEN, R.: *J. Physiol.* (London), *133*:70P (1956).

60. NASMYTH, P. A., and ANDREWS, W. H. H.: *Brit. J. Pharmacol., 14*:477 (1959).

61. BOURA, A. L. A., GREEN, A. F., McCOUBREY, A., LAURENCE, D. R., MOULTON, R., and ROSENHEIM, M. L.: *Lancet, 2*:July 11, 17 (1959).

62. MAXWELL, R. A., PLUMMER, A. J., SCHNEIDER, F., POVALSKI, H., and DANIEL, A. I.: *J. Pharmacol. & Exper. Therap., 128*:22 (1960).

63. PAGE, I. H., and DUSTAN, H. P.: *J.A.M.A., 170*:1265 (1959).

64. SHEPPARD, H., and ZIMMERMAN, J. H.: *Nature* (London), *185*:40 (1960).

65. FLECKENSTEIN, A.: *Verhandl. Deutsch. Ges. Inn. Med., 59*:17 (1953).

66. CARLSSON, A., ROSENGREN, E., BERTLER, Å., and NILSSON, J.: *Psychotropic Drugs.* S. Garattini and V. Ghetti, Eds. Amsterdam, Elsevier (1957).

67. SCHÜMANN, H. J.: *Arch. exper. Path. u. Pharmakol., 238*:41 (1960).

68. STJÄRNE, L.: Unpublished observations.

69. STJÄRNE, L., and SCHAPIRO, S.: *Nature* (London), *184*:2023 (1959).

70. EULER, U. S. VON: *Pharmacol. Rev., 11*:262 (1959).

71. WEIL-MALHERBE, H., and BONE, A. D.: *Biochem. J., 58*:132 (1954).

72. PRICE, H. L., and PRICE, M. L.: *J. Lab. & Clin. Med., 50*:769 (1957).

73. COHEN, G., and GOLDENBERG, M.: *J. Neurochem., 2*:71 (1957).

74. EULER, U. S. VON, and LISHAJKO, F.: *Acta physiol. scandinav.*, *45*:122 (1959).
75. BERTLER, Å., CARLSSON, A., and ROSENGREN, E.: *Acta physiol. scandinav.*, *44*:273 (1958).
76. VENDSALU, A.: *Acta physiol. scandinav.*, *49*:Suppl. 173 (1960).
77. CARLSSON, A., and WALDECK, B.: *Acta physiol scandinav.*, *44*:293 (1958).

XXIV

BIOCHEMISTRY OF THE CATECHOLAMINES

T. L. Sourkes

I. INTRODUCTION

A. Nomenclature

Through usage the word "catechol" has come to signify both *o*-dihydroxybenzene and pentahydroxyflavan. Because of this confusion of meanings the American Chemical Society[1] has recommended the older name "pyrocatechol" (Brenzcatechin) specifically for the former compound. In physiology "catechol" is conventionally reserved for the neurohumoral products of the sympatho-adrenal system. It will be applied here in this sense to the *o*-dihydroxyphenyl compounds associated biogenetically and structurally with β- (3,4-dihydroxyphenyl)-L-alanine (3,4-dopa). Thus, adrenaline and related compounds have come to be called *catecholamines (pyrocatecholamines)*. Other generic names deserve definition here. *Sympathin* is, of course, the name assigned by Cannon and Rosenblueth in 1933 to the neurohumoral effector agents of postganglionic sympathetic nerves and of the adrenal medulla. Its use is now restricted to unknown or uncharacterized sympathetic mediator(s) in the tissues and body fluids. For example, some years ago Holtz assigned the name *urosympathin*[2] to urinary extracts with pressor activity. Most of this activity is now known to be due to the noradrenaline content of the urine, the other catecholamine components of the urosympathin complex being adrenaline and dopamine. Encephalin[3] is a mixture of the catecholamines occurring in the brain. Some authors speak of *epinephrines* as a class term; this is regrettable, inasmuch as the word epinephrine has long ago been pre-empted for a specific compound: N-methyl-β-(3,4-dihydroxyphenyl)-β-hydroxyethylamine. *Aminochrome* has been tentatively suggested by Sobotka and Austin[4] for cyclic oxidation products of catecholamines having two oxygen functions in the 5- and 6-positions of dihydro indole, and including variants in the heterocyclic moiety. Adrenochrome is a well known aminochrome.

Adrenaline and noradrenaline are levorotatory as they occur in nature. This is determined by the orientation of the asymmetric β-carbon atom. The configuration of the *l*-catecholamines is optically related to that of D-mandelic acid[5] and probably to the *threo* form of 3,4-dihydroxyphenylserine.[6] Because the enzymes which catalyze the decarboxylation of the dihydroxyphenyl amino acids are specific for the L-isomers it can be assumed that the diastereoisomer generically related to the natural biologically active isomer of noradrenaline is *threo*-3,4-dihydroxyphenyl-L-serine.

During the growth of our knowledge of the catecholamines a large number of names have been applied to the various compounds in this group. In order to clarify this, a glossary of the catecholamines, their precursors, and related compounds is provided in Table I, along with their chemical structure. Some catecholacids are listed in Table II.

The dihydroxyphenylethylamine structure offers the theoretical possibility of 6 positional isomers, depending upon the location of the two phenolic groups on the ring. These correspond to the 6 isomers of dopa,* all of which have now been synthesized[7] and studied with respect to physical and chromatographic properties and to the action of tyrosinase[7] and of dopa decarboxylase[8] upon them. Of these isomers two have the pyrocatechol nucleus (2,3- and 3,4-dopa). Only 3,4-dopa among them has been found naturally occurring. It was first isolated from the broad bean *(Vicia faba)*.[9] 2,4-Dihydroxy-6-methylphenylalanine has been obtained form the corn cockle *(Agrostemma githago)*,[10] and at least one 2,5-dihydroxyphenyl compound, homogentisic acid, has been discovered as a normal intermediate in the metabolic degradation of tyrosine. Homogentisic acid is derived from 2,5-dihydroxyphenylpyruvic acid[11] which could theoretically be transaminated to form 2,5-dopa.

B. Natural Occurrences of Catecholamines and Related Phenolic Compounds

For almost 50 years after the isolation of adrenaline from the suprarenal medulla[12] adrenaline was the only catecholamine known to occur in animal tissues. That adrenaline could not be responsible for all the actions of the sympathomimetic mediator became apparent by the 1930's and recognition of this fact was written into the concept of two neurohumoral agents, sympathins E and I. Although noradrenaline was proposed during this period by several groups of investigators as a sympathetic neurohumor it remained for the investigations of Holtz,

---

*Where there is no possibility of confusion the 3,4-isomer will be referred to in this chapter simply as dopa.

TABLE I

CATECHOLAMINES AND RELATED COMPOUNDS

Common Name (and Synonyms)	4	3	5	2	6	β	α	N
Phenylalanine	H	H	H	H	H	H	COOH	H
Phenylserine	H	H	H	H	H	OH	COOH	H
Tyrosine (p-tyrosine)	OH	H	H	H	H	H	COOH	H
m-Tyrosine	H	OH	H	H	H	H	COOH	H
o-Tyrosine	H	H	H	OH	H	H	COOH	H
p-Hydroxyphenylserine (pops)	OH	H	H	H	H	OH	COOH	H
3,4-Dihydroxyphenylalanine (3,4-dopa)	OH	OH	H	H	H	H	COOH	H
3,4-Dihydroxyphenylserine (3,4-dops)	OH	OH	H	H	H	OH	COOH	H
β -Phenylethylamine	H	H	H	H	H	H	H	H
β -Phenyl-β -hydroxyethylamine	H	H	H	H	H	OH	H	H
Tyramine [β-(p-hydroxyphenyl)-ethyl-amine]	OH	H	H	H	H	H	H	H
Octopamine [β -hydroxy-β -(p-hydroxyphenyl)-ethyl-amine, β -hydroxytyramine]	OH	H	H	H	H	OH	H	H

Compound						
Dopamine [β-(3,4-dihydroxyphenyl)-ethylamine, 3-hydroxytyramine]	OH	OH	H	H	H	H
Epinine (N-methyldopamine)	OH	OH	H	H	H	CH₃
Noradrenaline [norepinephrine, arterenol, sympathin E, β-(3,4-dihydroxyphenyl)-β-hydroxyethylamine]	OH	OH	H	H	OH	H
Adrenaline [epinephrine, sympathin I, N-methyl-β-(3,4-dihydroxyphenyl)-β-hydroxyethylamine]	OH	OH	H	H	OH	CH₃
Isoproterenol (isuprel, N-isopropylnoradrenaline)	OH	OH	H	H	OH	CH(CH₃)₂
2,4,5-Trihydroxyphenylethylamine	OH	H	OH	OH	H	H
Adrenalone [β-(3,4-dihydroxyphenyl)-β-oxoethylamine]	OH	OH	H	H	O*	H
Metanephrine (m-methyladrenaline)	OH	OCH₃	H	H	OH	CH₃
Normetanephrine (m-methylnoradrenaline)	OH	OCH₃	H	H	OH	CH₃
Mescaline (3,4,5-trimethoxyphenylethylamine)	OCH₃	OCH₃	OCH₃	H	H	H

* keto group.

TABLE II

Some Catecholacids and Related Compounds

Compound	Trivial Names and Abbreviations
3,4-Dihydroxyphenylacetic acid	Dopacetic acid; dopac; homoprotocatechuic acid
3,4-Dihydroxymandelic acid	3,4-dihydroxyphenylglycollic acid; doma
3-Methoxy-4-hydroxyphenylacetic acid	Homovanillic acid; HVA
3-Methoxy-4-hydroxymandelic acid	Vanilmandelic acid; VMA
3,4-Dihydroxyphenylacrylic acid	3,4-Dihydroxycinnamic acid
3-Methoxy-4-hydroxyphenylacrylic acid	Ferulic acid
3-Hydroxy-4-methoxyphenylacrylic acid	*Iso*ferulic acid
2,5-Dihydroxyphenylacetic acid	Homogentisic acid

Credner, and Kroneberg on the chemical nature of urinary sympathin and von Euler on the sympathin of nervous tissue[13] to reveal the existence of *l*-noradrenaline as a normal constituent. Within the next few years this catecholamine was found in the adrenal gland[14] and many other organs,[15] as well as blood,[16] and cerebrospinal fluid.[17]

The discovery of noradrenaline as a neurohumor stimulated research on the biochemistry of the catecholamines, their precursors and metabolic derivatives. In 1950 Goodall detected dopamine in the sheep adrenal gland and in extracts of sheep heart,[18] and a year later von Euler, Hamberg, and Hellner found it in relatively large quantities in human urine.[19] Until this time it had been known as a natural product only in yellow broom, a plant of the *Genista* family, and as the quaternary base coryneine, in the Argentine cactus.[20] Its presence in the adrenal gland, where it comprises about 2% of the total catecholamines,[21] is now established. Dopamine makes up about 50% of the catecholamines in the sympathetic nerves and ganglia.[22] In addition, it occurs in the brain.[23,24] The catecholamines, particularly, dopamine, are found in some insects.[25] Noradrenaline has been identified in toad venoms and in the salivary gland of *Octopus vulgaris* where it is accompanied by tyramine and octopamine. Adrenaline also occurs in some toad venoms. Noradrenaline, dopamine and other amines are found in many fruits and vegetables.[26] Two other compounds of this series have been reported in animal tissues: isoproterenol[26a] and adrenalone,[26b] but their presence has not been confirmed. Adrenaline can be converted in metabolism to a new, biologically active substance.[26c]

Dopa has been identified in animal products on a few occasions. In 1932 Medes described a man with tyrosinosis who excreted what was reputed to be dopa, following the ingestion of a tyrosine load.[27] This finding has been evaluated by Lerner retrospectively,[28] and he concludes that the demonstration of dopa was not definitive. More recently, dopa and its 3-methyl ether have been reported present in the urine of some children with neuroblastoma.[28a] Dopa has also been found in small amounts in sheep adrenal extracts,[29] in brain,[30] and in normal pigmented mammalian skin.[31] More frequently organic acids possessing the 3,4-dihydroxyphenyl group have been detected: 3,4-dihydroxyphenylacetic acid in insects,[32] in spleen extracts,[33] in brain,[30] and in normal urine.[34] Dihydroxyphenyllactic acid has also been found in insect extracts.[35] An investigation of venous blood plasma of man failed to reveal any dihydroxyphenyl acids or dopamine.[36]

The concentrations of adrenaline, noradrenaline and dopamine in the tissues and body fluids vary considerably with species and with

TABLE III

NON-CONJUGATED CATECHOLAMINES IN ADULT HUMAN TISSUES AND BODY FLUIDS

	μg./gm. or μg./l.			
	Adrenaline	Noradrenaline	Dopamine	Reference
Brain	4.4	21.2	94.2	30
Adrenal Gland	0.5	0.1		37
Adrenal Medulla	1.26	0.21		37
Heart Muscle	0.23*			44
Urine	15	39	293	45, 45a
Venous Blood Plasma	0.01 ± 0.02	0.34 ± 0.04		46
Arterial Blood Plasma	0.10 ± 0.03	0.20 ± 0.03		46

*Adrenaline and noradrenaline.

physiological state. Information on this subject can be found in the following references: adrenal gland;[37] brain;[38-40] sympathetic nervous system;[22,41,42] and various mammalian tissues.[15,43] Some representative data are provided in Table III to show the amounts of these compounds in the brain, suprarenals, heart and body fluids of man.

II. INTRACELLULAR LOCATION OF CATECHOLAMINES

The catecholamines of the adrenal medulla are stored in granules within the chromaffin cells.[47] These granules contain very high concentrations of the amines, amounting to about one-sixth of the dry weight. This type of localization protects the amines from enzymic action and at the same time prevents them from exerting their metabolic and pharmacodynamic actions. The granules also contain unusually high concentrations of ATP (adenosine triphosphate), in amounts as high as 302 μmole/gm. of protein.[48] These chromaffin granules can be separated from much of the other cellular material by differential centrifugation of broken-cell preparations of the adrenal medulla, suspended in isotonic or hypertonic sucrose solutions. This procedure yields a "top layer" of low density particles, relatively rich in mitochondria, and a "bottom layer" of higher density material, rich in the granules containing catecholamines and ATP.[48,49] The granules also contain much phospholipid.[50] This is of interest in view of complex formation between catecholamines and lecithin.[51]

It seems likely that the amines are held in the granule in some type of ionic linkage with ATP.[52] Indeed, morphine and insulin, both of which cause release of the amines from the adrenal medulla, also cause a proportionate loss of ATP from the gland.[53] The release of catecholamines in vivo is under the control of the splanchnic nerves, whose mediator is acetylcholine; the effect of the neurohumor does not seem to be direct for carbachol is ineffective in releasing the amines from isolated chromaffin granules.[54] Compounds which release the amines from the isolated granules include detergents, lecithin, bile salts, "48/80," some amines (but not histamine), and sulfhydryl reagents.[52,54] In general, agents or physical conditions known to affect membrane permeability cause the release of catecholamines from their "bound" form.[52]

Catecholamines in other tissues are also bound to particles but not to the same extent as in the adrenal medulla. For example, much of the noradrenaline of the splenic nerve occurs in granules, but dopamine appears to be free in the supernatant fraction. Moreover, only a portion of the brain catecholamines is bound in particles.

The application of the density gradient technique, using sucrose solutions, in the fractionation of chromaffin granules has shown that adrenaline and noradrenaline are unevenly distributed in the layers. A noradrenaline-rich fraction sediments somewhat more readily than an adrenaline-rich fraction.[55] Hence, there is the possibility that two types of chromaffin cell occur, one containing noradrenaline and lacking the N-transmethylating enzyme system, and the other containing adrenaline. A special dopamine-containing cell has been described in the tissue of ruminants.[56]

III. CHEMISTRY OF THE CATECHOLAMINES*

A. Reactions of the Catechol Nucleus

1. With Boric Acid

Boric acid reacts with compounds bearing cis-hydroxyls on vicinal carbon atoms. Pyrocatechols react strongly to form anionic complexes

---

*The reactions discussed in this section have been selected for their pertinence to biochemical investigations.

in this way.[57] The oxidation of dihydric phenols proceeds differently in borate and phosphate buffers.[58]

2. With Oxidizing Agents

Adrenaline undergoes autoxidation in the presence of small amounts of metallic ions. The reaction is accelerated if a chelating agent such as edathamil (Versene) or a ferrihematin is added, or if it is carried out at an alkaline pH.

Oxidation is also effected by oxidants such as manganese dioxide, potassium ferricyanide, iodine, bromine, iodic acid, periodic acid, dipotassium mercuritetrathiocyanate, silver oxide, and others. Paramagnetic resonance studies show that oxidation of pyrocatechols proceeds through two successive single electron transfers, the intermediate being a paramagnetic o-semiquinone free radical[59] and the product (near pH 7 or below it) being the quinone of adrenaline, adrenoerythrin.[60] The half-life of this red compound is so short that studies of its independent physiological activity are precluded. It has been reported to exhibit pressor activity but this is presumed to be due to its reversible reduction in the body to the original adrenaline.

Adrenaline-quinone undergoes another reaction besides reduction. This is cyclization to 2,3-dihydro-3,5,6-trihydroxy-1-methylindole, also known as leucoadrenochrome. Under the conditions ordinarily employed to oxidize adrenaline the oxidant (oxygen, or a reagent containing a halogen or a metal) continues its action even after the rearrangement of the catecholamine-quinone. Leucoadrenochrome is oxidized to the aminochrome 2,3-dihydro-3-hydroxy-1-methylindole-5,6-quinone, or adrenochrome.[61] The use of iodine leads to the formation of 2-iodoadrenochrome,[62] the first aminochrome chemically characterized. Iodoaminochromes have also been prepared from noradrenaline, dopamine, isoproterenol, and epinine; they exhibit very marked dichroism.[63] Adrenochrome has been shown to exist, not in the o-quinone form, but as the zwitterionic p-quinoneimine.[64] The aminochromes are red compounds (iodoaminochromes are purple-red) with characteristic absorption spectra. In the presence of zinc or aluminum ions, or upon being made alkaline, adrenochrome isomerizes to form a fluorescent lutin, whose structure is 2,3-dihydro-5,6-dihydroxy-3-keto-1-methylindole. It exhibits keto-enol tautomerism, but the keto-form is the dominant species. The development of fluorescence from adrenaline and related compounds thus depends upon the presence of oxygen and is transient unless the lutin is stabilized against further oxidation to 2,3-dihydro-3,5,6-triketo-1-methylindole (oxoadrenochrome) and unknown products.

Adrenaline also undergoes oxidation to adrenochrome under the influence of enzymes such as mushroom catechol oxidase, cytochrome c-cytochrome oxidase, and ceruloplasmin.

The scheme of oxidation described above for adrenaline was the one actually postulated for dopa by Raper in 1927.[65] The rearrangement product of "dopachrome" was considered to be either 5,6-dihydroxyindole-2-carboxylic acid or 5,6-dihydroxyindole (as a result of decarboxylation at some stage). Indeed, the oxidation of 3,4-dopa proceeds under appropriate conditions to 5,6-dihydroxyindole, with the utilization of 4 moles of ferricyanide.[66] It is now known that the same route is followed also by adrenaline, noradrenaline, and related compounds. Oxidation of 2,5-dopa by ferricyanide results in the formation of 5-hydroxyindole, and 2,3-dopa forms 7-hydroxyindole. In these compounds the *o*-phenolic group is lost in the oxidation and only 2 moles of ferricyanide are required.[66]

The fluorescence of the lutins has been recognized for many years and the great value of this property for the quantitation of the catecholamines has been well appreciated.

The chemistry of the aminochromes has been reviewed by Heacock.[67]

3. Other Reactions

The pyrocatechols react with 2,6-dichloroquinone chloroimide and with diazotized sulfanilic acid among other phenol reagents. They rapidly reduce phosphotungstate, Folin's reagent for dihydroxy phenols. The reduction of arsenomolybdate to a blue compound absorbing maximally at 535 mμ. has been used in the colorimetric analysis of adrenaline and noradrenaline. Dopa, like other *o*-dihydroxybenzene derivatives, reacts with organophosphates but there is no evidence that it is useful in poisoning by such anticholinesterases.

B. Reactions of the Amino Group

Auerbach[68] has used β-naphthoquinone-4-sulfonic acid, a reagent for primary amines, to measure noradrenaline in pharmaceuticals.

The catecholamines react with aldehydes to yield products whose type depends upon the nature of the aldehyde used. The reacting aldehyde first forms a Schiff's base type of compound with the amine, and this rearranges to an isoquinoline. According to Eränkö[69] noradrenaline, but not adrenaline, forms a fluorescent derivative upon treatment with formaldehyde, and he has used this difference in differentiating two types of cell, depending upon the amine they contain, in the adrenal medulla of many species. Of great biological interest is the reaction of catecholamines with pyridoxal, the aldehyde form of vitamin B_6, to yield 1,2,3,4-tetrahydro-6,7-dihydroxyisoquinolines.[70] This condensation reaction assumes some physiological significance because it proceeds at appreciable rates at body temperature and at neutral pH.[71,72] The prime requisites for rapid reaction are (a) a free amino group, (b) the presence of a *meta*-hydroxyl group on the ring, and (c) an unsubstituted position on the ring *para* to this phenolic group (and *ortho* to the side chain).[71,73] Among the catecholamines examined the most reactive is noradrenaline, followed by dopamine. Adrenaline and isoproterenol react much more slowly. Masuoka *et al.* have taken advantage of this differential reactivity to separate precursor noradrenaline from enzymatically synthesized adrenaline by reacting the mixed amines with pyridoxal phosphate under controlled conditions.[74] 3,4-Dopa, 2,3-dopa, and 2,5-dopa combine with pyridoxal phosphate (in that order of descending reactivity), but 2,4-dopa does not. 2,6-Dopa, having both *ortho*-positions substituted, nevertheless reacts with the coenzyme, but does so anomalously.[8]

Adrenaline and noradrenaline rearrange in strong acid and with the application of heat, losing the elements of ammonia and forming 3,4-dihydroxyphenylacetaldehyde.[75]

C. Reactions of Aminochromes

1. Lutin Formation

The conversion of adrenochrome to adrenolutin has already been described. Many of the lutins can be stabilized by the addition of ascorbate or sulfite to the alkaline solution. If this protection is not provided the lutins decay, noradrenolutin more slowly than adrenolutin. This fact has been utilized occasionally in the differential estimation of the two compounds, but most investigators have preferred to apply other methodological principles.

2. Condensation with 1,2-diamines

Under appropriate conditions *o*-quinones condense with 1,2-diamines such as phenylenediamine or ethylenediamine to form colored or fluorescent products. Weil-Malherbe has reviewed the chemistry of this reaction.[76] The condensation can be achieved, for example, by autoxidation of the catecholamine at alkaline pH to the chrome, which is then trapped by ethylenediamine added to the reaction mixture. The chief product derived in this way from adrenaline is 2,3-dihydro-3-hydroxy-1-methyl-pyrrolo-[4:5-g]-quinoxaline.[77] The major derivative obtained from noradrenaline is the same as that obtained from pyro-catechol: 1,2,3,4-tetrahydro-1,4,5,8-tetraaza-anthracene. These products are extractable into organic solvents; the fluorophore prepared from dopa is, however, not extracted from an aqueous phase into these solvents.

Colored products are formed when catecholamines are reacted with 2,3-diaminonaphthalene,[78] but this test has very little specificity.

D. *Physico-chemical Determination of Catecholamines*

Within the last decade sensitive methods have been developed for the estimation of the catecholamines in the body fluids and tissues. This has been greatly facilitated by development of new instruments for fluorometry, both of the filter and of the grating types. The latter style of instrument can be used for the direct estimation of purified catecholamines through the intensity of their native fluorescence at or near 335 mμ. in strong acid when irradiated at 295 mμ.

Adrenaline and noradrenaline have been determined when they are present in fairly concentrated form, as in the adrenal medulla or in urines derived from cases of pheochromocytoma, through the color of their amino chromes. It is possible to distinguish between the two com-pounds methodologically, for adrenaline is readily oxidized to its aminochrome at pH values between 3 and 6, whereas noradrenaline is not oxidized at the lower pH under the test conditions. For the analysis of tissues other than the adrenal gland these methods are un-suitable. A higher order of sensitivity is required and this is attained by the fluorometric techniques, based upon formation of the amino-chromes and either (a) their rearrangement to the fluorescing lutins, or (b) their condensation with ethylenediamine. The former, or "tri-hydroxyindole" (THI), methods distinguish between adrenaline and noradrenaline in one of three ways: by taking advantage of the dif-ference in their rates of oxidation to the chromes at pH 3-4 and at pH 6, by utilizing differences in the intensity of fluorescence of the lutins at different activating wave-lengths, or by taking into account methodologically the differential rate of breakdown of the lutins in the absence of stabilizing compound. The last modification has been little used. In the THI methods dopamine is much less fluorescent than noradrenaline but because of its occurrence in substantial amounts in some tissues and in urine it may contribute appreciably to the "nor-adrenaline fraction." Otherwise it can be estimated independently by the fluorescence of its aminochrome in acid, stabilized by the addition of sodium sulfite. This lutin fluoresces in a different range than do the other catecholamines. Treatment of dopa solutions under comparable conditions yields fluorophores in the ultraviolet as for dopamine, and in the visible as for noradrenaline.

The ethylenediamine condensation method, sometimes referred to as the "quinoxaline" method, distinguishes between adrenaline and noradrenaline in mixtures either by measuring the fluorescense at two different sets of wavelengths or by differentially eliminating noradrenaline fluorescence with sodium thiosulfate.

Before fluorometry can be applied to the estimation of catecholamines in biological material, interfering substances must be removed. In some cases the catecholamines must be concentrated also. Among the adsorbents which have been used are silicic acid, aluminum hydroxide gel, and alumina. Ion exchange resins are being employed more widely for their specificity, not only in fractionating the catecholamines, but also in separating them from the metabolic catecholacids. Paper chromatography has also proven useful in identifying catecholamines and related compounds.

Methods for the chemical determination of catecholamines are described in detail in reference 79.

IV. BIOSYNTHESIS OF CATECHOLAMINES[80]

A. Alternate Pathways

As soon as the structure of adrenaline was known its biogenetic relation to tyrosine was suggested by Halle.[81] He claimed to have observed the conversion of this amino acid to catecholamine in adrenal medullary extracts. This was established 50 years later by Kirshner and Goodall.[82] The relationship of adrenaline to tyrosine has been amply substantiated in many other ways in recent years, beginning first of all with the experiments of Gurin and Delluva[83] who showed that radioactive DL-phenylalanine, the precursor of tyrosine, is converted to labeled adrenaline in the adrenal gland of the rat. In this work the side chain bore C^{14} in the carboxyl group or in the α-position, and the ring was labeled with tritium; the isolated adrenaline contained C^{14} derived from the α-carbon atom and tritium, but none of the carboxyl label. Formation of adrenaline has also been demonstrated in vivo using α-C^{14}-tyrosine and β-C^{14}-dopa.[84] In perfusion experiments with the calf adrenal gland it has been shown that tyrosine is the precursor of medullary noradrenaline.[85] This conversion also takes place in vitro, catalyzed by enzymes in slices of adrenal gland, as already mentioned, and in minced sympathetic nerves and ganglia.[86] Dopamine and noradrenaline are formed in both preparations; radioactive adrenaline formed from the labeled tyrosine is also found in the adrenal slices.

Another old view on the mode of formation of adrenaline was that of Rosenmund and Dornsaft[87] who suggested, on the grounds of synthetic organic chemistry, that a phenolic compound might condense with glycine to form dihydroxyphenylserine (3,4-dops); N-methylation and decarboxylation of this product would result in adrenaline. Actually the decarboxylation of 3,4-dops has since been shown to occur *in vivo* in the rabbit as well as in extracts of adrenal medulla, kidney, and liver, and the product is noradrenaline. Furthermore, an enzyme partially meeting the specifications of a catalyst for the Rosenmund-Dornsaft type of reaction has been found in the liver.[88] This "glycinogenase" cleaves β-hydroxy-α-amino acids. β-Phenylserine, for example, yields benzaldehyde and glycine. The reverse reaction, such as the formation of phenylserine or dops, has never been demonstrated, nor have the necessary aldehydes been identified in animal tissues. Phenylserine, moreover, is toxic if added to the diet of experimental animals.

An examination of Figure 1 reveals that starting with phenylalanine or tyrosine there are many alternative paths which might be followed *in vivo* to arrive at noradrenaline. Up to 1938 there was satisfactory experimental evidence for the oxidation of phenylalanine to tyrosine (Embden) and of the latter to 3,4-dopa (Raper). Tyramine was known as a product of bacterial action upon tyrosine, and it was regarded as

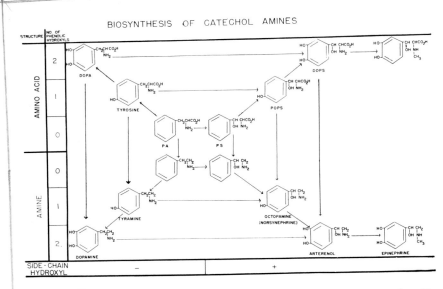

BIOSYNTHESIS OF CATECHOL AMINES

Fig. 1. Possible pathways of formation of catecholamines. (See text for discussion and Table I for nomenclature.)

a potential intermediate in catecholamine biosynthesis, but injected tyramine has been excluded as a precursor by isotope studies. The discovery by Holtz, Heise, and Lüdtke of an enzyme in animal tissues which actively decarboxylates dopa[89] immediately diverted attention to dopa and dopamine as putative precursors of noradrenaline and adrenaline. The participation of this newly found enzyme, dopa decarboxylase, in the biosynthesis of catecholamines was postulated by Blaschko[90] and Holtz[91] in 1939, since which time its role and that of dopa as an intermediate have been proven. The view was that the dopamine formed by the action of the enzyme was oxidized to noradrenaline and the latter was then methylated to adrenaline. These enzymatic reactions have now been described. Later on, Holtz and Kroneberg considered the possibility that some dopamine is N-methylated immediately and then oxidized on the side chain to adrenaline,[92] but there is no evidence for this path.

Another possibility may be considered, namely, that dopa is oxidized to dops, and this is then methylated and decarboxylated, or is decarboxylated directly. However, dops has never been detected as a metabolic product of labeled precursors in experiments designed to detect it, and N-methyldops is not decarboxylated *in vivo* or *in vitro*.

m-Tyrosine, an amino acid which has not yet been demonstrated in nature, can be converted to dopamine in the rat.[92a]

At the present time, therefore, the evidence from diverse types of experiments and from many different laboratories indicates that dopa is not only an obligatory intermediate in the biosynthesis of catecholamines but that it is also their immediate precursor.

B. Stepwise Transformation of Phenylalanine to Adrenaline

Phenylalanine is an essential amino acid, required for protein synthesis, growth, maintenance, and for tyrosine formation. It is oxidized through the intervention of an enzyme system requiring tetrahydrofolic acid, and oxygen.[93] The products are tyrosine, an oxidized pteridine, and water. The oxidized pteridine is reconverted to tetrahydrofolic acid through the action of a second enzyme utilizing reduced triphosphopyridine nucleotide. The mechanisms of these reactions have yet to be clarified. The phenylalanine oxidase appears to be absent in phenylketonuric individuals.

Tyrosine is oxidized to 3,4-dopa by mammalian tyrosinase[94] but this enzyme is only weakly active even in tissues such as the adrenal medulla where an active formation of catecholamines takes place; it is not known in which subcellular fraction it occurs.[94a] It is generally assumed that the non-enzymatic conversion first shown by Raper[95] and later by many others plays a role in the formation of dopa, but there are few experimental data on the relative importance of the enzymatic and non-enzymatic mechanisms. The role of ascorbic acid in non-enzymatic hydroxylations has been thoroughly studied.[96,97] Thus, in a system containing ascorbic or dehydroascorbic acid, ferrous ions and oxygen the hydroxylation of many organic compounds can occur. Ascorbic acid itself is not the hydroxylating agent but its presence is necessary, at least initially, for the reaction to take place. This non-enzymatic system acts upon phenylalanine to form both p-tyrosine and o-tyrosine. The former is converted to 3,4-dopa and hydroquinone.[98] It appears that non-enzymic hydroxylation catalyzed by ascorbic acid is a physiological process, for guinea pigs depleted of this vitamin hydroxylate certain aromatic compounds at a reduced rate.[99]

Another type of non-enzymatic formation of 3,4-dopa is effected by ultraviolet irradiation of p- or m-tyrosine[100] or by x-irradiation of p-tyrosine in aqueous solution and in the presence of oxygen.[101]

Unlike the preceding steps in the biosynthesis of catecholamines the mechanism of decarboxylation of dopa is well documented. In common with other amino acid decarboxylases the enzyme acting upon dopa has pyridoxal phosphate as its coenzyme. The simplest substrates upon which the enzyme is active are the o- and m-isomers of tyrosine;[102] the enzyme does not decarboxylate p-tyrosine. All six dopa isomers serve as substrates but are decarboxylated at quite different rates.[8] The N-substituted derivatives of susceptible substrates are not attacked because pyridoxal phosphate is unable to combine with them. Dopa decarboxylase is inhibited by carbonyl reagents, which combine with the coenzyme, and many other compounds which affect substrate-apoenzyme union. Two series of compounds which have been thoroughly studied for enzyme inhibition *in vitro* are derivatives of 3,4-dihydroxycinnamic acid[103] and of α-methylphenylalanine.[72] The most active inhibitors are 5-(3,4-dihydroxycinnamoyl)-salicylic acid, α-methyl-3,4-dopa, and α-methyl-m-tyrosine. As in the case of many other amino acids, administered dopa is decarboxylated *in vivo*. The dopamine formed has been assayed pharmacologically[104] and spectrophotofluorometrically.[105] This decarboxylation is inhibited significantly by pretreating the experimental animals with α-methyldopa[105,106] or with α-methyl-m-tyrosine.[107]

Dopa decarboxylase occurs in numerous tissues, including the adrenal medulla. The enzyme has been purified;[108,109] it may be identical with other aromatic amino acid decarboxylases such as 5-hydroxytryptophan decarboxylase.[109-111]

The conversion of dopamine to noradrenaline involves an asymmetric oxidation of the side chain, which has been studied in adrenal preparations and in brain. In the adrenal gland the enzyme occurs in association with the particulate matter of the cell and, in fact, may be located in the chromaffin granules.[94a] Levin *et al.* have purified the enzyme; ascorbic acid is a cofactor.[111a] Massart and Vercauteren[112] speculate that the *p*-quinonemethine of dopamine is an intermediate formed by the action of the oxidizing enzyme, and that the addition of the elements of water to this compound yields noradrenaline.

The formation of adrenaline from noradrenaline has been demonstrated in the intact rat and in adrenal extracts; the enzyme occurs in the supernatant fraction of homogenates. That the N-methyl group is derived from methionine[113] has been shown in experiments on the calf adrenal gland. When the organ is perfused with dopamine-1-C^{14}, labeled noradrenaline is formed along with small amounts of adrenaline, but the amount of C^{14}-adrenaline can be markedly increased by adding methionine to the perfusing medium. The transmethylation takes place in two steps: (1) the reaction of L-methionine and adenosine triphosphate to form adenosylmethionine;[114] and (2) transfer of the methyl group from the latter to noradrenaline. The conversion of noradrenaline to adrenaline appears to occur largely in the adrenal gland (in man), for bilaterally adrenalectomized humans excrete very little adrenaline.[115] The sites of non-adrenal formation of adrenaline are probably in the liver and kidneys.

Two other pathways have been suggested in addition to those discussed above. The discovery of octopamine (Table I) in an invertebrate[116] and more recently in mammals[117] raises the possibility that this compound is formed from tyramine and is then oxidized to noradrenaline. The latter oxidation is catalyzed by ultraviolet irradiation, so that part of this pathway is feasible. However, when labeled tyramine and phenylethylamine were tested as precursors of adrenal catecholamines in labeling experiments in the intact rat they were found to be completely inactive in this respect.[118] The origin, metabolism, and role of octopamine has, therefore, still to be clarified.

Another pathway is suggested by the observation that administered 3,4-dihydroxyphenylpyruvic acid is transaminated *in vivo* to form dopa, which is subsequently decarboxylated to dopamine.[119] Hence, there is the possibility of a by-pass from phenylpyruvic acid to dopa, involving two ring oxidations of the keto acid and transamination.

In summary, then, the weight of evidence on the formation of adrenaline in animal tissues is towards a pathway involving dopa, dopamine, and noradrenaline, in that sequence.

C. Nutritional Factors

It is clear that nutritional factors play a role in the biosynthesis of the catecholamines. Two essential amino acids are required: phenylalanine, to supply the carbon skeleton and the amino group, and methionine, for the conversion of noradrenaline to adrenaline. The amount of phenylalanine or tyrosine which the body diverts to the biosynthesis of catecholamines relative to the amounts of these amino acids ingested is so small that only by the use of special techniques has it been possible to demonstrate the dietary role of the amino acids in this process. For example, demonstration of the role of dopa as a precursor in acute experiments without benefit of radioisotopes has necessitated employing rats given large amounts of insulin to deplete their stores of adrenal catecholamines, and administering the amino acid by gavage. This treatment causes a significant increase in the adrenal catecholamines in 6 hours.[120] In a patient producing large amounts of catecholamines because of the presence of a pheochromocytoma Weil-Malherbe has shown that removal of amino acid precursors of the catecholamines (by instituting a protein-free diet) leads to a dramatic reduction in the output of urinary dopamine.[121]

To show a nutritional effect of methionine upon the biosynthesis of adrenaline it has been necessary to prepare experimental animals by maintaining them on a methionine-deficient diet for some time; then, those which are given a supplement of the missing amino acid show a small increase in the ratio of adrenaline to noradrenaline.[122] The matter of transmethylation may have other consequences. Because of the difference in pharmacological properties of noradrenaline and adrenaline it is conceivable that a significant alteration in the rate of transmethylation, that is, of either the formation of adenosylmethionine or its demethylative cleavage, could affect the functioning of the sympathetic nervous system. Clinically, a state of this kind occurs in cases of pheochromocytoma in which the amines are formed not only in large amounts but also in markedly abnormal ratios of one to the other. Methionine is related to the catecholamines in another way, for their inactivation by methylation of the m-phenolic group is an important metabolic pathway. Indeed, the O-methylation is affected by supplying an excess of compounds like guanidoacetic acid which are normally metabolized by N-methylation.[123]

Among the cofactors involved in the biosynthesis of the catecholamines are the pyridine nucleotides and pyridoxal phosphate. Thus, nicotinic acid and vitamin B_6 are necessary, the former in oxidative steps, the latter in the decarboxylation. Withholding pyridoxine from the diet for long periods does not affect the level of tissue catecholamines[107] but when such deficient animals are subjected to a "dopa-loading" test they convert much less of the exogenous amino acid to dopamine than do controls.[107,124] Two other vitamins have been tested similarly, riboflavin and thiamine. Deficiency of the former has some minor effects on tissue catecholamines; thiamine deficiency does not affect the catecholamine content of the adrenal gland.[107]

V. METABOLISM[125]

A. General

Small amounts of adrenaline, noradrenaline, and dopamine are normally excreted in the urine. A portion is found in the conjugated form. Conjugates with glucuronic and sulfuric acids have been detected, but the nature and amounts of the phenolic esters require more intensive investigation. The amounts of free catecholamines excreted daily by adults are given in Table III. Judged from infusion experiments in man these amounts represent but a few percent of the total produced by the body,[126] and hence signify the existence of other routes of metabolism which are quantitatively more important than conjugation or simple excretion through the kidney. Until recently the action of monoamine oxidase on catecholamines had made the route of oxidative deamination and further oxidation to the dihydroxyphenyl acids an important possibility and this was tested experimentally as soon as powerful monoamine oxidase inhibitors such as iproniazid, active *in vivo*, were discovered. It was then found that their administration affects only slightly the urinary output of adrenaline and noradrenaline, although they lead to increased catecholamine content of some organs, such as the brain. At about the same time as the physiological role of monoamine oxidase was being evaluated vanilmandelic acid (VMA, 3-methoxy-4-hydroxy-D-mandelic acid) (cf. Table II) was identified as a product of metabolism derived from noradrenaline.[127] It soon became clear that the most important path of metabolism of the catecholamines, in the quantitative sense, is through m-O-methylation.[125] Metanephrine and normetanephrine (Table I), the O-methyl derivatives of adrenaline and noradrenaline, respectively, occur in the urine both free and as their glucuronidates. The 3-methyl ether of dopamine is also found in the urine after parenteral administration of the amine. But a large portion of the methylated amines, as formed in the body, are oxidized by monoamine oxidase to VMA (adrenaline and noradrenaline) and to homovanillic acid (dopamine). Thus, monoamine oxidase functions in the degradation of the catecholamines, but its action is primarily on the m-O-methylated compounds. Catechol O-methyl transferase occurs in many tissues, particularly in the liver and kidney, but also in the spleen, intestine, brain and heart. The enzyme is activated by adenosine triphosphate and magnesium ions, and it is inhibited by sulfhydryl reagents,[128] o-catechol,[129] and pyrogallol.[130] Its activity is reduced in the hyperthyroid rat.[131] As in the N-transmethylation of noradrenaline to adrenaline, the immediate methyl donor is S-adenosylmethionine.

VMA is the major endogenous acidic metabolite of adrenaline and noradrenaline found in the urine.[132,133] In individuals infused with adrenaline or noradrenaline (labeled on the side chain with C^{14}) the main radioactive metabolite in the urine is also VMA (including its conjugates). If the subject has received iproniazid or some other inhibitor of monoamine oxidase beforehand, VMA is still found as a metabolite but in significantly reduced amounts.[133] The O-methyl compounds continue to be formed from the catecholamines and, because the oxidative pathway is blocked by the inhibitor, they accumulate sufficiently to permit their identification in tissue extracts. In this way metanephrine has been detected in the adrenal gland of the rat, and normetanephrine has been found in the spleen and brain, as well as in the adrenal gland. Minor acid metabolites include 3,4-dihydroxyphenylacetic acid, derived from dopamine, and 3,4-dihydroxy-D-mandelic acid, from adrenaline and noradrenaline. Because of its minimal action upon the nonmethylated amines under physiological conditions, monoamine oxidase can not be considered the sympathetic analog of cholinesterase (cf. ref. 134).

The conversion of an amine to the corresponding acid occurs in two enzymatic steps, the first of which is catalyzed by monoamine oxidase, and the second by a DPN-linked aldehyde dehydrogenase or xanthine oxidase. Monoamine oxidase catalyzes the oxidation of many amines to the corresponding aldehyde with the formation of hydrogen peroxide. The enzyme is usually associated with cytoplasmic particles, and thus far has been only partially purified. Little is known of its chemical nature[134,135] but riboflavin is thought to be involved in some phase of its action. The aldehydes formed from the catecholamines have been difficult to obtain in a suitable state for experimental work and therefore the identity of the specific enzymes converting the catecholaldehydes to the acids can only surmised. However, the aldehyde derived by enzymatic oxidation of dopamine is reported to be a substrate for a diphosphopyridine nucleotide-linked dehydrogenase, but not for the flavoenzyme, aldehyde oxidase.[136] A small portion of the aldehyde formed from metanephrine and normetanephrine undergoes reduction in vivo[137] to form 3-methoxy-4-hydroxyphenylglycol. m-Methoxydopamine probably follows a similar path.[138] This type of reaction was long ago described for several other aldehydes derived metabolically from amines.[139]

VMA is normally excreted to the extent of 1.5-3.5 μg./mg. of creatinine in urine or about 2-6 mg./24 hr. When this value is compared with the amounts of catecholamines usually excreted in the urine (about 0.3 mg./24 hr.) it can be appreciated that the combination of m-O-methylation and amine oxidation represents the major over-all route of metabolism. In specific tissues, however, m-O-methylation may play a less important role in relation to the primary action of monoamine oxidase. This is so in the the brain and heart,[140] organs in which there is very much more monoamine oxidase activity than catechol O-methyl transferase activity.

Some minor metabolic routes have been suggested. The possibility that the cytochrome system plays a role in the oxidation of adrenaline to its quinone and, further, to adrenochrome follows from the work of Ball and Chen[60] and of Green and Richter.[61] The presence of additional catalysts of catechol oxidation[141] in animal tissues, e.g., ceruloplasmin[142] and ferritin,[143] lends support to the views of Bacq who has emphasized the role of enzymatic oxidation of the catechol nucleus in the metabolism of the catecholamines.[144] Very little is known about metabolic products engendered by oxidation of the catechol nucleus— whether they are formed *in vivo* or how they are disposed of, if administered. It has been claimed that relatively large amounts of adrenochrome (or other aminochromes), of the order of 50[145] to 200[146] μg./l., occur in the blood plasma, but this has not been substantiated.[147] Adrenochrome is not found among the urinary products after the administration of labeled adrenaline to the rat,[148] but when adrenochrome itself is injected into the rabbit it appears in the urine where it can be measured as adrenolutin.[149] Demonstrations of the formation of adrenochrome from adrenaline have been achieved in plasma (due to ceruloplasmin?) under quite abnormal conditions of substrate concentration, whereas under physiological conditions the preformed catecholamines in platelet-rich plasma are perfectly stable.[16]

Some investigators have reported finding adrenalone in blood[26b,150] as a result of the action of a dehydrogenase. Kawamoto[151] has proposed that adrenalone is a normal intermediate in adrenaline metabolism, and that it is oxidized by monoamine oxidase and other oxidases to form protocatechuic acid as the terminal product. In their studies on the metabolic products of labeled adrenaline in the rat Schayer and Smiley noted that both sidechain carbon atoms remain fixed to the benzene ring, and for that reason they consider it unlikely that the adrenalone pathway actually functions as proposed.[148] Weil-Malherbe and Bone have sought evidence of an adrenaline dehydrogenase in rabbit and human plasma, as well as in extracts of rat liver, heart, spleen, and brain, without success.[36]

At various times it has been suggested that adrenaline undergoes demethylation to its precursor, noradrenaline. In perfusion experiments with the calf adrenal gland Rosenfeld *et al.* found no evidence for this reaction.[85] There is evidence, on the other hand, that an aerobic enzyme system, requiring reduced triphosphopyridine nucleotide, can remove the O-methyl group from O-methylated compounds.[152]

Small amounts of 2,4,5-trihydroxyphenylethylamine have been isolated from incubated preparations of adrenal medulla to which have been added dopamine.[153] Its formation is probably due to a non-enzymic oxidation.

Dehydroxylation of the catechol nucleus *in vivo* has been detected in respect to dopacetic acid and 3,4-dihydroxycinnamic acid.[154] The *p*-hydroxyl group is lost in these cases. This reaction presages others of a like nature, including the possible loss of the *m*-hydroxyl group.

To summarize: the catecholamines which are excreted in the urine as normal endogenous metabolites are adrenaline, noradrenaline, dopamine, and the corresponding *m*-O-methylated amines. Small amounts of 3-methoxy-4-hydroxyphenylglycol have been identified.[155] The catecholacids and their derivatives which have been found are dihydroxyphenylacetic, dihydroxymandelic, homovanillic,[156] VMA,[127] vanillic,[157] ferulic,[157] and 4-methoxy-3-hydroxycinnamic[158] acids.

B. Metabolism of Exogenous Dopa and Catecholamines

Information about the endogenous metabolism of these compounds has been sought by administration of very small amounts of their C^{14}-isomers, followed by separation of radioactive labeled metabolites in the urine. In the case of dopa,[159] dihydroxyphenylpyruvic acid, dopamine, noradrenaline, and dopac have been detected among the urinary products, but not dopa itself. In tests on humans ingesting large amounts of L-dopa[156] the most important metabolite excreted was HVA (see Table II). It has been considered possible that HVA is formed from dihydroxyphenylpyruvic acid which, in turn, is derived from dopa by transamination.[156] Other products of metabolism of orally administered dopa which have been found in rat and rabbit urine are dopac[154,160] and *m*-hydroxyphenylacetic acid.[154] The latter compound results from the dehydroxylation of the catechol nucleus. D-Dopa, like L-dopa, gives rise to dopamine in metabolism. Unlike the natural isomer, some of the D-amino acid can be detected in the urine of rats injected with it.[107,124]

Exogenous dopamine, noradrenaline and adrenaline exhibit similar patterns of metabolism. Only a small proportion of the radioactive label on the administered compound appears in the urine as the original amine; a much larger proportion occurs as the methylated compound. About one-fifth of administered noradrenaline[161] and up to one-half of injected adrenaline[162,163] are excreted as the conjugated derivatives of the respective methylated amines. In the rat all the conjugated metanephrine can be accounted for as the glucosiduronate; in man, too, this sugar acid is a very important conjugating agent but another conjugand (as yet unidentified) is also found.[163] Among the acidic products only small amounts of dopacetic acid and dihydroxymandelic acid are found. The m-O-methylated acids, however, account for large amounts of the administered radioactivity. Sixty percent of dopamine injected into rats is found in the 24-hour urine as HVA.[164] About one-third of noradrenaline[161] and adrenaline[162,165] administered to humans, and ten percent injected into rats[163] occur as the corresponding β-hydroxylated acid, VMA. In both man and rat, treatment with a suitable inhibitor of monoamine oxidase alters the proportion of aminated to acidic derivatives in favor of the former.

VI. SPECIAL BIOCHEMISTRY OF CATECHOLAMINES IN NERVOUS TISSUES

The occurrence of catecholamines in the nervous system has been known for many years. Adrenaline and noradrenaline were the first to be detected[13,42,166] and later dopamine was found also.[22-24,38] It is established that adrenaline occurs in the cerebral cells; noradrenaline and dopamine are present, each amine in varying concentration depending upon the specific site. The highest concentrations of noradrenaline occur in the hypothalamus, central gray matter of the mesencephalon, and the area postrema;[39,167] dopamine is localized in the corpus striatum and associated basal ganglia[38,39] to a large extent.

All steps in the biosynthesis of catecholamines have now been demonstrated in nerve and brain. The over-all process has been described by Goodall and Kirshner[86] starting with labeled tyrosine and dopa. For example, dopamine and noradrenaline are formed during incubation of these precursors with sympathetic nerves and ganglia. Dopa decarboxylase has been found in many types of nervous tissue, being highest in postganglionic sympathetic nerves and sympathetic ganglia, and lowest in cerebral cortex, preganglionic sympathetic nerves and vagus.[168] It is absent from the phrenic nerve. Dopamine-β-oxidase has been detected in the hypothalamus and caudate nucleus.[169] Nervous tissue, however, contains a very small complement of the noradrenaline N-transmethylase. This contrasts with adrenal medullary tissue in which this system is well developed, although present in changing concentrations during the growth of the animal.[37] In addition to the synthesizing enzymes brain also contains some enzymes concerned with the terminal metabolism of the catecholamines, namely, O-methyl transferase[170] and monamine oxidase.[171]

The catecholamine content of the brain can be grossly modified in several ways. The administration of noradrenaline[172] and adrenaline[173] causes the accumulation of small amounts of the amine in the hypothalamus; the pituitary gland and the sympathetic chain receive a portion of the injected amine also. Injecting dopa leads to an increase in cerebral dopamine;[105,174] the amino acid apparently passes into the brain, where it is decarboxylated. This conversion *in vivo* is inhibited by α-methyldopa[105] and by α-methyl-*m*-tyrosine.[107,121] Monoamine oxidase, which is quite evenly distributed through the brain, plays a significant role in the metabolism of the brain catecholamines, and by administering iproniazid or another inhibitor of the enzyme, noradrenaline[175] and normetanephrine[176] accumulate in the brain. Inhibition of catechol O-methyl transferase, however, does not bring about any change in the brain noradrenaline (cf. Crout[140]). Reserpine causes a remarkable loss of the catecholamines from the brain,[177] just as from other tissues. α-Methyldopa and α-methyl-*m*-tyrosine also lower the brain catecholamines, as one component of their action.[177a,177b]

VII. BIOCHEMICAL DISORDERS OF CATECHOLAMINE METABOLISM

A. Pheochromocytoma

Chromaffin tumors vary considerably in size, location, content of catecholamines, and rate of production of amines. The average ratio of adrenaline, noradrenaline and dopamine in normal human adrenal gland is of the order of 50:7:1 and in urine it is 1:3:12. In cases of pheochromocytoma these proportions are substantially changed. In the chromaffin tumor either adrenaline or noradrenaline predominates, although "mixed tumors" occur also. Dopamine is detected only occasionally.[178] The amounts of these catecholamines in the urine are quite variable when a tumor is present and range from normal values ("silent" tumors) to as high as 10 mg./day. Dopamine excretion has been little studied as yet.

Pheochromocytomatous tissue is rich in adenosine triphosphate.[179] It contains the necessary enzymes to convert dopa to dopamine and noradrenaline[179,180] and others concerned with the metabolism of the catecholamines: catechol O-methyl transferase and monoamine oxidase.[180] The methyl transferase accounts for the presence of normetanephrine in the tumor tissue.

The original finding of very large amounts of VMA in the urine of patients with pheochromocytoma[127] has been verified by other investigators. In patients with paroxysmal attacks of hypertension the urinary output of catecholamines fluctuates, being highest during the attack and falling to normal levels in remission,[181] but the excretion of VMA remains high during both phases.[127,181]

Elevated urinary catecholamines have been found in patients with extra-adrenal chromaffin tumors, e.g., functioning organs of Zuckerkandl.

B. Other Disorders

Excessive catecholaminuria has been reported in three cases of neuroblastoma in children,[182] but it is not a consistent finding in this disease.[183] Studnitz has found dopa and 3-methoxy-4-hydroxyphenylalanine in the urine of neuroblastoma cases.[28a]

It might be expected that in melanomatous conditions there would be an excess of catechol derivatives in some tissues and in the urine. In fact, in the urine of patients with malignant melanoma there is frequently much material having similar fluorescence characteristics to noradrenaline, but coming from some other compound.[45a]

Some changes in catecholamine metabolism have been described in basal ganglial diseases. In Parkinsonism the excretion of dopamine is subnormal.[184] At post-mortem the brain of Parkinsonian patients is deficient in dopamine.[185] Urinary dopamine is increased in hepatolenticular degeneration.[184]

REFERENCES

Valuable articles on the biochemistry of the catecholamines will be found in the proceedings of two symposia:

HERMANN, H. (Ed.): L'Adrénaline et la Noradrénaline dans la Régulation des Fonctions Homéostasiques. Paris, Centre National de la Recherche Scientifique, 1958.
KRAYER, O. (Ed.): Symposium on Catecholamines. *Pharmacol. Rev., 11:*232 (1959).

1. CAPELL, L. T.: *Chem. Eng. News, 35:*28 (1957).
2. HOLTZ, P., CREDNER, K., and KRONEBERG, G.: *Arch. exper. Path. u. Pharmakol., 204:*228 (1947).
3. RAAB, W., and GIGEE, W.: *Proc. Soc. Exper. Biol. Med., 76:*97 (1951).
4. SOBOTKA, H., and AUSTIN, J.: *J. Am. Chem. Soc., 73:*3077 (1951).
5. PRATESI, P., LaMANNA, A., CAMPIGLIO, A., and GHIZLANDI, V.: *J. Chem. Soc.,* 2069 (1958).

6. HARTMAN, W. J., POGRUND, R. S., DRELL, W., and CLARK, W. G.: *J. Am. Chem. Soc.*, *77*:816 (1955).

7. LAMBOOY, J. P.: *J. Am. Chem. Soc.*, *76*:133 (1954).

8. SOURKES, T. L.: *Rev. canad. biol.*, *14*:49 (1955).

9. GUGGENHEIM, M.: *Ztschr. physiol. Chem.*, *88*:276 (1913).

10. SCHNEIDER, G.: *Biochem. Ztschr.*, *330*:428 (1958).

11. KNOX, W. E.: In *Amino Acid Metabolism*, McElroy, W. D., and Glass, B., Eds. Baltimore, Johns Hopkins Press (1955).

12. ABEL, J. J., and CRAWFORD, A. C.: *Johns Hopkins Hosp. Bull.*, *8*:151 (1897); TAKAMINE, J.: *Am. J. Pharm.*, *73*:523 (1901).

13. EULER, U. S. v.: *Acta physiol. scandinav.*, *12*:73 (1946).

14. GOLDENBERG, M., FABER, M., ALSTON, E. J., and CHARGAFF, E. C.: *Science*, *109*:534 (1949).

15. EULER, U. S. v.: *Noradrenaline*. Springfield, Ill., Thomas (1956); MONTAGU, K. A.: *Biochem. J.*, *71*:91 (1959).

16. WEIL-MALHERBE, H., and BONE, A. D.: *Lancet*, *i*:947 (1953); *Biochem. J.*, *70*:14 (1958).

17. WEIL-MALHERBE, H., and LIDDELL, D. W.: *J. Neurol., Neurosurg., & Psychiat.*, *17*:247 (1954).

18. GOODALL, M.: *Nature*, *166*:738 (1950); *Acta physiol. scandinav.*, *24*:Suppl. 85 (1951).

19. EULER, U. S. v., HAMBERG, U., and HELLNER, S.: *Biochem. J.*, *49*:655 (1951).

20. GUGGENHEIM, M.: *Die biogenen Amine*. Basel, Karger (1951).

21. DENGLER, H.: *Arch. exper. Path. u. Pharmakol.*, *231*:373 (1957).

22. SCHÜMANN, H. J.: *Arch. exper. Path. u. Pharmakol.*, *227*:566 (1956).

23. WEIL-MALHERBE, H., and BONE, A. D.: *Nature*, *180*:1050 (1957).

24. CARLSSON, A., LINDQVIST, M., MAGNUSSON, T., and WALDECK, B.: *Science*, *127*:471 (1958).

25. ÖSTLUND, E.: *Acta physiol. scandinav.*, *31*:Suppl. 112 (1954).

26. UDENFRIEND, S., LOVENBERG, W., and SJOERDSMA, A.: *Arch. Biochem. & Biophys.*, *85*:487 (1959).

26a. LOCKETT, M. F.: *Brit. J. Pharmacol.*, *12*:86 (1957).

26b. IMAIZUMI, R., and KAWAMOTO, K.: *Med. J. Osaka Univ.*, *3*:269 (1952); TAKA-OKA, T., HABU, N., and WADA, M.: *Osaka Daigaku Igaku Zassi*, *7*:135 (1955) *(seen in Chem. Abst.*, *49*:11753i (1955)).

26c. AXELROD, J.: *Biochim. et biophys. acta*, *45*:614 (1960); EAKINS, K. E., and LOCKETT, M. F.: *Brit. J. Pharmacol.*, *16*:108 (1961).

27. MEDES, G.: *Biochem. J.*, *26*:917 (1932).

28. LERNER, A. B.: *Advances Enzymol.*, *14*:73 (1953).

28a. STUDNITZ, W. v: *Scandinav. J. Clin. & Lab. Invest.*, *12*:Suppl. 48 (1960); *Clin. chim. acta*, *6*:526 (1961).

29. GOODALL, M.: *Acta chem. scandinav.*, *4*:550 (1950).

30. MONTAGU, K. A.: *Nature*, *180*:244 (1957).

31. FOSTER, M., and BROWN, S. R.: *J. Biol. Chem.*, *225*:247 (1957).

32. SCHMALFUSS, H., HEIDER, A., and WINKELMANN, K.: *Biochem. Ztschr.*, *257*:188 (1933); SCHMALFUSS, H.: *Biochem. Ztschr.*, *294*:112 (1938).

33. EULER, U. S. v., and LISHAJKO, F.: *Acta physiol. scandinav.*, *42*:42 (1957).

34. EULER, U. S. v.: *Recent Progr. Hormone Res.*, *14*:483 (1958).

35. HACKMAN, R. H., PRYOR, M. G. M., and TODD, A. R.: *Biochem. J.*, *43*:474 (1948).

36. WEIL-MALHERBE, H., and BONE, A. D.: *Biochem. J.*, *67*:65 (1957).
37. WEST, G. B.: *Quart. Rev. Biol.*, *30*:116 (1955).
38. CARLSSON, A.: *Pharmacol. Rev.*, *11*:490 (1959).
39. SANO, I., TANIGUCHI, K., GAMO, T., TAKESADA, M., and KAKIMOTO, Y.: *Klin. Wchschr.*, *38*:57 (1960).
40. BERTLER, A., and ROSENGREN, A.: *Acta physiol. scandinav.*, *47*:350 (1959).
41. SCHÜMANN, H. J.: *Arch. exper. Path. u. Pharmakol.*, *233*:296 (1958).
42. EULER, U. S. v.: In *Metabolism of the Nervous System*, Richter, D., Ed. London, Pergamon (1957).
43. HÖKFELT, B.: *Acta physiol. scandinav.*, *25*:Suppl. 92 (1951).
44. BLOODWORTH, J. M. B., JR., and HAAM, E. v.: *Circulation*, *13*:573 (1956).
45. DRUJAN, B. D., SOURKES, T. L., LAYNE, D. S., and MURPHY, G. F.: *Canad. J. Biochem. & Physiol.*, *37*:1153 (1959).
45a. SOURKES, T. L., and MURPHY, G. F.: Unpublished data.
46. PRICE, H. L., and PRICE, M. L.: *J. Lab. & Clin. Med.*, *50*:769 (1957).
47. BLASCHKO, H., and WELCH, A. D.: *Arch. exper. Path. u. Pharmakol.*, *219*:17 (1953); HILLARP, N. A., LAGERSTEDT, S., and NILSON, B.: *Acta physiol. scandinav.*, *29*:251 (1953); BLASCHKO, H., HAGEN, P., and WELCH, A. D.: *J. Physiol.*, *129*:27 (1955).
48. BLASCHKO, H., BORN, G. V. R., D'IORIO, A., and EADE, N. R.: *J. Physiol.*, *133*:548 (1956); FORTIER, A., LEDUC, J., and D'IORIO, A.: *Rev. canad. biol. 18*:110 (1959).
49. BLASCHKO, H., HAGEN, J. M., and HAGEN, P.: *J. Physiol.*, *139*:316 (1957).
50. HILLARP, N. A., and NILSON, B.: *Acta physiol. scandinav.*, *32*:11 (1954).
51. NORLANDER, O.: *Acta physiol. scandinav.*, *21*:325 (1950); DENGLER, H., and DIEZEL, P. B.: *Naturwissenschaften 45*:244 (1958).
52. EADE, N. R.: *Rev. canad. biol.*, *17*:299 (1958).
53. CARLSSON, A., HILLARP, N., and HÖKFELT, B.: *J. Biol. Chem.*, *227*:243 (1957).
54. EADE, N. R.: *Brit. J. Pharmacol.*, *12*:61 (1957).
55. SCHÜMANN, H. J.: *J. Physiol.*, *137*:318 (1957); EADE, N. R.: *J. Physiol.*, *141*:183 (1958).
56. BERTLER, A., FALCK, B., HILLARP, N. A., ROSENGREN, E., and TORP, A.: *Acta physiol. scandinav.*, *47*:251 (1959).
57. BOESEKEN, J.: *Advances Carbohydrate Chem.*, *4*:189 (1949); ZITTLE, C.: *Advances Enzymol.*, *12*:492 (1951).
58. LAMER, V. K., and RIDEAL, E. K.: *J. Am. Chem. Soc.*, *46*:223 (1924).
59. ADAMS, M., BLOIS, M. S., JR., and SANDS, R. H.: *J. Chem. Phys.*, *28*:774 (1958).
60. BALL, E. G., and CHEN, T. T.: *J. Biol. Chem.*, *102*:691 (1933); RUIZ-GIJON, J.: *Arch. internat. physiol.*, *58*:5 (1950).
61. GREEN, D. E., and RICHTER, D.: *Biochem. J.*, *31*:596 (1937).
62. RICHTER, D., and BLASCHKO, H.: *J. Chem. Soc.*, *601*: (1937).
63. BLASCHKO, H., and LANGEMANN, H.: *J. Physiol.*, *112*:21P (1951).
64. HARLEY-MASON, J.: *Experientia*, *4*:307 (1948).
65. RAPER, H. S.: *Biochem. J.*, *21*:89 (1927); MASON, H. S.: *Advances Enzymol.*, *16*:105 (1955).
66. HARLEY-MASON, J., and BU'LOCK, J. D.: *Nature*, *166*:1036 (1950).
67. HEACOCK, R. A.: *Chem. Rev.*, *59*:181 (1959).
68. AUERBACH, M. E., and ANGELL, E.: *Science*, *109*:537 (1949).
69. ERÄNKÖ, O.: *Acta endocrinol.*, *18*:174 (1955).
70. HEYL, D., LUZ, E., HARRIS, S. A., and FOLKERS, K.: *J. Am. Chem. Soc.*, *74*:414 (1952).

71. SCHOTT, H. F., and CLARK, W. G.: *J. Biol. Chem., 196:*449 (1952).

72. SOURKES, T. L.: *Arch. Biochem. & Biophys., 51:*444 (1954); *Rev. canad. biol., 14:*49 (1955).

73. SCHOEPF, C., and SALZER, W.: *Ann. Chem., 544:*1 (1940).

74. MASUOKA, D. T., SCHOTT, H. F., AKAWIE, R. I., and CLARK, W. G.: *Proc. Soc. Exper. Biol. & Med., 93:*5 (1956).

75. FELLMAN, J. H.: *Nature, 182:*311 (1958).

76. WEIL-MALHERBE, H.: *Pharmacol. Rev., 11:*278 (1959); *Idem.: Biochim. et biophys. acta 40:*351 (1960).

77. HARLEY-MASON, J., and LAIRD, A. H.: *Biochem. J., 69:*59P (1958).

78. SULKOWITCH, H.: *Endocrinology, 59:*260 (1956).

79. QUASTEL, J. H. Ed.: *Methods in Medical Research,* Vol. 9. Chicago, Year Book Pub. (1961).

80. PELLERIN, J., LEDUC, J., and D'IORIO, A.: *Rev. canad. biol., 17:*267 (1958); BLASCHKO, H.: *Pharmacol. Rev., 11:*307 (1959).

81. HALLE, W. L.: *Beitr. chem. Physiol. Path., 8:*276 (1906).

82. GOODALL, M., and KIRSHNER, N.: *J. Biol. Chem., 226:*213 (1957).

83. GURIN, S., and DELLUVA, A. M.: *J. Biol. Chem., 170:*545 (1947).

84. UDENFRIEND, S., and WYNGAARDEN, J. B.: *Biochim. et biophys. acta, 20:*48 (1956).

85. ROSENFELD, G., LEEPER, L. C., and UDENFRIEND, S.: *Arch. Biochem. & Biophys., 74:*252 (1958).

86. GOODALL, M., and KIRSHNER, N.: *Circulation, 17:*366 (1958).

87. ROSENMUND, K. W., and DORNSAFT, H.: *Ber. deutsch. chem. Ges., 52:*1734 (1919).

88. VILENKINA, G. Y.: *Doklady Akad. Nauk SSSR, 69:*385 (1949); GILBERT, J. B.: *J. Am. Chem. Soc., 76:*4183 (1954).

89. HOLTZ, P., HEISE, R., and LÜDTKE, K.: *Arch. exper. Path. u. Pharmakol., 191:*87 (1938).

90. BLASCHKO, H.: *J. Physiol., 96:*50P (1939); *Ibid., 101:*337 (1942).

91. HOLTZ, P.: *Naturwissenschaften, 27:*724 (1939).

92. HOLTZ, P., and KRONEBERG, J.: *Klin. Wchschr., 26:*605 (1948).

92a. SOURKES, T. L., MURPHY, G. F., and RABINOVITCH, A.: *Nature, 189:*577 (1961).

93. KAUFMAN, S.: *Proc. Fourth Internat. Congr. Biochem.,* Vienna, 1958, Vol. 13. London, Pergamon (1959).

94. LERNER, A. B., FITZPATRICK, T. B., CALKINS, E., and SUMMERSON, W. H.: *J. Biol. Chem., 178:*185 (1949).

94a. KIRSHNER, N.: *Pharmacol. Rev., 11:*350 (1959).

95. RAPER, H. S.: *Biochem. J., 26:*200 (1932).

96. ABDERHALDEN, E.: *Fermentforsch., 15:*24 (1936); SCHAAF, F.: *Helvet. chim. acta, 18:*1017 (1936); VAN ARMAN, C. G., and JONES, K. K.: *J. Invest. Dermat., 12:*11 (1949).

97. UDENFRIEND, S., CLARK, C. T., AXELROD, A., and BRODIE, B. B.: *J. Biol. Chem., 208:*731 (1954).

98. BRODIE, B. B., AXELROD, J., SHORE, P. A., and UDENFRIEND, S.: *J. Biol. Chem., 208:*741 (1954).

99. AXELROD, J., UDENFRIEND, S., and BRODIE, B. B.: *J. Pharmacol. & Exper. Therap., 111:*176 (1954).

100. GONNARD, P.: *Ann. pharm. franc., 11:*283 (1953).

101. ROWBOTTOM, J.: *J. Biol. Chem., 212:*877 (1955).

102. BLASCHKO, H.: *Biochim. et biophys. acta, 4:*130 (1950).

103. HARTMAN, W. J., AKAWIE, R. I., and CLARK, W. G.: *J. Biol. Chem., 216:*507 (1955).

104. HOLTZ, P., CREDNER, K., and KOEPP, W.: *Arch. exper. Path. u. Pharmakol.*, *200*:356 (1942).

105. MURPHY, G. F., and SOURKES, T. L.: *Rev. canad. biol.*, *18*:379 (1959).

106. DENGLER, H., and REICHEL, G.: *Arch. exper. Path. u. Pharmakol.*, *234*:275 (1958); OATES, J. A., GILLESPIE, L. G., JR., UDENFRIEND, S., and SJOERDSMA, A.: *Science*, *131*:1890 (1960).

107. SOURKES, T. L., MURPHY, G. F., and WOODFORD, V. R., JR.: *J. Nutrition*, *72*:145 (1960).

108. WERLE, E., and AURES, D.: *Ztschr. physiol. Chem.*, *316*:45 (1959).

109. FELLMAN, J. H.: *Enzymologia*, *20*:366 (1959).

110. YUWILER, A., GELLER, E., and EIDUSON, S.: *Arch. Biochem. & Biophys.*, *80*:162 (1959).

111. WESTERMANN, E., BALZER, H., and KNELL, J.: *Arch. exper. Path. u. Pharmakol.*, *234*:194 (1958).

111a. LEVIN, E. Y., LEVENBERG, B., and KAUFMAN, S.: *J. Biol. Chem.*, *235*:2080 (1960).

112. MASSART, L., and VERCAUTEREN, R.: *Ann. Rev. Biochem.*, *28*:527 (1959).

113. KELLER, E. B., BOISSONNAS, R. A., and DU VIGNEAUD, V.: *J. Biol. Chem.*, *183*:627 (1950).

114. CANTONI, G. L.: *J. Biol. Chem.*, *204*:403 (1953).

115. EULER, U. S. V.: *Scandinav. J. Clin. & Lab. Invest.*, *4*:254 (1952); ELMADJIAN, F., LAMSON, E. T., and NERI, R.: *J. Clin. Endocrinol. & Metab.*, *16*:222 (1956).

116. ERSPAMER, V.: *Nature*, *169*:375 (1952).

117. KAKIMOTO, Y., and ARMSTRONG, M. D.: *Federation Proc.*, *19*:295 (1960).

118. UDENFRIEND, S., COOPER, J. R., CLARK, C. T., and BAER, J. E.: *Science*, *117*:663 (1953).

119. POGRUND, R. S., DRELL, W., and CLARK, W. G.: *Federation Proc.*, *14*:116 (1955); Idem.: *J. Pharmacol. & Exper. Therap.*, *131*:294 (1961).

120. VAN ARMAN, C. C.: *Am. J. Physiol.*, *164*:476 (1951).

121. WEIL-MALHERBE, H., and BONE, A. D.: *J. Clin. Path.*, *10*:138 (1957).

122. HUTCHEON, D. E., and PARKER, R. H. O.: *Brit. J. Pharmacol.*, *5*:604 (1950).

123. UDENFRIEND, S., CREVELING, C. R., OZAKI, M., DALY, J. W., and WITKOP, B.: *Arch. Biochem. & Biophys.*, *84*:249 (1959).

124. MURPHY, G. F., and SOURKES, T. L.: *Arch. Biochem. & Biophys.*, *93*:338 (1961).

125. AXELROD, J.: *Physiol. Rev.*, *39*:751 (1959).

126. EULER, U. S. V., and LUFT, R.: *Brit. J. Pharmacol.*, *6*:286 (1951); EULER, U. S. V., and ZETTERSTRÖM, B.: *Acta physiol. scandinav.*, *33*: (Suppl. 118), 26 (1955).

127. ARMSTRONG, M. D., McMILLAN, A., and SHAW, K. N. F.: *Biochim. et biophys. acta*, *25*:422 (1957).

128. AXELROD, J., and TOMCHICK, R.: *J. Biol. Chem.*, *233*:702 (1958); PELLERIN, J., and D'IORIO, A.: *Canad. J. Biochem. & Physiol.*, *36*:491 (1958).

129. BACQ, Z. M., GOSSELIN, L., DRESSE, A., and RENSON, J.: *Science*, *130*:453 (1959).

130. AXELROD, J., and LAROCHE, M. J.: *Science*, *130*:800 (1959).

131. D'IORIO, A., and LEDUC, J.: *Arch. Biochem. & Biophys.*, *87*:224 (1960).

132. ARMSTRONG, M. D., and McMILLAN, A.: *Pharmacol. Rev.*, *11*:394 (1959).

133. GOODALL, M.: *Pharmacol. Rev.*, *11*:416 (1959).

134. SOURKES, T. L.: *Rev. canad. biol.*, *17*:328 (1958).

135. BLASCHKO, H.: *Pharmacol. Rev.*, *4*:415 (1952).

136. FELLMAN, J. H.: *Biochim. et biophys. acta*, *35*:530 (1959).

137. KOPIN, I. J., and AXELROD, J.: *Arch. Biochem. & Biophys.*, *89*:148 (1960).

138. GOLDSTEIN, M., FRIEDHOF, A. J., POMERANTZ, S., and SIMMONS, C.: *Biochim. et biophys. acta, 39*:189 (1960).

139. GUGGENHEIM, M., and LÖFFLER, W.: *Biochem. Ztschr., 72*:325 (1916).

140. CROUT, J. R., CREVELING, C. R., and CATON, D.: *Federation Proc., 19*:297 (1960); PLETSCHER, A., and GEY, T.: *Helvet. physiol. et pharmacol. acta, 18*:C43 (1960).

141. SCHACTER, B.: *J. Biol. Chem., 184*:697 (1950).

142. HOLMBERG, C. G., and LAURELL, C. B.: *Scandinav. J. Clin. & Lab. Invest., 3*:103 (1951).

143. MAZUR, A., GREEN, S., and SHORR, E.: *J. Biol. Chem., 220*:227 (1956).

144. BACQ, Z. M.: *J. Pharmacol. & Exper. Therap., 95*:1 (1949).

145. HOFFER, A.: *Am. J. Psychiat., 114*:752 (1958).

146. PAYZA, A. N., and MAHON, M.: *Anal. Chem., 32*:17 (1960).

147. SZARA, S., AXELROD, J., and PERLIN, S.: *Am. J. Psychiat., 115*:162 (1958); FELDSTEIN, A.: *Ibid., 116*:454 (1959); LAYNE, D. S., and SOURKES, T. L.: *J. Nerv. & Ment. Dis., 130*:93 (1960); RANDRUP, A., and MUNKVAD, I.: *Am. J. Psychiat., 117*:153 (1960).

148. SCHAYER, R. W., and SMILEY, R. L.: *J. Biol. Chem., 202*:425 (1953).

149. FISHER, P., and LANDTSHEER, L.: *Experientia, 6*:305 (1950); FISHER, P., and LECOMTE, J.: *Bull. Soc. chim. biol., 33*:569 (1951).

150. IMAIZUMI, R., KAWAMOTO, K., KITA, T., and SATO, H.: *M. J. Osaka U., 3*:279 (1952).

151. KAWAMOTO, K.: *Sympos. Enz. Chem.* (Japan), *9*:52 (1954); seen in *Chem. Abst., 48*:7727b (1954).

152. AXELROD, J., and SZARA, S.: *Biochim. et biophys. acta, 30*:188 (1958); DALY, J. W., AXELROD, J., and WITKOP, B.: *J. Biol. Chem., 235*:1155 (1960).

153. SENOH, S., WITKOP, B., CREVELING, C. R., and UDENFRIEND, S.: *Proc. Fourth Internat. Congr. Biochem.,* Vienna, 1958, Vol. 13. London, Pergamon (1959).

154. DEEDS, F., BOOTH, A. N., and JONES, F. T.: *J. Biol. Chem., 225*:615 (1957).

155. AXELROD, J., KOPIN, I. J., and MANN, J. D.: *Biochim. et biophys. acta, 36*:576 (1959).

156. SHAW, K. N. F., MCMILLAN, A., and ARMSTRONG, M. D.: *J. Biol. Chem., 226*:255 (1957).

157. ARMSTRONG, M. D., SHAW, K. N. F., and WALL, P. E.: *J. Biol. Chem., 218*:293 (1956).

158. SMITH, P., and BENNETT, A. M. H.: *Nature, 181*:709 (1958).

159. PELLERIN, J., and D'IORIO, A.: *Canad. J. Biochem. & Physiol., 33*:1055 (1955); *35*:151 (1957).

160. LIN, K. H.: *J. Formosan M. A., 47*:1 (1948); quoted in ref. 154.

161. GOODALL, M., KIRSHNER, N., and ROSEN, L.: *J. Clin. Invest., 38*:707 (1959).

162. KIRSHNER, N., GOODALL, M., and ROSEN, L.: *Proc. Soc. Exper. Biol. & Med., 98*:627 (1958).

163. AXELROD, J.: *Pharmacol. Rev., 11*:402 (1959).

164. GOLDSTEIN, M., FRIEDHOFF, A. J., and SIMMONS, C.: *Biochim. et biophys. acta, 33*:572 (1959).

165. LABROSSE, E. H., AXELROD, J., and KETY, S. S.: *Science, 128*:593 (1958).

166. HOLTZ, P.: *Acta physiol. scandinav., 20*:354 (1950).

167. VOGT, M.: *J. Physiol., 123*:451 (1954).

168. HOLTZ, P., and WESTERMANN, E.: *Arch. exper. Path. u. Pharmakol., 227*:538 (1956); HOLTZ, P.: *Psychiat. et Neurol., 140*:175 (1960).

169. UDENFRIEND, S., and CREVELING, C. R.: *J. Neurochem., 4*:350 (1959).

170. AXELROD, J., ALBERS, W.. and CLEMENTE, C. D.: *J. Neurochem.*, 5:68 (1959).
171. BOGDANSKI, D. F., WEISSBACH, H., and UDENFRIEND, S.: *J. Neurochem.*, 1:272 (1957).
172. WHITBY, L. G., WEIL-MALHERBE, H., and AXELROD, J.: *Federation Proc.*, 19:296 (1960).
173. AXELROD, J., WEIL-MALHERBE, H., and TOMCHICK, R.: *J. Pharmacol. & Exper. Therap.*, 127:251 (1959); WEIL-MALHERBE, H., AXELROD, J., and TOMCHICK, R.: *Science, 129*:1226 (1959).
174. CARLSSON, A., LINDQVIST, M., and MAGNUSSON, T.: *Nature, 180*:1200 (1957).
175. SHORE, P. A., MEAD, J. A. R., KUNTZMAN, R. G., SPECTOR, S., and BRODIE, B. B.: *Science, 126*:1063 (1957).
176. AXELROD, J.: *Science, 127*:754 (1958); AXELROD, J., SENOH, S., and WITKOP, B.: *J. Biol. Chem., 233*:697 (1958).
177. HOLZBAUER, M., and VOGT, M.: *J. Neurochem., 1*:8 (1956); BRODIE, B. B., OLIN, J. S., KUNTZMAN, R., and SHORE, P. A.: *Science, 125*:1293 (1957).
177a. SOURKES, T. L.: *Rev. canad. biol., 20*:187 (1961).
177b. SOURKES, T. L., MURPHY, G. F., CHAVEZ, BEATRIZ, and ZIELINSKA, MARLA: *J. Neurochem. 8*:109 (1961).
178. MANGER, W. M., FLOCK, E. V., BERKSON, J., BOLLMAN, J. L., ROTH, G. M., BALDES, E. J., and JACOBS, M.: *Circulation, 10*:641 (1954).
179. GÉLINAS, R., PELLERIN, J., and D'IORIO, A.: *Rev. canad. biol., 16*:445 (1957); LEDUC, J., and D'IORIO, A.: *ibid., 19*:34 (1959).
180. SJOERDSMA, A., LEEPER, L. C., TERRY, L. L., and UDENFRIEND, S.: *J. Clin. Invest., 38*:31 (1959).
181. KRAUPP, O., STORMANN, H., BERNHEIMER, H., and OBENAUS, H.: *Klin. Wchschr., 37*:76 (1959).
182. ISAACS, H., MEDALIE, M., and POLITZER, W. M.: *Brit. M. J., i*:401 (1959).
183. GRAHAM, J. D. P.: *Nature, 183*:1733 (1959).
184. BARBEAU, A., MURPHY, G. F., and SOURKES, T. L.: *Science, 133*:1706 (1961).
185. EHRINGER, H., and HORNYKIEWICZ, O.: *Klin. Wchschr., 38*:1236 (1960).

XXV

SEROTONIN

IRVINE H. PAGE AND WILLIAM M. MCISAAC

SEROTONIN was first isolated in 1948 by Rapport, Green and Page[1] and in its short life has become the focal point about which many neurochemical investigations and theories have centered. The gradual unfolding of the ubiquitous importance of this hormone has proved to be a fascinating story, marred only by the difficulty of following its theme through an unprecedented volume of scientific literature. In a comprehensive review[2] written in 1958 reference was made to some 682 papers on this subject. The extent and novelty of this information makes it especially difficult to convey a true and comprehensive picture of the role played by this compound in the field of neurochemistry.

There is no substance with which we are acquainted that has been so provocative in eliciting suggested functions. It may be fruitful to determine its functions in lower animals as a clue to those in higher forms. For example, Mansour[3] has shown the presence of a most interesting system for synthesis of serotonin in liver flukes. These organisms metabolize carbohydrate anerobically at a high rate with large production of volatile fatty acids; only 4 to 8% is converted to lactic acid.[4] Serotonin and lysergic acid diethylamide (LSD) in low concentrations increase glucose utilization, glycogen breakdown and lactic acid production (two- to ten-fold increase) with little change in production of volatile fatty acids.[5] Neither epinephrine nor norepinephrine has any such action, in contrast with their effects in higher animals. Further, serotonin, but not epinephrine, increases phosphorylase activity and the formation of cyclic 3,5-adenosine-monophosphate.[6] Since Rall and Sutherland[7] found a similar stimulating action of epinephrine that increases the formation of active phosporylase in mammalian liver, the suggestion arises that possibly serotonin and related compounds have some of the same actions in invertebrates that epinephrine has in higher animals.

620

I. SEROTONIN IN BRAIN

Shortly after its discovery, serotonin was demonstrated by Twarog and Page[8] to occur in brain, but the significance of this finding was not appreciated until it was proposed by Gaddum[9] that lysergic acid diethylamide (LSD) acted as an hallucinogen by virtue of its antagonism to serotonin. The antagonism was demonstrated only on smooth muscle, not on cerebral function. The latter is difficult because of the lack of penetration of the blood-brain barrier. Serotonin given intravenously to patients during LSD hallucination could not be expected to act. Independently, Wooley and Shaw[10] suggested that serotonin was concerned in mentation and included mental disease as a consequence of disturbance of its metabolism.

The next definitive step was taken by Pletscher, Shore and Brodie[11] by showing that reserpine caused bound serotonin in the brain to be released, and its effect persisted long after the extractable reserpine had disappeared from the brain. This unusual observation has subsequently been extended to a variety of other tissues. Serotonin release has been shown not to be unique, as was originally thought, since norepinephrine is released as well.

One of the difficulties in understanding the physiological or pharmacological effects of serotonin is that it penetrates from the blood into the brain in only small quantities. In fact, it had been generally accepted that serotonin did not cross the barrier at all. But McIsaac and Page[12] using C^{14}-serotonin, found a significant amount of penetration when high perenteral dose levels were employed. Even when the blood serotonin is high as in carcinoid syndrome, there is no change in mental status, suggesting either that little penetration occurs, or the brain has adapted to higher concentrations and no longer reacts to them.[13] No increase is found in spinal fluid.[14]

The injection of small amounts of serotonin into arteries or veins of rats, anesthetized with Pentothal, causes strong inhibition of electrical activity of brain[15] indicating that some serotonin has passed the blood-brain barrier. The effect is similar to that of LSD. If no anesthesia is used, serotonin is excitatory, tending to increase frequency of the waves. Clearly, some serotonin gets into the brain from the blood stream and is effective in very small amounts.

The problem of how to cause a large increase in serotonin content of brain was solved by an ingenious method devised by Udenfriend, Weissbach and Bogdanski.[16] They showed that administered 5-hydroxytryptophan is converted to serotonin in brain tissue by 5-hydroxytryptophan decarboxylase and in this way the brain level is elevated to ten or more times the normal values. The clinical manifestations resulting from intravenously administered 5-hydroxytryptophan in dogs are remarkable. Bogdanski, Weissbach and Udenfriend[17] noted a variety of signs including muscle tremor, incoordination, salivation, lacrimation, piloerection, tachycardia, increased peristalsis, loss of response to visual stimuli, dilatation of pupils and loss of light reflex. They suggested that the signs were almost identical with those produced by LSD. Pretreatment of the dogs with iproniazid greatly augmented the action of the 5-hydroxytryptophan since the serotonin content of brain was, thereby, considerably further increased. In man, only 25 mg. could be tolerated without producing nausea and gastrointestinal disturbance. This was not enough to elicit mental change.

Serotonin potentiates the action of barbiturates and this is overcome by LSD.[18] After reserpine administration in animals hypotension and hypothermia occur. Restoration of normal temperature and arterial pressure is related to restoration of normal serotonin concentrations in the brain. In the presence of iproniazid, an inhibitor of serotonin breakdown, reserpine causes excitement, hyperthermia and hypertension; just the reverse of its usual effect. Iproniazid alone had no obvious effect in animals.

2. DISTRIBUTION OF SEROTONIN IN BRAIN

The finding by Paasonen, MacLean and Giarman[19] of relatively high serotonin values in the hippocampus, 0.26 μg./gm. and amygdala, 0.49 μg./gm. along with a fall off of serotonin concentration around the limbic lobe in either direction away from the olfactory trigone, poses an interesting question of function in relation to distribution. Equally interesting was their observation that the lowest serotonin level was in the neo-cortex, 0.01 to 0.08 μg./gm. Sympathetic ganglia contain no serotonin but have a high 5-hydroxytryptophan decarboxylase content.

The bovine pineal gland contains serotonin, catecholamines and histamine according to Giarman and Day.[20] In addition, acetylcholine, cholinesterase and choline acetylase have been found. The human gland contains the highest values, up to 22.82 μg./gm. for serotonin content recorded for any neural structure of any species, according to Giarman et al.[21] and simian pineal glands, 3.2 μg./gm. are richer in serotonin that bovine glands, 0.4 μg./gm. These (workers) suggest that the morphology of the pineal gland is well suited to a secretory function and that it well may participate in pituitary and adrenal control.

MacLean[22] has reviewed the problem of the functions of the large cerebral convolution called the limbic lobe. It is found in the brains of all mammals. Physiologically it is a common denominator of a variety of emotional and viscerosomatic functions. Most of the "old cortex" is contained in the limbic lobe and, as would be expected, it is structurally primitive. It has reciprocating pathways with the hypothalamus and the ancient structures of the brain stem. Portions of this limbic system are concerned with emotionally determined functions pertaining to preservation of the self or the species. The common property of having high serotonin concentrations in the limbic system and hypothalamus would tend to associate this neurohormone with the mechanisms of emotion.

There is much yet to be learned about the distribution of amines in the brain in terms of function. For example, dopamine is found localized almost exclusively in the nuclei of the corpus striatum of the cerebral hemispheres.[23,24]

Serotonin like norepinephrine is localized mainly in the older areas of the brain though the distribution of these two compounds within these areas do not exactly parallel each other. In the human brain, for example, the highest concentration of serotonin, 2.0 to 6.5 μg./gm. is in the caudate nucleus and putamen while the highest concentration of norepinephrine, 0.8–1.9 μg./gm. is in the rostral and intermediate portions of the hypothalamus. 5-Hydroxytryptophan decarboxylase and amine oxidase levels roughly parallel those of serotonin. Vogt[25] has noted that there is also a similar parallelism with norepinephrine. The tryptophan content of the hypothalamus, cerebellum and pons is about 100 times that of serotonin while the ratio is only three to ten times for the other parts of dog's, cat's and rabbit's brain.[26]

Following the injection of 5-hydroxytryptophan into rabbits, serotonin is found to accumulate in the hypothalamus and caudate nucleus of the brain. The least amount is found in the cerebral hemisphere and cerebellum. After 5-hydroxytryptophan injection into rabbits, Costa and Aprison[27] found the serotonin concentration to increase in the telencephalon, the hippocampus, the pons-medulla, and most of all, in the midbrain; the increase was much less in the cerebellum. During the first 2 hours EEG changes occurred consisting of monorhythmic diffuse high voltage activity, disappearance of cortical fast rhythms and hippocampal theta waves followed by generalized depressions of voltage. Chlorpromazine did not change the serotonin content of brain, yet pretreatment increased the ability of 5-hydroxytryptophan to elevate the serotonin level. Behavioral excitation was avoided by the chlorpromazine pretreatment.

Lerner et al.[28,29] isolated N-acetyl-5-methoxytryptamine from pineal gland and gave it the name "melatonin." This interesting substance is measured by its effect in lightening pigment cells of frogs, being approximately 100,000 times as active as norepinephrine. Further, they found[30] a chemically related, but inactive, compound identified as 5-methoxyindole-3-acetic acid. The amount of melatonin present can not be large since only 40 μg. were isolated per 100 gm. of pineal tissue. Melatonin is concentrated in the pineal gland but also occurs in other parts of the brain and peripheral nerves[31] but only in very small quantities.

3. POSSIBLE NEUROTRANSMITTER FUNCTION

By its properties, serotonin suggested itself as being a possible neurotransmitter. The invertebrate *Venus mercenaria* heart was found to be highly sensitive to serotonin.[32] Clam contains large quantities of serotonin as well and Welsh[32] has suggested that in *Venus* it may be the normal mediator of the cardiac excitatory nerves and acetylcholine the mediator of the inhibitory nerves.

Brodie and Shore[33] favor the suggestion that serotonin is involved in stimulation of parasympathetic centers in subcortical areas or, conversely, in inhibition of sympathetic centers.

Serotonin acts as an inhibitor of central synaptic transmission as measured in the transcallosal path of cats by Marrazzi and Hart.[34] Since LSD blocks the action of serotonin on smooth muscle, it is just possible that LSD, or something like it, blocks the action of serotonin in brain. No suitable studies have been carried out to prove or disprove these hypotheses.

There is some evidence that acetylcholine, choline acetylase and serotonin, all in bound form, are contained in simple vesicles at the nerve endings. These "synaptic vesicles" are thought by Whittaker[35] to be the source of bound transmitter substance. Part at least of the acetylcholine and serotonin may be released by freezing-thawing, hypotonic dilution, agitation, treatment with lecithinase, etc. The acetylcholine- and serotonin-containing particles are not the same. These interesting observations need extension and confirmation.

The distribution in brain of serotonin and of the sympathetic neurotransmitter norepinephrine is similar, in contrast to acetylcholine and histamine. Substance P, a polypeptide, has also been suggested as a possible neurotransmitter. The hypothalamus, basal ganglia and gray matter of the cord are relatively rich in it. Except for its high concentration in the dorsal roots, its distribution is similar to that of serotonin. All of these substances affect the central nervous system. While all have properties suggestive of neurotransmitter function, acetylcholine is the only one about which there is little doubt. However, it is likely that acetylcholine is not the only transmitter and serotonin possibly may be among the others.

A somewhat related function of serotonin that results in stimulation of smooth muscle is believed by Woolley[36] to be due to its ability to cause the passage of calcium ions through cell membranes. The passage of Ca^{++} and its reaction with actomyosin + adenosine triphosphate may explain why serotonin causes smooth muscle to contract. Serotonin combines with a specific lipid in the cell membrane, which Woolley calls "serotonin receptor," and this combination is followed by the binding of Ca^{++} by the receptor-serotonin compound. The resulting calcium-containing complex is soluble in fat and thus able to diffuse through the lipoidal cell membranes. Inside the membrane there seems to be an enzyme which attacks the complex and degrades it. The "serotonin receptor" has been extracted from smooth muscle and nerve[37] and recognized to be a lipid which combines specifically with serotonin.

4. TRANQUILIZATION

Largely through the work of Brodie and Shore,[33] the relationship between serotonin, reserpine and tranquilization has been illuminated. They demonstrated that reserpine changes brain serotonin from the bound to the free state.[38] Brodie, Prockop and Shore[39] suggested that serotonin is a neuro-hormone acting on what Hess called the trophotropic functions of the diencephalon which integrate with the parasympathetic system. Trophotropic stimulation results in drowsiness and sleep, increased parasympathetic activity, decreased skeletal muscle tone and activity and lowered responsiveness to external stimuli. Reserpine elicits such a syndrome presumably by stimulating the trophotropic division. Possibly serotonin is the transmitter since it is concentrated in the hypothalamus and is in stored form ready for release.

Thus, the sedative group of drugs such as the Rauwolfia alkaloids and the phenothiazine derivatives elicit trophotropic predominance. Brodie thinks that drugs can also produce similar central effects by quite different mechanisms. Trophotropic predominance could result either by stimulating the trophotropic division, for example with reserpine, or by depressing the opposing ergotropic division by chlorpromazine. Chlorpromazine thus could act by a mechanism not involving release of serotonin.

The primary action of reserpine is to impair the mechanism in brain cells that stores serotonin but without affecting its synthesis. The impairment of storage far outlasts the presence of reserpine in the brain. The effect of reserpine has been attributed to the free serotonin which might continue to stimulate synaptic junctions of the trophotropic division until the serotonin storage mechanism functions again. Brodie found a close relationship between the extent of serotonin release and the sedative potency of a variety of reserpine-like compounds. Some central stimulant effects, such as result from morphine given to cats, cause release of norepinephrine but not serotonin and elicit excitement rather than sedation.

In some ways reserpine, serotonin and chlorpromazine are similar, since Gangloff and Mournier[40] found that these drugs given intravenously to unanesthetized rabbits all produce the following electrographic effects:

(1) An initial transitory sleep pattern with drowsiness.

(2) Decrease of the arousal reaction to external sensory stimuli.

(3) Decrease of the electrical arousal reaction evoked by the electrical stimulation of the midbrain reticular formation.

(4) Decreased cortical excitability with increased threshold of the cortical after discharge.

(5) Partial block of the projections of the rhinencephalic system.

The differences are:

(1) The specific EEG patterns produced by reserpine and serotonin develop late and consist of a so-called mixed arousal and relaxation pattern associated with indifference but not sleep.

(2) The chlorpromazine EEG pattern develops early and is associated with sleep.

(3) The thalamus is slightly depressed by reserpine and serotonin but activated by chlorpromazine.

(4) Reserpine and serotonin do not depress the reticular formation while chlorpromazine elicits an initial depression.

Reserpine is often regarded as an antimetabolite of serotonin because of the similarity of the indole structure. Compounds which are not indoles also have been found to release brain serotonin as evidenced by Pletscher's report that some derivatives of 1,2,3,4,6,7,-hexahydroquinoline, e.g., tetrabenazine (the 2-oxo-3-isobutyl-9,10-dimethoxy derivative) have the same effect.[41] According to Quinn, Shore and Brodie[42] this drug has a selective action on brain serotonin and norepinephrine, releasing little or none of these amines peripherally. It has a greater effect on brain norepinephrine than on brain serotonin but the sedative effect seems to be related to change in serotonin rather than norepinephrine concentration. Tetrabenazine and reserpine seem to compete for the same receptors.

2-Phenylcyclopropylamine is a non-competitive inhibitor of serotonin metabolism. Maass and Nimmo[43] found that this non-hydrazine drug raised brain serotonin concentration when given by mouth.

α-Methyl tryptamine and α-ethyltryptamine inhibit monoamine oxidase activity while 5-hydroxy-α-methyl tryptamine is inactive *in vivo*. The two former, but not the latter, cause central stimulation of rats and mice. Their actions correlate with their ability to inhibit monoamine oxidase.[44]

The pharmacological effects of the monoamine oxidase inhibitors do not fit into a clear pattern. For example, despite the overall excitation, arterial blood pressure is reduced and these substances are of value in the treatment of angina pectoris where only a depressant would be expected to work.

Recently some doubt has been cast on the view that the stimulating effect of monoamine oxidase blocking agents is due to their ability to block the enzyme. Thus, Feldstein, Hoagland and Freeman[45] find that 1-benzyl-2-methyl-5-methoxytryptamine inhibits monoamine oxidase in man but acts as a tranquilizing agent rather than a stimulant.

The anticonvulsants are another group of substances capable of elevating brain serotonin. Bonnycastle, Giarman and Paasonen[46] noted in rats that such convulsing procedures as electric shock or administration of leptazol, picrotoxin and carbon dioxide did not change the level of serotonin, nor does elevating the serotonin content by administering 5-hydroxytryptophan protect against the convulsant action of leptazol. The rise in brain serotonin elicited by anticonvulsants is restricted to cerebral tissues. On the other hand, Garattini, Valsecchi and Valzelli[47] found an increase in brain serotonin in rats given electroshock, leptazol or cardiazol. Intestinal serotonin decreased. Bertaccini[48] found brain serotonin elevated only slightly. The problem clearly needs further study.

Harmaline and the hydrazine monoamine oxidase blocking agents seem to compete for the same site in the enzyme.[49]

5. PSYCHOTOMIMETIC COMPOUNDS CHEMICALLY RELATED TO SEROTONIN

The elucidation of the relationship between chemical structure and psychotomimetic activity may prove to be a most rewarding approach to better understanding of some mental diseases. The production of temporary psychotic phenomena in normal individuals, or of abnormal behavior patterns in experimental animals, by the use of chemical agents lends itself to the study of biochemical changes associated with psychoses.

Although the effects of plant extracts on the mind have been known for many years as evidenced by their role in some religious rites[50] it is only during the last decade that interest has grown rapidly regarding this particular aspect of psychopharmacology.

An incident which contributed considerable impetus to this field was the dramatic discovery by Hofman of the psychotomimetic properties of LSD. The minute dose (1 μg./kg.) required to produce these effects makes this compound unique.

So little is known of the normal occurrence, distribution and function of the varied, naturally occurring indoles that it would be rash indeed to attempt anything more than guesses as to their participation in the mechanisms of mental disease. In addition, no clear evidence has been found in patients to support any theory. But it must be added that, so far, little penetrating study has been given the problem.

It may be suggested further that the inhibition of central synpatic transmission found by Marrazzi and Hart[34] may be a part of the

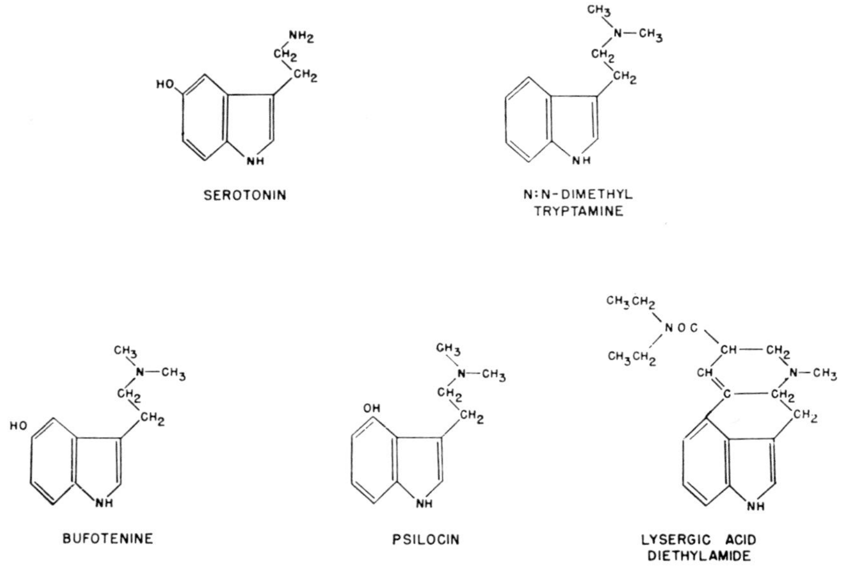

Fig. 1. Structural relationship between serotonin and some psychotomimetic indole derivatives.

mechanism of behavioral disturbance. One of the difficulties with relating this fact to mental change has been the finding that there seemed to be no relationship between the degree to which a substance blocks transmission and its ability to produce mental change. It must be kept in mind that mental change in animals may be something quite different from that in man.

2-Bromo-d-lysergic acid diethylamide depresses transmission in cats about as effectively as serotonin and may be an even more potent competitor of serotonin than LSD. But it is only slightly hallucinogenic while LSD is powerfully so.

Several attempts have been made to relate the indoles to mental disease. Feldstein et al.[51] measured blood serotonin and urinary 5-hydroxy-indole acetic acid in schizophrenic patients. No abnormality was found. Kopin[52] noted no difference in 5-hydroxyindole acetic acid excretion in normal and schizophrenic patients given 5 gm. oral doses fo tryptophan. Clearly such measurements do not necessarily reflect changes in the brain, or even change in the large bodily stores. Measurement of only one metabolic end product is often inadequate as an indicator of metabolic derangement. It is premature to draw sweeping conclusions either for or against a possible part the indoles play in mental disease. We are only beginning to understand the complex metabolism of serotonin itself, much less that of the many other similar indoles.

Some of the psychotomimetic compounds related to serotonin which have been extensively studied (see Fig. 1) are:

D-Lysergic Acid Diethylamide (LSD)

d-Lysergic acid diethylamide is a synthetic derivative of lysergic acid which is the nucleus of several of the ergot alkaloids. It is the most powerful psychotomimetic agent known and studies have revealed that whereas the dextro form is active the levo form is inactive. Substituents in the 2-position, e.g., bromine, modify the activity. The bromo derivative remains a potent serotonin antagonist but its psychotomimetic properties greatly diminish.[53] Two other factors necessary for psychotomimetic activity are the double bond between positions 9 and 10 and the diethyl substituents in the side chain. LSD is almost completely metabolized in vivo, only traces of the unchanged compound appearing in the urine or feces. In vitro it is metabolized by liver tissue, in a microsomal reaction requiring TPNH and oxygen, to 2-oxylysergic acid diethylamide which, being a hydroxy derivative in the 2 position, is devoid of the pharmacological actions of LSD.[54]

Bufotenine

Bufotenine was isolated from the secretion of the glands found on toads' backs and later from the seeds of Piptadenia peregrina.[55,56] These seeds have been used by South American Indians for the preparation of "cahoba," a psychotropic snuff.

Bufotenine has been reported to be psychotomimetic in humans and to cause behavioral changes in animals.[57-59] It possesses pharmacological properties including oxytocic, vasopressor and hexobarbital potentiation activity similar to those of serotonin.[60]

In bufotenine, the amine group is protected from monoamine oxidase action by the dimethyl substituents. It is not surprising therefore, that it has similar actions to serotonin but for a more prolonged time.

Psilocybin

The American ethnologist, Gordon Wasson, and his wife discovered that hallucinations experienced by some Mexican Indians during their religious rites were associated with the ingestion of mushrooms.[50] These fungi were identified as *Psilocybe Mexicana Heim.* The psychotropic principle, psilocybin, was isolated by Hofman *et al.*[61] and its structure confirmed by synthesis as the phosphoric ester of N:N-dimethyl-4-hydroxytryptamine.[62] The importance of the phosphate group is uncertain since psilocin, the non-phosphorylated analogue, possesses identical properties.[63]

Psychotomimetic effects, including hallucinations, have resulted from administration of 10 mg. of psilocybin to human subjects. It also produces pupillary dilatation, piloerection, tachycardia, tachypnea and hyperthermia.[64] It has a pressor effect similar to that of bufotenine and it potentiates barbiturate sleeping time.[59]

N:N-Dimethyl- and N:N-Diethyl-tryptamine

Szara (65) found that N:N-dimethyltryptamine produces psychotic effects similar to those induced by LSD. In the body it is metabolized to N-methyltryptamine, indole acetic acid, 6-hydroxydimethyltryptamine and 6-hydroxyindole acetic acid.[66] N:N-diethyltryptamine is similarly metabolized by hydroxylation and it has been claimed that its psychotomimetic properties are due to the formation of 6-hydroxy-N:N-diethyltryptamine.[67]

6. BIOGENESIS AND METABOLISM OF SEROTONIN

The biogenesis of serotonin from 5-hydroxytryptophan was first suggested by Udenfriend *et al.*[68] Radioactive tryptophan and metabolic balance methods have been used to demonstrate that tryptophan is the dietary precursor of serotonin in patients with carcinoid syndrome.[69] The excretion of 5-hydroxytryptophan in the urine of some patients with this syndrome also indicates that this compound is the immediate precursor of serotonin although the hydroxylation of tryptophan to 5-hydroxytryptophan has not been demonstrated in mammalian tissue. Such a conversion has been shown to occur in the bacteria *Chromobacterium violaceum*.[70]

The decarboxylation of 5-hydroxytryptophan to serotonin and carbon dioxide is accomplished by the enzyme 5-hydroxytryptophan decarboxylase which is highly specific since even 7-hydroxytryptophan will not serve as a substrate.[71] The enzyme's pH optimum is 8.1, which is high for an amino acid decarboxylase, and it requires metallic ions and pyridoxal phosphate as co-factors.[72,73] It is present in all tissues which contain serotonin, blood being the only notable exception.

Oxidative deamination of serotonin by monoamine oxidase is the major metabolic pathway. This enzyme is found in most tissues, is present in high concentrations in all parts of the brain, and is responsible for the deamination of other amines including the catecholamines. It converts serotonin to 5-hydroxyindoleacetaldehyde which is then converted quantitatively to 5-hydroxyindole acetic acid by aldehyde dehydrogenase.

A study of the metabolic fate of radioactive serotonin by McIsaac and Page[12] revealed the presence in the urine, in addition to 5-hydroxyindole acetic acid, of unchanged serotonin, serotonin glucuronide, N-acetyl serotonin and, in herbiverous species, 5-hydroxyindoleaceturic acid. Other metabolites described include the sulphates of 5-hydroxyindole acetic acid and 5-hydroxytryptamine[74,75] and an oxidation product thought to be a para-quinone imine.[76]

These metabolites appear to be devoid of physiological activity, the major significance being that N-acetylation provides the substrate for the formation of melatonin.

Biogenesis and Metabolism of O-Methyl Derivatives of Serotonin

The pineal gland, which according to the Cartesian concept was the seat of the soul, has become the center of renewed interest since it has been found to contain melatonin.[77] This, the most potent skin lightening agent known, causes the aggregation of melanin granules around the melanocyte nucleus. This aggregation is associated with a change in cytoplasmic colloidal state from a sol to a gel, with a consequent diminution of melanin production.[78]

Axelrod and Weissbach[79] found a specific enzyme localized in the pineal gland which transfers the methyl group from S-adenosylmethionine to N-acetyl-5-hydroxytryptamine to form melatonin. This hydroxy-O-methyl transferase is unlike catechol O-methyl transferase in that it does not require Mg^{++}. Serotonin can also be O-methylated by this enzyme though it is only one-tenth as good a substrate as N-acetyl-5-hydroxytryptamine.

Kopin *et al.*[80] and Kveder, McIsaac and Page[81] have shown that radioactive melatonin is largely metabolised by hydroxylation and subsequent conjugation, the major metabolite being N-acetyl-5-methoxy-6-hydroxytryptamine. This may be important since 6-hydroxylation of indoles has been shown to be associated with an increase in hallucinogenic activity.[67] The presence of a minor non-indolic metabolite[81] also suggests the possibility of cyclisation to 10-methoxyharmalan, an analogue of harmaline.

Since 5-methoxyindole acetic acid is the major metabolite of 5-methoxytryptamine[82,83] the isolation of the former from pineal tissue[77] indicates the presence of the latter. 5-Methoxytryptamine is biologically active[84,85] and, since melatonin is not deacetylated to any extent[83] and

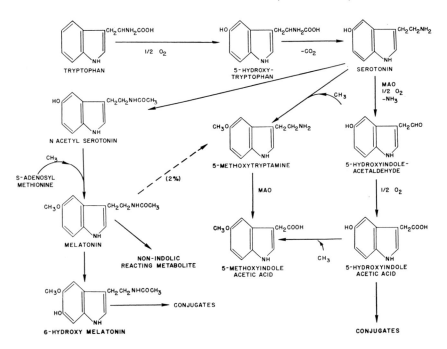

Fig. 2. Biogenesis and metabolism of serotonin. The metabolism of serotonin to 5-hydroxyindole acetic acid is a two step reaction, monoamine oxidase (MAO) being responsible for the first step. The methylation of N-acetyl serotonin to melatonin takes place only in pineal tissue. It is likely that 5-methoxytryptamine is formed directly from serotonin in a similar manner since the 2% deacetylation of melatonin would not account for the 5-methoxyindole acetic acid found.

the pineal gland is rich in serotonin,[21] it would seem probable that O-methylation of serotonin should occur.

The present concept of serotonin and melatonin metabolism is illustrated in Figure 2.

The O-methylation of hydroxyindoles to form biologically active compounds is in contrast to the O-methylation of the catecholamines which is an inactivation process.[84]

The significance of the production of physiologically active O-methyl derivatives of serotonin in mammalian pineal gland is still obscure, but the presence of a specific enzyme system in a localized site in the brain is a novel and provocative discovery.

REFERENCES

1. RAPPORT, M. M., GREEN, A. A. and PAGE, I. H.: *Science, 108:*329 (1948).
2. PAGE, I. H.: *Physiol. Rev., 38:*277 (1958).
3. MANSOUR, T. E.: *Brit. J. Pharmacol., 12:*406 (1957).
4. MANSOUR, T. E.: *Biochim. et biophys. acta, 34:*456 (1959).
5. MANSOUR, T. E.: *J. Pharmacol. & Exper. Therap., 126:*212 (1959).
6. MANSOUR, T. E., SUTHERLAND, E. W., RALL, T. W. and BUEDING, E.: *J. Biol. Chem. 235:*466 (1960).
7. RALL, T. W. and SUTHERLAND, E. W.: *J. Biol. Chem., 232:*1065 (1958).
8. TWAROG, B. M. and PAGE, I. H.: *Am. J. Physiol., 175:*157 (1953).
9. GADDUM, J. H.: *Ciba Foundation Symposium on Hypertension, Humoral and Neurogenic Factors,* p. 75. Boston, Little, Brown (1954).
10. WOOLLEY, D. W. and SHAW, E.: *Proc. Nat. Acad. Sc., 40:*228 (1954).
11. PLETSCHER, A., SHORE, P. A. and BRODIE, B. B.: *J. Pharmacol. & Exper. Therap., 116:*84 (1956).
12. McISAAC, W. M. and PAGE, I. H.: *J. Biol. Chem., 234:*858 (1959).
13. SCHNECKLOTH, R. E., PAGE, I. H. and CORCORAN, A. C.: *Circulation, 19:*766 (1959).
14. SJOERDSMA, A., WEISSBACH, H. and UDENFRIEND, S.: *Am. J. Med., 20:*520 (1956).
15. SLOCOMB, A. G., HOAGLAND, H. and TOZIAN, L. S.: *Am. J. Physiol., 185:*601 (1956).
16. UDENFRIEND, S., WEISSBACH, H. and BOGDANSKI, D. F.: *J. Biol. Chem., 224:*803 (1957).
17. BOGDANSKI, D. F., WEISSBACH, H. and UDENFRIEND, S.: *Ann. New York Acad. Sc., 66:*182 (1957).
18. SHORE, P. A., SILVER, S. L. and BRODIE, B. B.: *Experientia, 11:*272 (1955).
19. PAASONEN, M. K., MACLEAN, P. D. and GIARMAN, N. J.: *J. Neurochem., 1:*326 (1957).
20. GIARMAN, N. J. and DAY, M.: *Biochem. Pharmacol., 1:*235 (1958).
21. GIARMAN, N. J., FREEDMAN, D. X. and PICARD-AMI, L.: *Nature, 186:*480 (1960).
22. MACLEAN, P. D.: *Am. J. Med., 25:*611 (1958).
23. BERTLER, A. and ROSENGREN, E.: *Experientia, 15:*10 (1959).
24. BERTLER, A. and ROSENGREN, E.: *Acta physiol. scandinav., 47:*350 (1959).
25. VOGT, M.: *J. Physiol., 123:*451 (1954).
26. PRICE, S. A. P. and WEST, G. B.: *Nature, 185:*470 (1960).
27. COSTA, E. and APRISON, M. H.: *Am. J. Physiol., 192:*95 (1958).

28. LERNER, A. B., CASE, J. D., TAKAHASHI, Y., TU, T. H. and MORI, W.: *J.A.C.S.,* *80:*2587 (1958).
29. LERNER, A. B., CASE, J. D. and HEINZELMAN, R. V.: *J. Am. Chem. Soc., 81:*6084 (1959).
30. LERNER, A. B., CASE, J. D., BIEMANN, K., HEINZELMAN, R. V., SZMUSZKOVICZ, J., ANTHONY, W. V. and KRIVIS, A.: *J.A.C.S., 81:*5264 (1959).
31. LERNER, A. B., CASE, J. D., MORI, W. and WRIGHT, M. R.: *Nature, 183:*1821 (1959).
32. WELSH, J. H.: *Ann. New York Acad. Sc., 66:*618 (1957).
33. BRODIE, B. B. and SHORE, P. A.: *Ann. New York Ac., 66:*631 (1957).
34. MARRAZZI, A. S. and HART, E. R.: *Science, 121:*365 (1955).
35. WHITTAKER, V. P.: *Biochem. J., 73:*37P (1959).
36. WOOLLEY, D. W.: *Proc. Nat. Acad. Sc., 44:*197, 1202 (1958).
37. WOOLLEY, D. W. and CAMPBELL, N. K.: *Biochim. et biophys. acta, 40:*543 (1960).
38. SHORE, P. A., SILVER, S. L. and BRODIE, B. B.: *Science, 122:*284, (1955).
39. BRODIE, B. B., PROCKOP, D. J. and SHORE, P. A.: *Postgrad. Med., 24:*296 (1958).
40. GANGLOFF, H. and MOURNIER, M.: *Helvet. physiol. et pharmacol. acta, 15:*83 (1957).
41. PLETSCHER, A.: *Science, 126:*507 (1957).
42. QUINN, G. P., SHORE, P. A. and BRODIE, B. B.: *J. Pharmacol. & Exper. Therap., 127:*103 (1959).
43. MAASS, A. R. and NIMMO, M. J.: *Nature, 184:*547 (1959).
44. GRIEG, M. E., WALK, R. A. and GIBBONS, A. J.: *J. Pharmacol. & Exper. Therap 127:*110 (1959).
45. FELDSTEIN, A., HOAGLAND, H. and FREEMAN, H.: *Science, 130:*500 (1959).
46. BONNYCASTLE, D. D., GIARMAN, N. J. and PAASONEN, M. K.: *Brit. J. Pharmacol., 12:*228 (1957).
47. GARATTINI, S., VALSECCHI, A. and VALZELLI, L.: *Experientia, 13:*330 (1957).
48. BERTACCINI, G.: *J. Neurochem., 4:*217 (1959).
49. PLETSCHER, A., BESENDORF, H. and GEY, K. F.: *Science, 129:*844 (1959).
50. WASSON, V. P. and WASSON, R. G.: *Mushrooms, Russia and History.* New York. Pantheon Books (1957).
51. FELDSTEIN, A., HOAGLAND, H. and FREEMAN, H.: *J. Nerv. & Ment. Dis., 29:*62 (1959).
52. KOPIN, I. J.: *Science, 129:*835 (1959).
53. CERLETTI, A. and ROTHLIN, E.: *Nature, 165:*785 (1955).
54. AXELROD, J., BRADY, R. P., WITKOP, B., EVARTS, E. V.: *Nature, 178:*143 (1956).
55. WIELAND, H., HESS, G. and MITTASCH, H.: *Ber. dtsch. chem. Ges., 64:*2099 (1931).
56. STROMBERG, V. L.: *J. Am. Chem. Soc., 76:*1707 (1954).
57. FABING, H. B. and HAWKINS, J. R.: *Science, 123:*886 (1956).
58. EVARTS, E. V.: *Arch. Neurol. & Psychiat., 75:*49 (1956).
59. MAHLER, D. J. and HUMOLLER, F. L.: *Proc. Soc. Exper. Biol. & Med., 102:*697 (1959).
60. GESSNER, P. K., KHAIRALLAH, P., McISAAC, W. M. and PAGE, I. H.: *J. Pharmacol. & Exper. Therap. 130:*126 (1960).
61. HOFMANN, A., HEIM, R., BRACK, A. and KOBEL, H.: *Experimentia, 14:*107 (1958).
62. HOFMANN, A., HEIM, R., BRACK, A., KOBEL, H., FREY, A., OTT, H., PETRZILLAN, T. and TROXLER, F.: *Helvet. chim. acta, 42:*1557 (1959).
63. HOFMANN, A. and TROXLER, F.: *Experientia, 15:*101 (1959).
64. WEIDMANN, H., TACSCHLER, M. and KORZETT, H.: *Experientia, 14:*378 (1958).
65. SZARA, S.: *Experientia, 12:*441 (1956).

66. SZARA, S. and AXELROD, S.: *Experientia, 15:*216 (1959).
67. SZARA, S., HEARST, E. and PUTNEY, F.: *Federation Proc., 19:*23 (1960).
68. UDENFRIEND, S., TITUS, E., WEISSBACH, H. and PETERSON, R. E.: *J. Biol. Chem., 219:*335 (1956).
69. SJOERDSMA, A., WEISSBACH, H. and UDENFRIEND, S.: *Am. J. Med., 20:*520 (1956).
70. MITOMA, C., WEISSBACH, H. and UDENFRIEND, S.: *Nature, 175:*994 (1955).
71. CLARK, C. T., WEISSBACH, H. and UDENFRIEND, S.: *J. Biol. Chem., 210:*139 (1954).
72. BEILER, J. M. and MARTIN, G. J.: *Federation Proc., 13:*180 (1954).
73. BUZARD, J. A. and NYTCH, P. D.: *J. Biol. Chem., 227:*225 (1957).
74. CURZON, G.: *Arch. Biochem., 66:*497 (1957).
75. CHADWICK, B. T. and WILKINSON, J. H.: *Biochem. J., 76:*102 (1960).
76. BLASCHKO, H. and PHILPOT, F. J.: *J. Physiol., 122:*403 (1953).
77. LERNER, A. B., CASE, J. D. and TAKAHASHI, Y.: *J. Biol. Chem., 235:*1992 (1960).
78. LERNER, A. B.: *Nature, London, 184:*674 (1959).
79. AXELROD, J. and WEISSBACH, H.: *Science, 131:*1312 (1960).
80. KOPIN, I. H., PARE, C. M. B., AXELROD, J., WEISSBACH, H.: *Biochem. et biophys. acta, 40:*377 (1960).
81. KVEDER, S., MCISAAC, W. M. and PAGE, I. H.: *Biochem. J., 76:*28P (1960).
82. ERSPAMER, V.: *Pharmacol. Rev., 6:*425 (1954).
83. MCISAAC, W. M., KVEDER, S. and PAGE, I. H.: *Biochem. J., 76:*30P (1960).
84. ERSPAMER, V.: *Nature, 170:*281 (1952).
85. BARLOW, R. B. and KHAN, I.: *Brit. J. Pharmacol., 14:*265 (1959).
86. AXELROD, J.: *Physiol. Rev., 39:*751 (1959).

XXVI

γ-AMINOBUTYRIC ACID*

Eugene Roberts

γ-Aminobutyric acid (GABA†), a substance first synthesized in 1883 and known for a long time to be a product of microbial and plant metabolism, recently has been shown to have a unique occurrence in the central nervous system (CNS) in vertebrate organisms. It was thought that a substance with such an unusual distribution might have some characteristic physiological effects which might make it important for the function of the CNS. However, for several years after its discovery GABA was studied only from a biochemical point of view (see ref. 1 for summary of earlier work). The metabolism of GABA became of more general interest when the work of biologists and physiologists indicated that GABA actually might play a direct or indirect role in the regulation of neuronal activity. Recently a number of comprehensive papers have appeared in which the biochemcial and neurophysiological findings related to GABA were summarized in detail and a symposium has been devoted to the subject.[2-11] In the present brief review only some of the highlights will be considered and no attempt will be made to cover the literature completely.

SOME ASPECTS OF DISTRIBUTION OF FREE AMINO ACIDS IN NERVOUS TISSUE

Extensive studies of the distribution of free or loosely bound amino acids and related substances in animal tissues with the aid of two-dimensional paper chromatographic procedures showed that in a given species at a particular stage of development each normal tissue, including every type of blood cell, has a distribution of ninhydrin-reactive constituents which is characteristic for that tissue.[12] In general,

*Supported in part by a grant from the National Association for Mental Health and also grant No. 1615 from the National Institute for Neurological Diseases and Blindness, U.S.P.H.S.
†The following abbreviations are used: GABA, γ-aminobutyric acid; GAD, glutamic acid decarboxylase; GABA-T, GABA-α-ketoglutarate transaminase; CNS, central nervous system; TSC, thiosemicarbazide.

636

the significance of the presence of relatively large quantities of some of the amino acids in the free or easily extractable form in tissues is not known. Evidence at present indicates that GABA may play an important role in the physiological function of the CNS. Recently-reported data indicate that both glutamic and aspartic acids can produce spreading depression in rabbit cortex[13] and that aspartic and glutamic acids have an excitatory action on cat spinal neurons, while β-alanine and taurine, as well as GABA, have a depressant action.[14] All of the above substances are found in the free or easily extractable form in the CNS. Therefore, although a great deal of attention is now focused on problems related to the physiological role of GABA, it should be remembered that GABA is only one of the large number of freely extractable substances in nervous tissue which have physiological effects and that its activities and functions must always be considered in relation to the total chemical environment which contains many substances which may play a role in regulation of activity in the nervous system.

DETECTION AND QUANTITATIVE DETERMINATION OF γ-AMINOBUTYRIC ACID (GABA) IN TISSUE EXTRACTS

Most of the determinations of GABA which have been published to date have been performed by the use of standard paper chromatographic procedures. These are generally adequate for extracts containing relatively large amounts of GABA, since under these circumstances results can be interpreted easily. However, reports of the presence of small amounts of GABA in blood, urine, spinal fluid, etc., based solely on the use of ordinary paper chromatographic methods cannot be accepted without independent verification. The quantitative paper chromatographic procedure, variations of which have been employed extensively, is cumbersome and requires controls with every set of determination.[15] Newer procedures employing paper electrophoresis also have been employed.[16] Column chromatographic procedures have been devised by which GABA can be determined in extracts of tissue.[17,18] The latter methods are most suitable when accurate determinations of a variety of ninhydrin-reactive constituents are desired rather than when determinations of GABA alone are required, since the procedures are relatively complicated and time-consuming. Reports have been made of the determination of GABA by biological assay with crayfish stretch receptor.[4] Since this assay system responds not only to GABA but also to other substances, the values obtained by this procedure for crude tissue extracts are probably a composite for several substances with different specific activities. However, the crayfish stretch receptor can be used in an important qualitative way, for if no response is elicited by an extract in this extremely sensitive bioassay, it may be presumed that GABA is absent. A newly devised, specific spectrophotometric method for the microdetermination of GABA employing a bacterial enzyme has proven to be of great value and, as modified for brain extracts,[20] is now the method of choice. It combines specificity with the great sensitivity which can be achieved in the measurement of formation of TPNH.

DISTRIBUTION OF GABA IN ANIMAL TISSUES

In studies of tissues and body fluids in various vertebrates which included fish, amphibian, reptilian, avian, and mammalian species, GABA was detected unequivocally only in brain and spinal cord. All ninhydrin-reactive constituents other than GABA which were found on two-dimensional chromatograms of alcoholic extracts of brain and spinal cord also occurred in varying concentrations in the other tissues.[21] Although the extracts of brains of the different species studied showed marked variations in the contents of most of the detectable ninhydrin-reactive constituents, they all showed relatively high concentrations of GABA, glutamic acid, and glutamine. GABA was found to be present in large amounts in the cerebral cortex of dogs but was not detectable in extracts of the brachial plexus or optic nerve. It was detected in brain and spinal cord but not in sciatic nerve of the rabbit. GABA has not been detected in extracts of sympathetic ganglia, liver, spleen, or heart muscle[22] but has recently been reported to be present in retina and choroid but not in the iris or ciliary body of the eye of the dog and ox.[23] The above results emphasize the uniqueness of the occurrence of GABA in tissues of the CNS. Variations have been found in amounts of ninhydrin-reactive constituents in different parts of brain. The most marked differences generally have been noted in the content of GABA. Higher levels of GABA are found in gray than in white matter. In the rat, the corpora quadrigemina and diencephalic regions contained the highest levels of GABA, while the lowest levels were found in the whole cerebral hemispheres and the pons and medulla. In the chicken the optic lobes and diencephalon contained larger quantities of GABA than the cerebral hemispheres, hindbrain, or cerebellum.[24] Similar studies employing different parts of rabbit and monkey cortex have been performed. The differences in GABA content from one area to another in the various species are not readily interpretable at the present time in terms of the known physiological functions of these areas.

The amount of GABA present at any time in a particular area of the CNS is probably a reflection of the balance between the rate of formation and the rate of utilization. Parenterally administered GABA does not appear to enter the brain readily. Intravenous injection of as much as 3 gm. of GABA per kilogram into mice produced no change in the GABA levels of whole brain.[21] Similar results were obtained when GABA was injected intraperitoneally into rats.[4] At a time when the blood level was high no GABA was detectable in the cerebrospinal fluid of an unanesthetized monkey which had been given 200 mg./kg. of GABA.[4] These findings suggest that GABA generally does not pass the blood-brain barrier readily. However, physiologically disturbed or diseased areas of brain might allow passage into cerebral tissue of blood-borne GABA. Electrophysiological evidence indicates that systemically administered GABA ordinarily does not pass the blood-brain barrier in the cat but that following experimental local breakdown of the barrier penetration of intravenously injected GABA does take place.[25]

After injection of GABA solutions into mice or rats the amino acid was found distributed in liver, kidney, and muscle and was excreted in relatively large amounts in the urine.[21,26] Thus, GABA appears to enter quite readily from the bloodstream into tissues other than brain. There is no evidence that the GABA, which is formed in the brain, can leave the brain readily and enter the blood. GABA has not been detected in our laboratory in normal serum or in serum of patients with a variety of nonmalignant and malignant diseases at any time, nor has it been found in easily detectable amounts in specimens of cerebrospinal fluid in patients even after massive head injuries.

GABA appears to be taken up readily from solution by slices of cerebral cortex but not by liver or kidney slices or diaphragm sectors.[27] These results might reflect the affinity of nervous tissue for GABA and might be related to a specific capacity for binding of the amino acid by nervous tissue. At the present time it is difficult to relate the latter observations to what is known of the activity and function of GABA in the intact nervous system. It has been found that incubation of various phenothiazine derivatives with brain slices causes release of GABA into the bathing fluid, while a variety of other substances fail to show this effect.[28]

GABA levels in extracts of whole brain, as well as the amounts of other amino acids, tend to remain constant when experimental animals are placed under various physiological stresses.[12,21] For example, no significant changes were produced in GABA levels in whole brains of mice by a large variety of drugs tested in single effective doses or over a period of time. Inanition, dehydration, hypophysectomy, adrenalectomy, thyroidectomy, tumor growth, and diabetes also did not appear to alter the levels of brain GABA in rats.

METABOLIC RELATIONS OF GABA IN THE CNS

GABA is formed in brain to a large extent, if not entirely, from L-glutamic acid by the action of an L-glutamic acid decarboxylase (GAD), an enzyme found in mammalian organisms only in the CNS almost entirely in the gray matter [reaction (1)].

$$HOOCCH_2CH_2CH (NH_2)COOH \xrightarrow[\text{B}_6 \text{ coenzyme}]{\text{glutamic decarboxylase}}$$

L-Glutamic acid

$$HOOCCH_2CH_2CH_2NH_2 + CO_2$$
$$\text{GABA} \tag{1}$$

The decarboxylase reaction is essentially irreversible, no fixation of radioactive carbon from $C^{14}O_2$ into glutamic acid being noted under the anaerobic conditions employed for the manometric measurement of the maximal rate of the decarboxylation.

GABA-α-ketoglutarate transaminase (GABA-T) is found in the CNS also chiefly in the gray matter, but in contrast to GAD, it is also found in other tissues. It catalyzes the reversible transamination of GABA with α-ketoglutarate [reaction (2)].

$$HOOCCH_2CH_2CH_2NH_2 + HOOCCH_2CH_2C\!-\!COOH \underset{\text{B}_6 \text{ coenzyme}}{\overset{\text{GABA-}\alpha\text{-ketoglutarate transaminase}}{\rightleftharpoons}}$$
$$\text{GABA} \qquad\qquad \underset{\text{O}}{\overset{\|}{}}$$

α-Ketoglutaric acid

$$HOOCCH_2CH_2CHO \qquad + \qquad HOOCCH_2CH_2CH (NH_2)COOH$$
Succinic semialdehyde   L-Glutamic acid   (2)

If a continuous metabolic source of succinic semialdehyde were available, GABA could be formed by the reversal of reaction (2). However, to date no evidence has been adduced for the formation in brain of significant amounts of GABA by reactions other than the decarboxylation of L-glutamic acid.

Relative activities of GAD in whole brains of four species were as follows: monkey, 100; rabbit, 187; rat, 251; and mouse, 340. When individual areas of rabbit and monkey brain were compared, higher values were found in the rabbit brain for each area.[29] Refined microanalytical work[29,30] has borne out the original observations on grossly dissected portions of cat brain which showed clearly that the levels of GABA and GAD were much higher in gray than in white matter.[1]

Extremely low levels of GAD activity were found in the white matter from the monkey, rabbit, or rat brain. Insignificantly low levels of GABA-T were found in the white tracts and peripheral nervous tissue. Wide variations were found in both GAD and GABA-T activity within

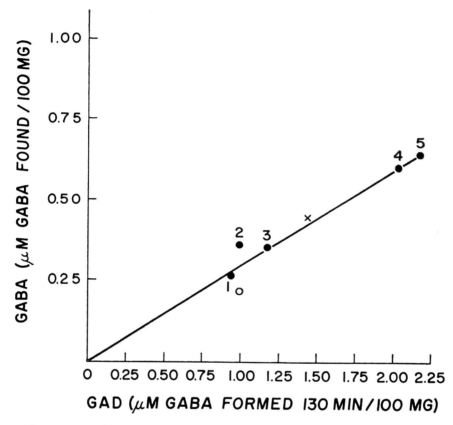

Fig. 1. Proportionality of GABA content and GAD activity. Maximal values obtained: 1, chick cerebellum; 2, chick hemisphere; 3, chick hindbrain; 4, chick optic lobe; 5, chick diencephalon; X, whole mouse brain; O, rabbit brain area 2-3.

the gray matter. The histological correlations with the measurements of enzyme activity suggest that both GAD and GABA-T are probably associated with nerve cell bodies rather than with axis cylinders, myelin, or oligodendroglia.

The GABA-T activity was highest in the subcortical structures, where the maximal potential activity in the various areas as measured in homogenates under optimal conditions was generally in excess of the measured GAD activity. In most cortical structures the rates of the two reactions were much more similar. The variations in GABA-T and GAD from one area to another did not parallel one another. In Figure 1 are plotted the GABA levels and GAD activity in various areas of chick brain, in mouse whole brain, and in rabbit brain cortical area 2-3. There is an essentially linear relationship between the amount of GABA and GAD activity. Similar results also were obtained when such a plot was made for different areas of guinea pig brain. The fact that the line can be extrapolated to zero lends support to the hypothesis that GAD is the major, if not the sole enzyme, responsible for the formation of brain GABA, and suggests that the steady state concentrations of GABA in various brain areas *normally* may be governed by the GAD activity and not by the GABA-T.

Brain also contains a dehydrogenase which catalyzes the rapid oxidation of succinic semialdehyde to succinic acid[31] [reaction (3)], which in turn can be oxidized via the reactions of the tricarboxylic acid cycle. An extensive study of the distribution of this enzyme has not been made yet.

$$\underset{\text{Succinic semialdehyde}}{\text{HOOCCH}_2\text{CH}_2\text{CHO}} + \text{DPN}^+ + \text{H}_2\text{O} \underset{\text{drogenase}}{\overset{\text{dehy-}}{\rightleftharpoons}} \underset{\text{Succinic acid}}{\text{HOOCCH}_2\text{CH}_2\text{COOH}} + \text{DPNH} + \text{H}^+$$

$$(3)$$

As would be expected from the above relationships, glutamic acid, GABA, and succinic semialdehyde can be oxidized by various brain preparations and can support oxidative phosphorylation, the P:O value for this oxidation approaching 3.[32]

GABA can also be metabolized in tissues other than the CNS since the GABA-T is not located exclusively in the CNS. A significant proportion of intraperitoneally administered GABA-1-C[14] could be isolated from the urine of intact rats as labeled succinate when a relatively large amount of nonradioactive succinate was administered simultaneously with the labeled GABA.[33] The carbon of intraperitoneally injected GABA-4-C[14] was distributed in glutamate, aspartate, alanine, and glycogen in rats.[34] The labeling patterns in the above compounds indicated that the succinate pathway can account for all of the metabolism of GABA under these conditions. Because of the complexity of the metabolic interrelationships in which glutamic acid and GABA participate and the many unknown parameters involved, no valid method has yet been devised to get a realistic assessment of the contribution of the GABA pathway to the energy metabolism of brain.

In summary, the reaction sequences shown by the heavier lines on Fig. 2 are those which appear to be unique to tissue of the CNS. Although GABA can be transaminated by extracts of tissues other than those of the CNS, the GAD appears to be located almost exclusively in the gray matter of the CNS. Therefore, the operation of the reactions involving GABA would not be anticipated to play an important role normally in tissues other than the gray matter of the CNS. Because of the essential irreversibility of GAD the entire sequence of reactions dealing with the metabolism of GABA also would be irreversible. Thus, in the CNS, but not in other tissues, there exists an irreversible shunt around the α-ketoglutarate oxidase system, the operation of

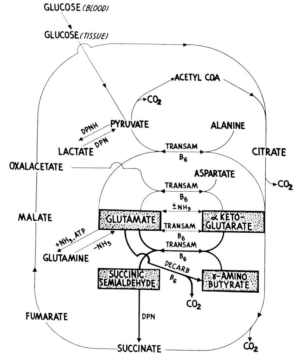

Fig. 2. Outline of metabolic relationships of GABA to the tricarboxylic acid cycle.

which depends on the unique occurrence of GAD and GABA in the CNS. Although it appears certain from the above that two alternate pathways for the oxidation of α-ketoglutarate exist in the tissue of the CNS, the experiments performed to date have not ruled out the possibility that in one cell or part of a cell the oxidation may take place entirely by the GABA shunt and in the other by the classical α-ketoglutarate oxidase system.

GABA AS A POSSIBLE PRECURSOR OF OTHER SUBSTANCES

(see ref. 35)

It has been suggested that GABA might serve as a precursor for a number of chemically related substances. γ-Guanidinobutyric acid, which has been isolated from calf brain, can be formed by the transamidination of GABA with arginine. The enzyme involved is the transamidinase which also is known to catalyze the synthesis of guanidinoacetic acid from glycine and arginine. This is the only enzymatically catalyzed reaction, other than the previously discussed transmination, in which GABA has been shown conclusively to be a precursor of another substance which has actually been proven to be present in brain. γ-Guanidinobutyric acid has been found to be active in various physiological test systems in which GABA has been shown to have an effect. It is considerably less effective than GABA in blocking sensory discharge in the crayfish stretch receptor system. Definitive isolation of β-hydroxy-GABA or proof of biosynthesis of this substance in brain has not been achieved yet. Homopantothenic acid, γ-aminobutyrylcholine, and γ-butyrobetaine have still not been proven to be present in brain by unambiguous procedures, and GABA has not been shown to be a precursor of carnitine, a substance of ubiquitous occurrence in the body. Recently γ-aminobutyrylhistidine has been isolated from brain,[36] but nothing is known yet about its biological function or mode of formation. Although a number of important trace substances of physiological importance may be formed from GABA in brain, there is no evidence yet for the *quantitatively* important participation of any pathways in the normal metabolism of GABA other than the transamination.

PHYSIOLOGICAL MECHANISM OF ACTION OF GABA

GABA is believed to participate in the inhibitory process which counteracts the depolarizing action of excitatory processes in nerve cells by maintaining the polarization of a cell at an equilibrium level near that of its resting value. Elegant work with precisely defined invertebrate and vertebrate test systems employing intracellular microelectrodes has indicated that the membrane stabilization process necessary for this inhibition is related to specific increases in the permeability of the postsynaptic membrane to potassium and/or chloride ions.[10,14]

A. Crayfish Stretch Receptor

Perhaps the most thoroughly studied invertebrate preparation has been the crustacean stretch receptor organ.[36A,37,38] The association of GABA with the crayfish stretch receptor occurred as a result of an extensive series of studies on the influence of factors present in extracts of beef brain which had inhibitory effects (Factor I) on the stretch receptor as well as in other physiological test systems. Eventually, GABA was shown to be the major factor exerting potent inhibitory action on the stretch receptor,[38A] and this opened the way for many investigations of the actions of GABA in a variety of invertebrate preparations. GABA appears to account for almost all the Factor I activity in extracts of whole rat, cat or beef brain. It was found that low concentrations of GABA had effects on the crayfish stretch receptor which were remarkably similar to those found on stimulation of the inhibitory nerve. GABA concentrations 1000 times stronger than those blocking afferent discharge did not block conduction in the sensory axons. GABA action, therefore, appears to be confined to the dendrites and cell body. The action of GABA is not localized necessarily on subsynaptic receptor sites, since it also was found to block the stretch discharge of the median receptor in the seventh thoracic segment, a structure possessing no demonstrable inhibitory synapses. GABA showed the most potent blocking action on the stretch receptor of a wide variety of related compounds tested, but guanidinoacetic and β-guanidinobutyric acid also were active. β-Hydroxy-GABA was approximately one-half as active as GABA in the stretch receptor system.

All of the active compounds appear to increase the flow of specific ions in the dendrites and cell body and to resemble the natural neural inhibitory transmitter in this respect. However, the evidence at the present time does not warrant assigning to GABA or any of the other compounds the role of the natural inhibitory transmitter substance, and the most recent evidence favors the view that some substance other than GABA is the naturally-occurring inhibitor in the crayfish system. Nonetheless, the study of the action of GABA in the crayfish system has given valuable fundamental information about the nature of the inhibitory process.

B. Vertebrate Nervous System

Results of experiments have been published recently in which intracellular recordings were made from motorneurons, interneurons, and Renshaw cells of the cat spinal cord while various substances were injected ionophoretically as cations onto the external surface of membranes by means of double-barrel, five-barrel, or multiple-coaxial micropipettes.[14] GABA, β-alanine, and taurine were found to be almost equally active in depressing activity of spinal neurons. These substances administered in this manner caused a reduction in amplitude of both excitatory and inhibitory postsynaptic potentials without a change in membrane potential, but with an increase in membrane conductance probably arising from an increase in permeability to chloride. The view has been expressed that GABA is more likely a membrane "stabilizer" rather than an inhibitory transmitter.

Since the first finding that topically applied solutions of GABA and β-hydroxy-GABA exerted inhibitory effects on electrical activity in the brain many experiments have been performed utilizing this technique in an attempt to elucidate the mechanism of action of GABA and to gain new information about the organization of the brain (see ref. 2 for numerous references). Direct application of GABA solutions on the cortex of cats induced marked changes in the nature of the evoked responses obtained at the point of application, the early negative component of these responses becoming positive. When GABA was applied to the cortical surface or given by deep injection the evoked responses recorded in the deeper layers were unchanged. The polarity of spindle bursts also was reversed by GABA to a surface positive form. Direct responses in the cerebellar surface were reduced in voltage but showed no change in polarity. These findings were interpreted to mean that GABA selectively blocks the depolarizing, excitatory synapses, which represent the surface-negative post-synaptic potentials in the cerebral cortex, and that the positive potentials observed are hyperpolarizing postsynaptic potentials, ordinarily masked by depolarization. The failure to observe positivity upon application of GABA to the cerebellar cortex was attributed to the relative lack of inhibitory synapses in the cerebellum, while inability to find an effect of topically applied GABA at deeper levels in the cerebral cortex was taken to indicate that the action was specific for exodendritic synapses.[9] An alternative interpretation of the reversal from negativity to positivity in the cortical-evoked potentials has been made in which it was suggested that subsequent to the blocking of the surface-negative waves the deep negative waves, inverted on the surface according to volume conductor theory, were reflected on the surface as positive waves.[4]

It is very difficult to accept fully any interpretation based on data obtained from such highly complex structures as the cerebral and cerebellar cortices employing gross recording electrodes. Because of our lack of understanding of the basic mechanisms underlying these potential changes, little can be concluded from the above results that will clarify the issue of the role of GABA in normal function of the CNS. The possibility also should be kept in mind that GABA normally might be a substance which is entirely intracellular and that application of the substance to the outer surface of neurons may give results which differ from those exerted by the endogenously formed and intracellularly contained GABA.

PHARMACOLOGY OF THE GABA SYSTEM

Both GAD, the enzyme that catalyzes the formation of GABA from L-glutamic acid, and GABA-T, the enzyme that catalyzes the first step in the chief pathway of utilization of GABA, require pyridoxal phosphate, a form of vitamin B_6, as a coenzyme.[1,30] The activity of both of these enzymes depends on the binding of the coenzyme to the enzyme. The experiments which have been performed to date suggest that the protein of GAD has a lower affinity for the coenzyme than the protein of GABA-T. Of the various tissues examined, brain is the richest source of pyridoxal kinase, the enzyme which makes the coenzyme from pyridoxal and adenosine triphosphate.[40] The first suggestion for a physiological role for GABA in mammals came from studies on the mechanism of the action of convulsant hydrazides.[8] Administration of a variety of hydrazides to animals uniformly resulted in production of repetitive seizures following a prolonged latent period. During the latent period susceptibility to seizures produced by either auditory or photic stimulation was greatly enhanced. The finding that the hydrazide-induced seizures could be prevented by parenteral administration of various forms of vitamin B_6 led to the suggestion that some enzyme system requiring pyridoxal phosphate as a coenzyme was being inhibited and that the decrease in the activity of this enzyme was somehow related to the production of the seizures. Attention was focused on GABA and GAD because of their unique occurrence in the CNS and because GAD had been shown to be inhibited by carbonyl trapping agents.[1] The hydrazide-induced seizures were accompanied by substantial decreases in the levels of GABA and reductions in GAD activity in various areas of brain studied. Experiments with glutamate-U-C^{14} intracerebrally administered to mice which had received a prior injection of thiosemicarbazide showed that this convulsant hydrazide significantly slowed the rate at which glutamic acid was converted to GABA even before seizures occurred.[33] Similarly, it was conjectured that there might be some relationship between the GABA system and the seizures found in almost all cases of vitamin B_6 deficiency in animals and humans. However, the above type of experiment demonstrated a correlation to occur but did not necessarily establish causal relationships between the GABA system and neuronal excitability. Great caution must be exercised in reaching conclusions from such observations since pyridoxal phosphate is a coenzyme for many enzymatic reactions, some of which are involved in the biosynthesis of physiologically active substances such as serotonin and epinephrine. Therefore, a deficiency of vitamin B_6, whether induced by dietary or chemical methods, might produce very complicated metabolic imbalances with far-reaching consequences in different areas of brain and spinal cord.

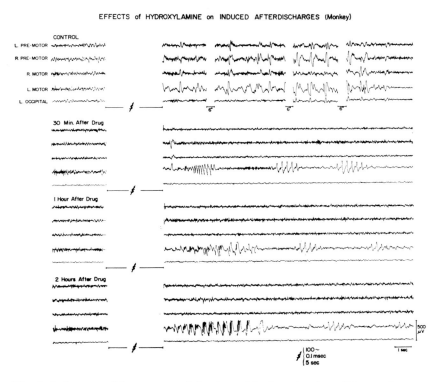

EFFECTS of HYDROXYLAMINE on INDUCED AFTERDISCHARGES (Monkey)

Fig. 3. Influence of intravenous injection of hydroxylamine (4.8 mg./kg.) on induction of electrically-induced afterdischarges in a conscious monkey with indwelling electrodes.

A direct demonstration of the reversal of the action of convulsant hydrazides by GABA itself proved to be difficult because of the lack of the ability of GABA to pass the blood-brain barrier in adult mammalian organisms. It was then shown that a preferential inhibition of GABA-T could be achieved *in vivo* with hydroxylamine (NH₂OH) which resulted in an increase in GABA levels in the CNS.[41] NH₂OH when administered alone, or with methylene blue to prevent the effects of methemoglobinemia which might result, has been found to elevate GABA levels in the brains of rats, cats, and monkeys.[11,41,42] Two-dimensional paper chromatography of the extracts showed the elevation of GABA to be specific, at least to the extent that the concentrations of the other ninhydrin-reactive constituents were, at most, only slightly affected. Administration of a number of methemoglobin-producing agents such as phenylhydrazine, p-aminopropriophenone, sodium nitrate, and acetanilide did not cause any significant elevations of GABA in various areas of rat brain. Elevations of levels of GABA by NH_2OH were correlated with the occurrence of electrophysiologically observable effects opposite to those found with convulsant hydrazides or B_6 antimetabolites. There was a remarkable reduction in the duration in spread of electrically-induced afterdischarges in cats in acute experiments and in conscious monkeys with indwelling electrodes (Fig. 3). In the case of rats, pretreatment with NH_2OH produced increases in GABA as well as a decrease in susceptibility to induction of seizures by Metrazol. Complete protection against an invariably effective dose of Metrazol (50 mg./kg.) was found between 1 and $1\frac{1}{2}$ hours after administration of $NH_2OH.HCl$ (40-100 mg./kg.).[11]

There are many difficulties involved in attempting to establish close correlations between such phenomena as gross seizures and changes in levels of a particular constituent in various areas of brain, particularly since the seizure phenomenon may be controlled by the activity of relatively small numbers of cells the properties of which either are not measured in the course of the chemical analyses or are obscured in the specimens studied because of the admixture of other tissue in which the change is not as marked. Nonetheless, in the three species studied the administration of NH_2OH produced increases in levels of GABA and a decrease in sensitivity to stimulation by some measurable criterion.

Experiments were then performed which showed that the convulsant effects of thiosemicarbazide (TSC) probably cannot be attributed solely to the inhibitory effect of this substance on the formation of GABA from glutamic acid. The results in Table I show that decreases of GABA were noted in the nine areas of rat brain studied when TSC was administered alone, while NH_2OH alone elevated GABA in all areas studied. However, when animals received both TSC and NH_2OH, seizures occurred which were characteristic of those usually produced by TSC alone, but in all instances the GABA levels in the areas of brain studied were either normal or elevated. These results indicate clearly that a general depression of GABA levels is not a necessary requirement for the induction of seizures by TSC. In view of the potent inhibition of pyridoxal kinase shown by hydrazones of pyridoxal[40] it

TABLE I

INFLUENCE OF NH₂OH AND TSC, ALONE AND IN COMBINATION, ON GABA LEVELS IN RAT BRAIN

GABA Levels (mg./100 gm. of Tissue, Wet Weight)

Brain Areas	Control (5)*		NH₂OH Only (3)		TSC Only (4)		TSC ½ hr. after NH₂OH (4)		TSC + NH₂OH Together (5)		TSC ½ hr. before NH₂OH (5)	
Cortex	25†	(24–27)	49	(45–54)	18	(16–20)	43	(35–57)	41	(36–57)	37	(28–47)
Medulla	25	(23–26)	33	(28–38)	17	(16–18)	34	(28–44)	29	(27–32)	26	(22–29)
Pons	27	(25–28)	42	(38–46)	18	(17–19)	42	(34–53)			31	(27–37)
Cerebellum	27	(25–30)	37	(35–38)	20	(19–23)	44	(38–51)	37	(30–49)	38	(29–43)
Hippocampus	31	(28–35)	41	(38–44)	20	(18–22)	42	(39–44)	39	(36–43)	39	(27–50)
Caudate Nucleus	31	(29–33)	46	(42–52)	22	(20–24)	45	(31–54)	41	(33–55)	43	(29–51)
Olfactory Lobes	48	(38–55)	61	(44–78)	43	(37–51)	65	(57–78)	62	(52–75)	61	(50–77)
Diencephalon	53	(46–60)	71	(62–75)	32	(27–36)	66	(54–88)	57	(52–63)	56	(42–71)
Colliculi	56	(52–60)	85	(77–95)	33	(31–35)	73	(60–94)	58	(54–65)	53	(38–66)

Animals receiving NH₂OH only were sacrificed at 90 to 120 minutes after injection. All animals receiving TSC, alone or in combination with NH₂OH, were sacrificed at time of first maximal tonic convulsion.

*Figures in parentheses indicate number of rats.

†Average for group; figures in parentheses indicate range.

still appears likely that some B_6-enzyme may be involved in the seizures. According to the scheme shown in Figure 4 it may be postulated
that in addition to inhibiting the formation of GABA (action one),
TSC may have either a direct or indirect excitatory effect on neuronal
membranes not related to an effect on the GABA system (action two),
or may inhibit one or more systems which are involved in the formation of some substance, X, from GABA (action three) which might
have more potent inhibitory effects in the CNS than GABA itself.
According to the above scheme, an increase in GABA resulting from
an inhibition of GABA-T (action four) with NH_2OH could cause a
decrease in neuronal excitability either because of the action of increased local concentration of GABA directly or because of the possible
enhancement by increased substrate concentration of the formation of

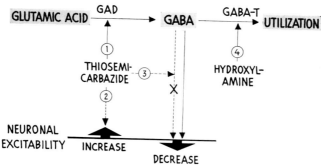

Fig. 4. Scheme showing the effects of thiosemicarbazide and hydroxylamine
on neuronal excitability and the GABA system.

X, an active derivative or metabolite of GABA. In experiments in
which both TSC and NH_2OH were injected, the elevations in GABA
content noted in most areas of brain indicated that with the doses
employed the *relative* decrease in GABA-T produced by NH_2OH was
greater than that produced in GAD activity by TSC. Although a correlation has been found in the occurrence of decreased neuronal excitability and elevation in the content of GABA when NH_2OH is administered, it cannot yet be concluded with certainty that a causal
relation exists. NH_2OH may have many effects on the CNS in addition
to the inhibition of GABA-T. Whether or not the anticonvulsant and
generally inhibitory effects can be attributed *solely* to the elevation of
GABA in the CNS cannot be determined from the measurements
which have been made to date.
     It was of interest to determine whether or not some direct relation-
ship existed between normally found levels of GABA and some meas-

urable criteria of seizure susceptibility. The results obtained in cats
show that virtually identical levels of GABA were found in three areas
of cat brain cortex which showed a threefold variation in seizure susceptibility.[43] The highest level of GABA was found in the hippocampus, which has an exceptionally low seizure threshold, requiring
only the mechanical stimulation of exploring electrodes to fire convulsive afterdischarges. These results appear to rule out the possibility
that there is a simple and direct relationship between seizure susceptibility and the level of GABA normally found in a particular cerebral
area.

DEVELOPMENTAL FEATURES OF THE GABA SYSTEM

In all species studied to date (mouse, chick, bullfrog, and rabbit)
there has been found to be a progressive increase in the content of
GABA in the brain during development. This was not found to be
the case for any of the other constituents detected on chromatograms

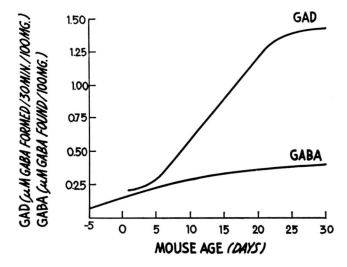

Fig. 5. Changes with age in GAD activity and GABA levels of whole mouse
brain.

of the extracts of the whole brain in these species. Figure 5 shows a
replot of previously published data on the changes with age in GAD
and GABA levels of whole mouse brain.[1] Up to 5 days after birth the
rate of increase of GABA content was approximately equal to that of
GAD activity. From the fifth to the twentieth day the rate of increase
of GAD activity was much greater than that of the increase in the

concentration of GABA. Similar results have been found in some parts of chick embryo brain[24] and in an area of rabbit cerebral cortex.[44]

GABA was first barely detectable in extracts of whole brain of the chick embryo on the fourth day of incubation, increasing in quantity with the age of the embryo.[21] The time course of increase of GABA, GAD, and GABA-T was determined in a single area of brain, the optic lobe, in the chick during embryonic development and after hatching.[45] The optic lobe was chosen for analysis because a preliminary survey had shown it to have the highest level of GABA in the chick embryo brain and because it furnished a well-defined, relatively large structure early in development which is of considerable functional importance in the activity of the avian CNS. Chromatograms of extracts obtained at various ages showed a progressive increase to occur in GABA levels and that no other ninhydrin-reactive constituent increased in a similar manner. The results in Figure 6 show that the

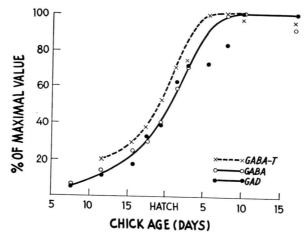

Fig. 6. Time-course of changes in GAD and GABA-T activities and GABA content in optic lobe of the brain of the chick.

GAD and GABA-T activities and GABA levels increased progressively with development of the optic tectum in a similar manner. It is interesting that the largest increment in the mass of the optic lobe occurs in the period prior to the beginning of the time during which the greatest rate of increase was noted in the biochemical variables studied. The structure attained 60% of its maximal weight at 15 days of incubation. The increases in the components of the GABA system take place at the same time that many other maturational changes are occurring in the optic lobe, the curve of increase of cholinesterase activity being remarkably similar to those of GABA-T and GAD.[45] Preliminary analyses have not revealed a particular variable which can be measured by histological methods and is well correlated with the changes in the GABA system. Insufficient knowledge is available of the pertinent intracellular variables to estimate to what extent the maximal potential activity measured in homogenates reflects the actual activity of the enzymes *in vivo*. However, the enzyme measurements are proportional to actual apoenzyme levels in the cell and to this extent probably furnish a valid measure of the rate of increase of the potentially active enzymatic proteins. It is hoped that the changes in the GABA system during development eventually will be linked to changes in physiologically measurable activities in the CNS.

CONCLUDING STATEMENT

Numerous difficulties are interposed between the finding of correlations and the establishment of causal relationships between chemically and electrically observed events in the CNS. In their attempts to elucidate the role of the GABA system in the function of the CNS the chemist and physiologist are faced with the problem which is common to all who attempt similar problems in any biological area. Enzyme measurements usually are performed in preparations which are fortified to elicit the maximal potential activity of which the system is capable. Whether or not measurements performed in this manner, in which the cellular structure has been destroyed and permeability barriers have been altered, reflect activities which are going on in neurons in particular areas at a particular time is a question which must be answered in each instance. Suitably designed isotope experiments scaled down sufficiently to give information about small groups of neurons may be helpful. It is difficult to interpret events at a cellular level from electrical measurements obtained from such highly complex structures as the cerebral and cerebellar cortices employing gross recording electrodes. Owing to the lack of understanding of the basic mechanisms underlying the potential changes there is little that can be concluded that will clarify the nature of the role of GABA in the normal function of the CNS. Even the results of intracellular recordings cannot yet be interpreted adequately in terms of the molecular events which are occurring in the neurons from which the measurements are being taken. There is much to be learned about the properties of the enzymes important to the GABA system: pyridoxal kinase, GAD, GABA-T, and succinic semialdehyde dehydrogenase. The intracellular localization of these enzymes must be elucidated. The determination of whether GABA itself is in free solution in neurons or

whether it is adsorbed or otherwise bound to structures within the
cell will be important for the understanding of its physiological role.
The possible therapeutic effects of elevation of GABA in various
neurological and mental disorders will undoubtedly be the subject
of much future clinical research.

REFERENCES

1. ROBERTS, E.: *Progr. Neurobiol., 1:*11 (1956).
2. ROBERTS, E., Ed.: *Inhibition in the Nervous System and γ-Aminobutyric Acid.*
   Oxford, Pergamon Press (1960).
3. BAXTER, C. F., and ROBERTS, E.: In *Neurochemistry of Nucleotides and Amino
   Acids,* p. 127, Brady, R. O., and Tower, D. B., Eds. New York, John Wiley
   and Sons (1960).
4. ELLIOTT, K. A. C., and JASPER, H. H.: *Physiol. Rev., 39:*383 (1959).
5. ELLIOTT, K. A. C.: In *Biochemistry of the Central Nervous System,* p. 251,
   Brücke, F., Ed. 4th Intern. Congr. of Biochemistry, Vienna. New York, Pergamon Press (1959).
6. TOWER, D. B.: In *Biochemistry of the Central Nervous System,* p. 213, Brücke,
   F., Ed. 4th Intern. Congr. of Biochemistry, Vienna. New York, Pergamon
   Press (1959).
7. ROBERTS, E., and BAXTER, C. F.: In *Biochemistry of the Central Nervous System,*
   p. 268, Brücke, F., Ed. 4th Intern. Congr. of Biochemistry, Vienna. New
   York, Pergamon Press (1959).
8. KILLAM, K. F.: *Federation Proc., 17:*1018 (1958).
9. GRUNDFEST, H.: *Federation Proc., 17:*1006 (1958).
10. KUFFLER, S. W., and EDWARDS, C.: *J. Neurophysiol., 21:*589 (1958).
11. ROBERTS, E., BAXTER, C. F., and EIDELBERG, E.: In *Function and Structure of
    the Cerebral Cortex,* p. 392, Tower, D. B., and Schadé, J. P., Eds., Amster-
    dam, Elsevier Press (1960).
12. ROBERTS, E., and SIMONSEN, D. G.: In *Jesse P. Greenstein Memorial Symposium:
    Amino Acids, Proteins and Cancer Biochemistry,* p. 121, Edsall, J. T., Ed.
    New York, Acad. Press (1960).
13. VAN HARREVELD, A.: *J. Neurochem., 3:*300 (1959).
14. CURTIS, D. R., and WATKINS, J. C.: In *Inhibition in the Nervous System and
    γ-Aminobutyric Acid,* p. 424, Roberts, E., Ed. Oxford, Pergamon Press (1960).
15. ROBERTS, E., and FRANKEL, S.: *J. Biol. Chem., 187:*55 (1950).
16. HANSON, A., and STUDNITZ, W.: *Acta chem. scandinav., 12:*1332 (1958).
17. BERL, S., and WAELSCH, H.: *J. Neurochem., 3:*161 (1958).
18. TALLAN, H. H., MOORE, S., and STEIN, W. H.: *J. Biol. Chem., 211:*927 (1954).
19. FLOREY, E., and FLOREY, E.: *J. Physiol. 144:*220 (1958).
20. BAXTER, C. F., and ROBERTS, E.: *Proc. Soc. Exper. Biol. & Med., 101:*811 (1959).
21. ROBERTS, E., LOWE, I. P., GUTH, L., and JELINEK, B.: *J. Exper. Zool., 138:*313
    (1957).
22. FLOREY, E., and McLENNAN, H.: *J. Physiol. 129:*384 (1955).
23. KOJIMA, K., MIZUNO, K., and MIYAZAKI, M.: *Nature, 181:*1200 (1958).
24. SISKEN, B., ROBERTS, E., and BAXTER, C. F.: In *Inhibition in the Nervous System
    and γ-Aminobutyric Acid,* p. 219, Roberts, E., Ed. Oxford, Pergamon Press
    (1960).
25. PURPURA, D. P., GIRADO, M., SMITH, T. G., and GOMEZ, J. A.: *Proc. Soc. Exper.
    Biol. Med., 97:*348 (1958).

26. VAN GELDER, N. M., and ELLIOTT, K. A. C.: *J. Neurochem., 3:*139 (1958).
27. ELLIOTT, K. A. C., and VAN GELDER, N. M.: *J. Neurochem., 3:*28 (1958).
28. ERNESTING, M. J. E., KAFOE, W. F., NAUTA, W. TH., OOSTERHUIS, H. K., and DE WAART, C.: *J. Neurochem., 5:*121 (1960).
29. LOWE, I. P., ROBINS, E., and EYERMAN, G. S.: *J. Neurochem., 3:*8 (1958).
30. ALBERS, R. W.: In *Neurochemistry of Nucleotides and Amino Acids*, p. 146, Brady, R. O., and Tower, D. B., Ed. New York, Wiley and Sons (1960).
31. ALBERS, R. W., and SALVADOR, R. A.: *Science, 128:*359 (1958).
32. McKHANN, G. M., and TOWER, D. B.: *Am. J. Physiol., 196:*36 (1959).
33. ROBERTS, E., ROTHSTEIN, M., and BAXTER, C. F.: *Proc. Soc. Exper. Biol. & Med., 97:*796 (1958).
34. WILSON, W. E., HILL, R. J., and KOEPPE, R. E.: *J. Biol. Chem., 234:*347 (1959).
35. PISANO, J. J., WILSON, J. D., and UDENFRIEND, S.: In *Inhibition in the Nervous System and γ-Aminobutyric Acid*, p. 226, Roberts, E., Ed. Oxford, Pergamon Press (1960).
36. PISANO, J. J., WILSON, J. D., COHEN, L., and UDENFRIEND, S.: *Federation Proc., 19:*334 (1960).
36a. ALEXANDROWICZ, J. C.: *Quart. J. Microscop. Sc., 92:*163 (1951); *93:*315 (1952).
37. FLOREY, E.: In *Inhibition in the Nervous System and γ-Aminobutyric Acid*, p. 72, Roberts, E., Ed. Oxford, Pergamon Press (1960).
38. EDWARDS, C.: In *Inhibition in the Nervous System and γ-Aminobutyric Acid*, p. 386, Roberts, E., Ed. Oxford, Pergamon Press (1960).
38a. BAZEMORE, A. W., ELLIOTT, K. A. C., and FLOREY, E.: *Nature, 178:*1052 (1956); *J. Neurochem., 1:*334 (1957).
39. BAXTER, C. F., and ROBERTS, E.: *J. Biol. Chem., 233:*1135 (1958).
40. McCORMICK, D. B., and SNELL, E. E.: *Proc. Nat. Acad. Sc., 45:*1371 (1959).
41. BAXTER, C. F., and ROBERTS, E.: *Proc. Soc. Exper. Biol. Med., 101:*811 (1959).
42. EIDELBERG, E., BAXTER, C. F., ROBERTS, E., SALDIAS, C. A., and FRENCH, J. D.: *Proc. Soc. Exper. Biol. & Med., 101:*815 (1959).
43. BAXTER, C. F., ROBERTS, E., and EIDELBERG, E.: *J. Neurochem., 5:*203 (1960).
44. BAXTER, C. F., SCHADE, J. P., and ROBERTS, E.: In *Inhibition in the Nervous System and γ-Aminobutyric Acid*, p. 214. Roberts, E., Ed. Oxford, Pergamon Press (1960).
45. SISKEN, B., SANO, K., and ROBERTS, E.: *J. Biol. Chem., 236:*503 (1961).
46. BONICHON, A.: *J. Neurochem., 5:*195 (1960).

XXVII

SOME POSSIBLE MEDIATORS OF NON-CHOLINERGIC CENTRAL TRANSMISSION

J. Crossland

It is now generally recognised that synaptic transmission in the central nervous system is everywhere effected by chemical mediators. It is also accepted that acetylcholine, for long the only serious contender for the role of transmitter substance, is not the mediator at all central synapses and in the past few years much effort has been expended in attempts to identify other transmitter substances.

Cholinergic nerves are characterized by the possession of appreciable quantities of acetylcholine and choline acetylase. As a result of his observations on the distribution of this enzyme, Feldberg was able to demonstrate a tendency to alternation of cholinergic and non-cholinergic neurones in several tracts of the central nervous system.[1,2] While there are obvious exceptions to this generalization, it is broadly true and it serves to emphasise the widespread distribution of cholinergic neurones. If the principle of alternation held rigidly it would be illogical to postulate the existence of more than one non-cholinergic mediator of excitation. The observed departures from strict alteration perhaps leave room for more than one transmitter substance among the population of non-cholinergic neurones, but their number must surely be strictly limited.

In peripheral autonomic fibres, nor-adrenaline forms the obvious alternative to acetylcholine, but it is found in only limited regions of the central nervous system and more attention has been paid to the central functions of the related substance, 5-hydroxytryptamine. Both are the subjects of earlier chapters in this volume; this writer's personal views on their functional significance can be found elsewhere.[3] It is sufficient here to state that there seem to be ample grounds for believing that neither is a major excitatory transmitter. It is necessary therefore to consider the claims of some other substances; these are the concern of this chapter. Inhibitory transmission, which is an important aspect of non-cholinergic activity, is ignored here save for an incidental mention in connection with the activities of Substance P. No difficulty arises yet in discussing excitatory transmission and its mediators as a quite separate problem.

It has become customary to adopt a list of characteristics which should supposedly be exhibited by all transmitter substances. The list is so well-known that it needs no reproduction here but it should be remarked that not all of the commonly-accepted criteria are of equal diagnostic importance.[3,4] It is, however, reasonable to demand that an excitatory transmitter, suitably administered to an experimental animal, should provide at least a caricature of the response it evokes when physiologically released. Its distribution, too, should be significant. A mediator of transmission is needed only at the termination of the fibres in which it is found so that it could, theoretically, be so concentrated there that its level in the fibre as a whole would be too low to allow its detection by pharmacological methods. This argument cannot be justifiably applied, however, to any substance which has already been found in quantity in a tract of fibres. All the compounds discussed in this chapter fall into this category; any that is a non-cholinergic transmitter substance ought to be present in at least a few tracts of fibres in which the choline acetylase activity in low and generally absent from those rich in acetylcholine. In the following pages, therefore, particular emphasis will be placed on the neuropharmacological actions and central distribution of the substances considered.

VASODILATOR SUBSTANCES IN SENSORY NERVE FIBRES

The simplest unit of central nervous activity is the monosynaptic reflex, in which impulses entering the spinal cord, by dorsal root fibres, directly influence effector neurones without involving any other nervous element. Since sensory nerves have a very low choline acetylase activity,[5] it seems reasonable to assume that the transmission of impulses across synapses between these fibres and adjacent neurones is non-cholinergic in type. Experimental support for this view is provided by the work of Eccles who showed, in the frog, that neither acetylcholine nor anti-cholinesterases had any influence on the behaviour of ventral root potentials monosynaptically evoked.[6] Nevertheless, Eccles was later able to demonstrate that reflex excitation of motoneurones does demand the intervention of a chemical mediator of some kind.[7] Its identification is clearly a matter of importance in view of the probability that the central nervous system employs a limited range of transmitter agents. The rather obvious way of assessing the transmitter potentiality of fractions of dorsal root extracts, by studying their actions on simple reflex systems or, more directly, on the membrane potential of motoneurones, has been neglected in favour of a simpler, but more indirect approach, first suggested as long ago as 1935 by Dale.[9] Mild mechanical stimulation of the skin causes vasodilatation in the stimulated area due, it is widely believed, to the operation of an axon reflex. Cutaneous sensory nerves arising from some skin receptors also receive branches from arterioles in the same area of skin. Impulses from the receptors travel along the sensory fibres into the cord in the usual way but, in addition, as they pass the point where the vascular branches join, they initiate impulses which pass centrifugally in these branches—in the opposite direction, that is, to that normally taken by impulses in sensory nerves—to produce a vasodilator response. A similar antidromic vasodilatation can be produced in the laboratory by electrical stimulation of certain sensory nerves. In both instances the vasodilator response is, presumably, brought about by a chemical mediator. Dale pointed out that a stimulated nerve is hardly likely to liberate different materials at its two ends so that the mediator of antidromic vasodilatation would also be liberated at the termination of the sensory nerve cell in the cord itself, where it would function as a synaptic transmitter substance. It is perhaps worth adding that Dale's general hypothesis has been verified in the special case of motor fibres whose recurrent collaterals, like the main trunk, are cholinergic in type.[9] Following Dale, attention has been focussed on the vascular actions of dorsal root extracts, and the three substances considered in this section received attention in the first instance because of their vasodilator properties rather than because of any striking effects on nerve cells.

Histamine

Lewis believed that irritation of the skin caused the liberation of a substance similar to, if not identical with, histamine.[10] This 'H-substance,' he postulated, produced capillary dilatation and a wheal; it also initiated an axon-reflex dilatation in the neighbouring arterioles. These three events constitute the 'triple response.' Lewis also supposed that 'H-substance' was liberated from the skin as a result of antidromic stimulation of sensory nerves by the irritative lesions of herpes zoster, thus producing the wheal so characteristic of this condition.[11] At no time did he suggest that his 'H-substance' was acting as a transmitter agent in the sense in which the term is used here. Kwiatkowski, however, proposed that antidromic vasodilatation was brought about by the liberation of histamine from the sensory nerves themselves which, he therefore concluded, were histaminergic in nature.[12] He based this view on his observations that the peripheral ends of nerves known to produce antidromic vasodilatation apparently contained large amounts of histamine. He also claimed to demonstrate the presence of histamine in the femoral vein of the cat during stimulation of the cut peripheral ends of its lumbar dorsal roots, though no attempt was made to establish that the active material actually came from the nerves. Kwiatkowski did point out, as a rather serious objection to his hypothesis, that the histamine content of sensory nerves rose progressively during degeneration. Transmitter substances are usually lost from a nerve, following separation from its cell body. (This rise in the histamine content of degenerating nerves is itself an intriguing finding which has not been further studied.)

Little other support for the existence of histaminergic nerves has been forthcoming. Holton and Perry showed that the course of antidromic vasodilatation in the rabbit ear was quite different from that produced by histamine and that it was unaffected by mepyramine, an anti-histamine compound.[13] This last finding confirmed an earlier observation by Parrot and Lefebvre[14] though Parrot[15] also found that anti-histamines did abolish axon-reflex vasodilatation brought about by mechanical stimulation of the skin. He believes that Lewis's 'H-substance' is indeed histamine but that the dilatation it produces, by the axon-reflex mechanism, involves the liberation at the arterioles of a specific transmitter substance. He and Ungar and their associates have attempted to identify this mediator by studying, as did Kwiatkowski, the properties of the material liberated into the femoral vein during stimulation of posterior roots.[16] Though chemically distinct from histamine, it shares some of its properties—thus it stimulates gastric secretion, lowers blood pressure and causes contraction of the isolated intestine.[17]

While there is, therefore, little evidence that histamine is the mediator of antidromic vasodilatation, it, or some closely-allied substance, does seem to be capable of stimulating sensory endings in the skin. This suggests the possession of electrogenic properties not dissimilar from those required of a transmitter agent and it is worth considering its occurrence and behaviour elsewhere in the nervous system.

Kwiatkowski reported that, though most parts of the brain contained no more than about 0.1 μg. histamine per gram, its concentration in the cerebellum of the cat and dog was as high as 2 μg./gm.[12] This was an interesting observation since the cerebellum has a very low choline acetylase activity.[5] Unfortunately Kwiatkowski's results have not been confirmed by later workers. Harris, Jacobsohn and Kahlson found appreciable quantities of histamine only in the hypothalamus[18] and even Cicardo and Stoppani who claimed to have detected extraordinarily large amounts (up to 20 μg./gm.) in the canine cerebrum, found none in the cerebellum.[19] Another report of appreciable quantities of histamine in the brain (over 4 μg./gm.), this time in the rat, came from Clouet, Gaitonde and Richter.[20] Because of the conflicting nature of these—and other—results, Crossland and Garven re-investigated the problem and attempted to see how far the discrepancies could be accounted for by variations in experimental technique, in the animals used and in their ante-mortem state and post-mortem treatment.[21] After eliminating the effects of substances in the extracts which interfered with the assay, it became clear that the histamine content of the brains, including the cerebellum, of all the species studied (rat, cat and rabbit) was generally very low. Only the hypothalamus yielded appreciable quantities of histamine. Nevertheless these results do not finally dispose of the possibility that histamine may be involved in fundamental processes in the nervous system, particularly the cerebellum, for it was also found that small quantities of histamine, added to cerebellar homogenates at room temperature, were quickly destroyed, or otherwise rendered biologically inactive. This inactivation, though possibly enzymic in nature, did not involve histaminase (diamine oxidase) since it was unaffected by aminoguanidine. Cerebral homogenates were much less active against added histamine.[21] Again, Crossland and Mitchell found that histamine influenced the electrical activity of the cerebellum.[22] In recent experiments White has shown that the brain can form histamine from histidine and can convert added histamine to methyl histamine and methylimidazole acetic acid.[23,24] A suitable methylating enzyme (imidazole-N-methyl transferase) has been isolated from cat brain by Brown, Tomchick and Axelrod.[25] Finally it must be remembered that, in our present state of knowledge, it is impossible to know what constitutes a physiologically 'low' concentration of any pharmacologically-active substance. The 0.1 to 0.5 μg. of histamine per gram of brain found by Crossland and Garven has been dismissed above as 'very low.' Yet it is common to state that the hypothalamus contains a 'high' concentration of 5-hydroxytryptamine though its actual content is no more than 0.3 μg./gm.[26]

The presence of histamine in quantity in the hypothalamus is not surprising, since this small area of the brain is embarrassingly well-endowed with a variety of active substances not all of which can be exerting a transmitter action. While the function of this hypothalamic histamine is unknown, the presence of histamine also in large quantities (up to 100 μg./gm.) in postganglionic sympathetic fibres[27] suggests that it might participate in the regulation of sympathetic nervous activity. This possibility is strengthened by the observations of Trendelenburg that histamine will stimulate both the hypothalamus[28] and the superior cervical ganglion.[29]

Marrazzi and his associates have shown that small quantities of histamine inhibit transcallosally-evoked potentials in the cat cortex and have suggested that it may function as a synaptic inhibitor.[30] However, similar experiments have led to their postulating an identical role for both adrenaline and serotonin[31] and more direct evidence would be needed before histamine could be accepted as a synaptic inhibitor. It is true that the administration to monkeys of large amounts of anti-histamine drugs can precipitate convulsions[32] and that convulsions might reasonably be expected as a consequence of blocking the action of an inhibitory substance. On the other hand more modest doses of anti-histamine compounds tend to be sedative in action.

Substance P

Euler and Gaddum, assaying acetylcholine in extracts of brain and intestine, detected the presence of another pharmacologically-active substance[33] which was later[34] called substance P. This name is rather more appropriate than its authors suspected thirty years ago, for it is now known that substance P is polypeptide in nature. Its physiological function, however, is still obscure.

Hellauer and Umrath found that simple extracts of spinal roots caused vasodilatation when subcutaneously injected into the denervated ear of the rabbit.[35] Dorsal root extracts were more active than ventral root extracts. Activity was also detected in sensory tracts from other parts of the central nervous system. For these reasons, Hellauer and Umrath considered that the active material in the root extracts might be the antidromic vasodilator substance and hence, also the mediator of transmission from sensory nerves. Interesting corroborative support for this view came from the observation that the vasodilator activity disappeared on incubation with extracts of nervous tissue, particularly sensory nerves,[36] and that this destruction was inhibited by strychnine and some other convulsant drugs. The most powerful convulsive agents were the most active inhibitors and there was a quantitatively close agreement between the relative convulsive and inhibitor potencies of the several compounds.[37,38] The idea that some substances precipitate convulsions by virtue of their ability to inhibit the destruction of an excitatory transmitter is both attractive and reasonable and it is in line with the fact that anti-cholinesterase drugs, which allow the accumulation of endogenously liberated acetylcholine in the brain, also have convulsant properties. No direct confirmation of these findings has yet been forthcoming. Holton and Perry,[13] indeed, showed that antidromic vasodilatation was unaffected by strychnine which, on this hypothesis, should preserve the transmitter and prolong the dilatatory action. How far this lack of effect of strychnine might be due to the fact that, *in vivo,* the destruction of the transmitter is already inhibited by other tissue components, as discussed in the next section, it is impossible to say. Other indirect evidence against Hellauer and Umrath's concept of strychnine action is provided by the observation of the Eccles group that strychnine had no action on the excitatory post-synaptic potential but that it considerably reduced inhibitory potentials.[39] Eccles therefore believes that strychnine excitation is due to inhibition of inhibitory transmission rather than to potentiation of excitatory processes. On the other hand, destruction of the cerebellar factor (see below) on incubation with tissue extracts is inhibited by strychnine.[40]

Umrath's view is that the sensory transmitter substances is related to, though not identical with, substance P. He has adduced evidence for the presence in dorsal roots of an enzyme which liberates the presumed transmitter substance from substance P.[41] He further believes that the latter is a constituent of 'proacetylcholine' from which acetylcholine is liberated during normal cholinergic transmission.[42] Thus the substance P of dorsal roots should be different from that of ventral roots, but the difference should be reduced after liberation of their respective transmitter moieties. Some of Umrath's experimental results favour this conclusion.[42] Until the active material in these extracts has been identified it will be impossible to adjudicate on the claim that it is a synaptic transmitter substance. All the investigations so far have been indirect, using vasodilator activity as an index of transmitter potential. If substance P is a constituent of both 'proacetylcholine' and the precursor of the sensory transmitter substance, its concentration in nerve tracts with high acetylase activity should run parallel with their acetylcholine content and it should, in addition, be present in some acetylcholine-poor tracts. This distribution in fact is not found.

The possibility has also to be considered that substance P itself has a transmitter function.[43] Intraventricular and subcutaneous injection of substance P is followed by an inhibition of spontaneous activity. Zetler investigated this tranquillizing action in greater detail and showed that, subcutaneously administered to mice, substance P could inhibit the psychomotor excitation brought about by morphine and methamphetamine. It had an anti-convulsant action against strychnine and picrotoxin and tremors due to harmine were reduced. Conversely, sleep and akinesia, induced by hexobarbitone and bulbocapnine respectively, were prolonged. The doses actually administered in these experiments were of the order of 9000 units per kilogram, corresponding to about 1 mg per kilo of the purest known preparation. A summary of this, and other work, can be found in the review by Zetler.[44] All of these observations would seem to suggest that substance P is related rather to inhibitory transmission, a *sine qua non* of whose mediator is, currently, its antagonism to strychnine. This conclusion is difficult to reconcile with the fact that a transmitter role for substance P was originally put forward on the grounds that it possessed the qualities demanded of the transmitter substance of the first sensory neurone —vasodilator action and a higher concentration in dorsal than in ventral roots—which is undoubtedly excitatory in type. However, Zetler[44] has obtained evidence that it causes hyperalgesia in mice, even after they have received analgesic doses of morphine, while Lechner and Lembeck observed an arousal reaction after the intracarotid injection of 30 to 100 units in the lightly anaesthetized rabbit.[45] Hyperalgesia could be a manifestation of an inhibitory process (just as the taking of alcohol, a central depressant, can lead to an apparent stimulation in man) but Zetler seems to favour the view that substance P is both an inhibitory transmitter and the sensory transmitter. Since there is no reason to believe that the first sensory neurone as such requires a unique transmitter substance, this hypothesis implies that the excitatory function of substance P is as widespread as its inhibitory function. There is nothing inherently improbable in the idea of a substance acting as both an excitatory and an inhibitory transmitter, but the transmitter role, if any, of substance P can be established only by direct experiments on specific synaptic systems. On Zetler's hypothesis any general neuropharmacological or behavioural action it exerts can be explained away as mirroring, as appropriate, either the excitatory or the inhibitory aspect of its function.

Several determinations of the distribution of substance P in the central nervous systems of oxen, cats, dogs and human beings have been made.[46-49] The more recent determinations have been made on the guinea pig ileum. The assays are usually performed in the presence of atropine, an anti-histamine and tryptamine which prevent the stimulant effect on the gut of acetylcholine, histamine and 5-hydroxytryptamine, any or all of which could be present in tissue extracts. These precautions do not entirely exclude the possibility that material other than Substance P is acting on the ileum and the absolute values obtained have shown some variations. Nevertheless, there is general agreement that the mid-brain, hypothalamus and caudate nucleus contain appreciable amounts of substance P. In addition, in the dog, the thalamus[48] and the floor of the fourth ventricle[49] have been found to be rich sources. In the human brain, the substantia nigra has a very high concentration.[47] The dorsal columns of the spinal cord—which represent the central extensions of those sensory root fibres whose secondary neurons arise in the medulla—and, particularly, the gracile and cuneate nuclei in which they terminate, also contain appreciable quantities of the polypeptide.[48,49] This would be expected if the transmitter of the first sensory neurone were substance P. Apart from this instance there is no obvious tendency for it to be concentrated in tracts of fibres with low choline acetylase activity. Further details of the distribution are to be found in the papers referred to: more are not given here since they seem to throw no useful light on the possible physiological function of substance P.

Zetler and Schlosser do not admit that the distribution of substance P is inconsistent with its being concerned in non-cholinergic transmission. They suggest that transmission is cholinergic in areas where choline acetylase activity exceeds substance P activity and non-cholinergic—and presumably mediated by substance P—where the reverse situation holds.[47] By this means it is possible to classify every region, however low its absolute concentration of either substance, but the justification of the method is doubtful. On this basis, transmission in the hypothalamus is not mediated by acetylcholine though its choline acetylase activity is as high as, or higher than, that of the thalamus and the red nucleus which are classified as 'cholinergic' areas. Moreover the method leads to some discrepancies. Transmission in the lateral geniculate body is undoubtedly non-cholinergic but according to Zetler and Schlosser's figures it is an area with a ratio of substance P to choline acetylase which favours the latter.

Holton has recently reported that, during the Wallerian degeneration of a sensory nerve, the substance P concentration of its distal end falls, while that of its proximal stump rises.[50] This forms presumptive evidence of its association with transmission processes. Umrath previously noted a similar, though smaller, fall in substance P concentration in degenerating nerves. The concentration of the presumed excitatory substance and of the enzyme responsible for splitting it from substance P fell much more sharply.[41]

Adenosine Triphosphate

Holton and her associates found that the intra-arterial injection into the rabbit ear of simple extracts of equine spinal roots resulted in vasodilatation, similar in its extent and time-course to that produced antidromically by electrical stimulation of the great auricular nerve.[51,52] These experiments were the same in intent as those of Hellauer and Umrath already referred to, but a more refined method of following the vascular changes allowed a more precise description of the behaviour of different vaso-active agents. It was found that, while antidromic vasodilatation proceeded in quite a different fashion from vasodilatation evoked by either histamine or substance P, it could be reproduced by ATP and ADP.[53] An elegant differential bio-assay led to a convincing demonstration that the active root extracts contained both these substances. Since ADP normally appears in tissue extracts only as a post-mortem breakdown product, it was considered that, in the living animal, antidromic vasodilatation, if due to the adenosine compounds, would depend exclusively on the triphosphate. More recently, Holton has been able to show, using the firefly luminescence method, that ATP is indeed released from stimulated sensory nerves.[54] It has been reported that sensory denervation of the ear increased the sensitivity of its vessels to dorsal root extracts but not to ATP.[55] This forms a minor obstacle to the acceptance of ATP as the mediator of vasodilatation.

The postulated mediator of antidromic vasodilatation should be found only in sensory nerves. Vasodilator activity was, however, detected in extracts of both dorsal and ventral roots as would be expected if the active agent were ATP, a substance whose metabolic function demands its presence throughout the nervous system. Nevertheless dorsal roots were shown to differ from ventral roots. Aqueous suspensions of acetone-dried powders of both lost their vasodilator activity during incubation at 38°C, but simple extracts of *fresh* dorsal roots (prepared without a stage of acetone-drying) retained their activity. Similarly-prepared extracts of ventral roots lost their vasodilator potency as rapidly as did extracts of powders. It was suggested that, while both motor and sensory fibres contain ATP and a catabolising enzyme, the effect of the latter was impeded in sensory fibres by some acetone-soluble factor. This might explain the fact, which has for long been remarked, that antidromic vasodilatation outlasts the period of nerve stimulation and it would readily account for the superior vasodilator activity of dorsal root fibres *in vivo*. It is more difficult to see how the possession of the inhibiting factor could be reconciled with the presumed central transmitter function of the antidromic vasodilator substance, for rapid inactivation of the mediator is regarded as an essential item in the transmission sequence and transmitter action at the first sensory synapse is known to be short-lived.[56]

Holton suggested that this persistence of vasodilator activity in fresh extracts might characterize other nerve fibres employing the sensory transmitter substance in synaptic processes and she and Harris accordingly studied the activity of incubated extracts of fresh tissue taken from different parts of the central nervous system. Among the areas studied it was found only in the dorsal columns and their nuclei, the caudate nucleus and the hypothalamus.[57] This distribution is suggestive of that shown by substance P and its significance is equally doubt-ful. Certainly there was no obvious tendency for the persistent vasodila-tor activity to be concentrated in those areas and tracts of the nervous system where the non-cholinergic transmitter would be expected to appear. It is possible to argue that the test used by Holton lays down an inappropriate criterion of fibres which liberate ATP as a synaptic transmitter substance. Even so, there is very little evidence that ATP has that central excitatory action which should be easily provoked by pharmacological doses of an excitatory transmitter substance. Rather large doses of ATP have been shown to stimulate some spinal cord and medullary neurones,[58,59,60] and Torda maintains that it has an excita-tory action similar to that of acetylcholine, on the rat cerebral cortex.[61] On the other hand, Robinson and Hughes demonstrated an antagon-ism between these two substances on the cat cortex.[62]

Thus while there is powerful evidence for the view that ATP initi-ates antidromic vasodilatation, the apparent corollary—that it is also a sensory transmitter substance—receives only flimsy support. One way of reconciling this contradiction might be to assume that two sub-stances, ATP and the sensory transmitter substance, are liberated from each end of stimulated sensory nerves. At the peripheral end, only ATP would be active, while at the central end the transmitter substance would perform its synaptic function. The inhibitor of ATP destruction would, on this hypothesis, be restricted to nerves which give rise to vasodilatation on antidromic stimulation, and its distribution would be irrelevant to the problem of noncholinergic transmission. Holton herself now seems to favour such a view.[54] Alternatively it may be, as Parrot has long argued,[17] that antidromic vasodilatation arises in nerves which, notwithstanding their entry into the cord by dorsal roots, are efferent in nature. Both of these explanations deny a central trans-mitter role to ATP while still admitting its importance in peripheral vascular control, and are therefore in harmony with the greater part of the available experimental information.

It is likely that Holton and her colleague have been studying a dif-ferent compound from that detected by Hellauer and Umrath, and it is best for the present to consider the two substances on their individual merits.

THE CEREBELLAR FACTOR

The cerebellum contains only small amounts of acetylcholine and should consequently, assuming the generality of chemical transmission, be a rich source of the mediator of non-cholinergic synaptic processes. Its mass is large in comparison with that of dorsal roots and its almost complete lack of histamine, substance P, nor-adrenaline and 5-hydroxytryptamine[3,4] should facilitate the production in quantity of any active material it contains in a pharmacologically more simple solution than that provided by dorsal root extracts.

Crossland and Mitchell made extracts of three large areas of the rabbit brain—the cerebral hemisphere, upper brain stem and cerebellum—and injected small amounts of these extracts into the decerebrate rabbits, the electrical activity of whose cerebellum was recorded. Very small amounts of all three extracts evoked an outburst of electrical activity which was often accompanied by other signs of cerebellar stimulation.[22] The activity of the extracts of cerebral hemisphere and upper brain stem was shown to be due to acetylcholine but that of the cerebellar extracts was due to another substance which differed from acetylcholine in being more stable in alkali than in acid solution. Its central action, however, was indistinguishable from that of acetylcholine in both the nature and duration of the cerebellar activity it provoked. Other experiments showed that on the electrical activity of the cortex, too, acetylcholine and the cerebellar factor had closely similar actions. Spinal reflexes were modified by the cerebellar factor but the responses were variable, as indeed are those due to acetylcholine.[64]

This parallelism between the actions of acetylcholine and the cerebellar factor disappeared when tests were made on a variety of smooth muscle preparations sensitive to acetylcholine. On all of these cerebellar extracts, freed of acetylcholine, were quite inactive. A similar lack of effect of the cerebellar factor has been found with other smooth muscle preparations.

The activity of the cerebellar factor was destroyed on incubation with homogenates of nervous tissue, particularly the cerebellum. It is interesting, in view of Hellauer and Umrath's work, to note that this inactivation was prevented by strychnine, but not by inhibitors of cholinesterase or of the amine oxidases.

Among a variety of substances tested, only histamine, in doses of about 0.08 μg., had an effect on the cerebellum similar to that due to the cerebellar factor and this action occurred only after a latent period of 60 to 70 seconds. All other substances tested—and these included substance P, ATP, 5-hydroxytryptamine and nor-adrenaline—were quite ineffective. While the cerebellar factor is certainly not histamine itself, this action of histamine is another pointer to the possibility that its importance in the central nervous system may be greater than has hitherto been supposed.

The cerebellar factor is unusual among active substances in that it is so much more active on nerve than on smooth muscle preparations. While this has proved to be an obstacle to its final identification, it does suggest that it might be particularly important in central nervous function, and a preliminary study has been made of its distribution. It has been found in the optic nerve and tract and in the grey matter (lateral geniculate body and superior colliculus) with which they stand in synaptic relationship; the dorsal roots; the spino-cerebellar tracts (and the peduncles through which they pass); the internal capsule and sensory cortex, and—though in smaller quantity than in the other areas mentioned—the pyramids. These are all areas of low, or negligible, choline acetylase activity. Conversely it has not been found in the peripheral fibres of the autonomic nervous system, nor in areas of the cortex with high choline acetylase activity. This inverse relationship between the content of acetylcholine and cerebellar factor was not everywhere apparent: the cerebellar factor was not found in the dorsal columns of the cord and was present in ventral roots, the richest source of choline acetylase in the whole nervous system. Its presence in dorsal roots and absence from the dorsal columns—the central continuation of some of the dorsal root fibres—suggests that dorsal root fibres are not chemically homogeneous. There is no reason why they should be so, although most studies have assumed a pharmacological uniformity in dorsal root fibres. The fact that substance P, while not noticeably restricted to areas of low choline acetylase activity, is found in the dorsal columns is of interest, and may be significant, in connection with the distribution of the cerebellar factor.

The cerebellar factor, though not entirely confined to fibres of low acetylcholine content nor present in all such fibres, does seem, from these early studies to have a distribution rather more in keeping with that to be expected of a non-cholinergic transmitter substance than the other substances discussed here. This, coupled with its activity on nerve cells, suggests that it might be involved in central transmission processes, though clarification of its physiological role demands a knowledge of its chemical identity and, more important, certain knowledge that the effects it produces can be attributed to a direct action on nerve cells.

OTHER SUBSTANCES

Brief mention should be made of other substances, concerning which little information has yet been published, but which might prove to be closely involved in central nervous function.

Hosein has reported the presence, in extracts made from the brains of convulsing rats, of γ-butyrobetaine, crotonbetaine and carnitine.[65] In extracts of normal rat brain these compounds appeared to be present as the Co-enzyme A esters; more recently these derivatives have been detected in brain extracts from convulsing rats.[66] The betaine esters produce convulsions and have acetylcholine-like properties,[66,67] but the free betaines are inactive, and Hosein has suggested that the Co-enzyme A derivatives act as excitatory transmitter substances. He has reported that they are present in the cerebellum in higher concentration than in the cerebral cortex but it is difficult to reconcile this finding with the assertion that they have acetylcholine-like actions, since by every known pharmacological test the acetylcholine-like activity of the cerebellum is only about one-tenth of that in the cortex. The betaine derivatives are clearly not identical with the cerebellar factor which is notably devoid of acetylcholine-like activity except on nervous tissue, and it is encouraging that the cerebellum, which has for long been an enigma by reason of its pharmacological poverty should at last begin to yield active substances.

Hayashi has studied the ability of a wide range of substances either to precipitate or to inhibit convulsive activity. This work is a sequel to earlier investigations into the nature of muscle excitation. Most of Hayashi's work has been concerned with the inhibition of convulsions and is therefore more relevant to inhibitory transmission which is discussed elsewhere; he has, however, drawn attention to the excitatory effects of carnosine (β-alanylhistidine), the longer chained ω-amino acids and glutamic acid. Lack of space prevents a more exhaustive treatment of this work. In any event, the interested reader should read the two remarkable books in which it is detailed, in order to appreciate the highly novel way in which the whole subject is approached.[68,69]

REFERENCES

1. FELDBERG, W. and VOGT, M.: *J. Physiol., 107:*372 (1948).
2. FELDBERG, W., HARRIS, G. W. and LIN, R. C. Y.: *J. Physiol., 112:*400 (1951).
3. CROSSLAND, J.: *J. Pharm. & Pharmacol., 12:*1 (1960).
4. CROSSLAND, J.: In *Metabolism of the Nervous System*, p. 523. Richter, Ed. London, Pergamon Press (1957).
5. HEBB, C. O. and SILVER, A.: *J. Physiol., 134:*718 (1956).
6. ECCLES, J. C.: *J. Neurophysiol., 10:*197 (1947).
7. BROCK, L. C., COOMBS, J. S. and ECCLES, J. C.: *J. Physiol., 117:*431 (1952).
8. DALE, H. H.: *Proc. Roy. Soc. Med., 26:*319 (1935).
9. ECCLE, J. C., FATT, P. and KOKETZU, K.: *J. Physiol., 126:*524 (1954).
10. LEWIS, T.: *The Blood Vessels of the Human Skin and Their Responses.* London, Shaw (1927).
11. LEWIS, T. and MARVIN, H. M.: *J. Physiol., 72:*xix (1926).
12. KWIATKOWSKI, H.: *J. Physiol., 102:*32 (1943).
13. HOLTON, P. and PERRY, W. L. M.: *J. Physiol., 114:*240 (1951).
14. PARROT, J.-L. and LEFEBVRE, J.: *Compt. rend. Soc. biol., Paris, 137:*316 (1943).
15. PARROT, J.-L.: *Compt. rend. Soc. biol., Paris, 136:*715 (1942).
16. UNGAR, G. and PARROT, J.-L.: *Compt. rend. Soc. biol., Paris, 129:*753 (1938).
17. PARROT, J.-L. and REUSE, J.: *J. physiol., Paris, 46:*99 (1954).
18. HARRIS, G. W., JACOHSOHN, D. and KAHLSON, G.: *Ciba Foundation Colloquia on Endocrinology*, Vol. 4, p. 186. London, Churchill (1952).

19. CICARDO, V. H. and STOPPANI, A. O. M.: *Prensa med., argent., 36*:173 (1949).
20. CLOUET, D. H., GAITONDE, M. K. and RICHTER, D.: *J. Neurophysiol., 1*:228 (1957).
21. CROSSLAND, J. and GARVEN, J. D.: Unpublished experiments.
22. CROSSLAND, J. and MITCHELL, J. F.: *J. Physiol., 132*:392 (1956).
23. WHITE, T.: *J. Physiol., 152*:299 (1960).
24. WHITE, T.: *J. Physiol., 149*:34 (1959).
25. BROWN, D. D., TOMCHICK, R. and AXELROD, J.: *J. Biol. Chem., 234*:2948 (1959).
26. AMIN, A. H., CRAWFORD, T. B. B. and GADDUM, J. H.: *J. Physiol., 126*:596 (1954).
27. EULER, U. S. VON: In *Histamine*, p. 235. Wolstenholme, E. W. and O'Connor, C. M., Eds. London, Churchill (1956).
28. TRENDELENBURG, U.: *J. Physiol., 129*:337 (1955).
29. TRENDELENBURG, U.: *Brit. J. Pharmacol., 9*:481 (1954).
30. GILFOIL, T. M., HART, E. R. and MARRAZZI, A. S.: *Federation Proc., 19*:262 (1960).
31. MARRAZZI, A. S.: In *Brain Mechanisms and Drug Action*, p. 45. Fields, Ed. Springfield, Ill., Thomas (1957).
32. CHUSID, J. G., KOPELOFF, L. M. and KOPELOFF, N.: *J. Appl. Physiol., 9*:271 (1956).
33. EULER, U. S. VON and GADDUM, J. H.: *J. Physiol., 72*:74 (1931).
34. GADDUM, J. H. and SCHILD, H.: *J. Physiol., 83*:1 (1934).
35. HELLAUER, H. F. and UMRATH, K.: *Pflügers Arch., 249*:619 (1948).
36. UMRATH, K. and HELLAUER, K.: *Pflügers Arch., 250*:737 (1948).
37. HELLAUER, H. F. and UMRATH, K.: *Z. Vitamin-, Hormon-Ferm.forsch., Wien, 3*:244 (1950).
38. UMRATH, K.: *Arch. exper. Path. u. Pharmakol., 219*:148 (1953).
39. BRADLEY, K., EASTON, D. M. and ECCLES, J. C.: *J. Physiol., 122*:474 (1953).
40. CROSSLAND, J., GARVEN, J. D. and MITCHELL, J. F.: *J. Physiol., 148*:20P (1959).
41. UMRATH, K.: *Pflügers Arch., 258*:230 (1953).
42. UMRATH, K.: *Pflügers Arch., 262*:368 (1956).
43. LEMBECK, F.: *Arch. exper. Path. u. Pharmakol., 219*:197 (1953).
44. ZETLER, G.: In *Polypeptides Which Affect Smooth Muscles and Blood Vessels*, p. 179. Schachter, Ed. Oxford, London, Pergamon Press (1960).
45. LECHNER, H. and LEMBECK, F.: *Arch. exper. Path. u. Pharmakol., 234*:419 (1958).
46. KOPERA, N. and LAZARINI, W.: *Arch. exper. Path. u. Pharmakol., 219*:214 (1953).
47. ZETLER, G. and SCHLOSSER, L.: *Arch. exper. Path. u. Pharmakol., 224*:159 (1955).
48. PERNOW, B.: *Acta physiol. scandinav., 29*:Suppl. 105 (1953).
49. AMIN, A. H., CRAWFORD, T. B. B. and GADDUM, J. H.: *J. Physiol., 126*:596 (1954).
50. HOLTON, P.: In *Polypeptides Which Affect Smooth Muscles and Blood Vessels*, p. 192. Schachter, Ed. Oxford, London, Pergamon Press.
51. HOLTON, F. A. and HOLTON, P.: *J. Physiol., 118*:310 (1952).
52. HILTON, S. M. and HOLTON, P.: *J. Physiol., 125*:138 (1954).
53. HOLTON, F. A. and HOLTON, P.: *J. Physiol., 126*:124 (1954).
54. HOLTON, P.: *J. Physiol., 145*:494 (1959).
55. FLOREY, E. and McLENNAN, H.: *Naturwissenschaften, 20*:561 (1955).
56. BREMER, F.: *J. Physiol. Path. Gén., 46*:963 (1954).
57. HARRIS, G. W. and HOLTON, P.: *J. Physiol., 120*:254 (1953).
58. BUCHTHAL, F., ENGBAEK, L., STEN-KUNDSEN, O. and THOMASEN, E.: *J. Physiol., 106*:3P (1947).
59. EMMELIN, N. and FELDBERG, W.: *Brit. J. Pharmacol., 3*:273 (1948).
60. FELDBERG, W. and SHERWOOD, S. L.: *J. Physiol., 123*:148 (1953).

61. TORDA, C.: *Am. J. Physiol., 178:*123 (1954).
62. ROBINSON, F. and HUGHES, R. A.: *J. Neurophysiol., 14:*387 (1951).
63. CROSSLAND, J. and MERRICK, A. J.: *J. Physiol., 125:*56 (1954).
64. CROSSLAND, J. and MITCHELL, J. F.: Unpublished experiments.
65. HOSEIN, E. A.: Personal communication.
66. HOSEIN, E. A.: *Nature, London, 187:*321 (1960).
67. HOSEIN, E. A. and McLENNAN, H.: *Nature, London, 183:*328 (1959).
68. HAYASHI, T.: *Chemical Physiology of Excitation in Muscle and Nerve.* Tokyo, Nakayama Shoten (1958).
69. HAYASHI, T.: *Neurophysiology and Neurochemistry of Convulsion.* Tokyo, Dainihon-Tosho (1959).

XXVIII

COMPARATIVE NEUROCHEMISTRY: INORGANIC IONS, AMINO ACIDS AND POSSIBLE TRANSMITTER SUBSTANCES OF INVERTEBRATES

Ernst Florey

THERE ARE well over one million different animal species on this planet, yet only a few have become laboratory animals and our knowledge of the chemistry of the nervous system is restricted to very few organisms indeed. Most of these are vertebrates, and of these the most prominent is the rat, followed by cat and dog. Whatever little we know about the neurochemistry of the other animals, particularly of invertebrate species, is the topic of this chapter. No attempt will be made to describe or discuss the kinetic aspects and the main purpose will be to summarize and evaluate the available data concerning the occurrence in nerve tissue of inorganic ions, amino acids, possible transmitter agents and related enzymes.

INORGANIC IONS AND AMINO ACIDS

It is generally assumed that the intracellular concentrations of various inorganic ions differ from those found in the extracellular fluid. In particular it appears that the intracellular concentrations of sodium and of chloride are low while that of potassium is high as compared with extracellular fluid. Specific investigations are restricted to the nervous system of decapod crustacea and the giant axons of decapod cephalopods (squid).

(a) *Cephalopoda.*—Data are available for isolated giant axons of *Sepia*[1] and for axoplasm of giant axons of *Loligo*.[2] The chief inorganic cations are potassium, sodium, magnesium and calcium in that order. In addition there is a considerable amount of organic, nitrogenous cation. The inorganic anions are largely chloride and phosphate. The majority of the anions are organic compounds of low molecular weight.

673

TABLE I

INORGANIC IONS AND AMINO ACIDS OF NERVE TISSUE OF INVERTEBRATES

(Amounts are expressed as microequivalents/gm. wet weight.)

	Homarus Vulgaris[1] Leg Nerve	Carcinus Maenas[1] Total	Carcinus Maenas[1] Leg Nerve Intracellular	Sepia Officinalis[1] Giant Axon Total	Loligo Pealii[2] Giant Axon Axoplasm	
Aspartate	112	138	⎫ 276–291	82	65	
Glutamate	25	35	⎬	39	10	fumarate
Alanine	33	33	⎭	21	15	succinate
Taurine	12	65	⎫ 157–165	103	100	
Glycine	35	5	⎬	5	220	Isethionic acid
					35	polycarboxylic acid
Sodium		152	30–53		65	
Potassium		260	412–432		344	
Magnesium		23			20	
Calcium		13			7	
Chloride		145	27		140	organic base
Sulfate		9				
Bicarbonate		9				
Phosphorus compounds		45			84	

By far the most prominent is isethionic acid, followed by an unknown polycarboxylic acid, aspartic, glutamic, fumaric and succinic acid. In addition there is a conspicuous amount of taurine and of another compound, possibly identical with N-methyl-picolinic acid (homarine).[2] Recent data are summarized in Table I.

(b) *Crustacea.*[1]—The chief cations in *Carcinus* nerve are potassium, sodium, magnesium and calcium in that order. Chloride is the most prominent inorganic anion but its concentration is too low to balance the cation concentration. The anion-deficit is met by organic anions. These are largely aspartic acid and glutamic acid. In addition, *Carcinus* nerve contains large quantities of taurine and alanine. The latter amino-acids seem to play an important role in the maintenance of osmotic balance between asoplasm and extracellular fluid (blood). The free amino acids of *Carcinus* nerve amount to about 25% of the dry weight. Similar results have been obtained for nerves of *Cancer, Maia, Homarus* and *Palinurus.* In the latter three species, glycine is also a conspicuous amino acid. Recent data are summarized in Table I.

TRANSMITTER SUBSTANCES AND RELATED COMPOUNDS

Actetylcholine (ACh), Cholinesterase, Choline Acetylase.—ACh-like activity has been detected in nerve tissue of many species. Unfortunately the identification of the active agent with ACh is uncertain in many cases because it is based on bio-assays only. There are several cholinesters which have biological actions similar to those of ACh. If tested on the *rectus abdominis* muscle of the frog, butyrylcholine is as potent as ACh and methylbutyrylcholine, propionylcholine and imidazolylpropionylcholine are respectively 1.38,1.6 and 3 times as active as ACh.[3] Several cholinesters have recently been identified in tissues of various animals, mostly in non-nervous tissue. So far the only indications that nerve tissue of invertebrate animals may contain cholinesters other than ACh is the finding of two unknown cholinesters in the heads of bees.[4] It is, of course, possible that these occur outside the brain. By combining chemical and pharmacological methods of identification it has been established that the ACh-like activity of extracts of central and peripheral nervous system of the lobster, *Homarus,* of heads of insects *(Apis,*[4] *Calliphora,*[5] *Musca*[6]*)* and of cerebral ganglia of *Octopus*[7] is practically all due to ACh. The ACh-values obtained from other sources must be accepted with the reservation in mind that they may represent the activity of different cholinesters. In most cases it has been ascertained that the ACh-like activity of the extracts is destroyed by alkali and vertebrate serum-cholinesterase. The data available from the literature are summarized in Table II.

ACh has not been found in Coelenterates and Sponges, nor has it

TABLE II

ACETYLCHOLINE CONTENT OF NERVE TISSUE OF INVERTEBRATES

(*Amounts are indicated as* μg./gm. *wet weight.*)

Phylum	Group	Genus and Species	Tissue	ACh	Reference
Porifera		Leuconia adperta	body	0	8
		Siphonocula crassa	body	0	8
Coelenterata	Cnidaria	Adamsia palliata	body	0	8
		rondeletti	body	0	8
		Rhizostoma pulmo	body	0	8
		Alcyonum palmatum	body	0	8
Mollusca	Gastropoda	Helix pomatia	ganglia	12	9
		Haliotis tuberculata	ganglia	20	9
		Aplysia depilans	peri-esophageal ganglia	2–3	8
		Busycon canaliculatum	ganglia	3–9	10
	Lamellibranchiata	Venus mercenaria	ganglia	1–5	10
		Pectunculus violascens	body	0.65	8
	Cephalopoda	Octopus vulgaris	cerebral ganglia	77	8
				90	9
Sipunculida		Sepia officinalis	cerebral ganglia	80	9
		Sipunculus nudus	body	0.8–0.9	8
			muscle	0.7	8
Annelida	Polychaeta	Spirographis spallanzanii	body	0.5–0.7	8
		Halla parthenopea	body	0.8	8
	Hirudinea	Haemopis sanguisuga	ventral nerve cord	6	11
Arthropoda	Crustacea	Lepas anatifera	body	0.15	8
		Callinectes sapidus	ventral ganglia	6.6	12
		Libinia emarginata	ventral ganglia	4.6	12
		Carcinus maenas	nervous system	2–4	13
		Cancer irroratus	ventral ganglia	3.1	12
		magister	leg nerves	2.0–6.7	14

	Cambarus virilis	motor fibers	0.1	14
		sensory fibers	1.9–6.9	14
		inhibitory fibers	0.1	14
		ventral nerve cord	9.8–14.4	12
	bartoni	ventral ganglia	16–30	15
		leg nerve and commissures	28	16
	limosus	ventral ganglia	9–10	16
		ventral nerve cord	10–66	16
		leg nerves	6–7	16
		central commissures	8	16
		leg nerves and commissures	8	16
	Astacus fluviatilis	brain	1–20	16
		ventral nerve cord	18–43	17
		proximal eyestalk	18–39	17
		distal eyestalk	2.5–15	17
			25–43	17
	Homarus americanus	ventral nerve cord	90	3
		leg nerves	46	3
		ventral ganglia	12–20	16
		leg nerves and connectives	8–10	16
		cardiac ganglion	0	18
		cardio-accelerators	0	18
Xiphosura	Limulus polyphemus	central ganglia	7.5–13.2	12
		leg nerves	10	18
		cardiac ganglion	0.3	12
Arachnida	Heteropoda regia	ganglia	35–50	19
	Buthus europaeus	ganglia	30–35	19
	Heterometrus maurus	ganglia	35–40	19
Insecta	Leptinotarsa decemlineata	head	3.5–10	19
	Carabus auratus	head	45–55	19
	Tenebrio molitor	head	20–35	19
	Carausius morosus	head	7.8	5
		head	8–9	19
	Gryllus domesticus	ganglionic chain	100–200	19
		head	7–10	19

TABLE II—*Continued*

Phylum	Group	Genus and Species	Tissue	ACh	Reference
		Periplaneta americana	cerebral ganglia	65	19
			head	8	19
				9.8	5
			nerve cord	36.7	5
				70	20
		Calliphora vomitoria erythrocephala	head	46–62	21
			head	20–35	19
			brain (estimated)	32.7	5
		Lucilia sericata	head	500	5
		Musca domestica	head	28.3	5
			head	26.1	5
		Xylocopa violacea	brain (estimated)	150	5
			brain	200	19
Echinodermata	Holothuroidea	Holothuria tubulosa	longitudinal muscle	1.5–1.7	8
			intestine	0.4	8
Chordata	Tunicata	Ciona intestinalis	body	0	8
		Phallusia mammilata	body	0	8

been found in the Tunicates. There are several phyla in which ACh has not yet been looked for. To these belong the *Kamptozoa, Priapulida, Onychophora, Linguatulida, Tardigrada, Tentaculata, Enteropneusta* and the *Chaetognatha.*

Cholinesterases have been detected in Coelenterates and in all those phyla in which ACh has been found. These are the *Nemathelminthes, Platyhelminthes, Nemertini, Mollusca, Sipunculida, Annelida, Arthropoda* and *Echinodermata.* In addition this enzyme system occurs in the *Tentaculata, Enteropneusta* and *Onychophora* (in the latter phylum its presence is only suggested by the fact that eserine potentiates the actions of ACh). The data on cholinesterase activity are summarized in Table III.

The cholinesterases are, of course, not restricted to the nervous system and in most cases determinations were made on extracts or homogenates of whole animals. It is not possible to simply distinguish between "true" and "pseudo-cholinesterase." In certain cases (e.g., *Terebratulina*[29]) the cholinesterase is even more specific than the true cholinesterase of mammalian red blood cells. The cholinesterases of different species are definitely different with regard to substrate specificity and optimum substrate concentrations. For a detailed account the reader is referred to the extensive papers of Augustinsson.[23,29] It must be kept in mind, however, that the behavior of cholinesterases as determined in studies of homogenates of whole organisms may not reflect true differences in the properties of cholinesterases of the different types of organism but rather a difference in relative amounts of different types of cholinesterase. Nevertheless, wherever it has been found that at optimal substrate concentration (about 10^{-3} M) ACh is hydrolyzed faster than acetyl-beta-methylcholine and that benzoylcholine is split at a very much lower rate, we can assume that the main enzyme activity can be ascribed to a true acetyl-cholinesterase. Esterases of this type appear to be present in all the forms listed in Table IV with the exception of *Sagartia, Mya, Dentalium, Tonicella, Maia* (muscle), and *Asterias* (intestine). In the latter cases benzoylcholine is split, indicating the presence of a non-specific cholinesterase.

Cholineacetylase presumably occurs in all those animals in which ACh is found. Specific measurements of its activity have been made only in cephalopods, crustacea and insects. The available data are given in Table IV.

ACh appears to be without effect in sponges and coelenterates. The fact that it has not been detected in organisms of these phyla is in itself no argument against the presence of this compound in the nervous system of these animals since the amount of nerve tissue within the parts or whole organisms taken for bio-assay is negligibly small.

TABLE III

CHOLINESTERASE CONTENT OF NERVE TISSUE

(Expressed as mg.ACh hydrolyzed by 100 mg. of tissue per hour (QChE).)

Phylum	Group	Genus and Species	Tissue	QChE	References
Porifera		Scypha, sp.	body	0	22
		Siphonocula crassa	body	0	8
Coelenterata	Cnidaria	Tubularia crocea	heads	0.137–0.267	28
		Metridium marginatum senile	body, parts	0.009–0.063	28
			sphincter muscle	0.004	28
		Sagartia luciae	body	0.035–0.068	28
		Cyanaea capillata	tentacles	0–0.013	28
		Aurelia aurita	subumbrellar neuro-muscular sheet	0.017	22
			subumbrellar neuro-muscular sheet plus marginal organs		
		Sagartia parasitica	body, upper part	0	22
		Rhizostoma pulmo	subumbrellar muscle	0.178	23
		Alcyonum palmatum	body	0	8
		Adamsia rondeleti	body	0	8
	Ctenophora	Mnemiopis leidyi	fragments of comb-plates and underlying parts (epithelium, jelly, cilia, nerve, muscle, etc.)	0	8
Platyhelminthes		Procotyla fluviatilis	body	0	23
		Planaria maculata	body	8–11.4	23
				11.4 and more	23
Nemertini		Cerebratulus lacteus	dorsal muscle	6.86	24
		Prostoma rubrum	body	510–899	25
Mollusca	Cephalopoda	Sepia officinalis	"liver"	0.972	23
		Loligo pealii	stellar nerve	0.486–0.840	26
			fin nerve	0.156–0.312	26

			Value	Ref.
Gastropoda	Eusepia	giant axon (whole)	0.15	27
	Eusepia	giant axon (sheath)	0.42	27
	Eusepia	brain	1.18	28
	Helix pomatia	muscle	0.076	28
	Helix pomatia	dart sac	14.677	23
	Helix pomatia	blood	9.428	23
	Patella vulgata	body	0.389	23
	Purpura lapillus	body	0.697	29
Soleneconae	Dentalium entalis	body	1.085	29
Lamellibranchia	Mya arenaria	body	0.219	29
	Astarte sulcata	body	0.113	29
	Modiolus	heart	8.73	30
	Venus mercenaria	heart	0.176	30
	Pecten	striated muscle	0.3	31
Placophora	Tonicella marmorata	body	0.372	29
Sipunculida	Phacolosoma spec.	retractor muscle	5–6	31
Annelida Polychaeta	Aphrodite aculeata	body	0	29
	Nereis virens	body	0	29
	Nereis spec.	body wall	5.5–7.5	31
	Spirographis Spallanzani	blood	0.081	23
Hirudinea	Haemopis sanguisug	ventral nerve cord	1.87–2.0	11
		muscle	1.20–1.25	11
	Pontobdella muricata	muscle	26–96	28
Oligochaeta	"Earthworm et al."	body wall	16–17	31
Arthropoda Insecta	Musca domestica	head	2.28	32
	Apis mellifica	head	2.08	32
	Melanoplus differentialis	brain	13–18	33
		brain	0.408	34
		ganglia	0.347	34
		ventral nerve cord	0.356	34
		wing muscle	0.134	34
		femur muscle	0.036–0.079	34
	Periplaneta americana	blood	0.059	34
		heart	0.040	34
		nerve cord	31–33	21

TABLE III—Continued

Phylum	Group	Genus and Species	Tissue	QChE	References
Arthropoda—Cont'd	Xiphosura	Limulus polyphemus	"ventral nerve"	1.749	30
			"cardiac nerve"	3.612	30
			heart	0.275–0.405	30
			intestine	0.145	30
			serum	0.340	30
			skeletal muscle	0.036	30
	Crustacea	Homarus vulgaris	ventral nerve cord	0.14	31
			ventral ganglia	15–20	35
			leg nerve	23	36
		americanus	abdominal muscles	10.0	36
			abdominal nerve cord proximal portion	0.160–0.225	28
			distal portion	7.192–17.820	26
			central nervous system	7.452–21.870	26
		Astacus fluviatilis	intestines	9–54	17
		Eupagurus bernhardus	muscles	0	29
			muscles	0	29
		Carcinus maenas	muscles	1.206	29
		Pagurus longicarpus	heart	0.397	30
		Libinia dubia	heart	0.230	30
		Callinectes sapidus	heart	0.413	30
		Maia squinado	muscles	0.421	29
		Pandalus montagui	body	0.283	23
		Balanus crenatus	body	0.016	23
Tentaculata	Brachiopoda	Terebratulina capud serpentis	body	0.340	29
Enteropneusta		Balanoglossus clavigerus	proboscis	0.551	29
			collar	0.259	29
			"liver sacs"	0.162	29

Echinodermata	Asteroidea	Asterias rubens	intestine, stomach	0.462	29
			ampulla, podia	0.194	29
		forbesi	radial nerve cord	0.384	22
	Ophiuroidea	Amphiura chiajai	body	0.152	29
	Echinoidea	Psammechinus miliaris	intestines	0.508	29
		Echinus esculentus	intestines	1.369	29
		Paracentrotus lividus	larvae (plutei)	9.072	23
	Holothurioidea	Thyone briareus	radial bands (muscle)	0.820	22
		Cucumarea lactea	body	1.517	29
		Mesothuria intestinalis	body	0.308	29
		Holothuria nigra	longitudinal muscles	0.037–0.194	28
Chordata	Tunicata	Ciona intestinalis	body	0	8

TABLE IV

CHOLINACETYLASE ACTIVITY OF NERVOUS TISSUE OF INVERTEBRATES

(Expressed as mg. of ACh synthesized per gm. of acetone dried powder per hour (QChA).)

Phylum	Group	Genus and Species	Tissue	QChA	References
Arthropoda	Insects	Lucilia sericata	heads	10	37
			brain (estimated value)	100	37
		"house fly"	heads	6	38
	Crustacea	Cancer irroratus	pooled nerve tissue	0.085–0.20	15
Mollusca	Cephalopoda	Sepia officinalis	retina	0–0.005	39
			retinal nerves	0–0.005	39
			optic ganglia	0.5	39
			inner part of opt. ggl.	0.340–2.60	39
			outer part of opt. ggl.	0.065–1.35	39
			optic nerve	0.050–0.145	39
			cerebellar ganglion	0.240–0.430	39

Bullock and Nachmansohn[22] in fact argued in favor of the hypothesis that ACh and cholinesterase are necessary attributes of any nervous system. They supported their argument by the demonstration of cholinesterase in coelenterates, the lowest forms known to possess a differentiated nervous system.

Nothing definite is known about the responses to ACh of *Kamptozoa, Priapulida* and *Nemathelminthes.* The cholinesterase activity reported by Kamemoto[25] for the nemertean *Prostoma rubrum* (see Table III) is the highest so far found in the whole animal kingdom. Although it contains much less cholinesterase, the dorsal muscle of another nemertean worm, *Cerebratulus lacteus,* was found to respond to ACh only if treated with eserine, and then only to high concentrations (5×10^{-5} gm./ml.).[24] There is as yet no proof for cholinergic transmission in nemerteans.

Among molluscs the existence of cholinergic neurons has been proven only in one case: the cardio-inhibitory fibers of *Venus mercenaria.* Here it has been shown by Prosser[40] and Welsh[41] that during stimulation of these neurones an ACh-like substance is released into the perfusion medium, that ACh imitates the action of the inhibitory nerves and that the drug mytolon blocks the action both of ACh and of the inhibitory cardiac nerves. The strikingly unequal distribution of choline acetylase in the cephalopod nervous system (see Table IV) makes it likely that there are cholinergic pathways. It must be admitted, however, that the evidence for this is not better (or worse) than that available for the central nervous system of mammals. The perfused mantle muscle of the squid *Eusepia* yields ACh but the output of this substance is not altered by stimulation of the mantle nerves and the response of the muscle to indirect stimulation is not potentiated by eserine, indicating that ACh is not the transmitter of the motoneurones.[42] Although the cephalopod heart responds to ACh, it has not yet been possible to demonstrate the cholinergic nature of the cardio-inhibitory nerves. It is interesting that in certain bivalves (e.g., *Mytilus californianus,*[18] *M.galloprovencialis, Amphidesma forsterianum, A.ventricosum*[43]) ACh causes a rise in tone, increase of heart rate and systolic contracture of the heart, while stimulation of the cardiac nerves can produce slowing and diastolic arrest.[44] Whether ACh has any normal role in the control of molluscan muscles other than those of the heart is still uncertain, although this compound has powerful actions in many cases, usually causing contraction. The transmission between second- and third-order giant axons in the stellar ganglion of squid appears to be non-cholinergic.[42]

The muscles of the bodywall and the pharyngeal retractor muscles of sipunculids contract in response to ACh.[42] Eserine increases this action as well as the response to indirect stimulation.[45]

The longitudinal muscles of the body wall of all annelids so far investigated contract in response to applied ACh. This action resembles that brought about by stimulation of the motor nerves. These in fact were shown (in *Hirudo*) to release an ACh-like substance upon stimulation. The effect of both ACh and nerve stimulation is potentiated by eserine and partially blocked by curare.[46] The gut of the earthworm *(Lumbricus)* is stimulated by ACh and this action as well as that of the augmentor nerves is potentiated by eserine and blocked by atropine.[47] The ACh content of the earthworm nervous system has not yet been described but ACh-like activity has been detected in extracts of whole earthworms.[47]

The longitudinal muscles of the onychophoran *Peripatopsis mosleyi* contract in response to applied ACh. The effect is potentiated by eserine.[48] It is not known whether the nervous system of this animal contains ACh.

The function of ACh in the arthropods still awaits clarification. The nervous system of all forms studied contains ACh or a similar ester, often in conspicuous amounts (see Table III). The cholinesterase activity is also most prominent and by far surpasses that found in mammalian organs. ACh has an accelerating action on the heart of certain insects (e.g., *Melanoplus*,[49] *Stenopelmatus*,[50] *Periplaneta*[51]), of *Limulus* and of many dekapod crustacea. In the latter two types the action is clearly on the cardiac ganglion which governs the heart beat. ACh appears to be without effect on synaptic transmission in the central nervous system of insects[52] and crustacea[53] but it may cause an increase in the spontaneous activity of the ventral nerve cord of crayfish.[54] ACh is without action on skeletal muscles of crustacea and insects[55] and there is no cholinesterase at insect motor endplates.[56] The ACh of crustacean peripheral nerve is present exclusively in the sensory fibers. Motoneurons and inhibitory neurones do not contain detectable amounts of this ester.[14] The cholinergic nature of crustacean sensory neurons has, however, not yet been established.

We are completely ignorant about possible cholinergic mechanisms in the phyla *Linguatulida, Tardigrada, Tentaculata, Enteropneusta* and *Chaetognatha.* There is, however, evidence for cholinergic mechanisms in echinoderms. Bacq[57] demonstrated the release of an ACh-like substance from longitudinal muscles of the sea cucumber. *Stichopus regalis,* during indirect stimulation. These muscles as well as those of other holothurians and the lantern adductor muscle of *Echinus esculentus* are very sensitive to ACh.[42] The contractions resulting from nerve stimulation or application of ACh are potentiated by eserine.

Catecholamines, Aminoxidase.—There is no substantial evidence that adrenaline or nor-adrenaline play a role as transmitter substance of neurons of invertebrates. Von Euler[58] detected small amounts of nor-adrenaline-like activity in the gill hearts of *Octopus vulgaris* and rather large amounts (10 μg./gm.) in the posterior salivary glands of this mollusc. It is quite possible that this nor-adrenaline is derived from octopamine[59] which is present in the gland in large quantities. Adrenaline and nor-adrenaline have been found in certain insects and annelids, in the latter they seem to be localized in the chromaffin cells of the central nervous system. Outside of these groups of animals these compounds do not seem to occur in invertebrates. The results of rather extensive studies of Oestlund,[60] supplemented by the data of von Euler,[58] are summarized in Table V.

Aminoxidase has been demonstrated in a number of annelids, echinoderms and molluscs.[61-66] The presence of large amounts of this enzyme in "liver" of various molluscs and in posterior salivary glands of the cephalopoda may indicate a function other than inactivation of nervous transmitter substances. No studies have been made on the presence of ortho-methyltransferase, the enzyme which is now recognized as chiefly responsible for the inactivation of nor-adrenaline in vertebrates

Oestlund[60] found an unknown compound in crustacean body extracts which he suspects to be a catecholamine and which he named "catechol-4." In insects there occur large amounts of oxytyramine (dopamine),[60] the precursor of nor-adrenaline (see Table V).

Adrenaline accelerates the pulsating blood vessels of annelids[67] and causes inhibition of the movements of the gut of the earthworm.[47] In spite of the fact that adrenaline and nor-adrenaline do not occur in crustacea, these substances have very definite actions on certain organs of these animals. They cause acceleration of the heart beat and stimulate the intestine to powerful contractions.[68] In the shrimp, *Crangon vulgaris* they cause expansion of the pigment in melanophores.[69] Cardioacceleration by adrenaline (and nor-adrenaline) has frequently been reported for insects and molluscs.[31]

With the exception of the nervous system of annelids, in particular that of the earthworm, catecholamines have not been shown to occur in *nerve tissue* of invertebrates.

Indole-alkylamines.—5-hydroxytryptamine (5-HT) has been found and identified (bio-assay, chromatography, fluorospectrography) in nerve tissue of various molluscs[41,70-73] and in a sea-anemone, *Calliactis parasitica.*[74] A similar compound, probably an ortho-dihydroxytryptamine, occurs in the nervous system of crustacea.[70,75] The biological actions of the latter are indistinguishable from those of 5-hydroxy-

TABLE V

ADRENALINE, NORADRENALINE AND DOPAMINE CONTENTS (OR EQUIVALENTS) IN BODY AND TISSUES OF VARIOUS INVERTEBRATES

(Expressed in $m\mu g./gm.$ wet weight.)

Phylum	Group	Genus and Species	Tissue	Noradr.	Adr.	Dopamine	References
Coelenterata	Cnidaria	Alcyonium digitatum	body		1.5	—	60
		Metridium dianthus	body		2.0	—	60
		Rhizostoma pulmo	body		0.3	—	60
Annelida	Polychaeta	Arenicola marina	body		32	—	60
	Oligochaeta	Lumbricus terrestris	body		45	—	60
			ventral nerve cord	320	1400	—	60
Mollusca	Gastropoda	Helix pomatia			4	—	60
	Lamellibranchia	Mytilus edulis			4	—	60
		Buccinum undatum			0.7	—	60
	Cephalopoda	Octopus vulgaris	gill heart		15–40	—	58
			posterior salivary gland		10,000	—	58
		macropus	posterior salivary gland		1,000	—	58
Arthropoda	Crustacea	Daphnia pulex	body		5	—	60
		Crangon crangon	body		1.7	—	60
	Insecta	Tenebrio molitor	imago, body	1100	15	—	60
			larva, body	1900–2200	16–300	2000–4000	60
		Vanessa urticae	larva, body	190	10	10,000–15,000	60
		Musca domestica	imago, body	1900	300	10,000–15,000	60
			larva, body	100	10	10,000–15,000	60
		Apis mellifica, worker	imago, body	750	50	4,000–8,000	60
			mature pupa, body	220	36	5,000–10,000	60
			immature pupa, body	45	49	2,000–4,000	60
			larva	300	10	—	60
			drone, imago, body	330	10	2,000–4,000	60
			immature pupa, body	100	13	5,000–10,000	60
			larva	760	75	5,000–10,000	60
		Forficula spec.	imago, body	1200	10	<1000	60
Chordata	Tunicata	Ciona intestinalis	body	—	0.8	—	60

tryptamine: both stimulate the crustacean and mollusc heart, the non-pregnant rat uterus and the guinea pig ileum.

The function of 5-HT in Calliactis is still unknown. No 5-HT was found in two other sea anemones, *Metridium* and *Anemonia*.[74]

The acceleratory action of 5-hydroxytryptamine on the heart of molluscs and crabs is up to hundred times stronger than that of adrenaline or nor-adrenaline.[70,76] The compound has, however, only a weak action on the crayfish intestine[18] and is without effect on chromatophores of shrimps.[18] Sensory nerve endings in crayfish are greatly excited by applied 5-hydroxytryptamine.[77]

The 5-HT (and dihydroxy tryptamine) content of nerve tissue of invertebrates is presented in Table VI.

On the basis of its occurrence in nerve tissue and of its actions, which resemble those of cardiac nerve stimulation, 5-hydroxytryptamine has been proposed as a transmitter substance of cardio-accelerator fibers in molluscs.[70,72] There is as yet no evidence for the function of the dihydroxytryptamine in peripheral nerves of crustacea, but there is suggestive evidence that this substance is the neuro-secretory produce of the pericardial organs[75] which are formed of a neuro-pile suspended within the pericardial cavity.

In molluscan tissues (posterior salivary glands of cephalopods) are also found tyramine and para-hydroxy-phenylethanolamine (octopamine).[59] The occurence of these agents in nerve tissue has not been demonstrated. For figures for the 5-HT content of non-nervous tissues of invertebrates (see refs. 73 and 78).

Substance I.—The peripheral and central nervous system of certain decapod crustacea (*Pachygrapsus*,[79] *Pacifastacus*, *Cancer*, *Homarus*[18]) was found to contain a substance which has strong inhibitory actions on striated muscle, heart ganglion, intestine and on stretch receptor neurons of crayfish.[79] The substance is not identical with gamma-aminobutyric acid but appears to be an amino compound (positive reaction with ninhydrin).[18] Although it has been isolated by means of paper chromatography its identity has not been established. Its actions are mimicked by gamma-aminobutyric acid. The action of both agents is blocked by picrotoxin.[80] The crustacean inhibitory agent has been named Substance I.[81]

A substance with similar chemical and pharmacological properties has been found in the nervous system of *Limulus*.[18]

Substance I seems to occur exclusively in the inhibitory neurons. It could not be found in motor or sensory fibers (*Cancer*).[14] It has also been found in the cardio-inhibitory fibers of *Homarus*.[18] Stimulation of the cardio-inhibitory fibers in crayfish causes the release of an inhibitory substance into the perfusion fluid of the heart. The action

TABLE VI

5-HYDROXY-TRYPTAMINE (5-HT) CONTENT OF NERVE TISSUE OF INVERTEBRATES*

(Amounts are indicated as μg./gm. wet weight (*) or μg./gm. dry weight (#). The data for crustacean tissues are also expressed in terms of 5-HT although the active agent is likely to be an ortho-dihydroxy-tryptamine.[75])

Phylum	Group	Genus and Species	Tissue	5-HT	References
Coelenterata	Cnidaria	Calliactis parasitica	tentacles	6–12#	74
			body wall	15–36#	74
			Coelenteric tissue	500–600#	74
		Metridium senile	body	0	74
		Anemonia sulcata	body	0	74
Mollusca	Cephalopoda	Sepia officinalis	optic ganglia	17.5–21.2#	70
			cerebral ganglia	present	70
			stellar ganglia	present	70
	Gastropoda	Busycon canaliculatum	pooled ganglia	17*	72
			connectives	8.4–9.7*	73
			ganglia and nerves	2–2.5*	73
				4.3–5.5*	73
	Lammellibranchiata	Venus mercenaria	pooled ganglia	15*	72
				12–52*	73
		Mytilus edulis	anterior byssus retractor muscle	0.75–1.0*	78
Arthropoda	Crustacea	Palinurus vulgaris	leg nerves	2*	70
		Dromia vulgaris	leg nerves	22.5–30.4#	70
			ventral ganglia	18.2–26.5#	70
			supraesophageal ganglion	19.7–24#	70

*Since the preparation of the manuscript an extensive list of the 5-HT contents of invertebrate tissues has been published by Welsh and Moorhead.[83]

of the inhibitory substance (Substance I) and of the inhibitory nerves is blocked by picrotoxin.[82] Substance I, therefore, can justly be assumed to be the transmitter substance of crustacean inhibitory neurones.

It is interesting that gamma-aminobutyric acid occurs only in small traces in the crustacean nervous system, in contrast to the vertebrate nervous system where it occurs in conspicuous amounts. Another difference between the two types of nervous system is the absence of glutamic acid decarboxylase in crustacean nerve tissue[18] *(Cancer magister)* and the insensitivity of decapod crustacea *(Pacifastacus, Orconectes)* to thiosemicarbazide,[18] a compound which in mammals inhibits glutamic acid decarboxylase and causes severe convulsions.

Comparative studies on the occurence of Substance I or related substances in the nervous systems of organisms other than crustacea have not yet been carried out.

REFERENCES

1. LEWIS, P. R.: *Biochem. J., 52:*330 (1952).
2. KOECHLIN, B.: *J. Biophys. Biochem. Cytol., 1:*511 (1955).
3. KEYL, M. J., MICHAELSON, I. A. and WHITTAKER, V. P.: *J. Physiol., 139:*434 (1957).
4. AUGUSTINSSON, K. B. and GRAHN, M.: *Acta physiol. scandinav., 32:*174 (1954).
5. LEWIS, S. E. and SMALLMAN, B. N.: *J. Physiol., 134:*241, 1956.
6. CHEFURKA, W. and SMALLMAN, B. N.: *Canad. J. Biochem. Physiol., 34:*731 (1956).
7. BACQ, Z. M. and MAZZA, F. P.: *Arch. internat. physiol., 42:*43 (1935).
8. BACQ, Z. M.: *Arch. internat. physiol., 42:*24 (1935).
9. CORTEGGIANI, E.: Thése de Sci., Paris (1938).
10. WELSH, J. H.: *J. Mar. biol. A. U. K., 35:*193 (1956).
11. SCHWAB, A.: *Ztschr. vergle. Physiol., 31:*506 (1956).
12. SCHALLEK, W.: *J. Cell. & Comp. Physiol., 26:*15 (1945).
13. JULLIEN, A. and VINCENT, D.: *Compt. rend. Soc. biol., Paris, 129:*845 (1938).
14. FLOREY, E. and BIEDERMAN, M. A.: *J. Gen. Physiol., 43:*509 (1960).
15. EASTON, D. M.: *J. Biol. Chem., 185:*813 (1950).
16. SMITH, R. I.: *J. Cell. & Comp. Physiol., 13:*335 (1939).
17. FLOREY, E.: *Pflanzenschutzberichte* (Wien), 7:81 (1951).
18. FLOREY, E.: Unpublished data.
19. CORTEGGIANI, E. and SERFATY, A.: *Compt. rend. Soc. biol., Paris, 131:*1124 (1939).
20. MIKALONIS, S. J. and BROWN, R. H.: *J. Cell. & Comp. Physiol., 18:*401 (1941).
21. TOBIAS, J. M., KOLLROS, J. J. and SAVIT, J.: *J. Cell. & Comp. Physiol., 28:*159 (1946).
22. BULLOCK, T. H. and NACHMANSOHN, D.: *J. Cell. & Comp. Physiol., 20:*239 (1942).
23. AUGUSTINSSON, K. B.: *Acta physiol. scandinav., 15:*Suppl. 52 (1948).
24. SMITH, C. C., JACKSON, B. and PROSSER, C. L.: *Biol. Bull., 79:*377 (1940).
25. KAMEMOTO, F. I.: *Science, 125:*351 (1957).
26. BULLOCK, T. H., GRUNDFEST, H., NACHMANSOHN, D. and ROTHENBER, M. A.: *J. Neurophysiol., 10:*11, 63 (1947).
27. BOELL, E. J. and NACHMANSOHN, D.: *Science, 92:*513 (1940).

28. BACQ, Z. M. and NACHMANSOHN, D.: *J. Physiol., 89*:368 (1937).
29. AUGUSTINSSON, K. B.: *Acta physiol. scandinav., 11*:141 (1946).
30. SMITH, C. C. and GLICK, D.: *Biol. Bull., 77*:321 (1939).
31. PROSSER, C. L.: *Comparative Animal Physiology.* Philadelphia, Saunders (1950).
32. BABERS, F. H. and PRATT, J. J.: *Physiol. Zool., 24*:127 (1951).
33. RICHARDS, A. G. and CUTCOMP, L. K.: *J. Cell. & Comp. Physiol., 26*:57 (1945).
34. MEANS, O. W.: *J. Cell. & Comp. Physiol., 20*:319 (1942).
35. MARNAY, A. and NACHMANSOHN, D.: *Compt. rend. Soc. biol.,* Paris, *125*:1005 (1937).
36. NACHMANSOHN, D.: *Compt. rend. Soc. biol.,* Paris, *127*:894 (1938).
37. SMALLMAN, B. N.: *J. Physiol., 132*:343 (1956).
38. FRONTALI, N.: *J. Insect Physiol., 1*:319 (1958).
39. FELDBERG, W., HARRIS, G. W. and LIN, R. G. Y.: *J. Physiol., 112*:400 (1951).
40. PROSSER, C. L.: *Biol. Bull., 83*:145 (1940).
41. WELSH, J. H.: *Arch. exper. u. Path. Pharmakol., 219*:23 (1953).
42. BACQ, Z. M.: *Arch internat. physiol., 44*:174 (1937).
43. PILGRIM, R. L. C.: *J. Physiol., 125*:208 (1954).
44. DIEDERICHS, W.: *Zool. Jahrb. Abt. Allg. Zool., 55*:231 (1935).
45. BACQ, Z. M. and COPPEE, G.: *Compt. rend. Soc. Biol.,* Paris, *124*:1244 (1937).
46. BACQ, Z. M. and COPPEE, G.: *Arch. internat. physiol., 45*:310 (1937).
47. MILLOT, N.: *Proc. Roy. Soc. London,* B, *131*:271 (1943).
48. EWER, D. W. and BERG, R. VAN DEN: *J. Exper. Biol., 31*:497 (1954).
49. HAMILTON, H. L.: *J. Cell. & Comp. Physiol., 13*:91 (1939).
50. DAVENPORT, D.: *Physiol. Zool. 22*:35 (1949).
51. KRIJGSMAN, B. J. and KRIJGSMAN, N. E.: *Nature, 165*:936 (1950).
52. ROEDER, K. D.: *Bull. Johns Hopkins Hosp., 83*:587 (1948).
53. SCHALLEK, W. and WIERSMA, C. A. G.: *J. Cell. & Comp. Physiol., 31*:35 (1948).
54. BONNET, V.: *Compt. rend. Soc. belge biol., 77*:804 (1938).
55. ELLIS, C. H., THIENES, C. H. and WIERSMA, C. A. G.: *Biol. Bull., 83*:334 (1942).
56. WIGGLESWORTH, V. B.: *Quart. J. micr. Sc., 99*:441 (1958).
57. BACQ, Z. M.: *Arch. internat. physiol., 49*:25 (1939).
58. EULER, U. S. VON: *Acta physiol. scandinav., 28*:297 (1953).
59. ERSPAMER, V. and BORETTI, G.: *Arch. internat. pharmacodyn. et therap., 88*:296 (1951).
60. OESTLUND, E.: *Acta physiol. scandinav., 31*:Suppl. 112 (1954).
61. BLASCHKO, H.: *J. Physiol., 99*:364 (1941).
62. BLASCHKO, H. and HAWKINS, J.: *Biochem. J., 52*:306 (1952).
63. BLASCHKO, H. and HAWKINS, J.: *J. Physiol., 118*:88 (1952).
64. BLASCHKO, H. and HIMMS, J. M.: *J. Physiol., 120*:445 (1953).
65. BLASCHKO, H. and HIMMS, J. M.: *J. Exper. Biol., 31*:1 (1954).
66. BLASCHKO, H. and HOPE, D. B.: *Arch. Biochem. & Biophys., 69*:10 (1957).
67. GASKELL, J. F.: *J. Gen. Physiol., 2*:73 (1919).
68. FLOREY, E.: *Z. vergl. Physiol., 36*:1 (1954).
69. FLOREY, E.: *Biol. Zentralbl., 71*:499 (1952).
70. FLOREY, E. and FLOREY, E.: *Ztschr. Naturfschg., 9b*:53 (1954).
71. WELSH, J. H.: *Anat. Rec., 117*:637 (1953).
72. WELSH, J. H.: *Ann. New York Acad. Sc., 66*:618 (1957).
73. WELSH, J. H. and MOOREHEAD, M.: *Science, 129*:1491 (1959).
74. MATHIAS, A. P., ROSS, D. M., and SCHACHTER, M.: *Nature, 180*:658 (1957).
75. CARLISLE, D. B.: *Biochem. J., 63*:32P (1956).
76. ERSPAMER, V. and GHIRETTI, F.: *J. Physiol., 115*:470 (1951).

77. FLOREY, E.: *Ztschr. Naturforschg., 9b:*540 (1954).
78. ERSPAMER, V.: *Rend. Sc. Farmitalia, 1:*1 (1954).
79. FLOREY, E.: *Arch Intern. Physiol., 62:*33 (1954).
80. ELLIOTT, K. A. C. and FLOREY, E.: *J. Neurochem., 1:*131 (1956).
81. FLOREY, E.: In *Inhibition in the Nervous System and Gamma-aminobutyric Acid.* E. Roberts, Ed. Pergamon, London (1960).
82. FLOREY, E.: *Naturwissenschaften, 44:*424 (1957).
83. WELSH, J. H. and MOORHEAD, M.: *J. Neurochem., 6:*146 (1960).

XXIX

CHEMICAL STUDIES IN RELATION TO CONVULSIVE CONDITIONS

L. S. WOLFE AND K. A. C. ELLIOTT

CONVULSIVE ACTIVITY may occur in animals and man in a wide variety of circumstances. Among these are hypoxia, high oxygen pressure, hypoglycemia, certain vitamin deficiencies, cerebral injuries, electroshock, genetic determination (e.g., audiogenic seizures), narcotic withdrawal, the administration of diverse chemical agents, the development of certain kinds of local brain lesions, as in focal epilepsy, and unknown causes as in idiopathic epilepsy. Convulsions may be associated with almost any disease of the brain. Other than the production of seizures no obvious common factor among these conditions has been discovered.

It should be noted that epileptiform activity, and even the initiation of such activity, are potentialities of normal brain if sufficiently and appropriately stimulated. Clinical and electroencephalographic observations of the spread of paroxysmal activity in the brain of man and of experimental animals shows that the spreading hyperactivity will excite surrounding normal neurones resulting in the transmission of the excitation across the cerebral cortex. Convulsive agents or conditions may initiate epileptiform activity or may lower some threshold so that epileptiform activity is initiated by normal stimuli. Current interest in the biochemistry of γ-aminobutyric acid and related substances has led to important contributions from neurochemists and neurophysiologists on the mechanism of regulation of neuronal excitability. Convulsive activity may now be conceived, not as an enhancement of the normal excitation of neurones, but as a partial or complete block of normal inhibition. A biochemical abnormality of some neurones is thought by many investigators to underlie the initiation of a gradually increasing depolarisation in their dendritic fields so that minimal stimuli may initiate a seizure discharge. The spread to adjacent neurones and the propagation axonally to other areas of

694

the nervous system of the discharge results in the striking manifestations of the convulsion.

The problem of convulsions should perhaps be considered from four aspects: (1) What factors determine susceptibility? (2) What are the mechanisms involved in the initiation of a seizure? (3) What processes are involved in the seizure itself? (4) What events occur as a result of the seizure? However, at the present stage of our knowledge it is difficult to decide to which aspect an observation is most relevant. Many factors are apparently concerned in several or all aspects. Chemical studies of convulsions are inseparable from the whole problem of the mechanism of nervous action. In the following survey only biochemical and physiological studies particularly concerned with convulsions are discussed.

GENERAL
Energy Metabolism

During convulsions the cerebral oxygen consumption and cerebral blood flow are greatly increased in a parallel fashion. These have been measured in the whole brain in monkeys by Schmidt, Kety and Pennes[1] and in cats by Geiger and Magnes[2] during drug-induced convulsions. Low values were found in the post-ictal semi-comatose state. The increased rate of circulation has been demonstrated in local regions of the brain during experimental convulsions in animals and in epileptic seizures in man by Gibbs, Lennox and Gibbs[3,4] and by Penfield, von Santha and Cipriani.[5]

The supply of oxygen is necessary for the maintenance of convulsive activity. Jasper and Erickson[6] found that apnea causes complete arrest of electrical activity of the cortex. Gurdjian, Webster and Stone[7,8] observed only brief metrazol-induced EEG changes, followed by cessation of electrical activity, in dogs breathing 4% oxygen. Seizures returned when air was again provided. The increased blood flow and oxygen consumption result from the convulsion and are not concerned in its initiation. The increase in blood flow begins a little time after the onset of local neuronal discharges and applies only to the parts of the cortex involved in the seizure.[5] Using oxygen electrodes Davies and Remond[9] found, in local areas of the cortex of curarized cats, that the rate of oxygen consumption began to rise and oxygen tension began to fall shortly after the onset of EEG seizure patterns induced by metrazol. Convulsions once initiated can be prolonged by additional oxygen or glucose.[10] The total cerebral blood flow and oxygen consumption of idiopathic epileptic patients between seizures is normal.[11] The effect of convulsant drugs on cerebral blood flow and oxygen consumption in man has not been studied (see ref. 12).

It is generally believed that the increased cerebral circulation during convulsions is brought about by the powerful cerebral vasodilator effect of extra carbon dioxide (see ref. 13) but other vasodilator products of metabolism such as lactic acid and liberated acetylcholine may be involved. The mechanism whereby the rate of combustion is increased is unknown. It may be connected with the greater energy demands of the ionic transport mechanisms during the recovery phase of the action-potentials probably mediated by reactions involving phosphate group transfers.

Related to the above observations are those of Jasper and Erickson[6] who demonstrated, after the commencement of epileptiform activity following Metrazol injection, a brief rise followed by a fall in cortical pH (see also ref. 16). The rise is presumably due to increased local blood circulation and the somewhat higher pH of the blood compared to brain tissue fluids.[14] The subsequent acid shift is likely due to the accumulation of lactic acid and other acid metabolites. The time of onset, intensity, and duration of the epileptiform activity were not affected by large variations in cortical pH induced by hyperventilation, carbon dioxide breathing, or injections of acid or alkali. No relation between pH and the EEG effects of local application of strychnine or electrical stimulation could be detected. Pope *et al.*[15] found that the pH of the surface of monkey cortex in a region rendered epileptogenic by alumina application was either the same as that of normal areas or slightly raised. Wang and Sonnenschein[16] demonstrated that convulsions induced by nitrogen mustard, DDT or agenized proteins were potentiated by carbon dioxide whereas convulsions induced by metrazol or electric shock were antagonized by carbon dioxide. The mechanism of this action of carbon dioxide is unknown.

Rapid-freezing of brain *in situ* with liquid air is the most satisfactory technique for studying the labile constituents of brain (see Thorn *et al.*[17]). Such studies have demonstrated decreased amounts of phosphocreatine, increased inorganic phosphate and lactic acid during metrazol-induced seizures in dogs.[7] Similar changes and decreases in glycogen, adenosine triphosphate and glucose were found in cats by Klein and Olsen[18] following the administration of convulsive agents and electric shock. Convulsive doses of sodium cyanide led to a fall in phosphocreatine which continued to fall with increasing duration of abnormal electrical activity of the brain. These observations indicate that during convulsive activity phosphocreatine and adenosine polyphosphates are lost with the formation of inorganic phosphate. In spite of the increased blood supply and increased oxygen consumption the oxygen tension of the brain tissue falls,[9] the anaerobic product lactic acid accumulates and cerebral glucose and glycogen content fall.

These changes are characteristic of the convulsive activity and not of the convulsive agent. The post-ictal electrical quiescence is probably due to an exhaustion of the tissue reserves of high energy phosphates.

In brain, frozen *in situ,* from dogs rendered epileptic by feeding agenized flour (see below), Gershoff, Newell and Stone[19] found no evidence of any chronic change in oxidative metabolism. No obvious differences from the expected normal have been found in respiratory rate and glycolysis, measured *in vitro,* of human epileptogenic focal tissue or of the brain of dogs suffering convulsions produced by agenized flour in the diet.[20] Most depressant drugs lower the respiration of cerebral tissue slices *in vitro* and this is accompanied by a decrease in phosphocreatine (see McIlwain[21]) but the addition of convulsant drugs such as Metrazol, picrotoxin and sodium fluoroacetate to respiring cerebral tissue slices does not alter their respiration, glycolysis or phosphate content except for some inhibition at very high concentrations.[22,23] McIlwain and his coworkers (see Chapter IX) have shown that the application of electrical pulses to cerebal cortex slices *in vitro* is capable of bringing about all the metabolic changes induced by convulsive agents *in vivo.*

Studies by Geiger and his coworkers on perfused cat brain (see Chapter VI) have shown that the increased rate of CO_2 production during convulsions is mainly due to the oxidation of non-carbohydrate materials[250] and there is increased incorporation of glucose carbon into amino acids[251] and protein.[252]

The observations so far discussed show that changes in oxidative metabolism and energy transfer occur in the brain during convulsions but appear not to be related to the initiation of the seizure but to its maintenance and to recovery from it. However, convulsions occur during hypoglycemia, hypoxia and cyanide poisoning. In these circumstances interference with the energy production in the brain could be the primary event in the initiation of seizures. In rats, following cyanide administration, the cytochrome oxidase of the brain was reduced by 50% at the end of convulsive activity.[24] Brooks, Ransmeier and Gerard[25] studied the effects on isolated frog brain of various substances known to affect nervous activity, with and without caffeine stimulation. They found that applications of methyl fluoroacetate, diisopropyl fluorophosphate, tetraethylpyrophosphate and atropine affect electrical activity in comparable rather than different ways. All except eserine inhibited oxygen consumption appreciably at concentrations which provoked functional changes. These drugs also inhibit a number of dehydrogenase systems in rat brain suspensions.[26] Further, fumarate which could diminish the action of fluoroacetate on oxygen consumption, and other dicarboxylic acids of metabolic importance, sometimes initiated large convulsive potentials. The authors concluded that function is disturbed by an interference with oxidative mechanisms.

The Acetylcholine System

There is considerable evidence that acetylcholine is a central synaptic transmitter substance and is involved in abnormal functioning of the central nervous system (see reviews by Feldberg[27] and Hebb[28]). Numerous workers (see Feldberg[29] and other articles in this volume) have found that acetylcholine (ACh) has stimulating and, in higher concentrations, depressing effects on the central nervous system or may facilitate response to other stimuli. Cholinesterase inhibitors such as eserine, prostigmine and diisopropylfluorophosphate produce similar effects or enhance the actions of ACh. Epileptiform spike discharges closely resembling those seen in epilepsy have been produced by local application of strong solutions of ACh to the cerebral cortex of cats.[30-32] Lower, but still "unphysiologically" high concentrations of ACh would produce the same effect if the cortex was pre-treated with anti-cholinesterase but it should be noted that ACh applied directly to the cortex might have limited access to the site of normal action because of the appreciable distance it must diffuse through membranes. Desynchronization and fast low amplitude activity of the EEG, as well as epileptiform discharges are observed following intraventricular or intracisternal injections of ACh and anticholinesterases[32-34] and in cats and man have produced generalized convulsions.[30,35] In earlier experiments[36,37] sleep rather than activation was produced following injections of ACh into cerebrospinal fluid and more recently Feldberg and Sherwood[38] reported "catatonia" in cats following intraventricular injections of ACh, physostigmine and diisopropyl fluorophosphate. Perhaps these findings can be interpreted as stimulation of cholinoceptive neurones in subcortical structures close to the ventricle and also the rostral extensions of the reticular formation. Unconsciousness is always associated with grand mal epilepsy. Freedman, Bales, Willis and Himwich[39,40] described in detail the epileptiform discharges observed in curarized rabbits following intracarotid injections of diisopropyl fluorophosphate. The resemblance to the discharge in grand mal epilepsy is striking. Further, Rinaldi and Himwich[41] found that the EEG alerting response to intracarotid injections of ACh was present in *cerveau isolé* preparations but absent from isolated cerebral hemispheres and suggested that the site of action is at the mesodiencephalic level. It is of some interest that the clinical studies of Penfield and Jasper[42] suggest that subcortical structures, called provisionally the centrencephalic system, are involved in some forms of petit mal and grand mal epilepsy.

Though ACh is not normally present in the cerebrospinal fluid in detectable amounts, it has been found by a number of workers (see ref. 29) in eserinized animals. Also it occurs in appreciable amounts in the cerebrospinal fluid in uneserinized cats and dogs following cerebral trauma,[35] in patients following cerebral trauma and electro-shock therapy, and in the majority of epileptic patients.[43] Intense hyperactivity of the brain appears to be associated with the release of ACh in sufficient amounts for some of it to escape destruction by cholinesterase and diffuse into the subarachnoid space or into fluids outside the pia-arachnoid surface of the cortex.[45]

The early studies of acetylcholine metabolism in relation to convulsant and narcotic agents were confusing. The ACh content of brains of anesthetized animals (pentobarbital, ether or chloralose) was found to be considerably increased and after administering Metrazol or picrotoxin the ACh fell towards normal values. If the convulsants were given to unanesthetized, curarized animals the ACh content was appreciably above normal.[44,45] In these experiments the tissue was immobilized in acid three minutes after excision. However, in experiments attempting to correlate *in vivo* brain activity with content of labile constituents it is essential to use rapid freezing techniques. Richter and Crossland[46] found that the ACh content in the brain of young rats dropped into liquid air varied with the state of activity of the nervous system. Increases in the ACh content were found during sleep and anesthesia. With convulsions induced by electric shock a rapid fall in ACh content occurred followed in 15 seconds by a return to the normal level and then a fall again as convulsions recommenced. Thus, during convulsions there is considerable depletion of ACh. It is important to realize that the ACh content of brain tissue depends on a balance between synthesis, storage in an inactive form, liberation and destruction. Convulsive activity appears associated with accelerated liberation of free ACh and consequent destruction so that the ACh content momentarily falls. This fall stimulates rapid resynthesis. On the other hand anesthesia and sleep decrease the rate of liberation and the ACh content rises. Unless the tissue is rapidly immobilized following treatment with convulsive agents the rapid fluctuations in ACh levels are not revealed. In insulin hypoglycemia the fall in ACh levels[47] is probably associated with a deficient synthesis.

In vitro studies by McLennan and Elliott[48] showed that the synthesis of free, soluble ACh by brain slices in the presence of a high potassium concentration was markedly stimulated by low concentrations of Metrazol and picrotoxin (2.5 mM and 0.02 mM respectively) corresponding to the estimated *in vivo* concentrations when convulsions are produced. Pentobarbital and Amytal (0.4 mM) caused a 50% inhibition of ACh synthesis. These concentrations of drugs had little effect on oxygen consumption.

Acetylcholine is present in the brain *in vivo* almost entirely in a bound, pharmacologically inactive, insoluble form associated with a granular, subcellular component of the tissue.[28,29,49] An equilibrium between free and bound forms has been suggested.[49] The release of bound ACh could be affected by various means. Thus, 50% of the bound ACh could be released by freezing and thawing, dialysis, osmotic dilution, treatment with lecithinases and shaking with glass Ballotini beads.[50,51] The entire amount of bound ACh is liberated by acidification or treatment with ether. When slices of normal cerebral cortex are incubated aerobically in a glucose-eserine-saline medium, free ACh accumulates and the bound ACh content also increases.[53,52] Tower and Elliott[53] reported that focal epileptogenic tissue produced free ACh at about the same rate as normal human tissue but its content of bound ACh failed to increase during incubation. A similar change from normal could be obtained with cat cortex when it was incubated under reduced oxygen tension or with cortex from cats to which methionine sulfoximine had been administered. The abnormality could be reversed by the addition of glutamine or asparagine. Tower[54] regarded the failure to produce bound acetylcholine together with a tendency, not statistically significant, to increased cholinesterase activity as among the few inter-ictal changes demonstrable in human epileptogenic tissue. However, recent attempts by Pappius and Elliott[55] to repeat these studies have failed. The production of bound ACh in human epileptogenic cerebral cortex was little different from normal tissue but the production of free ACh was appreciably lower and the presence of glutamine did not affect the bound or free ACh. Similar results were found for methionine-sulfoximine treated cats. The production of both bound and free ACh was decreased by lowering the oxygen tension. There is also no evidence to indicate that narcotics or convulsants affect the liberation of free ACh. Brodkin and Elliott[50] failed to find any effects of these agents on liberation or binding in brain suspensions. Thus, attempts to demonstrate abnormalities in ACh metabolism in epileptogenic tissues have been disappointing. Also it cannot be stated whether the rate of liberation of free ACh determines the level of nervous activity or is determined by it. Pharmacological actions of ACh and the anticholinesterases suggest the former possibility.

Recent physiological and biochemical studies are clarifying the nature of acetylcholine binding, and its relation to the "synaptic vesicle" theory of localisation of humoral transmitter substances (see reviews of Hebb[56] and Eccles[57]). Whittaker[58] has demonstrated, by gradient differential centrifugation, that most of the particle-bound ACh and

5-hydroxytryptamine from guinea pig and rat cerebral cortex is localized in a fraction appearing as simple vesicles (0.02 to 0.08 μ in size) in electron micrographs. It is possible that a re-investigation of the properties of the particles that contain ACh or other humoral agents in the central nervous system of normal and epileptogenic tissues may reveal a fundamental difference in the dynamics of acetylcholine release.

Recent studies by Hosein and his collaborators indicate that much of the active substance that has been considered to be ACh may be a mixture of coenzyme A derivatives of γ-butyrobetaine and related substances.[253,254] This finding will necessitate re-examination of the relation of ACh-like substances to convulsions.

Ammonia

It has been known for some time that functional activity of the nervous system is associated with ammonia formation.[59-61] Administration of ammonium salts to experimental animals produces convulsions.[62,63] Hepatocerebral intoxication in humans, when the liver is seriously damaged by acute or chronic disease, produces characteristic neurological effects of which the most frequent are coma and convulsions.[64] Ammonia is thought to be the principal toxic agent in this condition (see review by Sherlock[65]). Hepatectomized animals similarly become lethargic, comatose and die in convulsions.[66] Various authors have reported the presence of ammonia in the cerebrospinal fluid and its increase in epilepsy. But Richter, Dawson and Lees,[67] observing certain precautions in the determination, were unable to detect significant amounts of ammonia in the cerebrospinal fluid in normal subjects or in patients after electronarcosis, electroshock or grand mal epileptic seizures. Richter and Dawson[68] found that the ammonia content of rat brain (normally 0.28 to 0.47 mg./100 gm., depending on the method of killing) was lower than normal in tissue from animals under nembutal narcosis (0.06 to 0.19 mg.%) and higher in tissue from animals in metrazol or electroshock convulsions (0.45 to 0.94 mg.%.) By dropping the animals into liquid air after electroshock and before the onset of convulsions it was shown that the increase in ammonia levels preceded the convulsions. The authors suggest that ammonia increases brain irritability and may play a significant part in epilepsy. Brain ammonia also increased during short periods of anoxia and this may contribute to the convulsions often occurring under such conditions. Increases of ammonia levels in brain have also been reported following fluoroacetate administration.[69] Recently Tsukada et al.[70] reported increased ammonia levels in rat brain following brief electrical stimulation and following a conditioned stimulus. Within 120 minutes after the first stimulation a second stimulation caused no increase in ammonia. This finding is interpreted as an activation of the ammonia-binding system probably as glutamine. Hosein[71] has isolated γ-butyrobetaine from brains of convulsing animals and Hosein and Boisvert[72] found that the ethyl ester of this compound inhibits glutamic acid synthesis and ammonia utilization in rat brain cortex slices and in addition is a potent convulsant.

Takahashi, Nasu, Tamura and Kariya[255] find no correlation between ammonia levels and brain excitability, measured by electroshock seizure threshold and maximal seizure duration techniques. In fact chronic administration of ammonium salts decreased brain excitability. The conclusion reached was that the increase of ammonia content in the brain did not indicate convulsive activity as suggested by Richter and Dawson[68] but was a metabolic consequence of neuronal excitation. These findings are supported by those of Berl, Takagaki and Purpura[256] who failed to show alteration in the excitability of focal epileptogenic and non-epileptogenic lesions following intravenous ammonium acetate infusions. The development of paroxysmal discharges in traumatic cortical lesions did not appear to be causally related to increases in tissue ammonia concentration. Rapid intravenous infusions of ammonium salts induced generalized depression of electrocortical activity, whereas slow infusions over long periods induced a transient generalized hypersynchonous activity.

The metabolism of ammonia in brain and the metabolic changes occurring in ammonia intoxication are discussed elsewhere in this volume (see Chapter XV).

Glutamic Acid and Glutamine

Brain contains large amounts of glutamic acid[73] and glutamine.[68,73] The special role of the glutamate-glutamine system in cerebral metabolism and more particularly its relation to the operation of the Krebs cycle has been reviewed by several authors[74-76] and details will not be presented here. Glutamic acid is capable of maintaining the respiration of brain slices.[77] McIlwain[78] reported that human cerebral tissues differed from those of experimental animals in that glutamate not only maintained the respiratory rate of slices but also supported the respiratory response to applied pulses. Glutamic acid can combine with ammonia in brain slices with the production of glutamine.[79] Injections of glutamic acid have been reported to inhibit ammonium chloride convulsions.[62] Early reports that oral glutamic acid decreased "petit mal" seizures, increased mental alertness and aroused patients from insulin coma have had little clinical substantiation.[76,80] Tower[54,81-83] has studied the metabolism of glutamate in cerebral cortex slices from cats suffering seizures induced by methionine sulfoximine and 3-methyl-3-ethylglutarimide (Megimide). In contrast to the rise in glutamic acid levels seen in normal control slices, glutamic acid levels, after incubation, in slices from methionine sulfoximine-treated cats were significantly decreased and in addition glutamine synthesis was almost completely inhibited. With Megimide as the convulsant agent a marked decrease in glutamic acid was found during incubation as well as a fall in the γ-aminobutyric acid (GABA) level. Similarly, Tower[54] found that slices of human cortical epileptogenic foci showed a significant decrease in glutamic acid during incubation in contrast to a rise in normal slices. No significant decreases in GABA levels have as yet been found in human epileptogenic tissues. L-asparagine and GABA not only increased the glutamic acid production *in vitro* but appeared to have some effectiveness in controlling seizures and correcting the EEG abnormalities when administered orally to certain patients. Decreases in glutamic acid, glutamine and glutathione have been found in epileptogenic lesions produced by freezing[234] (see below).

γ-*Aminobutyric Acid*

Since the discoveries of the presence in brain of large amounts of GABA and of its neuro-inhibitory actions, neurochemical and neurophysiological interest in its metabolism and possible function as an inhibitor of neuronal excitation have been intense (see reviews[84-87] and Chapter XXVI in this volume). Brain contains the complete system for the metabolism of GABA. The formation of GABA by decarboxylation of glutamic acid and its removal by transamination with α-ketoglutarate to succinic semialdehyde have been clearly demonstrated in brain by Roberts and co-workers (see refs. 86, 88-90). This pathway, which is of unique occurrence in the nervous system, provides an alternative route around the α-ketoglutarate-succinate steps of the tricarboxylic acid cycle. Consequently alterations in carbohydrate metabolism, glutamic acid and glutamine metabolism, and the action of inhibitors of the vitamin B_6-dependent transamination and decarboxylation reactions might be expected to alter the levels of GABA (see also ref. 249). The concentration of GABA in the brain is the result of a steady state governed by transamination and decarboxylation. The neurophysiological studies of Purpura, Girado and Grundfest,[91] Iwama and Jasper[92] and others (see ref. 85) indicate that GABA acts as a modifier of neuronal activity. Convulsions occurring during vitamin B_6 deficiency caused by nutrition, antimetabolites or hydrazides are associated with a decreased activity of glutamic decarboxylase and decreased amounts of GABA extractable from the brain (see under

Vitamins below). Insulin hypoglycemia also causes a decrease in cerebral glutamic acid and GABA.[93,94] Similar reductions in GABA levels in brain have been reported in experimental animals suffering seizures induced by methionine sulfoximine and Megimide.[81] The pH optima of the decarboxylase and the transaminase are such that metabolic acidosis might be expected to increase and alkalosis to decrease the amount of GABA.[88] It is well known that acidosis decreases and alkalosis increases the incidence of epileptic seizures in man and animals. Hydroxylamine inhibits the GABA-α-ketoglutarate transaminase reaction more than glutamic acid decarboxylase. Studies of the anticonvulsant action of hydroxylamine[95,96] showed an elevated GABA level in rat brain after intraperitoneal injection.

Topical application of GABA has a powerful[97,92] blocking or depressing action on responses of the superficial layers of the cerebral cortex. This has been interpreted as a selective blockade of excitatory synapses ending on apical dendrites[97] (but see ref. 98). However, no appreciable amount of GABA enters the brain unless the blood brain barrier is broken. If this barrier is destroyed locally (by ethyl chloride spray or chloroform-methanol application) intravenous administration of GABA does block excitatory synapses and, further, paroxysmal activity is markedly reduced. The value of GABA as an anticonvulsant clinically is dubious not only because it fails to enter the brain but also because of its disturbing side effects when administered intravenously.

Although there is much evidence to suggest that certain seizure states are associated with alterations in GABA metabolism it is not possible at present to implicate it in all seizure mechanisms and particularly human epilepsy. Elliott and van Gelder[99] have suggested that the neurochemical importance of glutamate and GABA may reside in the balance in the brain of these substances in the free or occluded form and this might partly determine neuronal activity.

Carbonic Anhydrase System

Carbonic anhydrase is important in carbon dioxide transport across cell membranes. Inhibition of this enzyme by acetazolamide leads to carbon dioxide retention intracellularly. The studies of Millichap[100] have shown a direct relation between the activity of brain carbonic anhydrase and the susceptibility of animals to experimental seizures. Acetazolamide has been used successfully as an anticonvulsant in experimental animals and humans.[101,102] In the cat brain the hippocampus shows high acetazolamide uptake.[103] The threshold of seizure activity in the rhinencephalic system is known to be low and both the spontaneous and evoked activity in the ventral hippocampus is depressed by carbon dioxide.[104] Although the part played by the carbonic anhydrase system in the seizure process is unknown it has been suggested[85] that the decrease in intracellular pH following carbonic anhydrase inhibition might alter the rates of GABA formation and removal.

Vitamins
Thiamine

Thiamine deficiency in man affects principally the nervous and cardiovascular systems. The variability of its manifestations is related to the acuteness of the deficiency and the diet. Thus, in acute deficiency, confusion, convulsions, coma and an ophthalmoplegia (i.e., acute Wernicke's syndrome) predominate with little demonstrable pathology in the central nervous system. Only after repeated episodes does an encephalopathy appear. The more chronic effects of prolonged relative deficiency are manifest as a peripheral neuropathy and beriberi with minimal biochemical changes but well defined lesions in the nervous system.[105] The earliest signs of acute deficiency are the biochemical findings of hyperpyruvemia and decreased brain co-carboxylase levels.[106] Opisthotonus, neck retraction and convulsions are an important feature of the clinical picture of infantile beriberi.[107] Experimental animals sensitive to a dietary deficiency of the vitamin (e.g., cats[108]) die in convulsions. Halver[109] has reported the regular occurrence of convulsions in chinook salmon fry on a thiamine deficient diet.

Biochemical interest in thiamine deficiency started when Gavrilescu and Peters[110] described the convulsions, extreme opisthotonus, ataxia and peculiar rotation of the head occurring in pigeons fed a deficient diet. Incubation of minced brain from such pigeons in a glucose medium showed lowered oxygen uptake and the accumulation of pyruvate and lactate which could be returned to normal values by the addition of thiamine.[110-112] In 1936 Peters[113] introduced the term "biochemical lesion" to describe the pathological disturbances in tissue, illustrated by thiamine deficiency, initiated by a change in intracellular biochemistry. Subsequent studies by Peters and co-workers (see review by Peters[114]) showed that the decreased ability to oxidize pyruvate was due to a lack of the coenzyme thiamine pyrophosphate (co-carboxylase) necessary for the oxidative decarboxylation of pyruvate and other α-keto acids and the liberation of energy required for tissue metabolism. A lowered amount of thiamine pyrophosphate has been demonstrated in pigeons dying in convulsions due to thiamine deficiency.[115] Woolley and Merrifield[119] have made the important observation that convulsions occurred more frequently in animals that were forced to feed on a thiamine deficient diet that was rich in carbohydrate. In alcoholics, convulsions most frequently occur during the withdrawal phase when the dietary intake particularly of carbohydrate increases. There is little doubt that a defect in energy metabolism is the initial event leading to the acute neurological disturbances. It is the definition of the biochemical step which triggers the convulsive state in the presence of deficient energy supplies which is elusive. Recently Salem[116] has shown that not only pyruvate but also the more toxic methyl glyoxal accumulates in thiamine deficient tissues. Significant decreases in glutamic acid have been reported in the brains of thiamine-deficient animals with no changes in the glutamine or aspartic acid levels.[117] Thiamine pyrophosphate is also the coenzyme for transketolase[118] and the accumulation of pentose has been demonstrated in erythrocytes in thiamine deficiency. It is unlikely that this defect would affect the nervous system as glucose is primarily metabolized in brain by the glycolytic pathway and the pentose shunt is of little importance.

Thiamine deficiency can also be produced by administering the antivitamin pyrithiamine which acts by inhibiting the phosphorylation of thiamine.[120] The syndrome of weakness, ataxia, spastic paralysis and convulsions shown in silver foxes fed raw carp flesh (Chastek paralysis) is due to a thiaminase in the fish which splits thiamine at the methylene bridge into its pyrimidine and thiazole moeities.[121,122] One of these moeities, toxopyrimidine (2-methyl-4-amino-5-hydroxymethyl pyrimidine), is known to be a competitive inhibitor of pyridoxine. Consequently not only is thiamine destroyed but an antivitamin is produced in the process. The ataxia and generalized convulsions occurring in horses with bracken poisoning is due to thiaminases in the leaves of the plant.[123] In Japan "thiaminase disease" in humans showing beriberi-like symptoms is due to the presence of thiaminolytic bacilli in the gastrointestinal tract.[124] In all these conditions administration of thiamine corrects the neurological abnormalities.

Thiamine itself can be a convulsant agent. Vianna Diaz[125] produced generalized convulsions in dogs by topical application of thiamine or thiamine pyrophosphate onto the cerebral cortex. Hayashi[126] induced clonic convulsions in dogs after a latent period of 18 minutes by injecting 1.5 ml. of 0.2M thiamine hydrochloride into the cerebrospinal fluid. Thiamine pyrophosphate was a stronger convulsant than thiamine with a shorter latent period. These findings are peculiar since the pyrophosphate is believed to be less diffusible into nerve cells. Little is known of the breakdown of thiamine in mammals. Some apparently is split in a similar fashion to the action of thiaminase.[127] Perhaps toxopyrimidine residues liberated from the high local concentration of thiamine on the cerebral cortex penetrates into the neurons and produces the convulsive activity by its antivitamin action.

Pyridoxine

Epileptiform fits in rats fed a pyridoxine-deficient diet were first described by Chick, El Sadr and Worden.[128] Subsequently convulsions, ataxia and neuropathy have been reported following pyridoxine deficiency in a variety of animals (see reviews by Sherman[129] and Tower[130]). Rats suckled on pyridoxine-deficient mothers lose weight, convulse and die within three weeks. Convulsions resembling "grand mal" in human epilepsy are the most common feature of pyridoxine deficiency in mammals. Recently convulsions due to pyridoxine deficiency have been recognized in infants.[131-134] Two distinct types of deficiency have been found. One type is a pyridoxine dependency which occurs despite an adequate intake; in some cases this appears to be associated with the development of an abnormal need for the vitamin induced when the mother received excessive pyridoxine therapy for nausea and vomiting of pregnancy. The other type is related to variations in the pyridoxine requirements of infants and only appears when the intake for some reason (e.g., autoclaved proprietary formula) is lowered. Pyridoxine deficiency of the mother during pregnancy can also result in ataxia, spasticity and convulsions in the infant.[135] Convulsions ("rum fits") are part of the alcoholic withdrawal syndrome occurring 36 to 72 hours after cessation of an alcoholic spree. A pyridoxine deficiency has been demonstrated in these alcoholics and it has been possible to separate this group from those having an underlying tendency to epilepsy.[136] Some biochemical studies have been made of brain tissue of pyridoxine-deficient experimental animals. The activity of glutamic decarboxylase[137] and cysteine sulphinic acid decarboxylase[138] are markedly reduced and this leads to a decrease in the brain of GABA and taurine levels. Reduced glutathione levels in cortex, cerebellum and medulla have been reported.[139] Cystathionine, an intermediate in the transsulfuration of methionine, which occurs rapidly in brain, appears in the urine and accumulates in the brain in pyridoxine deficiency.[140,141] Cystathionase is a pyridoxine-dependent enzyme.

Acute pyridoxine deficiency can be induced by the antimetabolites 3- and 5-deoxypyridoxine and ω-methoxypyridoxine. Seizures develop 15 to 45 minutes after injection of these substances into mice, rats, rabbits, dogs and monkeys and can be stopped by injecting pyridoxine. The EEG shows generalized 14-18/sec. spike discharges.[142] Deoxypyridoxine, converted *in vivo* to the phosphate, can compete with pyridoxal phosphate for the apoenzyme and is most effective when pyridoxine intake is lowered.[143] In studies with the cat Purpura *et al.*[144] found that generalized seizures induced by the antivitamins were associated with decreases in glutamic acid and GABA and increases in glutamine in the brain. Injection of GABA after 3 hours of seizures reversed all these biochemical abnormalities but had no effect on the seizure pattern. They suggest, therefore, that these antimetabolites do not act by simple competitive antagonism but cause a constellation of metabolic abnormalities of which changes in GABA levels are one expression. Deoxypyridoxine also inhibits glutamic-aspartic transminase.[145] Thus, from these studies it is not possible to show a causal relationship between decreases in GABA levels and seizure activity (see ref. 95 and 257). Toxopyrimidine, the pyrimidine fragment of thiamine, will also produce convulsions and death within 3 hours in mice at doses of 7 to 15 mg./kg. and these convulsions are also blocked by pyridoxine.[146,147] The effect of toxopyrimidine on glutamic acid metabolism is still uncertain.

More convincing evidence for a causal relationship between glutamic acid metabolism and seizure activity is provided by recent studies of the convulsant hydrazides. Isonicotinic acid hydrazide (INH) is known to increase the excretion of pyridoxine and to cause a sensory neuritis and convulsive tendency in tuberculous patients receiving the drug for long periods.[148-150] Thiosemicarbazide is a convulsant for rats and mice after a certain latent period.[151,152] The most potent convulsant is thiocarbohydrazide.[153] Pyridoxine is antidotal[154] and Williams and Abdulian[155] suggested that the action of these convulsants is linked to the metabolic reactions of pyridoxine. Hydrazides are carbonyl trapping agents and combine with pyridoxal-5-phosphate to form hydrazones[156] and inhibit a number of enzymes in which it is the active coenzyme.[157] Hydrazine is also a convulsant to experimental animals.[158] Killam and Bain[159] showed that in vivo and in vitro hydrazides inhibit L-glutamic acid decarboxylase and cause a striking reduction in the levels of brain GABA. The seizures could be controlled by administration of pyridoxine. Pyridoxine also restored the activity of the decarboxylase. Strychnine, pentylenetetrazole or a convulsant barbiturate (sodium 5-ethyl-5 (1,3-dimethyl butyl) barbiturate) did not inhibit the decarboxylase.

Another interesting observation was made by Du Vigneaud, Kuchinskas and Horvath[160] who found that the inclusion of the sulfhydryl amino acid penicillamine (β-mercaptovaline) in the diet of rats led to pyridoxine deficiency symptoms. This substance also inhibited transaminase systems in vitro in liver and brain and this could be overcome by the addition of pyridoxal-5-phosphate. Recently Matsuda and Makino[258] have shown that DL-penicillamine, 0.3 mg per g. body weight, injected intravenously into mice caused symptoms of "running fits" followed by convulsions and death. These convulsions could be prevented by injection of pyridoxine. Further the brain glutamic decarboxylase isolated from penicillamine-treated animals was markedly inhibited and the activity of the inhibited enzyme could be completely restored by the addition of pyridoxal 5-phosphate. Similar results were obtained when glutamic decarboxylase was treated with penicillamine *in vitro*. Penicillamine reacts with the carbonyl group of pyridoxal to form thiazolidine structures. It also greatly increases the urinary excretion of pyridoxine as well as copper and has recently been used in the treatment of hepatolenticular degeneration. Penicillamine is a breakdown product of penicillin.[161] Penicillin is known to produce epileptiform discharges on topical application or injection into the cerebral cortex. Perhaps the convulsant effects of penicillin are due to the release of penicillimine during its breakdown in the brain and subsequent reaction with pyridoxine.

The evidence for a defect in glutamic acid metabolism in pyridoxine deficiency, whether nutritional or antimetabolic, is convincing. However, the connection of this kind of defect and decreased GABA levels with neuronal excitability is not clear cut. Pyridoxal and its derivatives have been shown to participate in amino acid and alkali metal ion transport in ascitic cells.[162] They may function similarly in the central nervous system. The importance of the vitamin in several other enzyme systems (histaminase, kynureninase, 5-hydroxytryptophan decarboxylase, etc.) must not be ignored. Balzer, Holtz and Palm[260] have shown that the relationship between hydrazides and pyridoxine, and convulsions and brain GABA in mice are complex.

Hormones

The part played by hormones in cerebral excitability is now becoming appreciated (see review, ref. 245 and Chapter 39). Of particular interest is the finding that adrenalectomy and the acute administration of ACTH and cortisol increase the susceptibility to seizures and decrease the GABA, glutamic acid and glutamine levels in the brains of dogs. On the other hand, desoxycorticosterone acetate and progesterone increase the electroshock threshold and the brain GABA levels. Woodbury[245] suggests that the effect of Dilantin is to increase the conversion of brain glutamic acid to glutamine and GABA whereas cortisol shunts glutamic acid away from GABA and glutamine synthesis into the Krebs cycle. These hormones may also regulate the electrolyte concentration in brain neurones.

Inorganic Ions

Potassium and calcium ions are closely concerned in all nervous activity. Bonnet and Bremer[163] observed stimulation of the electrical activity of the cortex, in cat "encéphale isolé" preparations, following very small intracarotid injections of potassium chloride. Calcium chloride or larger injections of the potassium salt depressed activity. Colfer and Essex[164] using micro-incineration techniques, demonstrated changes of total electrolyte, sodium and potassium in cortical neurones during metrazol, electric shock and audiogenic convulsions. These changes involved typically a diffuse increase of total electrolyte, a loss of potassium and a gain of sodium. Nerves and ganglia show hyperirritability or spontaneous activity when deprived of calcium.[165] (Complete lack of Ca blocks transmission through ganglia[261].) Convulsions occur immediately if citrate is injected intracisternally presumably because citrate immobilizes calcium ions. It is well known that in chronic hypocalcemia seizures are frequent. Hyperventilation alkalosis activates the EEG of epileptics probably partly by decreasing the level of ionized calcium.

Tower[166] has reported experiments with slices of cerebral cortex which demonstrate an impairment of the ability of epileptogenic tissue to maintain or build up intracellular levels of potassium. Normal slices of cerebral cortex in appropriate incubation media first lose 40% of their potassium to the medium but on incubation take back this potassium and expel sodium.[167,168] This re-concentration did not occur in epileptogenic tissue under the conditions studied. The failure to maintain intracellular potassium was interpreted as causing a greater tendency to depolarization and firing of the neurones. The addition of asparagine or glutamine to the medium appeared to reverse this defect.

Magnesium is also an important intracellular cation. An excess of it produces narcosis and decreased irritability of muscle and nerve. Exceedingly high values of blood magnesium occur in uraemia with central nervous system depression. Magnesium deficiency in man is associated with muscular weakness and hyperirritability.[169,170] Almost 30 years ago McCollum and co-workers[171] reported a spectacular syndrome in rats, rabbits, dogs and calves fed a magnesium deficient diet. The major features were dilatation of the cutaneous blood vessels, hyperirritability and convulsions. The role of magnesium in the physiology of the nervous system is still obscure. It is necessary for the activation or as a component of a number of enzymes and coenzymes[172] such as choline acetylase, glutamotransferase, and phosphorylative and pyruvate oxidative enzymes.

Fluoroacetate

Sodium fluoroacetate is a rodenticide known as compound 1080. Poisoning by it affects either the central nervous system producing convulsions or the heart leading to cardiac failure or both. An oral dose of 5 mg./kg. produces violent tonic convulsions in rats in 20 minutes. Dogs are particularly sensitive (0.01 mg./kg.), monkeys and man are relatively insensitive (20 to 60 mg./kg.) whereas frogs and toads are very resistant.[173] A cattle disease in the Transvaal is associated with eating Gifblaar ("poison leaf") shoots which contain fluoroacetic acid. Similarly the disease "broke-back" in Sierra Leone is caused by eating ratsbane, a plant containing another fluoro-fatty acid (see ref. 259). Only certain aspects of the work of Peters and his school on fluoro-acetate poisoning can be considered here (see ref. 174 and excellent review of Peters[175]). Fluoroacetate *in vivo,* and *in vitro* with kidney and liver, causes the accumulation of citrate. Fluoroacetate enters reactions in the tricarboxylic acid cycle as fluoroacetyl coenzyme A and fluoro-citrate is formed. Fluorocitrate competitively inhibits aconitase thus blocking the cycle at this stage and leading to the accumulation of citrate and interference with the energy supply. The term "lethal synthesis" was introduced by Peters to describe this enzymic synthesis of a toxic from a non-toxic substance.

It was originally thought that the accumulated citrate immobilized calcium ions with resultant effects on the brain and heart.[176] However, Chenoweth and co-workers[177,178] have produced evidence that the toxic effects of fluoroacetate cannot be correlated with the accumulation of citrate. Convulsions occurred when there was little increase in brain citrate. In isolated cerebral cortex preparations of the dog introduction of fluoroacetate or fluorobutyrate directly into the cortex caused convulsive EEG patterns spreading to adjacent areas unaccompanied by increase in citrate levels in such areas. Glycerol monoacetate and butyrate prevented the development of the seizures, but did not stop the citrate accumulation. Fluorocitrate but not fluoroacetate introduced into the subarachnoid space of pigeons, rabbits and rats induced violent convulsions after a variable latent period and injections of divalent ions had no effect (see ref. 175). Similarly fluorocitrate convulsions in mice could not be stopped by intravenus calcium gluconate.[179] Synthesis of acetylcholine is accelerated by citrate in cell-free brain preparations[181,182] and inhibited with brain slices.[183] Bovine brain tissue is capable of forming fluoroacetylcholine from fluoroacetic acid[180] and it might be argued that the convulsive action is exerted through a defective acetylcholine synthesis. However, all attempts to demonstrate this have failed. Fluoroacetate has been found to inhibit the respiration of mammalian brain tissue only slightly or not at all[23] but the methyl ester apparently inhibits some rat brain dehydrogenases[26] and the respiration of frog brain,[25] a species resistant to fluoroacetate. Bartlett and Baron[184] have reported an interference with the oxidation of acetate by fluoroacetate but brain tissue apparently does not activate acetate *in vitro*. Acetate, acetamide and monoacetin will protect animals (guinea-pig) from fluoroacetate convulsions and *in vitro* inhibit the formation of fluorocitrate by kidney particles.[185] A further curious finding is that intracisternal injections of sodium fluoroacetate into cats leads to long lasting seizures.[186] Brain does not convert fluoroacetate to fluorocitrate. It is likely that intracisternal fluoroacetate gets into the systemic circulation quickly and is converted extracerebrally to fluorocitrate. Apart from finding that glutamic acid and aspartic acid levels in rat brain are decreased in fluoroacetate convulsions[94] no studies have been made on amino acid metabolism.

At present all that can be said about the initiation of fluoroacetate convulsions is that a block in the metabolism of pyruvate by the citric acid cycle in brain tissue is produced by fluorocitrate and that this interference with energy supply might produce convulsive activity in a similar manner to that of hypoxia, hypoglycemia or acute thiamine deficiency.

Methionine Sulfoximine

A toxic material of great interest to the problem of convulsive activity is that produced by the action of nitrogen trichloride on certain proteins (e.g., gluten, zein, gliadin, casein, lactalbumin).[187] A disease in dogs called "canine hysteria" which is characterized by "running fits" has been known for many years and Wagner and Elvehjem[188] showed that this condition was associated with the presence of wheat gluten in the diet. In 1946 Mellanby[189] reported that this particular form of canine epilepsy was caused by a toxic material produced in wheat flour during the common process of bleaching and softening flour by treatment with nitrogen chloride which is known to the trade as "agene". The toxic material in agenized proteins has been isolated and identified as methionine sulfoximine.[190-192] It has now been synthesized (see refs. 193, 194 and review of early literature by Lewey[195]).

In dogs fed methionine sulfoximine or agenized proteins there is an initial phase of alimentary disturbances, ataxia and paresis particularly of hind limbs followed by seizures of intense fright, fits of running around in circles, episodes of salivation, mastication, barking, whining, fixed staring, diverse hallucinatory phenomena and, if the intoxication is high, the development of generalized tonic-clonic grand mal type seizures. Following the seizures, if death has not intervened, the dogs are confused and withdraw to a corner.[189,196,197] Similar effects occur in ferrets, cats, rabbits and mice on oral or parenteral administration.[189,191,198-201] Guinea pigs, monkeys and apparently man do not show toxic symptoms when fed agenized proteins although electroencephalographic changes have been seen in monkeys.[196,202] The dose of agenized flour used in the early studies was 30 to 40 gm./kg. providing approximately 60 to 90 mg./kg. of methionine sulfoximine. All symptoms are produced in dogs within 18 hours by 2 mg./kg. of methionine sulfoximine. In the rabbit or ferret 2 mg. produced convulsions in 48 hours although smaller doses spread over several days were also effective.[190,192] If the poisoned animals survive, the symptoms disappear with time only if the toxic material is removed from the diet. A parenteral dose of 10 to 15 mg./kg. produces generalized seizures in cats within 18 to 24 hours which persist for 24 hours.[201]

EEG studies by Newell and co-workers[198,203] and Silver and co-workers[196,204] showed that the seizures were generalized neuronal discharges comparable to those found in idiopathic epilepsy in man. However, no evidence has been obtained that highly agenized proteins in the diet of humans produces EEG changes. Gastaut, Toga and Naguet[197] re-examined the toxic syndrome in dogs and recorded epileptiform discharges in both the inter-ictal and ictal periods with predominance over the temporal lobe and demonstrated pathological changes maximal in the piriform lobe and cerebellum. The seizure patterns were analogous to human temporal lobe epilepsy on clinical, electrographic and pathological grounds. Pathological changes caused by methionine sulfoximine are similar to those produced by anoxia, insulin hypoglycemia or cytochrome oxidase inhibitors.[195,205,206] Recently Olszewski and Tower[207] found no pathological changes in cats examined 8 hours after the onset of methionine sulfoximine-induced seizures; this suggests that the seizure activity might have a biochemical origin.

The seizures induced by methionine sulfoximine are of particular interest to the neurochemist and neurophysiologist because of their resemblance to human epilepsy and their ready reproducibility in a variety of experimental animals. Newell and co-workers[202] found increases in blood magnesium and potassium but no other changes in dogs fed agenized gluten. No disturbances in cerebral respiration, oxidative metabolism, glycolysis or electrolyte metabolism have been found.[19,54,208] The impaired ability to produce bound acetylcholine by cerebral cortex slices from methionine sulfoximine treated animals reported earlier by Tower and Elliott could not be confirmed.[53,55,209] Reiner and Weiss[200] found that large doses of methionine would overcome the toxic effects. Methionine, glutamine or asparagine will control the seizures in mice and cats.[210]

Methionine sulfoximine inhibits the growth of microorganisms and this can be reversed by methionine or glutamine.[211,212] A closely related compound, methionine sulfoxide, similarly inhibits growth of various bacteria by preventing the amidation of glutamic acid to gluta-mine.[213-216] The formation of glutamine by purified preparations from pigeon liver is depressed by the sulfoxide.[217] Glutamine synthesis in brain requires the presence of glutamate, ammonia, adenosine triphos-phate, magnesium ions and glutamotransferase.[218,219] Methionine sul-foximine is an inhibitor of cerebral glutamine synthesis.[201,220] Peters and Tower[201] find that cerebral cortex slices from cats suffering methi-onine sulfoximine-induced seizures show greatly reduced levels of glu-tamic acid and glutamine and the glutamic acid levels continued to decrease during slice incubation. Additions of L-methionine, L-aspara-gine, adenosine triphosphate, GABA and its lactam, 2-pyrrolidinone, to the incubation media increased the glutamic acid levels but were ineffective in reversing the inhibition of glutamine synthesis. The addition of 10mM ammonium chloride resulted in an increase in slice glutamine content, which was further increased by L-methio-nine. These findings suggest an interference with the normal me-tabolism of ammonia. Further evidence for an inhibition of gluta-mine formation was obtained by Kolouskek and Jiracek[221] who found a decrease in protein, ammonia and amide nitrogen and an increase in non-protein nitrogen in the brains of rats six hours after methionine sulfoximine administration. It is of interest also to note that methi-onine sulfoximine brings about reversal of the inhibition by ammo-nium ions of the rate of formation of bound acetylcholine, methionine and glutamate having no such effect.[248]

In summary, the nature of the biochemical lesion in brain which leads to the induction of seizures caused by methionine sulfoximine is not clear. The poison acts both as a methionine antagonist and as an inhibitor of glutamic acid and glutamine synthesis. It is worth noting that methionine is an important methyl donor through which choline and creatine (methylated guanidinoacetate) are formed and is involved in the active transsulfuration reactions occurring in brain. However, the inhibition of glutamic acid production and the probable conse-quent reduction in GABA levels in brain appears at the present time more important to the initiation of seizure activity than the inhibition of glutamine formation.

Audiogenic Seizures

The susceptibility during certain periods of life of some strains of rats to seizures of the clonic-tonic type induced by sound stress has been known for a considerable time.[222,223] These audiogenic seizures have been compared to human epilepsy[224] and to Metrazol convul-sions.[225] Ginsburg and his group have identified some of the neuro-chemical mechanisms, possibly genetically controlled, associated with these seizures (see review, ref. 226). The seizures are exacerbated or alleviated by administering enzyme antagonists and substrates related to energy transfer mechanisms. A correlation was found between the susceptibility to convulsions and the acetylcholine level in the brain and the capacity to bind acetylcholine. Adenosine triphosphatase activity and P/O ratios were lowered. Sodium glutamate, succinate, lactate and α-ketoglutarate had a palliative effect on certain rat genotypes. Parenteral GABA had no effect. Ginsburg regards the most clearly defined metabolic lesion as a phosphorylative defect in which the synthesis of high energy phosphates is depressed in the animals during a susceptible period irrespective of whether or not convulsions have occurred. Koulousek et al.[227] found, in the brains of 16-week old rats susceptible to seizures, significantly larger amounts of amide nitrogen and smaller amounts of free ammonia nitrogen than in normals suggesting that there is also a disorder in glutamic acid metabolism.

Alumina Cream and Freezing

A chronic, recurrent paroxysmal disturbance of the brain closely resembling human focal epilepsy has been produced in monkeys and experimental animals by Kopeloff and co-workers by the implantation of aluminum hydroxide gel on the cortex or in subcortical structures.[228,229] The method has been successfully used by others[15,230] but the seizures take weeks to develop. Alumina cream damages the cerebral cortex leading to the production of a meningo-cerebral cicatrix and a surrounding glio-mesodermal reaction. In addition widespread ischemic lesions are found probably due to local edema following injection of the cream. Whether anoxia, mechanical pulling on neurones by the scarred tissue or the breakdown of the blood brain barrier by the formation of a pachymeningeal blood supply are the initiating factors leading to neuronal excitability is completely unknown. No biochemical studies have been made.

Another method of producing focal epilepsy in animals is by local freezing of the cerebral cortex by ethyl chloride spray.[231,232] Local discharging lesions are produced in a matter of hours and disappear in 7 to 10 days. The histological picture of the local lesions is one of demyelination, dense gliosis, dropping out of neurones and pallor of the superficial layers, again similar to human focal epilepsy.[233] There is also a local destruction of the blood brain barrier. Although this type of injury is the nearest approach experimentally to focal epilepsy there have been almost no detailed biochemical investigation. Berl, Purpura, Girado and Waelsch[234] have found a decreased level of glutamic acid, glutamine and glutathione but no changes in GABA in locally frozen cortex which shows EEG paroxysmal activity. On the other hand, intravenous administration of GABA, which could penetrate these regions of blood-brain barrier destruction, stopped the paroxysmal activity.[97]

Conclusions

In spite of the considerable amount of work which has been done on the biochemical changes associated with convulsions, induced by various means, it is still not possible to point to a specific lesion as the common cause. Changes in oxidative metabolism and energy transfer occur in the brain during convulsions but appear not to be related to the initiation of seizures but to maintenance of the seizures and to recovery processes. However, the convulsive effects of anoxia, hypoglycemia, fluorocitrate and possibly other agents indicate that interference with energy metabolism may initiate seizures. There is still no clear evidence to implicate acetylcholine or ammonia in the initiation of seizures. Studies of glutamic acid and GABA metabolism have failed to show a consistent relationship between altered amino acid metabolism and seizure susceptibility although in certain circumstances such as pyridoxine deficiency their importance seems well established. How altered amino acid metabolism and perhaps the metabolism of some of the compounds newly found in brain such as γ-guanidino-butyric acid,[235] β-hydroxy-γ-aminobutyric acid,[236] γ-aminobutyryl choline[273] and carnitine are related to neuronal excitability requires further investigation.

It should be emphasized that the results of determinations of labile constitutents in brain tissue from animals under various functional conditions must be interpreted with caution. Neurophysiological events occur in milliseconds or less and therefore the determination of substances concerned in such events can only indicate overall statistical effects. The techniques of rapid freezing in order to immobilize chemical activity are by no means instantaneous and may induce changes. Further, the activity of brain at any moment is often difficult to assess. Following the administration of convulsant drugs the EEG shows intermittent seizure patterns followed by greatly reduced activity. The bursts of high voltage brain waves during barbiturate narcosis are well known. These repetitive changes in activity must reflect chemical changes and it is difficult to know to what phase in the cyclic changes the chemical determinations refer. Finally, the brain is a multiple organ. Significant changes in a particular center may be obscured by determinations on the whole brain or on a region like the cerebral cortex which may not be primarily involved.

HUMAN EPILEPSY

Much effort has been expended in the attempt to correlate the epileptic condition with abnormalities of the composition of the blood and of systemic metabolism. This work has been reviewed by Goldstein and McFarland[238] and Penfield and Erickson.[239] Investigations into the basal metabolic rate, metabolism of carbohydrate, fat and protein, acid-base equilibria, water and salt balance, nutrition, endocrine activity, allergies and disorders of excretion have failed to indicate any causal relationship to epilepsy. Cerebral blood flow and oxygen consumption are normal between seizures.[240] Various authors have reported a tendency to hypoxemia, hypoglycemia, abnormal sugar tolerance, increased alkaline reserve and blood pH, low blood calcium and blood cholesterol in epileptic patients between seizures. Many of these reports are conflicting. The conditions apparently are not constant, and they throw little light on the epileptic mechanisms except perhaps to indicate disturbance of the autonomic system and often poor physical and emotional condition of the patient. Variability in blood constituents occurs to a greater extent in epileptic subjects than in normals as it does in most nervous and mental diseases. It has been reported that blood constituents estimated as guanidine are elevated in idiopathics[241] and rise sharply at the time of seizures but these findings have not been confirmed.[242] Decrease in alkali reserve and pH and increases in blood lactic acid, sugar, proteins and other nitrogenous materials and in plasma calcium, potassium and phosphate have been observed in association with seizures but all these changes can be considered as results of the excessive muscular and neuronal activity during seizures. The administration of glucose and oxygen can prolong seizures.

Changes in some of the factors mentioned above can precipitate seizures in epileptic and non-epileptic subjects. Both acute hypoxia and hypoglycemia, for instance, can precipitate seizures. Lowered carbon dioxide tensions of the blood and the consequent alkalosis produced by hyperventilation tend to activate the EEG and precipitate seizures in epileptic patients as also does the ingestion of alkali. Alkaline conditions favour neuronal hyperactivity, possibly as a result of deionisation of calcium. Epilepsy is of frequent occurrence in chronic hypocalcemia and the seizures frequently show features of tetany. As mentioned previously, acidosis decreases the incidence of seizures and this may be related to an increase in GABA content of the brain.[88] It is also possible that the effects of acidosis and alkalosis may result from changes in cerebral circulation caused by the blood carbon dioxide and pH changes. Though seizures may occur in chronic uremia there is no evidence that the retained chemicals are directly responsible but rather they are the effects of the associated hypertension. Excessive hydration either by drinking water or the administration of Pitressin has been used as a method for provoking epileptic seizures. Water intoxication in man results in delirium, convulsions and hyperreflexia[243] but again the mechanism is unknown. It might be due to changes in tissue permeability, salt balance and intracellular osmolarity associated with the expansion of intracellular compartments or to cerebral edema interfering with the circulation and setting up conditions similar to hypoxia. The brain in cerebral edema shows massive expansions of the oligodendrocytes and astrocytes surrounding neurones. Perhaps the changes in glial elements may affect the polarizability of neurones. Recent studies do suggest a function for the glia in water and ion metabolism, and ion transport in the brain.[244] Consumption of alcohol is well known as a precipitant of seizures in epileptics but the mechanism is not clear. The ketogenic diet used in the control of epilepsy may act by virtue of its dehydrating effect and the acidosis itself may have a sedative effect. There is no evidence that a disturbance of fat metabolism is involved.

Estrogens increase brain excitability (see ref. 245) and may have a direct convulsive effect or aggravate pre-existing epileptogenic foci. This has particular relevance to catamenial epilepsy where the estrogenic predominance near the menstrual period precipitates the spread of convulsive discharges in epileptic women.[246]

No consistent abnormalities of the cerebrospinal fluid have been found in epilepsy. As mentioned earlier, traces of acetylcholine have been detected in the fluid from the majority of epileptic patients.[43] Acetylcholine in the spinal fluid may simply be a result of continuous neuronal hyperactivity and not indicate the basis of this activity. Richter et al.[67] could not confirm earlier reports of the presence of ammonia in spinal fluid of epileptics.

Neurological, neurosurgical and neurophysiological studies of epilepsy (see refs. 42, 239) have shown that, in many cases, the epileptic discharge is initiated in a local area of grey matter, the epileptogenic focus, which is often situated close to a fibroglial scar. It would seem that any chemical changes or events peculiar to epilepsy should be found in such foci and that the spread of convulsive activity to other parts of the brain may involve normal tissue which is reacting to excessive stimulation from the focus. In cases in which no such foci can be identified it is likely that a derangement similar to that in a focus is present in a more diffuse form or in a less accessible site. Studies on focal brain tissue are therefore probably relevant to most forms of epilepsy.

Elliott and Penfield[20] found no significant differences in freshly excised epileptogenic foci from normal human cortex in the rates of oxygen uptake, carbon dioxide evolution, aerobic and anaerobic glycolysis. As previously mentioned Tower and Elliott[53] found that the total acetylcholine content of focal tissue, the rate of synthesis of free acetylcholine by slices *in vitro* and the accelerating effect of potassium on this synthesis fall into the normal range. The finding that bound acetylcholine did not increase in slices of focal tissue could not be repeated.[55] Somewhat higher levels of activity of cholinesterase have been reported. Tower[54] has observed significant decreases in glutamic acid synthesis by slices of focal tissue and a failure of such slices to reabsorb, during incubation under special conditions, the potassium lost to the medium at the start of incubation. There are no reports of an abnormality of GABA content in focal tissue. The value of GABA as an anticonvulsant is questionable because it fails to cross the blood brain barrier and has undesirable side effects. Thus, studies so far in the search for a biochemical mechanism for the abnormal firing of neurones in epileptogenic foci in man have been discouraging.

In considering such studies as these, three possibilities must be kept in mind: (1) the abnormal behaviour of epileptogenic tissue may be a response of normal neurones to an abnormal local environment; (2) the abnormal behaviour may be due to changes in the chemical potentialities of the neurones; (3) changes in the chemical potentialities may occur secondarily to hyperactivity, as an adaptation to, or deterioration resulting from, abnormal conditions and may not be essential to the epileptic process.

The writers feel that particular attention should be given to the first possibility. This is suggested by the negative results of studies on respiration and glycolysis. The studies of Penfield and his associates[42,239] indicate a probable impairment of local circulatory control in the neighbourhood of epileptogenic foci. This could cause acute and chronic changes in the chemical environment of neurones, such as variations in local pH or electrolyte concentration or of oxygen, glucose, carbon dioxide and other products of catabolism. All studies on the relation of such variables to neuronal function are pertinent to the problem of epilepsy. These studies should help clarify the essential problem of the initiation of the epileptic discharge. The function of glial cells and their metabolism is also particularly relevant. Madge and Sheibel[247] have demonstrated nerve fibres terminating on oligodendrocytes and it is possible that changes in the satellite oligodendrocytes may alter the functioning of neurones. Elucidation of the chemical actions of convulsive, narcotic and anticonvulsive agents should also help in understanding mechanisms underlying threshold, initiation and maintenance of epileptic discharge and lead to improved methods for the control of epilepsy.

REFERENCES

1. SCHMIDT, C. F., KETY, S. S. and PENNES, H. H.: *Am. J. Physiol., 143:*33 (1945).
2. GEIGER, A. and MAGNES, J.: *Am. J. Physiol., 149:*517 (1947).
3. GIBBS, F. A.: *Arch. Neurol. & Psychiat., 30:*1003 (1933).
4. GIBBS, F. A., LENNOX, W. G. and GIBBS, E. L.: *Arch. Neurol. & Psychiat., 32:*257 (1934).
5. PENFIELD, W., VON SÁNTHA, K. and CIPRIANA, A.: *J. Neurophysiol., 2:*257 (1939).
6. JASPER, H. and ERICKSON, T. C.: *J. Neurophysiol., 4:*333 (1941).
7. STONE, W. E., WEBSTER, J. E. and GURDJIAN, E. S.: *J. Neurophysiol., 8:*233 (1945).
8. GURDJIAN, E. S., WEBSTER, J. E. and STONE, W. E.: *A. Res. Nerv. & Ment. Dis., Proc., 26:*184 (1946).
9. DAVIES, P. W. and REMOND, A.: *A. Res. Nerv. & Ment. Dis., Proc., 26:*205 (1946).
10. RUF, H.: *Arkiv. Psychiat., 187:*97 (1951).
11. GRANT, F. C., SPITZ, E. B., SHENKIN, H. A., SCHMIDT, C. A. and KETY, S. S.: *Tr. Am. Neurol. A., 82* (1947).
12. SOKOLOFF, L.: *Pharmacol. Rev., 11:*1 (1959).
13. LASSEN, N. A.: *Physiol. Rev., 39:*183 (1959).
14. ELLIOTT, K. A. C. and JASPER, H. H.: *J. Neurosurg., 6:*140 (1949).
15. POPE, A., MORRIS, A. A., JASPER, H., ELLIOTT, K. A. C. and PENFIELD, W.: *A. Res. Nerv. & Ment. Dis., Proc., 26:*218 (1946).
16. WANG, R. I. H. and SONNENSCHEIN, R. R.: *J. Neurophysiol., 18:*130 (1955).
17. THORN, W., SCHOLL, H., PFLEIDERER, G. and MUELDENER, B.: *J. Neurochem., 2:*150 (1958).
18. KLEIN, J. R. and OLSEN, N. S.: *J. Biol. Chem., 167:*747 (1947).
19. GERSHOFF, S. N., NEWELL, G. W. and STONE, W. E.: *Arch. Biochem., 21:*74 (1949).
20. ELLIOTT, K. A. C. and PENFIELD, W.: *J. Neurophysiol., 11:*485 (1948).
21. McILWAIN, H.: *Biochemistry and the Central Nervous System,* p. 229. London, Churchill (1959).
22. MACLEOD, L. D. and REISS, M.: *J. Ment. Sc., 86:*276 (1940).
23. WEBB, J. L. and ELLIOTT, K. A. C.: *J. Pharmacol. & Exper. Therap., 103:*24 (1951).
24. ALBAUM, H. G., TEPPERMAN, J. and BODANSKY, O.: *J. Biol. Chem., 164:*45 (1946).
25. BROOKS, V. B., RANSMEIER, R. E. and GERARD, R. W.: *Am. J. Physiol., 157:*299 (1949).
26. MICHAELIS, L., ARANGO, N. I. and GERARD, R. W.: *Am. J. Physiol., 157:*463 (1949).
27. FELDBERG, W.: *Proc. Internat. Neurochem. Sympos., 2:*493 (1957); and in *Metabolism of the Nervous System,* p. 493. D. Richter, Ed. London, Pergamon (1957).
28. HEBB, C. O.: *Physiol. Rev., 37:*196 (1957).
29. FELDBERG, W.: *Physiol. Rev., 25:*596 (1945).
30. MILLER, F. R., STAVRAKY, G. W. and WOONTON, G. A.: *J. Neurophysiol., 3:*131 (1940).

31. BRENNER, C. and MERRITT, H. H.: *Arch. Neurol. & Psychiat.*, *48*:382 (1942).
32. FORSTER, F. M.: *Arch. Neurol. & Psychiat.*, *54*:391 (1945).
33. BORNSTEIN, M. B.: *J. Neurophysiol.*, *9*:349 (1946).
34. FELDBERG, W. and SHERWOOD, S.: *J. Physiol.*, *125*:488 (1954).
35. FIAMBERTI, A. M.: *Rev. sper. di. freniat.*, *61*:834 (1937).
36. DIKSHIT, B. B.: *J. Physiol.*, *81*:382 (1934).
37. HENDERSON, W. R. and WILSON, W. C.: *Quart. J. Exper. Physiol.*, *26*:83 (1936).
38. FELDBERG, W. and SHERWOOD, S.: Brit. J. Pharmacol.: *J. Physiol.*, *125*:488 (1954).
39. FREEDMAN, A. M., BALES, P. D., WILLIS, A. and HIMWICH, H. E.: *Am. J. Physiol.*, *156*:117 (1949).
40. FREEDMAN, A. M. and HIMWICH, H. E.: *Am. J. Physiol.*, *156*:125 (1949).
41. RINALDI, F. and HIMWICH, H. E.: *Arch. Neurol. & Psychiat.*, *73*:387 (1955).
42. PENFIELD, W. and JASPER, H. H.: *Epilepsy and the Functional Anatomy of the Human Brain.* Boston, Little, Brown (1954).
43. TOWER, D. B. and MCEACHERN, D.: *Canad. J. Res.*, *27*:105 (1949); *27*:120 (1949).
44. TOBIAS, J. M., LIPTON, M. A. and LEPINAT, A. A.: *Proc. Soc. Exper. Biol. & Med.*, *61*:51 (1946).
45. ELLIOTT, K. A. C., SWANK, R. L. and HENDERSON, N.: *Am. J. Physiol.*, *162*:469 (1950).
46. RICHTER, D. and CROSSLAND, J.: *Am. J. Physiol.*, *159*:247 (1949).
47. CROSSLAND, J., PAPPIUS, H. M. and ELLIOTT, K. A. C.: *Am. J. Physiol.*, *183*:27 (1955).
48. MCLENNAN, H. and ELLIOTT, K. A. C.: *J. Pharmacol. & Exper. Therap.*, *103*:35 (1951).
49. MANN, P. J. H., TENNENBAUM, M. and QUASTEL, J. H.: *Biochem. J.*, *33*:822, 1506 (1939).
50. BRODKIN, E. and ELLIOTT, K. A. C.: *Am. J. Physiol.*, *173*:437 (1953).
51. HEBB, C. O. and WHITTAKER, V. P.: *J. Physiol.*, *142*:187 (1958).
52. QUASTEL, J. H., TENNENBAUM, M. and WHEATLEY, A. H. M.: *Biochem. J.*, *30*:1668 (1936).
53. TOWER, D. B. and ELLIOTT, K. A. C.: *J. Appl. Physiol.*, *4*:669 (1952); *5*:375 (1953).
54. TOWER, D. B.: In Temporal Lobe Epilepsy, p. 301. Baldwin, M., and Bailey, P., Eds. Springfield, Thomas (1958).
55. PAPPIUS, H. M. and ELLIOTT, K. A. C.: *J. Appl. Physiol.*, *12*:319 (1958).
56. HEBB, C. O.: *Internat. Rev. Neurobiol.*, *1*:165 (1959).
57. ECCLES, J. C.: *The Physiology of Nerve Cells.* Baltimore, Johns Hopkins Press (1957).
58. WHITTAKER, V. P.: *Biochem. J.*, *72*:694 (1959).
59. TASHIRO, S.: *Am. J. Physiol.*, *60*:519 (1922).
60. WINTERSTEIN, H. and HIRSCHBERG, E.: *Biochem. Ztschr.*, *156*:138 (1925).
61. VRBA, R.: *J. Neurochem.*, *1*:12 (1956).
62. SAPIRSTEIN, M. R.: *Proc. Soc. Exper. Biol. & Med.*, *52*:334 (1943).
63. RUISSEAU, J. P. DU., GREENSTEIN, J. P., WINITZ, M. and BIRNBAUM, S. M.: *Arch. Biochem. & Biophys.*, *64*:355 (1956); *68*:161 (1957).
64. SEEGMILLER, J. E., SCHWARTZ, R. and DAVIDSON, C. S.: *J. Clin. Invest.*, *33*:984 (1954).
65. SHERLOCK, S.: *Am. J. Med.*, *24*:805 (1958).
66. MANN, F. C.: *Medicine*, *6*:419 (1927).
67. RICHTER, D., DAWSON, R. M. C. and LEES, L.: *J. Ment. Sc.*, *95*:148 (1949).
68. RICHTER, D. and DAWSON, R. M. C.: *J. Biol. Chem.*, *176*:1199 (1948).

69. BENITEZ, D., PSCHEIDT, G. R. and STONE, W. E.: *Am. J. Physiol., 176:*488 (1954).

70. TSUKADA, Y., TAKAGAKI, G., SUGIMOTO, S. and HIRANO, S.: *J. Neurochem., 2:*295 (1958).

71. HOSEIN, E. A., and PROULX, P.: *Nature, 187:*321 (1960).

72. HOSEIN, E. A. and BOISVERT, M.: *Proc. Canad. Fed. Biol. Soc., 2:*31 (1959).

73. KREBS, H. A., EGGLESTON, L. V. and HEMS, R.: *Biochem. J., 44:*159 (1949).

74. WEIL-MALHERBE, H.: *Physiol. Rev., 30:*549 (1950).

75. WAELSCH, H.: *Advances Protein Chem., 6:*299 (1951).

76. STRECKER, H. J.: In *Metabolism of the Nervous System,* p. 459. Richter, D., Ed. London, Pergamon Press (1957).

77. STERN, J. R., EGGLESTON, L. V., HEMS, R. and KREBS, H. A.: *Biochem. J., 44:*410 (1949).

78. MCILWAIN, H.: *J. Neurol., Neurosurg. & Psychiat., 16:*257 (1953).

79. KREBS, H. A.: *Biochem. J., 29:*1951 (1935).

80. PRICE, J. C., WAELSCH, H. and PUTNAM, T. J.: *J.A.M.A., 122:*1153 (1943).

81. TOWER, D. B.: *Clin. chim. acta, 2:*397 (1957).

82. TOWER, D. B.: *Proc. 4th Intern. Congr. Biochem., 3:*213 (1959).

83. HAWKINS, J. E. and SARETT, L. H.: *Clin. chim. acta, 2:*481 (1957).

84. ELLIOTT, K. A. C.: *Rev. canad. biol., 17:*367 (1958); *Proc. 4th Intern. Congr. Biochem., 3:*251 (1959).

85. ELLIOTT, K. A. C. and JASPER, H. H.: *Physiol. Rev., 39:*383 (1959).

86. ROBERTS, E. and BAXTER, C. F.: *Proc. 4th Intern. Congr. Biochem., 3:*268 (1959).

87. JINNAI, D. and MORI, A.: *Nissin Igaku, 45:*1-10 (1958).

88. ROBERTS, E., ROTHSTEIN, M. and BAXTER, C. F.: *Proc. Soc. Exper. Biol. & Med., 97:*796 (1958).

89. BESSMAN, S. P., ROSSEN, J. and LAYNE, E. C.: *J. Biol. Chem., 201:*385 (1953).

90. ALBERS, R. W. and BRADY, R. O.: *J. Biol. Chem., 234:*926 (1959).

91. PURPURA, D. P. M., GIRADO, M. and GRUNDFEST, H.: *Proc. Soc. Exper. Biol. & Med., 95:*791 (1957).

92. IWAMA, K. and JASPER, H. H.: *J. Physiol., 138:*365 (1957).

93. CRAVIOTO, R. O., MASSIEU, G. and IZQUIERO, J. J.: *Proc. Soc. Exper. Biol. & Med., 78:*856 (1951).

94. DAWSON, R. M. C.: *Biochim. et biophys. acta, 11:*548 (1953).

95. BAXTER, C. F. and ROBERTS, E.: *Proc. Soc. Exper. Biol. & Med., 101:*811 (1959).

96. EIDELBERG, E., BAXTER, C. F., ROBERTS, E., SALDIAS, C. A. and FRENCH, J. D.: *Proc. Soc. Exper. Biol. & Med., 101:*815 (1959).

97. PURPURA, D. P., GIRADO, M., SMITH, T. G. and GOMEZ, J. A.: *Proc. Soc. Exp. Biol. & Med., 97:*348 (1958).

98. JASPER, H. H.: In *Inhibition in the Nervous System and γ-Aminobutyric Acid,* Roberts, E., Ed. Pergamon Press (1960).

99. ELLIOTT, K. A. C. and VAN GELDER, N. M.: *J. Neurochem., 3:*28 (1958).

100. MILLICHAP, J. G.: *Proc. Soc. Exper. Biol. & Med., 96:*125 (1957); *97:*606 (1958).

101. KOCH, A. and WOODBURY, D. M.: *J. Pharmacol. & Exper. Therap., 122:*335 (1958).

102. MILLICHAP, J. G.: *Neurology, 6:*552 (1956).

103. ROTH, L. J., SCHOOLAR, J. C. and BARLOW, C. F.: *J. Pharmacol. & Exper. Therap., 125:*128 (1959).

104. DUNLOP, C. W.: *Am. J. Physiol., 190:*172 (1957); *191:*200 (1957).

105. DENNY BROWN, D.: *Federation Proc., 17:*35 (1958).

106. OCHOA, S.: In *Biology of Mental Health and Disease,* p. 97. New York, Hoeber (1952).

107. DAVIS, R. A. and WOLF, A.: *Pediatrics, 21*:409 (1948).
108. EVERETT, G. M.: *Am. J. Physiol., 141*:439 (1944).
109. HALVER, J. E.: *J. Nutrition, 62*:225 (1957).
110. GAVRILESCU, N. and PETERS, R. A.: *Biochem. J., 25*:1397 (1931).
111. PETERS, R. A. and SINCLAIR, H. M.: *Biochem. J., 27*:1910 (1933).
112. PETERS, R. A. and THOMPSON, R. H. S.: *Biochem. J., 28*:916 (1934).
113. PETERS, R. A.: *Lancet, 1*:1161 (1936).
114. PETERS, R. A.: *Brit. M. Bull., 9*:116 (1953).
115. GRUBER, M.: *Biochim. et biophys. acta, 10*:136 (1953).
116. SALEM, H. M.: *Biochem. J., 57*:227 (1954).
117. FERRARI, V.: *Acta Vitamin., 11*:53 (1957).
118. RACKER, E., DE LA HABA, G. and LEDER, I. G.: *J.A.C.S., 75*:1010 (1953).
119. WOOLLEY, D. W. and MERRIFIELD, R. B.: *Bull. Soc. chim. biol., 36*:1207 (1954).
120. KOEDAM, J. C.: *Biochim. et biophys. acta, 29*:333 (1958).
121. GREEN, R. G., CARLSON, W. E. and EVANS, C. A.: *J. Nutrition, 23*:165 (1942).
122. SEALOCK, R. R., LIVERMORE, A. H. and EVANS, C. A.: *J.A.C.S., 65*:935 (1943).
123. FIJITA, A.: *Advances Enzymol., 15*:389 (1954).
124. SARETT, H. P. and MORRISON, A. B.: *Ann. Rev. Biochem., 27*:339 (1958).
125. VIANNA DIAZ, M.: *Science, 105*:211 (1947).
126. HAYASHI, T.: *Neurophysiology and Neurochemistry of Convulsions.* Tokyo, Dainihon-Tosho, (1959).
127. HANDLER, P.: *Federation Proc., 17*:31 (1958).
128. CHICK, H., EL SADR, M. M. and WORDEN, A. N.: *Biochem. J., 34*:595 (1940).
129. SHERMAN, H.: *The Vitamins,* Vol. III, p. 265. Sebrell, W. H. and Harris, R. S., Eds. New York Acad. Press (1954).
130. TOWER, D. B.: *Am. J. Clin. Nutrition, 4*:329 (1956); *Proc. Nutr. Symp., 12*:21 (1956); *Nutrition Rev., 16*:161 (1958).
131. HUNT, A. D., STOKES, J., McCRORY, W. W. and STROUD, H. H.: *Pediatrics, 13*:140 (1954).
132. BESSEY, O. A., ADAM, D. J. and HANSEN, A. E.: *Pediatrics, 20*:33 (1957).
133. HUNT, A. D.: *Am. J. Clin. Nutrition, 5*:561 (1957).
134. COURSIN, D. B.: *Am. J. Dis. Child., 90*:344 (1955).
135. McGRANITY, W. J.: *Am. J. Clin. Nutrition, 4*:376 (1956).
136. LERNER, A. M., DECARLI, L. M. and DAVIDSON, C. S.: *Proc. Soc. Exper. Biol. & Med., 98*:841 (1958).
137. ROBERTS, E., YOUNGER, F. and FRANKEL, S.: *J. Biol. Chem., 119*:277 (1951).
138. BERGERET, B., CHATAGNER, F. and FROMAGEOT, C.: *Biochim. et biophys. acta, 17*:128 (1955).
139. ASHWOOD-SMITH, M. J. and SMITH, A. D.: *Nature, 184*:2028 (1959).
140. HOPE, D. B.: *Biochem. J., 66*:486 (1957); *J. Physiol., 141*:31 (1958); *Proc. 4th Intern. Congr. Biochem., 13*:63 (1959).
141. TALLAN, H. H., MOORE, S. and STEIN, W. H.: *J. Biol. Chem., 230*:707 (1958).
142. GAMMON, G. D. and GUMNIT, R.: *Tr. Am. Neurol. A., 57* (1957).
143. UMBREIT, W. W. and WADDELL, J. G.: *Proc. Soc. Exper. Biol. & Med., 70*:293 (1949).
144. PURPURA, D. P., BERL, S., GONZALEZ-MONTEAGUDO, O. and WYATT, A.: *Federation Proc., 17*:404 (1958).
145. DIETRICH, L. S. and BARRIES, E.: *Arch. Biochem. & Biophys., 64*:512 (1956).
146. ROSEN, F., HOLLAND, J. F. and NICHOL, F.: *Proc. Am. A. Cancer Res., 2*:243 (1957).
147. SAKURAGI, T. and KUMMEROW, F. A.: *Arch. Biochem. & Biophys., 71*:303 (1957).

148. BIEHL, J. P. and VILTER, R. W.: *Proc. Soc. Exper. Biol. & Med., 85*:389 (1954).
149. PLEASURE, H.: *Arch. Neurol. & Psych., 72*:313 (1954).
150. REILLY, R. H., KILLAM, K. F., JENNEY, E. H., MARSHALL, W. H., TAUSIG, T. and APTER, N. G.: *J.A.M.A., 152*:1317 (1953).
151. DIEKE, S. H.: *Proc. Soc. Exper. Biol. & Med., 70*:688 (1946).
152. PARKS, R. E., KIDDER, G. W. and DEWEY, V. C.: *Proc. Soc. Exper. Biol. & Med., 79*:287 (1952).
153. JENNEY, E. H. and PFEIFFER, C. C.: *J. Pharmacol. & Exper. Therap., 122*:110 (1958).
154. BAIN, J. A. and WIEGAND, R. G.: *J. Pharmacol. & Exper. Therap., 119*:131 (1957).
155. WILLIAMS, H. L. and ABDULIAN, D. H.: *J. Pharmacol. & Exper. Therap., 116*:62 (1956).
156. WIEGAND, R. G.: *J. Am. Chem. Soc., 78*:5307 (1956).
157. BOONE, I. V., MAGGE, M. and TURNEY, D. F.: *J. Biol. Chem., 221*:781 (1956).
158. FINE, E. A., KUNKEL, A. M. and WILL, J. H.: *Federation Proc., 9*:272 (1950).
159. KILLAM, K. F. and BAIN, J. A.: *J. Pharmacol. & Exper. Therap., 119*:255, 263 (1957).
160. DU VIGNEAUD, V., KUCHINSKAS, E. J. and HORVATH, A.: *Arch. Biochem. & Biophys., 66*:1 (1957); *68*:69 (1957).
161. CLARKE, H. T., JOHNSON, J. R. and ROBINSON, R.: *The Chemistry of Penicillin*, p. 55. Princeton, Princeton Univ. Press, (1949).
162. CHRISTENSEN, H. N.: *J. Biol. Chem., 209*:413 (1954); *234*:613 (1959); *Science, 122*:1087 (1955).
163. BONNET, V. and BREMER, F.: *Compt. rend. Soc. biol., 126*:1271 (1937).
164. COLFER, H. F. and ESSEX, H. E.: *Am. J. Physiol., 150*:27 (1947).
165. BRINK, F., BRONK, D. W. and LARRABEE, M. G.: *Ann. New York Acad. Sc., 47*:457 (1946).
166. TOWER, D. B.: *Neurology, 5*:113 (1955).
167. TERNER, C., EGGLESTON, L. V. and KREBS, H. A.: *Biochem. J., 44*:410 (1949).
168. PAPPIUS, H. M. and ELLIOTT, K. A. C.: *Canad. J. Biochem. & Physiol., 34*:1053 (1956).
169. FITZGERALD, M. G. and FOURMAN, P.: *Clin. Sc., 15*:635 (1956).
170. SUTER, C. and KLINGMAN, W. D.: *Neurology, 5*:691 (1955).
171. KRUSE, H. D., ORENT, E. and McCOLLUM, E. U.: *J. Biol. Chem., 96*:579 (1932); *Am. J. Physiol., 101*:454 (1932).
172. VALLEE, B. L.: *Advances Protein Chem., 10*:318 (1955).
173. CHENOWETH, M. B.: *Pharmacol. Rev., 1*:383 (1949).
174. PETERS, R. A.: *Brit. M. J., 2*:1165 (1952); *Brit. M. Bull., 9*:116 (1953); *Proc. Roy. Soc., B, 139*:143 (1952); *140*:143 (1952); *Biochem. J., 71*:245 (1959).
175. PETERS, R. A.: *Advances Enzymol., 18*:113 (1957).
176. BUFFA, P. and PETERS, R. A.: *J. Physiol., 110*:488 (1949).
177. KANDEL, A. and CHENOWETH, M. B.: *J. Pharmacol. & Exper. Therap., 104*:234 (1952).
178. HENDERSHOT, L. C. and CHENOWETH, M. B.: *J. Pharmacol. & Exper. Therap., 110*:344 (1954); *113*:160 (1955).
179. EEG-LARSEN, N. and NAESS, K.: *Acta pharmacol. et toxicol., 7*:331 (1951).
180. WOLLEMANN, M. and FEUER, G.: *Acta Physiol. Acad. Sc. Hung., 11*:165 (1957).
181. NACHMANSOHN, D. and JOHN, H. M.: *J. Biol. Chem., 158*:157 (1945).
182. FELDBERG, W. and MANN, T.: *J. Physiol., 104*:411 (1946).
183. McLENNAN, H. and ELLIOTT, K. A. C.: *Am. J. Physiol., 163*:605 (1950).

184. BARTLETT, G. R. and BARRON, E. S. G.: *J. Biol. Chem., 170*:67 (1947).
185. WAKELIN, R. W. and PETERS, R. A.: *Biochem. J., 67*:280 (1957).
186. KELEN, A. and McEACHERN, D.: *Canad. J. Res., 27*:146 (1949).
187. MORAN, T.: *Lancet, 253*:2:289 (1947).
188. WAGNER, J. R. and ELVEHJEM, C. A.: *J. Nutrition, 28*:431 (1944).
189. MELLANBY, E.: *Brit. M. J., 2*:885 (1946); 2:288 (1947).
190. BENTLEY, H. R., McDERMOTT, E. E., PACE, J., WHITEHEAD, J. K. and MORAN, T.: *Nature,* London, *164*:438 (1949); *165*:150 (1950).
191. REINER, L., MISANI, F., FAIR, T. W., WEISS, P. and CORDASCO, M. J.: *J. Am. Chem. Soc., 72*:2297 (1950).
192. CAMPBELL, P. N., WORK, T. S. and MELLANBY, E.: *Nature,* London, *165*:345 (1950).
193. MISANI, F. and REINER, L.: *Arch. Biochem. & Biophys., 27*:234 (1950).
194. BENTLEY, H. R., McDERMOTT, E. E. and WHITEHEAD, J. K.: *Nature,* London, *165*:735 (1950).
195. LEWEY, F. H.: *J. Neuropath. & Exper. Neurol., 9*:396 (1950).
196. SILVER, M. L., JOHNSON, R. E., KARK, R. M., KLEIN, J. R., MONAHAN, E. P. and ZEVIN, S. S.: *J.A.M.A., 135*:757 (1947).
197. GASTAUT, H., TOGA, M. and NAQUET, R.: In *Temporal Lobe Epilepsy,* p. 268. Baldwin, M. and Bailey, P., Eds. Springfield, Ill., Thomas (1958).
198. NEWELL, G. W., ERICKSON, T. C., GILSON, W. E., GERSHOFF, S. N. and ELVEHJEM, C. A.: *J.A.M.A., 135*:760 (1947).
199. RADOMSKI, J. L., WOODWARD, G. and LEHMAN, A. J.: *J. Nutrition, 36*:15 (1948).
200. REINER, L., MISANI, F. and WEISS, P.: *Arch. Biochem. & Biophys., 25*:447 (1950).
201. PETERS, E. L. and TOWER, D. B.: *J. Neurochem., 5*:80 (1959).
202. NEWELL, G. W., GERSHOFF, S. N., FUNG, F. H., and ELVEHJEM, C. A.: *Am. J. Physiol., 152*:637 (1948).
203. ERICKSON, T. C., GILSON, W. E., ELVEHJEM, C. A. and NEWELL, G. M.: *Proc. Ass. Res. Nerv. & Ment. Dis., 21*:164 (1946); *Proc. Soc. Exper. Biol. & Med., 65*:115 (1947).
204. SILVER, M. L., MONAHAN, E. P., KLEIN, J. R. and POLLACK, C. H.: *Arch. Neurol. & Psychiat., 60*:405 (1948).
205. SILVER, M. L.: *J. Neuropath. & Exper. Neurol., 8*:441 (1949).
206. HICKS, S. P. and COY, M. A.: *Arch. Path., 65*:378 (1958).
207. OLSZEWSKI, J. and TOWER, D. B.: In *Temporal Lobe Epilepsy,* p. 288. Springfield, Ill., Thomas (1958).
208. ELLIOTT, K. A. C. and PENFIELD, W.: *J. Neurophysiol., 11*:485 (1948).
209. TOWER, D. B. and ELLIOTT, K. A. C.: *Am. J. Physiol., 168*:747 (1952).
210. TOWER, D. B.: In *Chemical Pathology of the Central Nervous System,* Folch, J., Ed. London, Pergamon (1959).
211. HEATHCOTE, J. G. and PACE, J.: *Nature,* London, *164*:439 (1949); *166*:353 (1950).
212. NEWELL, G. W. and CARMAN, W. W.: *Federation Proc., 9*:209 (1950).
213. BOREK, E., MILLER, H. K., SHEINERS, P. and WAELSH, H.: *J. Biol. Chem., 163*:347 (1946).
214. WAELSCH, H., OWADES, P., MILLER, H. K., and BOREK, E.: *J. Biol. Chem., 166*:273 (1946).
215. McILWAIN, H., ROPER, J. A. and HUGHES, D. E.: *Biochem. J., 42*:492 (1948).
216. ELLIOTT, W. H. and GALE, E. F.: *Nature,* London, *161*:129 (1948).
217. SPECK, J. F.: *J. Biol. Chem., 179*:1405 (1949).
218. KREBS, H. A.: *Biochem. J., 29*:1951 (1935).

219. ELLIOTT, W. H.: *Nature*, London, *161*:128 (1948).

220. PACE, J. and McDERMOTT, E. E.: *Nature*, London, *169*:415 (1952).

221. KOLOUŠKEK, J. and JIRÁČEK, V.: *J. Neurochem.*, *4*:179 (1959).

222. SMITH, K. U.: *J. Comp. Psychol.*, *32*:311 (1941).

223. FRINGS, H. and FRINGS, H.: *J. Acoust. Soc. Am.*, *24*:163 (1952); *Behavior*, *5*:305 (1953).

224. LINDSLEY, D. B., FINGER, F. W. and HENRY, C. E.: *J. Neurophysiol.*, *5*:185 (1942).

225. MAIER, N. R. F. and SACKS, J.: *J. Comp. Psychol.*, *32*:489 (1941).

226. GINSBURG, B. E.: *Perspect. Biol. & Med.*, *1*:4:397 (1958).

227. KOLOUŠKEK, J., HORAK, F. and JIRÁČEK, V.: *J. Neurochem.* *4*:175 (1959).

228. KOPELOFF, L. M., BARRERA, S. E. and KOPELOFF, N.: *Am. J. Physiol.*, *98*:881 (1942); *100*:727 (1944).

229. KOPELOFF, N., WHITTIER, J. R., PACELIA, B. L. and KOPELOFF, L. M.: *EEG & Clin. Neurophysiol.*, *2*:163 (1950).

230. GASTAUT, H., NAQUET, R., MEYER, A., CAVANAGH, J. B. and BECK, I.: In *Temporal Lobe Epilepsy*, p. 240. Springfield, Ill., Thomas (1958): *J. Neuropath. & Exper. Neurol.*, *18*:270 (1959).

231. MORRELL, F. and FLORENZ, A.: *EEG & Clin. Neurophysiol.*, *10*:187 (1958).

232. KEITH, H. M. and BICKFORD, R. G.: *Am. J. Physiol.*, *179*:650 (1954).

233. MORRELL, F.: *Arch. Neurol. & Psychiat.*, *1*:141 (1959).

234. BERL, S., PURPURA, D. P., GIRADO, M. and WAELSCH, H.: *J. Neurochem.*, *4*:311 (1959).

235. McLENNAN, H.: *J. Physiol.*, *146*:358 (1959).

236. HAYASHI, T.: *J. Physiol.*, *145*:570 (1959).

237. KURIAKI, K., YAKUSHIJI, T., NORO, T., SHIMIZU, T. and SAJI, S. H.: *Nature*, London, *181*:1336 (1958).

238. GOLDSTEIN, H. and McFARLAND, R. A.: *Am. J. Physiol.*, *96*:771 (1939).

239. PENFIELD, W. P. and ERICKSON, T. C.: *Epilepsy and Cerebral Localization.* Springfield, Ill., Thomas (1941).

240. GRANT, F. C., SPITZ, E. B., SHENKIN, H. A., SCHMIDT, C. A. and KETY, S. S.: *Tr. Am. Neurol. A.*, 82 (1947).

241. MURRAY, M. and HOFFMAN, C. R.: *J. Lab. & Clin. Med.*, *25*:1072 (1940).

242. PALMER, H. D., SCOTT, D. B., McNAIR, and ELLIOTT, K. A. C.: *J. Lab. & Clin. Med.*, *28*:735 (1943).

243. DODGE, P. R., CRAWFORD, J. D. and PROBST, J.: *Tr. Am. Neurol. A.*, 83 (1958).

244. GERSCHENFELD, H. M., WALD, F., ZADUNAISKY, J. A. and DE ROBERTIS, E. D. P.: *Neurology*, *9*:412 (1959).

245. WOODBURY, D. M.: *Pharmacol. Rev.*, *10*:275 (1958).

246. LOGOTHETIS, J., HARNER, R., MORRELL, F. and TORRES, F.: *Neurology*, *9*:352 (1959).

247. MADGE, E. and SCHEIBEL, A. B.: In *Biology of Neuroglia*, p. 5. Springfield, Ill., Thomas (1958).

248. BRAGANCA, B. M., FAULKNER, P. and QUASTEL, J. H.: *Biochim. et biophys. acta*, *10*:83 (1953).

249. KINI, M. M. and QUASTEL, J. H.: *Nature*, *184*:252 (1959).

250. GEIGER, A., KAWAKITA, Y. and BARKULIS, S. S.: *J. Neurochem.*, *5*:323 (1960).

251. BARKULIS, S. S., GEIGER, A. and AGUILAR, V.: *J. Neurochem.*, *5*:339 (1960).

252. GEIGER, A., HORVATH, N. and KAWAKITA, Y.: *J. Neurochem.*, *5*:311 (1960).

253. HOSEIN, E. A. and PROULX, P.: *Nature*, *187*:321 (1960).

254. HOSEIN, E. A., ARA, R. and PROULX, P.: *Biochem. J. 83*:341 (1962) .

255. TAKAHASHI, R., NASU, T., TAMURA, T. and KARIYA, T.: *J. Neurochem.*, 7:103 (1961).

256. BERL, S., TAKAGAKI, G. and PURPURA, D. P.: *J. Neurochem.*, 7:198 (1961).

257. KAMRIN, R. P. and KAMRIN, A. A.: *J. Neurochem.*, 6:219 (1961).

258. MATSUDA, M. and MAKINO, K.: *Biochim. Biophys. Acta*, 48:192 (1961).

259. PETERS, R. A., HALL, R. J., WARD, P. F. V. and SHEPPARD, N.: *J. Biochem.*, 77:17 (1960).

260. BALZER, H., HOLTZ, P. and PALM, D.: *Naunyn-Schmiedeberg's Arch. exp. Path. Pharmak.*, 239:520 (1960).

261. BRONK, D. W.: *J. Neurophysiol.*, 2:38 (1939).

XXX

NEUROTROPIC DRUGS

James E. P. Toman

INTRODUCTION

Since the appearance of the first edition of this volume, a major revolution has occurred in the use of drugs in psychiatry. Such terms as "tranquilizer," "antidepressive," or "hallucinogen" were not to be found in the earlier index; drugs such as reserpine, the phenothiazines, the amine oxidase inhibitors, had barely reached the threshold of interest of clinical investigators. Somewhat less spectacular advances have been registered in the pharmacology of the neurological diseases within the last decade, but the number and variety of drugs in this field also has continued to multiply. It is more than timely, therefore, to reappraise the major drug groups which are now used for their effects upon the nervous system, and to take a second look at mechanisms of action which have been proposed in the past.

To give due weight to all of the drugs now in use or under study, and to give proper credit to all of the contributors to the exponentially increasing literature of neuropharmacology, it would be necessary to write a monograph at least as heavy as the entire present edition. Fortunately the other authors of these chapters will be giving detailed and scholarly attention to many current fields of interest. This writer will therefore take the privilege of surveying broadly the most recognizable groupings of neurotropic drugs, with special attention to some possible common mechanisms of action. In particular we will attempt to develop a theoretical approach relating the actions of certain drug groups to ultimate interactions at the molecular level with structural components of the nerve cell membrane, leading to a number of new classes of effects on excitation parameters.

This speculative approach will have to be done at the expense of a more scholarly review of the present status of neurotropic drugs, and the citation of the literature will be scanty. Certain sources which have been particularly useful to us in the preparation of this chapter are hereby gratefully acknowledged.[12,21,29,38,55,56,71] In an effort to avoid

728

duplication, we have barely touched upon some subjects which are given detailed treatment elsewhere in this present volume.[8,24,26,42,44,49,51,52,54,57,58,69] We have particularly neglected the field of neurohumoral mediators and related neurotropic drugs including some of special interest to psychopharmacology, but fortunately there are available many excellent critiques, reviews and monographs.[5,6,7,15,20,23,31,36,39,43,45,53,61,63,64,68]

CLASSIFICATION OF NEUROTROPIC DRUGS

The system used for classifying any group of objects will depend on the purpose served by classification. Thus in the general field of neuropharmacology we could avail ourselves of a number of possible methods of cataloguing drugs. For example:

(1) By intended clinical use: antiparkinson, antispastic, anticonvulsive, sedative, etc.

(2) By chemical structure: barbiturates, catecholamines, glycerol ethers, etc.

(3) By presumed relevant physiological neuronal mechanism: threshold-raising, anti-inhibitory, conduction-blocking, etc.

(4) By presumed relevant biochemical mechanism: anticholinesterase, monoamineoxidase inhibitor, catecholamine depleter, etc.

These are only a few of the possible variations, and perhaps not by far the most meaningful. Most classifications for didactic purposes are hybrid, traditional, colorful and misleading. The chief reason for this unsatisfactory state of affairs is the relative poverty of knowledge concerning mechanisms, either at the cellular or molecular levels of explanation, which would give a sound theoretical base for systematizing drugs. Lacking such a base, the easiest practical system is one in which the main groups relate to intended clinical use. Lest this seem too unphysiological, clinical grouping usually has the advantage of calling attention to those effects of each drug which are discernible in the smallest possible dosage. This is implicit in the clinical choice of a drug and a dosage just sufficient to produce a desired therapeutic action without causing side-effects. With this pragmatic consideration in mind, we can offer the following attempt at a clinical classification of neurotropic drugs which will at least furnish some descriptive terms for drugs discussed in the text:

I. Used primarily for suppression of specific central functions
   A. Anesthetic
   B. Sedative
   C. Antispastic
   D. Antiparkinson
   E. Anticonvulsant
   F. Antianxiety

G. Antischizophrenic
H. Analgesic
I. Antipyretic
J. Antiemetic
K. Antitussive
L. Others

II. Used primarily for stimulation of specific central functions
A. Convulsant
B. Alerting
C. Antidepressive
D. Hallucinogen
E. Others

III. Used primarily for suppression of specific peripheral functions
A. Local anesthetic
B. Ganglionic blocking
C. Neuroeffector blocking
D. Others

IV. Used primarily for stimulation of specific peripheral functions
A. Ganglionic stimulant
B. Neuroeffector stimulant
C. Others

V. Otherwise unclassified

It should be pointed out that the main classes are not mutually exclusive. Thus many drugs in class I can cause general anesthesia in high dosage, regardless of their more specific uses at lower dosage. In fact, almost any drug in any of these categories, regardless of its minimal effect, is capable of causing either anesthesia or convulsions if given in sufficient dose. "Enough of anything can do something to everything."

PATTERNS OF NEUROTROPIC DRUG ACTION

The simplest binary division of neurotropic drugs would be into depressant and stimulant classes. A few drugs would be easily sorted on this basis, for example a uniform excitant such as the convulsant pentylenetetrazole (Metrazol), or a uniform depressant such as the muscle relaxant mephenesin. Unfortunately, the majority of drugs do not show such uniform actions. As a homely example, ethyl alcohol is popularly known as a "stimulant," because of the effusive behavior it often evokes in a social setting. Furthermore, it may precipitate convulsions in occasional epileptic patients, superficially a stimulant action. Yet by all pharmacological criteria it is of course a central depressant, and was at one time the only available general anesthetic for surgical procedures. More striking paradoxes could be drawn with other drugs having more definitely mixed effects, such as reserpine, chlorpromazine, atropine, morphine, etc. An apparent stimulation may reflect only the release of a given system from inhibition by another which is slightly more depressed by the test drug.

Convulsions might be taken as a clear indication of a stimulant drug action regardless of particular mechanism. In a series of several thousand drugs tested on mice and drawn from almost every conceivable pharmacological grouping, we found the large majority to cause some type of convulsion in sufficient dose. In contrast, anesthesia without convulsions was limited to a more definite grouping of chemical forms. Apparently the normal mammalian brain contains all of the necessary feedback amplifier mechanisms to permit convulsions with either selective stimulation or selective depression. The normal regulatory mechanisms developed by the brain are more than adequate to prohibit convulsions from the ordinary constant play of nervous impulses, but the regulation can be overloaded easily by external intervention.[62] A particularly good case is given by the local anesthetics, which are well known to be capable of causing convulsions when administered systemically. Yet the action of these agents on particular central neurones and fibers appears to be universally an increase in threshold, just as in peripheral nerve. It must be that the particular pattern of threshold raising is sufficiently inhomogeneous to unbalance the normal mechanisms which regulate the brain against seizures. In the somewhat simpler brain of the frog, local anesthetics do not cause seizures, although stimulants such as pentylenetetrazole may do so.

I. Suppression of Specific Central Functions (cf. also refs. 2, 5, 21, 26, 39, 49, 55, 68)

Some drugs, for example certain typical barbiturates, have a useful range of action depending on dosage all the way from mildly tranquilizing to complete abolition of central nervous activity. Others are limited in the degree of depression which can be achieved, as with reserpine, or are found clinically useful only in their higher dosage range, as with ethyl ether. When we attempt to classify depressants by intended use, the examples given do not necessarily reflect a high degree of specificity for the desired action. It might be helpful at this point to list a series of levels of increasing neurological impairment which are sought clinically for particular therapeutic purposes.

(A) Placebo.—It is not uncommon to find marketed preparations of drug mixtures including barbiturates or other sedatives in such low dosage that the only conceivable benefit of this dosage to the patient is the psychological assurance that the prescription contains something to help him sleep.

(B) Reduction of Anxiety.—Above the placebo level many types of central depressant have minimal signs which might be called tranquilizing in that the patient's feelings of internal stress or external threat are reduced. This effect is seen with many sedatives, tranquilizers, analgesics, and antispastics. A feeling of well-being, or euphoria, is common with minimal doses of many drugs of both depressant and stimulant types. This phenomenon probably reflects the great delicacy of the neural mechanism for worry or anxiety, and helps to explain

the wide range of drugs used in the social phenomenon of drug addiction.

(C) Blockade of Special Neural Mechanisms.—Without notable impairment of consciousness or emotional reactivity, it is possible to block selectively a number of central functions particularly when they are pathologically altered. Thus certain drug families can be classified as anticonvulsant (for use in epilepsy), antiparkinson (to reduce the tremor and rigidity of paralysis agitans), antispastic (to reduce other forms of muscle rigidity), antiemetic (to reduce vomiting), antitussive (to diminish the cough reflex), analgesic (to block the central responses to painful stimuli), antipyretic (to stabilize the temperature control centers against substances causing fever), and so on. These specific drug classes are often noteworthy for their specificity of chemical structure.

(D) Reduction of Responsiveness to Stress.—As noted above, many drugs may allay anxiety, but some agents appear to be capable of blocking particular stress responses in a special way. Here we have in mind the reserpine and phenothiazine so-called tranquilizers. These drugs produce a type of reduction of motor function in animals and patients which is quite different from that seen with barbiturates or other more obvious central depressants. In part this change in behavior seems to represent a stabilization of peripheral autonomic and central emotional functions against external and internal stresses. The stress-stabilization seems to be involved in the favorable therapeutic action of these drugs against schizophrenia, although paradoxically this class of disorder is itself notable for evidences of apparent pathological affective stability.

(E) Making Sleep Possible.—Typical doses of sedatives such as barbiturates prescribed for bedtime use are not sufficient in themselves to cause unconsciousness, but allay anxiety and promote a feeling of pleasant drowziness encouraging to sleep.

(F) Causing Sleep.—Larger doses of sedatives may induce the uncontrollable desire to sleep, nevertheless permitting the patient to achieve wakeful alertness in the presence of sufficiently strong stimuli. This dosage level might be traditionally called hypnotic or soporofic, if a name is needed.

(G) Causing Stupor.—Still larger doses of typical sedatives may induce a state in which all higher functions are impaired even though the patient is sufficiently stimulated to keep him apparently awake and motorically active. Here there is definite interference with the learning mechanisms characteristic of the waking state, and with conditioned patterns of emotional behavior. The patient is "drunk." This state of central impairment may be utilized clinically in childbirth,

also in psychiatric practice to encourage the patient to babble in an uninhibited way (narcotherapy). The interference with conditioning mechanisms guarantees that the patient will have poor recall of the experience after recovery.

(H) Causing Unconsciousness.—Complete loss of memory mechanisms and muscular immobility are desirable for certain kinds of relatively non-traumatic surgical procedures, or in preparing patients for more traumatic surgery. Various non-volatile anesthetics are commonly employed, including barbiturates.

(I) Causing Anesthesia.—For major surgical procedures such as abdominal operations, it is necessary not only that the patient be unconscious and immobile but also that the most elementary pain reflexes of the spinal cord be blocked, so that muscular spasms will not interfere with the task. This is classical third stage anesthesia, achieved usually with gaseous anesthetics such as ethyl ether. At this stage the rugged centers of the medulla still produce rhythmic respiration and autonomic outflow sufficient to maintain blood pressure.

(J) Causing Complete Central Blockade.—It is sometimes necessary for a time to abolish even spontaneous respiration, as in surgical procedures on lungs or heart. Provided that artificial respiration is maintained and blood pressure supported by vasoconstrictor drugs, the brain is not permanently damaged even by long periods of suspended animation. Sometimes this procedure is further supported by artificial hypothermia, the body being chilled to a point where all metabolic processes are markedly reduced, the patient also being protected by suitable autonomic blocking agents against certain imbalances during the rewarming process. It is noteworthy that all brain functions including the retention of all previous learned material can survive such a drastic blockade of brain neurochemistry. This phenomenon is one of the strongest evidences that conditioned reflexes are built into stable anatomical structure.

We have already stated that drug groups vary widely in the combination and sequence of depressant and stimulant effects which they can achieve. For example, ethyl ether produces considerable excitement in low concentrations, while chlorpromazine shows excitatory effects in its high dosage range. Therefore central depression by drugs is not a linear one-dimensional process affecting all systems equally. The reduction of function of one system may release and exaggerate the function of a less depressed system. Thus it is not necessary to assume that a drug with mixed effects must necessarily act by more than one ultimate chemical mechanism on neurones. Conversely, a uniformly depressant drug is not necessarily restricted to one ultimate mechanism. In short, the complexity of brain is such that many patterns of depression are possible. For this reason we must be cautious, in searching for chemical explanations of depressant action, neither to minimize nor overstate the possibility of multiple molecular actions of a given drug.

II. Stimulation of Specific Central Functions (cf. also refs. 21, 22, 31, 36, 39, 53, 63, 68, 69)

As with central depressants, the central stimulants include some agents having a wide range of action and others with well-defined limits. Effects vary in intensity from placebo to convulsions. In roughly ascending order of degree of excitation, the following manifestations may be sought for clinical purposes:

(A) Placebo.—The reassurance to a patient who is mildly depressed or lacking in initiative that he is receiving a drug which is a "psychic energizer" may in itself initiate the necessary train of increased motor activity.

(B) Analeptic.—Stimulant drugs may be used to counteract the central depressant side-effects of drugs used for other purposes. For example, the drowziness caused by phenobarbital given for control of grand mal epilepsy may be counteracted by amphetamine without loss of the anticonvulsant protection.

(C) Alerting.—The most universally consumed drugs are those which help to maintain wakefulness and vigilance, usually caffeine in the form of a beverage such as tea or coffee. In various cultures ephedrine, cocaine and others have also been used. The usage of nicotine and of marihuana also appear to be based in part on their mildly alerting properties. Among synthetic agents, amphetamine receives far wider use than can be accounted for on the prescription pad. The enormous consumption of these eye-openers is attributable also to some degree of euphoriant action, although sometimes it appears that the euphoria is only relative to the unpleasant symptoms of abstention when a subject is sufficiently habituated. The allaying of feelings of hunger and fatigue are also contributory.

(D) Antidepressive.—One of the largest groups of psychiatric patients, and particularly in the older age range, is characterized by reduction in initiative and motor activity, with subjective feelings of inadequacy. Extreme manifestations include suicidal wishes and attempts. These depressive tendencies may not yield to treatment with amphetamine or other alerting drugs or for that matter to any of the common drugs with euphoriant properties. Recently a wave of new drugs including inhibitors of monoamine oxidase and adrenergic potentiators have appeared promising.

(E) Stimulation of Specific Neural Mechanisms.—There are many examples of relatively selective central stimulation, some of which have clinical utility. Often they appear to be based on specific central chemoreceptor mechanisms, as in the stimulation of respiration by carbon dioxide, or of vomiting by apomorphine. In some instances the central action may involve peripheral chemoreceptors, as in respiratory stimulation by nikethamide, nicotine, lobeline or cyanide.

(F) Hallucinogenic.—Various primitive peoples have used plant products such as mescaline, bufotenin, cocaine, atropine, ibogaine and others in oral doses sufficient to produce bizarre positive distortions of sensory experience, such as visual aberrations of color, form and movement, sometimes with equally bizarre behavioral manifestations. The apocryphal revelations induced by the hallucinogens were sometimes given special mystical significance by religious cults. More recently these and newer hallucinogens such as lysergic acid diethylamide have been used in psychiatric research and practice, occasionally as an adjunct to psychoanalysis. The ancient psychopharmacology of mystical revelation thus has its modern counterpart. A mundane explanation of the visual hallucinations is that they originate from mixed stimulation and depression of neurones along the visual pathways, including in the retina itself. A high degree of behavioral agitation to the point of maniacal actions without subsequent recall can be obtained with some hallucinogens, such as cocaine, and indicate more widespread actions than on sensory pathways alone.

(G) Convulsant.—A great many drugs useful for other purposes are capable of producing convulsions at higher dosage. The only valid clinical use of convulsions has been for the shock treatment or depressive and related psychoses, and the earlier use of pentylenetetrazole (Metrazol) for this purpose has been superseded by electroshock, and to a considerable extent recently by antidepressive drugs. There has been some usage of pentylenetetrazole for the activation of seizure foci in the EEG of epileptic patients. Otherwise the use of convulsant properties of drugs has been limited to the animal experimental laboratory for studies in the physiology and pharmacology of seizures.

III. Suppression of Specific Peripheral Functions
(cf. also refs. 14, 21, 25, 35, 43, 55, 56, 57, 59)

A major part of neuropharmacology concerns drugs used as blocking agents against neurohumoral mediators of the peripheral nervous system. Most of these are neuroeffector blocking agents, drugs which block chemical mediation of the responses of muscle and gland cells. A review of their uses would comprise a monograph in itself. Since our primary concern in this article is with neurones rather than effectors, we will limit attention to a representative listing of types of action of blocking agents.

1. Blocking of Impulse Conduction in Nerve Fibers and Other Excitable Tissues.—Local anesthetics such as procaine are capable of raising threshold and blocking impulse conduction in all cells having this property. Thus they find use in the prevention of pain by local application to skin, nerve trunks and spinal cord, but also in such nonneural usages as the blocking of cardiac arrhythmias.

2. Blocking of Cholinergic Mediation.—There are three principal classes of agents which block the effects of acetylcholine on target cells. Those which paralyze skeletal muscle by preventing the action of acetylcholine on the end-plate region of the muscle fiber may be called curariform or antinicotinic. The effect may be achieved by preventing cholinergic depolarization of the end-plate, as with d-tubucurarine, or by persistent depolarization, as with succinylcholine. Those which block cholinergic synaptic transmission at autonomic ganglia may also be classed as antinicotinic and include some curariform drugs, but not the more specifically useful ganglionic blockers such as tetraethylammonium. Those which block acetylcholine excitation of exocrine gland cells, or cause inhibition of cardiac muscle, and excitation or inhibition of smooth muscle depending on the cell type, are called antimuscarinic or atropinic, atropine being the prototype and most widely used of this class. In addition, there are some drugs which appear to block cholinergic mediation at various sites not by their action on the target cells but by preventing acetylcholine release from the input cell. This group would include botulinus toxin and an interesting new experimental series, the hemicholiniums.

3. Blocking of Adrenergic Mediation.—There are drugs available for the prevention of the effects of mediators of the autonomic sympathetic and other chromaffin systems on cardiac muscle, some glands, and a wide range of smooth muscle types, as well as upon many other cell types unrelated to the neuroeffector system. No single blocking agent is universal in its action on all of these cell types, as was noted also with the cholinergic system. The multiplicity of adrenergic mediators now known which are derived from tyrosine, as well as the related serotonin series derived from tryptophane, is probably further complicated by specific profiles of mediator sensitivity in the target cells themselves. Some attempts to systematize these profiles has been made, but not with complete success. The most universally acting blocking drugs are not those which attach to target cells but rather those which deplete the mediators at their source. This appears to be the principal action of reserpine and its closely related naturally occurring analog deserpidine. These drugs cause a transient release and prolonged deficit throughout the body of adrenaline, noradrenaline, dopamine and other presumed precursors of noradrenaline, as well as of serotonin. A number of other natural and synthetic depleting agents are more selective. A still different class of blocking agents, represented by the bretyllium series, may prevent mediator release.

4. Blocking of Histaminergic Mediation.—Although not clearly a neurotropic system, since the role of histamine as a neurohumor has never been established beyond reasonable doubt, it has long been evident that antihistaminic drugs such as diphenhydramine have effects both on brain and on peripheral nerve. Further, the presence of histamine in small-fibered sensory neurones and related brain centers is demonstrable. However, the chief effects of antihistamines are exerted on a wide range of smooth muscle and other peripheral target cells. In addition to drugs blocking target cells, some drugs can apparently deplete the histamine stores of neurones and other cells. Enzyme preparations containing a diamine oxidase system have also been used to speed destruction of histamine.

5. Blocking of Polypeptide Mediators.—Polypeptides of neural origin include antidiuretic hormone and oxytocin of the hypothalamic neurones with posterior pituitary terminations, adrenocorticotrophic-release hormone also of hypothalamic origin, substance P and slow-reacting substance of brain and peripheral origin, and probably many others. Some diuretic drugs such as caffeine may act by blocking the action of the antidiuretic hormone on renal target cells. Some presumed antihistamines may also act as polypeptide blockers. The new antiserotonin agent homochlorcyclizine may also block slow-reacting substance, a smooth-muscle excitant in several visceral organs.

IV. Stimulation of Specific Peripheral Functions
(cf. also refs. 7, 8, 18, 20, 22, 33, 58, 64, 65)

1. Stimulation of Sensory Receptors.—Although there are no useful applications other than experimental for nerve fiber stimulants such as the decalcifying agents, some useful drugs appear to act more specifically on the specialized end-structures of sensory nerves. The cooling action of menthol may be exerted directly on fibers which give rise to sensations of cold, while various liniments and other counterirritant preparations may behave likewise with respect to sensory fibers for warmth perception. Some drugs such as nikethamide which act as respiratory stimulants appear to do so by exciting chemoreceptor endings of the carotid body.

2. Cholinergic Stimulation.—In addition to acetylcholine itself, there are a number of synthetic agents such as carbaminoylcholine which mimic the actions of the mediator but have the advantage that they are less easily hydrolyzed by cholinesterase and therefore last longer. The synthetic agents and some which are suspect as naturally occurring cholinergic mediators are often more selective in their site of action than acetylcholine itself, showing special preference for skeletal muscle, postganglionic cells, or other targets. Some related drugs appear to facilitate cholinergic transmission rather than mimic it. Finally, the anticholineterases favor cholinergic transmission by preserving the mediator.

3. Adrenergic Stimulation.—In addition to many naturally occurring mediator catecholamines and their relatives in the serotonin family, various synthetic derivatives may also mimic mediators. The specificity for particular target cells is often notable. Another class of agents, such as amphetamine, may act at some sites by facilitating mediators already present through excitatory actions on target cells. Another large class, of interest because of their psychiatric use as antidepressives, are the monoamineoxidase inhibitors, represented by iproniazed. They intensify mediator action by slowing enzymatic destruction. However, many of these are also adrenergic facilitators in their own right. Other enzymatic blocking agents of interest included the O-methyl tranferase inhibitors, such as pyrogallol.

4. Others.—In addition to histamine and its mimics and facilitators, some agents such as stilbamidine have a histaminergic action by virtue of their ability to release histamine from an inactive complex. Some presumed monoamine oxidase inhibitors also may act on the diamine substrates, thus exerting histaminergic effects. Facilitators and releasers of polypeptide mediators are less well known; nicotine may be a direct stimulant for hypothalamic cells producing antidiuretic hormone.

MECHANISMS OF NEUROTROPIC DRUG ACTION

I. Physicochemical Characteristics of Neurotropic Drugs (cf. also refs. 29, 55)

Substances capable of altering central nervous function vary so widely that it seems most improbable that any single unifying rule could include them all. At one end of the structural range, nitrogen gas at sufficiently high atmospheric pressure may act as an anesthetic and simple derivatives of methane or ethane may be powerful anesthetics. At the other end of the range are structures of relatively great complexity, such as morphine, reserpine, bulbocapnine, strychnine and others, capable of producing highly selective actions. In between these extremes of size and complexity lie the great bulk of neurotropic drugs now in clinical use. Our ability to demonstrate rational relations between structure and activity will be best when we remain within particular families of drugs, such as the barbiturates, the volatile anesthetics, the anticonvulsants, etc. Nevertheless, certain broad principles of structure are sufficiently recurrent to provoke comment.

The association of exogenous chemical substances with endogenous tissue constituents can conceivably include the widest range of bonding energies from multiple covalent bonding further stabilized by resonance of the resultant complex at one extreme, to purely random physical collision at the opposite extreme.

Beginning with the latter, we might expect the poorest potency in that class of drugs which acts merely by diluting a liquid phase of tissue constituents. In the extreme case of water itself as the diluent, with an approximate concentration of 55 mols/l., it probably requires a shift of something like 5 mols/l. to produce notable effects on the nervous system; the significant shift is probably in concentration of osmotic particles, especially ions, rather than in water itself.

Water can to some extent be replaced and mimicked by urea. It is well known that some elasmobranch fishes accumulate a considerable fraction of urea, amounting to many mols/liter of body water. In peripheral nerve we have not observed notable actions of urea until more than half of the water medium has been replaced. The effects then seen are some increase in excitability, together with a lowering of spike amplitude and ultimately a remarkable increase in spike duration before complete failure of conduction.

Insofar as the simple alcohols may be considered organic homologs of water, let us consider them for the moment as purely diluting agents. Taking for example ethyl alcohol, it is evident that a 30 gm. schnapps distributed evenly through an 80 kg. man may have some minimal effects on the nervous system. If the alcohol is distributed in body water amounting to perhaps 50 liters, this subject will have replaced water by alcohol to the extent of 600 mg./l., or roughly 13 mMol/l. However, the lipid solubility of alcohol and its preference for association with non-polar moieties of protein structure suggest an additional mechanism of diluting action which we will now consider.

In general the neurotropic potency of saturated monoalcohols and many other simple series tends to increase with molecular weight. So also does the relative solubility in typical lipid solvents compared with water. The relationship is such that for a wide variety of substances of relatively poor potency the effective concentration in body lipids remains comparatively constant for a given neurological effect. This is essentially a statement of the classical Meyer-Overton rule regarding oil:water distribution coefficients of drugs.

However, it cannot be implied that drugs which follow this rule act only by dilution of the lipid phase of the neuronal membrane. Series similar to those of Meyer and Overton can be derived equally well from thermodynamic considerations by the calculations of Ferguson, giving essentially a hydrophobic index independent of the nonaqueous phase in which the test drug is assumed to distribute. Johnson, Eyring and Polissar[29] therefore raise the question whether typical lipid-soluble drugs need act on a lipid phase as such; they consider the possibility of association with hydrophobic moieties of proteins of specific enzyme systems, even when these are not in the lipid-phase portions of cell membranes.

In favor of the principle, however stated, of the importance of drug association with hydrophobic body constituents, there is a general rule that for homologous series the potency increases with alkyl chain length, as in alcohols, amides, carbamates, etc. This is essentially the classical rule of Traube, and gives series with decreasing aqueous solubility. It should be noted, however, that such series always come to a finite limit precisely because the drug must be carried in the aqueous phase if it is to reach the non-aqueous constituent.

It might be supposed that the saturated hydrocarbons would be the most effective neurotropic drugs, being hydrophobic and comparatively lipid-soluble. This is certainly not the case, since alcohols, amides, carbamates, halogens, ethers and esters are invariably more potently neurotropic than their hydrocarbon parent structures. In part the issue may turn on the necessity for aqueous transport. However, there may be a more direct significance of this relation of drug action, and in pursuit of a new rule we will now turn our attention to certain electrostatic considerations of structure.

If we arrange various neurotropic drugs, such as general anesthetic, sedative, muscle relaxant, in order of potency for specific effects, we cannot help but be impressed with the trend toward increasing potency with increasing noncarbon substituents, such as halogens, oxygen, nitrogen, sulfur. Furthermore, the tendency toward increasing potency with increasing unsaturation is notable more often than not. These trends, covering a wide range of potencies and structures, are opposed to Traube's rule regarding the effect of methylenic additions for particular heteroatom substituents of hydrocarbons. Nevertheless, the antimethylenic rule seems to hold over a wider range of structures, within which Traube's rule is followed in particular cases. We are therefore inclined toward the following rule regarding substituents of parent hydrocarbons: Members of extended drug series which act primarily by weak association with tissue constituents become more potent insofar as they present a molecular surface having greater negative electrostatic charge.

By electrostatic charge we are not here concerned with ionic forces, but with the inside-out polarization of non-ionic molecules. Thus saturated hydrocarbons may be visualized as having a relatively heavy protonic or electropositive external screening surface. As the saturated hydrocarbon is progressively replaced by heteroatoms having unshared electrons, or by unsaturation of bonds, or by distortion of bonds in highly strained ring structures such as cyclopropane, or by modifications forcing coplanarity, or merely by ring formation, the net electrostatic effect is to expose the outer electron orbitals at the surface of the invading drug molecule. Alternatively stated, increasing potency is associated with decreasing exposure of protons.

In some instances the tendency of such an effect will be to encourage the probability of hydrogen bonding with protons of hydrophilic tissue constituents. However, this will obviously not be the case with unsaturated carbon bonds and strained rings. It might be supposed that there is a tendency for preferential packing of surface-electronegative drug molecules with highly protonic and relatively surface-electropositive moieties of tissue constituents. However, it should be recognized that there can be important associations between molecules with the same relative surface electronegativities. Thus electron transfer complexes can exist between molecules based on the sharing of molecular orbitals.[30,40,48] Where the components of the complex are relatively equal, new orbitals can involve the entire molecular complex. With differences in polarity, an electron of one component may be drawn into a new molecular orbital of the other.

It appears for some series that the absolute numerical deficit in protons is more significant than the proton deficit ratio to molecular weight. This infers that the molecular mobility is less important than the inside-out charge of the individual molecule. In short, the surface charge effect is diluted when divided among separate smaller molecules having a random spatial distribution.

The effect which we have described can be expressed as "electron herniation." It implies a property of drug molecules which favors associations with tissue constituents limiting their degrees of freedom of motion. Since the rule, for what it is worth, seems to apply to relatively poorly potent classes of nonspecific central nervous depressants, it does not in any way compromise more sophisticated approaches to the actions of more specific drugs with potent and special effects on limited properties of neurones. For these we must consider the possibility of more precise bonding mechanisms.

The association between saturated hydrocarbons involves the weak-

est forces of all, and might be dismissed as Van der Waals forces if the
term had any meaning. Obviously something more specific is involved
in the tendency for association of non-polar structures. The orbitals
for C-H bonding electrons must necessarily extend well beyond the H
atom. They can thus provide an exchange force for a nearby H-C
moiety. If the bonding energies are similar, and therefore the equivalent frequencies, resonance effects by alternation can strengthen the
intermolecular association.

In short, there are forces, however weak, tending to associate similar
molecules or moieties of molecules, in addition to those forces existing between electrically dissimilar structures.

An example of an attempt to work out a system for prediction of
pharmacological properties from considerations of structure and solubility is that of Fujita.[19] Essentially it is a two-factor system taking
into account what he terms the "organic" and "inorganic" features of
organic molecules. The former is essentially a count of carbon atoms,
plus a correction to be made for certain noncarbon atoms and groups:
the latter is a correction applied to various atoms and groups which is
maximum for metal and least for halogens. The empirical corrections
are derived or interpolated from tables of solubility and other physical
properties of series of related compounds. The organic number appears
to represent the cumulative effect of covalent C-H and C-C bonds,
while the inorganic seems to represent polar features in bonds and is
greatest for electron-donating atoms, least for electron-receiving atoms.
At any rate the optimal pharmacological activity appears to lie in
molecules with about equal proportions of these two features. In some
respects the system reflects the hydrophilic-hydrophobic dualism, and
points up the lesson that physiologically active drugs must be soluble
in both water and lipid phase of tissues (or alternatively, must associate with both polar and non-polar moieties of the cell membrane).
This two-factor theory and its incident calculations also emphasize the
predictive features of knowledge of various physical characteristics of
drugs.

Another way of expressing the polar features of drug molecules is
in terms of their dipole moments, which tend to be large for many
simple drugs. However, the most potent drugs are multipolar rather
than simple dipoles, and it is hard to avoid the conclusion that their
potency resides in associations with multiple foci on the protein surface with which they interact. No simple physical measurement can be
expected to give information on the fine pattern of multipolar fields
surrounding the molecule. The calculations involved in determining
molecule orbitals are relevant, but most difficult even with computer
aid in the case of the larger drug molecules. An examination of molec-

ular models may sometimes assist speculation concerning the structure of the specific tissue constituent with which the drug interacts.

Most drugs are not particularly reactive in the ordinary sense of forming strong and stable bonds with known tissue constituents. Probably those few which are highly reactive, such as some nitrogen mustards, fluorophosphates, hydrazines, etc., tend to destroy the constituent with which they react, leading to prolonged action until new constituents are resynthesized.

For drugs which are capable of dissociation into ions there has been considerable interest in the calculation of dissociation constants. However, the role of ionic attractions with ionized moieties of tissue structure may be limited to such obvious cases as quaternary amines or those easily quaternized *in vivo*. Information on dissociation constants may be of value in the calculation of polar tendencies of unionized molecules.

II. The Model Membrane (cf. also refs. 4, 10, 18, 29, 33, 37, 41, 55, 56, 57, 71)

In order to develop a unified theoretical basis for the actions of drugs upon neurones, we will attempt to develop a schema which includes the principal features of the diffusion potential theory of Hodgkin,[27] but takes a somewhat unconventional approach toward the nature of the membrane diffusion barrier. Instead of a single barrier system perforated by occasional holes through which all ions must exchange, we will consider the possibility that the membrane resting and action potentials are developed at different levels in a more complex membrane. Specifically we will consider the properties of a folded membrane consisting of typical polypeptide chains (primary structure) laterally connected by hydrogen bonds between the carbonyl and amino moieties of peptide linkages (secondary structure) to form a sheet, which is thrown into folds linked primarily by bonds between atoms of the amino acid residues (tertiary structure). We will postulate that resting membrane potential arises from diffusion potentials across the entire thickness of membrane and is primarily dependent on secondary structure, while in contrast the action potential involves only partial transfer of ions into membrane folds and is therefore dependent on tertiary structure.

The basis for this speculative departure from previous membrane concepts is as follows:

(1) We accumulated from various investigators using intracellular microelectrodes a number of examples of action potentials of intracellular type without corresponding resting potentials. Although other

explanations may be invoked, it has seemed to us that the simplest premise would be the development of action potential in a layer or site external to membrane potential—i.e., penetration of the full thickness of membrane is not necessary for registration of the action potential.

(2) Some recent unpublished experiments in collaboration with A. Akcasu, involving stretching of axones in various ionic media, suggest the possibility of reversible enlargement of two sets of apertures in the membrane.

(3) The classical 4-layered flat membrane of Davson and Danielli[9] (protein-lipid-lipid-protein) appears to us to have a number of defects: for example:

(a) The membrane of approximately 50 Å thickness seen in electron photomicrographs is not limited to the surface of cells but appears to invaginate and encapsulate various cellular inclusions[10] and possibly to be the continuous form of all intracellular protein structure.[4] If so, the membrane would have to contain far more lipid than could be accounted for in many cells.

(b) The polypeptide backbone of the protein portion of the membrane ought to have curvatures and folds, if one can judge from attempts to build molecular models without bond strain.[29,46] Furthermore, it appears that enzymatically active protein monolayers on glass or aqueous surfaces are thick enough to imply folding.[29] If so, the Davson-Danielli model would be thicker than that seen in electron microscopy. The alternative is that the observed membrane is in fact a folded single layer. The supposed lipid phase of the membrane is then primarily the non-polar residues of particular amino acids forming the meshwork.

(c) Tissue culture phase lapse photomicrography reveals,[47] and electron microscopy suggests,[4] a constant dynamic process by many cells of bubbling, vacuole formation, invagination and evagination, continually changing and reconstituting the cell surface from what appears to be an inexhaustible supply of membranous material. From this and other cytological evidence, such as the mechanics of nuclear rotation, we are inclined to believe that the ground state of protoplasm, and the form in which it is synthesized, is membranous rather than particulate and molecular. If so, the occurrence of a protein surface double layer with interposed lipid seems to us geometrically improbable.

4. Certain soluble and easily isolated proteins appear to have a closely turned helical secondary structure. The strainless helices of Pauling[46] are based on maximal hydrogen bonding between polypetide

chains. Geometrical considerations suggest that strainless sheets with maximal bonding can be formed in similar fashion, and that these will occur in a folded structure. The side chain residues of polar type will be available for further tertiary bonding. Collision apertures can be calculated for both secondary and tertiary structure. Probability curves for apertures with various degrees of bonding can also be calculated. From such models, considered in an aqueous environment with typical concentrations of inorganic ions, it is possible to assess the probability of penetrance of particular ions across secondary or tertiary structure with various degrees of bonding. From these estimates in turn the ion resistances and finally the membrane voltage can be calculated.

5. The necessity for a new approach to membrane structure is motivated in part by a phenomenon which has never been adequately explained,—the sodium activation-inactivation-restoration cycle associated with the action potential.[56] Without plunging into the esoterics of this problem, it can be said simply that sodium behaves as if its inward diffusion caused the action potential, but also as if only a fraction of the available sodium could participate in this function. We have attempted to resolve this problem by the assumption that external sodium ion moves toward and into limited pockets of a folded membrane to produce the action potential.

If an electrical equivalent of the membrane is considered, the active inflow of sodium would be represented by a capacitative short-circuit across most of the sodium resistance of the resting membrane, rather than by a direct reduction of the sodium resistance.

III. Diffusion of Ions in the Model Membrane
(cf. also refs. 12, 13, 18, 22, 27, 28, 29, 37, 55, 56, 57, 70, 71)

The passive diffusion of ions along their gradients across the nerve membrane is limited by the following factors:

(1) The diameters of apertures within the secondary structure of the continuous protein membrane formed by hydrogen-bonding between adjacent polypeptide chains through their carbonyl and amino groups. This structure is universal and therefore has no qualitative difference from cell type to cell type which could serve to explain qualitative differences in action of drugs. However, the degree of bonding is dynamic and statistical, and depends both on the nature of the amino acids contributing to the polypeptide chains and upon the environmental conditions, including both physical parameters and chemical species. For conditions of maximal bonding the collision diameters of the atoms contributing to a unit hydrogen-bonded ring form an aperture which is definitely too small for penetration of a hydrated

sodium ion of 3.4 Å, and questionably so for a hydrated potassium ion of 2.2 Å. Larger absolute apertures are formed by the breaking of one or more successive hydrogen bonds. However, these apertures are also reduced by the existence of an ice-like water shell conditioned by the polypeptide structure.[30,55,60] Thus free penetration by ions is likely only if several successive hydrogen bonds are simultaneously ruptured, and sodium is always at a relative disadvantage compared to potassium or chloride. The latter ions therefore determine the polarity across the membrane, operating to create a relative internal negativity.

(2) Electrostatic conditions further limit ion penetration. The average resting diffusion potential created by the freer mobility of potassium and chloride opposes further diffusion of these ions, while favoring inward diffusion of sodium. However, local electrostatic effects also will tend to limit the admissable apertures within the polypeptide network. These will be created primarily by the side-chains of diamino and dicarboxylic amino acids, and therefore might be expected to differ considerably among cells with different protein structure. Also it should be noted that the average diffusion potential across the membrane will tend to orient the side-chains, and will also condition their state of ionization. Finally, the temporary trapping of free ions within the polypeptide mesh will offer attractive or repulsive forces to approaching ions.

(3) Even the relatively non-polar side-chains of amino acids will offer diffusion barriers by reason of their collision areas and also by the tendency of mobile non-polar solutes to become associated with them. The more polar side-chains will also tend to be associated with each other through forces varying from polar association and hydrogen bonds to disulfide and peptide bonds, the number and type depending on the repetition characteristic of the protein. It should be noted that these side-chain associations will form rings larger than, but fewer in number than, those formed by the polypeptide backbone, and that they might be expected to be much more specifically affected by particular solutes, including exogenous drugs. This looser and more variable meshwork forms the tertiary structure of the protein sheet, forming folds and pockets in what would otherwise be a continuous single surface of hydrogen-bonded polypeptide chains. To some extent the tertiary network may also form hydrogen bonds between apposed polypeptide chains not already fully bonded.

(4) The tertiary structure just described leads us to a conception of the membrane diffusion barrier which is considerably more complicated than that of the continuous single monolayer formed by secondary polypeptide chain hydrogen-bonding alone. The Davson-Danielli schema envisions two such secondary protein sheets with two

oriented lipid layers between. In contrast our conception is that of a single secondary sheet folded upon itself because of tertiary bonds, and therefore forming a pseudo double layer. Within the pockets thus formed by folding are entrapped polar and non-polar solutes, occasional inorganic ions, and a considerable shell of crystalline water structure. This total structure is assumed to be the membrane of some 50 Å thickness discernible in electron photomicrographs. It obviously presents a formidable barrier to the transport of any ion or solute approaching from either side. However, we come now to a critical point in excitation theory by asking whether it is necessary to have complete transfer of ions across the membrane in order to achieve an electrical change.

(5) Partial ion transport can occur through tertiary structure without penetration of secondary structure. An ion may thus transfer in or out of a pocket in the membrane. If for example a change in tertiary structure permitted an inward shift of sodium ions into externally-opening pockets previously free of ions (or possibly an inward shift of sodium ions from internally-opening pockets, or both) the net electrical effect would be an apparent transient increase in sodium permeability and a corresponding transient reversal of membrane potential. Such a shift would correspond precisely to the rising phase of the action potential, or the "activation" process, and the attainment of equilibrium in the pocket system would correspond to the falling phase or "inactivation." Complete recovery of excitability would require the trapping or extrusion of sufficient sodium ions to restore the original conditions of the tertiary pockets. In short, a mechanism can be envisioned whereby the action potential is created without gross transfer of sodium across the total thickness of membrane, and without the necessity of notable changes in other ion permeabilities. The critical factor would be the lability of the tertiary structure as a barrier to sodium transfer. The smaller hydrated volumes of the potassium and chloride ions would ordinarily permit their equilibration across tertiary structure and also sufficient permeability through secondary structure to maintain the resting membrane potential, which would be relatively unopposed by the sodium diffusion potential except during the overwhelming but transient partial shift of sodium. The resting impermeability of tertiary structure to sodium transfer would in turn be heavily dependent on the role of resting membrane voltage in maintaining suitable orientation of the side-chains contributing to tertiary bonding.

(6) Since a change in potassium permeability is not necessary for recovery in the schema of partial sodium transfer, it might be asked what role if any is played by potassium in this sequence. For vertebrate

axones the answer is apparently "none," since the evidence favors a
constant potassium permeability.[56] For squid axones it is evident that
a phase of increased potassium permeability supervenes, suggesting a
relative loosening of secondary structure.[27] For mammalian heart the
opposite probably occurs, a phase of prolonged potassium impermeability maintaining the depolarized state.[71] In all cases the potassium
gradient ultimately poises the resting membrane potential, without
which the critical sodium sequence would be impossible.

(7) The sodium extrusion cycle[28,54,56,70,71] may be considered a special case of random diffusion coupled with an as yet unspecified metabolic step. Let it be assumed that an intracellular sodium ion diffuses
through secondary membrane structure into an externally-opening
membrane pocket. Secondary structure is tightened under the orienting
influence of the hydrated ion, tending to seal the trap. However, the
local voltage gradient previously orienting tertiary structure is now
cancelled for the opening of the particular pocket, permitting outward
diffusion of the pocketed ion, after which the tertiary structure again
closes. This valve-like mechanism might conceivably operate without
energy expenditure, like a tiny Maxwell's demon, but it appears that
at least one of the four steps of structural change is not freely reversible,
and requires an oxidative step for reconstitution of structure. It might
also be asked why the valve mechanism does not operate for other ions
such as potassium or chloride. However, we have assumed from the
beginning that the penetration of these smaller ions is more probable
than for sodium through secondary structure; in short, the valve system is too leaky for ions of smaller diameter.

(8) Although the discussion has been exclusively concerned with
inorganic ions, it should be recognized that not all investigators accept
the unique role of sodium in the generation of action potential.[18,61]
Thus the role of organic quaternary ammonium ions has been champ-
ioned by Lorente de No, and by Nachmansohn for the particular case
of acetylcholine.[42] From another point of view the role of labile elec-
trovalences in structural components of the membrane has been stressed
by Ling.[37] Some organic cations, particularly hydrazine, have been
shown to replace sodium in its action potential function, as shown recently by Koketsu[34] and earlier by Lorente de Nó. But the sodium and
onium concepts are not mutually exclusive, since there is every reason
to suppose that membrane penetrance will be the same for any ions of
equal charge and hydration diameter. It is even conceivable that onium
cationic heads attached to long mobile side-chains in the membrane
could serve the role of sodium in penetrating tertiary structure for
the distance of a few angstroms, so that the fixed charge hypothesis is

also not incompatible with the sodium hypothesis, if one will accept the partial transfer theorem.

(9) One special set of phenomena to be considered in any ionic explanation of excitability is the accumulation of effects of repetitive stimulation. These include post-tetanic potentiation at central synaptic sites,[17] hyperexcitability in peripheral neurones,[62] etc., as well as various fatigue phenomena with more prolonged and rapid stimulation. In terms of the membrane model, it would appear that sodium penetration through tertiary structure is facilitated by previous action potential cycles. Since retention of sodium ion in the folds would impede rather than facilitate new cycles, it seems more likely that the cumulative change is in the tertiary structure, certain bonds being sluggishly restored once they are broken. In experiments with axones, we find some resemblance between the actions of decalcifying agents such as citrate, oxalate or phosphate, and the action of strong repetitive stimulation. It is therefore possible that calcium ion is the bonding agent in question, but this explanation is probably oversimplified even for the presumed decalcifying agents. In general, the tertiary stabilizers of either local anesthetic or anticonvulsant type which operate against effects of repetitive stimulation or decalcifying agents almost always have an aromatic moiety, which strongly suggest a role of phenylalanine, tyrosine or other aromatic side-chains in tertiary labilizer phenomena.

(10) There finally remains the question of alterations of membrane structure at specialized loci in the neurone, the synaptic areas. In contrast to conducting axones, these sites often appear to be incapable of generating a self-propagating action potential,[18] and are considered by Grundfest[22] to be electrically inexcitable. Nevertheless potential changes can be induced by mediator agents. The change must be toward depolarization for the excitatory case; for inhibition at least in mammalian spinal motoneurones, the change is hyperpolarizing, but this need not be universally true. In the schema of Eccles,[12,13] ion penetrations are increased in both cases, but the smaller ions are favored in the hyperpolarizing case while the differential permeability disappears in the depolarizing case. Interpreting the membrane model, it might be assumed that apertures within secondary structure are larger for inhibitory than for conducting membranes, largest of all for the excitatory synaptic type. But the incompletely bonded secondary structure is normally occluded by folding through tertiary linkages with which the mediator molecules may compete.

We do not necessarily accept the view that all central nervous interactions occur by means of organic mediators. Excitation by means of direct conduction appears as feasible for certain large synapses as it is known to be for the fused giant fiber segments of earth worms, the disc junctions of cardiac fibers, etc.[22,67] Non-synaptic interactions of both inhibitory and excitatory type can be shown between axones of isolated nerve and must certainly occur centrally. The proof for particular centrally acting mediators is convincing only for the special case of cholinergic activation of Renshaw cells by spinal motoneurone collaterals,[12] and even here is considerably less rigorous than for peripheral synapses. Nevertheless it seems probable that many naturally occurring substances may act as modulators of excitability even if they are not essential mediators of neuronal interaction. Therefore we will consider drug actions upon the membrane model independently of assumptions about the neural origin and release of presumed mediators.

IV. Drug Modifications of the Model Membrane (cf. also refs. 12, 13, 55, 56, 57)

On the basis of the foregoing model, it should now be possible to define some hypothetical changes induced by drugs. The four principal classes of drug action would be either tightening or loosening of either secondary or tertiary structure. Additional classes of action would include substances with charged moieties imitating specific inorganic ions, and finally metabolic inhibitors of sodium extrusion. Given these classes of action, it is also possible to subdivide drugs on the basis of their ability to penetrate to various depths of the complex surface. Finally, the tendency of some drugs to associate with particular amino acid sequences by multiple linkages must be taken into account. With these working variables, it is feasible to analyze the consequences of drug action on ion movement and on excitation properties.

(A) Tightening of Secondary Structure.—An agent which increased the probability of hydrogen bonding only in secondary protein structure would not necessarily have any effect on excitation threshold. It might be expected to cause slight resting hyperpolarization by further accentuating the difference between sodium and potassium penetration. It probably would encumber the sodium extrusion process and thus prolong refractoriness and increase fatiguability. The metabolic requirements for maintenance of resting potential would probably be reduced. The tightening of membrane secondary structure might have curious effects at synapses, such as converting depolarizing sites to hyperpolarizing or inhibitory. This description does not completely fit any known drug but is reminiscent of some actions of barbiturates. As to mechanism, it is not clear how a drug could exert a direct closing action on secondary bonds, but might act indirectly through association with side-chains, therefore requiring at least two points of linkage.

If so, it should have some effect also on functions of tertiary structure, such as increasing threshold. However, it is also possible to imagine an occlusive action of more lipid-soluble drugs preferentially concentrating in the folds in association with non-polar side-chains. In any event the drug would probably be required in considerable concentration to have any appreciable effect on secondary structure.

(B) Loosening of Secondary Structure.—An agent which favored larger secondary apertures would probably tend to reduce membrane potential by increasing the relative passive leak-back of sodium. Since total permeability would be increased, the metabolic requirement for maintenance of membrane potential would tend to increase. There would be no necessary change in threshold. Sodium extrusion would be handicapped by leak-back and refractoriness prolonged, as with the secondary membrane tighteners. At synapses, the loosening effect might convert inhibitory surfaces to excitatory. It is noteworthy that a labilizer of secondary structure might be a convulsant through one mechanism while depressing conduction by depolarizing. The only chemical requirement would be competition for hydrogen bonds, a condition satisfied by most drugs. The drugs would be of relatively poor potency because of the surface coverage required.

(C) Tightening of Tertiary Structure.—This action would operate primarily to raise threshold, with little if any effect on membrane potential. The local anesthetics such as procaine would be examples of this type of tertiary stabilizing action. A possible mechanism of stabilizing action would be the formation of multiple linkages between amino acid residues, thus reinforcing the existing tertiary structure. Therefore, the drug should possess multiple bonding sites. Furthermore, since relatively few bonds might give considerable reinforcement of structure, the drug might be expected to act in relatively low concentration. The attachment sites might be relatively critical for certain pairs of amino acid residues. At central synapses the tertiary stabilizers would tend to block both excitatory and inhibitory mediators. This is strongly suggestive of the mixed convulsant and depressant effects of procaine on the central nervous system.

(D) Partial Fixation of Tertiary Structure.—Drugs which stabilize that part of tertiary structure which is modified by repetitive activity should be considered separately from the previous class. Certain anticonvulsants such as diphenylhydantoin fall within this class. Their primary difference from the local anesthetics is their failure to raise threshold. With local anesthetics they share the ability to block hyperexcitability caused by decalcifying and other agents. Conversely, local anesthetics can be shown to have some interesting central anticonvulsant actions, despite their known propensity to cause convulsions.[3,62]

(E) Loosening of Tertiary Structure.—Drugs competing for tertiary bonds might be expected to lower threshold for sodium admittance, thereby increasing excitability and causing spontaneous firing in axones. Centrally, they should facilitate both excitary and inhibitory neurones, a function reminiscent of the amphetamine group. However, the amphetamine group has no excitatory actions on peripheral axones. Indeed, the axonal excitants are preponderantly decalcifying agents.

(F) Cationic Agents.—Drugs which resemble inorganic ions might be expected to cause effects dependent on their charge, size and special features of their residue structure.[55] On peripheral nerve both choline and acetylcholine behave like inert non-penetrating cations. If a small amount of sodium is provided, the remainder of the solution can be made isotonic with these agents without conduction failure. Some hyperpolarization occurs because of the loss of the normal sodium gradient. These cations are obviously too large to penetrate tertiary structure of axones, and it must be presumed that the tertiary structure is looser at synaptic sites where acetylcholine is active. Quaternization of various local anesthetics results in inactive ions,[50] presumably by reason of size. In contrast, tetraethylammonium ion has an excitatory effect on axones, while it is inhibitory at ganglionic synapses and relatively inactive at the neuromuscular junction. Presumably these qualitative differences in action are based on the increasing looseness of tertiary structure at these sites. Hydrazine and some guanidine-like substances can replace sodium at least partially in axone functions.[34] Ammonium ion itself is apparently small enough to resemble potassium rather than sodium.

(G) Metabolic Inhibitors.—Since the normal gradients of ions across the membrane are presumably maintained by metabolic work, it is certainly surprising that the action potential cycle can be maintained in the presence of a variety of metabolic poisons and various conditions unfavorable to oxidative metabolism, provided that the resting potential is maintained by exogenous current. Furthermore the reversibility of anoxic depolarization is faster than can be accounted for by redistribution of ions. It would seem therefore that either oxidative metabolism or exogenous anodal polarization may maintain the differential resting permeability and the membrane conditions necessary for the partial sodium transfer cycle during the action potential. The normal metabolic rate is also dependent to some extent on the sodium turnover cycle. Although many drugs, including barbiturates and urethanes, have been studied in vitro as metabolic inhibitors in various systems,[29,49] it seems likely that their in vivo neurotropic effects are exerted directly on the membrane parameters, while

their metabolic effects are secondary. As far as we know, none of the common classes of neurotropic drugs has yet been proved to act primarily through inhibition of oxidative metabolism.

(H) Other Enzyme Inhibitors.—The ability of physostigmine, diisopropylfluorophosphate, and other cholinesterase inhibitors to block nerve conduction has been used by Nachmansohn and coworkers[42] as evidence for a role of acetylcholine in the conduction process. On the basis of our own work with such agents it seems more likely that the anticholinesterases fall into the class of tertiary stabilizers, like local anesthetics. That the membrane itself may have esterasic properties is not denied, but it is not evident how if at all this property contributes to conduction of impulses. At central synapses anticholinesterases appear to have some mixed excitatory and depressant effects, as do also various cholinergic drugs. For the most part these effects are blocked by atropinic drugs, as at peripheral muscarinic synapses. Since the atropinics are also of the tertiary stabilizing class, it appears that the central actions of anticholinesterases in preserving cholinesters must be of some importance. However, the ability of atropine to block cholinesterasic effects without itself producing profound central disturbances should suggest that the cholinesters are modulators rather than essential mediators of central synaptic transmission.

Another group of enzyme inhibitors has recently come into some prominence because of their useful clinical antidepressive effects. These are the monoamine-oxidase (MAO) inhibitors, which presumably act through the preservation of catecholamines and serotonin. Without going into the central action of these latter mediator or modulator substances, we are inclined on the basis of our own work to consider many of the MAO inhibitors to act primarily as amphetamine-like tertiary labilizers.

Recapitulation.—To summarize this theoretical section, we have outlined a model of the neuronal membrane in which a sheet formed of hydrogen-bonded polypeptide chains is held in folds by linkages between amino acid residues. The critical event in excitation is assumed to be the limited diffusion of sodium ion or onium analogs into the folds. Based on this concept, a broad division of neurotropic drugs into four general classes is made: secondary (interpolypeptide) labilizers and stabilizers; tertiary (interfold) labilizers and stabilizers. Quantitative differences in structure between conducting axons and excitatory and inhibitory synapses give rise to qualitative differences in drug action at these various sites. Cationic drugs resembling the inorganic ions may also give qualitatively different effects at different sites depending on quantitative differences in structure.

V. Analysis of Some Neurotropic Drug Actions
(cf. also refs. 12, 21, 55, 56)

We will utilize the remaining text to illustrate the search for mechanism in only two groups, first the central depressants of relatively low potency such as general anesthetics, and secondly the local anesthetics. The first group illustrates some physical principles which can be extended also to the antispastic centrally acting muscle relaxants, the non-barbiturate sedatives, the barbiturate sedatives and the nonaromatic anticonvulsants. These drugs, in the approximate order given, appear to represent an ascending series of action beginning with labilization of secondary protein structure and passing over to stabilization with increasing complexity of multipolar profile. The second group illustrates a broad class of threshold-raising agents which are complex in their multipolar profile, have certain sequences of poles in common, and appear to act primarily as stabilizers of tertiary structure. The more obvious families within this class include, in addition to local anesthetics, such groups as atropinic, antiparkinson, and antihistaminics. The rules can be generalized also to more variant structural groups, including some anticholinesterases as well as cholinergic blocking agents, some antiadrenergic drugs as well as monoamine oxidase inhibitors and certain other antidepressives, anticonvulsant drugs with aromatic substituents, analgesics, and antipyretics. As a general rule this drug class shows a wide variety of specific peripheral and central blocking actions, often changing sharply with small changes in structure. Simplification of multipolar structure, as with aromatic alkylamines, brings a transition toward labilization of tertiary structure, with many specific examples of potentiating rather than blocking action. This fascinating array of multipolar drugs may provide in the future many pharmacological tools for the elucidation of the precise patterning of the residue structure of membrane protein at various sites in the nervous system.

(A) General Anesthetics and Related Central Depressants.—A number of volatile substances of low molecular weight are used in surgical procedures to produce central depression sufficient to permit painful manipulation on a relaxed body and without subsequent recollection by the patient. The depth of central depression required may vary from confusion and later amnesia in a childbirth to complete areflexia and cessation of respiratory movements in an open chest operation. In general these agents differ from non-volatile depressants of larger molecular weight such as barbiturates, which may also be used as surgical anesthetics, in that they do not produce preliminary tranquility or sleep. In fact, the volatile anesthetics are notable for production of

some degree of excitement during the induction period. Also as a rule they do not depress respiration as much as the non-volatile group for a corresponding degree of unconsciousness and analgesia, an important consideration in the average surgical operation.

Some representative volatile anesthetics are noted below, approximately in order of increasing potency as judged from percentage concentration required in inspired air.

nitrous oxide	N_2O	80%+
ethylene	$CH_2 = CH_2$	80%
acetylene	$CH \equiv CH$	75%
cyclopropane	$CH_2 - CH_2$ $\diagdown CH_2$	20%
ether	$(C_2H_5)_2O$	8%
ethyl chloride	C_2H_5Cl	4%
vinyl ether	$(CH_2{=}CH)_2O$	4%
trichloroethylene	$CHCl{=}CCl_2$	1%
chloroform	$CHCl_3$	1%

Generally these agents tend to have high oil:water distribution coefficients, and this would suggest that they tend to associate with non-polar groupings in the membrane. However, they invariably have some degree of proton deficit and corresponding polarity in comparison with hydrocarbons of similar molecular weight, which are relatively non-anesthetic. Therefore it might be assumed that in addition to non-polar association they tend to compete with other polar linkages in the membrane. The small size and the concentrations required in lipid would suggest a considerable membrane coverage. The mechanism of action might therefore be postulated as secondary labilization of interpolypeptide hydrogen bonding, in our previously suggested schema. If so, the ultimate effect on neurone membranes would be depolarization, by permitting increased resting sodium flux. In fact these agents are typical depolarizers of peripheral axones, and there is little reason to question similar central action. An additional central effect would be the weakening of inhibition by enlarging the apertures of secondary structure. This action might account for the excitatory and pseudoconvulsive manifestations noted during the induction stage with volatile anesthetics. These agents are not usefully anticonvulsant except in the special case of status epilepticus, where uncontrollable seizures may be abolished by full anesthetic doses as a life-saving measure.

Cyclopropane might seem to violate the structural rule concerning inactivity of saturated hydrocarbons, but it is noteworthy that in many physical properties cyclopropane and cyclopropyl derivatives behave more like their unsaturated analogs. The bond distortion approaches that of double bonds, and the proton deficit is equivalent to that of propylene, which also has anesthetic properties.

Related to the volatile anesthetic series are the so-called basal anesthetics, such as tribromoethanol, which are liquids or solids of low molecular weight with stronger polar associative tendencies, as shown by their higher boiling points. Continuous with this series are other agents of low molecular weight such as ethanol, used in various other applications as central depressants. Some representatives are given:

ethyl alcohol C_2H_5OH
tribromoethanol CBr_3CH_2OH
chloral hydrate $CCl_3CH(OH)_2$
paraldehyde $(CH_3CHO)_3$

As a general rule the higher boiling points and greater water solubilities tend to be associated with less excitation and more sedation than with the volatile anesthetics. Also the potency tends to increase with proton deficit. Thus in examining a large series of volatile and basal anesthetics and nonbarbiturate sedatives of low molecular weight, we have noted that there is approximately a ten-fold decrease in required dosage for a deficit of five protons, the deficit being compared with alkanes of similar molecular weight.

Since the larger proton deficits are contributed by more than one polar configuration on the molecule, a question arises concerning ultimate mechanism of action upon the nerve membrane. Although one electron-rich point on a molecule might tend to compete with and open up the hydrogen bonds of secondary structures, two or more such attractions might form bridges which stabilize the structure. Thus the multipolar group need not be depolarizers. Stability of secondary structure would also tend to reinforce inhibition and diminish excitation in the subsynaptic membranes. The smaller molecules would not occlude tertiary structure but might either labilize or stabilize depending on the separation of polar groups. Although these principles have not been tested in detail, it can be said that the ability of these smaller molecules to block conduction in axones without depolarizing increases with the number of polar groups. The mechanism appears to be interference with sodium influx, as shown by fall in action potential spike. Ability to raise threshold, in the manner of local anesthetics, is less marked. Interference with the recovery process is notable in all of these substances.

As to the relative effect on central inhibition, which should be reduced for the monopolar and increased for the multipolar molecules if our hypothesis is correct, we have already indicated the more sedative effect of the higher members of the series. Another tentative index of the relative ratio of central inhibition to excitation, based on the theory of feedback circuits, would be the tendency to slow electrical rhythms. It is notable that the volatile anesthetics tend as a rule to produce reduced EEG potentials of asynchronous character, while the more sedative and non-volatile group tend to produce large, slow synchronous effects and eventually synchronous bursts with periods of silence, for comparable degrees of anesthesia in experimental animals. As one ascends the multipolar series, it is also evident that the doses required for central depression are relatively less than required for conduction block, again emphasizing the possibility of inhibition by stabilization of secondary structure at synaptic membranes.

It is evident that we have here a qualitative difference in mechanism of central depression arising from a quantitative increase in the number of attraction centers of central depressant molecules. Ultimately this trend also appears to be superceded in still larger molecules by stabilization of tertiary structure, leading to interesting mixtures of excitation and depression which will be discussed later.

A final word is in order about the polar structure of the central depressant molecules of low molecular weight. Features contributing to the polarity are unsaturation, bond distortion, and electron-rich substituents. Unmasking of negative field zones by proton deficit is a common factor. The molecules are usually relatively unreactive. Hydrogen bond formation by proton acceptance is a common but not a universal feature. Non-bonding electrostatic attractions for protons bonded to membrane structure would be a common feature, even for the bifunctional alcoholic drugs.

In contrast to these drugs are various organic substances of low molecular weight which are not central depressant. Ionized molecules, such as the simple organic acids, have little known effect on central function, while on peripheral nerve they are usually excitatory, especially the polycarboxylic acids. Cationic quaternary ammonium molecules have little central or peripheral effect unless they meet certain size specifications, and then their actions are most notable at those peripheral synaptic sites where acetylcholine is implicated as a sodium-like mediator of depolarization. Amines of small to moderate molecular weight are not notably depressant. Other nitrogenous substances are likely to be depressant only insofar as they form acidic groups as in amides, acylureas, other imides, barbiturates, carbamates, etc. Thus by exclusion the requirements for central depression appear to be molecular foci of intermediate electronegative and proton-attracting character, anchored to proton-rich alkyl groups.

It should also be noted that excessive polar character even of intermediate type may reduce the central depressant effect. Thus the typical sugars are relatively inert, as is glycerol, while alkyl ethers of smaller polyalcohols are depressant.

Aromatic substituents do not contribute notably to central depression, but have certain specific features of action in connection with threshold which will be discussed later.

To summarize this section, we have tried to give some unifying characterization to a very heterogeneous group of drugs having general depression of the central nervous system as a common effect. The presumed common denominator would appear to be attraction for the amine hydrogen of the polypeptide chain of membrane protein, although the interpolypeptide hydrogen bonds may be either weakened or strengthened depending on the number of polar foci in the depressant drug. In addition the drugs must associate with non-polar amino acid moieties.

(B)   Local Anesthetics.—The local anesthetics include a large number of substances which are used primarily for their ability to block nerve conduction. In this application they may be applied topically to injured surfaces to allay pain or irritation, injected around small nerves for local anesthesia, around large nerve trunks to anesthetize an entire region, or even into the vertebral canal to block nerve conduction bilaterally for the lower body segments. The purpose of such blockade is almost always the relief of pain, itching or burning or the prevention of pain during surgical manipulations of particular organs or body areas. To accomplish this end it is important that the local anesthetic should not itself produce irritation of nerve fibers or endings, and should have a transient and completely reversible blocking action.

The prototype drugs possessing these actions are the plant alkaloid cocaine and the synthetic procaine. The great majority of local anesthetics in clinical use are related to these both in structure and pharmacological properties, but there are many more substances which can be shown experimentally to block conduction in a similar manner. These include atropine and related antimuscarinic synaptic blocking agents, many antiparkinson agents of atropinic type, some antihistaminics, anticholinesterases, antispastics, antispasmodics, etc. Many but not all of this larger local anesthetic class are structurally similar to the conventional local anesthetics.

A typical local anesthetic is likely to be a dialkylaminoethanol ester of a substituted benzoic acid. Thus procaine is the diethylaminoethanol ester of paraminobenzoic acid. Considerable variation may be made on this structure without loss in potency. The most general requirement appears to be the root A-x $(CH_2)_n$ N $(R)_2$, although even this is not inviolable. Here A is an aromatic ring system, x is is a heteratom system such as an ester linkage, the number n of carbons is usually 2, and the R substituents of the amine are short alkyls or an equivalent saturated ring. Variants in the heteratom portion include ethers, amides, amidines, urethanes and others.

Before proceeding further with a consideration of structure-activity relations, it will be necessary to give some attention to the mechanism of action of local anesthetics.

The key feature of local anesthetic action is the ability to block the conduction of nerve impulses. This is apparently accomplished primarily by raising threshold to a point where the impulse is no longer self-propagating. In a typical frog sciatic preparation treated with procaine, the block occurs when threshold is increased from two to three-fold. At this point local non-progagating spikes can still be recorded, but these diminish in size in association with a further increase in local threshold until finally the membrane behaves like a passive network in response to induced changes in membrane potential. During this development the resting membrane potential remains practically normal. We have also noted in frog fibers that there is little if any change in the resting membrane resistance, as judged from measurement of membrane length and time constants. Therefore the principal effect seems to be upon the mechanism permitting influx of sodium during the action potential. Procaine causes first an increase in the amount of depolarization required to permit a large increase in sodium permeability, and finally blocks sodium influx even with large depolarizing currents.

We have earlier discussed the action potential spike as a transient and limited influx of extracellular sodium into a fraction of the membrane. The membrane potential, in contrast, represents the summation of diffusion potentials and permeabilities of various ions across the entire thickness of membrane. The principal cation gradients involved are those of potassium, tending to polarize, and sodium, tending to depolarize. Local anesthetics do not prevent depolarization by extracellular increase in potassium. However, the following evidence suggests that local anesthetics tend to reduce the resting permeability to sodium in a specific way:

Some unpublished data of H. W. Bond[3a] demonstrate indirectly the role of local anesthetics in limiting the resting sodium influx. Stampfli and Nishie[58a] had shown that hypocalcemic depolarization failed to occur in the absence of external sodium, suggesting that calcium itself restricted resting sodium influx. Bond found an average reduction of 9mv in resting potential of desheathed nerve when calcium-free solutions were used. Procaine, cocaine and dibucaine were able to reverse the hypocalcemic depolarization in concentrations which did not block conduction. The rate of repolarization was almost as rapid as that caused by added calcium itself, and comparable to the rate of change of potential as external sodium concentration is varied.

Thus the local anesthetics behave like calcium insofar as they block a fraction of the resting sodium permeability. They also resemble calcium with regard to their effects on excitability. Calcium ion raises threshold, and decalcifying agents such as citrate, oxalate and phosphate lower it to the point of spontaneous firing. Procaine in doses considerably below that required for conduction block can prevent the induced hyperexcitability.

The common action of calcium and procaine in this regard is the stabilization of the membrane against active sodium influx. But calcium and procaine are by no means equivalent. Hyperpolarization appears to be a feature of conduction block by calcium but not by procaine. Procaine is also considerably more potent as a blocking agent. Furthermore it is difficult to envision the same site of action for these two agents, as far as bonding of tissue constituents is concerned. However, the action may be common insofar as it indicates a stabilization of that region of membrane structure involved both in the active sodium influx and in part of the passive influx. In our schema of the membrane this region would be the external fraction of the tertiary structure of membrane proteins.

Another set of phenomena in which local anesthetics appear to be involved in stabilization against sodium influx is exemplified in their interactions with veratrine and related substances, as shown by the work of Herr and Akcasu.[25] Veratrine has a number of actions,[21,59] which need not be detailed here, indicative of widespread increase in membrane permeability to sodium. Resting membrane potential is reduced in a sodium-dependent manner. The action potential threshold is at first reduced, but conduction eventually fails after changes suggestive of inability of the membrane to extrude the excess of sodium influx. Herr and Akcasu showed that local anesthetics in low concentration could unblock the veratrinized nerve, while veratrine intensified the block produced by higher concentrations of local anesthetics. But in both cases the veratrine depolarization was prevented. As with decalcifying agents, it is evident that veratrine is not a direct antagonist of local anesthetics.

The blocking action of local anesthetics seems to be universal for all types of excitable cells, muscle as well as nerve, which might be expected on the basis of the universality of the mechanism of the conducted action potential spike. Therefore it seems important to explain the apparently excitatory effects of local anesthetics on the central nervous system, the convulsions which can be demonstrated in laboratory mammals and which occasionally occur in human patients with accidental intravenous administration of an injection intended to be local.

The local anesthetics are not convulsants in the same sense as strychnine, pentylenetetrazole, etc. We have observed that procaine or cocaine can alter electrically induced maximal seizures in a manner similar to many anticonvulsants. Furthermore, procaine seizures can be prevented by small doses of barbiturates which do not ordinarily have anticonvulsant effects. Barbiturate depression is potentiated by procaine. The apparent excitatory effects seem to be confined to higher levels, the medulla and cord being depressed. Even in cortex the threshold of evoked EEG responses to direct electrical stimulation is raised, but the radiation of responses may be widespread. The effect is suggestive of a reduction in inhibition. Probably the procaine attacks neurones indiscriminately whether they are excitatory or inhibitory in their end effects, giving rise to convulsions only in centers where inhibitory relations are dominant. In the simpler brain of the frog, procaine causes only depression. In mammalian brains the convulsant effects when demonstrable are associated with other evidences of central depression.

Among the local anesthetics cocaine is unusual in its ability to produce hallucinations and other behavioral and subjective changes, which are the basis of its illegal use by drug addicts. These changes probably represent in part the result of indiscrimate suppression of both inhibitory and excitatory cells. In addition there may also be a component of adrenergic action, not shared by most other typical local anesthetics. Cocaine is notable peripherally as a vasoconstrictor and potentiator of adrenergic agents. Other drugs which are known to have both local anesthetic and specific autonomic actions, such as atropinics and some antihistaminics, are notable for their mixed effects on higher nervous function.

Returning to peripheral nerve blockade, it is widely believed that the local anesthetics block conduction most easily in the small unmyelinated C fibers which are responsible for certain types of pain perception and also form the principal outflow of the autonomic system. Erlanger and Gasser[16] reported preferential blocking of C fibers. However, we have re-examined this problem in collaboration with Everett in a variety of nerve types in various species and failed to find such a general rule. Preferential block of A fibers can be demonstrated in some types of preparation. The preference may even change from the central to the peripheral end of a given nerve. Subgroups among A and C fibers may show differential sensitivity. In any case, the dif-

ferences are not great, and it is well-nigh impossible to abolish conduction in one fiber group with affecting others. Most clinical applications do not involve differential blocking. The universality of local
anesthetic block appears to be relatively quantitative.

Returning at last to the subject of structural relations and the ultimate molecular site of action, it is often assumed that the local anesthetics must penetrate the membrane. Part of this reasoning is based
on the inactivity of the quaternary amine derivatives of local anesthetics. The assumption is compounded by the belief that local anesthetics,
which are ordinarily administered as acid salts, must enter the membrane as the undissociated amine, then dissociate in the interior.

However, it appears to us that the involvement of local anesthetics
with sodium influx denotes a superficial site of action. Also, in desheathed frog sciatic nerve some effects of procaine develop as rapidly
as the effects of external changes in ion concentration, which is not
necessarily true of other classes of quaternaries. Again, the inactivity
of quaternaries is not necessarily an evidence for penetration of active
lesser amines. Richards[50] has recently compared some central convulsant actions of substances known to have local anesthetic effects as well,
in their tertiary amine forms. The quaternary analogs were antag-
onistic to the tertiary in a manner suggesting partial competition for
the same sites. We would conclude that if the quaternaries do not
penetrate, then the tertiary or secondary amines likewise need not
penetrate, and the locus of action is superficial. The physiological
inactivity of the particular quaternaries then must be based on an
obvious feature of their structure, their inability to act as acceptors
of protons or alkyl radicals. Conversely, the activity of the lesser basic
amines would reside in their ability to act as acceptors. In short, only
a non-quaternary can quaternize.

This consideration leads to the presumption that the amine linkage
occurs with free carboxyl groups of glutamic or aspartic acid residues,
or with the amides of these. It would be these groups which would
ordinarily be polarized to orient outward under the vector of the
membrane resting potential. They would also be capable of cross
linkage by calcium.

In addition to the amine, there are two other association zones on
a typical local anesthetic, an ester or other hydrogen-bond accepting
sequence, and an aromatic group, capable of forming complexes
through the electron transfer mechanisms of Mulliken.[40] An electron-
sharing transfer with relatively equivalent amino acid residues such
as phenylalanine, tyrosine, tryptophane or histidine is conceivable.

Whatever the linkages we may speculate on, they seem to occur in
such a way as to present a barrier to sodium influx, and to be more

resistant than the natural anti-sodium barrier to lowering of membrane voltage.

To summarize, the prime function of local anesthetics and related drugs is the elevation of neuronal threshold, which is accomplished by forming stable linkages which somehow impede sodium influx. The linkages involve amino acid residues of the membrane protein. They are furthermore restricted to the external aspects of the membrane. Local anesthetics are, by this definition, multipolar stabilizers of external tertiary membrane structure.

In the development of this thesis we have been most strongly motivated by the writings of Shanes,[56] whose work could have been quoted extensively both for and against these notions.

CONCLUSION

This discussion has been largely a speculative search for general rules of neurotropic drug action which would reflect aspects both of drug structure and of membrane structure, and would give meaningful interpretations to the functional nervous changes produced by various classes of drug-membrane association. Although the search is undoubtedly worthy, it is still unsuccessful to the extent that we have as yet rather poor and meager evidence on which to base conclusions of great generality. Furthermore, the reader may discount the logic of an argument which is founded on a relatively unsophisticaled level of theoretical chemistry. Nevertheless we hope we have at least presented a suitable target for the more critically-minded, and a sort of projection test to stimulate further free association among the more speculative.

Addendum

For a more comprehensive discussion of drug groups, with structural formulae of many agents mentioned, see equivalent chapter in first edition of this volume.

Many of the statements in this chapter are based on previously unpublished observations resulting from research supported by the following USPHS Grants: M-1422, M-4545, and MY-3775. We are likewise indebted to Abbott Laboratories for support, and specifically to Drs. G. M. Everett, J. Taylor and R. K. Richards for collaboration and counsel.

REFERENCES

1. AHLQUIST, R. P.: *J. Pharmacol Exper. Therap., 127:*146 (1959).
2. ANICHKOV, S. V.: In *Symposia and Special Lectures, XXI Internat. Cong. Physiol. Sci., Buenos Aires,* p. 23 (1959).

3. BERNHARD, C. G., and BOHM, E.: *Br. J. Pharmacol., 110:*288 (1955).
3a. BOND, H. W.: M. A. thesis. University of Illinois (1960).
4. BOURNE, G. H.: *An Introduction to Functional History.* London, Churchill, (1960).
5. BREMER, F.: *Actualités Pharmacol., 10:*25 (1957).
6. BRODIE, B. B., SPECTOR, S., and SHORE, P. A.: In *Symposium on Catecholamines,* p. 548. Baltimore, Williams & Wilkins (1959).
7. CARLSSON, A.: In *Symposium on Catecholamines,* p. 490. Baltimore, Williams & Wilkins (1959).
8. CROSSLAND, J.: Chapter 27 of this volume.
9. DAVSON, H., and DANIELLI, J. F.: *The Permeability of the Natural Membrane.* New York, Macmillan (1943).
10. DEROBERTIS, E. D. P., and SABATINI, D. D.: *Federation Proc., 19:*70 (1960)
11. EADE, N. R.: *Bret. J. Pharmacol., 12:*61 (1957).
12. ECCLES, J. C.: *The Physiology of Nerve Cells.* Baltimore, Johns Hopkins Press, (1957).
13. ECCLES, J. C.: In *Neurophysiology,* Vol. 1, p. 59, Washington, D. C., Am. Physiol. Soc. Publ. (1959).
14. EHRENPREIS, S. and KELLOCK, M. G.: *Biophys. Biochem. Res. Comm., 2:*311, (1960).
15. ELLIOTT, K. A. C., and JASPER, H. H.: *Physiol. Rev., 39:*383 (1959).
16. ERLANGER, J., and GASSER, H. S.: *Electrical Signs of Nervous Activity.* London, Oxford Univ. Press (1937).
17. ESPLIN, D. W.: *J. Pharmacol. Exper. Therap., 120:*301 (1957).
18. FATT, P.: In *Neurophysiology,* Vol. 1, p. 199, Washington, D. C., Am. Physiol. Soc. Publ. (1959).
19. FUJITA, A.: *Pharmaceut. Bull. (Japan), 2:*163 (1954).
20. FURCHGOTT, R. F.: In *Symposium on Catecholamines,* p. 429. Baltimore, Williams & Wilkins (1959).
21. GOODMAN, L. S., and GILMAN, A.: *The Pharmacological Basis of Therapeutics,* 2nd. Ed. New York, Macmillan (1955).
22. GRUNDFEST, H.: In *Neurophysiology,* Vol. 1, p. 147, Washington, D. C., Am. Physiol. Soc. Publ. (1959).
23. HAYASHI, T.: *Neurophysiology and Neuropharmacology of Convulsion.* Tokyo, Dainihon-Tosho Co. (1959).
24. HEBB, C. O.: Chapter 20 of this volume.
25. HERR, F., and AKCASU, A.: *J. Pharmacol. Exper. Therap., 130:*328 (1960).
26. HIMWICH, H. H.: Chapter 31 of this volume.
27. HODGKIN, A. L.: *Proc. Roy. Soc. B., 148:*1 (1958).
28. HOKIN, L., and HOKIN, M. R.: *Internat. Rev. Neurobiol., 2:*99 (1960).
29. JOHNSON, F. H., EYRING, H., and POLISSAR, M. J.: *The Kinetic Basis of Molecular Biology,* New York, Wiley and Sons (1954).
30. KARREMAN, G.: *Gordon Res. Conf. Med. Chem.,* p. 9 (1960).
31. KILLAM, K. F.: *Federation Proc., 17:*1018 (1958).
32. KLOTZ, I. M.: *Science, 128:*815 (1958).
33. KOELLE, G. B.: *Science, 132:*1495 (1960).
34. KOKETSU, K.: In Symposium on *Biophysics of Physiological and Pharmacological Actions,* Washington, D. C., A.A.A.S. Publ. (1961).
35. KUFFLER, S. W., and EYZAGUIRRE, C: *J. Gen. Physiol., 39:*155 (1955).
36. LEAKE, C. D.: *The Amphetamines.* Springfield, Ill., Thomas (1958).
37. LING, G: *A Physical Theory of the Living State.* New York, Blaisdell (1961).

38. LORENTE DE NO, R.: *Stud. Rockefeller Inst.*, *131* and *132:* (1942).
39. MONNIER, M.: In *Symposia and Special Lectures, XXI Internat. Cong. Physiol. Sci.*, p. 149. Buenos Aires (1959).
40. MULLIKEN, R. S.: *J. Am. Chem. Soc.*, 72:600 (1950).
41. MULLINS, L. J: In *Conference on Current Problems in Microbiology.* Washington, D. C., A.A.A.S. Publ. (1961).
42. NACHMANSOHN, D: Chapter 21 of this volume.
43. NICKERSON, M: In *Symposium on Catecholamines,* p. 443. Baltimore, Williams & Wilkins (1959).
44. PAGE, I. H: Chapter 25 of this volume.
45. PATTON, H. D.: *Ann. Rev. Physiol.*, 20:509 (1958).
46. PAULING, L., COREY, R. B., and BRANSON, H. R.: *Proc. Nat. Acad. Sc.*, 37:205 (1951).
47. POMERAT, C. M., and LEAKE, C. D: *Ann. New York Acad. Sc.*, 58:1110 (1954).
48. PULLMAN, B., and PULLMAN, A: *Rev. Mod. Physics, 32:*428 (1960).
49. QUASTEL, J. H: Chapter 19 of this volume.
50. RICHARDS, R. K., and KUETER, K. E: *Federation Proc.*, 20:165 (1961).
51. ROBERTS, E: Chapter 26 of this volume.
52. ROSSITER, R. J.: Chapter 36 of this volume.
53. ROTHBALLER, A. B.: In *Symposium on Catecholamines,* p. 494. Baltimore, Williams & Wilkins (1959).
54. SCHOLEFIELD, P: Chapter 17 of this volume.
55. SCHUELER, F. W.: *Chemodynamics and Drug Design.* New York, Blakiston-McGraw-Hill (1960).
56. SHANES, A. M.: *Pharmacol. Rev.*, 10:59 (1958).
57. SHANES, A. M.: Chapter 22 of this volume.
58. SOURKES, T: Chapter 24 of this volume.
58a. STÄMPFLI, R., and NISHIE, K.: *Helv. Physiol. Acta, 14:*93 (1956).
59. STRAUB, R.: *Helvet. Physiol. Acta, 14:*1 (1956).
60. SZENT-GYORGI, A: *Bioenergetics.* New York, Acad. Press (1957).
61. TASAKI, I: In *Neurophysiology.* Vol. 1, p. 75, Washington, D. C., Am. Physiol. Soc. Publ. (1959).
62. TOMAN, J. E. P: In *Symposia and Special Lectures, XXI Internat. Cong. Physiol. Sci.*, p. 158. Buenos Aires (1959).
63. TOWER, D. B.: *Neurochemistry of Epilepsy.* Springfield, Ill., Thomas (1960).
64. VOGT, M: In *Symposium on Catecholamines,* p. 483. Baltimore, Williams & Wilkins (1959).
65. VON EULER, U. S: In *Neurophysiology,* Vol. 1, p. 215. Washington, D. C., Am. Physiol. Soc. Publ. (1959).
66. WASER, P. G.: In *Symposia and Special Lectures, XXI Internat. Cong. Physiol. Sci.*, p. 30. Buenos Aires (1959).
67. WATANABE, A., SMITH, T. G., and GRUNDFEST, H.: *Federation Proc.*, 19:298 (1960).
68. WIKLER, A: *The Relation of Psychiatry to Pharmacology.* Baltimore, Williams & Wilkins (1957).
69. WOLFE, L. S., and ELLIOTT, K. A. C.: Chapter 29 of this volume.
70. WOODBURY, D. M., KOCH, A., and VERNADAKIS, A: *Neurology,* 8 (suppl. I):113 (1958)
71. WOODBURY, J. W., and PATTON, H. D: In *Medical Physiology and Biophysics* T. C. Ruch and J. F. Fulton, Ed. Philadelphia, Saunders (1960).

XXXI

PSYCHOPHARMACOLOGICAL ASPECTS OF
THE NERVOUS SYSTEM

Harold E. Himwich

The new advances in psychoneuropharmacology have yielded beneficial results in patients with mental disease and have stimulated a great volume of experimental work on animals and man in an effort to find correlates for the behavioral effects in terms of the basic sciences. Prominent among the new data are those in the field of biochemistry and especially brain biochemistry. Many of the psychotropic drugs affect the concentrations of various brain constituents and alter the metabolism of the indole amines and the catechol amines. A consideration of the relation of these drugs to the amine metabolism of the brain is a chief purpose of this chapter. We shall present some of the most pertinent observations in this field and then discuss hypotheses that have been advanced to explain them.

Not all of the new psychopharmacologic drugs produce biochemical changes in the brain of animals, especially with the relatively small amounts used in the treatment of patients. Some, like meprobamate, modify electrical potentials, but, with doses within the human therapeutic range alterations in brain constituents have not been reported in animals. Other medications affect both electrophysiological phenomena and brain chemistry. Our present concern is with the influence of this group of drugs on the biochemical processes whether or not they are accompanied by other changes in neurophysiological features. Perhaps it should be mentioned that a biochemical effect observed in the brain of a given species of animal may not occur with equal intensity, or may not take place at all in other species. Thus, it is not wise to extrapolate freely results obtained on animals to man.

BRAIN AMINES AND PSYCHOTROPIC DRUGS

A. Reserpine and Other Amine Releasing Compounds.—The oldest member of this group of drugs is reserpine, an ester alkaloid, originally

766

isolated from the root of the plant, Rauwolfia serpentine, in 1952[1] and now produced synthetically. Reserpine decreases the serotonin level in the rabbit intestine[2] where the argentaffin cells in the mucous membrane of the gastrointestinal tract are the source of more than 90% of the serotonin content of the body.[3] Reserpine also releases serotonin from the brain of rabbits and cats.[4] The power of amphetamine to release serotonin is much weaker than that of reserpine. The latter in relatively low dosage, 0.5 mg./kg., reduces the concentration of serotonin in dog brain to vanishing amounts, while amphetamine in large toxic quantities, 20 to 30 mg./kg., cuts serotonin concentrations only to approximately half the control values.[5,6] In view of the marked behavioral changes associated with alterations in serotonin levels of the brain, it is surprising that only 1% of the serotonin of the body is found in that organ[7] where, however, it has a rapid turnover rate.[8] Reserpine releases serotonin from other sites, in fact wherever it occurs, including the mast cells of rat,[9] the spleen[10] and blood platelets, the latter amounting to about 1 mg. in man.[11-13] Other Rauwolfia alkaloids which are as active as reserpine in eliminating serotonin from the brain are rescinnamine (Moderil, Pfizer Laboratories) and 11-desmethoxyreserpine (Harmonyl, Abbott Laboratories).[14] The stereoisomer, isoreserpine, however, does not diminish brain amines.

Reserpine lowers the catechol amine content of the cat's hypothalamus.[15] In view of the fact that adrenaline forms only 7 to 14% of the brain catechol amines[16] it is not surprising that the decrease of brain catechol amines is predominantly in the form of noradrenaline.[17] The fibers and ganglia of adrenergic neurons of rabbits, cats and dogs also lose a large fraction of their noradrenaline when the animals are injected with reserpine.[18] When the depletion of noradrenaline is severe and has persisted for more than 4 hours, it may lead to failure of response from the organ innervated by the adrenergic nerves to indirect electrical stimulation. Thus a functional pharmacological sympathectomy may be performed by reserpine[18,19] as the release of catechol amines into the blood stream usually following the stimulation of the adrenergic nerves fails to occur.[20] Bretylium produces a similar effect as it prevents the release of noradrenaline from the stimulated adrenergic nerves.[21,22] Tyramine which is active only in the presence of an intact adrenergic system[23] ceases to evoke an increase of blood pressure after the administration of reserpine. In general not only tyramine but all sympathomimetic amines affect the binding sites for the catechol amines, thus causing the release of these amines and exposing them to the metabolic action of enzymes.[24] Reserpine[25,26] and cocaine[27] also accelerate amine metabolism but unlike reserpine, cocaine not only prevents the uptake of noradrenaline by tissues but also hinders its release.

The intravenous injection of rabbits with 5 mg./kg. reserpine not only caused the rapid decline of brain noradrenaline but also that of brain serotonin. A comparison of the shape and duration of the curves for the loss of these two amines from the brain revealed that they were practically identical.[17] For both amines a definite drop was observed in $\frac{1}{4}$ hour, about 90% disappeared within 4 hours and thereafter there was a slow return toward normal in 7 days.[17] Though tetrabenazine, a non-indole benzoquinoline derivative, depletes brain serotonin and noradrenaline, its actions are distinctive from those of reserpine in important ways. First, brain serotonin is depressed less than brain noradrenaline. Second, the effects of the benzoquinoline derivatives pass rapidly so that unlike reserpine the former do not show accumulative action. Two other benzoquinoline derivatives, Ro 4-1284* and Ro 4-1398,† also act much more briefly than reserpine.[28,29] Finally, tetrabenazine does not exhibit the power of reserpine to deplete peripheral stores. Thus the use of tetrabenazine is associated neither with the diarrhea nor the hypotension induced by reserpine.[30] P-2647,** another benzoquinoline derivative, is even weaker and except in large doses fails to release either serotonin or noradrenaline from the brain.[30a] Concerning the amine releasing effects of raunescine and isoraunescin, there is a difference of opinion. The use of the bioassay technique disclosed that the noradrenaline stores are depleted to a greater extent than those of serotonin.[31,32] On the other hand, results with fluorimetric methods indicate that these drugs are equally effective in lowering both amines.[28] A selective release of brain noradrenaline, however, is evoked by another reserpine analog, Su 5171 (Ciba Pharmaceuticals) Methyl 18-0-(3-N,N-dimethylamine benzoyl) resperate.[33] Syrosingopine, a compound structurally related to resepine[34] evokes a peripheral release of noradrenaline greater than that exhibited in the brain.[34]

Reserpine also frees the catechol amines of the adrenal glands.[35,36] With small doses of reserpine, 0.4 mg./kg., the catechol amines of the adrenal medulla, quantitatively their most important single depot, were diminished more in the innervated adrenal gland than in the denervated contralateral organ.[15,17] On the other hand larger doses

---

*2-hydroxy-2-ethyl-3-isobutyl-9,10-dimethoxy-1,2,3,4,6,7-hexahydro-11bH-benzo   (a) quinolizine.

†2-hydroxy-2-(3′-methoxybutyl)-3-ixobutyl-9,10-dimethoxy-1,2,3,4,6,7-hexahydro-11bH-benzo (a) quinolizine.

**The acetate of 2-hydroxy-3-diethylcarbamyl-9,10-dimethoxy-1,2,3,4,6,7-hexahydro-11bH-benzoquinolizine.

of reserpine, 5 mg./kg., emptied the rat's adrenal gland of its catechol amines whether it was denervated or not.[37,38] Species seems to be a determining factor in the relative efficacy of central and peripheral effects. In the rat and cat[36] the action seems to be predominantly peripheral, while in the rabbit[39] the central influence is more important. Reserpine depletes the noradrenaline in the heart[35,40] as well as in lungs and spleen[17] while adrenaline remains relatively unaffected. Reserpine has the power to release serotonin and noradrenaline wherever they are found in the brain but it is well to emphasize that these amines are not evenly distributed but occur in characteristic patterns which are similar in cat, dog[16,41] and man.[42,43] Both noradrenaline and serotonin occur in the brainstem with highest concentrations in diencephalic structures including the hypothalamus and in the mesencephalon. Somewhat lower levels are found in the thalamus and medulla oblongota while the neocortex and the cerebellum have the smallest amounts. In general, then, the older parts of the brain contain the greater concentrations of these two amines. Though the total amounts of the two catechol amines, noradrenaline and dopamine[16,41,42,43,44] are similar, their distribution is entirely different for dopamine is concentrated in subcortical areas of telencephalon where more than 80% of the dopamine is found in the neostriatal caudate nucleus and putamen.[44] Dopamine resembles the other amines in sensitivity to reserpine which releases practically all dopamine from rabbit brain.[45]

B. Iproniazid and Other Drugs Inhibiting Monoamine Oxidase.— The inhibitors, in contrast to the reserpine group of drugs, raise the levels of brain amines and do so in proportion to the monoamine oxidase activity of the tissues concerned, though other enzymes, for example decarboxylase, are involved in the accumulation of the amines. The MAOI (monoamine oxidase inhibitor) drugs interfere with oxidative deamination[3] and in man cause the appearance of increased amounts of tryptamine, serotonin and other indole products in the urine[46] while temporarily diminishing that of 5HIAA.[12] For the same reason the metabolic breakdown of intravenously administered radioadrenaline is inhibited.[98] A similar action occurs against the oxidative deamination of dopamine, tyramine, noradrenaline and adrenaline, metadrenaline and normetadrenaline. Because of a turnover which is faster for serotonin than for noradrenaline, the former rises more rapidly and to a greater extent in the brain.[47] In fact MAOI activity is usually inferred from amine accumulation. Iproniazid, the prototype of MAOI[48] and other hydrazine-containing drugs including phenylisopropyl hydrazine, nialimide and isocarboxazid, are irreversible inhibitors. When the exception of N-benzyl-N-methyl-2-propynyla-

mine hydrochloride (MO 911, Abbott Laboratories), isopropyl hydrazine is probably the active group responsible for the monoamine oxidase inactivation which involves a dehydrogenation of the inhibitor.[49]
In contrast a competitive action occurs with tranylcypromine, harmaline and harmine, powerful inhibitors, and the much weaker alpha-
methyltryptamine[50,51] and alpha-ethyltryptamine (Etryptamine, Upjohn Company). Amphetamine[6] also an inhibitor of monoamine
oxidase is too weak to be effective in doses that can be given safely
in vivo.[10] In general the newer monoamine oxidase inhibitors are more
rapid in their activity and exhibit more specificity for the brain than
does iproniazid. The efficacy of MAOI increases in the series starting
with iproniazid and progressing to nialimide, isocarboxazid and tranylcypromine. In contrast to brain, liver amines are not elevated by
MAOI due to the greater importance of other catabolic pathways in
that organ. With bioassay methods for serotonin it was shown that
anticonvulsant compounds[52] and barbiturates[53] evoke rises in brain
serotonin. Such increases, however, occurring as early as 5 minutes after
drug injections, are difficult to reconcile with known rates of serotonin turnover.[54]

   C. Chlorpromazine and Imipramine.—Chlorpromazine has been
variously reported to be without effect[55,56] on brain serotonin and
noradrenaline or to cause small rises.[57,58] If there is any action of
imipramine to augment brain serotonin it also is of a small order.[58]
In contrast, the action of chlorpromazine to impair the elevation of
brain serotonin induced by iproniazid is well established especially in
rats.[57,59,55,56] Dr. Clara Morpurgo, in this laboratory, has demonstrated
that this decrease is dependent upon a chlorpromazine-induced fall of
temperature and therefore a slowing of all bodily reactions. It is
doubtful that chlorpromazine can reduce 5HTP decarboxylase below
critical values. The interaction of iproniazid and chlorpromazine left
brain amine levels higher than those of the controls and suggests that
iproniazid has two synergistic actions, the first to antagonize monoamine oxidase and the second to diminish permeability.[55] Chlorpromazine restored normal permeability and thus lowered amines to levels
commensurate only with the elevation associated with the inhibition
of MAO.[55] On the other hand the observation that the reserpine reduction of serotonin was prevented to a certain degree by chlorpromazine indicated that the chief action of chlorpromazine was to reduce
permeability of the granular membrane thereby diminishing the entrance and release of monoamines of the amine-bearing granules.[56] Chlorpromazine would appear to restore the permeability
impaired by iproniazid but to decrease permeability in the absence of
that drug. Impaired permeability may also explain why chlorproma-

zine and imipramine diminish the uptake of circulating radio-nora-
drenaline by heart and adrenal medulla.[60A] That chlorpromazine effects permeability is supported by a large body of observations.[60-62]
Still another suggestion for the action of chlorpromazine is that it
serves as a powerful electron donor and the action of this drug is
therefore due to charge transfer.[63]

D. Brain Amines and Behavior.—With the tools at hand to increase
or decrease brain amines, and, for that matter brain amino acids too,
we have available the opportunity to investigate the relationships between these brain constituents and behavior. Are behavioral changes
associated with an excess or a deficiency of one of these brain constituents? And, as a corollary, does an excess or deficiency create an
imbalance responsible for changes in behavior? Illustrating the latter
possibility are the differential EEG effects of iproniazid on one side
and phenylisopropyl hydrazine or tranylcypromine on the other. The
usual alternations between sleep and alert patterns observed in the
EEG of curarized artificially respired rabbits were continued after the
administration of a single dose of iproniazid which evoked slow increases both of serotonin and noradrenaline. In contrast, either phenylisopropyl hydrazine or tranylcypromine induced persistant desynchronization associated with an imbalance created by a rapid rise in brain
serotonin and only minimal changes in noradrenaline.[64] It is true that
we are looking for changes only in the areas where we have biochemical means of attack, and that there may be other brain constituents
more relevant to this problem. In fact, it is still to be proved that
there are positive correlations between such biochemical changes and
behavior. This concept, however, has been put to preliminary tests
in experiments on animals and man. In a series of observations on
psychotic patients we administered isocarboxazid and reserpine separately and together for an average of 15 days for each type of medication.[65-67] Daily examinations of patients for their psychiatric status
revealed that periods of disturbed behavior were preceded, as well as
accompanied, by increased eliminations of 5-hydroxyindole acetic acid
(5HIAA) and to a lesser extent of 3-indoleacetic acid (3IAA). This
association between increased excretions of indole compounds and
behavioral disturbances occurred either spontaneously or with reserpine therapy. In regard to the latter it is well known that improvement
from drug therapy with chlorpromazine and especially reserpine may
be preceded by a short period of increased disturbance.[68] In 5 of 9
schizophrenic patients even greater rises in the elimination of the
indole metabolites were observed following the cessation of combined
therapy with reserpine and isocarboxazid than on reserpine alone.
These rises occurred at a time when the activations of psychotic symp-

toms were most severe. In our patients we observed not only periods of behavioral worsening, but also of tranquilization. The latter were associated with more moderate increases of 5HIAA than those occurring with the activation of psychotic symptoms. It would seem that under our experimental conditions tranquilization was accompanied by moderate increases of free serotonin in the body, while greater rises occurred previous to and during the activation of the psychosis in 5 of our 12 schizophrenic patients.

Other explorations of possible associations between indole amines and behavior are suggested by administration of dimethyltryptamine which is followed by a psychotic state and by the observation that 6-hydroxydimethyltryptamine is a stronger psychotomimetic than its parent substance.[69] A similar situation is reported for diethyltryptamine which is converted to 6-hydroxydimethyltryptamine in the body.[70] Whether or not such substances are produced when the concentrations of indole compounds are increased, as observed in our work, is still to be determined. In any event these biochemical findings reflect, to the greatest extent, changes in parts of the body other than the brain. It is therefore interesting that a similar biphasic effect of serotonin has been noted in animal experiments,[71] tranquilization being associated with smaller increases of free serotonin than those which occur with disturbed behavior. An EEG analysis of rabbits reveals that small doses of 5-hydroxytryptophan, a serotonin precursor, evoke a sleep pattern while larger ones are alerting.[72] In addition the two different patterns appear to be associated with two different levels of serotonin in the brain. Moderate increases of less than three times the control value occur with sleep patterns and larger ones, from three to four times the control are observed with EEG activation.[64] Additional evidence of the effect of serotonin on behavior reveals that with 5 to 30 mg./kg. 5-hydroxytryptophan, dogs exhibited a decrease of spontaneous activity while in contrast the administration of 40 to 60 mg./kg. caused excitement, disorientation and changes of motor control and sensory function.[73] This double action has also been demonstrated[74] in dogs premedicated with the MAOI, tranylcypromine, 2 mg./kg., without observable behavioral changes for 6 hours. At the end of that period the injection of 2 mg./kg. 5HTP induced sedation, but when the dose of that amino acid was increased to 5 to 7 mg./kg. in the same animal a relatively brief calming action was followed by signs of excitement, including motor restlessness, ataxia, obstinate progression, festination of hind legs, aggressiveness, hostility and a rise in temperature.[74] The reader should note that these experiments with raised levels of serotonin do not necessarily throw light on the normal functions of that compound in the brain.[10,75]

Because MAOI raised levels of all brain amines it is necessary to distinguish between the behavioral effects of serotonin and noradrenaline and for that matter for other amines as well. Iproniazid given for periods of 4 to 5 days raised the levels of both biogenic amines though the increase of serotonin started earlier, attained higher levels and continued longer than that of noradrenaline.[76] But only during the period when the noradrenaline contents of the brainstem were highest was there a marked degree of spontaneous motor activity, increased motor response to tactile stimuli and constriction of the blood vessels of the ear in rabbits.[76A] These signs disappeared with the fall of noradrenaline though serotonin still remained elevated.[76] In dogs and cats MAOI failed to evoke marked changes in behavior, unlike their effects on rodents such as mice, rats, guinea pigs and rabbits. It is therefore worthy of note that dogs and cats respond to MAOI with elevations of serotonin in the brain but not of noradrenaline.[16,76] It should be noted that an increase of catechol amines may occur not only as a result of drug action but also secondary to stress. The results in our patients[65-67] reveal that the urinary catechol amines[77] increase in concentration with disturbed behavior, especially with anxiety. The time relationships, however, were different from those noted with indole amines. The rise of catechol amines seems to follow rather than to precede signs of increased anxiety.

In our search for possible stimulating compounds occurring naturally in the brain dopamine must be considered. For example, a large dose of 200 mg./kg. dopa reversed the reserpine-induced sedation as well as the blepherospasm and myosis of rabbits.[78] In other experiments, in which dopa was given without reserpine, increased motor activity and sympathetic stimulation seemed to correlate with the accumulation of dopamine and especially so in the caudate nucleus.[79] Similar alleviations of sedation were seen in mice pretreated with 100 mg./kg. of reserpine and then given 100 mg./kg. of iproniazid before the injection of 200 mg./kg. of dopa.[80] In general dopa appears effective only in large doses. In view of the fact that reserpine-induced sedation is relieved in the same manner by desoxyephedrine, methyphenidate[80,81] and amphetamine, one wonders whether this relief is due to nonspecific stimulatory action or to the restoration of depleted brain amines.

DRUGS AND INTRACELLULAR METABOLISM OF BRAIN AMINES

We have seen that some psychotropic drugs change concentrations of amines in brain and other parts of the body. We shall now go deeper and examine the intracellular processes involved in such alterations. Of three factors important in determining the concentrations of amines in chromaffin cells some, like the enzyme decarboxylase, tend to raise levels while in contrast MAO lowers indole amines and catechol amines.[82] Catechol-O-methyltransferase (COMT) functions in this way particularly for noradrenaline and adrenaline. The final factor is a dynamic equilibrium between bound and free amines. It is hardly necessary to point out that the concentrations of amines resulting from centrifugation of tissue homogenates do not necessarily represent quantitatively the free and bound forms in the living tissue. Though it does not seem likely that the amines in the supernatant are bound to particles too difficult to sediment,[83] the granules probably lose portions of their amine content upon resuspension and recentrifugation.[84] Furthermore, the amines in the precipitate are not only held by granules but may also be adsorbed to cytoplasmic particles.[83]

   A. Bound Amines, Reserpine and MAOI.—There is some controversy as to the site of action of reserpine for it has been reported that the initial release of the catechol amines, adrenaline, noradrenaline and dopamine from rabbit brain was from the soluble cytoplasmic fraction.[85] In contrast, however, it has also been noted that noradrenaline passed from the particulate fraction to the supernatant.[86] Moreover, direct evidence that reserpine effected a release of noradrenaline from suspensions of transmitter granules isolated from bovine splenic nerves has been obtained.[87] In the case of brain serotonin, that drug exerts its prime action against the bound form as it suffers a greater depression than does the supernatant[88,84] Additional evidence is afforded from adrenal medullas of animals given reserpine and then injected with DOPA, for though the total amount of catechols rose, there was less in the bound form and more in the free.[89,90] The action of reserpine is thus directed against the formation of bound amine complexes. The chronic administration of reserpine might be expected to deplete the stores of serotonin and of noradrenaline but exert differential effects on the free forms. In contrast to free noradrenaline, free serotonin rises above control levels because the rate of formation of serotonin is more rapid that that of noradrenaline.[76] Though reserpine probably exerts both direct effects on the adrenal medulla and indirect ones via the splanchnic nerves the action of reserpine on that tissue is similar to that of stimulation in so far as ATP and catechol amines[36] are eliminated together and in equivalent amounts from the large medullary granules. In this way at least reserpine produces the same effects on the adrenal medulla as do various stimulants upon this tissue.[16,91-93] That reserpine is effective is indicated by the observation that the large, heavier granules lose 90% of their catechol amines.[36] Data on the effects of reserpine on the amine granules of low density are lacking but examinations of total adrenal tissue disclosed that reserpine administration consistently caused a disproportionally greater elimination of catechol amines than of adenine nucleotides, thus suggesting in this case the release of catechol amines from a binding site not involving ATP.[94]

In studies of the *in vitro* uptake of noradrenaline, adrenaline and serotonin by blood platelets reserpine was found to block the uptake from amine-rich plasma.[11] In these structures ATP remained normal after amine depletion as if ionic bonds between ATP and amines had been sundered. In this way platelets are different from amine-bearing tissues in their response to reserpine.[36] It must be remembered, however, that platelets are a sort of surviving structure somewhat like the red blood corpuscles and therefore reserpine may act in a way not characteristic for other tissues. It is not improbable that the other tranquilizing Rauwolfia alkaloids and the benzoquinoline derivatives also prevent amine binding.

B. Interactions of Reserpine and MAOI on Bound Amines.— Another point requiring consideration is the interaction of MAOI and reserpine on free and bound amines. Following the injection of iproniazid into rats the levels of brain serotonin were raised and more so in the supernatant than in the precipitate fraction,[84] an observation in accordance with the conception that serotonin is formed in cell sap and that MAOI blocks a primary catabolic pathway of brain serotonin. The increases of free and bound serotonin were practically the same whether iproniazid, 100 mg./kg., was given alone or with reserpine, 5 mg./kg. Because of the relative constancy of the bound form in both instances the suggestion has been made that the MAOI interferes with the activity of reserpine to release serotonin.[84] In parallel experiments on catechol amines, tranylcypromine also caused an increase of free noradrenaline that was greater in the supernatant than in the residue.[86] Intraperitoneal injections of reserpine into rats pretreated with tranylcypromine erased the accumulated excess of noradrenaline but did not reduce concentrations either in the supernatant or in the residue below the control levels. In fact the ratio of free to bound catechol amines closely approximated the premedication values.[86] It would therefore seem that tranylcypromine inhibited the ability of reserpine to set free catechol amines. It has also been suggested[76] that reserpine still releases bound amines despite the presence of MAOI and that the free amines accumulate intracellularly. It is not improbable that the free amine levels in the cells do rise with MAOI as a result of cellular impermeability. On the other hand, direct observations indicate that the particulates are not depleted either of indole amines[84] or of catechol amines.[86] With the use of iproniazid or pyrogallol to block the MAOI and COMT pathways, respectively, it has been shown that to some degree these two pathways for catechol amine metabolism can compensate for each other. MAOI increased activity of the COMT system while that of pyrogallol enhanced the function of the MAO route.[95] The relatively greater importance of the COMT system for the metabolism of catechol amines in the circulating blood[96] was demonstrated by experiments in which radioactive adrenaline was injected intravenously into rats[97] and pyrogallol markedly inhibited the degradation of the circulating amine, an effect imputed chiefly to the action of the liver on the blood passing through that organ. In contrast iproniazid produced strong increases of catechol amine contents of both brain and heart. It would therefore seem that MAO furnishes a primary pathway in heart and brain though the function of COMT remains as an alternate route in these organs. The combined blockade of both enzyme systems by a MAOI and pyrogallol, however, does not stop catechol amine metabolism but results in the formation of a new adrenaline catebolite as well as other changes.[99] The metabolism of dopamine, too, can be inhibited by MAOI[100] as well as by pyrogallol.[99,101]

C. Drugs Influencing Decarboxylase Functioning.—Drugs can also influence the function that decarboxylase performs identically for dopa and 5HTP[102-104] an enzyme which occurs in the cytoplasmic sap.[105,106] Semicarbizide depresses decarboxylase.[10] More powerful inhibitors are alpha-methyldopa and alpha-methyl- 3-hydroxyphenylalanine[107] which decrease the cellular concentrations of serotonin[108] and noradrenaline.[102] In experiments on man alpha-methyldopa was found to diminish the urinary excretions of serotonin, tyramine and tryptamine.[109] In rats and guinea pigs under the influence of alpha-methyldopa[110] the serotonin content of brain and heart fell rapidly and returned to control levels within 15 hours as the enzyme inhibition wore off. Brain dopamine was reduced to 30% of the control and had returned to normal levels by 24 hours.[111] Noradrenaline, however, continued at very low levels for several days. This prolonged decrease of noradrenaline could not be explained entirely by a depression of decarboxylase activity[110] and might be due to a differential effect on noradrenaline binding sites.[111] The depressions of decarboxylation observed in insulin hypoglycemia[112] and with imipramine and chlorpromazine[113] were weak and probably not capable of reducing the amines to critical levels.

BIOCHEMICAL CHANGES PRODUCED ON BRAIN CONSTITUENTS OTHER THAN AMINES

The earliest attempts to discover the mechanism of action of chlorpromazine[114] disclosed a fall of body temperature and a depression of oxygen consumption of excised guinea pig cerebral cortex.[114] Many *in vitro* studies using not only chlorpromazine but also its congeners, methylene blue and phenergan[115-121] made on brain slices, separated cerebral tissues, minces, homogenates and mitochondria confirmed the depressant effects on the brain respiration using glucose, fructose, pyruvate, L-glutamate and alpha-ketoglutarate acid as substrates. Also inhibited by chlorpromazine are hexokinase, cytochrome oxidase, ATP-ase, D-amino-acid oxidase as well as the processes of oxidative phosphorylation.[115-120,122] Because of the high concentrations of cholorpromazine used in these experiments it is probable that these results express the toxicological possibilities of chlorpromazine on cellular metabolism rather than the pharmacological mechanism of their therapeutic effects. Chlorpromazine given to experimental animals in concentrations much greater than the largest doses administered therapeutically still failed to induce changes in phosphate metabolism.[123] Though reserpine depressed the activity of cytochrome oxidase and ATP-ase it did so in concentrations which were considerably higher than ordinary pharmacological doses.[119] Similar conclusions apply to hydroxazine[124] and meprobamate.[125] The respiration of guinea pig brain minces are susceptible to d-lysergic acid diethylamide (LSD-25), to its brominated derivative (2-bromo-d-lysergic acid diethylamide) (BOL-140),[126] as well as to mescaline sulfate[120] but the concentrations of the psychotomimetics used in these experiments were greatly in excess of those employed in man. A dose of 5 mg./kg. reserpine administered to mice decreased brain GABA concentrations, an effect antagonized by 150 mg./kg. iproniazid. In this instance an acid underwent changes similar to those produced by these drugs on some brain amines.[126B] In contrast in other experiments on rats both reserpine and MAOI raise the concentrations of lactic and pyruvic acids in the blood. The authors ascribed the higher levels to alterations in monoamine metabolism.[126A]

On the other hand it must be emphasized that the *in vivo* effects of psychotropic drugs are not limited to their influences on brain amines. On the contrary these drugs are active on a broad biological basis even with the small doses used therapeutically. Comparatively high concentrations of chlorpromazine and azacyclonol depressed the incorporation of P[32] into lipid phosphorus of guinea pig brain slices while with low concentrations increases were observed.[127] The importance of dosage is illustrated by experiments in which 10^{-3}M chlorpromazine inhibited the incorporation of acetate-1-^{14}C mevalonic acid-2-^{14}C and glucose-G^{-14}C into brain phospholipids fatty acid while a concentration of 10^{-5}M exerted opposite effects as did 3.5 mg./kg. of chlorpromazine *in vivo*.[128] The latter dose is considerably smaller than the maximum given to disturbed schizophrenic patients three or four times daily. Similarly, the low concentration of 0.1mM imipramine has been shown to decrease the uptake of radioglycine by cortical slices.[129] These observations underscore the pharmacological dictum that many drugs have widespread effects not limited to a special site considered responsible for the desired therapeutic action.

Observations on man[130] disclosed that neither chlorpromazine[131,132] nor promazine[133] in doses producing soporific results affected cerebral metabolic rate (CMR). The intravenous injection of reserpine in therapeutic doses did not lower cerebral metabolism.[134-136] Methylphenadate (Ritalin, Ciba Pharmaceuticals) even though a CNS stimulant, also failed to raise CMR in therapeutic doses.[133] In a similar fashion the administration of LSD-25 in amounts adequate to evoke characteristic psychotomimetic alterations in behavior produced no detectable changes in metabolism both in controls and schizophrenic patients.[137] It may therefore be safely concluded that therapeutic doses of these drugs are without significant effects on the metabolic rate of the brain as a whole and accordingly behavioral changes induced by these drugs are not to be imputed to an influence on CMR.

ACTIONS OF DRUGS ADMINISTERED INTRAVENTRICULARLY

In contrast to the stimulating effect of adrenaline administered peripherally, intrathecal injections produced a fall in body temperature, analgesia and a sort of model sleep in unanesthetized dogs,[138,139] and cats.[140] With different intraventricular doses of acetylcholine conditions resembling either sleep[141,142] or convulsions[143,144] were observed in animals and man. Other drugs injected intraventricularly into man include pilocarpine and atropine[145] as well as cholinesterase, procaine, pentamethonium iodide and flaxedil.[146]

As a result of studies on mice[147] as well as cats[148-150] dogs[151] and human beings mentioned above, data have been accumulated which, in general, apply to the four species studied. In the first place there are reactions in common to many drugs which have been injected intraventricularly, an observation to be expected in view of the fact that they can all influence the functions of brain structures lining the ventricular walls adjacent to the cerebrospinal fluid. The reactions to such stimulation include licking, swallowing, salivation, retching, vomiting, defecation, miturition, and tachypnea. What is more important, however, is that in many instances the alterations produced are characteristic for a given drug or a small group of drugs.[152] For example, convulsions are caused by the intraventricular injection of curare and tubocurarine while decamethonium induces spastic paresis, yet peripheral administrations of these drugs produce paralysis of the neuromyal junction. The administration of eserine sulfate (10 to 100 μg.) and of DFP (100 μg.) is followed by various behavioral changes including catatonia. These drugs also cause itching of central origin, a property also shared by morphine, KCl and sodium fluoracetate.

The differences in the results between the intraventricular and peripheral administration of these drugs may not be qualitative in nature but may rest on a quantitative basis due to greater magnitude of dosage within the ventricle than can be attained by parenteral injections. In fact the same effects produced by central injections can be observed if the parenteral dose is 20 to 40 times as great as that given intraventricularly.[147] For example, a catatonic condition can be induced by the subcutaneous administration of bulbocapnine, 20 to 30 mg./kg., in contrast to a total intraventricular dose of 1 mg required to achieve the same behavioral results.[153] The intravenous injection of adrenaline at the rate of 40 μg./kg./min. evokes the usual stimulating effects of the peripheral administration of adrenaline. Under these conditions the entrance of adrenaline into the various cerebrospinal fluid receptacles may vary between 20 to over 100 nanograms per minute, concentrations of a lower order than the 30 to 80 μg. required for the intraventricular analgesia of adrenaline.[154] The peripheral administration of mescaline can cause bouts of scratching in mice but the dose employed is 100 mg./kg. while the intraventricular dose for this purpose is 30 μg.[155] Similarly, serotonin[156] injected into the brain of mice evoked scratching, a result not seen by other routes of administration. Sedation and other results of the intraventricular injections of chlorpromazine occurred with amounts too small to be effective by intravenous route.[157] Psychic estrus was induced in the castrate estrogen-primed hamster with an intraventricular dose of progesterone, a phenomenon not achieved when the same dose was injected systemically.[158] In view of the consistency of all these results, and others, it is surprising that the peripheral administration of reserpine is more effective than the intraventricular one in attenuating avoidance responses in cats.[159]

Sites of Action.—The data indicate that the intraventricular effects of drugs are produced by central and not peripheral actions. Furthermore, they are caused by effects on subcortical rather than cortical areas. Flooding exposed cerebral cortex with tubocurarine does not produce convulsions nor is there necessarily any tubocurarine on the cortex after intraventricular injection.[152] Though these drugs are injected into the lateral ventricle it is not improbable that most of the results are produced by structures lining the third and fourth ventricles. Convulsive activity appears to be as characteristic for the periventricular gray matter as is contraction for muscle.[152] Furthermore, the analgesic-like state produced by adrenaline is reminiscent of the condition imposed by drugs which block the reticular formation, a structure lying beneath the fourth ventricle. Noradrenaline injected into the third ventricle induced ovulation in estrogen-treated rabbits, a phenomenon which was prevented by pre-treatment with atropine or pentobarbital. The evidence therefore suggests a basal tuberal or posterior hypothalamic site of action for that adrenergic agent.[160]

REFERENCES

1. MUELLER, J. M., SCHLITTLER, E. and BEIN, H. J.: Reserpin, der sedative Wirkstoff aus Rauwolfia serpentina Benth, *Experientia, 8*:338 (1952).
2. PLETSCHER, A., SHORE, P. A. and BRODIE, B. B.: Serotonin release as a possible mechanism of reserpine action. *Science, 122*:374-375 (1955).
3. ERSPAMER, V.: Pharmacology of indolealkylamines. *Pharmacol. Rev., 6*:425-487 (1954).
4. PLETSCHER, A., SHORE, P. A. and BRODIE, B. B.: Serotonin as a mediator of reserpine action in the brain. *J. Pharmacol. & Exper. Therap., 116*:84-89 (1956).
5. PAASONEN, M. K. and VOGT, MARTHE: The effect of drugs on the amounts of substance P and 5-hydroxtryptamine in mammalian brain. *J. Physiol., 131*:617-626 (1956).
6. MANN, P. J. G. and QUASTEL, J. H.: Benzedrine (beta-phenylisopropylamine) and brain metabolism. *Biochem. J., 34*:414-431 (1940).
7. COREALLE, P.: The occurrence and distribution of 5-hydroxytryptamine (enteramine) in the central nervous system of vertebrates. *J. Neurochem., 1*:21-33 (1956).
8. BRODIE, B. B., SPECTOR S., KUNTZMAN, R. G. and SHORE, P. A.: Rapid biosynthesis of brain serotonin before and after reserpine administration. *Naturwissenschaften, 10*:244-245 (1958).
9. HAGEN, P., BARRNETT, R. J. and LEE, F.: Biochemical and electron microscopic study of particles isolated from mastocytoma cells. *J. Pharmacol. & Exper. Therap., 126*:91-108 (1959).
10. COSTA, E.: The role of serotonin in neurobiology. *Internat. Rev. Neurobiol., 2*:175-227 (1960).
11. HUGHES, F. B. and BRODIE, B. B.: The mechanism of serotonin and catecholamine uptake by platelets. *J. Pharmacol. & Exper. Therap., 127*:96-102 (1959).
12. HUGHES, F. B., SHORE, P. A. and BRODIE, B. B.: Serotonin storage mechanism and its interaction with reserpine. *Experientia, 14*:1-6 (1958).
13. BORN, G. V. R., INGRAM, G. I. C. and STACEY, R. S.: The relationship between 5-hydroxytryptamine and adenosine triphosphate in blood platelets. *Brit. J. Pharmacol., 13*:62-64 (1958).

14. SHORE, P. A., CARLSSON, A. and BRODIE, B. B.: Mechanism of serotonin release by reserpine. *Federation Proc.*, 15:483 (1956).

15. HOLZBAUER, M. and VOGT, MARTHE. Depression by reserpine of the noradrenaline concentration in the hypothalamus of the cat. *J. Neurochem.*, 1:8-11 (1956-57).

16. VOGT, MARTHE: The concentration of sympathin in different parts of the central nervous system under normal conditions and after the administration of drugs. *J. Physiol.*, 123:451-481 (1954).

17. BRODIE, B. B., OLIN, JACQUELINE, KUNTZMAN, R. G. and SHORE, P. A.: Possible interrelationships between release of brain norepinephrine and brain serotonin by reserpine. *Science*, 125:1293-1294 (1957).

18. MUSCHOLL, E. and VOGT, MARTHE: The action of reserpine on the peripheral sympathetic system. *J. Physiol.*, 141:132-155 (1958).

19. CARLSSON, A.: The occurrence, distribution and physiological role of catechol amines in the nervous system. *Pharmacol. Rev.*, 11:490-493 (1959).

20. BERTLER, A., CARLSSON, A., LINDQUIST, M. and MAGNUSSON, T.: On the cortical amine levels in blood plasma after stimulation of the sympathoadrenal system. *Experientia*, 14:184-185 (1958).

21. BOURA, A. L. A., COPP, F. C., DUNCOMBE, W. G., GREEN, A. F. and McCOUBREY, A.: The selective accumulation of bretylium in sympathetic ganglia and their postganglionic nerves. *Brit. J. Pharmacol.*, 15:265-270 (1960).

22. BOURA, A. L. A., and GREEN A. F.: The actions of bretylium: adrenergic neurone blocking and other effects. *Brit. J. Pharmacol.*, 14:536-548 (1959).

23. FURCHGOTT, R. F.: The pharmacology of vascular smooth muscles. *Pharmacol. Rev.*, 7:183-265 (1955).

24. BURN, J. H. and RAND, M. J.: Sympathetic postganglionic cholinergic fibres. *Brit. J. Pharmacol.*, 15:56-66 (1960).

25. AXELROD, J. and TOMCHICK, R.: Increased rate of metabolism of epinephrine and norepinephrine by sympathomimetic amines. *J. Pharmacol. & Exper. Therap.*, 130:367-369 (1960).

26. BURN, J. H. and RAND, M. J.: The action of sympathomimetic amines in animals treated with reserpine. *J. Physiol.*, 144:314-336 (1958).

27. WHITBY, L. G., HERTTING, G., AXELROD, J. Effect of cocaine on the disposition of noradrenaline labelled with tritium. *Nature*, 187:604-605 (1960).

28. BRODIE, B. B. Selective release of norepinephrine and serotonin by reserpine-like compounds. *Dis. Nerv. System*, Supp., 21:107-109 (1960).

29. PLETSCHER, A., BESENDORF, H. and GEY, K. F.: Depression of norepinephrine and 5-hydroxytryptamine in the brain by benzoquinoline derivatives. *Science*, 129:844 (1959).

30. QUINN, GERTRUDE, P., SHORE, P. A. and BRODIE, B. B.: Biochemical and pharmacological studies of RO 1-9569 (Tetrabenazine), a non-indole tranquilizing agent with reserpine-like effects. *J. Pharmacol. & Exper. Therap.*, 127:103-109 (1959).

30a. FINGER, K. F., WEISMAN, A., and TRETTER, J. R.: Behavioral and biochemical activity of a new series of benzoquinoline derivatives. *The Pharmacologist*, 3:75, 1961.

31. KARKI, N. T. and PAASONEN, M. K.: Selective depletion of noradrenaline and 5-hydroxytryptamine from rat brain and intestine by rauwolfia alkaloids. *J. Neurochem.*, 3:352-357 (1958-59).

32. PAASONEN, M. K. and DEWS, P. B.: Effects of raunescine and isoraunescine on

behavior and on the 5-hydroxytryptamine and noradrenaline contents of brain. *Brit. J. Pharmacol., 13:*84-88 (1958).

33. BRODIE, B. B., FINGER, K. F., ORLANS, F. B., QUINN, G. P. and SULSER, F.: Evidence that tranquilizing action of reserpine is associated with change in brain serotonin and not in brain norepinephrine. *J. Pharmacol. & Exper. Therap., 129:*250-256 (1960).

34. ORLANS, F., BARBARA, HUGHES, F. B., FINGER, K. F., BRODIE, B. B.: Pharmacological consequences of the selective release of peripheral norepinephrine by syrosingopine (SU 3118). *J. Pharmacol. & Exper. Therap., 128:*131-139 (1960).

35. BERTLER, A., CARLSSON, A. and ROSENGREN, E.: Release by reserpine of catecholamines from rabbits' hearts. *Naturwissenschaften, 43:*521 (1956).

36. HILLARP, N. A.: Effect of reserpine on the adrenal medulla of sheep. *Acta physiol. scandinav., 49:*376-382 (1960).

37. MARKIN, B. L.: Catecholamine depletion in the rat's denervated adrenal gland following chronic administration of reserpine. *Nature, 182:*113-114 (1958).

38. CALLINGHAM, B. A. and MANN, MONICA: Replacement of adrenaline and noradrenaline in the innervated and denervated adrenal gland of the rat following depletion with reserpine. *Nature, 182:*1020-1021 (1958).

39. KRONEBERG, G. and SCHUMANN, H. J.: Die Wirkung des Reserpine auf den Hormongehalt des Nebennierenmarks. *Arch. Exper. Path. u. Pharmakol., 231:*349-360 (1957).

40. PASSONEN, MATTI, K. and KRAYER, O.: The release of norepinephrine from the mammalian heart by reserpine. *J. Pharmacol. & Exper. Therapy., 123:*153-160 (1958).

41. AMIN, A. H., CRAWFORD, T. B. B. and GADDUM, J. H.: The distribution of substance P and 5-hydroxytryptamine in the central nervous system of dog. *J. Physiol., 126:*596-618 (1954).

42. SANO, I., GAMO, T., YAKIMOTO, Y., TANIGUCHI, K., TAKESADA, M. and NISHINUMA, K.: Distribution of catechol compounds in human brain. *Biochem. et biophys. acta, 32:*586-587 (1959).

43. COSTA, E. and APRISON, M. H.: Studies on the 5-hydroxytryptamine (Serotonin) content in human brain. *J. Nerv. & Ment. Dis., 126:*289-293 (1958).

44. BERTLER, A. and ROSENGREN, E.: On the distribution in brain of monoamines and of enzymes responsible for their formation. *Experientia, 15:*382-388 (1959).

45. CARLSSON, A., LINDQUIST, M., MAGNUSSON, T. and WALDBECK, B.: On the presence of 3-hydroxytramine in brain. *Science, 127:*471 (1958).

46. SJOERDSMA, A., LOVENBERG, W., OATES, J. A., CROUT, J. R. and UDENFRIEND, S.: Alterations in the pattern of amine excretion in man produced by a monomine oxidase inhibitor. *Science, 130:*225 (1959).

47. SPECTOR, S., SHORE, P. A. and BRODIE, B. B.: Biochemical and pharmacological effects of the monoamine oxidase inhibitors, iproniazid, 1-phenyl-2-hydrazine-propane (JB 516), 1-phenyl-2-hydrazinobutane (JB 835), *J. Pharmacol. & Exper. Therap., 128:*15-21 (1960).

48. ZELLER, E. A., BARSKY, J. and BERMAN, E. R.: Amine oxidases. XI. Inhibition of monoamine oxidase by 1-isonico-tinyl-2-isopropylhydrazine. *J. Biol. Chem., 214:*267-274 (1955).

49. DAVISON, A. N.: The mechanism of the irreversible inhibition of rat liver monoamine oxidase by iproniazid (Marsilid). *Biochem. J., 67:*316-322 (1957).

50. GREIG, MARGARET, WALK, R. A. and GIBBONS, ANNA, J.: The effect of three tryptamine derivatives on serotonin metabolism in vitro and in vivo. *J. Pharmacol. & Exper. Therap., 127:*110-115 (1959).

51. McGEER, P., McGEER, E., FELDSTEIN, A., HOAGLAND, H., RIVIERA, M. R. and FREEMAN, H.: Metabolism of radioactive serotonin in psychotics treated with MAO inhibitor. *J. Neuropsychiat., 1:*274-275 (1955).

52. BONNYCASTLE, D. D., GIARMAN, N. J. and PAASONEN, M. K.: Anticonvulsant compounds and 5-hydroxytryptamine in rat brain. *Brit. J. Pharmacol., 12:*228-231 (1957).

53. ANDERSON, E. G. and BONNYCASTLE, D. D.: A study of the central depressant action of pentobarbital, phenobarbital and diethyl ether in relationship to increases in brain 5-hydroxytryptamine. *J. Pharmacol. & Exper. Therap., 130:*138-143 (1960).

54. BONNYCASTLE, D. D., BONNYCASTLE, M. F. and ANDERSON, E. G.: The effects of a number of central depressant drugs upon brain 5-hydroxytrptamine levels in the rat. *J. Pharmacol. Exper. Therap., 135:*17-20 (1962).

55. EHRINGER, H., HORNYKIEWICZ, I. and LECHNER, K.: Die Wirkung des Chlor-promazine auf den Katecholamin—und 5-Hydroxytryptaminstoffwechsel im Gehirn der Ratte. *Arch. exper. Path u. Pharmakol., 239:*507-519 (1960).

56. PLETSCHER, A. and GEY, K. F.: Wirkung von chlorpromazin auf pharma-cologische veranderungen des 5-Hydroxytryptamine und noradrenalin-Gehaltes im Gehirn. *Med. Exper., 50:*259-265 (1960).

57. BARTLET, A. L.: The 5-hydroxytryptamine content of mouse brain and whole mice after treatment with some drugs affecting the central nervous system. *Brit. J. Pharmacol., 15:*140-146 (1960).

58. COSTA, E., GARATTINI, S. and VALZELLI, L.: Interactions between reserpine, chlorpromazine and imipramine. *Experientia, 16:*460-461 (1960).

59. CAMANNI, F., MOLINATTI, G. M. and OLIVETTI, M.: Abolition by chlorpromazine of the inhibiting effect of iproniazid on the depletion of adrenal catechol-amines induced by reserpine. *Nature, 184:*65-66 (1959).

60. BULLE, P. H.: Effects of reserpine and chlorpromazine in prevention of cere-bral edema and reversible cell damage. *Proc. Soc. Exper. Biol. & Med., 94:*553-556 (1957).

60A. AXELROD, J., WHITBY, L. G. and HERTTING, G.: Effect of psychotropic drugs on the uptake of H³-norepinephrine by tissues. *Science, 133:*No. 3450, 383-384 (1961).

61. BAUER, K. FR., and LEONHARDT, H.: A contribution to the pathological physi-ology of the blood-brain-barrier. *J. Comp. Neurol., 106:*363-370 (1956).

62. CHRISTENSEN, J., FENG, Y. S. L., POLLEY, E. and WASE, A. W.: Influence of chlorpromazine on transport of ions into cerebral tissues. *Federation Proc., 17:*358 (1958).

63. KARREMAN, G., ISENBERG, I., and SZENT-GYÖRGYI, A.: On the mechanism of ac-tion of chlorpromazine. *Science, 130:*1191-1192 (1959).

64. COSTA, E., PSCHEIDT, G. R., VAN METER, W. G. and HIMWICH, H. E.: Brain concentrations of biogenic amines and EEG patterns of rabbits. *J. Pharma-col. & Exper. Therap., 130:*81-88 (1960).

65. BRUNE, G. G. and HIMWICH, H. E.: Biphasic action of reserpine and isocar-boxazid on behavior and serotonin metabolism. *Science, 133:*190-192 (1961).

66. BRUNE, G. G. and HIMWICH, H. E.: Correlations between Behavior and Uri-nary Indole Amines during Treatment with Reserpine and Isocarboxazid, Separately and Together. *Neuro-Psychopharmacology, 2:*465-494 (1961).

67. Brune, G. G. and Himwich, H. E.: *Effects of Reserpine on Urinary Trypta-mine and Indole-3-acetic Acid Excretion in Mental Deficiency, Schizophrenia and Phenylpyruvic Oligophrenia.* Bologne, in press.

68. Rinaldi, F., Rudy, L. H. and Himwich, H. E.: Clinical evaluation of azacy-clonol, chlorpromazine and reserpine on a group of chronic psychotic pa-tients. *Am. J. Psychiat., 112:*678-683 (1956).

69. Szara, S. and Axelrod, J.: Hydroxylation and N-dimethylation of N, N-dime-thyltryptamine. *Experientia, 15:*216-219 (1959).

70. Szara, S., Hearst, E. and Putney, F.: Metabolism of hallucinogenic trypta-mine derivatives. *Federation Proc., 19:*23 (1960).

71. Brodie, B. B., Shore, P. A.: A concept for a role of serotonin and norepine-phrine as chemical mediator in the brain. *Ann. New York Acad. Sc., 66:*631-642 (1957).

72. Monnier, P. M. and Tissot, R.: Action de la reserpine et de ses mediateurs (5-hydroxytryptophan-serotonine et dopa-noradrenaline) sur le comporte-ment et le cerveau du lapin. *Helvet. physiol. acta, 16:*255-267 (1958).

73. Bogdanski, D. F., Weissbach, H. and Udenfriend, S.: Pharmacological studies with the serotonin precursor, 5-hydroxytryptophan. *J. Pharmacol. & Exper. Therap., 122:*182-194 (1958).

74. Himwich, W. A. and Costa, E.: Behavioral changes associated with changes in concentration of brain serotonin. *Federation Proc., 19:*838-845 (1960).

75. Vogt, Marthe: Theory and facts about the functional role of noradrenaline, 5-hydroxytryptamine (serotonin) and other amines found in mammalian brain. Paper read at Tenth Anniversary Celebration, Galesburg State Re-search Hospital, 1960.

76A. Chessin, M., Kramer, E. R. and Scott, C. C.: Modifications of the pharma-cology of reserpine and serotonin by iproniazid. *J. Pharmacol. & Exper. Therap., 119:*453-460 (1957).

76. Brodie, B. B., Spector, S. and Shore, P. A.: Interaction of drugs with norepi-nephrine in the brain. *Pharmacol. Rev., 11:*548-564 (1959).

77. Pscheidt, G., Brune, G. G. and Himwich, H. E.: Effect of therapeutic doses of psychotropic drugs on clinical symptomatology and urinary amines. *Phy-siologist, 3:*126 (1960).

78. Carlsson, A., Lindquist, M. and Magnusson, T.: 3,4-dihydroxyphenylalanine and 5-hydroxytryptophan as reserpine antagonists. *Nature, 180:*1200 (1957).

79. Bertler, A. and Rosengren, E.: On the distribution in brain of monoamines and of enzymes responsible for their formation. *Experientia, 15:*382-388 (1959).

80. Everett, G. M. and Toman, J. E. P.: Mode of action of rauwolfia alkaloid and motor activity. *Biol. Psychiat. 1:*75-81 (1959). Jules H. Masserman, ed. Grune and Stratton, New York.

81. Plummer, A. J., Maxwell, R. A., Earl, A. E.: The influence of Ritalin (methylphenidate) on the behavioral and circulatory effects of reserpine. *Schweiz. med. Wchnschr.,* 60, 370 (1957).

82. Blaschko, H., Richter, D. and Schlossmann, H.: The inactivation of adren-aline. *J. Physiol., 90:*1-17 (1937).

83. Bertler, A., Hillarp, N. A. and Rosengren, E.: "Bound" and "free" catechol amines in the brain. *Acta physiol. scandinav., 50:*113-118 (1960).

84. Giarman, N. J. and Schanberg, S.: The intracellular distribution of 5-hydroxy-tryptamine (HT; Serotonin) in the rat's brain. *Biochem. Pharmacol., 1:*301-306 (1958).

85. WEIL-MALHERBE, H. and BONE, A. D.: The effect of reserpine on the intracellular distribution of catecholamines in the brain stem of the rabbit. *J. Neurochem.*, 4:251-263 (1959).

86. GREEN, H. and SAWYER, J. L.: Intracellular distribution of norepinephrine in rat brain. I. Effect of reserpine and the monoamine oxidase inhibitors, trans-2-phenylchlorpropylamine and 1-isanecatenyl-2-isopropyl hydrazine, *J. Pharmacol. & Exper. Therap.*, 129:243-249 (1960).

87. VON EULER, U. S. and LISHAJKO, F.: Effect of reserpine on release of noradrenaline from transmitter granules in adrenergic nerves. *Science, 132:*351 (1960).

88. WALASZEK, E. and ABOOD, L. G.: Fixation of 5-hydroxytryptamine by brain mitochondria. *Proc. Soc. Exper. Biol. & Med., 101:*37-40 (1959).

89. BERTLER, A., ROSENGREN, A. M. and ROSENGREN, E.: In vivo uptake of dopamine and 5-hydroxytryptamine by adrenal medullary granules. *Experientia, 16:*418-419 (1960).

90. BERTLER, A., HILLARP, N. A. and ROSENGREN, E.: Storage of new-formed catechol amines in the adrenal medulla. *Experientia, 16:*419-420 (1960).

91. CARLSSON, A., HILLARP, N. and HOKFELT, B.: The concomitant release of adenosine triphosphate and catechol amines from the adrenal medulla. *J. Biol. Chem., 227:*243-252 (1957).

92. HILLARP, N. A. and THIEME, G.: Nucleotides in the catechol amine granules of the adrenal medulla. *Acta physiol. scandinav., 45:*328-338 (1959).

93. CARLSSON, A. and HILLARP, N. A.: Release of adenosine triphosphate along with adrenaline and noradrenaline following stimulation of the adrenal medulla. *Acta physiol. scandinav., 37:*235-239 (1956).

94. WEINER, N., BURACK, W. R. and HAGEN, P. B.: The effect of insulin on the catechol amines and adenine nucleotides of adrenal glands. *J. Pharmacol. & Exper. Therap., 130:*251-255 (1960).

95. GODDALL, M., KIRSHNER, N. and ROSEN, L.: Metabolism of noradrenaline in the human. *J. Clin. Invest., 38:*707-714 (1959).

96. AXELROD, J.: Metabolism of epinephrine and other sympathomimetic amines. *Physiol. Rev., 39:*751-776 (1959).

97. CROUT, J., CREVELING, C. R. and CATON, D.: Norepinephrine metabolism in rat brain and heart. *Federation Proc., 19:*297 (1960).

98. RESNICK, O. The influence of amine oxidase inhibitors in epinephrine metabolism in man. *Ann. New York Acad. Sc., 80:*726-731 (1959).

99. DESCHAEPDRYVER, A. F. and KIRSHNER, N.: Metabolism of DL-adrenaline-2-C^{14} in the cat after blockade of monoamine oxidase and catechol-O-methyltransferase. *Science, 133:*586-587 (1961).

100. ROSENGREN, E.: On the role of monoamine oxidase for the inactivation of dopamine in brain. *Acta physiol. scandinav., 49:*370-375 (1960).

101. GOLDSTEIN, M., FRIEDHOFF, A. J., POMERANTZ, S. and SIMMONS, C.: The characterization of a new metabolite of dopamine. *Biochim. et biophys. acta, 39:*189-191 (1960).

102. UDENFRIEND, S.: Serotonin metabolism and the central nervous system. Read at the IVth International Congress of Biochemistry, Vienna, 1958.

103. WESTERMAN, E., BALZER, H. and KNELL, J.: Hemmung der serotoninbildung durch alphamethyl-dopa. *Arch. Exper. Path. u. Pharmakol., 234:*194-205 (1958).

104. ROSENGREN, E.: Are dihydroxyphenylalanine decarboxylase and 5-hydroxy-tryptophan decarboxylase individual enzymes? *Acta physiol. scandinav.*, *49*:364-369 (1960).

105. BLASCHKO, H., HAGEN, P. and WELCH, A. D.: Observations on the intracellular granules of the adrenal medulla. *J. Physiol.*, *129*:27-49 (1955).

106. SCHUMANN, H. J.: Uber die Verteiling von Noradrenalin und Hydroxytyramine in sympathischen Nerven (Milznerven). *Arch. exper. Path. u. Pharmakol.*, *234*:17-25 (1958).

107. SOURKES, T. L.: Inhibition of dihydroxyphenylalanine decarboxylase by derivatives of phenylalanine. *Arch. Biochem. & Biophys.*, *51*:444-456 (1954).

108. SMITH, S. E.: The pharmacological actions of 3,4-dihydroxyphenyl-a-Methylalanine (alpha-methyldopa) an inhibitor of 5-hydroxytryptophan decarboxylase. *Brit. J. Pharmacol.*, *15*:319-327 (1960).

109. OATES, J. A., GILLESPIE, L., UDENFRIEND, S. and SJOERDSMA, A.: Decarboxylase inhibition and blood pressure reduction by alpha-methyl 3,4-dihydroxy-DL-phenylalanine. *Science*, *131*:1890-1891 (1960).

110. HESS, S. M., OZAKI, M. and UDENFRIEND, S.: The effects of alpha-methyl dopa and alpha-methyl meta tyrosine on the metabolism of serotonin and norepinephrine. *Pharmacologist, 2*:81 (1960).

111. HESS, S. M., CONNAMACHER, R. H. and UDENFRIEND, S.: Effect of alpha-methyl-amino acids on catecholamines and serotonin. *Federation Proc.* (1961).

112. COSTA, E. and HIMWICH, H. E.: Brain serotonin metabolism in insulin hypoglycemia. In *Biochemistry of the Central Nervous System*, Vol. 3, pp. 283-290. Hoffman and Ostenhol, Eds. New York, Pergamon Press (1960).

113. HIMWICH, W. A., COSTA, E. and HIMWICH, H. E.: Brain serotonin in relation to imipramine interaction with a monoamine oxidase inhibitor. *Neuropsychopharmacology, 2*:485-489 (1961).

114. COURVOISIER, S., FOURNEL, J., DUCROT, R., KOLSKY, M. and KOETSCHUT, P.: Proprietés Pharmacodynamiques du Chlorhydrate de Chloro-3-(Dimethylamino-3-prophyl)-10-Phenothiazine (4560 R.P.). *Arch. internat. pharmacodyn., 92*:305-314 (1953).

115. BERHSOHN, J., NAMAJUSKA, I. and COCHRANE, L. S. G.: The effect of chlorpromazine on respiration and glycolysis in rat brain. *Arch. Biochem. & Biophys.*, *62*:274-283 (1956).

116. LISOVSKAYA, N. P., and LIVANOVA, N. B.: The effect of some pharmacological agents upon respiration, ATP content and phosphoprotein metabolism in slices of the rat cerebral cortex. *Biokhimika, 5*:24, 799-810 (1959).

117. ABOOD, L. G.: Effect of chlorpromazine on phosphorylation of brain mitochondria. *Proc. Soc. Exper. Biol. & Med., 88*:688-690 (1955).

118. KORSHOW, V. A.: Effect of aminazine upon respiration and oxydizing phosphorylation in the animal tissue. *Problems of Experimental Pathology.* Ch. 23, pp. 253-9, Braines, S. N. (1959).

119. CENTURY, E. and HORWITT, M. K.: Actions of reserpine and chlorpromazine hydrochloride on rat brain oxidative phosphorylation and adenosine triphosphate. *Proc. Soc. Exper. Biol. & Med., 91*:493-496 (1956).

120. LEWIS, J. L. and McILWAIN, H.: The action of some ergot derivatives, mescaline and dibenamine on the metabolism of separated mammalian cerebral tissues. *Biochem. J., 57*:680-684 (1954).

121. LINDAN, O., QUASTEL, J. H. and SVED, S.: Biochemical studies on chlorpromazine. The effect of chlorpromazine on respiratory activity of isolated rat brain cortex. *Canad. J. Biochem. & Physiol., 35*(12):1135-1144 (1957).

122. YAGI, K., NAGATSU, T. and OZAWA, T.: Inhibitory action of chlorpromazine on the oxidation of D-amino-acid in the diencephalon part of the brain. *Nature, 177*:891-892 (1956).

123. WEINER, N.: Effect of CPZ on levels of adenine nucleotides and creatine phosphate of brain. *Federation Proc., 19*:30 (1960).

124. NISHI, S., KOKETSU, K., CERF, J. A. and ABOOD, L. G.: Some electrophysiological and biochemical studies with hydroxyzine. *J. Pharmacol. & Exper. Therap., 126*:148-154 (1959).

125. DESCI, L. and MEHES, J.: Increases similarity of the hydrothalamic cells to the uncoupling effect of tranquilizing drugs. *Arch. internat. pharmacodyn., 119*:294-304 (1959).

126. GERONIMUS, L. H., ABRAMSON, H. A. and INGRAHAM, L. J.: Lysergic acid diethylamide (LSD-25): XXIII. Comparative effects of LSD-25 and related ergot drugs on brain tissue respiration and on human behavior. *J. Psychol., 42*:157-168 (1956).

126A. GEY, K. F. and PLETSCHER, A.: Increase of pyruvic and lactic acid in rat blood by inhibitors of monoamine oxidase. *Experientia, 17*:25-26 (1961).

126B. BALZER, H., HOLTZ, P. and PALM, D.: Reserpin und gamma-aminobuttersäuregehalt des Gehirns. *Experientia, 17*:38-40 (1961).

127. MAGEE, W. L., BERRY, J. F. and ROSSITER, R. J.: Effect of chlorpromazine and azacyclonol on the labelling of phosphatides in brain slices. *Biochim. et biophys. acta, 21*:408-409 (1956).

128. GROSSI, E., PAOLETTI, P. and PAOLETTI, R.: The in vitro and in vivo effects of chlorpromazine on brain lipid synthesis. *J. Neurochem., 6*:73-78 (1960).

129. QUASTEL, J. H.: Carbohydrate metabolism in the brain cortex in vitro and the effects of neurotropic agents. *Proc. Assoc. Nerv. Ment. Dis.* In press (1962).

130. KETY, S. S. and SCHMIDT, C. F.: The nitrous oxide method for the quantitative determination of cerebral blood flow in man: theory, procedure and normal values. *J. Clin. Invest., 27*:476-483 (1948).

131. FAZEKAS, J. E., ALBERT, S. N. and ALMAN, R. W.: Influence of chlorpromazine and alcohol on cerebral hemodynamics and metabolism. *Am. J. M. Sc., 230*:128-132 (1955).

132. MORRIS, G., PONTIUS, R., HERSCHBERGER, R. and MOYER, J. H.: Cerebral hemodynamics following administration of chlorpromazine. *Federation Proc., 14*:371-372 (1955).

133. EHRMANTRAUT, W. R., SHEA, J. G., TICKTIN, H. E. and FAZEKAS, J. F.: Influence of promazine and methylphenidate on cerebral hemodynamics and metabolism. *Arch. Int. Med., 100*:66-69 (1957).

134. HAFKENSCHIEL, J. H., SELLERS, A. M., KING, G. A. and THORNER, M. W.: Preliminary observations on the effect of parenteral reserpine on cerebral blood flow, oxygen and glucose metabolism, and electroencephalograms of patients with essential hypertension. *Ann. New York Acad. Sc., 61*:78-84 (1955).

135. KLEH, J. and FAZEKAS, J. F.: The use of reserpine in the hypertensive arteriosclerotic syndrome. *Am. J. M. Sc., 228*:560-562 (1954).

136. KLEH, J. and FAZEKAS, J. F.: Effects of hypotensive agents on subjects with cerebral vascular insufficiency. *J. Am. Geriat. Soc., 4*:18-23 (1956).

137. SOKOLOFF, L., PERLIN, S., KORNETSKY, C. and KETY, S. S.: The effects of d-lysergic acid diethylamide on cerebral circulation and over-all metabolism. *Ann. New York Acad. Sc., 66*:468-477 (1957).

138. BASS, A.: Über eine Wirkung des Adrenalin auf das Gehirn. *Ztschr. Ges. Neurol. u. Psychiat., 26*:600-601 (1914).

NEUROCHEMISTRY

NEUROCHEMISTRY

NEUROCHEMISTRY

139. BECHT, F.: Studies of the cerebrospinal fluid. *J. Physiol.*, *51*:1-125 (1920).

140. LEIMDORFER, R., ARANA, R. and HACK, M.: Hyperglycemia induced by the action of adrenaline on the central nervous system. *J. Physiol.*, *150*:588-595 (1947).

141. DIKSHIT, B. B.: Action of acetylcholine on the "sleep centre." *J. Physiol.*, *83*:42 (1935).

142. BORNSTEIN, M. B.: Presence and action of acetylcholine in experimental brain trauma. *J. Neurophysiol.*, *9*:349-366 (1946).

143. BRENNER, C. and MERRITT, H. H.: Effect of certain choline derivatives on electrical activity of the cortex. *Arch. Neurol. & Psychiat.*, *48*:382-385 (1942).

144. FIAMBERTI, A. M.: Accessi a carattere epilettico provocati con l'introduzione sotto cipitale di sostanze vasodilatrici. *Riv. sper. franiat.*, *61*:834-840 (1937).

145. CUSHING, H.: The action of atropine in counteracting the effects of intraventricular pituitrin and of pilocarpine. *Proc. Nat. Acad. Sc.*, *17*:163-170 (1931).

146. SHERWOOD, S. L.: Intraventricular medication in catatonic stupor. *Brain*, *75*:68-75 (1952).

147. HALEY, T. J. and McCORMICK, W. G.: Pharmacological effects produced by intracerebral injection of drugs in the conscious mouse. *Brit. J. Pharmacol.*, *12*:12-15 (1957).

148. FELDBERG, W. and SHERWOOD, S. L.: A permanent cannula for intraventricular injections in cats. *J. Physiol.*, *120*:3 (1953).

149. SCHWARZ, M. D., KHALIL, G. W., BICKFORD, R. G., LICHTENHELD, F. R.: Behavioral and electroencephalographic effects of hallucinogenic drugs. *Arch. Neurol. & Psychiat.*, *75*:83-90 (1956).

150. BHATTACHARYA, B. K. and FELDBERG, W.: Perfusion of the ventricular system of the brain in the anesthetized cat. *J. Physiol.*, *135*:4-5 (1957).

151. WEINBERG, S. J. and HALEY, T. J.: Centrally medicated effects of cardiac drugs: Strophanthin-K, Quindine and Procaine Amide. *Circulation Res. 3*:103-109 (1955).

152. FELDBERG, W. S.: Behavioral changes in the cat after injection of drugs into cerebral ventricle. In *The Brain and Human Behavior*, ARNMD, Vol. 36, pp. 401-423. H. C. Solomon, S. Coff and W. Penfield, Eds. Baltimore, Williams & Wilkins (1958).

153. FELDBERG, W. and SHERWOOD, S. L.: Injection of bulbocapnine into the cerebral ventricles of cats. *Brit. J. Pharmacol.*, *10*:371-374 (1955).

154. DRASKOCI, M., FELDBERG, W. and HARANATH, P. S. R. K.: Passage of circulating adrenaline into perfused cerebral ventricles and subarachnoidal space. *J. Physiol.*, *150*:34-39 (1960).

155. FELLOWS, E. J. and COOK, L.: The comparative pharmacology of a number of phenothiazine derivatives. *Psychotropic Drugs*, pp. 397-404. S. Garattini and V. Ghetti, Eds. Amsterdam, Elsevier (1957).

156. HALEY, J.: Intracerebral injection of psychotomimetic and psychotherapeutic drugs on conscious mice. *Acta pharmacol. et toxicol.*, *13*:107-112 (1957).

157. SPECTOR, S., BOGDANSKI, D. F. and BRODIE, B. B.: Evidence that chlorpromazine exerts a generalized central sympatholytic action. *Federation Proc.*, *16*:337 (1957).

158. KENT, G. C. JR., and LIBERMAN, M. J.: Induction of psychic estrus in the hamster with progesterone administered via the lateral brain ventricle. *Endocrinology*, *45*:29-32 (1949).

159. JOHN, E. R., WENZEL, BERNICE, M. and TSCHIRGI, R. D.: Differential effects on various conditioned responses in cats caused by intraventricular and intramuscular injections of reserpine and other substances. *J. Pharmacol. & Exper. Therap., 123:*193-205 (1958).

160. SAWYER, C. H.: Activation and blockade of the release of pituitary gonadotropin as influenced by the reticular formation. In *Reticular Formation of the Brain,* pp. 223-230. H. H. Jasper, L. D. Proctor, R. S. Knighton, W. C. Noshay, and R. T. Costello, Eds. Boston, Little Brown (1958).

161. GREEN, H., and ERICKSON, R. W.: Further studies with tranylcypromine (monoamine oxidase inhibitor) and its interaction with reserpine in rat brain. *Arch. Internat. Pharmacodynamic Therap., 135:*407-425 (1962).

Addendum

According to Green and Erickson,[161] "Paper chromatographic and fluoresence spectrum analyses of acid homogenates of brains of rats several hours after the intraperitoneal administration of reserpine (5 mg./kg.) failed to show the presence of detectable quantities of authentic 5HT."

XXXII

EFFECTS OF ANAESTHETICS, DEPRESSANTS AND TRANQUILISERS ON BRAIN METABOLISM

J. H. Quastel

Narcotics* and anaesthetics include a large variety of structural types such as hydrocarbons, alcohols, ethers, urethanes, sulphones, amides, ureides, barbiturates, nitrous oxide etc. and it is evident that their common property of inducing narcosis in animals must depend on certain physicochemical characters which they have in common rather than upon the possession of any special chemical constitution.

The knowledge that brain and nerve tissues are rich in lipoidal substances led to the idea that lipoid solubility is in some way related to narcosis. Overton[1] and Meyer[2] independently suggested a parallelism between the affinity of an anaesthetic for lipoids and its anaesthetic effect. Using oil-water partition coefficients as measures of lipoid affinity, it was found that in many cases anaesthetic potency is related to the coefficient. On the other hand it is known that many substances, more soluble in oil than in water, have no narcotic action, and that inorganic ions such as magnesium may induce anaesthesia and have little or no solubility in oil. Traube[3] advanced the theory that narcotics alter cell surface properties as a result of lowering of the surface tension of water, but not all narcotics lower the surface tension of water. Höber[4] suggested that permeability of the central nervous system is depressed by many anaesthetic agents and Winterstein[5] noted a decrease in permeability of muscle cells when treated with anaesthetics. Narcotic effects of nitrogen and the inert gases, argon, krypton and xenon, at high pressures have been attributed to lipoid solubility[6,7] but Case and Haldane[8] doubt if this is the correct explanation. Ferguson[9]

---

*Morphine and allied substances are not included among the narcotics considered in this chapter. They appear to act by mechanisms different from those described here. The narcotics considered in this chapter are also referred to as anesthetics.

has reasoned that narcotic action may depend on a mechanism governed by the equilibrium existing between the concentration of the narcotic in the external phase and its concentration in a special, sensitive, phase. He concludes that equal narcotic effects are produced at equal thermodynamic activities in the sensitive phase, and many calculations seem to support this conclusion (see Brink and Posternak[10]). The rule, however, does not apply very rigorously, but even if it did, it would fail to show more than that the physical characteristics of the narcotic either determines its entry into a cell, or into a special phase of the cell, or its orientation at a specific surface. It gives no obvious clue to the mechanism of action of the narcotic. It may be recalled that substances (e.g., camphor) having water solubilities and oil-water distribution coefficients similar to those of the narcotics may be devoid of narcotic power. Butler[11] concludes "that the study of the physical properties of anaesthetics is a method possessing distinctly limited possibilities for disclosing the actual mechanism of narcosis. . . . The nature of the physical effect is not clarified and the consequences of the primary action that lead to depression of cellular function remain to be described."

It has long been known that narcotics as a general rule inhibit enzymic and respiratory processes but until recently there has been reluctance to associate narcosis with a suppression of oxidative events. Verworn's classical theory[12] claimed that narcosis was a sort of asphyxia but the fact that narcotics could paralyse activities of anaerobic organisms created a disbelief in such a point of view. Henderson[13] went so far as to state that there could be no relation between narcosis and oxidative events, and Butler[11] has also presented arguments against such an association. The reluctance in associating narcosis with oxidative events has been partly due to the fact that the quantities of narcotics required to induce narcosis in an animal are usually of a far smaller order than those required to inhibit most enzymic reactions. Moreover, there has not been until recently any clear evidence that during narcosis in an animal there is any fall in respiratory activity in the nervous system where the narcotics might be expected to exert their greatest effects.

McClure et al.[14] have, however, demonstrated the existence of anoxia in the CNS during the anaesthesia brought about by barbiturates and other narcotics. Himwich and co-workers[15] have found that, under pentothal, oxygen consumption of the cerebral cortex is decreased more than that of the lower centres. With thiopental anaesthesia the average oxygen intake is lowered about 35%.[16] According to Shaw et al.[17] ether anaesthesia is associated with a decrease in the difference between the oxygen contents of arterial and venous bloods. Dameshek

et al.[18] have shown that in the human subject under the influence of
Amytal there is a small but definite inhibition of oxygen uptake and
dextrose utilization by the brain. The depression of cerebral function
by barbiturates indeed parallels the reduction of oxygen uptake. This
fall in oxygen uptake *in vivo,* however, may only be a reflection of the
diminished cerebral activity obtained under narcosis. It does not itself
point to an interference with respiratory activity by the responsible
drugs.

Very many facts point to the profound influence of brain oxidations
on its functional activity. Moreover, it has been clearly established
that glucose is a principal substrate of the brain in the living animal
(though of course it is not the only one) and that oxygen utilized by
the brain is mainly concerned with combustion of glucose supplied
by the blood. A deprivation of glucose from the brain has as dire
physiological effects on the central nervous system as a deprivation of
oxygen (see Quastel[19]). It is known, however, that a variety of substances, other than those directly involved in glucose breakdown are
burned by the brain, as for example, glutamic acid[20] and a variety of
amines.[21] Possibly such substances assume greater quantitative importance when availability of glucose has for some reason diminished.

The physiological facts (e.g. see ref. 22) point to a very high degree
of dependence of mental function on the maintenance of oxygen and
glucose supply to the central nervous system. Any interference with
the respiratory activity of the nervous system, or with some important
aspect of this, by the action of the drug would be expected to disturb
its functional activity. The action of the drug, i.e. its biochemical
effect, may be highly localized even if its distribution in the brain as
a whole is uniform, for the significant factor is the accessibility of the
drug to the enzyme systems affected. A change of biochemical events
at a particular centre in the central nervous system, paralysing the
functional activity of this centre, and affecting, therefore, all branches
of the central nervous system influenced by this centre, would not necessarily be accompanied by similar biochemical changes throughout the
entire central nervous system. In fact, significant and vital chemical
changes at a particular centre may be quite obscured by a series of
other biochemical changes taking place in the nervous system as a
whole as a direct consequence of the paralysis of the centre in question.
It is for this reason that the biochemical findings obtained in studies
of the brain in the intact animal following drug administration must
be interpreted with great caution. They may have little relation to the
direct effect of the drug on the particular nervous centre affected.

ANAESTHETICS AND RESPIRATION OF THE BRAIN *IN VITRO*

Anaesthetics have the power of inhibiting, at low concentrations, the respiration of brain tissue either in the form of a mince or of intact thin slices.[23] Studies of the effects of seven alkyl-barbiturates on the oxygen uptake of minced guinea pig brain respiring in the presence of glucose showed[24] that there is a rough parallelism in this series of barbiturates between hypnotic powers and inhibitive effects on brain respiration. This parallelism is shown among narcotics of different chemical types.[25]

Results, shown in Table I, obtained by using brain cortex slices,[23] made it clear that a variety of narcotics, at their narcotizing concentrations, produces inhibitions of respiration varying from 6% to 32%. The inhibitions recorded represent the effects of the narcotics on the respiration of the entire brain cortex of the animal. Local inhibition will be much higher if the narcotic is localized or specifically absorbed at particular centres. This seems likely as Swank and Cammermeyer[26] have obtained evidence that narcotics have differential effects on the neurones in brain. According to Elliott and Sutherland[27] the addition of pentobarbital (0.002 M) brings about a large inhibition of oxygen uptake of human cerebral cortex slices in presence of glucose, human brain cortex being a little more sensitive than rat brain cortex. When very dilute concentrations of a narcotic are investigated, the effect sometimes, e.g., with pentobarbital,[28] is to bring about a small increase of respiration (of about 5 to 10%) of the brain cortex slice, the effect being dependent on the calcium and magnesium concentrations.

TABLE I

NARCOTIC CONCENTRATION AND EFFECTS ON THE RESPIRATION OF BRAIN CORTEX SLICES IN A GLUCOSE MEDIUM

Narcotic	Animal	Estimated Narcotic Dose gm./kg.	Narcotising Concentration (M.)	Per Cent Inhibition of Isolated Brain Tissue Respiration by Narcotising Concentration
Ethyl urethane	Rat	2	0.022	6
Magnesium ions	Rat		0.005	13
Magnesium ions	Rabbit		0.005	12
Chloral hydrate	Rat	0.22	0.0013	10
Luminal	Rat	0.2	0.00079	15
Chloretone	Rat	0.18	0.001	20
Evipan	Guinea pig	0.16	0.00062	17
Avertin	Rat	0.3	0.0011	31
Chloretone	Guinea pig	0.18	0.0010	32

Wilkins, Featherstone, Schwidde, and Brotman[29] have shown in experiments which combined a dog's brain biopsy method and the manometric technique, that the oxygen consumption *in vitro* of brain cortex, basal ganglion or hypothalamus may be depressed to the extent of 70% in presence of 0.04% pentobarbial. Moreover Schueler and Gross[30] have estimated the oxygen consumption of rat brain cortex slices in which the suspension medium consisted of whole blood drawn from a dog before and at given intervals after the administration of 36 mg./kg. nembutal. They found that highly significant inhibitions (25 to 33%) of brain respiration are obtained using blood drawn 3, 15, 30 and 60 minutes after administration of the narcotic.

NARCOTICS AND SPECIFICITY OF OXIDATIVE INHIBITION

Narcotics do not inhibit all oxidative processes to the same extent. Sen[31] for example showed that urethane, at the high concentrations that inhibit succinic dehydrogenase, has no effect on xanthine oxidase. The oxidations of glucose, lactate and pyruvate are most affected by the narcotics, while those of succinate and p-phenylenediamine are undisturbed.[24] Data obtained by the tissue slice technique are shown in Table II where the effects of luminal on rat brain cortex oxidations are recorded.

TABLE II

EFFECTS OF PHENOBARBITAL (0.08%) ON BRAIN RESPIRATION IN PRESENCE OF VARIOUS METABOLITES (RAT BRAIN CORTEX SLICES)

Metabolite	Q_{O_2} *without Narcotic*	Q_{O_2} *with Narcotic*	*Per Cent Effect of Narcotic on* Q_{O_2}
Nil	2.9	2.75	− 5
Glucose 0.01 *M*	12.2	5.5	−55
Na D-Lactate 0.02 *M*	13.5	8.8	−35
Na Pyruvate 0.02 *M*	11.1	8.1	−27
Na L-Glutamate 0.02 *M*	8.0	6.8	−15
Na Succinate 0.02 *M*	9.5	10.2	+ 7

The high sensitivity to the narcotics of glucose oxidation in brain is a striking feature of narcotic action *in vitro,* and in view of the great importance of glucose oxidation in the functional activity of the central nervous system, this sensitivity must be a significant factor in any consideration of the mechanism of narcotic action.

The total respiration of tissues other than brain is also affected by narcotics though not to the same degree. A result with evipan is shown in Table III. Examination of the inhibitive action of narcotics on the respiration of a variety of tissues has shown that narcotics inhibit the oxidation of glucose, lactate and of pyruvate in tissue such as liver, kidney, or diaphragm, to about the same extent as in brain. It would seem that the effects of narcotics at low concentrations are confined, as in brain, largely to the inhibition of the combustion of substances associated with carbohydrate metabolism. With brain, in contrast to such tissues as liver and kidney, carbohydrate breakdown is the dominant feature of metabolism and it is this fact which throws into prominence the specific inhibitory effect of narcotics in brain metabolism. Nevertheless[23] narcotics will also inhibit the oxidation of fatty acids and amino acids by isolated liver.

TABLE III

EFFECT OF 0.033% EVIPAN* ON RESPIRATION OF GUINEA PIG TISSUES IN PRESENCE OF GLUCOSE

Tissue	Respiration (Q_{O_2})	Respiration (Q_{O_2}) in Presence of Narcotic	Per Cent Inhibition by Narcotics
Brain	14.2	9.5	33
Spleen	7.7	6.4	17
Liver	4.25	4.15	2
Testis	8.65	7.25	16
Kidney	15.2	15.95	Nil

*Na N-methyl-cyclohexenyl methyl barbiturate.

REVERSIBILITY OF NARCOTIC ACTION *IN VITRO*

The effects of narcotics such as the barbiturates, chloretone, or hyoscine, on the respiration of brain slices are reversible. This is shown simply by washing the brain slices in a narcotic free medium after their immersion for an hour at 37° in the narcotic solution. The slow constant rate of oxygen uptake found in presence of the narcotic is raised immediately to a higher level which remains constant (Quastel and Wheatley[32]). High concentrations of narcotics, however, produce irreversible effects.

Analysis[23] of the kinetic data indicates that two effects of a narcotic on brain respiration *in vitro* take place:

(1) Rapid attainment of an equilibrium between the narcotic and a constitutent of the respiratory system. The inhibition of respiration is that to be expected from a simple mass action equation (Jowett[33]) as observed with small concentrations of narcotic producing inhibitions not greater than 40% This applies to narcotics such as urethane, chloral, chloretone, barbiturates, avertin (tribromoethyl alcohol) and magnesium ions.

(2) Relatively slow development of irreversible changes, leading to increased inhibitions of respiration that cannot be restored to normal by removal of the narcotic. This takes place with most narcotics such as barbiturates or chloretone at relatively high concentration. It occurs, however, at low concentrations with ether[34] and chloroform. Irreversibility of action also occurs with indole which is also a powerful inhibitor of brain respiration.[32] Conceivably this is due to gradual irreversible denaturation of the proteins with which these narcotics become associated. It is of interest to note that Hutchinson and Stotz[35] have shown that administration of indole to rats in amounts adequate to yield an *in vitro* inhibition of 30 to 50% on brain metabolism leads to clonic convulsions rather than narcosis. As has been emphasized by Himwich[16] this may be due to differential inhibitions, there being less effect on motor activity than on other activities of the nervous system.

RESPIRATION *IN VITRO* OF BRAINS OF ANAESTHETISED ANIMALS

The brains of anaesthetised animals do not, usually, show a smaller rate of respiration *in vitro* than those of the normal. This is doubtless due to the diffusion of the narcotic from the brain slices into the surrounding medium, thereby diminishing the narcotic concentration in the brain. For example, Wortis[36] found that the oxygen uptake of minced brains from rats injected with butyl-bromallyl barbiturate and sodium amytal was not diminished *in vitro* with glucose as substrate. Elliott and Henderson[37] found that slices of brains of rats and rabbits injected with pentobarbital showed no inhibition of oxygen uptake *in vitro*. Swift[38] gave lethal doses of barbital and avertin to rats but found that their brains *in vitro* showed no diminished rates of respiration from the normal. These negative results are to be expected if the narcotic effect *in vitro,* is, as has been shown may be the case, freely reversible. Taylor *et al.*,[39] however, have found that when tridione and 3-ethyl oxazolidinedione are injected into mice, the oxygen uptakes of the brains *in vitro* are inhibited 13% as compared with the controls, while injection of 120 mg./kg. of phenobarbital results in 8% inhibition. These authors found that the tridione content of brains of anaesthetised mice is approximately 0.0175 M, a concentration that produces 10% inhibition of the normal oxygen uptake *in vitro*.

STIMULATED BRAIN METABOLISM

The respiration of isolated brain cortex slices in a normal physiological (glucose containing) medium is about half that found *in vivo* and it may be increased by two methods to values approximating to those found *in vivo*:

(a) Alteration of the cationic composition, notably the K+/Ca++ ratio, of the medium in which the brain slice is incubated (see Chapter X).

(b) Application of electrical impulses.[43-45]

There is little doubt that both methods of respiratory stimulation have a common basis, namely cationic displacements at the brain cell membrane. What is important, however, is the fact that the stimulated respiration of isolated brain tissue has the magnitude of brain respiration *in vivo* and possesses some of the characteristic feature of brain *in vivo* such as response to drug action. It may be considered a working hypothesis that the stimulated brain slice is an approximation, so far as its biochemical characteristics are concerned, to the functioning brain, that is, to brain tissue *in vivo*, stimulated by sensory impulses. It must be borne in mind, however, that brain slices, under the best experimental conditions obtained so far, do not show the electrophysiological responses to stimulation nor the spontaneous activity associated with brain *in vivo*. Nevertheless, even as an approximation to the *in vivo* condition, they are able to yield valuable biochemical data that bear upon the properties of the functioning brain.

EFFECTS OF ANAESTHETICS, ETC., ON STIMULATED BRAIN METABOLISM

It was found by Jowett and Quastel[23] that the steady state of the diminished respiration of brain slices brought about by small concentrations of anaesthetics, such as phenobarbital or chloretone is greatly dependent on the K+ concentration of the medium. The presence of 12.8 meq./l.K+ secures a steady inhibition of respiration by chloretone, lower concentrations of K+ producing a fluctuating and unstable state, possibly due to loss of K+ from the brain cells. This unstable state depends on the temperature and is less evident at 29° than at 39°.

Anaesthetics (and, as will be shown, depressants and tranquilisers) exercise much larger inhibitory effects on the respiration of nerve tissue, stimulated either electrically, or by the presence of high K+/Ca++, than on that of the unstimulated preparation. Bronk and Brink[44] showed that the rate of oxygen uptake by resting frog nerve is reduced 15% by 2 mM chloretone but that the increment in the rate of oxygen uptake by nerves carrying impulses at the rate of 50 impulses/sec. is decreased by 50% by the same quantity of narcotic. McIlwain[45] demonstrated that narcotics such as the barbiturates and choral inhibit the respiration of electrically stimulated brain cortex slices at concentrations having relatively little effect on the respiration of the unstimulated tissue. He also showed that potassium-stimulated respiration is more sensitive to the action of barbiturates and chloral than the unstimulated. Jowett and Quastel[23] found that luminal inhibition is greater in absence of Ca++ than in its presence. Removal of Ca++ has effects on narcotic sensitivity similar to that due to added K+.[42] Ghosh and Quastel[46] made it clear that it is the increased portion of brain respiration, due to K+ stimulation, which is highly sensitive to luminal, chloretone or ethanol and that, in fact, the narcotic suppresses the K+ stimulation (see Tables IV and V).

TABLE IV

EFFECTS OF LUMINAL ON RAT BRAIN CORTEX RESPIRATION IN PRESENCE OF
POTASSIUM CHLORIDE[46]

Additions	Q_{O_2} without Added KCl	Q_{O_2} with Added KCl (0.1 M)	Average Per Cent Increase Due to KCl
Glucose	14.2, 12.6, 11.5	24.5, 20.0, 21.0	70
Glucose + 3.3 mM Luminal	9.5, 7.4, 6.9	10.5, 8.5, 7.8	12

TABLE V

EFFECTS OF CHLORETONE ON THE KCl STIMULATED RESPIRATION OF RAT BRAIN
CORTEX SLICES IN PRESENCE OF DIFFERENT SUBSTRATES (10 mM)[46]

		Q_{O_2} No Chloretone Present	Q_{O_2} In Presence of 3.3 mM Chloretone
Glucose,	Without added KCl	12.5	8.3
	With 0.1 M KCl	20.5	9.2
Sodium Pyruvate,	Without added KCl	13.2	10.1
	With 0.1 M KCl	18.8	11.2
Sodium L-Glutamate,	Without added KCl	7.5	5.0
	With 0.1 M KCl	7.0	5.0
Sodium Succinate,	Without added KCl	10.8	10.5
	With 0.1 M KCl	9.0	8.5

The largest effects of K+/Ca++ stimulation on rates of oxygen consumption occur with the substrates, glucose, fructose, pyruvate and lactate and little or none is seen with L-glutamate or succinate. The presence of increased K+/Ca++ does not affect the action of narcotics on glutamate or succinate oxidation. The enhanced inhibitory effects

TABLE VI

EFFECTS OF NARCOTICS AND DEPRESSANTS ON $C^{14}O_2$ FORMATION FROM GLUCOSE-U-C^{14} IN PRESENCE OF RAT BRAIN CORTEX SLICES[47]

(Initial activity of glucose = 100,000 c./min./vessel; glucose = 10 mM)

Drugs Added	Amytal		Doriden			Ethanol (in presence of 10 mM L-glutamate)		
	Nil	0.5 mM	Nil	2.5 mM	10 mM	Nil	0.2 M	0.4 M
$C^{14}O_2$ evolved in 90 min. K^+ = 5 mM (c./min./mg.)	211	145	215	217	200	101	102	101
$C^{14}O_2$ evolved in 90 min. K^+ = 105 mM, (c./min./mg.)	528	165	485	416	179	200	178	161
% inhibition by drug of stimulated $C^{14}O_2$ output	—	94	—	25	100	—	23	39

Doriden = alpha ethyl alpha phenylglutarimide; narcotic concentration (rat) = 700 mg./kg.
Ethanol: narcotic concentration (rat) = 4 to 8 gm./kg.

of narcotics is restricted to the substrates whose oxidation is accelerated by the increased K^+/Ca^{++}. Recent evidence[48] indicates that the cationic stimulation of respiration is due to the increased rate of operation of the citric acid cycle in the brain cell, the rate limiting step that is (indirectly) affected being the conversion of pyruvate into acetyl-CoA.

Investigations using radioactive glucose and estimating the rates of formation of $C^{14}O_2$ instead of oxygen consumption show very clearly the effects, at low concentrations, of Amytal, Doriden (a-ethyl-a-phenyl-glutarimide) and ethanol in suppressing the potassium stimulation (Table VI).

In view of the properties of brain tissue stimulated *in vitro*, by changed electrolyte concentration or by application of electric impulses, and of the approximation of the behaviour of such excited tissue *in vitro* to that of functioning brain, the results on the effects of narcotics on stimulated brain *in vitro* have an obvious physiological significance.

Such results do not, of course, imply that all nerve cells in the brain are equally affected by the drug when it causes anaesthesia or narcosis or mental changes, nor that a depression of total brain respiration should necessarily ensue. They do imply, however, that the affected cells can no longer carry on their normal biochemical, and functional, behaviour and, therefore, that those parts of the nervous system controlled by the activities of the affected cells will also be affected, with resulting effects on the nervous system as a whole that will vary according to the location and neurophysiological significance of the affected cells.

NARCOTICS AND UNCOUPLING OF PHOSPHORYLATION

Narcotics at low concentrations will dissociate phosphorylations from oxidations sometimes without any apparent effect on the respiratory rate. It is well known that during respiration organic phosphate esters are built up from inorganic phosphate in the tissues, and that drugs such as dinitrophenol and gramicidin will inhibit this phosphate uptake without affecting the rate of respiration. It has been shown by Brody and Bain,[49] that barbiturates at low concentrations will also bring about the same phenomenon, an uncoupling of phosphorylation from oxidation (see Table VII). Definite decreases of the P/O ratio seem, however, to occur when the rate of oxygen uptake is also affected, contrary to what occurs with dinitrophenol (see also, Case and Mc-Ilwain[50] who have shown that the rates of both phosphorylation and respiration are equally lowered by chloral). The evidence[51] makes it clear that the behaviour of narcotics on metabolic processes in the brain differs from that of a typical uncoupling agent, such as 2,4-dinitro-phenol.

Experiments with cell preparations gave rise to the conclusion (Michaelis and Quastel[52]) that the site of action of anaesthetics (e.g., chloretone) on brain respiration is located with a process playing an intermediate role between cytochrome oxidase and a flavoprotein concerned with oxidation of reduced diphosphopyridine nucleotide

TABLE VII

EFFECTS OF THIOPENTAL ON OXIDATIVE PHOSPHORYLATION BY RABBIT BRAIN MINCE[49]

M. Concentration of Thiopental	O_2 Uptake (microatoms)	P Uptake (microatoms)	$\dfrac{P}{O}$
Nil	4.8; 3.8	9.6; 8.0	2.0; 2.1
5×10^{-5}	5.5; 3.2	8.0; 6.4	1.6; 2.0
1×10^{-4}	4.3; 3.2	8.0; 6.0	1.8; 1.9
2.5×10^{-4}	4.6; 3.1	5.6; 5.6	1.4; 1.8
5×10^{-4}	3.7; 3.2	2.4; 2.2	0.6; 0.8
7.5×10^{-4}	3.6; 1.8	0.0; 0.0	0.0; 0.0
1×10^{-3}	2.9; 2.2	0.0; 0.0	0.0; 0.0

($DPNH_2$). In accordance with this conclusion, it has been found by Ernster, Löw and Lindberg[53] that Amytal is a highly effective inhibitor of the oxidation of $DPNH_2$. As it is now well known that the biological oxidation of $DPNH_2$ is accompanied by the phosphorylation of adenosine diphosphate (ADP) to adenosine triphosphate (ATP), it follows that the narcotic is also inhibitory to oxidative phosphorylation. This is shown in the following reaction:

$$DPNH_2 + ADP + P_i + O \xrightarrow[\text{Amytal}]{\text{Inhibited by}} DPN + ATP + H_2O$$

The suppression of $DPNH_2$ oxidation by Amytal thus has the double effect of suppressing the citric acid cycle (as pyruvate oxidation requires DPN for its conversion to acetyl-CoA) and ATP formation.

The interference of narcotics with ATP synthesis in the brain is shown by their suppression of acetylcholine synthesis[54-56] and by their inhibitory effects (e.g., those of 4 mM chloretone or 1 mM Nembutal) on P^{32} incorporation (from phosphate) into phosphoproteins and organic phosphorus compounds in cat brain slices respiring in presence of glucose.[57] A striking demonstration of the effect of a low concentration of a narcotic (Amytal) on ATP formation in brain slices is shown by its action in suppressing glutamine synthesis, a reaction that requires the participation of ATP in the condensation of glutamate and ammonia. Results illustrating this phenomenon are shown in Table VIII,[58] where it is obvious that a very large fall in the yield of labelled glutamine from labelled glucose occurs. Other changes also take place and these can be satisfactorily explained by the conclusion that Amytal has a two-fold effect:

(a) Diminution of DPN formation from $DPNH_2$.

(b) Diminution of ATP formation.[58]

Reduced triphosphopyridine nucleotide oxidation in brain is not affected by Amytal.[59]

TABLE VIII

INFLUENCE OF 0.5 mM SODIUM AMYTAL ON RADIOACTIVE AMINO ACID FORMATION FROM GLUCOSE-U-C[14] IN PRESENCE OF RAT BRAIN CORTEX SLICES
(*Glucose-U-C[14] = 5 mM; 10^6 c/m. Aerobic Condition. $K^+ = 105$ meq./1.*)

(*Amino acid values expressed as counts/min./100 mg. wet weight tissue.*)

Amino Acid Formed	No Amytal Added	Amytal 0.5 mM
Glutamic acid	5516 ± 475	6761 ± 450
Aspartic acid	1183 ± 185	661 ± 51
Glutamine	2397 ± 209	111 ± 10
Alanine	794 ± 49	386 ± 36
γ Aminobutyric acid	1491 ± 164	1479 ± 123

Inhibitive effects of narcotics, anaesthetics, or a tranquiliser such as chlorpromazine, on ATP synthesis in the brain do not necessarily involve immediate falls in respiration in the brain cells affected. A situation may arise where the increased concentration of ADP, which has a rate limiting effect on metabolic reactions involved in glucose breakdown, can give rise to an increased rate of oxygen consumption. This is a frequent effect of the addition of respiratory "uncouplers." Nevertheless this effect may be transient, depending on a variety of conditions, and the ultimate effect of suppression of so important a process as $DPNH_2$ oxidation must be a suppression of respiration.

The effects of these drugs on oxidative synthesis of ATP and, therefore, on the synthesis of acetylcholine, especially that bound in subcellular particles, to be drawn upon during the functional activity of the nerve cell, may account for a diminished rate of recovery of the cell to its normal condition. This slowing of recovery rate may well be a dominant factor in causing paralysis of the nerve cell or centres specifically affected by the drugs.

Narcotics, such as pentobarbital and ethanol, exercise a larger percentage depression of respiration in the adult than the young rat brain,[64] a result that is to be expected on the evidence that the activity of the citric acid cycle increases with age during the early days of post natal life and that the effects of K^+ on aerobic nerve metabolism is greatly decreased in infant animal brain. There is a significant positive correlation between rate of respiration at different ages, and sensitivity to barbiturates.[65] Apparently in old age the inhibitory effects of barbiturates in respiration diminish, the maximum effects occurring in the young adult.

EFFECTS OF CHLORPROMAZINE ON BRAIN METABOLISM *IN VITRO*

Chlorpromazine also exerts an inhibitory activity on the respiration of brain cortex slices in presence of glucose, pyruvate or L-glutamate but not with succinate.[61] This inhibitory effect is greatly increased with brain cortex slices stimulated by the presence of potassium ions, a definite inhibition occurring with 0.2 mM chlorpromazine. Moreover, the drug diminishes the incorporation of labelled glycine into brain proteins during incubation of brain cortex slices in a glucose-Ringer medium. This inhibition is associated with reduction of ATP available for amino acid incorporation into proteins. The effect is also brought about by Amytal and ethanol at low concentrations (Table IX).

TABLE IX

EFFECTS OF CHLORPROMAZINE, ETHANOL AND AMYTAL ON GLYCINE-1-C[14] INCORPORATION INTO RAT BRAIN CORTEX PROTEINS[61,66] AFTER AEROBIC INCUBATION IN A SALINE-PHOSPHATE-GLUCOSE MEDIUM

Drug	Concentration	Percentage Inhibition of Glycine Incorporation
Chlorpromazine	0.2 mM	20
	0.3 mM	30
Amytal	0.1 mM	4
	0.5 mM	55
Ethanol	0.4 M	53

Chlorpromazine at low concentrations reduces the enhanced respiration due to electrical excitation[60] just as it reduces the increased oxygen uptake found with potassium ion stimulation.[61] The addition of chlorpromazine (at 0.1 mM) to guinea pig brain slices brings about changes in labelling of lipid phosphorus in presence of P^{32}, namely decreases of phosphatidylethanolamine and phosphatidylcholine and increase of phosphoinositide; with higher concentrations of the drugs there is a considerable decrease in labelling of lipid phosphorus.[62]

Recent results[67] indicate that chlorpromazine uncouples phosphorylation coupled to the oxidation of ferrocytochrome c and inhibits

DPNH$_2$-cytochrome c reductase, the effect being mainly due to an effect on the coupled phosphorylation reaction.

Thus chlorpromazine, like Amytal, brings about an inhibition of oxidative phosphorylation in brain cortex respiration. However, the action of chlorpromazine *in vitro* differs from that of the barbiturates in bringing about progressive inhibitions and in its high binding power with tissue proteins (probably lipoproteins). The drug after combining with tissue components gradually diffuses into the brain cell bringing about its metabolic inhibitions.[61] The conclusion that chlorpromazine, like Amytal, affects DPNH$_2$ oxidation (in phosphorylating systems such as those in brain cortex *in vitro*) has been confirmed with the use of liver mitochondrial systems[67] where it was also shown that 0.2 mM chlorpromazine brings about a marked inhibition of incorporation of P[32] into ATP. These facts do not imply that chlorpromazine and Amytal act at the same locations in the nervous system. It is possible, in fact, that the differences between the clinical effects of these two drugs are due more to their different sites of action than to essential differences in biochemical mechanism.

EFFECTS OF ALIPHATIC ALCOHOLS ON BRAIN METABOLISM

The addition of ethanol at small concentrations diminishes[46,68] the oxygen consumption of rat brain cortex slices respiring in a glucose-phosphate medium when this has been stimulated by the presence of 100 meq./l. K$^+$. Potassium-stimulated respiration of rat brain slices is much more affected by ethanol at low concentration than the normal respiration, the concentration being of the same order as those necessary to bring about the narcotic state in the rat. The behaviour of ethanol is similar in this respect to that brought about by anaesthetics such as the barbiturates or chloretone. These results have been confirmed by Fischer,[69] Sutherland *et al.*[70] and by Wallgren and Kulonen,[71] who have also shown that ethanol causes a decrease in the respiration of electrically stimulated brain tissue in presence of glucose.

The inhibitory effects of the alcohols increase markedly as the length of the carbon chain increases and with increase of their concentration, and the potassium ion stimulation of brain cortex respiration is diminished or abolished by concentrations of alcohols that have little effect on the unstimulated respiration.[68] n-Pentanol is much more effective than ethanol in effecting an inhibition of the stimulated respiration and there seems to take place a rapid establishment of equilibria between the alcohols and the components that influence the brain respiratory system. In confirmation of the results of Wolpert *et al.,*[72] it has been found[68] that brain mitochondrial respiration is relatively insensitive to concentrations of alcohols that considerably depress stimulated rat brain slice respiration. In this respect, the alcohols differ from the barbiturates but resemble perhaps the action of chlorpromazine.[73] The results support the conclusion that the alcohols exercise their inhibitory effects of brain respiration at some site located in the brain cell membranes. If this is true, it must be concluded that a significant proportion of the brain cell respiration is controlled by the cell membrane where presumably the potassium ion stimulation takes place. The alternative explanation that the effects are due to oxidation of the alcohols to the highly toxic aldehydes or that the alcohols block the entry of substrates into the cell has been ruled out.

BRAIN ATP DURING NARCOSIS

Analyses of brain tissue taken from animals during narcosis may show levels of ATP higher than those in the normal brain. Experiments, reported by Bain,[90] show also that injection of P^{32} into mice during Amytal or thiopental narcosis leads to increased quantities of P^{32} being incorporated into ATP of mouse brain. It is possible to understand this effect if it is considered that with decreased cerebral activity following the inhibition of certain activating centres by the narcotic, there is a lessened stimulation of nerve cells in many parts of the brain (not immediately affected by the drug) with a smaller rate of ADP formation. It is now well known that stimulation (cationic or electrical) of brain leads to increased ADP production. It follows that higher values of ATP in the brain following narcosis are a reflection of lessened cerebral activity, or lessened nerve stimulations, consequent upon the paralysis of nerve cells in special regions, or possibly highly localized sites, of the brain.

EFFECTS OF SALICYLATES ON BRAIN METABOLISM

Salicylates, like 2:4-dinitrophenol, suppress the formation of radioactive glutamine from radioactive glucose in presence of rat brain cortex slices. Representative results are shown in Table X.[74] There can be little doubt that the inhibition is due to the suppression of oxidative phosphorylation.[75,76] The effect, however, is more pronounced with the cation-stimulated metabolism than with the unstimulated. The effects of salicylate and 2:4-dinitrophenol are not identical. The former strongly depresses alanine formation with but little effect on that of γ-aminobutyrate, whilst the latter has the reverse effect (Table X). Whilst these effects indicate that the two drugs do not have identical effects, it is evident that major effect is that of un-

TABLE X

EFFECTS OF SALICYLATES AND 2:4-DINITROPHENOL ON RADIOACTIVE AMINO ACID
FORMATION FROM GLUCOSE-U-C^{14} (5 mM) IN RAT BRAIN CORTEX SLICES[74]

| | | | 0.05 mM DNP | | 5 mM Sodium Salicylate | |
| | 5 mM KCl | 105 mM KCl | | | | |
(Amounts expressed as mμatom carbon derived from glucose incorporated per hr. per 100 mg. wet wt. tissue)			5 mM KCl	105 mM KCl	5 mM KCl	105 mM KCl
Glutamate	858	965	825	850	830	905
Glutamine	191	341	92	30	115	56
γ-Aminobutyrate	220	325	185	207	200	310
Aspartate	250	264	291	255	225	261
Alanine	145	162	133	155	91	94

coupling phosphorylation from respiration. The different clinical effects are presumably to be attributed to the different sites of action in the body.

EFFECTS OF AMYTAL ON THE INCORPORATION OF P^{32} INTO ADENOSINE TRIPHOSPHATE (ATP), ADENOSINE DIPHOSPHATE (ADP) AND PHOSPHOCREATINE (CrP)

Dawson and Richter[77] have shown that electrical stimulation of the brain causes a drop in the content of ATP and a rise of inorganic phosphate in it, whilst Shapot[78] has given evidence that excitation of the brain increases the ADP/ATP ratio. It is now well known that concentrations of ADP (or phosphate ions) may be rate limiting in mitochondrial respiration. Hence stimulation of the brain *in vitro* by reactions increasing ADP (or phosphate) may result in acceleration of oxygen consumption and other dependent metabolic events.

The organic phosphates of brain slices undergo considerable changes in presence of increased K$^+$. There is a fall of ATP and CrP.[79-81] This effect of cationic stimulation is shown in representative results[74] given in Table XI where it is seen that the incorporation of P^{32} from radioactive phosphate is diminished in ATP, and CrP and increased in ADP. This would be expected if cation stimulation causes an increased rate of conversion of ATP to ADP, with resultant fall in CrP according to the reaction:

$$ADP + CrP \rightleftharpoons ATP + Cr.$$

In presence of Amytal (0.5 mM), however, there is, with the normal (5 mM) KCl concentration, a fall in the labelled CrP which is larger than that of labelled ATP. These effects are greatly increased in the presence of 105 mM KCl. It is evident that at normal concentrations of K+ the fall in ATP due to Amytal is diminished by the transphosphorylation due to CrP present. With high concentrations of K+, there is less CrP available to react with ADP (whose phosphorylation is suppressed by Amytal) and hence there is a diminished ATP level.

Thus the increased sensitivities of the stimulated metabolism of brain cortex to a narcotic, such as Amytal, may be partly due to the fact that stimulation diminishes the content of phosphocreatine and its ability, therefore, to restore ATP levels.

TABLE XI

EFFECTS OF AMYTAL ON THE INCORPORATION OF P^{32} INTO ATP, ADP AND CrP IN RAT BRAIN CORTEX SLICES INCUBATED AEROBICALLY IN GLUCOSE-RINGER MEDIUM CONTAINING 10 mM $Na_2HP^{32}O_4$ (10^7 C./M.)[74]

Addition	KCl Present	ATP	ADP	CrP
		(c./m./100 mg. wet tissue)		
Nil	5 mM	3100	100	1900
Nil	105 mM	2150	550	950
Amytal (0.5 mM)	5 mM	2950	150	1450
Amytal (0.5 mM)	105 mM	1250	50	400

MODE OF ACTION OF ANAESTHETICS AND ALLIED SUBSTANCES

It is possible to understand the effects of anaesthetics, depressants and tranquilisers, so far studied, by their suppression of: (a) mitochondrial oxidations, and/or (b) cation transfer at the brain cell membrane. The effects on mitochondrial respiration may be summarized in the following reactions:

(1) Pyruvate + DPN + CoA

O $\downarrow$ Stimulated by increased K+/Ca++ (or electrically) by cytoplasmic increase of ADP (at expense of ATP and CrP)

Acetyl-CoA + $DPNH_2$ + CO_2

(2) $DPNH_2$ + ADP + P_i

O $\downarrow$ Inhibited by Amytal etc.

DPN + ATP + H_2O

The effects at the brain cell membrane may be understood if the transport carriers at the membrane that are responsible for cation movements associate with, or are rendered inert by, the responsible drugs. Such effects would result in the diminution, or abolition, of $K+/Ca++$ (or electrical) stimulation and hence would have ultimately a similar effect to that of a respiratory inhibitor acting at the mitochondria. Substances affecting the cell membrane, in the manner visualized, would not necessarily be "uncouplers" of respiration.

It seems most probable that the narcotics influence both mitochondrial and nerve cell respiration by their adsorption, or combination, with lipid groups present in the membranes, these groups being involved in the establishment of ionic gradients and respiratory metabolism of the cells. It is already known[82] that breakdown of phospholipid groups at the membrane brings about, as its first effect, an uncoupling of phosphorylation from respiration (a fall in P/O ratio). It is not, therefore, unreasonable to assume that the attachment of narcotics to such groups will also lead to the same result, i.e., interference with electron transport and oxidative phosphorylation. This results in a suppression of the functional activities of the cell. This concept of the mode of action of narcotics, which links the physicochemical characters of the drugs with their effects on oxidative processes makes it possible to relate their metabolic effects to their established physical attributes embraced in the classical Overton-Meyer hypothesis.

NARCOTICS AND GLYCOLYSIS

The mechanism of anaerobic breakdown of glucose in brain involves the interplay of dehydrogenases that are also involved in the aerobic breakdown of the sugars. The absence of any effect of chloretone[52] on glycolysis indicates that the narcotic-sensitive oxidative system, important in the aerobic breakdown of glucose, is either absent from, or is without influence in, the reactions involved in the anaerobic breakdown of glucose by brain. There is now evidence, indeed, to show that narcotics increase aerobic glycolysis, by suppression of the Pasteur effect. Possibly this is the explanation for the observation of Edwards and Larrabee[83] that narcotics at low concentrations accelerate glucose consumption by excised rat superior cervical ganglia. This conclusion is in conformity with the observations of Greig,[84] Rosenberg *et al.*[85] and Webb and Elliott[86] that in presence of narcotics there is an increased rate of breakdown of glucose, though there is suppression of respiration. The latter authors[86] suggest that the local increase of hydrogen ion concentration due to the increased aerobic glycolysis might be of as much physiological significance as the depression of respiration.

EFFECTS OF NARCOTICS ON BIOLOGICAL ACETYLATIONS

In presence of quantities of narcotics that suppress respiration, acetylcholine synthesis by brain is also greatly suppressed. This was first shown using ether.[54] McLennan and Elliott[55] have shown considerable depression of synthesis by brain slices by various drugs, and Johnson and Quastel[56] have obtained similar results. There is always a concomitant drop in rate of respiration but this need not necessarily be as large.

Narcotics do not diminish, or only slightly diminish,[55,56] the anaerobic synthesis of acetylcholine by ATP in presence of brain extracts. The known phosphorylations by ATP (e.g., those involved in hexokinase activity and in glycolysis) are not impeded by narcotics at low concentrations. At concentrations that impede respiration, no inhibitory effect was found on the acetylation of sulfanilamide by enzymes present in the liver.

When the acetylating system is linked with a respiratory system such as that present in brain, the ATP necessary for the acetylation by these systems being formed by the energy of respiration, the presence of narcotics secures large inhibitory effects on the acetylation.[56] Thus, nembutal (0.0005 M) and chloretone (0.004 M), at concentrations that do not affect anaerobic synthesis of acetyl sulfanilamide in presence of ATP, exert marked effects on the aerobic synthesis in absence of added ATP. Moreover the addition of ATP to the aerobic system brings about a considerable alleviation of the inhibitory effect of the narcotic. The most obvious explanation of the inhibitory phenomena

TABLE XII

INHIBITION OF RESPIRATION OF RAT BRAIN HOMOGENATE BY STEROIDS AND STILBESTROL[87]

	A.R.U.*	Per Cent Inhibition in Presence of	
		0.2 Per Cent Glucose	0.2 M Succinate
Desoxycorticosterone	1.0	87	15
Progesterone	2.0	28	10
Testosterone	7.0	24	1
α-Estradiol	>20.0	14	3
Stilbestrol	20.0	91	44

*Anaesthetic rat unit (Selye[89]).

that take place aerobically is that the narcotics inhibit those links in the respiratory chain (e.g. $DP\dot{N}H_2$ oxidation) which are responsible for the oxidative synthesis of ATP.

STEROIDS

Results given in Table XII show that steroids which have anaesthetic potency also affect rat brain (homogenate) respiration in presence of glucose but not in presence of succinate (Gordan and Elliott,[87] see also Eisenberg et al.[88]). The inhibitions parallel anaesthetic activities. There is an anomalous action of stilbestrol which is possibly accounted for by the special oxidative reactions undergone by this substance.

It is not known yet if steroid inhibitions of brain metabolism are affected by stimulation of the brain though it is evident that steroid hormones interfere with tissue oxidations. Recent evidence[63] shows that the site of action of corticosterone, and possibly other steroid hormones, lies in the respiration chain between the flavoproteins and cytochrome c, a site already suggested as the point of action of many narcotics.[52]

REFERENCES

1.   OVERTON, E.: Studien über Narkose. Jena (1901).
2.   MEYER, H. H.: Arch. exper. Path. u. Pharmakol., 42:109 (1899).
3.   TRAUBE, J.: Pflüger's Arch. ges. Physiol., 105:541 (1904).
4.   HÖBER, R.: Pflüger's Arch. ges. Physiol., 120:492 (1907).
5.   WINTERSTEIN, H.: Biochem. Ztschr., 70:130 (1915).
6.   LAWRENCE, J. H., LOOMIS, W. F., TOBIAS, C. A. and TURPIN, F. H.: J. Physiol., 105:197 (1946).
7.   MEYER, K. H. and HOPFF, H.: Ztschr. physiol. Chem., 126:281 (1923).
8.   CASE, E. M. and HALDANE, J. B. S.: J. Hyg., 41:225 (1941).
9.   FERGUSON, J.: Proc. Roy. Soc. London, B, 127:387 (1939).
10. BRINK, F. and POSTERNAK, J. M.: J. Cell. & Comp. Physiol., 32:211 (1948).
11. BUTLER, T. C.: Pharmacol. Rev., 2:121 (1950).
12. VERWORN, M.: Narcosis. In Harvey Lectures (1911-12). Philadelphia, Lippincott (1912).
13. HENDERSON, V. E.: Physiol. Rev., 10:171 (1930).
14. McCLURE, R. D., HARTMANN, F. W., SCHNEDORF, J. G. and SCHELLING, V.: Ann. Surg., 110:836 (1939).
15. HIMWICH, W. A., HOMBURGER, E., MARESCA, R. and HIMWICH, H. E.: Am. J. Psychiat., 103:689 (1947).
16. HIMWICH, H. E.: Brain Metabolism and Cerebral Disorders. Baltimore, Williams & Wilkins (1951).
17. SHAW, J. L., STEELE, B. F. and LAMB, C. A.: Arch. Surg., 35:1 (1937).
18. DAMESHEK, W., MYERSON, A. and LOMAN, J.: Am. J. Psychiat., 91:113 (1934).
19. QUASTEL, J. H.: Physiol. Rev., 19:135 (1939).
20. QUASTEL, J. H. and WHEATLEY, A. H. M.: Biochem. J., 26:725 (1932).
21. PUGH, C. E. M. and QUASTEL, J. H.: Biochem. J., 31:286 (1937).
22. GIBBS, F. A., GIBBS, E. L. and LENNOX, W. G.: Tr. Am. Neurol. A., 63:129 (1937).

23. JOWETT, M. and QUASTEL, J. H.: *Biochem. J., 31*:565 (1937).
24. QUASTEL, J. H. and WHEATLEY, A. H. M.: *Proc. Roy. Soc.,* B, *112*:60 (1932).
25. FUHRMAN, F. A. and FIELD, J.: *J. Pharmacol. & Exper. Therap., 77*:392 (1943).
26. SWANK, R. and CAMMERMEYER: *J. Cell & Comp. Physiol., 34*:43 (1949).
27. ELLIOTT, H. W. and SUTHERLAND, V. C.: *J. Cell. & Comp. Physiol., 40*:221 (1952).
28. WESTFALL, B. A.: *J. Pharmacol. & Exper. Therap., 96*:193 (1949).
29. WILKINS, D. S., FEATHERSTONE, R. M., SCHWIDDE, J. T. and BROTMAN, M.: *J. Pharmacol. & Exper. Therap., 98*:36 (1950).
30. SCHUELER, F. W. and GROSS, E. G.: *J. Pharmacol. & Exper. Therap., 98*:28 (1950).
31. SEN, K. C.: *Biochem. J., 25*:849 (1931).
32. QUASTEL, J. H. and WHEATLEY, A. H. M.: *Biochem. J., 28*:1521 (1934).
33. JOWETT, M.: *J. Physiol., 92*:322 (1938).
34. JOWETT, M. and QUASTEL, J. H.: *Biochem. J., 31*:1101 (1937).
35. HUTCHISON, M. C. and STOTZ, E.: *J. Biol. Chem., 140*:lxv (1941).
36. WORTIS, S. B.: *Arch. Neurol. & Psychiat., 33*:1022 (1935).
37. ELLIOTT, K. A. C. and HENDERSON, N.: *J. Neurophysiol., 11*:473 (1948).
38. SWIFT, M. N.: *Anaesthesiology, 8*:453 (1947).
39. TAYLOR, J. D., RICHARDS, R. K., EVERETT, G. M. and BERTCHER, E.: *J. Pharmacol. & Exper. Therap., 98*:392 (1950).
40. DICKENS, F. and GREVILLE, G. C.: *Biochem. J., 29*:1468 (1935).
41. ASHFORD, C. A. and DIXON, K. C.: *Biochem. J., 29*:157 (1935).
42. BUCHEL, L.: *Anesth. et analg., 10*:No. 1, 1 (1953).
43. WINTERSTEIN, H.: *Bethe's Handbuch,* 9. Berlin, Springer (1929).
44. BRONK, D. W. and BRINK, F.: *Federation Proc. 10*:19 (1951).
45. MCILWAIN, H.: *Biochem. J., 53*:403 (1953).
46. GHOSH, J. J. and QUASTEL, J. H.: *Nature,* London, *174*:28 (1954).
47. PARMAR, S. S. and QUASTEL, J. H.: In Quastel, J. H., *Proc. 4th Inter. Cong. Biochem. Vienna,* Vol. 3, p. 90. Brücke, F., Ed. Pergamon Press (1959).
48. KINI, M. M. and QUASTEL, J. H.: *Nature, 184*:252 (1959); KIMURA, Y. and NIWA, T.: *Nature, 171*:881 (1953); TSUKADA, Y. and TAKAGAKI, G.: *Nature, 175*:725 (1955); TAKAGAKI, G., HIRANO, S. and TSUKADA, Y.: *J. Biochem.* (Japan), *45*:41 (1958).
49. BRODY, T. M. and BAIN, J. A.: *Proc. Soc. Exper. Biol. & Med., 77*:50 (1951).
50. CASE, E. M. and MCILWAIN, H.: *Biochem. J., 48*:1 (1951).
51. JOHNSON, W. J. and QUASTEL, J. H.: *J. Biol. Chem., 205*:163 (1953).
52. MICHAELIS, M. and QUASTEL, J. H.: *Biochem. J., 35*:918 (1941).
53. ERNSTER, L., LÖW, H. and LINDBERG, O.: *Acta. chem. scandinav., 9*:200 (1955). ERNSTER, L., JALLING, O., LÖW, H. and LINDBERG, O.: *Exper. Cell. Res.,* Suppl., *3*:124 (1955).
54. MANN, P., TENNENBAUM, M. and QUASTEL, J. H.: *Biochem. J., 32*:343 (1938).
55. MCLENNAN, H. and ELLIOTT, K. A. C.: *J. Pharmacol. & Exper. Therap., 103*:35 (1951).
56. JOHNSON, W. J. and QUASTEL, J. H.: *Nature,* London, *171*:602 (1953).
57. FINDLAY, M., STRICKLAND, K. P. and ROSSITER, R. J.: *Canad. J. Biochem. & Physiol., 32*:504 (1954).
58. KINI, M. M. and QUASTEL, J. H.: *Nature, 184*:252 (1959).
59. GIUDITTA, A. and STRECKER, H. J.: *J. Neurochem., 5*:50 (1959).
60. MCILWAIN, H. and GREENGARD, O.: *J. Neurochem., 1*:348 (1957).
61. LINDAN, O., QUASTEL, J. H. and SVED, S.: *Canad. J. Biochem. & Physiol., 35*:1135, 1145 (1957).

62. MAGEE, W. L., BERRY, J. F. and ROSSITER, R. J.: *Biochem. et biophys. acta, 21:*408 (1956).
63. JENSEN, P. K.: *Nature, 184:*Suppl. 7, 451 (1959).
64. HIMWICH, H. E., SYKOWSKI, P. and FAZEKAS, J. F.: *Am. J. Physiol., 132:*640 (1941).
65. DESBARATS-SCHONBAUM, M. L. and BIRMINGHAM, M. K.: *J. Gerontology, 14:*284 (1959).
66. QUASTEL, J. H.: *Biochemistry of the Central Nervous System,* Proc. 4th Inter. Congr. Biochem. Vienna, Vol. 3, p. 90. Brücke, F., Ed. Pergamon Press (1959).
67. DAWKINS, M. JR., JUDAH, J. D. and REES, K. R.: *Biochem. J., 73:*16 (1959); *72:*204.
68. BEER, C. T. and QUASTEL, J. H.: *Canad. J. Biochem. & Physiol., 36:*543, 531 (1958).
69. FISCHER, E.: *Alcoholism* (AAAS), p. 19 (1957).
70. SUTHERLAND, V. C., HINE, C. H. and BURBRIDGE, T. N.: *J. Pharmacol. Exper. & Therap., 116:*469 (1956).
71. WALLGREN, H. and KULONEN, E.: *Biochem. J., 75:*150 (1960).
72. WOLPERT, A., TRUITT, E. B., BELL, F. K. and KRAUTZ, J. L.: *J. Pharmacol. Exper. & Therap., 117:*358 (1956).
73. BERGER, M., STRECKER, H. J. and WAELSCH, H.: *Nature, 177:*1234 (1956); *Ann. New York Acad. Sc., 66:*806 (1957).
74. GONDA, O. and QUASTEL, J. H.: In press (1962).
75. SMITH, M. J. H. and JEFFREY, S. W.: *Biochem. J., 64:*589 (1956).
76. MANCHESTER, K. L., RANDLE, P. J. and SMITH, G. H.: *Brit. M. J., i:*1028 (1958).
77. DAWSON, R. M. C. and RICHTER, D.: *Am. J. Physiol., 160:*203 (1950).
78. SHAPOT, V. S.: *Metabolism of the Nervous System,* p. 257. D. Richter, Ed. New York, Pergamon Press (1957).
79. MCILWAIN, H.: *Biochem. J., 52:*289 (1952).
80. GORE, M. B. R. and MCILWAIN, H.: *J. Physiol., 117:*471 (1952).
81. HEALD, P. J.: *Biochem. J., 57:*673 (1954).
82. PETRUSHKA, E., QUASTEL, J. H. and SCHOLEFIELD, P. J. G.: *Canad. J. Biochem. & Physiol., 37:*975, 989 (1959).
83. EDWARDS, C. and LARRABEE, M. G.: *Federation Proc. 12:*37 (1953).
84. GREIG, M. E.: *J. Pharmacol. & Exper. Therap., 91:*317 (1947).
85. ROSENBERG, A. J., BUCHEL, L., ETLING, N. and LEVI, J.: *Compt. rend. Acad. sc., 230:*480 (1950).
86. WEBB, J. L. and ELLIOTT, K. A. C.: *J. Pharmacol. & Exper. Therap., 103:*24 (1951).
87. GORDAN, G. S. and ELLIOTT, H. W.: *Endocrinology, 41:*517 (1947).
88. EISENBERG, E., GORDAN, G. S., ELLIOTT, H. W. and TALBOT, J.: *Proc. Soc. Exper. Biol. & Med., 73:*140 (1950).
89. SELYE, H.: *Endocrinology, 30:*437 (1942).
90. BAIN, J. A.: *Progress in Neurobiology, 2:*139, H. Waelsch, Ed. New York, Hoeber (1957).

XXXIII

BACTERIAL NEUROTOXINS

J. W. Stevenson

Tʜᴇ ᴍᴏsᴛ potent nerve poisons known are produced by two species of the anaerobic spore-forming bacteria, *Clostridium botulinum* and *Clostridium tetani,* the causal agents of the diseases botulism and tetanus respectively. The principal toxic substance produced by each of these organisms exerts its effect specifically upon nerve tissue and accounts for all of the symptoms of the disease.

There are a few infectious diseases of bacterial origin, such as diphtheria, in which neurotoxic symptoms may appear infrequently, diseases in which such symptoms are regarded more as complications than as integral parts of the clinical picture. It has not been established with certainty whether involvement of the nervous system in such instances is due to specific neurotoxic substances or whether the neurological symptoms are due to the same toxins as those which account for the classical symptoms of the disease. There is, on the other hand, at least one instance of a bacterium which produces a toxin capable of inducing a paralytic syndrome in experimental animals but which appears to produce no neurological symptoms in the naturally occurring human disease, or if so, only in the exceedingly rare case. This is *Shigella dysenteriae,* the causal agent of a severe form of bacillary dysentery.

BOTULINUM TOXIN

Botulism

Botulism is a form of food-poisoning in which symptoms follow the ingestion of preserved foodstuffs in which *Cl. botulinum* has grown and liberated toxin. The disease is a pure intoxication, unaccompanied by infection, since the organism, a soil saprophyte, has no capacity to establish itself in living tissues under ordinary conditions. Symptoms have their onset within 12 to 72 hours after ingestion of the spoiled food, and take the form initially of visual disturbances such as diplopia, blepharoptosis, mydriasis, and loss of reflex to light.

813

Pharyngeal and laryngeal paralyses appear early in the course of the disease and eventually the paralysis extends to involve the skeletal musculature, causing a general muscular weakness or flaccid paralysis which may be marked but which is rarely complete. Death, when it occurs, is due to respiratory paralysis or cardiovascular collapse. The mortality rate in North America has been about 65%; fortunately the disease is not a common one. In those who survive, a period of some months is ordinarily required for complete return to normal muscle function.

The Toxins of Cl. botulinum

Five types of the single species *Cl. botulinum* designated A, B, C, D and E, are recognized on the basis of serological specificity of the toxins that they produce. There would appear to be two closely related strains of the type C organism, Cα and Cβ. The Cα antitoxin neutralizes both the Cα and Cβ toxins, whereas the Cβ antitoxin neutralizes only the homologous Cβ toxin. Despite their antigenic dissimilarity all five toxins produce identical symptoms and there is no reason to believe that they differ in the mechanism by which they produce paralysis. They do show, however, fairly marked quantitative differences in potency for different animal species. Botulism in man has been due almost exclusively to the A, B and E toxins. Types C and D have been associated with the disease in the lower animals, the Cα toxin accounting for large outbreaks of botulism in wild ducks, and the Cβ and D toxins causing naturally occurring botulism in cattle, horses and sheep. The Rhesus monkey is resistant to the C and D toxins when they are administered *per os*,[1] and it is possible that man is equally insusceptible, since these types would appear not to have been implicated in human botulism, or if so, only in the very rare instance. A variety of animals are susceptible to the toxin of *Cl. botulinum* when given *per os* and by parenteral injection, although animal species vary widely in their susceptibility to the different types.

Properties of Botulinum Toxin

Of the five toxin types the A toxin has been the one most intensively studied. Whole culture autolysates of high potency may be obtained by growing the organisms in media containing casein or tryptic digests of casein, glucose and corn-steep liquor[2-5] with yields of toxin ranging from 1 to 2 x 10^6 mouse intraperitoneal LD 50's per ml. of culture autolysate. Barron and Reed[6] have produced type A cultures containing 40 to 50 million lethal mouse doses per ml. by growing the organisms in cellophane sacs suspended in such media. The toxin would appear to be an integral part of the protoplasm which is only liberated into the culture fluid when the cells undergo autolysis.[4,5,7-10]

The toxin was isolated in crystalline form in 1946, the first bacterial toxin to be obtained in the crystalline state, by two groups working independently and employing different methods (Abrams, Kegeles and Hottle;[11] Lamanna, Eklund and McElroy[12]). Duff *et al.*[13] have, within more recent years, described a simplified procedure for purification of the type A toxin.

The crystalline type A toxin is a substance of extraordinary potency. The intraperitoneal LD 50 for the 20 gm. white mouse is in the range of 0.00003 μg. (32 billion mouse LD 50's per gm. of pure toxin and 220 to 240 x 10^6 LD 50's per mg. of nitrogen[12]). If one assumes that man has the same degree of susceptibility, on a unit weight basis, as the mouse, and there is good reason to believe that he has, then it may be calculated that the lethal dose for an adult would be approximately 0.12 μg. by injection. Botulinum toxin is the most poisonous substance known and although the lethal dose by ingestion is considerably higher than by parenteral injection, it is not surprising that individuals have contracted fatal botulism through simply tasting foods suspected of spoilage. Various experimental animals are highly susceptible to the type A toxin; the guinea pig, for example, is some two times more susceptible to the toxin on a unit weight basis than is the mouse.[4] It should be noted here that although it is the convention to describe potency on a unit weight basis Lamanna has shown that in the mouse the potencies of types A, B and C botulinal toxins are independent of the weights of individual animals.[14]

The type A botulinal toxin is a simple heat coagulable protein with an isoelectric point of pH 5.6[11] and a molecular weight calculated on the basis of physical data of from 900,000[15] to 1,130,000.[16] The molecule contains 16.29% nitrogen, 0.052 to 0.059% phosphorous and 0.437% sulphur, and is composed of nineteen amino acids which account for all of the nitrogen.[17] Analytical data provide no clue as to the nature of the configuration of the molecule which might account for its specific toxicity. The amino acids are naturally occurring forms, biologically active and connected through peptide bonds. The percentages of aspartic acid, tyrosine and threonine are higher than are ordinarily encountered in nontoxic proteins of known composition;[17] the significance of this in terms of toxicity is not clear. Denaturation of the molecule accompanied by a loss of solubility leads to irreversible detoxification.[12]

Since its initial crystallization some doubt has arisen about the homogeneity of preparations of purified type A botulinum toxin. Although the crystalline toxin does behave as a homogeneous substance in electrophoresis and ultracentrifugation studies it was noted that the phase-rule solubility test for homogeneity could not be met.[15,18] Lamanna[19] has shown that crystalline preparations contain a component, distinct from the neurotoxin, which has the capacity to agglutinate the red cells of a number of animal species. The haemagglutinin which is antigenically identical to a haemagglutinin in purified type B botulinal toxin may be separated from the toxin by absorption on red cells with no loss of neurotoxic activity.[20] It is possible, perhaps, that the haemagglutinin and neurotoxin may form a relatively stable complex under some circumstances and this might account for the very high molecular weight reported for the crystalline product. It has been observed[21] that crystalline botulinum toxin dissociates at an alkaline pH to much smaller molecules with no loss in potency of the preparation. Similarly with absorption of the haemagglutinin the remaining toxin shows a change in the diffusion coefficient indicating a smaller molecular size than that reported for the whole preparation.[18]

The type B toxin was first obtained in pure form by Lamanna and Glassman.[22] The methods for purification of the A toxin available at the time were not applicable to the isolation of the B type. The toxin was described as a simple protein with an estimated molecular weight of 60,000. Its toxicity for the mouse was 110 to 200 x 10^6 mouse intraperitoneal LD 50's per mg. of nitrogen, that is, of the same order as that of the crystalline type A toxin. Some confusion exists concerning molecular weight and solubility properties of the type B toxin. Wagman and Batemann[23] have reported the molecular weight to be in the range of 500,000, a figure which approaches that of the A toxin, and Duff and his associates[24] have recently reported that their method of purification of the A toxin[15] is applicable to the B type and that the A and B toxins prepared by the same procedure differ little except in serological specificity; the similarity of the sedimentation constants of the two proteins suggest that they may not differ greatly in molecular weight. It is possible that chemical differences noted by Lamanna and Glassman might have resulted in part, at least, from the fractionation methods involved in isolation. Whole culture autolysates of *Cl. botulinum,* type B possess, like the A toxin, haemagglutinating activity. It would be of interest to know if the low molecular weight type B preparation of Lamanna and Glassman had been freed of the haemagglutinating component and if the larger molecules prepared by others had retained this component. The type B toxin does differ, however, from the A toxin in that efforts to crystallize it have failed thus far.

Within the past few years the other type toxins C, D and E have been obtained in a purified and highly active form.[25-29]

The Pharmacodynamics of Botulinum Toxin

Upon ingestion botulinum toxin is absorbed, largely from the upper part of the small intestine into the lymph stream from which it makes its way into the systemic circulation.[30] Its potency upon ingestion may be accounted for by the fact that in the crude form as it exists in whole culture autolysates, and presumably in spoiled foodstuffs, it is resistant to the action of pepsin and trypsin.[31-33] It is true that the crystalline product is digested with a loss in neurotoxic activity by pepsin, trypsin, chymotrypsin and other proteolytic enzymes.[34-36] It is possible that substances in crude culture autolysates and foodstuffs may protect the toxin from enzymatic inactivation. Indeed there is evidence that the A, B and E toxins are elaborated initially in an atoxic, perhaps macromolecular form, the so-called protoxin, which is converted to toxin by the action of pepsin, trypsin and other proteolytic enzymes.[37-41]

Symptoms referable to the central nervous system are rarely, if ever, seen in botulism. The lack of central involvement may be explained possibly by the large size of the toxin molecule which may fail to traverse the blood brain barrier.

Early workers[42-47] firmly established the concept that botulinum toxin exerted its effect peripherally by bringing about a block in the transmission of nerve impulses in the region of the myoneural junctions of somatic motor nerves and the parasympathetics and actually mapped out on the basis of the distribution of paralysis, those nerve fibers which we now recognize as cholinergic nerves. The paralysis was regarded as "curare-like" in nature in that it left the muscle directly excitable but inexcitable indirectly through the end plates. It was shown that the muscle response to direct stimulation was unaffected by the toxin and that conduction within a nerve trunk bathed in high concentrations of toxin was unimpaired; oscillograms of an excised nerve were not affected by large concentrations of toxin over a period of several hours.[48] By a process of elimination it was reasoned that the toxin acted at the myoneural junction.

Guyton and MacDonald,[49] Ambache,[50] Burgen, Dickens and Zatman,[51] Brooks[52-55] and others, have, in more recent years confirmed and extended many of the earlier observations. Most of the experimental work has been carried out with the type A toxin. Guyton and MacDonald studied the effect of the toxin *in vivo,* a method involving the production of local paralysis in the gastrocnemius muscle of the intact living animal; Ambache has investigated the local effects induced by the intraocular injection of the toxin in rabbits and Burgen *et al.* have employed in their studies the isolated rat phrenic nerve-

diaphragm preparation of Bülbring.[56] The experiments substantiate
earlier claims that the toxin exerts no effect upon conduction in the
nerve trunk proper and no direct effect upon the muscle fibers as such.
The specificity of the toxin for cholinergic fibers is well brought out
in experiments involving intraocular inoculation where in one and
the same organ adrenergic and sensory systems are unimpaired although they are exposed to a concentration of toxin which is adequate
to paralyse cholinergic nerves.[50] This supports the contention that
the toxin does not interfere with conduction in nerve trunks proper
since there is no reason to believe that the basis of nervous conduction
in cholinergic nerves is intrinsically different from that of other nerve
fibers of the body. In the intact living animal muscles which are paralysed for several months become fibrotic and lose mass as though the
nerve had been sectioned but such muscles remain responsive to direct
electrical stimulation.[49] Burgen and his associates[57] have shown that
the property of post-tetanic potentiation whereby a short tetanus of
the motor nerve increases the muscular tension developed in succeeding single twitches, is unchanged in partially paralysed muscles. Since
post-tetanic potentiation is a muscular phenomenon[57] the fact that
botulinum toxin brings about no change is regarded as further evidence of the lack of direct action on the muscle.

It would appear quite clearly established that the site of action of
the toxin is distal to the nerve trunk and yet proximal to the muscle
fibrils.

The mechanism by which botulinum toxin blocks the transmission
of nerve impulses seems to be entirely different from the mode of
action of curare. Curare renders motor end plates insensitive to the
acetylcholine released from the nerve endings. This is not the case in
botulism where completely paralysed muscles remain normally responsive to the injection of acetylcholine;[49-51] the response to acetylcholine is unaltered during all stages of the poisoning. Nicotine has
the same effect upon the poisoned muscles as does acetylcholine.[49]
Cholinesterase inhibitors, such as eserine and prostigmine, have a
potent decurarizing action but these drugs do not, in any dose, significantly decrease the paralysis brought about by botulinum toxin.[49,51,58]
Similarly such drugs as tetraethylpyrophosphate, adrenaline and KCl
which are said to exert an anticurare action[59,60] have no appreciable
effect upon the rat nerve-diaphragm preparation poisoned with botulinum toxin.[51] Burgen et al.[51] have further demonstrated, in nerve-
diaphragm preparations partially paralysed by the toxin, that the
normal type of tetanic response and normal summation curves may
be obtained, a situation quite different from that seen when such
preparations are partially paralysed with curare.

Guyton and MacDonald[49] assumed that the poisoning took place at some point proximal to the site at which acetylcholine is released and postulated that the paralysis was the result of the failure of production of acetylcholine. That this is so has been substantiated by Burgen and his associates.[51] In rat nerve-diaphragm preparations almost completely paralysed by the toxin, the output of acetylcholine, on motor nerve stimulation, is very markedly reduced. The poisoning would appear to follow the all or none principle, in that cholinesterase inhibitors fail to bring about any reversal of the paralysis. The normal type of tetanic response and the normal summation curves suggest that a partially paralysed muscle contains some motor units which are unaffected and which behave normally in all ways, and blocked motor units in which transmission is not restored by conditioning stimuli or other means.

In a comparison of the mode of action of the A and B botulinal toxins[51] it has been noted that the rat nerve-diaphragm is relatively insensitive to the B toxin as compared to the A type, and this correlates closely with the natural relative resistance of the rat to the B toxin. The guinea pig is, on the other hand, almost equally susceptible to both A and B toxins and this is reflected in experiments with the isolated guinea pig nerve-diaphragm where the type B toxin exerts an effect as potent as that obtained with the A toxin. It is suggested that the differing sensitivity of mammalian species to botulinum toxin of a given type is related to the specific sensitivity of their nerve terminals rather than to differing modes of distribution or disposal of the toxin.

The diminished secretion of acetylcholine at the nerve endings in botulinum poisoning might be brought about in a number of possible ways: (1) the synthesis of acetylcholine at the nerve endings might be inhibited by the toxin; (2) acetylcholine might be destroyed as rapidly as it is formed due to enhanced cholinesterase activity; (3) the release of acetylcholine might be prevented, perhaps, by a permeability change in the nerve endings; (4) although it is clearly established that the toxin exerts no effect on conduction in the nerve trunk proper, it is possible that it might block the transmission of the nerve impulse through terminal unmyelinated fibrils, in which case failure of the production of acetylcholine would be secondary to failure of the nerve impulse to reach the "acetylcholine release" region.

Effect of Botulinum Toxin on the Synthesis of Acetylcholine

Torda and Wolff[61] reported that the type A and B toxins strongly inhibited the *in vitro* synthesis of acetylcholine by frog and mouse brain homogenates and stated that brain tissue from poisoned animals synthesized some 60% less acetylcholine than did brain tissue from healthy controls. Others have failed to confirm these findings. Burgen et al.[51] have been unable to detect any inhibitory effect of the toxin on choline acetylase in minced mouse brain or in the more active system utilising an acetone dried powder of rat brain as a source of enzyme. Torda and Wolff used a culture filtrate of unspecified purity as their source of toxin, and it is possible that impurities present in toxin preparations available at that time might have been responsible for the inhibition of acetylation of choline recorded in their experiments. The co-enzyme for choline acetylase is the same as that involved in the liver enzyme system responsible for the acetylation of aromatic amines, that is, co-enzyme A. Botulinum toxin has no inhibitory effect upon this system as it is involved in the acetylation of sulphanilamide[51] and it may be concluded from the foregoing experiments that it does not affect co-enzyme A as it functions in the acetylation of choline.

Burgen and his associates report that 100 LD 50's of toxin per ml. of reaction mixture had no significant effect *in vitro* on the oxygen uptake of rat brain slices determined in the Warburg apparatus nor did the Qo_2 of brain slices from poisoned rats differ from normal values.

That the toxin does not affect adenosinetriphosphate is obvious in that ATP must be included as a source of energy in the choline acetylating system where acetone dried powders of nerve tissue are employed as a source of choline acetylase. Stevenson, Fairbairn and Campbell[62] failed to demonstrate any effect of the toxin on adenosine-triphosphatase (ATP-ase) activity.

It is reasonable to conclude that botulinum toxin has no effect upon choline acetylase, coenzyme A, the sources of energy or the substrates. This conclusion is supported by the work of Stevenson and Girvin[63] who tested the effect of the type A toxin on the bacterial acetylation of choline. The microbial synthesis of acetylcholine by a bacterium *Lactobacillus plantarum* involves a mechanism of acetylation of choline identical to that of mammalian cells,[64,65] and bacterial choline acetylase has been obtained in the cell free state.[65] It has been shown that botulinum toxin in high concentrations does not inhibit: (1) the synthesis and secretion of free acetylcholine by actively proliferating lactobacilli in culture; (2) the synthesis and storage of "bound" acetylcholine by actively proliferating cells; (3) the synthesis and secretion of acetylcholine by washed non-proliferating bacterial cells incubated in a suitable chemically defined substrate, and (4) the toxin exerts no effect upon the activity of cell-free bacterial choline acetylase nor upon other essential components of the acetylating system such as coenzyme A and adenosinetriphosphate.

Effect of the Toxin on Cholinesterase Activity

A rapid disappearance of acetylcholine due to enhanced cholinesterase activity can be excluded as an explanation of the mode of action of the toxin since the output of acetylcholine in the *in vitro* experiments[51] was measured in the presence of eserine, a cholinesterase inhibitor. Moreover, it has been shown that botulinum toxin in high concentration has no effect on the activity of the "true" or the "pseudo" cholinesterases of guinea-pig serum.[51]

Effect of the Toxin on Cell Permeability

It seems unlikely that the effect of the toxin is to inhibit the release or diffusion of acetylcholine at the nerve endings although this is a mechanism which cannot be conclusively discounted at the present time. A permeability change in the nerve endings would not be likely to follow the all or none principle which applies to the effect of botulinum toxin.[51] Moreover, experiments with bacterial cells[63] indicate that the toxin has no effect upon the secretion of acetylcholine through the cell membrane. It may be argued, of course, that bacterial cell membranes and the membranes of mammalian nerve endings may differ radically in their properties in this respect.

Effect of the Toxin on Unmyelinated Terminal Nerve Fibers

Burgen *et al.*[51] concluded, by a process of elimination based on their observations and the experiments of others, that the toxin exerted its effect by interacting with some component of the terminal unmyelinated nerve fibrils entering the end plate region in such a way as to block transmission of the nerve impulse. The failure of production of acetylcholine would then be secondary to the failure of the stimulus to reach the "acetylcholine release" region; this is in accord with the all or none principle of botulinum poisoning and the lack of effect of cholinesterase inhibitors. Guyton and MacDonald[49] noted a striking increase of latency of action potentials in the partially paralysed guinea-pig's gastrocnemius, a delay which might possibly have occurred in the terminal nerve fibrils.

Brooks[52,53] studied action potentials in the end plate zone of single motor units in poisoned muscle preparations and concluded that botulinum toxin rendered terminal motor nerve filaments, just proximal to the end plates, inexcitable to impulses originating in the nerve trunk proper. It was felt, at the time, that the acetylcholine release

mechanism per se was unimpaired, in that, although it was not activated by way of the poisoned terminal nerve filaments, it was still
responsive to electrical current impulses applied directly through the
surrounding bath medium.[53] It was noted, however, that after junctional transmission was blocked with botulinum toxin, post-tetanic
potentiation could be readily induced by way of the motor nerve. Del
Castillo and Katz[67] have shown that after almost complete blockage
of neuromuscular transmission by certain agents that repeated nerve
volleys give rise to an increase in the discharge of spontaneous miniature end plate potentials due probably to changes in motor nerve
terminals and that externally applied currents are as effective as nerve
volleys in this respect.[68] On the basis of these observations Brooks[54,55]
has examined the effect of botulinum toxin on miniature end plate
potentials and finds that the toxin causes a reduction in the frequency
of spontaneous miniature end plate potentials which can be restored
to approximately normal values by post-tetanic potentiation. It is concluded that the probable site of action of botulinum toxin is at the
tips of the motor nerve terminals, the acetylcholine release region.
Stover et al.[66] in a study of summation curves in isolated frog nerve-
muscle preparations noted that spaced repeated stimuli applied by
way of the nerve trunk within 4 to 18 msec. resulted in a muscle action
potential. Their interpretation is that the first stimulus releases only
a threshold quantity of acetylcholine which when added to that released by the second stimulus is sufficient to induce muscle contraction.
It is argued that the paralytic effect of the toxin is due, not to impairment of conduction but rather to poisoning of the acetylcholine release mechanism.

Whatever the process of botulinum intoxication, it is unlikely to
be a purely physical one. When the toxin is administered to animals
in doses of 1 to 2 M.L.D., a latent period of some 17 to 20 hours
ensues before the onset of any signs of paralysis and a characteristic
lag period is seen in isolated nerve-muscle preparations which cannot
be explained on the basis of slow diffusion of a large molecule since
replacing the bath fluid in the latent period, a procedure which reverses the diffusion gradient into muscle, does not alter the subsequent
development of paralysis.[51] In the same connection it has been noted
that once the toxin has been allowed sufficient contact with nerve for
fixation in isolated nerve-muscle preparations, the addition of large
doses of antitoxin during the latent period fails to forestall the subsequent development of paralysis. It may be presumed that during the
latent period the toxin is irreversibly fixed to its target site and produces some gradual change which ultimately leads to paralysis. The
latent period is short and the progress of the paralysis most rapid at

temperatures of 30 to 37°C.; at lower temperatures the latent period and the progress of paralysis are very much prolonged.[51] This effect is apparent in nerve-muscle preparations of both the warm-blooded and the cold-blooded animals. The process of intoxication then has a high temperature coefficient which is characteristic of a chemical reaction rather than a purely physical one.

Pappenheimer[69] feels that the characteristic latent period and the extraordinary potency of the toxin suggest that it does not act by direct inhibition of enzymes or as an enzyme itself but rather by interfering with the synthesis of some essential enzyme. Toxic symptoms would not become manifest until the excess of essential enzymes had been depleted. It will be noted, however, that in experiments with the bacterial acetylation of choline, the cultures were initiated from a small inoculum, the cells multiplied normally in the presence of relatively high concentrations of toxin and the descendants of the seed cells, many generations removed from the origincal inoculum, synthesized acetylcholine in normal amounts.[63]

Botulinum toxin does not appear to act as a destructive poison, that is, in the sense of producing specific histological changes in the end plate region. The period required for complete recovery of a totally paralyzed muscle in experimental animals is one year, some ten times the period required for recovery following crushing of the nerve. Guyton and MacDonald[49] suggest, on the basis of this observation, that the toxin exerts its effect, whatever it may be, on some structure or component of nerve which cannot be repaired or reconditioned as quickly as can the nerve fibrils per se.

Immunization experiments contribute little to our knowledge of the mode of action of botulinum toxin except, perhaps, to point to the irreversible nature of the poisoning. Passive immunization of isolated nerve-diaphragm preparations follows the same rules as apply in passive immunization of the living animal.[51] The addition of antitoxin prior to the union of homologous toxin and nerve tissue prevents the development of paralysis, whereas treatment with antitoxin late in the lag period or subsequent to the appearance of paralysis fails to prevent or to bring about any reversal in the progress of the paralysis.

THE NEUROTOXIN OF CL. TETANI

Tetanus

Tetanus is a disease of man and of the lower warmblooded animals which occurs when the anaerobic spore-forming bacterium, *Cl. tetani,* an organism widely distributed in the soil and also present in animal faeces, infects wounded or otherwise injured tissues. *Cl. tetani* is not an invasive organism. The spores will only germinate, and the vegetative cells so formed will only multiply, in dead fragments of tissue or foreign materials in the wound where conditions of anaerobiosis prevail, as a result of which we have in tetanus a strictly localized infection which may, at times, be insignificant in extent even in a fatal case. Tetanus is akin to botulism in that all of the symptoms of the disease are due to the specific action of a potent toxin on nerve tissue. It differs, however, in its pathogenesis, from botulism in that there is infection, the neurotoxin being produced as a result of growth of the organisms in the tissues. The manner in which the toxin which is elaborated locally in the wound, makes its way to the central nervous system where it exerts its major action, has been a subject of much controversy.

The incubation period in tetanus may range, in cases where no prophylaxis has been attempted, from 2 to 21 days. Not infrequently the first symptoms take the form of local tetanus with spasm and rigidity of the muscles in the neighbourhood of the wound. Generalized tetanus develops insidiously with gradually increasing stiffness and tonic spasms of the skeletal muscles. Trismus or tonic spasm of the masseters is often an early and characteristic sign; the muscles of the trunk and limbs are progressively involved. Any slight stimulus, tactile, auditory or visual may initiate a reflex paroxysm of violent muscular contractions. As the disease progresses the spasms become more frequent and more prolonged. The clinical picture in tetanus differs from that of strychnine poisoning in that in tetanus there is a sustained muscular rigidity and tremor between the reflex paroxysmal convulsive seizures. Death, when it occurs, may be due to spasm of the respiratory muscles or those of the larynx or at times it may be attributed to sheer exhaustion. The mortality rate bears a definite relationship to the incubation period. It may be as high as 80% when the incubation period is very short, and as low as 17% when the period of incubation is much prolonged.

Properties of Tetanus Toxin

Cl. tetani produces two antigenically distinct toxins, a haemolysin (tetanolysin) and a highly potent neurotoxin. Tetanolysin may be disregarded in any discussion of tetanus since it plays no part whatever in the development of the toxaemia. All of the symptoms of the disease are due to the neurotoxin variously referred to as spasmin, tetanospasmin, or simply tetanus toxin. All strains of *Cl. tetani,* unlike *Cl. botulinum,* produce the same antigenic type of neurotoxin which can be neutralized by a single antitoxin.

Various media have been devised for the preparation of tetanus toxin in high yield in culture.[70-72] The growth requirements for the production of toxin are not completely defined in that semi-synthetic media will support good yields only when supplemented with a beef heart infusion. The toxin is formed in a fully active state within the bacterial cells from which it can be extracted by various means;[74-80] it is presumably released into culture fluids or the tissue fluids in infection upon autolysis of the cells. In a casein digest beef heart infusion medium supplemented with cystine, tyrosine and glucose[71] yields of extracellular toxin ranging from 200,000 to 800,000 mouse M.L.D.'s per ml. may be obtained.[73]

Tetanus toxin was obtained in the pure crystalline form in 1946 by Pillemer, Wittler and Grossberg.[81] The procedure involves fractional precipitation of culture filtrates with methanol at low temperatures and under rigidly controlled conditions of pH, ionic strength and protein concentration. Crystalline tetanal toxin is a protein with an estimated molecular weight of 67,000 to 68,000[82,83] and contains 15.7% nitrogen, 0.065% phosphorus and 1.04% sulphur.[82] The percentages of 13 amino acids in the protein molecule have been determined.[82] It is noteworthy that tetanal toxin contains exceptionally high percentages of aspartic acid and lysine as compared to most other proteins. The aspartic acid content is about 50% greater than that of leucine, a relationship that is also seen in type A botulinum toxin[17] but one that is reversed in most other proteins of known composition. Among all of the lethal poisons known crystalline tetanus toxin ranks second only to botulinum toxin, having a potency of some 75×10^6 mouse M.L.D.'s per mg. of nitrogen[81] and symptoms of tetanus may be produced in the mouse with as little as 0.000013 mg. of the crystalline product.[84] There are, of course, variations in animal susceptibility to tetanus toxin, just as is the case with the toxin of *Cl. botulinum*. Man and the horse are said to be among the most highly susceptible.

Upon standing at 0°C. or when treated with minute concentrations of formalin tetanus toxin undergoes toxoiding which would appear to involve polymerization of two toxin molecules which have a sedimentation constant of 4.5 Svedberg units to a dimeric compound with a sedimentation constant of 7 S.[85,86] It is suggested that condensation occurs through the toxic groups leaving those radicles responsible for antigenicity unimpaired.

The Transport and Sites of Action of Tetanus Toxin

Tetanus toxin acts centrally upon motor nerve cells of the spinal cord and medulla and peripherally at cholinergic nerve endings. Theories concerning the pathway by which the toxin reaches the central nervous system have been a subject of much dispute over the

years and a voluminous literature has grown about this subject. At
the turn of this century Marie,[87] Marie and Morax[88] and Meyer and
Ransom,[89] on the basis of a series of ingenious experiments, formulated the theory of nerve carriage. It was concluded that tetanus toxin
is absorbed from the site of injection in experimental toxaemia or in
the infected tissues in the naturally occurring disease by the end organs
of motor nerves and that it travels in a centripetal current along the
axis cylinders to the cord and medulla. The phenomenon of local
tetanus, which at the onset of the naturally occurring disease is often
seen in the region of the infected part and which, in the experimental
toxaemia, first develops in groups of muscles into which the toxin
has been injected, supported the axis cylinder theory of toxin transport. If the toxin were to make its way directly along the motor fibers
of the inoculated area, it would be expected that the first cells of the
central nervous system to be affected should be those anterior horn
cells giving rise to the fibers and innervating the muscles of the area;
subsequent diffusion of toxin throughout the cord would then give
rise to the progressive development of generalized tetanus. Toxin
absorbed into the blood stream or injected intravenously was said to
gain access to the central nervous system only after having been absorbed by motor endings. It was claimed that toxin could be demonstrated in the motor nerves of an injected limb, but that a severed
nerve took up toxin slowly, a degenerate nerve not at all. It was noted
that the inoculation of a very minute dose of toxin into a limb resulted in tetanus localized entirely to the limb; if the motor nerve to
the limb was severed prior to the inoculation tetanus failed to develop.

The Marie-Meyer theory of axis cylinder transmission of tetanus
toxin has been vigourously challenged by Abel and his associates.[90-96]
Early workers had believed that the toxin exerted its effect solely upon
the central nervous system. Abel *et al.* claim that tetanus toxin exerts
a dual action, a central and a peripheral effect, each of which can be
elicited quite independently of the other and both of which can be
recognized as distinct physiological entities even when they occur together. The injection of very minute amounts of toxin, as for example,
a total of $1/200$ of the lethal dose, distributed to various parts of a
limb, is said to induce purely local tetanus characterized by sustained
muscular rigidity independent of external stimuli and with none of
the reflex excitability seen in generalized tetanus. This is said to be a
peripheral effect resulting from fixation of the toxin upon the motor
end organs of the striated muscles. The application of toxin directly
to the cord in the region of the anterior horns produces, after a latent
period of a few hours, only reflex spasmodic activity of the muscles
innervated by the affected segment of the cord with none of the per-

sistent rigidity of local tetanus. The subcutaneous, intramuscular or intravenous injection of a full lethal dose of toxin gives rise to the complete picture of generalized tetanus, that is, the paroxysmal motor spasms which may be induced by various stimuli, the central effect, and the superimposed muscular rigidity which is sustained at all times, the peripheral effect.

On the basis of their experimental studies Abel and his colleagues concluded that tetanus toxin is not carried along the axis cylinders to the central nervous system but rather that it reaches the anterior horn cells via the systemic lymph and blood streams. They objected to the theory of axis cylinder transport on both anatomical and physiological grounds, and noted that when doses greater than a minimum lethal dose were injected into a limb a high proportion of the toxin could be demonstrated in the vascular and lymphatic systems whereas they failed to demonstrate toxin in the axis cylinders. It was further stated that the injection of a sublethal dose of toxin directly into the sciatic nerve did not give rise to tetanus if precautions were taken to prevent leakage of the toxin into the surrounding tissues.

Since the appearance of local tetanus was not observed when the toxin was injected after section of the regional motor nerve supply, and failing to recognize a peripheral effect of the toxin, it was natural that earlier workers should suppose that functional connection with the spinal cord was essential to the development of tetanus. However, Harvey[97] has observed that if toxin is injected into a muscle soon after a nerve has been cut, that local tetanus is produced, and that it does not disappear until the motor nerve endings have lost their transmitting function. It is suggested that the determining factor in the development of local tetanus is the integrity of the motor nerve endings and not the connection with the spinal cord.

The foregoing investigations have by no means settled the controversy concerning transport of the toxin. Friedemann,[98] Wright,[99,100] Baylis[101] and their colleagues have in more recent years presented convincing evidence that tetanus toxin may be carried to the central nervous system by nerves. Transection of the spinal cord in the lumbar region prevents generalized tetanus and death from an otherwise lethal dose of toxin inoculated into a lower limb or sciatic nerve.[98,101] It is reported, in agreement with the findings of earlier investigators, that toxin injected into the calf muscles of the rabbit can be identified in the sciatic nerve[101] and chemical sclerosis of the sciatic nerve proximal to the level of injection of toxin is said to impede the transport of toxin and prevent the development of local tetanus.[100,101] If toxin is injected into a cranial nerve, as the vagus, the sequence of development of localizing symptoms suggests a radial spread of toxin from the motor nucleus of that nerve to neighbouring motor nuclei.[99]

The Central Action of Tetanus Toxin

The major symptoms of tetanus, that is, the reflex paroxysmal muscle spasms, are the result of action of tetanus toxin on components of the central nervous system and resemble very closely the symptoms of strychnine poisoning. The sustained rigidity of muscles between the convulsive seizures in tetanus, the result of action of the toxin at peripheral nerves, is not seen in strychnine poisoning.

Strychnine would appear to act by depressing inhibitory synapses along polysynaptic pathways;[102,103] it has no effect upon monosynaptic reflexes. Acheson in 1942[104] demonstrated that in local tetanus produced in cats polysynaptic reflexes were increased whereas the mono-synaptic reflexes remain essentially normal. Brooks and his associates, in view of the similarity of the central effects of strychnine and tetanus toxin, have made a detailed study of the action of the tetanus toxin on the inhibition of motor neurones.[105,106] The work confirms the observations of Acheson and his associates that, like strychnine, the toxin is without effect upon monosynaptic reflexes whereas it increases polysynaptic reflexes. In anaesthetized spinal cats all forms of spinal inhibition investigated were abolished following the injection of toxin either peripherally into a mixed nerve trunk or directly into the spinal cord. The toxin would appear to exert its effect near the synaptic junctions between the specific interneurones of the inhibitory pathway and the motor neurone. It is suggested that the toxin might act either by blocking receptors of the subsynaptic inhibitory areas or upon presynaptic terminals of inhibitory interneurones preventing the production or release of an inhibitory transmitter substance.[106]

Van Heyningen[107-109] has attempted to identify the substance at the inhibitory synapse upon which the toxin acts. Wassermann and Takaki in 1898 reported that emulsions of brain tissue had the capacity of entering into combination with tetanus toxin and removing it by fixation from a toxin solution.[110] Landsteiner and Botteri[111] subsequently showed that an extract of nerve tissue, a mixture of sphingolipids, particularly the cerebrosides and sphingomyelins, had the greatest toxin receptor activity and apparently a specific one since it does not apply to a variety of other proteins such as botulinum, diphtheria, *Cl. oedematiens*, *Cl. welchii*, staphylococcal and dysentery toxins and various non-toxic proteins.[108,111-114] Van Heyningen[109] has identified the specific receptor of tetanus toxin in the grey matter of nervous tissue, not as a cerebroside as was thought by earlier workers, but as a closely related substance, a ganglioside containing fatty acids, sphingosine, glucose, galactose, acetylgalactosamine, acetylneuraminic acid and amino acid residues. The ganglioside which is, in the isolated form, water soluble, occurs in nervous tissue in the form of water insoluble complexes with cerebrosides and sphingomyelins. The significance of the fixation of tetanus toxin by the gangliosides is not clear at the present time. It is suggested that combination between the toxin and the ganglioside may be the first step leading to the specific pharmacological action of the toxin.

The Peripheral Action of Tetanus Toxin

From a study of muscular responses in local tetanus Harvey[97] concluded that the phenomena of local tetanus resembled in some respects the early changes seen in denervated muscle and in other respects the changes occurring with eserine poisoning, and might be explained if one were to assume that the toxin acted at motor nerve endings in such a way as to result in an abnormal leakage of acetylcholine, and at the same time a diminution of cholinesterase or a depression of cholinesterase activity.

Ambache, Morgan and Wright[115] have studied the effect of tetanus toxin upon the rabbit's iris. There are clinical features of tetanus, rather over-shadowed by the more dramatic skeletal muscle spasms, such as atonic bladder, tachycardia and constipation, which suggest that parasympathetic nerves may be involved in the disease. The injection of a small amount of tetanus toxin into the anterior chamber of the rabbit's eye is followed, after a latent period of one to two days, by a persistent mydriasis, failure of the pupil to react to light, and failure of the pupil to contract after stimulation of the third nerve, all of which suggest that in this form of local tetanus cholinergic transmission to the sphincter pupillae is almost completely paralysed. That the toxin exerts no effect upon the smooth muscle of the sphincter pupillae is shown by the immediate myosis that follows the injection of acetylcholine and carbaminocholine. Electrical stimulation of the oculo-motor nerve, which on the normal side produces prompt myosis, brings about little or no reduction in the diameter of the dilated pupil of the poisoned eye; the response to oculomotor stimulation is partially restored by the instillation of eserine into the conjunctival sac, a fact which suggests that the toxin interferes with humoral transmission.

In contradiction to Harvey's hypothesis of increased production of acetylcholine, Ambache et al. show that the acetylcholine content of an intoxicated iris falls gradually to a concentration of about 50% of that of the normal eye, and that of the aqueous humor to some 15 to 25% of the normal. The diminished secretion of acetylcholine would appear not to be due to any effect of the toxin on the enzymatic acetylation of choline. Torda and Wolf[116] found, if anything, an increased synthesis of acetylcholine *in vitro* in the presence of all but very large doses of the toxin and Schaefer[117] states that the toxin has no effect upon the enzyme choline acetylase.

The experiments of Ambache and his collaborators give support to the contention that the phenomena associated with local tetanus resemble in certain features the after-effects of denervation of skeletal muscle. Doses of carbaminocholine that are insufficient to produce any effect in the normal control eye cause a marked myosis of the iris of the intoxicated eye. It is known that cholinergic effector systems become more sensitive to acetylcholine and parasympathomimetic drugs after their innervation has been destroyed.[118]

The possibility that tetanus toxin might affect the cholinesterase content of tissues or depress cholinesterase activity, has received much attention.[115,117,119,120-123] The little evidence that exists that cholinesterase might be inhibited by tetanus toxin is derived from *in vitro* studies where no distinction appears to have been made between "true" and "pseudo" cholinesterase. Thus Labenz and Genuit[120] reported that, *in vitro*, tetanus toxin was a potent cholinesterase inhibitor, whereas others have been unable to support this claim.[120-123] There would appear to be no diminution of the cholinesterase content of the spinal cord, the brain or of smooth and skeletal muscles in either local or generalized tetanus intoxication;[115,119,124] in some of the experiments, at least, due regard was given to total cholinesterase, "true" cholinesterase and "pseudo" cholinesterase. In this respect the effect of tetanus toxin would appear to differ from that of nerve degeneration where the concentration of cholinesterase undergoes a considerable decrease.

It is clear that the manner in which the toxin induces peripheral disturbances is still unknown. The toxin would appear to be fixed at cholinergic nerve endings or possibly in the course of terminal unmyelinated fibrils proximal to the acetylcholine release region since, although there is a diminution in the production of acetylcholine *in vivo*, the toxin appears not to depress the enzymatic acetylation of choline. The decreased release of acetylcholine might possibly be secondary to some derangement in transmission of the impulse just proximal to the acetylcholine release region, or to some impairment of the acetylcholine release mechanism per se. Whatever the exact site of action, fixation of the toxin on peripheral nerves produces physiological disturbances resembling in some ways those accompanying the post-traumatic degeneration of nerve. It is worthy of note that the period required for complete recovery in local tetanus is within the range of time required for repair of a crushed nerve in marked contrast to the situation in local botulism.

As in botulism, the derangement of function in tetanus would appear to have a purely physiological background, and animals which succumb to tetanus intoxication show no specific morphological changes in nerve or other tissues.[84] Pappenheimer has suggested,[69] as in the case of botulism, on the basis of the characteristic latent period seen in experimental tetanus toxaemia and the extraordinary potency of the toxin, that it might act, not directly upon enzymes concerned in nerve function but rather by interfering with the synthesis of some essential enzyme. It is possible that normal neuromuscular relationships might be upset by an interference with the energy-yielding biochemical reactions that are vital for normal nerve and muscle metabolism. However, Pillemer and Muntz[86] were unable to detect any effect of crystalline tetanus toxin upon the *in vitro* glycolysis in mouse brain homogenates, or upon adenosinetriphosphatase activity of nerve and muscle tissue of animals poisoned with massive doses of toxin. It has been repeatedly suggested that tetanus toxin might act not directly on nerve tissue but rather that it might produce in the body some secondary substance responsible for the symptoms. Thus Courmont and Doyen claimed to have isolated a strychnine-like material from tetanic muscles. However, later investigations have failed to confirm the existence of any secondary substance in poisoned nerve or muscle.[84,86,98]

A number of authors[49,50,82,115] have stressed points of resemblance between tetanus and botulinum toxins which are of more than trivial interest. The toxins are produced by closely related species of the one genus, *Clostridium*. Both are proteins, the elemental and amino acid concentrations of which provide no clue to the high degree of toxicity that they exhibit. They have essentially the same qualitative composition of amino acids and both show in common certain peculiarities in the relative proportions of some of the amino acids as contrasted with other proteins of known composition. Peripherally at least, both toxins exert an effect on cholinergic nerve endings which result in a diminished output of acetylcholine, despite the fact that neither substance depresses the *in vitro* acetylation of choline. On superficial examination the clinical pictures in botulism and tetanus appear to differ considerably, but it is known that in botulism there is a preliminary excitatory period for at least the parasympathetic system and, in tetanus, paralytic symptoms resembling those of botulism may at times occur. Thus there is some reason to believe that the active groups of these two toxins may be closely related.

BACTERIAL 'NEUROTOXINS' OF SECONDARY
IMPORTANCE

The Toxin of Corynebacterium diphtheriae

Although neurological symptoms are not an integral part of the classical clinical picture in diphtheria some form of paralysis may occur as a late complication of the disease, ordinarily making its appearance in the second or third week of convalescence. The muscles or the soft palate are the most frequently affected. Ocular paralysis in some form is usually seen and occasionally the pharynx, the diaphragm, and the muscles of the extremities may be involved. In severe cases respiratory paralysis, due to involvement of the phrenic nerves, may result in death. If the patient survives, rapid and complete recovery of muscle function ensues.

Virulent strains of *C. diphtheriae* secrete a potent soluble toxin which accounts for the major symptoms of the disease. The growth requirements of *C. diphtheriae* are fairly well defined and it is now possible to obtain high yields of toxin in semi-synthetic and chemically defined media.[125-127] The concentration of iron in the medium bears a critical relationship to the production of toxin.[128] Maximum toxin production occurs only over a narrow range of iron concentration, with an optimum of about 0.1 microgram of iron per ml. Further additions of iron, although improving growth, result in a rapid fall in toxin production, and when a concentration of 0.5 microgram per ml. is reached toxin is no longer produced.

Diphtheria toxin has been isolated in varying degrees of purity and characterized by Eaton,[129] Pappenheimer[130] and others.[131-137] The purest preparation obtained by Pappenheimer was a heat-labile protein with an isoelectric point of pH 4.1 and an estimated molecular weight of about 72,000.[138] The purified product contained 16% nitrogen, 0.75% sulphur and less than 0.05% phosphorus. The minimum lethal dose of purified toxin for the guinea-pig was approximately 1 μg. By the application of gel-diffusion methods, Pope and his colleagues[139] in 1950, showed that the purest toxin preparations available at the time contained some fourteen distinct antigens; Pope and Stevens[132,134-136] have since reported the isolation of a crystaline protein with the *in vivo* and *in vitro* properties of diphtheria toxin which, despite repeated crystallization still contains three or four antigens. As with botulinum and tetanus toxins, all methods which denature or in any way alter the protein molcule bring about a simultaneous loss of toxicity.

Whether separate neurotoxic and "classical" toxin molecules are produced by *C. diphtheriae* has been, in the past, a matter of some dispute. Ehrlich[140] believed, on the basis of observations made in the course of toxin-antitoxin neutralization studies that the organism produced a neurotoxin distinct from the toxin which accounts for the classical symptoms of the disease. However, on the basis of our present knowledge, it would appear to be clearly established that diphtheria toxin is a single substance with a relatively low affinity for nerve tissue as compared to other tissues of the body.[141,142] In contrast to botulinum and tetanus toxins diphtheria toxin appears to be quite non-specific in its action with respect to the tissues it attacks. The lesions produced by diphtheria toxin take the form of cellular degeneration with oedema and haemorrhage and may be found in almost any of the tissues of a susceptible animal. In general there has been considerable disagreement concerning the extent and the nature of the nerve lesions. The available evidence indicates that degenerative changes involve the nerves associated with the paralysed areas and take the form of an ascending peripheral toxic neuritis. Histologically the changes are similar to those of Wallerian degeneration seen following division of a nerve but rarely are they so severe or complete.

The mechanism by which diphtheria toxin produces its characteristic lesions is not clear. Pappenheimer and Hendee[69,143,144] suggest that the toxin may interfere with cellular oxidations. As has been noted, toxin is liberated into the medium only when the level of iron in the medium is reduced to a low level, and only under aerobic conditions. A porphyrin is found in culture filtrates only when the iron concentration is reduced and its production parallels the secretion of toxin. The addition of iron into the culture medium in concentrations above those for optimal toxin production results in the disappearance from the culture filtrates of the porphyrin, iron and diphtheria toxin in a molar ratio of 4:4:1. All of the iron added over the range in which toxin production is inhibited can be found in the cells. Further evidence strongly suggests that the toxin is related to cytochrome b, the main iron porphyrin pigment of the organism. Pappenheimer has suggested that diphtheria toxin might be the protein moiety of cytochrome b, which in the absence of iron cannot be incorporated into the complete cytochrome molecule, and that the toxin might act by blocking the synthesis of mammalian cytochrome b or some related enzyme in the susceptible animal. It is of interest to note, in this connection, that in the *Cecropia* silk-worn maximum sensitivity to diphtheria toxin has been found to be a characteristic only of these developmental stages which show a cytochrome system.[145] Yoneda and Pappenheimer[146] have shown in the past year, however, that a toxigenic strain of *C. diphtheriae* and a nontoxigenic strain from which the former had been derived by infection with temperate bacteriophage β behave in the same manner in their relationship to the iron content of the medium. With low concentrations of iron the yields of protein and porphyrin are the same for both strains, but toxin is not a component of the protein fraction secreted by the nontoxigenic strain. Clarke[147,148] using in his studies a toxigenic strain of *C. diphtheriae* different from that employed by Pappenheimer, has also found that the effect of iron in decreasing the formation of toxin is not associated quantiatively with the formation of cytochrome b.

Shigella dysenteriae "Neurotoxin"

In common with other members of the genus *Shigella, Sh. dysenteriae* contains a heat stable endotoxin, a protein-polysaccharide-lipoid complex of the somatic antigens,[149-154] which when injected parenterally into experimental animals causes diarrhoea and pathological lesions in the intestinal tract which closely resemble those found in clinical cases of bacillary dysentery.

Unlike other organisms of the group, *Sh. dysenteriae* produces a thermolabile toxin which, despite the fact that it is only released upon autolysis of the cells,[149-151,155] is commonly referred to as an exotoxin. The exotoxin, which is produced only by rough variants of the organism, induces paralytic symptoms in rabbits and mice, a fact which has led observers to class it as a neurotoxin.

Highly purified preparations of the so-called neurotoxin have been prepared by various procedures.[156-160] The most potent preparation has been obtained by van Heyningen and Gladstone[160] in an electrophoretically homogeneous state. It is a protein containing some 15.7% nitrogen. The purified preparation is highly active, 1 mg. containing 750 LD 50's per kg. of mouse weight and 1,150,000 LD 50's per kg. of rabbit weight.

Unlike the endotoxin, the neurotoxin of *Sh. dysenteriae* may be toxoided with formalin to produce an effective antigen. The immunological studies of Boroff[155,161] suggest that the neurotoxin is simply the protein component of the somatic antigen. Both the S and R variants of the organism produce this protein but it would appear that the S form incorporates the protein into the whole protein-polysaccharide-lipid complex, whereas the R form fails to do so.

There has been much controversy concerning the existence of a specific neurotoxic activity of the exotoxin. Although degenerative changes have been described in ganglion cells of some animal species, neurological lesions can not be induced in all species nor does it appear that the action of the toxin is entirely specific, since it produces changes in parenchymatous organs, vasoconstriction and capillary haemorrhage. Even in those animals which have a high degree of susceptibility to the neurotoxic activity of the exotoxin, this toxin would appear to have a relatively low affinity for nerve tissue per se. Rabbits and mice, for example, actually survive longer when toxin is injected into the medulla oblongata, than when it is injected into the blood stream.[162] There is no evidence that the toxin can be transported in nerve trunks, nor does it exert any effect on peripheral nerve endings.[162]

The multiplicity of toxic constituents in crude preparations complicated the efforts of investigators to evaluate the separate activities of the endotoxin and the exotoxin of *Shigella dysenteriae*. The problem has been resolved through the use of purified neurotoxin prepared by van Heyningen and Gladstone. Employing pure toxin in their studies Bridgwater,[163] Cavanagh[164] and their associates conclude that the toxin has no specific affinity for nerve cells proper and that the damage to nerve tissue is simply mediated through primary damage to the endothelium of small vessels. Following the intravenous injection of purified "neurotoxin" in rabbits, focal haemorrhages appear in the grey matter of the spinal cord enlargements some time before the onset of neurological symptoms. Degenerative changes in neurones are definitely related to the distribution of the affected vessels and are not seen until some hours after the development of the focal haemorrhages. It is also noted that intestinal changes are frequently present in animals inoculated. Since all of the diverse lesions are believed to have a basic vascular origin it is doubtful if *Sh. dysenteriae* exotoxin can be regarded as a neurotoxin in the strict sense of the term as we apply it to botulinum and tetanus toxins.

REFERENCES

1. GUNNISON, J. B. and MEYER, K. F.: *Proc. Soc. Exper. Biol. & Med., 26*:89 (1928).
2. LEWIS, K. A. and HILL, E. V.: *J. Bact., 52*:213 (1947).
3. STEVENSON, J. W., HELSON, V. A. and REED, G. B.: *Canad. J. Res., E25*:9 (1947).
4. STEVENSON, J. W., HELSON, V. A. and REED, G. B.: *Canad. J. Res., E25*:14 (1947).
5. HELSON, V. A., STEVENSON, J. W. and REED, G. B.: *Canad. J. Res., E25*:25 (1947).
6. BARRON, A. L. and REED, G. B.: *Canad. J. Microbiol., 1*:108 (1954).
7. BOROFF, D. A.: *J. Bact., 70*:363 (1955).
8. BOROFF, D. A., RAYNAUD, M. and PRÉVOT, A. R.: *J. Immunol., 68*:503 (1952).
9. KINDLER, H., MAGER, J. and GROSSWICZ, N.: *Science, 122*:926 (1955).
10. BONVENTRE, P. F. and KEMPE, L. L.: *Appl. Microbiol., 7* (6):374 (1959).
11. ABRAMS, A., KEGELES, G. and HOTTLE, G. A.: *J. Biol. Chem., 164*:63 (1946).
12. LAMANNA, C., EKLUND, H. W., and McELROY, O. E.: *J. Bact., 52*:1 (1946).
13. DUFF, J. T., WRIGHT, G., KLERER, J., MOORE, D. E. and BIBLER, R. H.: *J. Bact., 73*:42 (1957).
14. LAMANNA, C., JENSEN, W. I. and BROSS, I. D.: *Am. J. Hyg., 62*:21 (1955).
15. PUTNAM, F. W., LAMANNA, C. and SHARP, D. G.: *J. Biol. Chem., 165*:735 (1946).
16. KEGELES, G. J.: *J. Am. Chem. Soc., 68*:1670 (1946).
17. BUEHLER, H. J., SCHANTZ, E. J. and LAMANNA, C.: *J. Biol. Chem., 169*:295 (1947).
18. LAMANNA, C.: *Science, 130*:763 (1959).

19. LAMANNA, C.: *Proc. Soc. Exper. Biol. & Med., 69:*332 (1948).
20. LAMANNA, C. and LOWENTHAL, J. P.: *J. Bact., 61:*751 (1951).
21. WAGMAN, J.: *Arch. Biochem. & Biophys., 50:*104 (1954).
22. LAMANNA, C. and GLASSMAN, H. N.: *J. Bact., 54:*575 (1947).
23. WAGMAN, J. and BATEMAN, J. B.: *Arch. Biochem. & Biophys., 31:*424 (1951).
24. DUFF, J. T., KLERER, J., BIBLER, R. H., MOORE, D. E., GOTTFRIED, C. and WRIGHT, G. C.: *J. Bact., 73:*597 (1957).
25. CARDELLA, M. A., DUFF, J. T., GOTTFRIED, C. and BEGEL, J. S.: *Bact. Proc., 56:*90 (1956).
26. CARDELLA, M. A., DUFF, J. T., GOTTFRIED, C. and BEGEL, J. S.: *J. Bact., 75:*360 (1958).
27. GORDON, M., FIOCK, M. A., YARINSKY, A. and DUFF, J. T.: *J. Bact., 74:*533 (1957).
28. RAYNAUD, M., PRÉVOT, A. R., BRYGOO, J. and TURPIN, A.: *Internat. Cong. Microbiol.,* 6th, *4:*135 (1955).
29. WENTZEL, L. M., STERNE, M. and POLSON, A.: *Nature, 166:*739 (1950).
30. MAY, A. J. and WHALER, B. C.: *Brit. J. Exper. Path., 39:*307 (1958).
31. SCHÜBEL, K.: *Arch. exper. Path. u. Pharmakol., 96:*193 (1923).
32. BRONFENBRENNER, J. J. and SCHLESINGER, M. J.: *J. Exper. Med., 39:*509 (1924).
33. CHISTYAKOV, F. M. and RODOPULO, A. K.: *Ztschr. Microbiol. Epidemiol. Immunitätsforsch* (U.S.S.R.), *9:*88 (1943). Cited from *Chem. Abst., 39:*3323 (1945).
34. COLEMAN, I. W.: *Canad. J. Biochem. & Physiol., 32:*27 (1954).
35. HALLIWELL, G.: *Biochem. J., 58:*4 (1954).
36. MEYER, E. A. and LAMANNA, C.: *J. Bact., 78:*175 (1959).
37. SAKAGUCHI, G. and TOHYAMA, Y.: *Japan. J. Med. Sc. & Biol., 8:*255 (1955).
38. DUFF, J. T., WRIGHT, G. C. and YARINSKY, A.: *J. Bact., 72:*455 (1956).
39. DOLMAN, C. E.: *Canad. J. Pub. Health, 48:*187 (1957).
40. SAKAGUCHI, G. and SAKAGUCHI, S.: *J. Bact., 78:*1 (1959).
41. BONVENTRE, P. F. and KEMPE, L.: *J. Bact., 78:*892 (1959).
42. COWDRY, E. V. and NICHOLSON, F. M.: *J. Exper. Med., 39:*827 (1924).
43. DICKSON, E. C. and SHEVKY, R.: *J. Exper. Med., 37:*711 (1923).
44. DICKSON, E. C. and SHEVKY, R.: *J. Exper. Med., 38:*327 (1923).
45. EDMUNDS, C. W. and LONG, P. H.: *J. A. M. A., 81:*542 (1923).
46. EDMUNDS, C. W. and LLOYD, P. C.: *J. A. M. A., 80:*1875 (1923).
47. SCHÜBEL, K.: *Arch. exper. Path. u. Pharmakol., 96:*193 (1923).
48. BISHOP, G. H. and BRONFENBRENNER, J. J.: *Am. J. Physiol., 117:*393 (1936).
49. GUYTON, A. C. and MACDONALD, M. A.: *Arch. Neurol. & Psychiat., 57:*578 (1947).
50. AMBACHE, N.: *J. Physiol., 108:*127 (1949).
51. BURGEN, A. S. V., DICKENS, F. and ZATMAN, L. J.: *J. Physiol., 109:*10 (1949).
52. BROOKS, V. B.: *Science, 117:*334 (1953).
53. BROOKS, V. B.: *J. Physiol., 123:*501 (1954).
54. BROOKS, V. B.: *Federation Proc., 15:*25 (1956).
55. BROOKS, V. B.: *J. Physiol., 134:*264 (1956).
56. BÜLBRING, E.: *Brit. J. Pharmacol., 1:*38 (1946).
57. BROWN, G. L. and VON EULER, U. S.: *J. Physiol., 93:*39 (1938).
58. EDMUNDS, C. W. and KEIPER, G. F.: *J. A. M. A., 83:*495 (1924).
59. ROSENBLUETH, A., LINDSLEY, D. B. and MORRISON, R. S.: *Am. J. Physiol., 115:*53 (1936).
60. WILSON, A. T. and WRIGHT, S.: *Quart. J. Exper. Physiol., 26:*127 (1936).

61. TORDA, C. and WOLFF, H. G.: *J. Pharmacol. & Exper. Therap., 89*:320 (1947).
62. STEVENSON, J. W.: FAIRBAIRN, D. and CAMPBELL, A. J.: Unpublished (1946).
63. STEVENSON, J. W. and GIRVIN, G. T.: *Atti. Del. VI congresso Internazionale di Microbiologia*, Rome, *4*:XII, 133 (1953).
64. STEPHENSON, M. and ROWATT, E.: *J. Gen. Microbiol., 1*:279 (1947).
65. GIRVIN, G. T. and STEVENSON, J. W.: *Canad. J. Biochem. & Physiol., 32*:131 (1954).
66. STOVER, J. H. JR., FINGERMAN, M. and FORESTER, R. H.: *Proc. Soc. Exper. Biol. & Med., 84*:146 (1953).
67. DEL CASTILLO, J. and KATZ, B.: *J. Physiol., 124*:574 (1954).
68. DEL CASTILLO, J. and KATZ, B.: *J. Physiol., 124*:585 (1954).
69. PAPPENHEIMER, A. M., JR.: *Federation Proc., 6*:479 (1947).
70. MUELLER, J. H. and MILLER, P. A.: *J. Immunol., 50*:377 (1945).
71. MUELLER, J. H. and MILLER, P. A.: *J. Immunol., 56*:143 (1947).
72. TAYLOR, E. M.: *J. Immunol., 50*:385 (1945).
73. PICKETT, M. J., HOEPRICK, P. D. and GERMAIN, R. O.: *J. Bact., 49*:515 (1945).
74. RAYNAUD, M.: *Ann. Inst. Pasteur, 80*:356 (1951).
75. RAYNAUD, M., TURPIN, A., MANGALO, R. and BIZZINI, B.: *Ann. Inst. Pasteur, 88*:24 (1955).
76. MILLER, P. A., EATON, M. D. and GRAY, C. T.: *J. Bact., 77*:733 (1958).
77. MIR, C. H. and NAZARI, F.: *Arch. Inst. Hessarek., 11*:9 (1959).
78. MIR, C. H. and NAZARI, F.: *Arch. Inst. Hessarek., 11*:13 (1959).
79. MIR, C. H. and NAZARI, F.: *Arch. Inst. Hessarek., 11*:17 (1959).
80. VAILLARD, L. and VINCENT, H.: *Ann. Inst. Pasteur, 5*:1 (1891).
81. PILLEMER, L., WITTLER, R. and GROSSBERG, D. B.: *Science, 103*:615 (1946).
82. DUNN, M. S., CAMIEN, M. N. and PILLEMER, L.: *Arch. Biochem., 22*:37 (1949).
83. LARGIER, J. F.: *J. Immunol., 76*:393 (1956).
84. PILLEMER, L. and WARTMAN, W. B.: *J. Immunol., 55*:277 (1947).
85. PILLEMER, L. and MOORE, D. H.: *J. Biol. Chem., 173*:427 (1948).
86. PILLEMER, L. and MUNTZ, J. A.: Cited from Pillemer, L. and Robbins, K. C.: *Ann. Rev. Microbiol., 3*:265 (1949).
87. MARIE, A.: *Ann. Inst. Pasteur, 11*:591 (1897).
88. MARIE, A. and MORAX, V.: *Ann. Inst. Pasteur, 16*:818 (1902).
89. MEYER, H. and RANSOM, F.: *Arch. Path. Pharm., 49*:369 (1903).
90. ABEL, J. J., EVANS, E. A., HAMPIL, B. and LEE, F. C.: *Bull. Johns Hopkins Hosp., 56*:84 (1935).
91. ABEL, J. J., HAMPIL, B. and JONAS, A. F.: *Bull. Johns Hopkins Hosp., 57*:317 (1935).
92. ABEL, J. J. and HAMPIL, B.: *Bull. Johns Hopkins Hosp., 57*:343 (1935).
93. ABEL, J. J., EVANS, E. A. and HAMPIL, B.: *Bull. Johns Hopkins Hosp., 59*:307 (1936).
94. ABEL, J. J., HAMPIL, B., JONAS, A. F. and CHALIAN, W.: *Bull. Johns Hopkins Hosp., 62*:522 (1938).
95. ABEL, J. J., FIROR, W. M. and CHALIAN, W.: *Bull. Johns Hopkins Hosp., 63*:373 (1938).
96. FIROR, W. M. and JONAS, A. F.: *Bull. Johns Hopkins Hosp., 62*:91 (1938).
97. HARVEY, A. M.: *J. Physiol., 96*:348 (1939).
98. FRIEDMANN, U., HOLLANDER, A. and TARLOV, I. M.: *J. Immunol., 40*:325, (1941).
99. WRIGHT, E. A., MORGAN, R. S. and WRIGHT, G. P.: *J. Path. & Bact., 62*:569 (1950).

100. Wright, E. A., Morgan, R. S. and Wright, G. P.: *Brit. J. Exper. Path., 32:*169 (1951).
101. Bayliss, J. H., Mackintosh, J., Morgan, R. S. and Wright, G. P.: *J. Path. & Bact., 64:*33 (1952).
102. Bradley, K., Easton, D. M. and Eccles, J. C.: *J. Physiol., 122:*474 (1953).
103. Coombs, J. S., Eccles, J. C. and Fatt, P.: *J. Physiol., 130:*396 (1955).
104. Acheson, G. H., Ratnoff, O. D. and Schoenbach, E. B.: *J. Exper. Med., 75:*465 (1942).
105. Brooks, V. B., Curtis, D. R. and Eccles, J. C.: *Nature, 175:*120 (1955).
106. Brooks, V. B., Curtis, D. R. and Eccles, J. C.: *J. Physiol., 135:*655 (1957).
107. van Heyningen, W. E.: *J. Gen. Microbiol., 20:*291 (1959).
108. van Heyningen, W. E.: *J. Gen. Microbiol., 20:*301 (1959).
109. van Heyningen, W. E.: *J. Gen. Microbiol., 20:*310 (1959).
110. Wassermann, A. and Takaki, T.: *Berl. klin. Wchnschr., 35:*5 (1898).
111. Landsteiner, K. and Botteri, A.: *Zentralbl. Bakt.* (Orig.), *42:*562 (1906); Cited from van Heyningen, W. E.: *J. Gen. Microbiol., 20:*291 (1959).
112. Coleman, G. E.: *J. Infect. Dis., 34:*614 (1924).
113. Pons, R.: *Compt. rend. Soc. biol.,* Paris, *129:*209 (1938).
114. Fulthorpe, A. J.: *J. Hyg.,* Camb., *54:*315 (1956).
115. Ambache, N., Morgan, R. S. and Wright, G. P.: *Brit. J. Exper. Path., 29:*408 (1948).
116. Torda, C. and Wolff, H. G.: *Federation Proc., 6:*377 (1947).
117. Schaefer, H.: *Arch. exper. Path. u. Pharmakol., 203:*59 (1944).
118. Cannon, W. B.: *Am. J. M. Sc., 198:*737 (1939).
119. Martini, E., Torda, C. and Zironi, A.: *J. Physiol., 96:*818 (1939).
120. Labenz, K. and Genuit, H.: *Arch. exper. Path. u. Pharmakol., 198:*369 (1941).
121. Werle, E. and Stütgen, G.: *Klin. Wchnschr., 21:*821 (1942).
122. Ammon, R.: *Ergebn. Enzymol., 9:*35 (1943).
123. Vincent, D. and De Prat, J.: *Compt. rend. Soc. biol., 139:*1146 (1945).
124. Pillemer, L. and Robbins, K. C.: *Ann. Rev. Microbiol., 3:*265 (1949).
125. Pappenheimer, A. M. Jr., Mueller, J. H. and Cohen, S.: *Proc. Soc. Exper. Biol. & Med., 36:*495 (1937).
126. Mueller, J. H. and Miller, P. A.: *J. Immunol., 40:*21 (1941).
127. Drew, R. M. and Mueller, J. H.: *J. Bact., 62:*549 (1951).
128. Pappenheimer, A. M. Jr. and Johnson, S. J.: *Brit. J. Exper. Path., 17:*335 (1936).
129. Eaton, M. D.: *J. Bact., 31:*347 (1936).
130. Pappenheimer, A. M. Jr.: *J. Biol. Chem., 120:*543 (1937).
131. Lepow, I. H. and Pillemer, L.: *J. Immunol., 69:*1 (1952).
132. Pope, C. G. and Stevens, M. F.: *Lancet, 2:*1190 (1953).
133. Norlin, G.: *Brit. J. Exper. Path., 36:*599 (1955).
134. Pope, C. G. and Stevens, M. F.: *Brit. J. Exper. Path., 39:*139 (1958).
135. Pope, C. G. and Stevens, M. F.: *Brit. J. Exper. Path., 39:*150 (1958).
136. Pope, C. G. and Stevens, M. F.: *Brit. J. Exper. Path., 39:*490 (1958).
137. Poulik, M. D. and Poulik, E.: *Nature, 181:*354 (1958).
138. Pappenheimer, A. M. Jr.: *J. Bact., 43:*273 (1942).
139. Pope, C. G., Caspary, E. A. and Fenton, E. L.: *Brit. J. Exper. Path., 32:*246 (1951).
140. Ehrlich, P.: *Deutsch. med. Wchnschr., 24:*597 (1898).
141. Dreyer, G. and Madsen, T.: *Ztschr. Hyg. u. Infektionskr., 37:*250 (1901).
142. Olitzki, L., Stuczynski, L. A. and Crosswicz, N.: *J. Immunol., 60:*419 (1948).

143. PAPPENHEIMER, A. M. JR. and HENDEE, E.: *J. Biol. Chem., 171*:701 (1947).
144. PAPPENHEIMER, A. M. JR. and HENDEE, E.: *J. Biol. Chem., 180*:597 (1949).
145. PAPPENHEIMER, A. M. JR. and WILLIAMS, C. M.: *J. Gen. Physiol., 35*:727 (1952).
146. YONEDA, M. and PAPPENHEIMER, A. M., JR.: *J. Bact., 74*:256 (1957).
147. CLARKE, G. D.: *J. Gen. Microbiol., 18*:698 (1958).
148. CLARKE, G. D.: *J. Gen. Microbiol., 18*:708 (1958).
149. BOIVIN, A. and MESROBEANU, L.: *Compt. rend. Soc. biol., 124*:442 (1937).
150. BOIVIN, A. and MESROBEANU, L.: *Compt. rend. Soc. biol., 126*:222 (1937).
151. BOIVIN, A. and MESROBEANU, L.: *Compt. rend. Soc. biol., 126*:323 (1937).
152. MORGAN, W. T. J.: *Biochem. J., 31*:2003 (1937).
153. MORGAN, W. T. J. and PARTRIDGE, S. M.: *Biochem. J., 34*:169 (1940).
154. MORGAN, W. T. J. and PARTRIDGE, S. M.: *Biochem. J., 35*:1140 (1941).
155. BOROFF, D. A.: *J. Bact., 57*:617 (1949).
156. ANDERSON, C. G., BROWN, A. M. and MACSWEEN, J. C.: *Brit. J. Exper. Path., 26*:197 (1945).
157. DUBOS, R. J. and GEIGER, J. W.: *J. Exper. Med., 84*:143 (1946).
158. ENGLEY, F. B., JR.: *Bact. Proc., 49*:97 (1949).
159. ENGLEY, F. B., JR.: *Bact. Proc., 16*:153 (1952).
160. VAN HEYNINGEN, W. E. and GLADSTONE, G. P.: *Brit. J. Exper. Path., 34*:202 (1953).
161. BOROFF, D. A.: *J. Bact., 58*:387 (1949).
162. HOWARD, J. C.: *Brit. J. Exper. Path., 36*:446 (1955).
163. BRIDGWATER, F. A. J., MORGAN, R. S., ROWSON, K. E. K. and PAYLING WRIGHT, G.: *Brit. J. Exper. Path., 36*:447 (1955).
164. CAVANAGH, J. B., HOWARD, J. G. and WHITBY, J. L.: *Brit. J. Exper. Path., 37*:272 (1956).

XXXIV

NEUROCHEMICAL EFFECTS OF
SNAKE VENOMS

Beatriz M. Braganca and I. Aravindakshan

Snake venoms are powerful toxins to man and animals. Their poisonous nature has been recognized from early times, Atreya[1] one of the ancient physicians living in India before 5th century B.C.[2] pointed out that snake venoms were the most potent among animal toxins. The minimum lethal dose for rabbits has been found to range from 0.01 to 3.0 μg/kg. weight of the animal.[3]

These venoms are complex mixtures containing a variety of enzymes.[4,5] It is clear from recent studies that the composition of snake venoms even from the same species of snakes shows great variation.

The literature bearing on the general properties of snake venoms has been extensively reviewed by Kellaway,[6] Essex[7] and by Boquet.[3] Studies relating particularly to the neurochemical effects of snake venoms have been reviewed by the author[8] in the 1st edition of *Neurochemistry*. During the last few years numerous reports have appeared relating specially to the constitution of "neurotoxins" and to the biochemical changes produced by snake venoms on tissue metabolism.

Due to limitation of space the present review will attempt to describe essentially the more recent investigations with only a brief reference to the literature reported in the earlier review.[8]

PHARMACOLOGICAL EFFECTS OF SNAKE VENOMS

Among the various classes of snakes the *Colubridae* and the *Crotalidae* secrete venoms which have pronounced effects on the nervous system. The Indian cobra *(Naja naja)* is a typical member of the colubrid class of snakes. Numerous physiological studies have established that nearly all snake venoms possess to some extent the curare-like effects, the venoms of the *colubridae* and the *crotalidae* being more potent than those of the vipers. It is believed that victims of these snakes generally die through paralysis of the respiratory muscles. All attempts to reverse the paralysing action of venoms by compounds known to reverse the action of curare have been unsuccessful.[9-11] Houssay and associates[12] first demonstrated that some venoms have an inhibitory effect on the irritability of the muscle to direct stimulation. This effect paralleled the haemolytic action of these venoms on dog erythrocytes, indicating that the phospholipase present in these venoms was implicated in the phenomenon. The direct action of cobra venom on muscle tissue has been confirmed by Sarkar and Maitre.[13] Recent evidence obtained by Hadidian[14] shows that venoms of *Agkistrodon piscivorus* can render skeletal muscle unresponsive to direct stimulation or to stimulation through its nerve. The deterioration of the muscular tissue once started is irreversible. Fraser and Elliott[15] first demonstrated that introduction of venom from the colubrid class of snakes directly into the brain near the bulba centres caused a cessation of respiration. Direct effects of cobra venom on the central nervous system have been confirmed by several authors.[17-19] Recently Morrison and Zamecnik[16] have observed that venoms of cobra and rattle snake can produce demylination on incubation with portions of spinal chord or brain tissue.

Several reports have appeared on the physiological effects of active protein fractions separated from venoms of *Crotalus terrificus*. Barrio and Brazil[20] have found two varieties of *Crotalus terrificus*, one of which produces convulsions followed by a phase of hypotonia. These effects were partially reversed by $MgSO_4$, $CaCl_2$, chloral hydrate and nembutal. The other variety caused paralysis.

Mussatché and Vieira[21] observed that the contracture induced in rat muscle by *Crotalus t.terrificus* venoms resembles a Lundsgaard contracture such as is produced by substances known to interfere with the glycolytic cycle. Similar effects could be reproduced with the crotamine fraction. Goncalves[22] has separated three fractions from the venom of *Crotalus terrificus* capable of producing distinct physiological effects: (a) crotamine which brings about paralysis of posterior extremities; (b) crotoxin which is able to inhibit epileptic seizures induced in frogs by quick cooling of spinal chord; (c) a proteolytic enzyme fraction which can produce contraction of guinea pig ileum suspended in Tyrode solution.

CONSTITUTION OF NEUROTOXINS

The components responsible for the direct action of venoms on the central nervous system as well as its peripheral effects are generally referred to as the "neurotoxins."

In 1860 Weir Mitchell[23] separated, for the first time, a toxic protein fraction from the venom of rattle snake. The toxic fraction was non-coagulable by boiling but could be precipitated by various salts and by 95% alcohol. Overwhelming evidence accumulated during the last century has indicated that the toxic components of venoms are proteins. Refinements in techniques available for purification of proteins from complex mixtures have been successfully employed for the isolation of very potent toxic fractions from venoms. In 1938 Slotta and Fraenkel-Conrat[24] reported the isolation of a neurotoxin of rattle snake *Crotalus terrificus terrificus,* in crystalline form. This protein was named "Crotoxin" and possessed phospholipase activity. Subsequently Li and Fraenkel-Conrat[25] and Gralen and Svedberg[26] showed it to be homogenus by electrophoretic and ultracentrifugal studies. The molecular weight was 30,000. The toxicity of "Crotoxin" is of the order of 8 μg. per mouse and it is stable to 70°C. in acid solution.[27] It has been shown to contain 18 of the common amino acids having a high proportion of sulphur amino acids[28] and aromatic amino acids.[29] Analytical data indicates that this protein is very sensitive to a variety of inactivating agents.[27] Attempts to split the crotoxin into biologically active fractions have not been encouraging according to some authors. Fraenkel-Conrat subjected crotoxin to partition chromatography but obtained fractions which were biologically inactive.[30] Treatment with dinitrofluorobenzene also resulted in separation of two fractions which were non-toxic.[31-33] Crotoxin has been analysed for the end groups. The biological activity was retained after removal of 3 amino acid residues with carboxypeptidase.[33] Habermann and Neumann[34,35] obtained crotoxin from rattle snake venom. Three fractions have been separated from this preparation by ionic exchange chromatography. Of the toxicity 60% was found in a fraction named "Crotactin," apparently free from phospholipase. This fraction had a paralysing action and increased capillary permeability. The mother liquor obtained after precipitating the "Crotactin" contained a basic protein having convulsive properties. The phospholipase was present in a third fraction.

Goncalves and associates[36,37] have applied the method of electrophoresis quite extensively for the separation of biologically active components from *Crotalus terrificus terrificus.* These investigations have clearly demonstrated that there is wide variation in the composition of active proteins of venoms from snakes of the same species. An active component "Crotamine" has been separated from venom of *Crotalus terrificus terrificus* prevalent in southern regions of Brazil and Argentina. This component was absent in venom of the same species of snakes found in other regions of the country. "Crotamine" was dialysable and sedimentation data suggests a molecular weight in the region of 10,000 to 15,000.

Barrio[38] has separated three main fractions from *Crotalus terrificus* by electrophoresis: (a) crotamine which caused paralysis in mice and respiratory failure; (b) proteolytic enzymes; (c) a neurotoxin corresponding to crotoxin which is haemolytic and causes death in mice.

Studies on Formosan cobra by Sasaki[39,40] indicate that the distribution of phospholipase in these snake venoms does not parallel the toxicity. A neurotoxic component capable of causing respiratory paralysis (MLD in mice 0.08 to 0.1 μg./gm.) was separated. This had very little phospholipase activity. On the other hand a fraction rich in phospholipase was obtained having much less toxicity (MLD in mice 12-13 μg./gm.). The latter was found to contain a carbohydrate component. Bussard and Cote[41] working with cobra venom *(Naja naja)* claim the separation of phospholipase and a fraction free from this enzyme which contained all the toxicity of the original material. Radomski and Deichman[42] have obtained two fractions from cobra venom *(Naja naja)* by ethanol fractionation. The fraction relatively richer in phospholipase, adenosinetriphosphatase and diphosphopyridine nucleotidase was less toxic than the other fraction which contained these enzymes in lesser amounts. Since the enzymic activities did not parallel the toxicity it is concluded that these enzymes are not implicated in the primary toxic action of this venom. Doery[43] drew similar conclusions as a result of studies on Australian tiger snake *Notechis scutatus scutatus* venom.

In view of the complex nature of venoms, it is not surprising that more than one factor contributes to the overall toxicity. Since none of the fractions was completely free of the enzymic activity (phospholipase)[42,43] the evidence is not adequate to conclude that enzymes are not implicated in the neurotoxic action of these venoms. The results of studies showing that venom contains factors which can change the permeability of nerve tissue, are pertinent to this point. Hadidian[14] has demonstrated that the rate of penetration of procaine into the isolated nerve preparation is increased if the nerve is exposed to a solution of venom *(Agkistrodon piscivorus)*. Experiments described in a later section also show that the phospholipase A of cobra venom can penetrate the blood-brain barrier causing destruction of phospholipid structures. It is therefore conceivable that factors which could not reach the central nervous system otherwise may find their way into the brain in presence of small quantities of phospholipase and so cause neurotoxic changes.

Carel and Wright[44] have fractionated the venom of the sea snake *Enhydrina schistoses*. Of the initial toxicity 90% was dialysable,

whereas most of the lecithinase activity was non-dialysable. Furthermore, the dialysable toxic component was more heat labile than phospholipase. Apparently in this venom the main toxic component is not
phospholipase.

Suzuki *et al.*[45] have crystallised phospholipase from cobra venom
(Naja naja) by heat treatment and ammonium sulphate fractionation.
Crystalline material prepared by this method was five times as toxic
as the crude material on protein basis, and its phospholipase activity
was increased six-fold.[46]

ENZYMIC COMPONENTS OF SNAKE VENOMS

It has been known for a long time that venoms contain a number of
very active enzymes. Several studies reviewed in other sections indicate that the enzymic components of venoms may play an important
role in its toxic effect. The list of enzymes present in snake venoms includes several types of proteases, phospholipase, choline esterase, hyaluronidase, ribonuclease, desoxyribonuclease, phosphomonoesterase,
phosphodiesterase, adenosine triphosphatase, diphosphopyridine nucleotidase, 5'-nucleotidase and L-amino acid oxidase.[4,5] The phosphodiesterase[47] and cholinesterase[48] have been obtained in a high state of
purity. The L-amino acid oxidase[49] and phospholipase[45] have been
crystallised. The L-amino acid oxidase was non-toxic whereas crystalline phospholipase from cobra venom *(Naja naja)* was found to be
highly toxic. Literature on enzymes in snake venoms has been extensively reviewed by Zeller.[4,5] The following section will attempt to review the studies appearing since the last edition of this book.

PHOSPHOLIPASE

Suzuki *et al.*[45] have described a procedure for crystallisation of phospholipase from cobra venom *(Naja naja atra)* by heat treatment and
ammonium sulphate fractionation. Phospholipase crystalised as fine
needles. As mentioned earlier crystalline phospholipase obtained by
this procedure from cobra venom *(Naja naja)* was toxic to mice.[46]

Hanahan,[50] Long and Penny[51] and Davidson *et al.*[52] have studied
the fatty acids liberated by the action of venom phospholipase on
lecithin and concluded that only fatty acids in the α-position of lecithin
were removed from the lecithin molecule. Recent studies by Marinetti
et al.[53] suggest that cobra venom phospholipase may attack the fatty
acids both in the α and the β position of lecithin. In these studies the
glycerol residue was analysed after treatment of lecithin with venom
phospholipase and it was shown that a mixture of α and β lysolecithins
had been produced. More conclusive evidence has been obtained by de

Haas *et al.*[54] with the synthetic lecithins having fatty acids of known constitution in the different positions. The results of these studies have clearly shown that phospholipase from *Crotalus adamenteus* brings about hydrolysis of fatty acids attached to the β-position of lecithin. These experiments do not exclude the possibility of the presence of more than one enzyme in the venom capable of degrading the phospholipid. Very recently Rosenthal and Gayer[55] have succeeded in synthesising DL-2,3-distearoyloxypropyl (dimethyl)-β-hydroxyethyl-ammonium acetate, a compound somewhat related to lecithin which is a powerful inhibitor of phospholipase A. Kinetic studies have shown that the inhibition produced is of a competitive type. It was found to protect the erythrocytes from the haemolytic action of venom. The compound has low toxicity and was found to significantly protect mice against the toxic action of venom. The protective action could be demonstrated, however, only if injected together with the venom.

PHOSPHATASES

Purification of phosphodiesterase from rattlesnake venom by column chromatography has led to the complete separation of this enzyme from 5′-nucleotidase, ophio-adenosine triphosphatase, diphosphopyridine nucleotidase and ribonuclease.[3]

Johnson *et al.*[56] have clearly demonstrated the formation of pyrophosphate and adenylic acid as products of reaction of venom (rattle snake and *Naja naja*) adenosinetriphosphatase on adenosine triphosphate. Adenosine formed by the action of 5′-nucleotidase present in venom was also detected among the products of reaction. Since these products are known to produce profound effects on cardiac tissue the suggestion is made that they may be implicated in the hypotensive action of venoms.

THE EFFECT OF VENOMS ON ENZYME SYSTEMS IN TISSUES

Biochemical mechanisms underlying the neurotoxic action of a variety of snake venoms have been explored actively during the last few years. These investigations relate essentially to the effect produced by venoms on a number of enzymatic processes in animal tissues, with special reference to nervous tissue.

Fleckenstein and associates[57,58] have extensively studied the action of crude venom on various dehydrogenases. Specific antivenom serum has been demonstrated to reverse the destructive effects of crude cobra venom on enzymes in experiments *in vitro*. Since many of the inflamatory and pain-producing compounds of known constitution also inhibit dehydrogenases it is concluded that these biochemical effects are implicated in some of the pharmacological actions of venom. As a result of studies with crude venoms, Ya-Pin Lee[59] concludes that DPN-pyrophosphatase is responsible for the inactivating effect of venom on DPNH-cytochrome c reductase of animal tissues.

The evidence obtained in experiments *in vitro* using crude venoms cannot be conclusive in view of the multiplicity of enzymes present in the crude material which may influence the course of reaction. Braganca and Quastel[60,61] have employed in their studies heated cobra venom which is toxic and does not contain many of the enzymes present in the crude material. The heated product containing phospholipase A was inhibitory to enzymes concerned with the over-all oxidation of several substrates in brain and liver homogenates. The cytochrome oxidase was particularly susceptible to the destructive action of heated venom.

Since only enzymes associated with mitochondrial bodies, and which require intact mitochrondial structure for their optimum activities, were inactivated by venom, the authors concluded that the phospholipase of the venom was the responsible factor.

Nygaard[62] has demonstrated that phospholipase A (crotoxin) is a strong inhibitor of succinic-cytochrome c reductase and DPH-cytochrome c reductase. Nygaard and Sumner[63] have shown that the succinic oxidase in rat liver homogenates and in mitochondrial suspensions was completely inactivated when approximately 10% of the hydrolysable lecithin was degraded by phospholipase. Edwards and Ball[64] have confirmed these results using cytochrome oxidase from beef heart, and heated venom as the source of phospholipase. They suggested that the effects are brought about through destruction of mitochondrial phospholipids which serve as cement substances to bind together the interacting groups of enzymes. The stimulation of respiration generally observed to precede the inactivating action of heated venoms on the respiratory enzymes in isolated tissue preparations has been studied in greater detail by Petrushka *et al.*[65,66] Experiments with pyruvate labelled with C[14] have indicated that the increased respiratory activity is due to the oxidation of added substrate and does not result from liberation of endogenous substrates. Habermann[67] demonstrated that oxidative phosphorylation in liver homogenates is uncoupled by venoms of *Naja nigricollis*, *Vipera ammodytes* and *Naja haje*. The inhibitory factor was heat stable which indicated that it may be phospholipase. Studies with liver[65] and brain mitochondria[68] have clearly demonstrated that small quantities of heated venoms which stimulate respiratory activity bring about considerable inactivation of the accompanying phosphorylations. Aravindakshan and Braganca[68] have found complete correlation between the effect of venom on the P:O ratio observed in experiments *in vitro* and changes produced in the mitochondria of animals injected with cobra venom. Crystalline phospholipase produced similar destructive effects on the phosphorylations in mitochondria.[69] Phospholipase A has been found to penetrate the blood-brain barrier and bring about hydrolysis of brain phospholipids.[69] Since phospholipids are known to play an important role in phosphorylations, this mechanism could explain the inhibition of P:O ratio observed in animals injected with venom. The experiments of Hudson, Quastel and Scholefield[70] have also demonstrated that there is less incorporation of P^{32} in the 'ATP-ADP' fraction of spinal chord of rats injected intrathecally with cobra venom. It is well established that the phosphorylations accompanying oxidation of substrates by mitochondrial enzymes occur in steps in different regions of the respiratory chain.[71] Phospholipase A from cobra venom has been shown to inactivate preferentially the phosphorylations coupled to cytochrome oxidase in brain and liver mitochondria. These effects have been observed both in experiments *in vitro* and in the animals injected with the material. The phosphorylations occurring in the region of DPNH-cytochrome c are apparently quite resistant to the destructive action of venom.[72]

Heated venoms containing phospholipase produce profound changes in the mitochondrial membrane. Petrushka, Quastel and Scholefield[65] have demonstrated that additions of small quantities of heated *Agkistrodon piscivours* venom increases the swelling of liver mitochondria. Similar changes have been observed in animals injected with crude cobra venom *(Naja naja)* or crystalline phospholipase.[69] The effects could be demonstrated 30 minutes after injection of doses lethal in 18 hours. Changes in swelling properties of the mitochrondria are found to precede the inhibitory effect on the phosphorylation process. Alterations in mitochondrial permeability resulting from the action of phospholipase have been shown to lead to leakage of various enzymes into the surrounding medium.[73] Several studies have demonstrated that phospholipase as well as lysolecithin can produce swelling of mitochondria and uncouple oxidative phosphorylation.[65-67,74,75] Studies designed to explore the mechanism by which venoms produce destructive effect on mitochondrial functions indicate direct action of phospholipase on mitochondrial phospholipids. Nygaard and Sumner[63] demonstrated that mitochondria preincubated with phospholipase (crotoxin) was not more effective than phospholipase alone in inactivating succinic oxidase. Petrushka *et al.*[66] demonstrated that phospholipase C from *Cl. welchii*, which does not give rise to lysophospholipids, was just as effective as phospholipase A (heated venom) in inhibiting respiration. Quantitative studies with crystalline phospholipase A (from cobra venom) and pure lysolecithin have also shown that much larger quantities of lysolecithin are required to inhibit mitochondrial functions than could be expected to be produced from amounts of venom which are effective.[69] *In vitro* experiments have further demonstrated that lecithin can reverse the action of heated venom on the swelling properties as well as the inhibition of P:O ratio in mitochondria. The reversal presumably arises through the competitive action of lecithin with the tissue phospholipids for venom phospholipase.[65,69] Electron microscopic studies by Nygaard *et al.*[76] have shown that the structural changes produced in the mitochondria by phospholipase A are qualitatively different from those produced by lysolecithin.

It is apparent from the biochemical findings that phospholipase of cobra venom can penetrate the blood-brain barrier and bring about destruction of phospholipids essential for important metabolic activities in these particles. The resulting inactivation of ATP synthesis may reasonably be expected to block several essential functions of the organism. It is seen that changes in mitochondrial permeability can be detected very early after injection of cobra toxin. Such an effect besides disturbing the various functions described, could also affect fundamental processes such as the ion transport across cellular membrane. It could also enable other components of venom to penetrate into the central nervous system, as well as into other tissues. Thus components in cobra venom, otherwise innocuous, could become toxic in presence of phospholipase. With regard to the role of phospholipase in the neurotoxic action of snake venoms it is of interest that recent studies[77] have indicated that the axon membrane is composed of a bimolecular layer of lipids on which protein molecules are adsorbed. Furthermore, experiments of Skou[78] indicate that physical changes in lipid-containing interface of the axon membrane have a direct bearing on the blockage of nerve impulses during anaesthesia. Cobra venom for instance is known to have anaesthetic properties. These studies point to the nature of mechanisms which can correlate changes produced by phospholipase on tissue metabolism with some of the neurotoxic effects of certain snake venoms such as the cobra venom.

REFERENCES

1. CHARAKASAMHITA: *Shree Gulab Kumuerba Ayurvedic Society, Jamnagar,* 2140 (1949).
2. AUROBINDO, SRI.: *The Message of the Gita,* Anil Bharan, Ed. London, George Allen and Unwin Ltd. (1946).
3. BOQUET, P.: *Venins de serpents et Antivenins.* Medicales Flamarion (1947).
4. ZELLER, E. A.: *Advances Enzymol., 8:*458 (1948).

5. ZELLER, E. A.: *The Enzymes,* Vol. 1, p. 2:987. Acad. Press (1951).
6. KELLAWAY, C. H.: *Ann. Rev. Biochem., 8:*557 (1939).
7. ESSEX, H. E.: *Physiol. Rev., 25:*148 (1945).
8. BRAGANCA, B. M.: *Neurochemistry,* p. 612. Elliott, K. A. C., Page, I. H., and Quastel, J. H., Eds. Springfield, Ill., Thomas (1955).
9. KELLAWAY, C. H.: *Australian J. Exper. Biol. & Med. Sc., 10:*195 (1932).
10. CUSHNY, A. R., and YAGI, S.: *Phil. Tr. Roy. Soc.* (B), *208:*1 (1918).
11. GAUTRELET, J., HALPREN, N., and CORTEGGIANI, E.: *Arch. internat. physiol., 38:*293 (1934).
12. HOUSSAY, B. A., MAZZOCCO, P., and NEGRETTE, J.: *Compt. rend. Soc. biol., 11:*823 (1922).
13. SARKER, N. K., and MAITRE, S. R.: *Am. J. Physiol., 163:*209 (1950).
14. HADIDIAN, Z.: *A.A.A.S.,* Publ. No.44:205 (1954).
15. FRASER, R. H., and ELLIOTT, T. R.: *Proc. Roy. Soc., 74:*104 (1905).
16. MORRISON, J. R., and ZAMECNIK, P. C.: *Arch. Neurol. & Psychiat., 63:*367 (1950).
17. CHOPRA, R. N., and ISWARIAH, V.: *Indian J. M. Res., 18:*1113 (1931).
18. HOUSSAY, B. A., and HUG, E.: *Compt. rend. Soc. biol., 99:*1509 (1928).
19. MACHT, D. I.: *Ann. Int. Med., 11:*1824 (1938).
20. BARRIO, JR. A., and BRAZIL, O. V.: *Rev. Inst. Malbrán, 16:*22 (1954).
21. MOUSSATCHÉ, H., GONCALVES, J. M., VIEIRA, G. D., and HASSON, A.: *A.A.A.S.,* Publ. No.44:275 (1954).
22. GONCALVES, J. M.: *A.A.A.S.,* Publ. No.44:261 (1954).
23. WEIR MITCHELL, S.: *Smithsonian Contrib. to Knowledge, 12:*1866 (1860).
24. SLOTTA, K. H., and FRAENKEL-CONRAT, H. C.: *Nature, 142:*213 (1938).
25. LI, C. H., and FRAENKEL-CONRAT, H. C.: *J. Am. Chem. Soc., 64:*1586 (1842).
26. GRALEN, N., and SVEDBERG, T.: *Biochem. J., 32:*1375 (1938).
27. FRAENKEL-CONRAT, H.: *Biochim. et biophys. acta, 5:*98 (1950).
28. SLOTTA, K. H., and FORSTER, W.: *Ber., 71:*1082 (1938).
29. SLOTTA, K. H.: *A.A.A.S.,* Publ. No.44:253 (1954).
30. FRAENKEL-CONRAT, H.: *A.A.A.S.,* Publ. No.44:271 (1954).
31. NEUMANN, W. P.: *Naturwissenschften, 42:*370 (1955).
32. NEUMANN, W. P.: *Biochem. Ztschr., 327:*170 (1955).
33. FRAENKEL-CONRAT, H., and SINGER, B.: *Arch. Biochem. & Biophys., 60:*64 (1950).
34. HABERMANN, E., and NEUMANN, W. P.: *Arch. exper. Path. u. Pharmakol., 228:*217 (1956).
35. NEWMANN, W. P., and HABERMANN, E.: *Biochem. Ztschr., 327:*170 (1955).
36. GONCALVES, J. M., and VIEIRA, L. G.: *Anais acad. brazil. cienc., 22:*141 (1950).
37. GONCALVES, J. M.: *A.A.A.S.,* Publ. No.44:261 (1954).
38. BARRIO, JR., A.: *Rev. inst. Malbràn* (Beunos Aires), *16:*215 (1954).
39. SASAKI, T.: *Yakugaku Zasshi, 77:*845 (1957).
40. SASAKI, T.: *Yakugaku Zasshi, 78:*516 (1958).
41. BUSSARD, A., and COTE, R.: *Compt. rend., 239:*915 (1954).
42. RADOMSKI, J. L., and DEICHMANN, W. B.: *Biochem. J., 70:*293 (1958).
43. DOERY, H. M.: *Biochem. J., 70:*535 (1958).
44. CAREY, J. E., and WRIGHT, E. A.: *Nature, 185:*103 (1960).
45. SUZUKI, T., IWANAGA, S., and KAWACHI, S.: *Yakugaku Zasshi, 78:*568 (1958).
46. ARAVINDAKSHAN, I., and BRAGANCA, B. M.: Unpublished data.
47. DE CARILHE, M. P., and LASKOWSKI, M.: *Biochim. et biophys. acta, 18:*370 (1955).
48. CHOUDHURY, D. K.: *Science and Culture, 8:*238 (1942).
49. SINGER, T. P., and KEARNEY, E. B.: *Arch. Biochem., 29:*190 (1950).
50. HANAHAN, D. J.: *J. Biol. Chem., 207:*879 (1954).

51. LONG, C., and PENNY, I. F.: *Biochem. J.*, *58*:XV (1954).

52. DAVIDSON, F. M., LONG, C., and PENNY, I. F.: *Proc. 2nd Intern. Conf. Biochemical Problems of Lipids.* Popjack, G., and Liberton, E. Eds. New York (1950).

53. MARINETTI, G. V., ERBLAND, J., and STOTZ, E.: *Biochim. et biophys. acta, 33*:403 (1959).

54. DE HASS, G. H., MULDER, I., and VAN DEENEN, L. L. M.: *Biochem. & Biophys. Res. Comm., 3*:287 (1960).

55. ROSENTHAL, A. F., and GEYER, R. P.: *J. Biol. Chem., 235*:2202 (1960).

56. JOHNSON, M., KAYE, M. A. G., HEMS, R., and KREBS, H. A.: *Biochem. J., 54*:625 (1953).

57. FLECKENSTAIN, A., TIPPELT, H., and KRONER, H.: *Arch. Exper. Path. u. Pharmakol., 210*:380 (1950).

58. FLECKESTAIN, A., BERG, G. GAYER, J., and SCHONIG, S.: *Arch. Exper. Path. u. Pharmakol., 213*:265 (1951).

59. YA-PIN LEE: *J. Formasan M. A., 53*:353 (1954).

60. BRAGANCA, B. M.: Doctoral Thesis, McGill University (1951).

61. BRAGANCA, B. M., and QUASTEL, J. H.: *Biochem. J., 53*:88 (1953).

62. NYGAARD, A. P.: *J. Biol. Chem., 204*:655 (1953).

63. NYGAARD, A. P., and SUMNER, J. B.: *J. Biol. Chem., 200*:723 (1953).

64. EDWARDS, S. W., and BALL, E. G.: *J. Biol. Chem., 209*:619 (1954).

65. PETRUSHKA, E., QUASTEL, J. H., and SCHOLEFIELD, P. G.: *Proc. Canad. Cancer Conf., 2*:106 (1957).

66. PETRUSHKA, E., QUASTEL, J. H., and SCHOLEFIELD, P. G.: *Canad. J. Biochem. & Physiol., 37*:975 (1959).

67. HABERMANN, E.: *Naturwissenschaften, 41*:429 (1954).

68. ARAVINDAKSHAN, I., and BRAGANCA, B. M.: *Biochim. et biophys. acta, 31*:463 (1959).

69. ARAVINDAKSHAN, I., and BRAGANCA, B. M.: *Biochem. J., 79*:84 (1961).

70. HUDSON, A. J., QUASTEL, J. H., and SCHOLEFIELD, P. G.: *J. Neurochem., 5*:177 (1960).

71. CHANCE, B., and WILLIAMS, G. R.: *Advances Enzymol., 17*:65 (1956).

72. ARAVINDAKSHAN, I., and BRAGANCA, B. H.: *Biochem. J., 79*:80 (1961).

73. MCARDLE, B., THOMPSON, R. H. S., and WEBSTER, G. R.: *J. Neurochem., 5*:135 (1960).

74. WITTER, R. F., MORRISON, A., and SHEPARDSON, G. R.: *Biochim. et biophys. acta, 26*:120 (1957).

75. WITTER, R. F., and COTTONE, M. A.: *Biochim. et biophys. acta, 22*:372 (1956).

76. NYGAARD, A. P., DIANZANI, M. U., and BAHR, G. F.: *Exper. Cell Res., 6*:453 (1954).

77. DAVSON, H., and DANIELLI, J. F.: *The Permeability of Natural Membranes,* Cambridge, Univ. Press (1943).

78. SKOU, J. C.: *Biochim. et biophys. acta, 30*:625 (1958).

XXXV

THE TOXIC EFFECT OF OXYGEN ON NERVOUS TISSUE

Frank Dickens

INTRODUCTION

The problem of the mechanism of poisoning by oxygen at pressures above one atmosphere is still an unsolved one, but partly for that very reason much interest attaches to the considerable amount of knowledge that has been acquired during the past 20 years concerning the toxic effects of oxygen on enzymes and tissue metabolism, particularly since almost nothing was known of the toxic action on brain and nervous tissue before 1940. Since that date, mainly because of Naval requirements, there have been several detailed studies, and the technical difficulties of the investigation of metabolic reactions at pressures above one atmosphere have been overcome.

The history of oxygen poisoning, even more than the somewhat related subject of high-altitude physiology, was securely founded on an experimental basis by that great pioneer of respiration physiology, Paul Bert. In *La Pression Barometrique*,[1,2] published in 1878, Bert proved conclusively that the principal features of mountain sickness arose from the diminished partial pressure of oxygen, and not as had been thought by many physiologists from the fall of barometric pressure per se. But in this monumental work he also showed that *increase* of oxygen pressure above one atmosphere* was highly toxic, and described these effects in the following terms:

1. Oxygen acts like a poison which is rapidly fatal
2. The poisoning is characterized by convulsions
3. The convulsions are accompanied by a considerable fall of body temperature.

---

*Oxygen pressure is throughout expressed in atmospheres, 100% oxygen at normal pressure being one atmosphere. The term High Oxygen Pressure (HOP) denotes pressures of oxygen above one atmosphere.

Bert believed these convulsions to be central in origin ("an exaggera-
tion of the excito-motor power of the spinal cord"), and according to
the intensity of the symptoms they appeared to him to resemble "the
different types of tetanus, strychnine, phenol, epilepsy, etc." (Hitchcock and Hitchcock's translation, 1943[2]). But he also recognized clearly
that oxygen also affects other organs and tissues, very high oxygenation paradoxically being capable of diminishing tissue oxidations with
consequent fall of body temperature: "Consumption of oxygen, production of carbonic acid and urea, breaking down of glucose in the
blood, all chemical phenomena which can be measured easily, appear
to be considerably slowed down by the action of oxygen under high
tension. . . . . Nor is it astonishing to see that death is the consequence
of such a depression in the intensity of the physico-chemical acts of
nutrition." Bert further believed qualitative changes in metabolism
to occur during exposure to high pressure oxygen (HOP), which led
to the formation of a toxic substance the elimination of which was
necessary for recovery of the organism observed to occur on its return
to normal conditions. However, the formation of such toxic substances
has not yet been established by other investigators.

Bert's observations on oxygen convulsions have been repeatedly confirmed. Figure 1 collects some of the data on the toxic effects of oxygen
in various species. For a more detailed account of this and other general aspects of oxygen poisoning the excellent reviews by Stadie, Riggs
and Haugaard[3] and Bean[4] should be consulted. Comprehensive bib-
liographies up to 1955 have been prepared for the U. S. Navy Department.[5,5a,5b] As will be evident from Figure 1, the time of onset of toxic
symptoms is a function of both the pressure of oxygen and the time
of exposure. Different authors have taken different threshold symptoms, some having used only minor twitchings while others have waited
for the development of violent clonic convulsions. Nevertheless there
is a rough general relationship, empirically represented by the writer
by the equation:

$$\log t = 3 - 2.6 \log p$$

in the broken curve shown in Figure 1, where t is the time in minutes
for the appearance of toxic symptoms and p is the pressure of oxygen
expressed in atmospheres. The *lethal* exposures for mice are about 6
times greater, and approximate to the equation of the continuous
curve shown in Figure 1 (Gerschman *et al.*[17])

$$\log t = 3.78 - 2.73 \log p$$

for values of p of 1 atmosphere or above. The reasons underlying the
very wide divergence of sensitivity to HOP shown by various animal

species (see for example Marks[18]) are not adequately understood and would repay detailed study.

Whereas at pressures around one atmosphere the lungs are primarily affected, at higher pressures the typical convulsive effects quickly de-

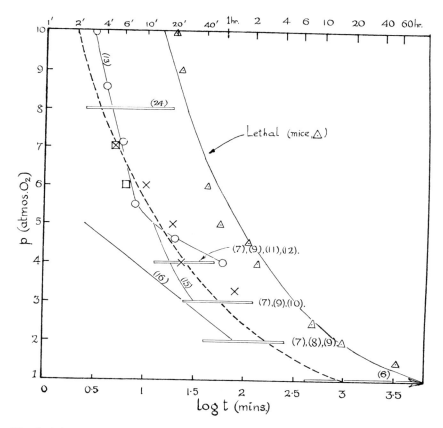

Fig. 1. *Time of exposure of mammals to oxygen necessary for onset of toxic symptoms, in relation to the pressure of oxygen.* Numbers in brackets are references: X mice (ref. 14), O man (ref. 13), □ man (ref. 12). The broken line is an attempt to fit a curve to these observations, and is plotted for the equation given in the text. The continuous heavy line and the points marked △ (ref. 17) represent the *lethal* times for mice, included for comparison.

velop. Cold-blooded animals are more resistant to oxygen,[3,4] and the fact that species which are devoid of haemoglobin (Drosophila) are also susceptible to oxygen poisoning indicates that the mammalian type of transport of blood gases is not a necessary condition for poisoning by oxygen (see ref. 4). On the other hand, even in Drosophila, carbon dioxide sensitizes the animals to oxygen (see ref. 4; also the recent mammalian studies of Taylor[19,20]; also refs. 21, 22).

It is now proposed to proceed directly to the description of the known toxic effects of oxygen on isolated tissues and on enzyme systems; when this has been done, an attempt will be made to see how far these observations can at present be correlated with the effects of oxygen poisoning in the whole animal.

THE TOXIC EFFECTS OF OXYGEN ON BRAIN TISSUE

1. Oxygen at about One Atmosphere Pressure

The first indication of a possible toxic effect of oxygen on the respiration of brain tissue *in vitro* appears to be contained in publications of Noyons and Van Goor[25] and Van Goor and Jongbloed.[26] (These publications made in 1940–1942 in Holland were not available in England until after the war.) It was found that after about 90 minutes in absence of glucose and after 260 minutes in presence of glucose, the respiration of chopped brain of the cat fell off in pure oxygen at one atmosphere pressure rather abruptly compared with control portions in air.[25] However, this was believed to be due to exhaustion of the substrate (ref. 25, p. 597), for on addition of extra glucose the respiratory rates (measured by the CO_2 production using the diaferometer of Noyons) were increased to about the same level in air and in oxygen (ref. 25, p. 574). In the second paper,[26] it was shown that HOP (3 atmos. O_2) definitely poisons the cellular respiration, the effect here being not caused by substrate exhaustion, and not being restored either by returning the tissue to air or adding extra glucose.

Van Goor and his colleagues used very large amounts of chopped brain (1 gm. fresh cerebral tissue plus 2 ml. saline containing 0.01 M glucose), and calculation shows that substrate exhaustion may well have been responsible for the fall of respiration observed by them at one atmosphere, as they themselves suggest. On the other hand they appear to have been the first investigators to show the toxic effect of HOP (3 atmos.) on brain tissue respiration, and their findings on this point are quite clear and definite.

In the meantime, in England and U. S. A. Mann and Quastel[27] and Elliott and Libet[28] had independently observed a toxic effect of one atmosphere of oxygen on brain respiration. (For security reasons, the former authors did not publish their observations, made early in 1941 (see footnote to p. 139 of ref. 27), until after the war.) Mann and Quastel found that the respiration of chopped or crushed rat brain falls off to a greater extent in the presence of oxygen than in the presence of air, particularly when the substrate is glucose (0.01 M), sodium lactate or pyruvate (0.027 M). There was less sensitivity to oxygen when sodium succinate (0.05 M) was the substrate. Elliott and Libet[28] found like Mann and Quastel that the initial rates of respiration of homogenates of whole rat brain in presence of glucose were the same in air and in oxygen at one atmosphere, but that the rate in oxygen started to fall below the rate in air during the second hour, and during the third and fourth hours of the experiment is was only 55 and 35% respectively of that in air. (The similar figures for Mann and Quastel's two experiments are for the second hour 95 and 82%; for the third hour 68 and 39% of the control in air.) It does not seen possible that any of these results could have been due to substrate exhaustion (glucose 5 to 6 mg. in 3 ml. total volume containing 200 or 300 mg. brain, total oxygen uptake in 4 hours not more than about 1 ml. Total oxygen equivalent for complete oxidation of glucose added = about 4.6 ml. at N. T. P.) Moreover, the total oxygen consumption was higher in air than in oxygen. Consequently these authors should be credited with the first proof of the toxic nature of oxygen at one atmosphere pressure on brain tissue respiration. These results of Mann and Quastel and of Elliott and Libet were confirmed by Dickens[29] who used slices of brain cortex suspended in phosphate Ringer solution containing glucose. Elliott and Libet[28] had reported a single result with slices in isotonic sodium chloride and in this experiment the fall of respiration in oxygen was more marked than that observed by Dickens. There is some reason to think that the fall of respiration which occurs in oxygen is lessened by the presence of the other ions, particularly calcium and even more so magnesium, and this may account for the quantitative differences in the effects observed (see Dickens[29]). In any case the full extent of oxygen toxicity at one atmosphere develops only very slowly, usually not until the fourth or fifth hour of the exposure of the tissue to the gas in the case of tissue slices; homogenates and chopped brain are more rapidly affected.

2. Oxygen at Pressures above One Atmosphere

As has already been mentioned, Van Goor and Jongbloed[26] were the first to show that oxygen at pressures above one atmosphere was highly toxic to brain respiration, although as they measured only the CO_2 production there remains some possibility of error in attributing the estimations solely to tissue respiration. Figure 3 of their paper (p. 413 of ref. 26) shows, however, that they observed initially a surprisingly high rate of CO_2 output (Q_{CO_2} about 24) for rat brain in oxygen at 3 atmos.; this rate fell rapidly after about 1.5 hours until after 3.5 hours it was only about $Q_{CO2} = 3$. In air, the rate of CO_2 production was lower and was fairly steady at about $Q_{CO2} = 7.5$. They showed that this inhibition due to HOP was irreversible on restoring the tissue to air at one atmosphere. Unlike the earlier findings at one atmosphere,[25] the fall in this case was proved not to be due to substrate-exhaustion (p. 415 of ref. 26).

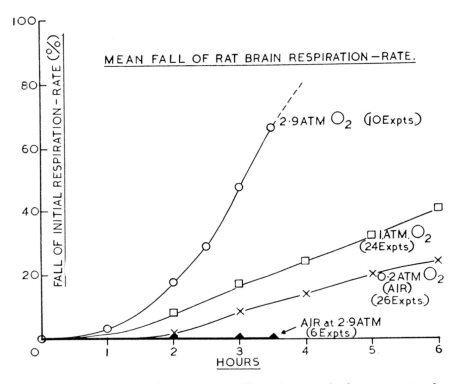

Fig. 2. *Mean fall of respiration rate of slices of rat cerebral cortex exposed to various pressures of oxygen.* (Data of Dickens.[29]) Suspension medium: Ringer-phosphate solution containing 0.2% glucose. 37°C.

In ignorance of these interesting experiments, Dickens[29] in London and Stadie, Riggs and Haugaard[24] in Philadelphia independently studied the effect of HOP on the respiration of slices and homogenates of rat brain cortex.*

Both investigations showed that an inhibitory effect of oxygen was

---

*Dickens' experimental findings were reported to the Medical Research Council in March, 1944, but publication was not permitted until later.

regularly obtained. Figure 2 shows observations on cortex slices by Dickens, mostly made by observation within a large pressure chamber maintained at 2.9 atmos. pressure in which ordinary Warburg mano-meters were filled either with air or pure oxygen, the observers being subjected to the same pressure but of course breathing air. At this pressure of air the tissue respiration remained almost perfectly linear for more than 3 hours, while in pure oxygen it began to fall after about one hour's exposure, the fall becoming very rapid after about 2 hours (Fig. 2). The Figure also includes Dickens's observations at one atmosphere in air and in oxygen, where the toxic effect of oxygen on the slices is much less marked but nevertheless is clearly shown when the mean of many experiments is plotted in this way (Fig. 2).

Stadie, Riggs and Haugaard[24] used a highly ingenious enclosed small high pressure chamber containing the manometers, which could be read and operated by external observers by means of controls ma-nipulated from outside the chamber (Stadie and Riggs[30]). This is a greatly improved version of a similar earlier instrument devised by Libbrecht and Massart.[31] It enabled the Philadelphia workers to study the effect of HOP up to 8 atmos., which would not have been prac-ticable in the arrangement used by Dickens, owing to the toxic effect of prolonged exposure to such high pressures on the observer. Stadie *et al.* found that the respiration rate of rat cortex slices at one atmos-phere O_2 was within 5% rectilinear for 3 hours but at 8 atmos. O_2 the respiration rate fell quite rapidly after 60 minutes (p. 200 of ref. 24).

Neither Dickens nor Stadie *et al.* found significantly higher initial respiratory rates of cerebral cortex in HOP as compared with oxygen at one atmosphere. There was no alteration in the respiratory rate of slices of brain tissue taken from rats which had been previously ex-posed to convulsive doses of HOP, but Stadie *et al.* found that the respiratory rate of homogenates prepared from such brains was less well sustained as a result of the preliminary exposure of the rats to HOP. Stadie *et al.*[24] also showed that the respiratory quotient of brain tissue was unaffected by previous exposure of the whole animals to HOP, though possibly it was slightly lowered by exposure to 8 atmos. O_2 *in vitro.* Both Dickens and Stadie *et al.* found that the inhibitory effect of HOP on brain respiration was completely irreversible on restoration of the poisoned tissue to normal pressures of oxygen or air.

Table I summarises these observations and shows that there is fairly satisfactory agreement on the time-course of oxygen poisoning of brain slices. The actual time-course of the poisoning fits a probability curve.[29] All the observations so far considered refer to brain tissue suspended in a medium containing glucose. As is well known, the respiration of brain falls rather rapidly in a substrate-free medium whatever the oxygen pressure, but Stadie *et al.*[24] showed that addition of glucose to brain tissue which had been previously incubated for 60 minutes at 8 atmos. O_2 in absence of glucose, did not produce any considerable increase of respiration, i.e. the toxic effect is also exerted in absence of glucose. This agrees with observations of Mann and Quastel[27] and Elliott and Libet[28] made at one atmosphere of oxygen.

TOXIC EFFECT OF OXYGEN ON BRAIN TISSUE RESPIRATION IN PRESENCE OF SUBSTRATE OTHER THAN GLUCOSE

Stadie *et al.*[24] showed that brain slices during exposure to 8.2 atmos. O_2 continue to utilize glucose, as determined by its disappearance from the suspension medium, though at a diminished rate. There was possibly some increase of aerobic lactic acid formation compared with control slices at one atmosphere. Similar experiments on the disappearance of substrates other than glucose have not been made, but indirect evidence on substrate utilization has been obtained from the oxygen uptake of brain exposed to HOP in presence of various substrates.

Mann and Quastel[27] found that at one atmosphere O_2, oxidation of lactate and pyruvate fell off similarly to that of glucose, but succinate oxidation was little affected. Dickens[29] and Stadie *et al.*[24] found that at higher pressures of oxygen the same degree of poisoning occurred for glucose, fructose, lactate and pyruvate. Stadie *et al.* state that succinate oxidation was also poisoned at 8 atmos., but Dickens found that at 3.4 to 4.6 atmos. O_2 considerable succinate oxidation persisted in brain slices, and to some extent the oxidation of L-glutamate also. The presence of glucose together with succinate during exposure to HOP protected the subsequent ability of the tissue to oxidize succinate. These experiments, like those of Mann and Quastel, show that succinate oxidation appears to be more stable to oxygen than that of hexoses or pyruvate. It may be mentioned here that the glycolytic system of brain, as measured by the ability to form lactic acid anaerobically from glucose, is also destroyed by HOP (Dickens[29]).

COMPARISON OF SENSITIVITY TO HOP OF BRAIN WITH THAT OF OTHER TISSUES

The effect of raised oxygen tension on the total gaseous metabolic exchange of animals has been reviewed by Stadie, Riggs and Haugaard,[3] who conclude that while the inhalation of one atmosphere O_2 for 24 hours produces no significant change, there is evidence of a decreased oxygen uptake (Bean [32]) and decreased CO_2 output (Hill and Macleod[33]) at oxygen pressured (or partial pressures) above one atmosphere. This confirms earlier statements of Bert[1] already mentioned. Stadie and Haugaard,[34] however, later reported no decrease of oxygen consumption at 8 atmos. O_2 even in obviously poisoned mice.

Bert found similar effects in isolated strips of beef muscle.[1] Bean and Bohr[4,35] using smooth muscle, observed loss of tone on exposure to HOP which pharmacologically resembled that produced by anoxia or cyanide poisoning: they postulated the inactivation by oxygen of respiratory enzyme systems, or "hyperoxic anoxia." Whereas Bert concluded that nerve tissue was the more sensitive to HOP, Bean and Bohr considered that the nerve fibre and myoneural junction were "apparently no more profoundly affected by high O_2 than the muscle itself" (p. 105 of ref. 4). Bean and Bohr's observations have been confirmed by Riggs,[36] inasmuch as the rate of onset of HOP convulsions in the intact animal. But Riggs found no corresponding fall in the oxygen uptake of the isolated muscle subjected to HOP, and although cyanide and azide could both inhibit the muscle respiration by 70%, only the former prevented the loss of tonus on exposure to HOP.

The importance of these observations lies in the close correlation in time of these effects with the onset of convulsions. Bean and Bohr believed that the oxygen was necessarily acting through a cyanide-sensitive system (cytochrome oxidase) to inactivate the dehydrogenase systems. It is evident that this explanation is difficult to reconcile with Riggs observations, and the mechanism is therefore still obscure.

Issekutz[37] did not observe any inhibitory effect of 5 atmos. O_2 on the oxygen uptake of thick slices of muscle, liver or kidney: but the internal oxygen tension was probably insufficient under the conditions adopted. Stadie, Riggs and Haugaard[38] found that rat diaphragm muscle was the most resistant to oxygen of the tissues examined by them (liver, kidney, lung, the order of sensitivity agreeing generally with that given by Dickens,[29] viz.:

Brain > spinal cord > liver > testis > kidney > lung > muscle.
The much greater sensitivity of brain tissue is shown by the fact that its respiration was 50% poisoned in 1 hour, as compared with 3.5 hours for liver, when exposed to 8 atmos. O_2.[38] Dickens observed a sensitivity of spinal cord similar to that of brain but his samples of rat liver appeared rather less resistant to HOP than those of Stadie et al., both nervous and liver tissues being much more susceptible to oxygen poisoning than the others in the above series.

CONDUCTION BLOCK IN NERVE PRODUCED BY
OXYGEN AT HIGH PRESSURE

Stein and Perot at the U.S. Naval Medical Research Institute, Bethesda, have recently described important effects of exposure to HOP on isolated peripheral nerve. Toxic effects on the frog sciatic nerve-muscle preparations by "15 superoxygenated atmospheres" acting for 2 hours were originally recorded by Bert[1] and this finding was confirmed by Hill & Macleod[33] and by Bean & Bohr.[23] That a conduction block was produced in frog sciatic nerve exposed to 12 atmos. oxygen for 4.5 hours was shown by Stein & Perot;[39] the block was partially reversible on rapid restoration to atmospheric pressure. Consistent with the greater susceptibility to HOP of the mammal, ulnar nerve trunks from the cat were more rapidly affected;[40] at 13 atmos. oxygen and 37° the mean time for block was 56 min., whereas in 12 atmos. helium plus 1 atmos. oxygen conduction continued unimpaired. Slow recovery (2 hours) of conduction occurred if decompression of the nerve was performed within a few minutes of the suppression of conduction by oxygen. From the data of these authors[40] one may calculate the relationship of time in minutes (t) for conduction block in cat nerve, to pO_2 in atmospheres:

$$\log t = 2.91 - 1.03 \log p$$

corresponding with much longer exposures to HOP in the isolated nerve than those necessary for occurrence of toxic signs in the intact animal, and somewhat longer than even the fatal periods of exposure for mice (see Fig. 1). According to Marks[18] cats are only slightly more resistant to oxygen toxicity than mice (at 4.05 atmos. O_2). However, it is quite conceivable that extension of these highly interesting results on peripheral nerve to cerebral tissue might exhibit a still closer correlation in the time of onset of toxicity with that observed in the whole animal.

Consistent with this possibility, Kaplan and Stein[41] have demonstrated the occurrence of a fairly rapid impairment (50% in 90 minutes at 6.6 atmos. O_2) of ion transport in guinea-pig brain cortex slices, resulting in loss of K and of glutamate from the slices, accompanied by the entry of Na from the medium. An increase of brain Na also occurred after similar exposure of intact guinea-pigs to HOP,[42] the period of 2 hours being sufficient to produce evidence of incipient oxygen toxicity in the animals. Adrenalectomized animals, which are known to have an increased brain Na content, also show increased brain excitability to electro-shock. However, adrenalectomized animals are reported to show increased resistance to oxygen toxicity.[43,44]

THE POSSIBLE RELATIONSHIP BETWEEN OXYGEN TOXICITY AND IRRADIATION EFFECTS

Gerschman, Fenn and colleagues at the University of Rochester School of Medicine have since 1954 developed the general hypothesis that some basic similarity exists between oxygen poisoning and the effects produced by exposure to x-rays. Various substances which protected animals against the lethal effects of x-rays were tested for their action on oxygen toxicity[45] on the basis that oxygen and x-rays can produce similar chromosome aberrations, increased oxygenation increases the effect of radiation, and both radiation and oxygen have been considered to produce oxidizing free radicals within the tissues. These facts suggest the possibility of a factor common to these two apparently widely differing types of treatment.

The experimental findings[45,17] give some support to this concept, significant protection against the lethal effects of 6 atmos. oxygen in mice being given by the sulphydryl compounds cysteamine, reduced glutathione and thiourea and also by diethyldithiocarbamic acid (sodium salt). All of these substances have been stated to give protection against x-radiation. However, at other pressures of oxygen conflicting results were obtained; for example the above-mentioned sulphydryl compounds were detrimental at pressures of oxygen from 1 to 1.5 atmos. Cobalt, which was found by Dickens[29] to protect brain tissue respiration *in vitro* and by Marks[18] to protect intact mice against HOP, has been stated also to protect mice against x-rays.[46] Here again, Gerschman *et al.,*[17] observed protection only at 1 atmosphere O_2 in mice, not at higher pressures. In spite of these difficulties and inconsistencies, this type of approach is likely to yield important results eventually, both for oxygen toxicity and radiation research.

EFFECTS OF VARIOUS HORMONES, VITAMINS AND AUTONOMIC DRUGS ON OXYGEN TOXICITY

For convenience, a number of little understood observations are briefly mentioned under this heading.

Adrenalectomy increases the survival time and protects against the C.N.S. effects in rats submitted to HOP.[47-49] Epinephrine partially reversed this protection and was detrimental in normal animals exposed to HOP, whilst cortical hormones could completely abolish the protective effects of adrenalectomy, indicating that probably both cortex and medulla are concerned in this effect, though perhaps principally the cortex.

Tocopherols protected rats against HOP, whilst vitamin E-deficient rats showed increased sensitivity.[50] The effects of pantothenic acid deficiency on oxygen poisoning resembled those of adrenalectomy, and this may be correlated with the adrenal atrophy seen in this avitaminosis.[51] Coenzyme A has also been said to have some protective effects.[45]

Sympatho-mimetic agents (oxytyramine, tryptamine) and parasympatho-mimetic agents (Doryl and Mecholyl chloride) showed a protective action against both HOP and X-radiation,[43] and both protective actions of the latter group were abolished by atropine. Atropine alone also diminished the survival time of the animals on exposure to HOP.[43]

THE POISONING BY OXYGEN OF ISOLATED ENZYME SYSTEMS AND THE MECHANISM OF THIS ACTION

The activities of a number of enzymes are poisoned by oxygen: it is not proposed to catalogue these are they are fully detailed in recent reviews.[3-5] The most noteworthy are—SH enzymes of the type of succinic dehydrogenase (Lehmann,[54] Libbrecht and Massart;[31] also Stadie and Haugaard,[61] Dickens[52]), a component of the pyruvic oxidase system (Barron,[55] Mann and Quastel,[27] Dickens[29,52]), and triosephosphate dehydrogenase (Dickens[52]). The dehydrogenases of malic, glutamic and ketoglutaric acids may also be inactivated,[53] and also preparations of choline oxidase and phosphoglucomutase.[52] Choline acetylase activity is also rapidly destroyed by oxygen when cell-free preparations are studied, but the choline acetylase activity of slices of rat brain was not affected even by HOP at 8 atmospheres.[56] It is not known whether the poisoning in extracts is related to the oxidation of the enzyme itself or of coenzyme A, its sulphydryl-containing co-factor. The flavoprotein enzyme, D-amino acid oxidase is also stated to be inhibited, but only in cell free preparations, where it is highly susceptible even to the air. In tissue slices it is quite stable to 7 atmos. O_2.[57]

Indeed it seems as if oxygen under the right conditions is a fairly general inhibitor of most—SH enzymes (see ref. 52), oxygen therefore belonging to the class of thiol-removing substances described by Bacq.[58] Such substances have marked pharmacological activity.[58] In this sense, excess oxygen may be regarded as a "protoplasmic poison." This does not exhaust the possibilities, however, since some metallo-enzymes, and possibly flavoproteins,[27] may also be inactivated by oxygen.[3,52]

Very recently it has in fact been shown that the flavoprotein enzyme, DPNH-cytochrome c reductase, is also very highly susceptible to poisoning even by oxygen at 1 atmosphere or on exposure to the air.[59] The half-life of the cell-free enzyme preparation is only 6 minutes at 38° and 1 atmosphere O_2, although anaerobically the enzyme is quite stable. The nature of the oxidizable group is unknown, though in the rather similar inactivation by atmospheric oxygen of the flavocyto-chrome enzyme yeast lactic dehydrogenase (or cytochrome b_2), mere exposure to the air appears to cause a rapid dissociation of some of the riboflavin phosphate accompanied by aggregation of the protein.[60]

Dixon et al.,[59] suggest that inactivation of cytochrome reductase by oxygen may be important in connection with oxygen poisoning. This interesting suggestion needs to be tested by the study of the enzyme in the living cell, since, as already mentioned, various enzymes which are readily inactivated by oxygen in extracts are apparently quite stable to HOP in situ.

We have seen that succinic dehydrogenase is not readily inactivated in brain tissue under oxygen poisoning. This enzyme is protected by malonate[52,61] or high concentrations of succinate[61] and the liver enzyme after oxygen inactivation is capable of being reactivated by reduced glutathione or cysteine.[61] The protection against oxygen poisoning of other—SH enzymes by their coenzymes, activators, or substrates is stressed by Dickens.[52] Presumably all these substances render the —SH groups of the enzyme-protein molecule less accessible to oxygen (see ref. 52), either by combination with the —SH group itself (metal activa-tors) or by a steric shielding action (substrates, coenzymes, competi-tive inhibitors).

Apart possibly from DPNH-cytochrome c reductase, the inactivation of the other principal enzyme systems by oxygen appears to be either by oxidation of the —SH enzyme proteins themselves or else of es-sential —SH coenzymes, such as coenzyme A and lipoic acid, which are concerned for example in the oxidative metabolism of α-ketoacids and in activation of acetyl radicals. Now that the complex mechanism of the pyruvate oxidase system is better understood, it would be most informative to see which component accounts for the inactivation by oxygen of this important system, which has been observed both in homogenates and in the tissue slice.[29,53]

THE POSSIBLE ROLE OF HYDROGEN PEROXIDE IN OXYGEN POISONING

Hydrogen peroxide and peroxide radicals have pharmacological properties which are attributed by Bacq[58] to their ability to oxidize —SH groups. H_2O_2 is also toxic to the oxidation of lactate and pyru-vate,[27] succinate[27,29] or glucose[29] by brain tissue. Brain has a low catalase content and its susceptibility to H_2O_2 is consistent with this fact, but the susceptibility to oxygen poisoning of tissues other than brain is not related to their content of catalase.[29] Moreover Dickens[29] could not detect any peroxide formation when a very sensitive test was applied to brain tissue which had been exposed to HOP either in presence or absence of cyanide or azide to inhibit the destruction of H_2O_2 by catalase. It is of course quite probable that oxygen inactivation of some preparation of isolated enzymes (e.g., xanthine oxidase, cf. ref. 27) may be due to accumulation of H_2O_2, but such a mechanism has still to be shown to operate in animal tissues under the usual conditions of oxygen poisoning.

CAN THE EFFECTS OF HOP ON ISOLATED TISSUES BE CORRELATED WITH OXYGEN POISONING IN THE INTACT ANIMAL?

The time of onset of signs and symptoms of oxygen poisoning (t minutes) in man and animals is related to the pressure of oxygen (p atmos). by the approximate equation already suggested:

$$\log t = 3 - 2.6 \log p \text{ or } t = \frac{1000}{p^{2.6}}$$

From the data of Table I the time (T minutes) for 50% poisoning of respiration of brain slices in vitro is approximately related to the pressure of oxygen (P atmos.) as follows:

$$\log T = 2.56 - 0.77 \log P \text{ or; } T = \frac{360}{P^{0.77}}$$

TABLE I

TIME COURSE OF POISONING OF BRAIN TISSUE RESPIRATION BY HIGH PRESSURE OXYGEN

Oxygen Pressure (atmos.)	Average Time for 50% Poisoning (mins.)	Observer
2.9	180	Dickens[29]
(3.0)	(105*)	Van Goor & Jongbloed[26]
3.38	150	Dickens[29]
4.4	100	Dickens[29]
5.08	80	Dickens[29]
8.0	75	Stadie et al.[24]

*Chopped (rat?) brain tissue (other observations are for *slices* of rat brain cortex).

While there is evidently some rough general similarity in these relationships, the powers of p or P are very different. Thus at any given O_2 pressure, A atmos.,

$$\frac{T}{t} = 0.36 \text{ A}^{1.83}$$

Thus the time for a given percentage poisoning of isolated brain tissue respiration does not vary with the oxygen pressure in the same way as the behaviour of the whole animal. Moreover, even if one assumes that at any given external pressure of oxygen the brain of the animal is subjected to the same oxygen pressure as slices of tissue respiring *in vitro* (which it is not; see ref. 62), the percentage of brain poisoning calculated from the *in vitro* respiration is very small at a time of exposure which will produce convulsions in the intact animal (see ref. 29). Even if the excised tissue is exposed to CO_2 as well as HOP this is true.[24] There is thus a discrepancy between the time course of the two processes which is difficult to explain if poisoning of the brain respiration as a whole is the primary cause of oxygen poisoning. Obviously a selective poisoning of some essential *part* of brain oxidations is not excluded by these considerations (see refs. 29, 34).

In other tissues the oxygen-sensitivity of the respiration is even less than that of brain, muscle being one of the most resistant in this respect (see above). Nevertheless, the tension of isolated muscle preparations is diminished by oxygen pressures which do not measurably affect the oxygen uptake of the sliced muscle, and this effect occurs at a rate similar to that of oxygen poisoning in the intact animal.[36] Unlike the oxygen poisoning of tissue respiration, this effect on muscular tonus is reversible on decompression, just as the acute effects of oxygen poisoning are reversible in the whole animal. Again, these observations do not appear to require the assumption of a "hyperoxic anoxia,"[4] since respiration was not affected, at least in muscle slices.

Thus these valuable observations on muscle raise many further puzzling questions, which can only be resolved by much more detailed investigation of the metabolism, preferably in the intact muscle preparation as well as in slices and extracts. Among these an outstanding contribution would be the investigation of the effect of HOP on the adenosinetriphosphatase activity of myosin preparations, which can be inactivated by oxidation of myosin —SH groups and the inactivation can be resersed by —SH compounds:[63] oxidants also prevent actomyosin formation.[64] Whether the adenylic acid deaminase activity of myosin[65] is similarly affected does not appear to have been studied, but it is said to be less selectively blocked by —SH reagents.[65] The adenosine triphosphatase activity of myosin preparations can be inhibited by low concentrations of hydrogen peroxide in presence of traces of divalent metal ions or of adrenochrome;[66] and hydrogen peroxide (5 x 10^{-4} molar) also renders the phrenic nerve-diaphragm preparation insensitive to indirect stimulation.[67] It is not yet known if these observations can be related to the effects of exposure to HOP resulting both in conduction-block in peripheral nerve[39,40] and in serious impairment of ion transport in brain cortical tissue,[41,42] which have been already described. The phosphagen level and adenosine triphosphatase activity of brain and nervous tissue also need to be explored in this way. The opinion has been expressed by N. Haugaard (p. 8 of ref. 5b) that in the intact animal the acute symptoms of oxygen toxicity may be related to an oxidation of essential coenzymes (glutathione, lipoic acid, coenzyme A and possibly co-carboxylase) rather than to an inactivation of the tissue enzymes themselves. This possibility might accord well with the reversible nature of this stage of oxygen poisoning *in vivo,* although direct measurements of the effects on these coenzymes are lacking at present. On the other hand, the oxidative inactivation of DPNH cytochrome c reductase, a mechanism suggested by Dixon *et al.,*[59] is apparently irreversible, at least *in vitro.*

These suggestions merely serve to illustrate the serious gaps at present confronting any attempt to explain oxygen poisoning on the basis of enzyme inactivation. The protection against HOP afforded by metallic ions, especially Mn, Co, Mg and Ca (Dickens[29]) on the respiration of brain needs to be brought into line with further studies of this kind. It should also be noted that in hypoxia which like HOP is capable of causing convulsions in man and animals and has been considered to affect the same fundamental processes (Bean[4]), there is primarily an increase of lactic acid and a decrease of phosphocreatine in the dog's brain, followed by partial decomposition of adenosine-triphosphate near the animal's limit of tolerance, when the phosphocreatine has been almost completely decomposed (Gurdjian *et al.*[68]). The appearance of cerebral glycolysis *in vivo* at low oxygen tensions (25 mm. Hg. in the cerebral venous blood) is not inconsistent with the similar behaviour of cortical cell suspensions *in vitro* below 4 mm. Hg. (Elliott and Henry[69]).

Finally a brief reference should be made to two quite different hypotheses for which the evidence cannot yet be considered satisfactory. Taylor[19,20] has revived interest in the part played by tissue CO_2 in oxygen poisoning (see refs. 3, 4).

However, these results[19,20] have been severely criticised on technical grounds (ref. 70; see also p. 25 of ref. 5b), and several workers have failed to confirm them.[62,70,71] Consequently the whole question of the role of CO_2 in oxygen poisoning remains an open one.

The second hypotheses is that originally proposed by Bert,[1] i.e., the formation of a toxic substance in animals exposed to HOP. Although blood histamine has been reported (Campbell[72]) to be increased three-fold in rats exposed to 5 atmos. O_2, neither histamine nor blood or tissue-extracts from rats poisoned with HOP duplicated the effects or augmented the symptoms of oxygen poisoning. No toxic substances have been detected by others (see ref. 4).

It must therefore be concluded that in spite of the numerous toxic effects of oxygen which have been clearly demonstrated to occur both in enzyme systems and in isolated tissues, none as yet can be regarded as providing a satisfying basis for an explanation of the mechanism of oxygen poisoning in the intact animal.

REFERENCES

1. BERT, P.: *La Pression Barometrique*. Paris (1878).
2. HITCHCOCK, MARY A. and HITCHCOCK, F. A.: *Barometric Pressure* (translation of ref. 1). Columbus, Ohio, College Book Co. (1943).
3. STADIE, W. C., RIGGS, B. C. and HAUGAARD, N.: *Am. J. M. Sc.*, 207:84 (1944).
4. BEAN, J. W.: *Physiol. Rev.*, 25:1 (1945).
5. HOFF, E. C.: *A Bibliographical Sourcebook of Compressed Air, Diving, and Submarine Medicine*. Washington, D.C., Bur. Med. & Surg., Navy Dept. (1948).
5a. HOFF, E. C. and GREENBAUM, L. J. JR.: *A Bibliographical Sourcebook of Compressed Air, Diving & Submarine Medicine*, Vol. II (1954).
5b. GOFF, L. G. (ED.): *Proc. Underwater Physiol. Sympos.* Publ. 377, Nat. Acad. Sc., Washington, D.C. (1955).
6. See Ref. 3, p. 100 (Table 1) for data at approx. 1 atmos. O_2.
7. BEHNKE, A. R., JOHNSON, F. S., POPPEN, J. R. and MOTLEY, E. P.: *Am. J. Physiol.*, 110:565 (1934-5).
8. BORNSTEIN, A. and STROINK, M.: *Deutsch. med. Wchnschr.*, 38:1495 (1912).
9. HILL, L.: *Quart. J. Exper. Physiol.*, 23:49 (1933).
10. BEHNKE, A. R.: *Ann. Int. Med.*, 13:2217 (1939-40).
11. THOMSON, W. A. R.: *Brit. M.J.*, 2:208 (1935).
12. HALDANE, J. B. S.: *Nature*, 148:458 (1941).
13. DEMANT, CAPT. G. C. C.: Cited by Jenkinson, S.: *Brit. J. Surg.*, 27:767 (p. 769) (1939-40).
14. PRIKLADOVIZKY, S. I.: *Fiziol. zhur.*, 20:518, cited by ref. 5 (1936).
15. DONALD, K. W.: *Report of the Admiralty Experimental Diving Unit.* No. 9 (1943); see also *Brit. med. J.* i:712 (1947).
16. HALDANE, J. B. S. and SPURWAY, H.: *Statistical Appendix* to K. W. Donald, Report to Royal Naval Personnel Committee of the Medical Research Council, No. 95.
17. GERSCHMAN, R., GILBERT, D. L. and CACCAMISE, D.: *Am. J. Physiol.*, 192:563 (1958).
18. MARKS, H. P.: Report to the Royal Naval Personnel Committee, Medical Research Council, No. 101 (1944).
19. TAYLOR, H. J.: *J. Physiol.*, 108:264 (1949).
20. TAYLOR, H. J.: *J. Physiol.*, 109:272 (1949).
21. LAMBERTSEN, C. J., STROUD, M. W., EWING, J. H. and MACK, C.: *J. Appl. Physiol.*, 6:358 (1953).
22. LAMBERTSEN, C. J., OWEN, S. G., WENDEL, H., STROUD, M. W., LURIE, A. A., LOCHNER, W. and CLARK, G. F.: *J. Appl. Physiol.*, 14:966 (1959).
23. BEAN, J. W. and BOHR, D. F.: *Am. J. Physiol.*, 124:576 (1938).
24. STADIE, W. C., RIGGS, B. C. and HAUGAARD, N.: *J. Biol. Chem.*, 160:191 (1945).
25. NOYONS, A. K. M. and VAN GOOR, H.: *Arch. néerl. Physiol.*, 25:553 (1940-41).
26. VAN GOOR, H. and JONGBLOED, J.: *Arch. néerl. Physiol.*, 26:407 (1942); see also *Enzymologia*, 13:313 (1949) and *Acta brev. néerl. Physiol.*, 17:49 (1950).

27. MANN, P. J. G. and QUASTEL, J. H.: *Biochem. J., 40*:139 (1946).
28. ELLIOTT, K. A. C. and LIBET, B.: *J. Biol. Chem., 143*:227 (1942).
29. DICKENS, F.: *Biochem. J., 40*:145 (1946).
30. STADIE, W. C. and RIGGS, B. C.: *J. Biol. Chem., 154*:669 (1944).
31. LIBBRECHT, W. and MASSART, L.: *Compt. rend. Soc. biol., 124*:299 (1937).
32. BEAN, J. W.: *Proc. Soc. Exper. Biol. & Med., 26*:832 (1929); *J. Physiol., 72*:27 (1931).
33. HILL, L. and MACLEOD, J. J. R.: *J. Hyg., 3*:401 (1903).
34. STADIE, W. C. and HAUGAARD, N.: *J. Biol. Chem., 164*:257 (1946).
35. BEAN, J. W. and BOHR, D. F.: *Am. J. Physiol., 130*:445 (1940).
36. RIGGS, B. C.: *Am. J. Physiol., 145*:211 (1945).
37. ISSEKUTZ, B., HARANGOZO-OROSZY, M., MURANYI, A. and BUGYI, B.: *Arch. exper. Path. u. Pharmakol., 202*:550 (1943); ISSEKUTZ, B.: *Math. naturw. Anz. unger. Akad. Wiss., 62*:214 (1943).
38. STADIE, W. C., RIGGS, B. C. and HAUGAARD, N.: *J. Biol. Chem., 160*:209 (1945).
39. STEIN, S. N. and PEROT, P. L., JR.: *Research Rep. to Naval Med. Res. Inst., Nat. Naval Med. Center, Bethesda, 13*:759 (1955).
40. PEROT, P. L., JR. and STEIN, S. N.: *Am. J. Physiol., 197*:1243 (1959).
41. KAPLAN, S. A. and STEIN, S. N.: *Am. J. Physiol., 190*:157 (1957).
42. KAPLAN, S. A. and STEIN, S. N.: *Am. J. Physiol., 190*:166 (1957).
43. GERSCHMAN, R., GILBERT, D. L., NYE, S. W., PRICE, W. E., JR. and FENN, W. O.: *Proc. Soc. Exper. Biol. & Med., 88*:617 (1955).
44. TAYLOR, D. W.: *J. Physiol., 140*:23 (1958).
45. GERSCHMAN, R., GILBERT, D. L., NYE, S. W., DWYER, P. and FENN, W. O.: *Science, 119*:623 (1954).
46. PARR, W., O'NEILL, T., BUSH, S. and KREBS, A.: *Science, 119*:415 (1954).
47. BEAN, J. W. and JOHNSON, P. C.: *Am. J. Physiol., 180*:438 (1955).
48. GERSCHMAN, R. and FENN, W. O.: *Am. J. Physiol., 176*:6 (1954).
49. TAYLOR, D. W.: *J. Physiol., 140*:23 (1958).
50. TAYLOR, D. W.: *J. Physiol., 140*:37 (1958).
51. TAYLOR, D. W.: *Nature,* London, *183*:257 (1959).
52. DICKENS, F.: *Biochem. J., 40*:171 (1946).
53. HAUGAARD, N.: *J. Biol. Chem., 164*:265 (1946); see also pp. 8-12 in ref. 5b.
54. LEHMANN, J.: *Skandiv. Arch. Physiol., 72*:78 (1935).
55. BARRON, E. S. G.: *J. Biol. Chem., 113*:695 (1936).
56. STADIE, W. C., RIGGS, B. C. and HAUGAARD, N.: *J. Biol. Chem., 161*:189 (1945).
57. STADIE, W. C. and HAUGAARD, N.: *J. Biol. Chem., 161*:181 (1945).
58. BACQ, Z. M.: *Experientia, 2* (1946).
59. DIXON, M., MAYNARD, J. M. and MORROW, P. F. W.: *Nature,* London, *186*:1032 (1960).
60. ARMSTRONG, J. McD., COATES, J. H. and MORTON, R. K.: *Nature,* London, *186*:1033 (1960).
61. STADIE, W. C. and HAUGAARD, N.: *J. Biol. Chem., 161*:153 (1945).
62. LAMBERTSEN, C. J., KOUGH, H., COOPER, D. Y., EMMEL, G. L., LOESCHKE, H. H. and SCHMIDT, C. F.: *Abstr. XVIII Internat. Physiol. Cong.,* p. 322 (1950).
63. ZIFF, M.: *J. Biol. Chem., 153*:25 (1944).
64. BAILEY, K. and PERRY, S. V.: *Biochem. et biophys. acta, 1*:506 (1947).
65. HERMANN, V. S. and JOSEPOVITS, G.: *Hung. Acta Physiol., 2*:64, 73 (1949); cited by Straub, F. B., *Ann. Rev. Biochem., 19*:377 (1950).
66. DICKENS, F. and GLOCK, G. E.: *J. Physiol., 113*:24P (1951); *Biochim. Biophys. Acta, 7*:578 (1951).

67. HOBBIGER, F.: *J. Physiol., 113:*14P (1951).
68. GURDJIAN, E. S., WEBSTER, J. E. and STONE, W. E.: *Am. J. Physiol., 156:*149 (1949).
69. ELLIOTT, K. A. C. and HENRY, M.: *J. Biol. Chem., 163:*351 (1946).
70. LAMBERTSEN, C. J., STROUD, M. W., EWING, J. H. and MACK, C.: *J. Appl. Physiol., 6:*358 (1953).
71. TAYLOR, D. W.: *J. Physiol., 143:*149 (1958).
72. CAMPBELL, J. A.: *J. Physiol., 90:*91 (1937); *Brit. J. Exper. Path., 18:*191 (1937).

XXXVI

THE MYELIN SHEATH, METABOLISM OF MYELIN AND EXPERIMENTAL DEMYELINATION

R. J. ROSSITER

THE MYELIN SHEATH

THE CHEMICAL nature of the myelin sheath is of interest because demyelination, or the destruction of the myelin sheath, is a prominent feature in many neurological disorders. For this reason, neurochemists have continued to study the metabolism of myelin and pathologists have persisted in their attempts to produce experimental demyelination in laboratory animals.

Since pure "myelin" is not available for direct chemical analysis, the neurochemist has been compelled to deduce the constituents of myelin from such analyses as are practicable. This has been done (a) by comparing the chemical composition of peripheral nerve or white matter of brain, tissues containing many myelinated fibers, with gray matter, which contains more cell bodies and comparatively few myelinated fibers, (b) by comparing the concentration of certain chemical constituents in the brain of immature animals, at a period before myelination has begun, with that of the same constituent in the brain of adult animals, i.e., at a period when myelination is complete, (c) by studying the chemical changes in peripheral nerve throughout the course of experimental Wallerian degeneration, during which time myelin disappears from the nerve, and (d) by applying chemical techniques to the study of demyelinated areas in autopsy material obtained from patients with demyelinating diseases.

In addition, it is possible to reach some conclusions concerning the chemical nature of myelin from metabolic studies. In subsequent sections it will be shown that the lipids of myelin are formed characteristically in the brains of young animals at the time of myelination, but not readily in the brains of adult animals. Also myelin, once formed,

870

persists in the brain without significant metabolic turnover for long periods of time. Metabolic experiments such as these provide valuable confirmatory evidence as to whether or not certain lipids are components of the myelin sheath.

Comparison of White Matter with Gray Matter

A comparison of the chemical constituents of white matter of brain with those of gray matter may be found in Tables II-V of chapter II. It can be seen that white matter contains considerably more plasmalogens, sphingomyelins, cerebrosides, cholesterol (Table II), proteolipids (Table III) and residue organic phosphorus (Table IV) than gray matter. To these should be added sulfatides[1] and diphosphoinositides, but not monophosphoinositides.[2]

It will be noted that there is more "cephalin" in white matter than in gray matter. The figures quoted include phosphatidyl ethanolamines, phosphatidyl serines, diphosphoinositides and plasmalogens. Quantitatively plasmalogens are the most important of these substances.[3,4] Changes in the concentration of plasmalogens alone are almost sufficient to account for the greater concentration of "cephalin" in white matter than in gray matter, although diphosphoinositides also may contribute.[2] It has been proposed that phosphatidyl serines may be components of myelin.[5,6] Since this suggestion is in conflict with other findings,[7] the point should be investigated further.

From data of this type, lecithins and the mucolipids would appear not to be constituents of myelin.

Chemistry of Brain during Development

The biochemistry of the developing nervous system formed the subject of a symposium held at Oxford in 1954.[8] In particular, the reader is referred to a paper by Folch[7] for a review of previous findings and to a subsequent critical review by Folch et al.[9] The topic also is discussed by Sperry elsewhere in this volume.

During early development, many chemical substances are laid down in the brain and in the spinal cord as the result of two processes: (a) growth, and (b) myelination. These two processes may take place at the same time, although not necessarily at the same rate. Pertinent data on the chemical changes in brain during development have been provided by Brante,[5] Edgar and Smits[10] and Davison and Wajda[11] for the rabbit, Folch[7] and Uzman and Rumley[12] for the mouse, Korey and Orchen,[13] Erickson and Lands[14] and Kishimoto and Radin[15] for the rat, and Johnson, McNabb and Rossiter,[16] Brante,[5] Tingey[17] and Cumings et al.[18] for man.

Taken together, the findings indicate that plasmalogens, sphingo-myelins, cerebrosides, sulfatides, cholesterol and proteolipids, but not lecithins, phosphatidyl serines or mucolipids, are deposited in the brain more rapidly at the time of myelination.

Chemistry of Wallerian Degeneration

The chemical changes that accompany Wallerian degeneration were reviewed by Johnson, McNabb and Rossiter[19] and more recently by Rossiter.[20] The most comprehensive study on the changes in the concentration of lipids during Wallerian degeneration are those of Johnson, McNabb and Rossiter[21] for the cat, and Brante[5] and McCamen and Robins[22] for the rabbit. The latter workers reported results for Wallerian degeneration in the central nervous system as well as in peripheral nerve.

In general there is a coincident decrease in the concentration of sphingomyelins, cerebrosides and free cholesterol, with the appearance of cholesterol ester, as the myelin sheath disappears. There is also a decrease in the concentration of residue organic phosphorus.[23] For further details concerning the chemistry of Wallerian degeneration the reader is referred to a recent review (Rossiter[20]).

Some interest attaches to the classical Marchi reaction, used for the detection of degenerating nerve fibers. Because of our present lack of knowledge concerning (a) the specificity of histochemical tests, particularly those for the detection of lipids, and (b) the precise nature of the chemical components of the myelin sheath (see below) and the changes that they undergo during Wallerian degeneration, any explanation of the Marchi test in chemical terms is still little better than speculation. It is usually considered that the Marchi staining becomes positive as the result of the formation of some new lipid or lipid degradation product. Wolman,[24] however, has suggested that the formation of a non-acidic polysaccharide is responsible.

The possibility that the Marchi test depends upon the physical rather than the chemical state of the degenerating myelin has been considered. Adams[25] recently suggested that normal myelin is Marchi-negative because of its hydrophilic properties, whereas the products of myelin degradation are Marchi-positive because of their hydrophobic nature.

Demyelination in Man

Cumings[26,27] compared the concentration of lipids in demyelinated areas with that of similar constituents in normal areas of brains from patients with multiple sclerosis, and other demyelinating conditions. For further details, see Blackwood and Cumings[28] and Cumings.[29] In each instance, there was a decrease in the concentration of sphingo-myelins, cerebrosides, and free cholesterol in the demyelinated areas, with little change in the concentration of lecithins and "cephalins." In addition, cholesterol ester was present in the demyelinated areas and there was a decrease in the concentration of residue organic phosphorus. Thus the changes in the concentration of lipids in the demyelination of multiple sclerosis are quite similar to those described above for the demyelination of Wallerian degeneration.

It is hardly surprising that Bernsohn and Namajuska[30] were unable to detect changes in the distribution of lipids in the serum of patients with multiple sclerosis, but it is of interest that Green et al.[31] reported an increase in the concentration of cholesterol in the cerebrospinal fluid, more than 60% of which was in the esterified form.

Chemical Constituents of Myelin

When all the evidence is considered together, it seems reasonable to assume that plasmalogens, sphingomyelins, cerebrosides, sulfatides, diphosphoinositides and non-esterified cholesterol are the principal lipid components of the myelin sheath. Such lipids were called *myelin lipids* by Johnson et al.[19] and *sheath typical* lipids by Brante.[5] To these the proteolipids of Folch and Lees,[32] and possibly some component that contributes to the residue organic phosphorus, may be added.

LeBaron and Folch[33] have suggested that the classical neurokeratin contains the protein moiety of the proteolipids. This could be interpreted as evidence for the view that proteolipids are constituents of myelin, for both chemical[34] and histological[35] observations indicate that neurokeratin is located in the myelin sheath. Additional evidence is provided by the findings, described above, that foetal brain contains little proteolipid and that there is more proteolipid in white matter of brain than in gray matter. The problem is still somewhat unclear, however, because it has been reported from two laboratories that no proteolipid is obtained from peripheral nerve when the methods used for the successful preparation of proteolipids from the central nervous system are applied to this tissue.[36,37] A similar uncertainty surrounds the lipophilic protein, neurosclerin, studied by Uzman and co-workers.[38-40] This substance, which probably represents a major portion of the proteolipid protein of Folch and Lees,[32] increases in brain at the time of myelination,[38] but the concentration in peripheral nerve is much less than that in brain.[40]

The nature of the myelin component that contributes to the residue organic phosphorus is still uncertain. The possibility that the phosphorus is derived from the phosphatidopeptides of LeBaron and Folch,[33] the triphosphoinositides of Dittmar and Dawson[41] or the three diphosphoinositides of Hörhammer *et al.*,[42] which are said to be present chiefly in white matter of brain,[2] is discussed in Chapter II of this volume.

A discussion of how the myelin constituents, both lipid and protein, are arranged together to form the myelin sheath is not possible here. As the result of the application of a number of physical techniques, such as those of polarization optics, x-ray diffraction and electron microscopy, a concept of the pattern of organization between the lipids and proteins in the myelin sheath has gradually emerged. For summaries of this important work the reader is referred to publications of Fernández-Morán,[43] Fernández-Morán and Finean,[44] Finean[45] and Finean and Robertson.[46]

METABOLISM OF MYELIN
Formation of Myelin Lipids

Phosphatides.—When a suitable isotopically-labelled precursor is administered to an animal, the label is incorporated into the phosphatides of most tissues, including brain, spinal cord and peripheral nerve. This is true of a wide variety of precursors, e.g., inorganic P labelled with P^{32}; fatty acid labelled with deuterium, C^{14}, I^{131}, or elaidic acid; acetate labelled with deuterium or C^{14}; glycerol labelled with C^{14}; choline, ethanolamine or serine, labelled with C^{14}, N^{15} or tritium; inositol labelled with C^{14} or tritium.

Similar labelling experiments carried out *in vitro* with tissue slices suggest that for the nervous system, like most other tissues, the phosphatides are formed *in situ* from the appropriate low molecular weight precursors (see Rossiter[47] for references). Such isotope experiments, although they show that lipid synthesis can occur, give little information as to the metabolic pathways involved. Recently, largely as the result of the notable contributions of Kennedy,[48,49] much has been learned concerning the formation of glycerophosphatides in chicken liver. There is good reason to believe that similar pathways are operative in brain and nerve.[50-52] Recent reviews on the biological formation of phosphatides are those of Kennedy,[48,49] Rossiter[53] and Rossiter and Strickland.[54,55]

Plasmalogens.—Korey and Orchen[13] showed that when acetate 1-C^{14} or palmitate-1-C^{14} was administered to rats, some of the radioactivity was incorporated into the unsaturated ether side-chain of the plasmologens. In addition, the *in vitro* incorporation of palmitate-1-C^{14} into the aldehydogenic side-chain of plasmalogens by a rat-brain preparation was described by Gambal and Monty.[56] These authors also made the interesting observation that the incorporation was stimulated by the addition of cytidine 5′-triphosphate (CTP) and ethanolamine.

A further step forward was the report of Kiyasu and Kennedy[57] that rat liver contains an enzyme that catalyzes the formation of choline-containing plasmalogen from cytidine diphosphate choline (CMP-PC) and "plasmalogenic diglyceride":

CMP-PC + "plasmalogenic diglyceride" $\rightleftharpoons$ choline plasmalogen + CMP $---$ (1)

The "plasmalogenic diglyceride," prepared enzymically by the action of phospholipase D on the choline plasmalogen of beef heart, is defined as a D-α,β-diglyceride in which one ester linkage has been replaced by an α',β'-unsaturated ether bond. The reaction is catalyzed by a phosphorylcholine transferase similar to the phosphorylcholine-glyceride transferase shown to participate in the biosynthesis of lecithin.[48,49]

Kiyasu and Kennedy[57] also presented evidence that the rat-liver enzyme was capable of catalyzing the formation of ethanolamine plasmalogen from "plasmalogenic diglyceride" and cytidine diphosphate ethanolamine, a reaction more important in the formation of brain plasmalogen and one consistent with the observations of Gambal and Monty[56] referred to above.

Sphingomyelin.—Ansell and Spanner[58] showed that when inorganic P[32] was injected into rats, some of the isotope was incorporated into the sphingomyelin of the brain. This activity was greatest in young rats at the time of myelin deposition.

The experiments of Zabin and Mead[59] and Sprinson and Coulon[60] with C[14]-labelled precursors showed that carbon atoms 1 and 2 and the nitrogen atom of sphingosine are derived from the carbon atoms 3 and 2 and the nitrogen of serine. The remaining carbon atoms, 3-18, are derived from acetyl coenzyme A (acetyl CoA) and were thought to enter the sphinogosine molecule by way of a long-chain 16-carbon intermediate. The *in vivo* findings were extended by the *in vitro* experiments of Brady and Koval,[61] who showed that palmityl coenzyme A (palmityl CoA) may be the precursor of carbon atoms 3-18 of sphingosine and that the addition of reduced triphosphopyridine nucleotide (TPNH) to the reaction mixture was necessary when serine and palmityl CoA were the precursors. Manganous ions and pyridoxal phosphate also were required. Zabin[62] described a system from rat brain, with similar coenzyme requirements, that formed ceramide (N-acyl sphingosine) from serine and palmityl CoA. Subsequently Brady et al.[63] showed that when sphingosine was formed from palmityl CoA and serine, the first stage was the formation of palmitaldehyde from palmityl CoA. The reduction, which required TPNH, was catalyzed by an enzyme present in rat brain:[61]

Palmityl CoA + TPNH + H$^+$ $\rightleftharpoons$ palmitaldehyde + CoA + TPN$^+$ $-----$ (2)

The palmitaldehyde then condensed with serine to form dihydrosphingosine and CO_2:

$$\text{Palmitaldehyde} + \text{serine} \longrightarrow \text{dihydrosphingosine} + CO_2 \quad ------- \quad (3)$$

It was stated that reaction 3 required pyridoxal phosphate and manganous ions. Brady et al.[63] produced evidence for the formation of a Schiff base-metal complex between serine, pyridoxal phosphate and manganous ions. The resonance-stabilized carbanion so formed can then participate in the carbon-to-carbon addition reaction with palmitaldehyde to form dihydrospingosine and CO_2. It was further suggested that dihydrosphingosine could be converted to sphingosine by a flavoprotein enzyme present in brain tissue:[61,63]

$$\text{Dihydrosphingosine} + \text{flavin} \longrightarrow \text{sphingosine} + \text{flavin } H_2 \quad ------- \quad (4)$$

Presumably the sphingosine is esterified by fatty acyl CoA to form N-acyl sphingosine:

$$\text{Sphingosine} + \text{fatty acyl CoA} \rightleftharpoons \text{N-acyl sphingosine} + \text{CoA} \quad ------- \quad (5)$$

Sribney and Kennedy[64] demonstrated that chicken liver contains an enzyme that catalyzes the transfer of phosphorylcholine from CMP-PC to ceramide:

$$\text{CMP-PC} + \text{ceramide} \rightleftharpoons \text{sphingomyelin} + \text{CMP} \quad ---- \quad (6)$$

The enzyme was called phosphorylcholine-ceramide transferase. Reaction 6 is similar to the phosphorylcholine-glyceride transferase reaction in the biosynthesis of lecithin and the similar reaction (equation 1) in the formation of plasmalogen. The observation of Rossiter et al.[50,51] that some of the radioactivity of CMP-P^{32} was incorporated into the alkali-resistant fraction of rat brain suggests that reaction 6 also occurs in brain tissue.

In more detailed reports of the above work, Sribney and Kennedy[65,66] showed that phosphorylcholine-ceramide transferase is present in brain as well as in other animal tissues and that it is specific not only for CMP-PC but also for a particular ceramide. In order for the ceramide to be active, the sphingosine moiety must have the trans-configuration of the double bond, and the hydroxyl group of carbon 3 must be threo in relation to the amino group on carbon 2 (i.e., the active sphingosine is threo-1,3-dihydroxy-2-amino-4-trans-octadecene). The product of reaction 6 also contained the threo- and trans-configuration, in contrast to the erythro- and trans-configuration of naturally-occurring sphingomyelins.[66,67] Sribney and Kennedy[66] suggested that in vivo threo-sphingomyelin may be converted to erythro-sphingomyelin by a second enzyme system.

Cerebroside.—The in vivo experiments of Radin et al.,[68] Burton,

Sodd and Brady[69,70] and Moser and Karnovsky[71] indicate that both C^{14}-labelled galactose and C^{14}-labelled glucose are incorporated into the cerebroside of the brain of young rats and mice. In contrast to the findings for the mucolipids, which also become radioactive under similar conditions, the rate of labelling of cerebrosides from glucose-C^{14} or from serine-3-C^{14} was greatest at the time of greatest myelin deposition,[69-72] further evidence that cerebrosides, but not mucolipids, are myelin lipids.

When glucose-C^{14} labelled in carbon-6 was administered to mice, almost all of the radioactivity of the cerebroside galactose was recovered from that carbon atom, indicating that the carbon skeleton of glucose is transferred to the galactose of brain cerebroside as a unit. Burton, Sodd and Brady[69] showed that a microsome preparation from the brain of young rats contained the enzymes necessary for the incorporation of glucose and galactose in cerebroside and that uridine diphosphogalactose (UDP-gal) was the primary hexose donor. Subsequently Cleland and Kennedy[73] described an enzyme preparation from brains of young rats and guinea pigs that catalyzed the formation of psychosine (galactosyl-sphingosine) from UDP-gal and sphingosine.

Thus the steps leading to the formation of cerebroside are:[69,73]

From glucose

$$\text{G-1-P}^* + \text{UTP} \rightleftharpoons \text{UDPG} + \text{PP} - - - - - - - - - - - - - \quad (7)$$
$$\text{UDPG} \rightleftharpoons \text{UDP-gal} - - - - - - - - - - - - - - - - - - \quad (8)$$

From galactose

$$\text{Gal-1-P} + \text{UDPG} \rightleftharpoons \text{UDP-gal} + \text{G-1-P} - - - - - - - - - \quad (9)$$

Common pathway

$$\text{UDP-gal} + \text{sphingosine} \longrightarrow \text{psychosine} + \text{UDP} - - - - - -(10)$$
$$\text{psychosine} + \text{acyl-CoA} \longrightarrow \text{cerebroside} + \text{CoA} - - - - -(11)$$

Reactions 7-9 are well known and have been shown to occur in brain.[69] Cleland and Kennedy[73] studied reaction 10. The enzyme, galactosyl-sphingosine transferase was found to be specific for UDP-gal and for the natural *erythro-trans* isomer of sphingosine. The enzyme was less active towards other isomers of sphingosine. It was inactive towards ceramides, a finding which led Cleland and Kennedy[73] to suggest that cerebrosides are formed by the esterification of psychosines (reaction 11), rather than by the direct transfer of galactose from UDP-gal to ceramides.

---

*Abbreviations: G-1-P, glucose-1-phosphate; UTP, uridine 5'-triphosphate; UDPG, uridine 5'-diphosphate glucose; PP, pyrophosphate; gal-1-P, galactose-1-phosphate; UDP, uridine 5'-diphosphate.

Sulfatides.—Radin *et al.*[68] showed that both galactose-1-C[14] and sulfate-S[35] were incorporated into the sulfatides of the brain of young rats. More recently both Bakke and Cornatzer[74] and Davison[74a] showed that sulfate-S[35] was incorporated into the brains of young rats much more rapidly than into the brains of mature animals. The persistence of radioactivity in the sulfatide fraction is consistent with the suggestion that sulfatide is a myelin lipid. The experiments of Goldberg[75] indicate that the sulfate is derived from 3'-phosphoadenosine-5'-phosphosulfate, the "active sulfate" of Robbins and Lipmann.[76]

Diphosphoinositide.—Although a certain amount is known concerning the formation of inositol lipids in both brain and other tissues (see refs. 55, 77 for reviews), in these experiments the end product would appear to have been monophosphoinositide or phosphatidyl inositol. As pointed out above, such a compound is not a myelin lipid. Little is known concerning the biosynthesis of brain diphosphoinositide.

Cholesterol.—Isotope experiments indicate that the cholesterol of the brain of adult animals is relatively inert metabolically, whereas in the brains of young animals cholesterol appears to be formed quite readily. Thus Bloch *et al.*[78] found that when cholesterol labelled with deuterium was fed to a dog, none of the label could be recovered from brain cholesterol, although the cholesterol of all other tissues studied contained considerable amounts of the isotope. When young animals are used in this type of experiment, however, brain cholesterol is labelled quite readily. Thus Davison *et al.*, demonstrated the incorporation of cholesterol-C[14] into the brain cholesterol of newly-hatched chickens[79] or young rabbits.[80]

A similar conclusion can be drawn from the experiments of Waelsch, Sperry and Stoyanoff,[81] who showed that deuterium was not incorporated into the brain cholesterol of adult rats whose body fluids had been enriched with deuterium oxide (D_2O), whereas in young animals both D_2O[82] and tritiated water (H^3_2O)[83] is incorporated into brain cholesterol. Also van Bruggen *et al.*[84] reported negligible incorporation of isotope into brain cholesterol of adult rats after the administration of acetate-1-C[14]. However, McMillan *et al.*[85] found that the cholesterol of the brain of adult rats was labelled after intracisternal injection of either acetate-1-C[14] or pyruvate-2-C[14], but that considerably more of the isotope could be recovered from brain cholesterol when young rats were used. Similar results were reported for acetate-2-C[14] by Nicholas and Thomas[86] and for glucose-C[14] by Moser and Karnovsky.[71]

That cholesterol can be formed *in situ* in brain was demonstrated by the *in vitro* experiments of Srere *et al.*[87] These workers showed that radioactivity from acetate-1-C[14] could be incorporated into the cholesterol of brain slices. Again slices from young animals were much more active than those from adults.

Little work has been done on the metabolic pathways leading to the biosynthesis of cholesterol in brain. In other tissues cholesterol is formed from acetate by way of mevalonic acid, squalene and lanosterol. For further details the reader is referred to a recent summary of this work by Cornforth.[88] The observations that both *in vivo*[89] and *in vitro*[90] radioactivity from mevalonic acid-2-C^{14} is incorporated into brain cholesterol suggest that cholesterol is formed by a similar pathway in the nervous system. In the *in vitro* formation of cholesterol from mevalonic acid-2-C^{14}, brain slices from young animals again were shown to be much more active than those from adults.[91]

Myelinogenesis

The early experiments of Spiedel[92,93] on the formation of myelin in the nerves of the tails of tadpoles and those of Clark and Clark[94] on myelin formation in the nerves of the rabbit ear suggested that in peripheral nerve myelin is produced by Schwann cells. This view can now be considered as established, largely as the result of two more recent complementary investigations: that of Peterson and Murray[95] on myelination in tissue culture and that of Geren,[96] who used the electron microscope to study myelination in the developing chick embryo. The findings of Geren[96] have been confirmed by Robertson[97] for reptilian nerve and by Terry and Harkin[98] for mammalian nerve regenerating after section.

It is, therefore, of interest to consider metabolism of nerves degenerating after section, because it is well known that such nerves are abundantly provided with the Schwann cells that are responsible for the formation of myelin. In nerves undergoing Wallerian degeneration the phospholipid is more readily labelled from inorganic P^{32} both *in vivo*[99,100] and *in vitro*.[101-103] In addition, the radioactivity from a wide variety of C^{14}-labelled precursors is more readily incorporated into the phospholipids[104,105] and that of acetate-1-C^{14} is more readily converted into cholesterol.[106] It thus may be seen that the comparison between intact and degenerating nerves is analogous to that between adult and immature brain referred to above.

It is tempting to conclude from experiments of this type that the observed increase in the *in vitro* labelling of phospholipid is related to the proliferation of Schwann cells and that it indicates that such nerves are more amply provided with the metabolic machinery necessary for the formation of myelin lipids. Such nerves have the ability to form myelin, and indeed they do form myelin when a suitable opportunity presents itself, i.e., when the degenerating nerve fiber receives a growing axon tip from the central stump. This interpretation, which possibly may be true in a general sense, is, however, complicated by the experimental finding that the increase in labelling is not confined to myelin lipids. A more detailed discussion of this problem is given in a recent review (Rossiter[20]).

In the central nervous system Luse[107] has shown that oligodendrocytes play a role analogous to that of the Schwann cells in peripheral nerve. Essentially similar results were reported by Peters.[108]

Whether myelin lipids are formed from smaller molecules at the time of myelination, whether they are formed from precursors of high molecular weight already present in the satellite cell, or whether myelination merely represents a reorientation of myelin lipids formed some time previously, is not known. The publication of Uzman and Rumley[12] suggests the latter possibility.

That cholesterol ester may be related in some way to the process of myelination is suggested by the demonstration of cholesterol ester both in peripheral nerves regenerating after crush (Burt, McNabb and Rossiter[109]) and in the developing spinal cord (Adams and Davison[110]).

Metabolic Stability of Myelin

It has been known for some time that certain of the myelin lipids, in particular cholesterol, are not readily formed in the brains of adult animals. It was pointed out above, however, that in the brains of immature animals and in peripheral nerves regenerating after section, two situations where myelination is proceeding, cholesterol is formed quite readily from precursors of low molecular weight. There is evidence, also referred to above, that the same applies to other myelin lipids, such as the plasmalogens, sphingomyelins, cerebrosides and sulfatides. In experiments of Thompson and Ballou[83] radioactivity from tritiated water remained in certain of the lipids of rat brain for long periods of time, suggesting that such lipids were inert metabolically. Persistence of radioactivity in brain cholesterol labelled from acetate-1-C^{14}, pyruvate-2-C^{14} or acetate-2-C^{14} also has been reported[85,86] Recently the concept of the metabolic stability of the myelin lipids has been extended greatly by a series of experiments reported by Davison, Payling Wright and colleagues.

Davison et al.[79,80] showed that, when cholesterol-4-C^{14} was administered to newly hatched chickens or to rabbits 17 days after birth, radioactive cholesterol persisted in the brain for periods of time up to one year, whereas by this time there was no appreciable activity in other tissues such as liver, kidney, heart or blood plasma. In the rabbits there was some loss of activity from brain gray matter during the first few months, but there was little loss from brain white matter, spinal cord or peripheral nerve.

Results of a similar nature were reported when inorganic P[32] was administered to young rats[111,112] or rabbits,[113] when serine -3-C[14] was injected into rabbits[114] and when inorganic S[35] or glycerol-1-C[14] was injected into rats.[74a,112,115] With each precursor radioactivity persisted in the brain, spinal cord and peripheral nerve for periods of time up to 200 days. In experiments where the brain was separated into white matter and gray matter, radioactivity persisted longer in white matter than in gray matter. In experiments where the lipids were separated chromatographically, radioactivity persisted in sphingomyelins, cerebrosides and cholesterol, but not in lecithins and cephalins.

It was suggested that the persistence in the lipids of the nervous system of radioactivity from labelled cholesterol and from the labelled lipid precursors results from the deposition of radioactive lipids in myelin. Myelin is formed during development but, once it is deposited, it remains inert metabolically. Indeed, current views concerning the structure of myelin are such (see Finean and Robertson[46] for references) that it is difficult to imagine how enzyme proteins, necessary for metabolic reactions, could come into proximity with the oriented lipids of the myelin sheath.

On the basis of metabolic turnover it seems likely that the lipids of the nervous system may be divided into two components: (a) one located largely in the white matter of brain, spinal cord and peripheral nerve that is relatively inert, except during periods of myelination, and (b) one located largely in gray matter of brain that has appreciable metabolic turnover. It is the latter component that is responsible for most of the lipid metabolism of adult brain. The inert component represents myelin lipid. It is of interest to note that metabolic experiments, such as those of Davison and colleagues, again suggest that the principal myelin lipids are sphingomyelins, cerebrosides, sulfatides and cholesterol.

EXPERIMENTAL DEMYELINATION

Pathological lesions involving chiefly the white matter of the nervous system are not limited to man. Spontaneous demyelinating diseases are known to occur in apes and monkeys, newborn and sucking lambs, horses, moose, dogs, foxes and goats. Many factors have been implicated as a cause of demyelination: the administration of certain toxic chemicals, including a number of metabolic inhibitors, infective agents and their endogeneous toxins, hemolysins, lipolytic enzymes, vascular thromboses, nutritional deficiencies, immunological reactions, vascular spasm, and constitutional and hereditary factors. In fact Hurst[116] conceived of demyelination not "as a specific process due to any one cause," but as a "type of response of the white matter to noxious stimuli insufficient to cause full necrosis of tissue."

There is little evidence that the demyelination produced by such a variety of conditions as those listed is the same in every instance. It is possible that true demyelination is an outward manifestation of one of a number of chemical or physical processes taking place within the myelin sheath. In addition, demyelination may be secondary, i.e., it may follow the destruction of the nerve cell or axon. The characteristics of true demyelination in human diseases have been described by Adams and Kubick[117] and more recently by Adams.[118]

Below are given some of the contributions of neurochemists to the study of experimental demyelination. The topic is considered further in reviews by Cavanagh and Thompson[119] and Thompson.[120]

Experimental Encephalomyelitis

The literature contains a number of reports of the occurrence of paralyses and demyelinating lesions in the brain of both man and experimental animals following the injection of suspensions of rabbit spinal cord in the Pasteur treatment of rabies. It was soon established that these symptoms were caused by the presence of normal brain or spinal cord in the injected material. Much of the early work in this field was summarized by Hurst[121] in 1932. Reviews of subsequent developments are those of Hurst,[122] Cavanagh,[123] Waksman,[124] Condie and Good[125] and a recent monograph by Kies and Alvord.[126]

Rivers and his associates[127,128] produced a disseminated encephalomyelitis, characterized by foci of demyelination, by the repeated injection of suspensions of rabbit brain into monkeys. Similar results were obtained by Ferraro and Jervis.[129] In 1947 Kabat, Wolf and Bezer[130,131] succeeded in producing a high incidence of encephalomyelitis in monkeys after relatively few injections of heterologous brain tissue, to which had been added the adjuvants of Freund and McDermott.[132] Independently, Morgan[133] obtained similar results. With this technique demyelinating lesions have been produced in guinea pigs,[134] rabbits,[135] mice,[136] dogs,[137] sheep,[138] goats[139] and rats.[140]

The manner in which the lesions are produced suggests that an allergic mechanism is involved. It is postulated that the demyelination is associated with the reaction of antibodies, produced in response to antigen or antigens in the injected brain tissue, with the brain tissue of the animal receiving the injection. The evidence both for and against this view was summarized in a recent review by Robbins.[141]

Since neither specific antigen nor antibody has been characterized, the attractive allergy hypothesis still remains unproven. Few results have been described, however, that are not consistent with such an hypothesis. The hypothesis is further supported by claims that the incidence of encephalomyelitis is greatly reduced by the administration of corticotropin,[142] cortisone,[143] large doses of salicylates[144] or 6-mercaptopurine,[145] all substances known to inhibit the production of antibody. The wide acceptance of the allergy hypothesis is illustrated by the general use of the term *experimental allergic encephalomyelitis* for the condition.

Encephalitogenic Factors.—The nature of encephalitogenic factor or factors is of considerable interest to the neurochemist. It was early established that encephalitogenic activity is present in the brain of man, monkey, rabbit, dog, sheep, guinea-pig, mouse, rat and chicken, and that white matter is more active than gray matter.[130,133,146] Other organs such as muscle, kidney, liver, pancreas, spleen, testis and adrenal were found to be inactive. It also was found that there was much less activity in foetal brain[130,146] and in peripheral nerve.[133,146-148] However, the chemical nature of the active factor remained in doubt. For example, activity was reported in the lipid fraction of brain,[139,146] the water-soluble fraction,[149,150] or both.[151]

Unfortunately the situation has not been clarified by more recent studies. Olitsky and Tal[152] reported that proteolipids A and B, as isolated by Folch and Lees,[32] were active. Similar results were described by Goldstein et al.[153,154] and by Wacksman et al.,[155] who found activity in the proteolipid C fraction also. The minor discrepancies in the results of these workers may be due to a species difference; Olitsky and Tal[152] used bovine cord and homologous brain in mice, Goldstein et al.[153,154] used homologous brain in guinea-pigs, whereas Wacksman et al.[155] used bovine brain in rabbits. Recently the preparation of a more active lipid-soluble substance from a petroleum ether extract of spinal cord was described by Lipton.[156]

In 1956 Kies, Roboz and Alvord[157] claimed that water-soluble material, described as a glycoprotein, prepared from bovine spinal cord had encephalitogenic activity in guinea-pigs. Subsequently Roboz et al.[158] described the preparation from bovine spinal cord of a purified collagen-like protein, shown by Kies, Alvord and Roboz[159] to have high encephalitogenic activity when tested in guinea-pigs.

From the time of the earliest studies, the possibility had been considered that the active factor might be a constituent of myelin. The possibility that the proteolipids, which are absent from foetal brain and peripheral nerve, might be components of myelin, has been discussed previously. The distribution of encephalitogenic activity parallels that of the proteolipids and, with the important exception that peripheral nerve is inactive, the distribution of encephalitogenic activity parallels that of myelin. Such findings suggest that the encephalitogenic factor is a constituent of myelin. Recently Buetner *et al.*,[160] using the fluorescent antibody technique, showed that there was at least one active antigen in the myelin sheath. There is no evidence that the collagen-like protein of Roboz *et al.*[158] is a component of myelin.

The fact that encephalitogenic activity has been observed in both lipid-soluble and water-soluble material suggests that there may be more than one active substance. Waksman[161] presents evidence for the supposition that the encephalitogenic factor is multiple. He instances species differences in the responses to the same preparation of antigen. Thus guinea-pigs were more sensitive than rabbits to the collagen-like protein of Roboz *et al.*[158]

Despite the difficulties in characterizing the encephalitogenic factor or factors, experimental encephalomyelitis remains a useful means of producing demyelination in the laboratory. The relation of experimental encephalomyelitis to demyelinating diseases of man was discussed by Hurst[122] and more recently by Adams.[118]

Nutrition and Demyelination

Experimental Animals.—In the early days of nutritional research many pathological changes were described in the brain, spinal cord and peripheral nerves of experimental animals maintained on diets deficient in one or more of the vitamins. Lesions in the nervous system were at different times attributed to lack of vitamin A, vitamin E, thiamine, riboflavin, nicotinic acid, pyridoxine, pantothenic acid, or biotin. It is probable that in some of these experiments mixed deficiencies were produced and that in others the lesion in the nervous system was not primarily demyelinating. In 1939 Phillips and Engel[162] described a pathological condition in the spinal cord of chicks characterized by a degeneration of the myelinated fibers, although there were also some degenerative changes in the axis cylinders. The condition could be prevented by feeding pantothenic acid, but not nicotinic acid, riboflavin or thiamine. Lippincott and Morris[163] described a similar myelin degeneration in the spinal cord and sciatic nerves of mice, which likewise could be prevented by feeding excess pantothenic acid. These observations are in no way conclusive, but they do indicate the importance of dietary factors in maintaining the normal myelin sheath in experimental animals. In this regard it is of interest to note that Swank and Bessey[164] described histological changes in the myelin sheath of the peripheral nerves of rats subjected to starvation alone.

Man.—In man, too, lesions of the nervous system have been described that may be of nutritional origin. This topic is considered elsewhere in this volume. It is unlikely, however, that uncomplicated pantothenic acid deficiency, for instance, is the cause of demyelinating conditions in man. Siegel, Putnam and Lynn[165] reported that the concentration of pantothenic acid in the blood of patients with disseminated sclerosis was normal.

It is well known that in thiamine deficiency, and possibly in other nutritional deficiencies,[120,166] the concentration of pyruvic acid in the blood is increased. Jones *et al.*[167] in 1950 reported high concentrations of pyruvic acid in the blood of patients with multiple sclerosis. More recent studies, however, have failed to substantiate this claim.[168-170] The possibility that multiple sclerosis may be of dietary origin was considered by Brickner and Brill.[171]

Copper.—Interest in a possible nutritional factor in demyelinating disease was further stimulated by the work of Bennetts and colleagues[172,173] in Australia and Innes and Shearer[174] in England. These workers investigated a demyelinating condition of newborn lambs called swayback or enzoötic ataxia. In Australia the disease is associated with a low concentration of copper in the pasture, in the blood and liver of the parent ewe, and in the blood and liver of the affected lamb. The condition may be prevented by feeding small amounts of copper to the pregnant ewes. In England the beneficial effects of copper feeding were confirmed, but it was found that the disease often occurred in areas where the copper content of the soil and pasture was normal. Despite this, there was usually a low concentration of copper in the blood and liver of both the parent ewe and in the tissues, including brain, of the affected lamb.[138,175] Innes[138] suggested a number of possible explanations for this finding: (a) that the copper is present in the pasture in a form that the pregnant ewe cannot absorb; (b) that there is some dysfunction of the alimentary tract of the pregnant ewe; or (c) that some unknown factor, possibly an excess of molybdenum, inhibits the absorption of copper.

Other similar demyelinating conditions have been reported. Thus from Iceland Pálsson and Grímsson[176] described demyelination in the brain of lambs from ewes fed seaweed during the pregnancy. Despite a normal intake of copper, the concentration of copper in the blood and liver of affected lambs was low. A field experiment showed that the disorder could be prevented by giving a supplement of copper to the pregnant ewes. Similarly, Mills and Fell[177] were able to produce demyelination experimentally in lambs by feeding the parent ewes a diet supplemented by large quantities of sulfate and molybdenum. Again the concentration of copper in the liver of the lambs was low.

These demyelinating conditions have in common a low concentration of copper in the liver and other tissues. Gubler *et al.*[177a] produced experimental copper deficiency in pigs and Gallagher *et al.*[178] produced a similar deficiency in rats and hens. Both groups showed that the condition was associated with a decrease in the activity in the enzyme cytochrome oxidase in the liver. Subsequently Howell and Davison[175] reported that the activity of this enzyme, now thought to contain copper[178a-d], was decreased in the brains of swayback lambs. These observations all point to the possibility that a decrease in the activity of cytochrome oxidase, or perhaps another copper-containing enzyme, may be related in some imperfectly understood way to the development of demyelination.

Although the pathological findings in swayback and other conditions associated with copper deficiency in lambs are very similar to those observed in certain types of demyelinating disease in man, the investigation of copper metabolism in man has proved disappointing. Mandelbrote *et al.*[179] failed to show any significant change either in the concentration of copper in the serum, or in the excretion of copper in the urine of patients with multiple sclerosis. Thus copper deficiency, like pantothenic acid deficiency, would appear to play no part in the etiology of this disease. However, observations such as those reported above have helped a great deal to orientate our thinking on the general problem of demyelination.

Toxic Substances and Demyelination

A condition, usually described as demyelination, can be produced in the white matter of the nervous system by the administration of certain toxic substances to laboratory animals. Work on experimental demyelination of this type was reviewed in 1944 by Hurst[180] and Ferraro.[181] Among the substances that have been used are potassium cyanide,[182-185] hydrogen cyanide vapour,[186] carbon monoxide,[184,187,188] sodium azide,[184] tetanus toxin[188,189] and *Clostridium welchii* toxin.[190] Monkeys, cats, dogs, rabbits and rats have been used as experimental animals.

It will be noted that many of these substances, e.g., cyanide, azide and carbon monoxide, are metabolic poisons that inhibit the cytochrome system in surviving tissue preparations. Although other metabolic inhibitors, such as fluoroacetate,[186] hydroxylamine and the narcotics,[184] can produce pathological changes in the nervous system, the lesions are not confined to the white matter, and are not primarily demyelinating. Similar histochemical changes, also not characteristically demyelinating, can be produced by prolonged insulin hypoglycaemia[186] and anoxia (see Morrison[191] for references). Putnam[192] produced pathological changes, probably the result of prolonged anoxia, in the brains of dogs by means of experimental venous thromboses. The possible relation of vascular lesions such as these to human demyelinating disease has been discussed by Putnam.[193] Experimentally, the lesions produced by cyanide, and similar inhibitors of the cytochrome system, appear to be more characteristically demyelinating than do those produced by anoxia or by other toxic substances. It is tempting to speculate that normally the maintenance of the integrity of the myelin sheath requires the presence of an enzyme, possibly the cytochrome system, and that an interference with the action of this enzyme system by a metabolic inhibitor causes the sheath to degenerate. The relation between copper deficiency, demyelination and the activity of cytochrome oxidase was commented upon in the previous section.

Organo-phosphates.—For some years considerable interest has centered around the findings that demyelination may be produced in the spinal cord and peripheral nerve of some species of laboratory animals by the prolonged administration of certain organo-phosphorus compounds. In 1930, a localized outbreak of "ginger paralysis" occurred in the United States among persons who had consumed drinks prepared from extracts of ginger imported from Jamaica. Smith and Elvove[194,195] showed that tri-*ortho*-cresyl phosphate (TOCP) was the harmful ingredient in the extract. Since that time a number of instances of accidental TOCP poisoning have been reported (see Hunter *et al.*,[196] Earl and Thompson,[197] and Susser and Stein[198] for references), the most recent being in Morocco where some thousands of persons were poisoned from consuming cooking oil adulterated with lubricating oil containing TOCP (Smith and Spalding[199]).

After the Jamaica ginger incident Smith and Lillie[200] showed that TOCP could produce demyelinating lesions in experimental animals, particularly in chickens. They described TOCP as being "essentially a myelin poison." Subsequently Earl and Thompson[197,201] confirmed the finding of Smith and Lillie[200] and they further showed that the non-specific or pseudo-cholinesterase, but not the specific or true cholinesterase, was inhibited in the plasma, brain and spinal cord of birds poisoned with TOCP. It was suggested that the pseudocholinesterase of the nervous system might be associated in some way with the maintenance of the myelin sheath, and that the inhibition of this enzyme by TOCP might be responsible for the demyelination. Such a suggestion was of widespread interest because of the rapidly increasing use of a great variety of organo-phosphorus cholinesterase inhibitors in agriculture and horticulture.

Barnes and Denz[202] reported that two other organo-phosphorus compounds, di*iso*propylfluorophosphate (DFP) and bis-mono*iso*propyl-amino-fluorophosphine oxide (mipafox), like TOCP, produced paralyses and demyelinating lesions in the spinal cord and peripheral nerves of chickens. However, Davison[203] and Austin and Davies[204] found that a number of other organo-phosphorus compounds, although they inhibited the activity of pseudocholinesterase in chickens in a manner similar to TOCP, DFP and mipafox, did not cause demyelination or paralyses. There would thus appear to be no obvious relation between the prolonged inhibition of pseudocholinesterase activity and the production of demyelination. It is of interest that Jefferson[205] was unable to detect any change in the activity of either the pseudo- or the true cholinesterase in the cerebrospinal fluid of patients with multiple sclerosis, an observation confirmed by Webster and Mackenzie.[206]

In describing the pathological findings of patients poisoned with TOCP, Aring[207] reported extensive damage to axons as well as to myelin sheaths. In careful experimental studies with chickens Cavanagh,[207a] using TOCP, and Fenton,[207b] using DFP, also observed that axons were destroyed as well as myelin sheaths. Neither worker could find evidence that the demyelination was primary. However, Majno and Karnovsky[208] reported that mipafox caused a decrease in the *in vitro* incorporation of acetate-C^{14} into the lipid of rat sciatic nerve and Austin[209] described similar results when DFP was administered to chickens. In contrast, Webster[210] reported that demyelination in the chicken produced by TOCP was not associated with any change in the incorporation of inorganic P^{32} into the lipid phosphorus of peripheral nerve or spinal cord. Thus not only is the demyelination caused by TOCP and other organo-phosphorus compounds not associated with inhibition of pseudocholinesterase activity, but there is also considerable doubt, despite frequent statements to the contrary (see, for example Susser and Stein[198]), as to whether the demyelination caused by TOCP poisoning is, in fact, primary.

Lipolytic Enzymes and Demyelination

Marburg[211] in 1906 suggested that demyelinating diseases may be caused by an excess of lipolytic enzymes in the plasma. In 1930, Brickner[212] incubated sections of rat spinal cord with plasma from normal subjects or from patients with multiple sclerosis. He claimed that the incidence and the severity of histological changes characteristic of demyelination was greater in the cords that had been incubated with the plasma from the diseased patients. Weil and Cleveland[213] confirmed these findings and Weil and Luhan[214] reported the presence of a similar neurotoxic substance in the urine of patients with multiple sclerosis. However, the presence of this neurotoxic substance in the serum and urine is in no way characteristic of demyelinating disease. Positive tests were obtained in a number of unrelated conditions, including diseases of the liver. Weil and Cleveland[213] concluded that this *in vitro* myelinolytic effect was not related to the demyelination of multiple sclerosis.

In addition, Brickner[215,216] claimed that there was an increase in the concentration of both an esterase and an enzyme capable of hydrolyzing lecithin in the serum of patients with multiple sclerosis. This work has yet to be confirmed. Crandall and Cherry[217] reported that the activity of lipase (i.e., an enzyme capable of hydrolyzing olive oil) was increased in the serum of a high percentage of patients with multiple sclerosis, but there was no change in the activity of esterase (i.e., an enzyme capable of hydrolyzing ethyl butyrate). A similar percentage of patients with liver or pancreas disease also had an increase in the serum lipase activity with no change in the activity of the esterase. More recent studies have confirmed that the esterase activity of the serum of patients with multiple sclerosis is not increased.[218]

In an experimental investigation, Weil and Crandall[219] ligated the common bile duct or pancreatic duct of dogs. In either condition there was an immediate increase in the activity of the serum lipase followed by a later rise in the neurotoxic activity of the serum, as judged by Brickner's rat spinal cord test. Thus the increase in lipase activity did not parallel the increase in neurotoxic activity. Also the lipase activity could be destroyed by heating the serum, a procedure that had no effect on the neurotoxic activity. They concluded that in experimental hepatic damage a neurotoxic agent, which is not lipase, is present in the serum. This, together with the work of Weil and Cleveland[213] and Crandall and Cherry[217] described above, throws serious doubt on the importance of serum lipase or the serum neurotoxic substance in human demyelinating disease.

Demyelination In Vitro

Many workers have attempted to produce changes similar to those of demyelination by incubating sections of brain or spinal cord *in vitro* with certain enzymes. In 1902 Flexner and Noguchi[220] described the neurotoxic effects of snake venom, an observation later confirmed by Weil.[221] Frazer *et al.*[190] produced an *in vitro* demyelination in nerve tissue with the toxin of *Clostridium welchii*. Negative results were obtained with pancreatic lipase by Weil and Cleveland,[213] but Vogel[222] was able to produce demyelination by injecting a purified lipase into the brains of rabbits. The enzyme also caused a demyelination on segments of spinal cord incubated *in vitro*.

A thorough investigation of the *in vitro* effects of enzymes on the nervous system was undertaken by Morrison and Zamecnik.[223] These workers incubated sections and blocks of rabbit spinal cord and brain with either cobra venom or a *Clostridium welchii* filtrate (consisting chiefly of the alpha toxin). In each instance there was demyelination. In sections incubated with cobra venom lecithin was thought to be broken down into lysolecithin, since cobra venom is known to contain a phospholipase A, whereas in the sections incubated with *Clostridium welchii* filtrate lecithin was thought to be broken down into diglyceride and phosphorylcholine by phospholipase D known to be present in the filtrate.[224]

In assessing the results of experiments such as these, it should be borne in mind that mechanisms other than those postulated may be responsible for the observed changes. In addition to phospholipase A, cobra venom contains a number of other enzymes, and Macfarlane[225] showed that sphingomyelin, a known constituent of the myelin sheath, is also hydrolyzed by the *Clostridium welchii* alpha toxin. In 1930 Weil[221] reported that a number of hemolytic compounds, including such non-enzymic substances as saponin and sodium taurocholate, can produce a demyelination *in vitro,* presumably as a result of a physical action on myelin. It may well be that an enzyme can cause a demyelination, not by its direct action on the lipids of the myelin sheath, but by producing a substance which is itself myelinolytic. As Morrison and Zamecnik[223] pointed out, lysolecithin, formed from the hydrolysis of lecithin by the cobra venom, may be such a myelinolytic substance. But the importance to experimental pathology of experiments such as those of Vogel[222] and Morrison and Zamecnik[223] remains. They demonstrate that each of three quite different enzymes, lipase and phospholipases A and D, can produce *in vitro* changes in the myelin sheath that strongly resemble demyelination produced *in vivo.*

A detailed account of the effects of neurotoxins and venoms is given elsewhere in this volume.

REFERENCES

1. LEES, M., FOLCH, J., SLOANE-STANLEY, G. H. and CARR, S.: *J. Neurochem., 4:*9 (1959).
2. HÖRHAMMER, L., WAGNER, H. and HÖLZL, J.: *Biochem. Ztschr., 232:*269 (1960).
3. RAPPORT, M. M. and LERNER, B.: *Biochim. et biophys. acta, 33:*319 (1959).
4. WEBSTER, G. R.: *Biochim. et biophys. acta, 44:*109 (1960).
5. BRANTE, G.: *Acta physiol. scandinav.* (suppl. 63), *18:*1 (1949).
6. ROBINS, E., EYDT, K. M. and SMITH, D. E.: *J. Biol. Chem., 220:*677 (1956).
7. FOLCH, J.: In *Biochemistry of the Developing Nervous System,* p. 121. H. Waelsch, Ed. New York, Acad. Press (1955).
8. WAELSCH, H. (ED.): *Biochemistry of the Developing Nervous System.* New York, Academic Press (1955).

9. Folch, J., Casals, J., Pope, A., Meath, J. A., LeBaron, F. N. and Lees, M.: In *The Biology of Myelin*, p. 122. S. R. Korey, Ed. New York, Hoeber (1959).

10. Edgar, G. W. F. and Smits, G.: *J. Neurochem., 3:*316 (1959).

11. Davison, A. N. and Wajda, M.: *J. Neurochem., 4:*353 (1959).

12. Uzman, L. L. and Rumley, M. K.: *J. Neurochem., 3:*170 (1958).

13. Korey, S. R. and Orchen, M.: *Arch. Biochem. & Biophys., 83:*381 (1959).

14. Erickson, N. E. and Lands, W. E. M.: *Proc. Soc. Exper. Biol. & Med., 102:*512 (1959).

15. Kishimoto, Y. and Radin, N. S.: *J. Lipid Res., 1:*79 (1959).

16. Johnson, A. C., McNabb, A. R. and Rossiter, R. J.: *Biochem. J., 44:*494 (1949).

17. Tingey, A. H.: *J. Ment. Sc., 102:*851 (1956).

18. Cumings, J. N., Goodwin, H., Woodward, E. M. and Curzon, G.: *J. Neurochem., 2:*289 (1958).

19. Johnson, A. C., McNabb, A. R. and Rossiter, R. J.: *Arch. Neurol. & Psychiat., 64:*105 (1950).

20. Rossiter, R. J.: In *Pathology of the Nervous System*, p. 207. J. Folch, Ed. London, Pergamon Press (1961).

21. Johnson, A. C., McNabb, A. R. and Rossiter, R. J.: *Biochem. J., 45:*500 (1949).

22. McCamen, R. E. and Robins, E.: *J. Neurochem., 5:*18 (1959).

23. Logan, J. E., Mannell, W. A. and Rossiter, R. J.: *Biochem. J., 51:*482 (1952).

24. Wolman, M.: *J. Neurochem., 1:*370 (1957).

25. Adams, C. W. M.: *J. Neurochem., 2:*178 (1958).

26. Cumings, J. N.: *Brain, 76:*531 (1953).

27. Cumings, J. N.: *Brain, 78:*554 (1955).

28. Blackwood, W. and Cumings, J. N.: *J. Neurol., Neurosurg. & Psychiat., 17:*33 (1954).

29. Cumings, J. N.: In *Biochemical Aspects of Neurological Disorders*, p. 180. J. N. Cumings and M. Kremer, Eds. Oxford, Blackwell (1959).

30. Bernsohn, J. and Namajuska, I.: *Proc. Soc. Exper. Biol. & Med., 88:*124 (1955).

31. Green, J. B., Papadopoulos, N., Cevallos, W., Forster, F. M. and Hess, W. C.: *J. Neurol., Neurosurg. & Psychiat., 22:*117 (1959).

32. Folch, J. and Lees, M.: *J. Biol. Chem., 191:*807 (1951).

33. LeBaron, F. N. and Folch, J.: *J. Neurochem., 1:*101 (1956).

34. Kühne, W. and Chittenden, R. H.: *Ztschr. Biol., 26:*291 (1889).

35. Koenig, H.: *J. Neurochem., 4:*93 (1959).

36. Finean, J. B., Hawthorne, J. N. and Patterson, J. D. E.: *J. Neurochem., 1:*256 (1957).

37. Folch, J., Lees, M. and Carr, S.: *Exper. Cell Res.*, Suppl. 5, p. 58 (1958).

38. Uzman, L. L.: *Arch. Biochem. & Biophys., 76:*474 (1958).

39. Uzman, L. L. and Rosen, H.: *Arch. Biochem. & Biophys., 76:*490 (1958).

40. Uzman, L. L. and Rumley, M. K.: *Arch. Biochem. & Biophys., 89:*13 (1960).

41. Dittmer, J. C. and Dawson, R. M. C.: *Biochim. et biophys. acta, 40:*379 (1960).

42. Hörhammer, L., Wagner, H. and Richter, G.: *Biochem. Ztschr., 331:*155 (1959).

43. Fernández-Morán, H.: In *Metabolism of the Nervous System*. D. Richter, Ed. London, Pergamon Press (1957).

44. Fernández-Morán, H. and Finean, J. B.: *J. Biochem. Biophys. Cytol., 3:*725 (1958).

45. Finean, J. B.: *Exper. Cell Res.*, Suppl. 5, p. 18 (1958).

46. Finean, J. B. and Robertson, J. D.: *Brit. M. Bull., 14:*267 (1958).

47. ROSSITER, R. J.: In *Metabolism of the Nervous System,* p. 355. D. Richter, Ed. London, Pergamon Press (1957).
48. KENNEDY, E. P.: *Canad. J. Biochem. & Physiol., 34*:334 (1956).
49. KENNEDY, E. P.: *Federation Proc., 16*:847 (1957).
50. ROSSITER, R. J., MCMURRAY, W. C. and STRICKLAND, K. P.: *Federation Proc., 16*:853 (1957).
51. ROSSITER, R. J., MCLEOD, I. M. and STRICKLAND, K. P.: *Canad. J. Biochem. & Physiol., 35*:945 (1957).
52. ROSSITER, R. J., PRITCHARD, E. T. and STRICKLAND, K. P.: *Neurology* (Suppl. 1), *8*:34 (1958).
53. ROSSITER, R. J.: In *Metabolic Pathways,* 2nd Ed., Vol. 1, p. 357. D. M. Greenberg, Ed. New York, Acad. Press (1960).
54. ROSSITER, R. J. and STRICKLAND, K. P.: *Ann. New York Acad. Sc., 72*:790 (1959).
55. ROSSITER, R. J. and STRICKLAND, K. P.: In *Lipide Metabolism,* p. 69. K. Bloch, Ed. New York, John Wiley & Sons (1960).
56. GAMBAL, D. and MONTY, K. J.: *Federation Proc., 18*:232 (1959).
57. KIYASU, J. Y. and KENNEDY, E. P.: *J. Biol. Chem., 235*:2590 (1960).
58. ANSELL, G. B. and SPANNER, S.: *Biochem. J., 79*:176 (1961).
59. ZABIN, I. and MEAD, J. F.: *J. Biol. Chem., 205*:271 (1953); *211*:87 (1954).
60. SPRINSON, D. B. and COULON, A.: *J. Biol. Chem., 207*:585 (1954).
61. BRADY, R. O. and KOVAL, G. J.: *J. Biol. Chem., 233*:26 (1958).
62. ZABIN, I.: *J. Am. Chem. Soc., 79*:5834 (1957).
63. BRADY, R. O., FORMICA, J. V. and KOVAL, G. J.: *J. Biol. Chem., 233*:1072 (1958).
64. SRIBNEY, M. and KENNEDY, E. P.: *Federation Proc., 16*:253 (1957).
65. SRIBNEY, M. and KENNEDY, E. P.: *J. Am. Chem. Soc., 79*:5325 (1957).
66. SRIBNEY, M. and KENNEDY, E. P.: *J. Biol. Chem., 233*:1315 (1958).
67. CARTER, H. E. and FUJINO, Y.: *J. Biol. Chem., 221*:879 (1956).
68. RADIN, N. S., MARTIN, F. B. and BROWN, J. R.: *J. Biol. Chem., 224*:499 (1957).
69. BURTON, R. M., SODD, M. A. and BRADY, R. O.: *J. Biol. Chem., 233*:1053 (1958).
70. BURTON, R. M., SODD, M. A. and BRADY, R. O.: In Symposium III. *Biochemistry of the Central Nervous System,* p. 202. F. Brücke, Ed. London, Pergamon Press (1959).
71. MOSER, H. W. and KARNOVSKY, M. L.: *J. Biol. Chem., 234*:1990 (1959).
72. GARCIA, L. and BURTON, R. M.: *Federation Proc., 19*:144 (1960).
73. CLELAND, W. W. and KENNEDY, E. P.: *J. Biol. Chem., 235*:45 (1960).
74. BAKKE, J. E. and CORNATZER, W. E.: *J. Biol. Chem., 236*:653 (1961).
74a. DAVISON, A. N.: *Biochem. J., 78*:4P (1961).
75. GOLDBERG, I. H.: *J. Lipid Res. 2*:103 (1961).
76. ROBBINS, P. W. and LIPMANN, F.: *J. Biol. Chem., 229*:837 (1957).
77. PAULUS, H. and KENNEDY, E. P.: *J. Biol. Chem., 235*:1303 (1960).
78. BLOCH, K., BERG, B. N. and RITTENBERG, D.: *J. Biol. Chem., 149*:511 (1943).
79. DAVISON, A. N., DOBBING, J., MORGAN, R. S. and PAYLING WRIGHT, G.: *J. Neurochem., 3*:89 (1958).
80. DAVISON, A. N., DOBBING, J., MORGAN, R. S. and PAYLING WRIGHT, G.: *Lancet, i*:658 (1959).
81. WAELSCH, H., SPERRY, W. M. and STOYANOFF, V. A.: *J. Biol. Chem., 135*:291 (1940).
82. WAELSCH, H., SPERRY, W. M. and STOYANOFF, V. A.: *J. Biol. Chem., 135*:297 (1940), *140*:885 (1941).
83. THOMPSON, R. C. and BALLOU, J. E.: *J. Biol. Chem., 208*:883 (1954), *223*:795 (1956).

84. VAN BRUGGEN, J. T., HUTCHENS, T. T., CLAYCOMB, C. K. and WEST, E. S.: J. Biol. Chem., 200:31 (1953).
85. MCMILLAN, P. J., DOUGLAS, G. W. and MORTENSEN, R. A.: Proc. Soc. Exper. Biol. & Med., 96:738 (1957).
86. NICHOLAS, H. J. and THOMAS, B. E.: J. Neurochem., 4:42 (1959).
87. SRERE, P. A., CHAIKOFF, I. L., TREITMAN, S. S. and BURNSTEIN, L. S.: J. Biol. Chem., 182:629 (1949).
88. CORNFORTH, J. W.: J. Lipid Res., 1:3 (1959).
89. NICHOLAS, H. J. and THOMAS, B. E.: Biochim. et biophys. acta, 36:583 (1959).
90. GARATTINI, S., PAOLETTI, P. and PAOLETTI, R.: Arch. Biochem. & Biophys., 80:210 (1959).
91. KOREY, S. R. and STEIN, A.: Federation Proc., 18:264 (1959).
92. SPEIDEL, C. C.: J. Exper. Zool., 61:279 (1932).
93. SPEIDEL, C. C.: J. Comp. Neurol., 61:1 (1935).
94. CLARK, E. R. and CLARK, E. L.: Anat. Rec. (Suppl. 3), 70:14 (1938).
95. PETERSON, E. R. and MURRAY, M. R.: Am. J. Anat., 96:319 (1955).
96. GEREN, B. B.: Exper. Cell. Res., 7:558 (1954).
97. ROBERTSON, J. D.: J. Biochem. Biophys. Cytol., 1:271 (1955).
98. TERRY, R. D. and HARKIN, J. C.: Exper. Cell. Res., 13:193 (1957).
99. BODIAN, D. and DZIEWIATKOWSKI, D.: J. Cell. & Comp. Physiol., 34:155 (1950).
100. SAMUELS, A. J., BOYARSKY, L. L., GERARD, R. W., LIBET, B. and BRUST, M.: Am. J. Physiol., 164:1 (1951).
101. MAGEE, W. L. and ROSSITER, R. J.: Biochem. J., 58:243 (1954).
102. MIANI, N. and MARINI, I.: Bull. Soc. Ital. Biol. Sper., 31:29 (1955).
103. MAGEE, W. L., BERRY, J. F., MAGEE, M. and ROSSITER, R. J.: J. Neurochem., 3:333 (1958).
104. MAJNO, G. and KARNOVSKY, M. L.: J. Exper. Med., 108:197 (1958).
105. PRITCHARD, E. T. and ROSSITER, R. J.: J. Neurochem., 3:341 (1958).
106. KLINE, D., MAGEE, W. L., PRITCHARD, E. T. and ROSSITER, R. J.: J. Neurochem., 3:52 (1958).
107. LUSE, S. A.: J. Biochem. Biophys. Cytol., 2:777 (1956).
108. PETERS, A.: J. Biochem. Biophys. Cytol., 7:121 (1960).
109. BURT, N. S., MCNABB, A. R. and ROSSITER, R. J.: Biochem. J., 47:318 (1950).
110. ADAMS, C. W. M. and DAVISON, A. N.: J. Neurochem., 4:282 (1959).
111. DAVISON, A. N. and DOBBING, J.: Biochem. J., 73:701 (1959).
112. DAVISON, A. N. and DOBBING, J.: Biochem. J., 75:565 (1960).
113. DAVISON, A. N. and DOBBING, J.: Biochem. J., 75:571 (1960).
114. DAVISON, A. N., MORGAN, R. S., WAJDA, M. and PAYLING WRIGHT, G.: J. Neurochem., 4:360 (1959).
115. DAVISON, A. N.: Biochem. J., 74:1P (1960).
116. HURST, E. W., COOKE, B. T. and MELVIN, P.: Australian J. Exper. Biol. & Med. Sc., 21:115 (1943).
117. ADAMS, R. D. and KUBIK, C. S.: Am. J. Med., 12:510 (1952).
118. ADAMS, R. D.: In "Allergic" Encephalomyelitis, p. 183. M. W. Kies and E. C. Alvord, Eds. Springfield, Ill., Thomas (1959).
119. CAVANAGH, J. B. and THOMPSON, R. H. S.: Brit. M. Bull., 10:47 (1954).
120. THOMPSON, R. H. S.: In Biochemical Aspects of Neurological Disorders, p. 35. J. N. Cumings and M. Kremer, Eds. Oxford, Blackwell (1959).
121. HURST, E. W.: J. Hyg., 32:33 (1932).
122. HURST, E. W.: Am. J. Med., 12:547 (1952).
123. CAVANAGH, J. B.: Guy's Hosp. Rep., 105:39 (1956).

124. WAKSMAN, B. H.: *Internat. Arch. Allergy Appl. Immunol.* (Suppl.), *14*:1 (1959).
125. CONDIE, R. M. and GOOD, R. A.: In *The Biology of Myelin,* p. 321. S. R. Korey, Ed. New York, Hoeber (1959).
126. KIES, M. W. and ALVORD, E. C. (EDS.): *"Allergic" Encephalomyelitis.* Springfield, Ill., Thomas (1959).
127. RIVERS, T. M., SPRUNT, D. M. and BERRY, G. P.: *J. Exper. Med., 58*:39 (1933).
128. RIVERS, T. M. and SCHWENTKER, F. F.: *J. Exper. Med., 61*:689 (1935).
129. FERRARO, A. and JERVIS, G. A.: *Arch. Neurol. & Psychiat., 43*:195 (1940).
130. KABAT, E. A., WOLF, A. and BEZER, A. E.: *J. Exper. Med., 85*:117 (1947).
131. WOLF, A., KABAT, E. A. and BEZER, A. E.: *J. Neuropath. & Exper. Neurol., 6*:333 (1947).
132. FREUND, J. and MCDERMOTT, K.: *Proc. Soc. Exper. Biol. & Med., 49*:548 (1942).
133. MORGAN, I. M.: *J. Exper. Med., 85*:131 (1947).
134. FREUND, J., STERN, E. R. and PISANTI, T. M.: *J. Immunol., 57*:179 (1947).
135. MORRISON, L. R.: *Arch. Neurol. & Psychiat., 58*:391 (1947).
136. OLITSKY, P. K. and YAGER, R. H.: *J. Exper. Med., 90*:213 (1949).
137. THOMAS, L., PATERSON, P. Y. and SMITHWICK, B.: *J. Exper. Med., 92*:133 (1950).
138. INNES, J. R. M.: *Brit. Vet. J., 106*:93 (1950).
139. LUMSDEN, C. E.: *Brain, 72*:517 (1949).
140. LIPTON, M. M. and FREUND, J.: *J. Immunol., 71*:98 (1953).
141. ROBBINS, F. C.: In *"Allergic" Encephalomyelitis,* p. 467. M. W. Kies and E. C. Alvord, Eds. Springfield, Ill., Thomas (1959).
142. MOYER, A. W., JERVIS, G. A., BLACK, J., KOPROWSKI, H. and COX, H. R.: *Proc. Soc. Exper. Biol. & Med., 75*:387 (1950).
143. KABAT, E. A., WOLF, A. and BEZER, A. E.: *Tr. Am. Neurol. A., 76*:128 (1951).
144. GOOD, R. A., CAMPBELL, B. and GOOD, T. A.: *Proc. Soc. Exper. Biol. & Med., 72*:341 (1949).
145. HOYER, L. W., CONDIE, R. M. and GOOD, R. A.: *Proc. Soc. Exper. Biol. & Med., 103*:205 (1960).
146. ALVORD, E. C.: *J. Immunol., 61*:355 (1949).
147. WAKSMAN, B. H. and ADAMS, R. D.: *J. Exper. Med., 102*:213 (1955).
148. WAKSMAN, B. H. and ADAMS, R. D.: *J. Neuropath. & Exper. Neurol., 15*:293 (1956).
149. HOTTLE, G. A., NEDZEL, G. A., WRIGHT, J. T. and BELL, J. F.: *Proc. Soc. Exper. Biol. & Med., 72*:289 (1949).
150. FERRARO, A. and ROIZIN, L.: *J. Neuropath. & Exper. Neurol., 10*:394 (1951).
151. KOPROWSKI, H. and JERVIS, G. A.: *Proc. Soc. Exper. Biol. & Med., 69*:472 (1948).
152. OLITSKY, P. K. and TAL, C.: *Proc. Soc. Exper. Biol. & Med., 79*:50, *81*:590 (1952).
153. GOLDSTEIN, N. P., KOLB, L. C., MASON, H. L., SAYRE, G. P. and KARLSON, A. G.: *Neurology, 3*:609 (1953).
154. GOLDSTEIN, N. P., KIES, M. W., KARLSON, A. G., KOLB, L. C., MASON, H. L. and SAYRE, G. P.: *Neurology, 5*:550 (1955).
155. WAKSMAN, B. H., PORTER, H., LEES, M. D., ADAMS, R. D. and FOLCH, J.: *J. Exper. Med., 100*:451 (1954).
156. LIPTON, M. M.: In *"Allergic" Encephalomyelitis,* p. 300. M. W. Kies and E. C. Alvord, Eds. Springfield, Ill., Thomas (1959).
157. KIES, M. W., ROBOZ, E. and ALVORD, E. C.: *Federation Proc., 15*:288 (1956).
158. ROBOZ, E., HENDERSON, N. and KIES, M. W.: *J. Neurochem., 2*:254 (1958).
159. KIES, M. W., ALVORD, E. C. and ROBOZ, E.: *J. Neurochem., 2*:261 (1958).

160. BEUTNER, E. H., WITEBSKY, E., ROSE, N. R. and GERBASI, J. R.: *Proc. Soc. Exper. Biol. & Med., 97*:712 (1958).

161. WAKSMAN, B. H.: In *"Allergic" Encephalomyelitis*, p. 263. M. W. Kies and E. C. Alvord, Eds. Springfield, Ill., Thomas (1959).

162. PHILLIPS, P. H. and ENGEL, R. W.: *J. Nutrition, 18*:277 (1939).

163. LIPPINCOTT, S. W. and MORRIS, H. P.: *J. Nat. Cancer Inst., 2*:39 (1941).

164. SWANK, R. L. and BESSEY, O. A.: In *Multiple Sclerosis and Demyelinating Diseases*, p. 133. Baltimore, Williams and Wilkins (1950).

165. SIEGEL, L., PUTNAM, T. J. and LYNN, J. G.: *Proc. Soc. Exper. Biol. & Med., 47*:362 (1941).

166. JOINER, C. L., McARDLE, B. and THOMPSON, R. H. S.: *Brain, 73*:431 (1950).

167. JONES, H. H., JONES, H. H. JR. and BUNCH, L. D.: *Ann. Int. Med., 33*:831 (1950).

168. HENNEMAN, D. H., ALTSCHULE, M. D., GONCZ, R. M. and ALEXANDER, L.: *Arch. Neurol. & Psychiat., 72*:688 (1954).

169. BAUER, H.: *Biochem. Z.: 327*:491 (1956).

170. McARDLE, B.: Quoted by Thompson, R. H. S. in ref. 120.

171. BRICKNER, R. M. and BRILL, N. Q.: *Arch. Neurol. & Psychiat., 46*:16 (1941).

172. BENNETTS, H. W. and CHAPMAN, F. E.: *Australian Vet. J., 13*:138 (1937).

173. BENNETTS, H. W. and BECK, A. B.: Bull. 147, Council for Scientific and Industrial Research of Australia (1942).

174. INNES, J. R. M. and SHEARER, G. D.: *J. Comp. Path. & Therap., 53*:1 (1943).

175. HOWELL, J. McC. and DAVISON, A. N.: *Biochem. J., 72*:365 (1959).

176. PÁLSSON, P. A. and GRÍMSSON, H.: *Proc. Soc. Exper. Biol. & Med., 83*:518 (1953).

177. MILLS, C. F. and FELL, B. F.: *Nature, 185*:20 (1960).

177a. GUBLER, C. J., CARTWRIGHT, G. E. and WINTROBE, M. M.: *J. Biol. Chem., 224*:533 (1957).

178. GALLAGHER, C. H., JUDAH, J. D. and REES, K. R.: *Proc. Roy. Soc. London, s.B., 145*:134, 195 (1956).

178a. WAINIO, W. W., WENDE, C. V. and SHIMP, N. F.: *J. Biol. Chem., 234*:2433 (1959).

178b. SANDS, R. H. and BEINERT, H.: *Biochem. Biophys. Res. Comm., 1*:175 (1959).

178c. TAKEMORI, S.: *J. Biochem. (Tokyo), 47*:382 (1960).

178d. GRIFFITHS, D. E. and WHARTON, D. C.: *Biochem. Biophys. Res. Comm., 4*:199 (1961).

179. MANDELBROTE, M., STANIER, M. W., THOMPSON, R. H. S. and THURSTON, M. N.: *Brain, 71*:212 (1948).

180. HURST, E. W.: *Brain, 67*:103 (1944).

181. FERRARO, A.: *Arch. Neurol. & Psychiat., 52*:443 (1944).

182. FERRARO, A.: *Arch. Neurol. & Psychiat., 29*:1364 (1933).

183. HURST, E. W.: *Australian J. Exper. Biol. & Med. Sc., 18*:201 (1940), *20*:297 (1942).

184. LUMSDEN, C. E.: *J. Neurol., Neurosurg. & Psychiat., 13*:1 (1950).

185. HICKS, S. P.: *Arch. Path., 49*:111 (1950).

186. LEVINE, S. and STYPULKOWSKI, W.: *Arch. Path., 67*:306 (1959).

187. MEYER, A.: *Ztschr. Neurol. u. Psychiat., 112*:187 (1928).

188. PUTNAM, T. J., McKENNA, J. B. and MORRISON, L. R.: *J.A.M.A., 97*:1591 (1931).

189. CLAUDE, H.: *Arch. Physiol. norm. Path., 29*:843 (1897).

190. FRAZER, A. C., ELKES, J. J., SAMMONS, H. G., GOVAN, A. D. T. and COOKE, W. T.: *Lancet, i*:457 (1945).

191. MORRISON, L. R.: *Arch. Neurol. & Psychiat., 55:*1 (1946).
192. PUTNAM, T. J.: *Arch. Neurol. & Psychiat., 33:*929 (1935).
193. PUTNAM, T. J.: *Arch. Neurol. & Psychiat., 37:*1298 (1937).
194. SMITH, M. I. and ELVOVE, E.: *Pub. Health Rep., 45:*1703 (1930).
195. SMITH, M. I., ELVOVE, E. and FRAZIER, W. H.: *Pub. Health Rep., 45:*2509 (1930).
196. HUNTER, D., PERRY, K. M. A. and EVANS, R. B.: *Brit. J. Indust. Med., 1:*227 (1944).
197. EARL, J. C. and THOMPSON, R. H. S.: *Brit. J. Pharmacol., 7:*683 (1952).
198. SUSSER, H. V. and STEIN, Z.: *Brit. J. Indust. Med., 14:*111 (1957).
199. SMITH, H. V. and SPALDING, J. M. K.: *Lancet, ii:*1019 (1959).
200. SMITH, M. I. and LILLIE, R. D.: *Arch. Neurol. & Psychiat., 26:*976 (1931).
201. EARL, C. J. and THOMPSON, R. H. S.: *Brit. J. Pharmacol., 7:*261 (1952).
202. BARNES, J. M. and DENZ, F. A.: *J. Path. & Bact., 65:*597 (1953).
203. DAVISON, A. N.: *Brit. J. Pharmacol., 8:*212 (1953).
204. AUSTIN, L. and DAVIES, D. R.: *Brit. J. Pharmacol., 9:*145 (1954).
205. JEFFERSON, M.: *Clin. Sc., 13:*599 (1954).
206. WEBSTER, G. R. and MACKENZIE, I. C. K.: *Guy's Hosp. Rep., 106:*239 (1957).
207. ARING, C. D.: *Brain, 65:*34 (1942).
207a. CAVANAGH, J. B.: *J. Neurol. Neurosurg. & Psychiat., 17:*163 (1954).
207b. FENTON, J. C. B.: *J. Path. & Bact., 69:*181 (1955).
208. MAJNO, G. and KARNOVSKY, M. L.: *Federation Proc., 14:*250 (1955).
209. AUSTIN, L.: *Brit. J. Pharmacol., 12:*356 (1957).
210. WEBSTER, G. R.: *Biochem. J., 57:*153 (1954).
211. MARBURG, O.: *Jahrb. Psychiat., 27:*211 (from Ferraro[181]) (1906).
212. BRICKNER, R. M.: *Arch. Neurol. & Psychiat., 23:*715 (1930).
213. WEIL, A. and CLEVELAND, D. A.: *Arch. Neurol. & Psychiat., 27:*375 (1932).
214. WEIL, A. and LUHAN, J. A.: *Arch. Neurol. & Psychiat., 34:*459 (1935).
215. BRICKNER, R. M.: *Bull. Neurol. Inst. New York, 1:*105 (1931).
216. BRICKNER, R. M.: *Bull. Neurol. Inst. New York, 2:*119 (1932).
217. CRANDALL, L. A. and CHERRY, I. S.: *Arch. Neurol. & Psychiat., 27:*367 (1932).
218. RICHARDS, C. H. and WOLFF, H. G.: *Arch. Neurol. & Psychiat., 43:*59 (1940).
219. WEIL, A. and CRANDALL, L.: *Ztschr. Neurol. u. Psychiat., 140:*577 (1932).
220. FLEXNER, S. and NOGUCHI, H.: *J. Exper. Med., 6:*279 (1902).
221. WEIL, A.: *Arch. Path., 9:*828 (1930).
222. VOGEL, F. S.: *J. Exper. Med., 93:*297 (1951).
223. MORRISON, L. R. and ZAMECNIK, P. C.: *Arch. Neurol. & Psychiat., 63:*367 (1950).
224. MACFARLANE, M. G. and KNIGHT, B. C. J. G.: *Biochem. J., 35:*885 (1941).
225. MACFARLANE, M. G.: *Biochem. J., 42:*587 (1948).

XXXVII

NEUROMUSCULAR DISORDERS*

J. E. Desmedt

The term 'neuromuscular disorders' includes the clinical conditions which affect the lower motor neuron and its axon, the neuromuscular junction and the skeletal muscle fibers. These structures which together constitute the motor unit (Sherrington) are intimately interrelated so that disturbance to any one of them is apt to affect the others. Another reason for grouping these diseases together is that they lend themselves to similar diagnostic and investigative technics.

GENERAL CONSIDERATIONS

Deterioration of motor performance in disease can result from many causes, e.g., intoxication, infection, hormonal imbalance, inadequate dietary intake or conditioned nutritional deficiency,[221,134] inherited metabolic defect, and the motor unit complex may be involved at many different levels.[160,105,471,26,109,380] In order to identify the primary biochemical lesion consideration has to be paid to each of the sequential elementary processes (Fig. 1) which enable the nerve impulse[205,232] initiated in the motor nerve cell[126] to activate skeletal muscle[67,225,320,139] and elicit the contractile response.[368,215,216,217,62] Further potential sites of clinical disorders are the metabolic processes called into play to sustain prolonged activity, such as the processes of energy mobilization in muscle,[323,99] the likely increase in acetylcholine synthesis in presynaptic endings whose transmitter stores would otherwise be rapidly depleted in repetitive synaptic activation (cf. refs. 50, 347, 281), and the adaptative changes in muscle local circulation[166,16] and in systemic circulation and pulmonary ventilation.[15] The motor unit itself should be viewed as a dynamic organization implying long-term interactions[441] of which only a few have been investigated, e.g., the dependance of the motor axon on its parent cell for the continuous supply of enzymes

*Supported by a research grant from the Muscular Dystrophy Associations of America Inc.

and other constituents synthesized in close relation to the cell nucleus,[443,218,197] the trophic influence of the motor nerve on the attached
muscle fibers,[144,185,463,109] and the possible function of continuous subthreshold acetylcholine release by nerve endings[140,225] in the regulation of the end-plate cholinoceptive reactivity.[226,405] The striking differences in the order of involvement of the various muscle groups in
different diseases, and sometimes even in different patients with the
same disease, suggest that motor units possess some kind of biochemical
individuality (cf. ref. 441) and a differential vulnerability to noxious
agents. In some of these diseases the biochemical lesion may be at-
tenuated and even repaired in spontaneous or induced remissions.

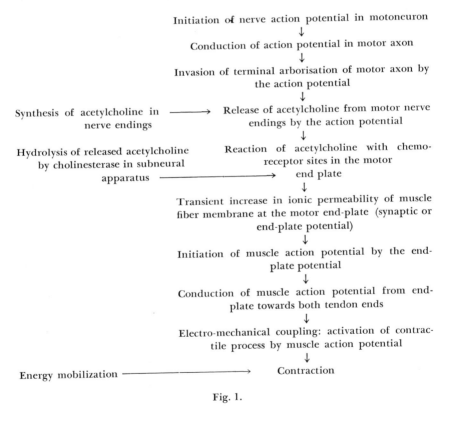

Fig. 1.

Even severe degenerative changes may be followed by attempts to compensate for the loss : muscle cells possess a remarkable power to re-
generate after injury[75,104] and, in partially denervated muscle, collateral
sprouting enables surviving motor axons to reinnervate additional

muscle fibers thus expanding residual motor units beyond normal dimensions.[442,425,127,460,461,79]

Skeletal muscle dysfunction expresses itself clinically by weakness with or without wasting, pain,[152] and impaired movement related to spasm (myotonia) or to fibrosis. The precise identification of specific syndromes implies an increasing dependance on special methods of analysis. Microscopical examination of muscular and neuromuscular biopsies[3,171,79,77,461] provides valuable information about the state of intramuscular nerves and muscle fibers and its diagnostic value is well established especially in the myopathies. Specific biochemical lesions may however fail to express themselves in recognizable patterns owing to the limited repertoire of histopathological reactions. Tissue culture,[159] histochemistry[20] and electron microscope[183] are now extending the range of anatomical studies.

Electromyography, i.e., the recording of spontaneous and voluntary electrical activity by means of needle-electrodes inserted into the muscles, is currently used for the diagnosis of neurogenic and myogenic paralyses and for the study of the organization of motor units.[57,242,406,56,45] The investigation of electrical and mechanical responses to nerve stimulation in a well-chosen muscle group allows the quantitation of weakness and fatigue and identification of dynamic patterns of responses characteristic of specific syndromes.[193,203,294,220,396,124,108,110,163,248,125] Technics for inserting glass microelectrodes into skeletal muscle fibers *in situ* seem very promising.[27] Human muscle can also be excised during surgery and tested *in vitro* under satisfactory conditions.[90,112] Pharmacological properties have been assessed with intravenous or intra-arterial injections.[192,59,131,180]

Standard biochemical technics are applied to test enzymic activity and metabolic reactions in excised muscle samples.[311,381] When investigating electrolyte contents, it is preferred to express the concentrations in relation to intracellular water rather than to muscle wet or dry weight.[194,43,86] This reference base is justified by the success achieved in unfolding the properties of excitable tissues in terms of movements of ions along or against their electrochemical gradients across the cell membrane.[204,205] Several methods allow a rough estimation to be made of extracellular space and, by subtraction of intracellular water.[289,86] Tissue analysis meets with special difficulties in patients with muscle atrophy or dystrophy when muscle architecture suffers distortions and the biopsy specimens contain an increased amount of fat and connective tissue. Muscle contents can then be expressed relative to the non-collagen nitrogen base which is defined as muscle nitrogen soluble in dilute alkali.[265] This base offers an approximation to the true functioning muscle tissue.[14,18] Skeletal muscle accounts for about 40% of body weight of the normal adult male and it contains about two thirds of the total body potassium and one third of the total body magnesium.[451,148] By virtue of its bulk, metabolic changes in diseased muscle are able to exert significant influences as indicated by studies of body composition by isotopic dilution technics,[128,32,391] of metabolic balance sheets, and of biochemical changes in blood and urine.

Blood circulation through skeletal muscle can be investigated with venous occlusion plethysmography,[16] dye dilution method[9] and local clearance of isotopic tracer.[228,433] Uptake or release of metabolites by muscles *in situ* is estimated from forearm bloodflow and from differences in concentrations in arterial blood and in venous blood collected from a deep vein draining forearm muscles.[87,8,81,314,380]

Only selected topics will be treated in this chapter on account of the limited space available. The problems raised by neurogenic atrophies and the trophic influence of the motor nerve on skeletal muscle have been left out but recent surveys can be consulted.[144,375,109,185]

PROGRESSIVE MUSCULAR DYSTROPHY

This is one of the most common muscular diseases and in spite of extensive research, neither its primary cause nor the mechanism involved have been elucidated. Muscular dystrophy is an inherited disorder which manifests itself by a slowly progressive weakness and wasting due to degenerative changes in the muscles without any lesion in peripheral or central nervous systems. Proximal muscles are generally affected first but the entire skeletal musculature may eventually be involved. No therapy is known to arrest or revert the dystrophic process. Recent nosological studies on large groups of patients currently distinguish three main types with different modes of inheritance: [423,402,262,19,439,252,434,435,36] (a) The *Duchenne type* is the commonest and most serious form. It begins in early childhood, chiefly in males, involving first pelvic girdle and later shoulder girdle but not the face. This form is rapidly progressive. It is carried by a sex-linked recessive gene. Sporadic cases may depend on new mutations. (b) The *facio-scapulo-humeral type*[255] occurs in both sexes and usually starts in the second decade. The wasting occurs first in the shoulder girdle and usually involves the face. The course is slow. This type is generally due to an autosomal dominant gene.[421] (c) The *limb-girdle type* discloses intermediate features and is less clearly defined. It appears to be inherited by recessive factors. Two other rare types of slowly progressive familial dystrophies have been described, e.g., the *distal myopathy*[445] with an unusual distribution to distal part of the limbs and the *ocular myopathy*[233,21] which involves external ocular muscles.

Pathological examination of dystrophic muscles discloses a slowly progressive and randomly distributed atrophy, scattered fibers showing hypertrophy or degenerative changes, only little evidence of regenerative changes, and interstitial accumulation of connective tissue and fat. Inflammatory cells are typically absent.[3,437] The behavior of muscle fibers following injury or in tissue culture deviate from the normal.[3,436,159] Cardiac muscles may be involved[367] but smooth muscles are not affected. Electromyography discloses changes consistent with the diffuse pattern of myopathic alterations. Due to random muscle fiber degeneration, the motor unit suffers a progressive loss of its component muscle fibers[240,242,61] resulting in a decrease in duration and voltage of the potentials and in the motor unit territory. The spike is conducted with normal velocity in surviving muscle fibers but changes have been described in refractory period[138] and in mechanical properties.[40]

Muscular dystrophies presumably depend on an inborn error of metabolism which has not yet been identified since the known biochemical changes appear secondary to dystrophic muscle breakdown.

Serum Enzymology.—Schapira and Dreyfus have found a striking increase in the serum level of aldolase, the enzyme which splits fructose 1,6-diphosphate into triose-phosphates.[376,373,219,22,10,136,393,408,450] The increase may be as high as 30 times above the normal. Increased levels in serum have also been found for other enzymes such as phospho-hexo-isomerase, lactic dehydrogenase, glutamic pyruvic transaminase and glutamic oxalacetic transaminase which are also present in high concentrations in the muscle cell but normally only appear in very small amounts in the systemic circulation.[373,377,341,120,450] These enzymes are also elevated in other primary diseases of muscle such as polymyositis, but not in the neural atrophies nor in neuromuscular diseases without wasting (e.g., myasthenia gravis). A transient rise in serum enzymes may occur in patients with acute cellular damage, e.g., in cardiac infarction or hepatitis.[393,450,430,224] The higher values occur in the younger patients with rapidly progressing muscular dystrophy while only moderate increases are found in adult patients or when the dystrophy is far advanced.[10,341,120,450] The level of enzymes in serum may remain elevated continuously for many months.[10,408,450] Serum enzymology provides a new useful approach though it cannot indicate the primary disorder because too many enzymes are involved and the changes seem to reflect loss into the blood of intracellular soluble proteins in the course of the dystrophic process.

Creatine Metabolism.—The occurrence of a marked creatinuria and of a reduced urinary elimination of creatinine in the myopathies is well known but it is now generally agreed that these changes occur in any generalized muscle wasting and reflect the reduction in total muscle mass in the body.[301,302,388,300,93,264] Adult men do not normally excrete significant amounts of creatine, but creatine is regularly eliminated by children and occasionally by women. Isotopic studies are in agreement with the view that, while creatine synthesis in liver and other sites proceeds at a fairly normal rate, much of the newly formed creatine fails to be taken up by the atrophied muscles and is thus eliminated.[24] However the interpretation of creatinuria may be difficult because it also occurs in metabolic disorders without actual muscle wasting, e.g., in pituitary diseases[92] and in thyrotoxicosis or following thyroid therapy.[173] Antithyroid treatment (thiouracil) suppresses the creatinuria in hyperthyroidism but not in other conditions.

A more reliable index of the reduction in functional muscle mass is actually provided by the decrease in urinary excretion of creatinine in patients on a creatinine-free diet. The normal adult male excretes daily 23 mg. creatinine per kg. body weight, the normal adult female 16.5 and infants about 10.[300] The value of the creatininuria as an index of the functional muscle mass simply results from the fact that the creatinine excreted by the kidney originates essentially from the creatine phosphate present in muscle tissue.[35,38,24]

Aminoaciduria.—No significant anomaly in total nitrogen balance has been noted in muscular dystrophy[388] but studies centered on the amino nitrogen, which normally represents only 2-4% of nitrogen excretion, have shown that the number and the concentration of amino acids excreted seem to be above normal limits.[7,214,33] Similar changes have been described in normal relatives of the patients[33] which would suggest that the aminoaciduria may not be secondary to dystrophic degeneration.

Pentosuria.—Excretion of abnormal amounts of ribose has been reported[308,334,117] but satisfactory evidence for such an anomaly could not be obtained by other groups.[292,438,358,346] The discrepancies are perhaps in part to be ascribed to differences in estimation procedure[116] and recent discussions should be consulted.[416,346]

Muscle Composition.—On the basis of intracellular water, biopsied dystrophic muscle is low in potassium and high in sodium, as if the mechanism for selective potassium accumulation had deteriorated.[212] A low potassium content is also found when the estimation is referred to the non-collagen nitrogen basis.[264] The turnover of K_{42} in the muscle sample is within normal limits.[391] This does not contradict the reduction in total exchangeable potassium in the body (isotope dilution method)[32,391] because the latter change reflects the important reduction in total mass of muscle tissue which normally contains about

70% of body potassium. The properties of muscle proteins have been investigated.[378,211] The concentrations of many constituents, referred to non-collagen nitrogen basis, are abnormal in muscular dystrophy, but generally not very different from what is found in the neural atrophies; there is a reduced content of myosin, myoglobin and glycolytic enzymes, while the activities of the oxidative enzymes seem normal.[118,429] Muscle iron increases in neural atrophy but remains normal in muscular dystrophy.[373,374]

Miscellaneous.—In contrast to myotonic dystrophy, progressive muscular dystrophy is not accompanied by consistent abnormalities of the endocrines.[420,95,364] Changes in protein fractions in serum such as an increase in alpha-2 globulin may be detected but this is not specific.[269,270,332] The basal metabolic rate is within normal range and occasional low figures can be explained by the extensive muscle wasting which is not reflected in total surface area.[388,420] Non-specific metabolic changes[102] are likely to occur simply as a consequence of prolonged immobilization.

Vitamin E Deficiency.—Experimental deprivation of dietary vitamin E in various mammals induces muscular weakness and wasting with excessive creatine elimination and degeneration of muscle fibers.[164, 135,284,339,448] Infants with biliary atresia or cystic fibrosis of the pancreas fail to absorb fat-soluble vitamins and may develop vitamin E deficiency.[48,97] These cases may present creatinuria and an occasional muscle lesion, but do not exhibit classical muscular dystrophy.[471,327,330] No defect in tocopherol has yet been demonstrated in muscular dystrophy, and the serum and muscle levels in tocopherol are normal in this disease.[307,291] Tocopherol administration may cure the nutritional myopathy and eliminate the creatinuria,[286,306,300,285,447] but is without effect in muscular dystrophy.[300,191] Tocopherol deficiency also differs from muscular dystrophy in the occurrence of a marked increase in oxygen consumption by muscles, both *in vivo* and *in vitro*,[426,213,469] which results in an elevated metabolic rate of the animal.[227] Glycogenolytic enzymes are not much reduced in muscle tissue and their concentration in the blood is not increased as in human muscular dystrophy.[373,23] The biochemistry of vitamin E has been recently reviewed.[41] Nutritional myopathies unrelated to tocopherol have been described.[72]

Hereditary Myopathy in Mice.—A mutation in an inbred strain (No. 129) of mice has resulted in a myopathy without neural involvement which is inherited by a recessive autosomal gene.[299] Successful breeding of these mice has been achieved and, in view of the added possibility of using unaffected litter mates as controls, dystrophic mice now afford an important research tool even though it is not proved that the biochemical lesion is identical with the one in human muscular dystrophy. A number of metabolic studies are available.[12,13,374,331,440] Dystrophic mice present a creatinuria which is unaffected by tocopherol administration.[222] The serum aldolase is increased.[379,440,466,467,450,195] C_{14} amino-acid incorporation studies suggest an accelerated turnover of muscle proteins, in which synthesis does not keep pace with catabolism.[395] Resting potentials in muscle fibers, measured with intracellular microelectrodes, are normal but are abnormally susceptible to electrolyte change.[85] An increased muscular irritability to mechanical stimulation suggests some similarities to human myotonic dystrophy.[283] The mechanical properties of dystrophic mouse muscles have also been analysed.[370]

POLYMYOSITIS

Until recently the terms myositis or dermatomyositis referred to a rather circumscribed entity with skin changes and aching weak muscles. However this acute form is much less common than the now well-recognized syndrome called subacute or chronic polymyositis in which skin changes and muscle tenderness are minimal.[122,322,157,37,437] The differentiation of the latter from other myopathies may raise problems, but recognition of its true incidence is important because cortisone may be of considerable value in treatment.[412,390,122,437] The electromyogram of polymyositis discloses a myopathic pattern (see above) but also repetitive discharges of fiber potentials which might be related to hyperirritability of muscle fibers in active degeneration.[186,348,356,437] Microscopical examination discloses degenerative changes of variable severity, regenerative activity of remaining muscle fibers and interstitial collections of inflammatory cells.[122,157,37,437] Polymyositis seems closely linked to the collagen diseases, e.g., rhumatoid arthritis, lupus erythematosus, . . . in which similar muscle changes occur. The etiology is obscure and the role of hypersensitivity reaction has been considered.[437]

In polymyositis the level of aldolase and other enzymes in serum is increased and it returns to normal with successful therapy.[394,341,120,408,53] Creatine metabolism is affected in proportion to muscular involvement[300,73] and serum gamma globulins are increased.[270] Basal metabolic rate tends to be elevated.[122,157] Myopathies resembling in some respects human polymyositis have been described in farm animals.[39,187]

McARDLE DISEASE

In this peculiar condition, apparently confined to skeletal muscle, initial strength is normal but exercise, especially if intensive, leads to local pain, weakness and cramps.[272] Movements become progressively awkward, stiff and soon impossible. The stiff muscles cannot be relaxed and passive extension is painful. Recovery always occurs in 5 to 10 minutes. There is no evidence of muscle wasting. Neurological examination is negative. After ischemic exercise, electrically silent localized swellings have been noticed in the muscle and interpreted as true reversible contractures (cf. refs. 158, 369). The concentration of lactate both in systemic blood and in blood coming from forearm muscles is decreased from normal. McArdle suggested that the incapacitation and the development of contractures resulted from the inability of the muscle to break glycogen down to lactic acid. He pointed out the likely similarity to iodoacetate-treated muscle which goes into contracture after a few induced contractions and is defective in glycogenolysis[271] as a result of poisoning of glyceraldehyde phosphate dehydrogenase.[297,298] The subsequent finding that intravenous infusions of glucose[381,344] and also of fructose[343] considerably increased the exercise tolerance of these patients pointed to an enzymic block closer to the phosphorolysis of glycogen. Biochemical studies on muscle biopsies have now identified the lesion as a specific defect in phosphorylase.[311,381,382,258] The affected muscles also present an excessive storage of glycogen, the latter apparently possessing a normal branched structure.[311] The disorder only involves the initial step of glycogen breakdown, and hexose phosphates added to extracts of the muscles are normally metabolized.

IDIOPATHIC PAROXYSMAL MYOGLOBINURIA

This rare disorder is characterized by attacks of muscle tenderness and stiffness with incapacitation, accompanied by the emission of a red or even dark-brown urine containing spectroscopically demonstrable myoglobin.[296,100,2,399,198,355,237] The symptoms subside in a few hours or a few days and thereafter the patient is able to use the affected muscles normally. Heavy muscular exertion is a frequent precipitating factor in susceptible patients. The most serious complication arises from renal failure. The only prophylactic measure is restriction of muscular activity. Myoglobinuria may be familial.[198] A similar syndrome occurs in horses.[66] A muscle biopsy taken just after an attack discloses marked widespread damage of muscle fibers with segmental necrosis but little interstitial reaction. Some time after an episode, only moderate and scattered changes may remain.[372,55,399,198,28,355,162]

Myoglobin, which functions as a short-term oxygen store in muscle[305,31] has a molecular weight of about a quarter of that of hemoglobin and its renal threshold is much lower (15 to 20 mg. per ml. blood[464]). It may thus color the urine while the plasma is clear, whereas in hemoglobinuria both plasma and urine are colored. Visible myoglobinuria (28 mg./100 ml. or more[342]) may occur in any extensive disruptive lesion of the muscles, e.g., in crush injuries.[64] Increased amounts of creatine and of amino acids are also eliminated in the urine in attacks of myoglobinuria[41] and there occurs a transient increase in the serum level of aldolase, transaminase and phosphohexoisomerase.[342,364] Myoglobinuria is only the most readily observable effect of the acute muscle damage, the etiology of which is unknown.

MYOTONIA

Myotonia is a symptom consisting in abnormal delay in relaxation of muscle fibers after cessation of the stimulus—be it voluntary, mechanical or electrical. The patient experiences difficulties in initiating movement after rest because of muscle stiffness. With repetition the movement becomes progressively more rapid and freely performed, with normal relaxation. Alleviation of myotonic spasm in one set of muscles does not prevent its occurrence in another. Myotonia returns after a period of rest. It is accentuated by cold exposure. It occurs in two well-recognized and distinct diseases:[407] (a) *Myotonia congenita* (Thomsen's disease[409]) is a relatively benign anomaly involving only muscular contraction and not associated with dystrophic features. It is usually inherited as a mendelian dominant trait. There is a marked generalized myotonia which becomes manifest in early life. The muscles are hypertrophic with uniform increase in muscle fiber diameter without histopathological changes.[3] A hereditary disease similar to myotonia congenita occurs in goats.[261,236,76] (b) *Myotonic dystrophy* (Steinert's disease[401]) is a slowly progressive myopathy of late onset with moderate myotonic features. It tends to be dominant and does not overlap with pedigrees of Thomsen's disease or of progressive muscular dystrophy.[353,407] The myopathic process is similar to the one in muscular dystrophy[459,3] but it involves first and foremost the distal muscle groups and extends to facial, extraocular and other bulbar-innervated muscles. There are also prominent dystrophic features in non-muscular tissues, e.g., cataract, skeletal anomalies, testicular atrophy and other endocrine disorders.

The myotonic spasms which appear electromyographically as bursts of high frequency potentials during attempted relaxation[57,254,147,406] seem primarily related to changes in muscle fiber membrane rather than in motor nerve or myoneural junction. The myotonic response to direct stimulation persists after degenerative section of the nerve in goats[51] and it is not abolished by full curarization of the muscle.[253,254,147,161] The elicitation of a muscle action potential apparently triggers an autorhythmic discharge in this condition. In fact infiltration of the muscle with a local anesthetic can block the afterspasm selectively.[57,147] Various drugs are known to intensify or diminish the myotonic symptoms.[236,51,352,89] Some of these effects may result from changes in the amount of neuromuscular excitation reaching the muscle rather than from a modification by the drug of the intrinsic myotonic process. With respect to therapy, quinine,[462,407] cortisone,[390] procaine amide[161] and prednisone[371] have been found of use in both forms of myotonia.[267,263]

Biochemical findings are somewhat different in the two clinical forms, in view of the associated dystrophy in Steinert's disease. In myotonia congenita both creatine tolerance and creatinine elimination tend to be elevated.[349,304] There is no evidence of myopathic changes. Chromatograms of phosphate esters from muscle samples have disclosed the presence of an unidentified fraction and of changes in creatine phosphate which might be due to mechanically induced myotonic activity during biopsy procedure.[65] Serum enzymology is normal. In myotonic dystrophy, the metabolic findings are similar to those in other myopathies, but generally less marked and less constant than in muscular dystrophy and polymyositis. Creatinine elimination is reduced in proportion to muscle wasting and the creatinuria is more or less marked.[303,304,93,470] The serum level of aldolase and other enbymes is normal or moderately elevated.[120,136,408,243,245,450] The protein fractions in serum have also been studied.[270,244]

Myotonic muscles appear to have a lowered potassium content.[91,114] Administration of potassium-binding ion exchange resin, which decreases serum potassium, has been found to relieve myotonic symptoms.[184,413] Myotonia seems to be reduced after meals or after administration of insulin and epinephrine,[352,249,338] i.e., in situations promoting a shift of potassium into the muscles (cf. ref. 94).

MYASTHENIA GRAVIS

Myasthenia gravis is characterized by loss of strength of exercised muscles and at least partial recovery after a period of rest. The extraocular and brainstem-innervated muscles are most frequently affected but the distribution of symptoms varies. The condition may be mild and restricted to a few muscle groups, or it may lead to a severe incapacity and even death from failure of pulmonary ventilation.[325,335, 175,428,386,111] There are no obvious changes in the muscles, no pain and no wasting and no sensory symptoms. Biochemical features associated with myopathic degeneration, such as elevated serum aldolase, creatinuria etc., do not occur in uncomplicated myasthenia gravis.[324, 302,325,300,120,364]

The disorder is related to a peculiar block of neuromuscular transmission. While the response of a rested myasthenic muscle to a single nerve shock is fairly normal, repetitive stimulation, even at low frequency (e.g., 2/sec.), leads to a marked reduction in the amplitude of successive responses. The features are not unlike those seen in d-Tubocurarine poisoning but further electrophysiological tests disclose fundamental differences between the two conditions. In myasthenic patients, a brief phase of electrically induced or voluntary activity is followed, after a fleeting facilitation, by a marked increase in neuromuscular block which takes many minutes to recover.[106,110] This 'post-tetanic exhaustion' phenomenon is obviously the counterpart of the pathological fatigue seen clinically. No such post-tetanic exhaustion occurs in a curarized muscle tested similarly, but it has been found in muscle poisoned with hemicholinium HC3,[107] a compound which strongly inhibits the synthesis of acetylcholine by nervous tissue.[384,282,281] On the basis of this and other evidence it appears likely that the myasthenic neuromuscular block depends on a presynaptic neurochemical defect chronically impairing acetylcholine synthesis in motor nerve endings, thereby preventing prompt replenishment of the acetylcholine stores which are being depleted during periods of increased activity.[107,110,111] No change need be postulated in the process of acetylcholine ejection from nerve endings. The myasthenic block is thus believed to differ considerably from the neuromuscular failure seen in botulinum intoxication where a single shock on the motor nerve evokes a very small muscle response and repetitive stimulation leads to a marked facilitation of successive responses.[290] The botulinum disorder apparently results from an impaired acetylcholine release[49] while acetylcholine synthesis is not affected.[63,403]

The reduced safety margin of neuromuscular transmission in myasthenia accounts for the exaggerated sensitivity of these patients to injected d-Tubocurarine,[25,121,345] and muscle relaxants.[121] Myasthenic muscle is fairly normally sensitive to arterially injected acetylcholine.[456,59,131] Changes in motor end-plate pharmacology have been suggested[180,175] but they might be secondary to enduring alteration in the presynaptic cholinergic mechanism.[111] Myasthenic patients, especially when only mildly affected by the disease exhibit an unexplained tolerance to intravenous decamethonium.[74] Anticholinesterase compounds such as Prostigmin, Mestinon and Mytelase are able to relieve myasthenic weakness for a period of hours following oral administration and they are in current use in the medical management of these patients.[335] These drugs do not remove the myasthenic neuro-muscular defect but only provide a non-specific and limited compensation thereof by prolonging and reinforcing the effect of synaptically liberated acetylcholine on the motor end-plates.[110] In severely affected patients the anticholinesterase drugs may become less effective and, when administered in too large amounts, they may aggravate muscular weakness by inducing 'cholinergic crisis.'[175,335] The relief of motor incapacitation by Prostigmin[427] and by the shorter-acting Tensilon[336] provides in most cases an unequivocal confirmation of the diagnosis of myasthenia gravis.[175,335,428,366] Some problem may arise however in the case of mild myasthenic-like symptoms when the response to the prostignin test is doubtful, especially if the patient presents in addition myopathic or atypical symptoms.[157,365,366,437] Useful information should be derived from nerve stimulation tests to titrate myasthenic involvement[248,109,110] and neuromuscular biopsies to show changes in motor nerve endings.[78,276,30]

The reason why patients develop a myasthenic defect at their myo-neural junctions is still obscure.[111] The incidence of genetic factors in etiology is far from established.[246] One possibility is that the enzyme cholineacetylase or some other essential component of the cholinergic manufacturing system in motor nerve endings fail to be supplied adequately to the nerve endings as a result of a biochemical disorder in the corresponding motor nerve cell in the spinal cord or medulla. The idea of an inborn or acquired error of motoneuron metabolism in myasthenia is still very tentative.[110] Another hypothesis postulates the release of some toxic compound into the blood, possibly by the thymus gland.[277,457] Abnormalities in thymic tissue (germinal center formation) are common in myasthenic patients,[69] thymic tumours occur in approximately 15% of them[70,69,231,175,335,428] and surgical thymectomy can definitely alleviate the myasthenic symptoms at least in a proportion of the patients.[230,231,385,123,397,175,335,428] Extracts have been prepared from the thymuses thus removed at operation and they have been assayed on neuromuscular preparations for curare-like properties.[455,457] Myasthenic serum has also been tested.[321] The hypothesis of a circulating metabolite with short-term depressant effect has not been substantiated. Many features of the disease would be better explained by an auto-immune process which could initiate a long-term neuro-chemical lesion at neuromuscular synapses.[398,320a,111] Changes in level of complement in serum during active phases of myasthenia provide the only evidence for the latter hypothesis.[320a]

NEUROMUSCULAR DISORDERS ASSOCIATED WITH MALIGNANCY

Patients suffering from cancer may present various kinds of neurological disorders not directly produced by metastases. Carcinomatous sensory neuropathy with chronic degeneration of posterior root ganglions[103] and cortical cerebellar degeneration[170,44] are well-known. Cases with muscular weakness and/or wasting unaccountable by malignancy cachexia have also been described and the lesions responsible may involve various levels of the neuromuscular system.

Carcinomatous Polymyositis.—The incidence of tumor in patients with polymyositis is reported to be as high as 8 to 17%.[437,364,454] The most common sites of the growth are stomach, breast, ovaries, lung and reticulo-endothelial system in that order. The muscular symptoms, generally in the form of a florid dermatomyositis but sometimes without skin involvement, may precede and dominate those of the tumor. The latter is sometimes necropsy finding. Diseases of the collagen group are also associated with malignancy.[360]

Carcinomatous Neuromyopathy.—This is a relatively infrequent association and the neoplasm is in most cases a bronchogenic carcinoma. The clinical features are those of a peripheral neuropathy or of a proximal myopathy of variable severity sometimes with bulbar palsy and ophthalmoplegia, and with a tendancy to spontaneous remissions.[260,200,196,44,199] Abnormal fatigue, which may respond more or less clearly to Prostigmin, sensory loss, muscular atrophy and depressed reflexes may occur in this rather heterogenous group of patients. Microscopical examination discloses various features singly or in association, viz. demyelination of peripheral nerve fibers, slight and scattered changes in the muscles with variable atrophy, and degeneration in posterior columns and motoneurons in spinal cord.[260,200,196,199] The relation of these cases to those in the next section is not yet clear.

The Lambert-Eaton Syndrome.—Nerve stimulation studies have identified a remarkable syndrome in patients with bronchogenic carcinoma and progressive weakness mainly in proximal muscles.[250,124,359,251] In contrast to myasthenia gravis, the weakness is more obvious at the initial effort and muscle strength improves with sustained or repeated activity. The response to Prostigmin is poor or absent. However the sensitivity to injected d-Tubocurarine is clearly increased, as in myasthenia. On maximal electrical stimulation of the motor nerve, the muscle electrical response is found to be small, only 2 to 30% of normal voltage but when the shocks are repeated at 10/sec., the successive muscle responses grow to several times the initial voltage. This facilitation presumably accounts for the temporary increase in muscle strength following exercise and perhaps also for the fact that Prostigmin is not clearly helpful to these patients. The occurrence of a marked initial block which is overcome by postactivation facilitation is reminiscent of the neuromuscular defect in botulinum intoxication. It could be postulated by analogy that the disorder involves primarily the acetylcholine ejection mechanism in motor nerve endings. In view of the peculiar features of this syndrome it seems desirable to avoid confusion with myasthenia gravis by using a designation such as the one proposed here.

Comment.—Motor disorders in carcinomatous patients raise many problems especially in view of the variety of the lesions observed. It seems strange that neuromyopathies should be associated with carcinoma of the bronchus rather than with malignancy in general. The nature of the association is not clear. Toxic effects seem excluded because the neuromuscular symptoms may appear long before a tumor is detected and because they may remit spontaneously in spite of further progress of the growth.[260,44] Other mechanisms which have been considered are virus infection,[235] conditioned nutritional deficiency,[103] and hypersensitivity reaction of nerve or muscle tissues to some product of the tumor.[437,44] The effects of tumor therapy on the neuromuscular disorder are equivocal.[44] In one case of Lambert-Eaton syndrome the removal of the bronchogenic carcinoma was followed by a slow repair of the neuromuscular defect (E. H. Lambert, personal communication).

TICK PARALYSIS

An acute ascending motor paralysis may occur in man and domestic animals following the bite of ticks of various genera (Dermacentor, Ixodes, . . .). The disease has a widespread distribution. It is well known in the Rocky Mountains but also occurs in Eastern United States, Australia, South Africa and Europe.[1] Over 300 human cases with a mortality of 12% have been recorded in North America.[362] Tick paralysis is more common and more severe in children than in adults. The patient experiences weakness followed by symmetrical flaccid paralysis involving first the legs and progressing to the upper extremities and eventually affecting the muscles innervated by cranial nerves. Death may follow from respiratory difficulty.[1] Tick paralysis is to be distinguished from the specific diseases transmitted by ticks and from the allergic manifestations which may follow tick bites. Recovery from paralysis is strikingly rapid if the tick is removed from the skin. Non-specific supportive measures may fail to prevent death if the tick is not removed.

Tick paralysis seems related to an as yet unidentified neurotoxin which is secreted by the salivary glands of the feeding female tick and is continuously injected into the body of the victim.[363,172] Tick eggs may contain a toxin similar to the one in salivary glands.[354,337] The syndrome of ascending flaccid paralysis has been reproduced by applying living wild female ticks to the skin of dogs and other animals.[188,363,54,315,361,130] The paralysed muscles respond to direct electrical stimulation but fail to contract when shocks are delivered to the motor nerve.[315,316,361,130] The presence of a normal response to arterially injected acetylcholine[316,130] and the absence of recovery with Prostigmin exclude a competitive (d-Tubocurarine-like) neuromuscular block. Synaptic potentials cannot be elicited at the myoneural junction and no additional acetylcholine appears in the venous effluent of a perfused paralysed muscle when the motor nerve is stimulated.[316,318,130] However the failure of nerve impulses to liberate acetylcholine is not primarily related to a biochemical disorder in cholinergic mechanisms because: (a) the resting output of acetylcholine is not reduced in unstimulated paralysed muscle and it can be increased on perfusion with excess potassium;[317] (b) the acetylcholine content and cholinacetylase activity of ventral spinal roots are within normal limits,[317] and (c) tick paralysed muscles, in contrast to myasthenic or hemicholinium-treated muscle,[107] do not exhibit a decrement in successive responses to low-frequency nerve stimulation.[317] The defect in tick paralysis thus appears to be located proximally to the acetylcholine release mechanisms and it could depend on inadequate invasion of the axonal arborisation by the motor nerve spike. A puzzling question is whether the orderly ascending progression of paralysis should be related to a corresponding differential susceptibility of the motor nerves to tick toxin.

PERIODIC PARALYSIS AND DISTURBANCES OF POTASSIUM METABOLISM

Hypokalemic Periodic Paralysis (Westphal Disease).—This is characterized by recurrent attacks of flaccid paralysis usually starting with proximal lower limbs and involving more or less rapidly the trunk, upper limbs and neck.[389,404,29,155,273] The muscles innervated by cranial nerves are rarely involved. Artificial respiration may be necessary in severe cases to prevent asphyxial death. There is no sensory loss and consciousness is not affected. The attacks may last from a few hours up to 1 to 2 days. They are more likely to occur when the patient is at complete rest subsequent to a large evening meal or to a period of excitement or vigorous exercise. The patient may thus awaken from sleep to find himself unable to move. Similar episodes can be experimentally induced in patients with the disease by administration of glucose, insulin or epinephrin. Exposure of a limb to cold has been reported to increase the weakness locally. Attacks are less likely to occur in the fasting patient.[288] Local exercise, when possible, results in an improvement in strength and the patient may use local exercise to abort a mild attack.[465,6,404,29] The paralyzed muscles do not respond to electrical stimulation.[449,465,153,181,182] After the attack these abnormalities disappear and muscle function is practically normal. Attacks first make their appearance in childhood or adolescence and become less frequent, or disappear, in later life. The disease has a familial incidence and appears inherited as a dominant trait.[329,29] Periodic paralysis has been described in association with hyperthyroidism. The latter condition, or thyroid feeding, increase the severity of periodic paralysis which may in such cases be relieved by anti-thyroid therapy.[389,278,266]

Attacks of paralysis are generally associated with a fall in potassium concentration in serum, but there is no critical level for the onset of muscular weakness.[4,404,273] The episodes may be prevented or terminated by the ingestion of an adequate dose of potassium. Renal elimination of potassium decreases when the paralysis develops[6,350,142,153,96] which implies a shift of the cation from blood to some intracellular site. The total exchangeable potassium, measured with K_{42}, does not appear to be changed.[274] Recent studies on forearm bloodflow and arterio-venous differences have demonstrated a net uptake of potassium by skeletal muscle during the development of a spontaneous or induced attack of paralysis and, conversely, a net release of potassium from muscle into blood during subsequent spontaneous recovery.[468] The hypokalemia thus appears to be only a consequence of the extra demand for potassium in the muscles, the cause of which is unknown. If a biochemical error were responsible for the abnormal potassium shift, it would be likely to affect carbohydrate metabolism.[273,392] It is known that potassium normally moves into cells during glucose assimilation and that it is involved in phosphorylation reactions.[42,257] Although the procedures known to facilitate the occurrence of attacks involve glucidic metabolism, the latter has not yet been proved to be abnormal in these patients.[273] The fact that episodes of hypokalemic paralysis become less easy to induce after large amounts of carbohydrate have been ingested suggests that the storage mechanism can become saturated.[279]

Electrophysiological studies also locate the defect primarily in the muscle itself. The muscle action potential is not normally propagated during the paralysis.[154,295,182] Anomalies in electro-mechanical coupling (cf. refs. 368, 216) and in contractile process are not excluded and should be considered because the mechanical tension developed by the muscle during an attack appears more reduced than the voltage of the simultaneously recorded action potential.[295,182] It is not known whether these abnormal features result from a disorder in dynamic ionic transfer processes in the membrane. During the attack the muscle fibers take up not only potassium but also water, hence the relative stability of intracellular potassium concentration and of resting membrane potential.[392] This increase in fibre volume accounts for the increase of the circumference of the paralysed extremities seen clinically.[29,465,392] Histopathological studies of periodic paralysis disclose thick fibers with dissociated myofibrils and central vacuoles, but no interstitial reaction.[165,465,183,392]

Hyperkalemic Periodic Paralysis or Adynamia Episodica Hereditaria (Gamstorp Disease).—This presents similar clinical features of recurrent attacks of flaccid paralysis.[155,156,223,129,234] It is also inherited as a dominant trait. The episodes likewise occur in the patient at rest and they are reduced by exercise. However attacks are accompanied by an elevated serum potassium level and an increased potassium elimination by the kidney, which points to a shift of the cation from the cells (possibly muscle) into the blood plasma. The attacks can be precipitated by oral administration of 1 to 3 gm. potassium and they are prevented or relieved by glucose or epinephrine. They are more liable to occur in the fasting patient and frequent small carbohydrate feedings between meals can reduce their incidence.[155,129] These precipitating conditions are exactly the reverse of those for hypokalemic paralysis.

Electromyograms performed during attacks disclose signs of hyperexcitability with spontaneous discharges and increased sensitivity to injected acetylcholine and also a reduction in the number of muscle fibers which can be activated.[60] These effects could be explained if the muscle fibers were excessively depolarized by a reduction in potassium ratio across the membrane.

Secondary Dyskalemia.—Disturbances in potassium metabolism occur in a variety of clinical conditions and, when severe, they may lead to ascending flaccid quadriplegia.[149,414,310] In primary aldosteronism[83,84] muscle paralysis develops in relation to a marked potassium depletion and hypokalemia. There is an excess intracellular sodium and reduced potassium in biopsied muscles, owing to the intense sodium retention induced by an aldosterone-secreting adrenal cortex adenoma. Additional symptoms are tetany related to metabolic alcalosis, polyuria, polydipsia and hypertension. Surgical removal of the adenoma relieves the clinical and biochemical abnormalities.

Episodes of paralysis depending on a similar excessive potassium loss may be noticed in patients with Addison's disease treated with large doses of desoxycorticosterone.[411] Hypokalemic paralysis may occur in severe diabetes when a number of factors are present, such as potassium loss by polyuria and vomiting, or potassium movement into cells with insulin therapy.[207,326,280,149] Muscular weakness related to potassium deficiency has also been recognized in patients subjected to withdrawal of gastro-intestinal secretions by vomiting, diarrhea or suction-drainage, and in such cases the administration of potassium-free parenteral solutions can increase the ionic imbalance.[256]

Hyperkalemic paralysis can be seen in renal diseases with oliguria and reduced potassium elimination.[293,309]

INTOXICATION BY CHOLINESTERASE INHIBITORS

Organophosphorus cholinesterase[383,209] inhibitors represent a great potential danger in view of their outstanding toxicity and adaptation as chemical warfare agents (tabun, sarin . . .) and of the utilization of a number of them (parathion or E 605, hexaethyl tetraphosphate, . . .) as insecticides in agriculture.[383,208,209,101] These anticholinesterases play only a minor role as therapeutic agents because they are not so manageable as the Prostigmin-like compounds.[335,175,386] Severe intoxications, some of them fatal, have occurred in man following accidental exposure (inhalation of vapor, absorption of fluid).[88,174,417,82,319,133] Surprisingly low concentrations of these phosphoryl compounds can inactivate, frequently irreversibly, the cholinesterase enzymes and produce marked muscarine-like, nicotine-like and, if the compound is liposoluble, central nervous system symptoms. Neuromuscular block results from accumulation at the motor end-plate of paralysing concentrations of acetylcholine both from local and distant sites.[113] Death follows from circulatory and/or respiratory failure, the latter resulting from weakness of respiratory muscles and obstruction of airways by excessive secretions and bronchoconstriction.[176,208,101,178,209] The treatment of such poisoning has relied mainly on artificial ventilation, aspiration of secretions and administration of large doses of atropine which alleviates most symptoms except neuromuscular block. Significant progress has resulted from the recent advent of powerful antidotes such as pyridine-2-aldoxime methiodide (PAM) and related compounds which can reactivate the phosphoryl cholinesterase.[229,201, 202,52,458] An intravenous injection of 0.5 to 2 gm. of PAM has no influence on muscle function in normal man but produces a striking relief of alkylphosphate poisoning, and especially of the neuromuscular block.[319,178] This effect is parallel to the regeneration of red blood cell cholinesterase. PAM has also been found helpful to reverse cholinergic crisis induced in patients with myasthenia gravis by treatment with excessive amounts of anticholinesterase drugs.[179]

TETANY

This syndrome is characterized by episodes of muscular spasms and paresthesias of sudden onset which involve primarily the distal territories (e.g., carpo-pedal spasm, 'main d'accoucheur' attitude) and spread in centripetal direction. The severity and extent of the attacks varies and when the tetany is latent, appropriate measures such as hyperventilation or the ischemia produced by an inflated cuff around the arm may elicit the spasms.[5] The heightened nerve excitability in tetany can be demonstrated between attacks by the decrease in galvanic threshold[132] and in accommodation to the slowly established electric currents[238,452] and by the occurrence of multiple discharges of motor units in the electromyogram.[419,241,71] The tetanic cramps are associated with intense motor unit activity. The main site of hyperexcitability is located in the proximal part of the larger peripheral nerve fibers and this region seems to act as a 'trigger zone' transforming single voluntary nerve impulses into repetitive discharges.[239,241] The experimental tetany induced by parathyroidectomy in dogs persists after the supraspinal centers have been excluded by a spinal section, but tonic spasms are not found in chronically denervated muscles.[446] A neuromuscular location of the trouble is unlikely since reduced calcium depresses acetylcholine liberation.[68,141,67]

Hypocalcemia and alcalosis are the two main common denominators in the tetany syndrome.[453,137,5] The effect of calcium lack in promoting the nerve autorhythmic behavior and in changing properties such as accommodation and Monnier's damping index is well documented,[143,11,47,247,312,313,46,387] and is being analysed in terms of membrane ionic currents.[150,206,151] The effect of changes in pH are less clearly understood;[259] they seem largely independent of changes in calcium ion concentration[287,46] and appear to involve a specific action of carbon dioxide tension on the nerve.[268,313] Blood calcium decreases in parathyroid tetany, e.g., following experimental removal of the parathyroid glands[275] or in idiopathic hypoparathyroidism.[115,410,400] Another common form of hypocalcemic tetany occurs in children suffering from rickets.[453,137,5] The intensity of clinical manifestations of tetany is not necessarily proportional to the decrease in serum calcium. A chronic hypocalcemia is better tolerated than an acute one. The presence of bound and ionized forms of calcium in serum has also to be considered.[357] It is true that a reduction restricted to the physiologically active ionized form is exceptional,[190] yet the level of total calcium in blood may be misleading, e.g., when there is a marked drop in bound calcium as in hypoproteinemia. Methods for estimation or calculation of ionized calcium have been described.[287,210,190]

Alcalotic tetany can occur in a variety of conditions. Vigorous and sufficiently prolonged hyperventilation by normal man will induce typical tetanic spasms with a concomitant increase in blood pH.[167] Hyperventilation with air enriched in carbon dioxide does not lead to tetany. States of metabolic alcalosis with tetany can occur, e.g., after large losses of gastric secretions by vomiting and in primary aldosteronism.[83,98]

Disturbances in Magnesium Metabolism.—A prolonged dietary deprivation of magnesium in mammals produces vasodilation, muscle twitching, restlessness and convulsions.[333,169,168] Hypomagnesemic tetany is also known to occur spontaneously in quickly growing calves which depend on a whole milk diet containing inadequate amounts of magnesium.[34]

Nearly all foods contain magnesium. When the dietary intake is experimentally restricted in normal man, the excretion rapidly falls and only moderate negative magnesium balance can be produced.[145,17] States of severe magnesium deficiency have been described in malnourished and debilitated patients suffering large losses of gastro-intestinal secretions by vomiting, diarrhea or suction drainage.[189,146,432,424,351] These patients lose much sodium and potassium as well and it is indeed only after the deficiencies in these two cations are corrected that a magnesium deficiency syndrome clearly emerges. The parenteral administration of magnesium-free fluids is a frequently quoted precipitating or enhancing factor. The symptoms of magnesium deficiency are muscle twitching, tremor and psychic excitement. The serum calcium is unchanged whereas the serum magnesium is decreased below the normal range of 1.75 to 2.5 mEq./l. Magnesium therapy relieves the symptoms within a few hours. Calcium is ineffective and may even enhance the magnesium deficiency tetany[351,431,418] presumably by increasing magnesium elimination.[80] Magnesium administration to deficient subjects is followed by a significant retention of the cation[432,351] whereas normal man eliminates parenterally injected magnesium.[145]

Hypomagnesemic tetany may be thought to be primarily related, like the classical tetany, to hyperexcitability of the peripheral nerves on which magnesium is known to exert a stabilizing action like that of calcium.[150,151] It is of great interest that the two cations are not interchangeable in the therapy of the corresponding deficiency states. This suggests that different specific neurochemical processes may be involved. Indeed calcium and magnesium are known to affect in opposite ways various enzyme systems. At the myoneural junction the process of acetylcholine release from motor nerve endings is potentiated by calcium and depressed by magnesium.[67,225]

REFERENCES

1. ABBOTT, K. H.: *Proc. Staff Meet., Mayo Clin., 18:*39 (1943).
2. ACHESON, D. and MCALPINE, D.: *Lancet, 2:*372 (1953).
3. ADAMS, R. D., DENNY-BROWN, D. and PEARSON, C. M.: *Diseases of Muscle, A Study in Pathology.* New York, Hoeber (1953).
4. AITKEN, R. S., ALLOTT, E. N., CASTLEDEN, L. I. M. and WALKER, M.: *Clin. Sc., 3:*47 (1937).
5. ALAJOUANINE, T., CONTAMIN, F. and CATHALA, H. P.: *Le syndrome tétanie.* Paris, Baillière (1958).
6. ALLOTT, E. N. and MCARDLE, B.: *Clin. Sc., 3:*229 (1938).
7. AMES, S. R. and RISLEY, H. A.: *Proc. Soc. Exper. Biol. & Med., 68:*131 (1948).
8. ANDRES, R., CADER, G. and ZIERLER, K. L.: *J. Clin. Invest., 35:*671 (1956).
9. ANDRES, R., ZIERLER, K. L., ANDERSON, H. M., STAINSBY, W. N., CADER, G., GRAYYIB, A. S. and LILIENTHAL, J. L.: *J. Clin. Invest., 33:*482 (1954).
10. ARONSON, S. M. and VOLK, B.: *Am. J. Med., 22:*414 (1957).
11. ARVANITAKI, A.: *Arch. internat. physiol., 49:*209 (1939).
12. BAKER, N., BLAHD, W. H. and HART, P.: *Am. J. Physiol., 193:*530 (1958).
13. BAKER, N., TUBIS, M. and BLAHD, W. H.: *Am. J. Physiol., 193:*525 (1958).
14. BALDWIN, D., ROBINSON, P. K., ZIERLER, K. L. and LILIENTHAL, J. L.: *J. Clin. Invest., 31:*850 (1952).
15. BANNISTER, R. G.: *Brit. M. Bull., 12:*222 (1956).
16. BARCROFT, H. and SWAN, H. J. C.: *Sympathetic Control of Human Blood Vessels.* London, Arnold (1953).
17. BARNES, B. A., COPE, O. and HARRISON, T.: *J. Clin. Invest., 37:*430 (1958).
18. BARNES, B. A., GORDON, E. B. and COPE, O.: *J. Clin. Invest., 36:*1239 (1957).
19. BECKER, P. E.: *Deutsch. Ztschr. Nervenheilk., 173:*482 (1955).
20. BECKETT, E. B. and BOURNE, G. H.: In *The Structure and Function of Muscle,* Vol. 3. New York, Acad. Press (1961).
21. BECKETT, R. S. and NETSKY, M. G.: *Arch. Neurol. & Psychiat., 69:*64 (1953).
22. BECKMANN, R.: *Klin. Wchuschr., 34:*1237 (1956).
23. BECKMANN, R. and BUDDECKE, E.: *Klin. Wchuschr., 34:*818 (1956).
24. BENEDICT, J. D., KALINSKY, H. J., SCARRONE, L. A., WERTHEIM, A. R. and STETTEN, DR., JR.: *J. Clin. Invest., 34:*141 (1955).
25. BENNETT, A. E. and CASH, P. T.: *Arch. Neurol. & Psychiat., 49:*537 (1943).
26. BENNETT, H. S., SZENT-GYORGYI, A., DENNY-BROWN, D., ADAMS, R. D. and ROSE, A. S.: *Neurology, 8:*65 (1958).
27. BERANEK, R.: *Čs. fysiol., 8:*172 (1959).
28. BERENBAUM, M. C., BIRCH, C. A. and MORELAND, J. D.: *Lancet, 1:*892 (1955).
29. BICKERSTAFF, E. R.: *J. Neurol., Neurosurg., & Psychiat., 16:*178 (1953).
30. BICKERSTAFF, E. R. and WOOLF, A. L.: *Brain, 83:*10 (1960).
31. BIÖRCK, G.: *Acta med. scandinav., 133:*suppl. 226 (1949).
32. BLAHD, W. H., BAUER, F. K., LIBBY, R. L. and ROSE, A. S.: *Neurology, 5:*201 (1955).
33. BLAHD, W. H., BLOOM, A. and DRELL, W.: *Proc. Soc. Exper. Biol. & Med., 90:*704 (1955).

34. BLAXTER, K. L. and SHARMAN, G. A. M.: *Veterinary Rec.*, *67*:108 (1955).
35. BLOCH, K., SCHOENHEIMER, R. and RITTENBERG, D.: *J. Biol. Chem.*, *138*:155 (1941).
36. BLYTH, H. and PUGH, R. J.: *Ann. Human Gen.*, *23*:127 (1959).
37. BOGAERT, L. VAN, RADERMECKER, M. A., LOWENTHAL, A. and KETELAER, C. J.: *Acta neurol. belg.*, *11*:869 (1955).
38. BORSOOK, H. and DUBNOFF, J. W.: *J. Biol. Chem.*, *168*:493 (1947).
39. BOSANQUET, F. D., DANIEL, P. M. and PARRY, H. B.: *Lancet*, *2*:737 (1956).
40. BOTELHO, S. Y., BECKETT, S. B. and BENDLER, E.: *Neurology*, *10*:601 (1960).
41. BOYER, P. D.: In *The Enzymes*, Vol. 3, Chap. 18, p. 353. Boyer, P. D., Lardy, H. and Myrbäck, K. Eds. New York, Acad. Press (1960).
42. BOYER, P. D., LARDY, H. A. and PHILLIPS, P. H.: *J. Biol. Chem.*, *146*:673 (1942).
43. BOYLE, P. J. and CONWAY, E. J.: *J. Physiol.*, *100*:1 (1941).
44. BRAIN, W. R. and HENSON, R. A.: *Lancet*, *2*:971 (1958).
45. BREININ, G. M.: *Arch. Ophth.*, *59*:177 (1958).
46. BRINK, F.: *Pharmacol. Rev.*, *6*:243 (1954).
47. BRINK, F., BRONK, D. W. and LARRABEE, M. G.: *Ann. New York Acad. Sc.*, *47*:457 (1946).
48. BRINKHOUS, K. M. and WARNER, E. D.: *Am. J. Path.*, *17*:81 (1941).
49. BROOKS, V. B.: *J. Physiol.*, *134*:264 (1956).
50. BROWN, G. L. and FELDBERG, W.: *J. Physiol.*, *88*:265 (1936).
51. BROWN, G. L. and HARVEY, A. M.: *Brain*, *62*:341 (1939).
52. BROWN, R. V., KUNKEL, A. M., SOMERS, L. M. and WILLS, J. H.: *J. Pharmacol.*, *120*:276 (1957).
53. BRUMLIK, J., WACHS, H., HUMMEL, W. and BOSHES, B.: *Quart. Bull. North Western Univ. M. School.*, *33*:22 (1959).
54. BRUMPT, E.: *Compt. rend. Acad. sc.*, Paris, *197*:1358 (1933).
55. BUCHANAN, D. and STEINER, P. E.: *Arch. Neurol. & Psychiat.*, *66*:107 (1951).
56. BUCHTHAL, F.: *An Introduction to Electromyography*. Copenhagen, Gyldendal (1957).
57. BUCHTHAL, F. and CLEMMESEN, S.: *Acta psychiat. et neurol.* *16*:143 (1941).
58. BUCHTHAL, F. and CLEMMESEN, S.: *Acta psychiat. et neurol.* *16*:389 (1941).
59. BUCHTHAL, F. and ENGBAEK, L.: *Acta psychiat. et neurol. 23*:3 (1948).
60. BUCHTHAL, F., ENGBAEK, L. and GAMSTORP, I.: *Neurology*, *8*:347 (1958).
61. BUCHTHAL, F., ROSENFALCK, P. and ERMINIO, F.: *Neurology*, *10*:398 (1960).
62. BUCHTHAL, F. and STEN-KNUDSEN, O.: *Ann New York Acad. Sc.*, *81*:422 (1959).
63. BURGEN, A. S. V., DICKENS, F. and ZATMAN, L. J.: *J. Physiol.*, *109*:10 (1949).
64. BYWATERS, E. G. L.: *J.A.M.A.*, *124*:1103 (1944).
65. CALDWELL, P. C. and PRANKERD, T. A. J.: *J. Neurol., Neurosurg. & Psychiat.*, *17*:127 (1954).
66. CARLSTRÖM, B.: *Skandinav. Arch. Physiol.*, *61*:161 (1931).
67. CASTILLO, J. DEL and KATZ, B.: *Progr. Biophys. & biophys. Chem.*, *6*:121 (1956).
68. CASTILLO, J. DEL and STARK, L.: *J. Physiol.*, *116*:507 (1952).
69. CASTLEMAN, B.: *Atlas of Tumor Pathology*, fasc. 19. A.F.I.P., Washington, (1955).
70. CASTLEMAN, B. and NORRIS, E. H.: *Medicine*, *28*:27 (1949).
71. CATHALA, H. P. and CONTAMIN, F.: *Rev. Franc. Études clin. et biol.*, *2*:358 (1957).
72. CAVANAGH, J. B. and MACDONALD, I.: *Quart. J. Exper. Physiol.*, *43*:235 (1958).
73. CHRISTIANSON, H. B., O'LEARY, P. A. and POWER, M. H.: *J. Invest. Dermat.*, *27*:431 (1956).

74. CHURCHILL-DAVIDSON, H. C. and RICHARDSON, A. T.: *J. Physiol., 122*:252 (1953).
75. CLARK, W. E. LEGROS: *J. Anat., 81*:24 (1946).
76. CLARK, S. L., LUTEN, F. H. and CUTLER, J. T.: *J. Nerv. & Ment. Dis., 90*:297 (1939).
77. COËRS, C. and DESMEDT, J. E.: *Neurology, 9*:238 (1959).
78. COËRS, C. and DESMEDT, J. E.: *Acta neurol. et psychiat. belg., 59*:539 (1959).
79. COËRS, C. and WOOLF, A. L.: *The Innervation of Muscle.* Oxford Blackwell (1959).
80. COLBY, R. W. and FRYE, C. M.: *Am. J. Physiol., 166*:408 (1951).
81. COLES, D. R., COOPER, K. E., MOTTRAM, R. F. and OCCLESHAW, J. V.: *J. Physiol., 142*:323 (1958).
82. CONLEY, B. E.: *J.A.M.A., 163*:1338 (1957).
83. CONN, J. W.: *Arch. Int. Med., 97*:135 (1956).
84. CONN, J. W. and LOUIS, L. H.: *Ann. Int. Med., 44*:1 (1956).
85. CONRAD, J. T. and GLASER, G. G.: *Tr. Am. Neurol. A., 84*:170 (1959).
86. CONWAY, E. J.: *Physiol. Rev., 37*:84 (1957).
87. COOPER, K. E., EDHOLM, O. G. and MOTTRAM, R. F.: *J. Physiol., 128*:258 (1955).
88. Council on Pharmacy and Chemistry: *J.A.M.A., 144*:104 (1950).
89. COVERNTON, J. S. and DRAPER, M. H.: *M. J. Australia,* 161 (1947)
90. CREESE, R., DILLON, J. B., MARSHALL, J., SABALAWA, P. B., SCHNEIDER, D. J., TAYLOR, D. B. and ZINN, D. E.: *J. Pharmacol., 119*:485 (1957).
91. CUMINGS, J. N.: *Brain, 62*:153 (1939).
92. CUMINGS, J. N.: *Brain, 67*:265 (1944).
93. CUMINGS, J. N.: *Brain, 76*:299 (1953).
94. CUMINGS, J. N. and MAAS, O.: *Brain, 62*:422 (1939).
95. DANOWSKI, T. S., BASTIANI, R. M., MCWILLIAMS, F. D., MATEER, F. and GREENMAN, L.: *Am. J. Dis. Child., 91*:356 (1956).
96. DANOWSKI, T. S., ELKINGTON, J. R., BURROWS, B. A. and WINKLER, A. W.: *J. Clin. Invest., 27*:65 (1948).
97. DARBY, W. J., FERGUSON, M. E., FURMAN, R. H., LEMLEY, J. M., BALL, C. T. and MENEELY, G. R.: *Ann. New York Acad. Sc., 52*:328 (1949).
98. DARROW, D. C. and HELLERSTEIN, S.: *Physiol. Rev., 38*:114 (1958).
99. DAVIES, R. E., CAIN, D. and DELLUVA, A. M.: *Ann. New York Acad. Sc., 81*:468 (1959).
100. DEBRÉ, R., GERNEZ, C. and SÉE, G.: *Bull. Soc. Med. Hôp. Paris, 50*:1640 (1934).
101. DE CANDOLE, C. A., DOUGLAS, W. W., LOVATT EVANS, C., HOLMES, R., SPENCER, K. E. V., TORRANCE, R. W. and WILSON, K. M.: *Brit. J. Pharmacol., 8*:466 (1953).
102. DEITRICK, J. E., WHEDON, G. D. and SHORR, E.: *Am. J. Med., 4*:3 (1948).
103. DENNY-BROWN, D.: *J. Neurol., 11*:73 (1948).
104. DENNY-BROWN, D.: *J. Neuropath., 10*:94 (1951).
105. DENNY-BROWN, D.: *Am. J. Med., 15*:368 (1953).
106. DESMEDT, J. E.: *Nature, London, 179*:156 (1957).
107. DESMEDT, J. E.: *Nature, London, 182*:1673 (1958).
108. DESMEDT, J. E.: *Acta neurol. et psychiat. belg., 58*:977 (1958).
109. DESMEDT, J. E.: *Am. J. Phys. Med., 38*:248 (1959).
110. DESMEDT, J. E.: In *Second Symposium on Myasthenia Gravis,* H. R. Viets, ed., Springfield, Ill., Thomas (1961).
111. DESMEDT, J. E.: *Physiol. Rev., 42, in press* (1962).
112. DILLON, J. B. and SABAWALA, P. B.: *Neurology, 9*:62 (1959).
113. DOUGLAS, W. W. and PATON, W. D. M.: *J. Physiol., 124*:325 (1954).

114. DRAGER, G. A., HAMMIL, J. F. and SHY, G. M.: *Arch. Neurol. & Psychiat., 80:*1 (1958).
115. DRAGSTEDT, L. R.: *Physiol. Rev., 7:*499 (1927).
116. DREW, A. L.: *Am. J. Phys. Med., 35:*309 (1955).
117. DREW, A. L. and SELVING, B. T.: *Neurology, 3:*563 (1953).
118. DREYFUS, J. C., SCHAPIRA, G., SCHAPIRA, F. and DEMOS, J.: *Clin. chim. acta, 1:*434 (1956).
119. DREYFUS, J. C., SCHAPIRA, G. and DEMOS, J.: *Clin. chim. acta, 3:*571 (1958).
120. DREYFUS, J. C., SCHAPIRA, G. and SCHAPIRA, F.: *Ann. New York Acad. Sc., 75:*235 (1958).
121. EATON, L. M.: *M. Clin. North America, 31:*907 (1947).
122. EATON, L. M.: *Neurology, 4:*245 (1954).
123. EATON, L. M., CLAGETT, O. T. and BASTRON, J. A.: *A. Res. Nerv. & Ment. Dis., Proc., 32:*107 (1953).
124. EATON, L. M. and LAMBERT, E. H.: *J.A.M.A., 163:*1117 (1957).
125. EBELING, P., GILLIATT, R. W. and THOMAS, P. K.: *J. Neurol., 23:*1 (1960).
126. ECCLES, J. C.: *The Physiology of Nerve Cells.* Baltimore, Johns Hopkins Univ. Press (1957).
127. EDDS, M. V.: *Quart. Rev. Biol., 28:*260 (1953).
128. EDELMAN, I. S., OLNEY, J. M., JAMES, A. H., BROOKS, L. and MOORE, F. D.: *Science, 115:*447 (1952).
129. EGAN, T. J. and KLEIN, R.: *Pediatrics, 24:*761 (1959).
130. EMMONS, P. and MCLENNAN, H.: *Nature, 183:*474 (1959).
131. ENGBAEK, L.: *EEG & Clin. Neurophysiol., 3:*155 (1951).
132. ERB, W.: *Arch. Psychiat., 4:*271 (1874).
133. ERDMANN, W. D. and LENDLE, L.: *Ergebn. inn. Med. u. Kinderh., 10:*104 (1958).
134. ERSHOFF, B. H.: *Physiol. Rev., 28:*107 (1948).
135. EVANS, H. M.: *J. Mount Sinai Hosp., 5:*233 (1940).
136. EVANS, J. H. and BAKER, R. W. R.: *Brain, 80:*557 (1957).
137. FANCONI, G.: *Schweiz. Med. Wchschr., 84:*429 (1954).
138. FARMER, T. W., BUCHTHAL, F. and ROSENFALCK, P.: *Neurology, 9:*747 (1959).
139. FATT, P.: In *Handbook of Physiology,* Amer. Physiol. Soc., Neurophys. I, 199 (1959).
140. FATT, P. and KATZ, B.: *J. Physiol., 117:*109 (1952).
141. FATT, P. and KATZ, B.: *J. Physiol., 118:*73 (1952).
142. FERREBEE, J. W., ATCHLEY, D. W. and LOEB, R. F.: *J. Clin. Invest., 17:*504 (1938).
143. FESSARD, A.: *Propriétés rythmiques de la matière vivante.* Paris, Hermann (1936).
144. FISCHER, E.: *Am. J. Phys. Med., 35:*212 (1955).
145. FITZGERALD, M. G. and FOURMAN, P.: *Clin. Sc., 15:*635 (1956).
146. FLINK, E. B., MCCOLLISTER, R., PRASAD, A. S., MELBY, J. C. and DOE, R. P.: *Ann. Int. Med., 47:*956 (1957).
147. FLOYD, W. F., KENT, P. and PAGE, F.: *EEG & Clin. Neurophysiol., 7:*621 (1955).
148. FORBES, G. B. and LEWIS, A. M.: *J. Clin. Invest., 35:*956 (1956).
149. FOURMAN, P.: In *Lectures on the Scientific Basis of Medicine,* Vol. 7, p. 451. London, Athlone Press (1959).
150. FRANKENHAEUSER, B. and HODGKIN, A. L.: *J. Physiol., 137:*217 (1957).
151. FRANKENHAEUSER, B. and MEVES, H.: *J. Physiol., 142:*360 (1958).
152. GAMMON, G. D.: *M. Clin. North America, 42:*1629 (1958).

153. GAMMON, G. D., AUSTIN, J. H., BLITHE, M. D. and REID, C. G.: *Am. J. M. Sc.*, *197*:326 (1939).

154. GAMMON, G. D., HARVEY, A. M. and MASLAND, R. L.: *Biol. Symp.*, *3*:291 (1941).

155. GAMSTORP, I.: *Acta Paediat.*, *108*: suppl. (1956).

156. GAMSTORP, I., HAUGE, M., HELWIG-LARSEN, H. F. MJÖNES, H. and SAGILD, U.: *Am. J. Med.*, *23*:385 (1957).

157. GARCIN, R., LAPRESLE, J., GRUNER, J. and SCHERRER, J.: *Rev. Neurol.*, *92*:465 (1955).

158. GASSER, H. S.: *Physiol. Rev.*, *10*:35 (1930).

159. GEIGER, R. S. and GARVIN, J. S.: *J. Neurol.*, *Neurosurg. & Psychiat.*, *16*:532 (1957).

160. GERARD, R. W. and TAYLOR, R. E.: *Am. J. Med.*, *15*:83 (1953).

161. GESCHWIND, N. and SIMPSON, J. A.: *Brain*, *78*:81 (1955).

162. GILLETT, R. L.: *New England J. Med.*, *260*:1156 (1959).

163. GILLIATT, R. W.: *J. Neurol.*, *Neurosurg. & Psychiat.*, *22*:344 (1959).

164. GOETSCH, M. and PAPPENHEIMER, A. M.: *J. Exper. Med.*, *54*:145 (1931).

165. GOLDFLAM, S.: *Deutsch. Ztschr. Neurol.*, *7*:1 (1895).

166. GRANT, R. T.: *Clin. Sc.*, *3*:157 (1937).

167. GRANT, S. B. and GOLDMAN, A.: *Am. J. Physiol.*, *52*:209 (1920).

168. GREENBERG, D. M., BOELTER, M. D. D. and KNOPF, B. W.: *Am. J. Physiol.*, *137*:459 (1942).

169. GREENBERG, D. M. and TUFTS, E. V.: *Am. J. Physiol.*, *121*:416 (1938).

170. GREENFIELD, J. G.: *The Spinocerebellar Degenerations*. Springfield, Ill., Thomas (1954).

171. GREENFIELD, J. G., SHY, G. M., ALVORD, E. C. and BERG, L.: *An Atlas of Muscle Pathology in Neuromuscular Diseases*. Edinburgh, Livingston (1957).

172. GREGSON, J. D.: *Proc. Entomol. Soc. Brit. Columbia*, *48*:54 (1952).

173. GRIFFITHS, W. J.: *Lancet*, *2*:467 (1951).

174. GROB, D.: *Arch. Int. Med.*, *98*:221 (1956).

175. GROB, D.: *J. Chronic Dis.*, *8*:536 (1958).

176. GROB, D., GARLICK, W. L. and HARVEY, A. M.: *Bull. Johns Hopkins Hosp.*, *87*:106 (1950).

177. GROB, D. and HARVEY, A. M.: *J. Clin. Invest.*, *37*:350 (1958).

178. GROB, D. and JOHNS, R. J.: *Am. J. Med.*, *24*:497 (1958).

179. GROB, D. and JOHNS, R. J.: *Am. J. Med.*, *24*:512 (1958).

180. GROB, D., JOHNS, R. J. and HARVEY, A. M.: *Bull. Johns Hopkins Hosp.*, *99*:153 (1956).

181. GROB, D., JOHNS, R. J. and LILJESTRAND, A.: *Am. J. Med.*, *23*:356 (1957).

182. GROB, D., LILJESTRAND, A. and JOHNS, R. J.: *Am. J. Med.*, *23*:340 (1957).

183. GRUNER, J. E. and PORTE, A.: *Rev. Neurol.*, *101*:501 (1959).

184. GRÜTTNER, R. and MERTENS, H. G.: *Klin. Wchschr.*, *31*:868 (1953).

185. GUTMANN, E.: *Am. J. Phys. Med.*, *38*:104 (1959).

186. GUY, E., LEFEBVRE, J., LERIQUE, J. and SCHERRER, J.: *Rev. neurol.*, *83*:278 (1950).

187. HADLOW, W. J.: *Lab. Invest.*, *8*:1478 (1959).

188. HADWEN, S.: *Parasitology*, *6*:283 (1913).

189. HAMMARSTEN, J. F. and SMITH, W. D.: *New England. J. Med.*, *256*:897 (1957).

190. HARNAPP, G. O.: *Ztschr. ges. inn. Med.*, *9*:681 (1954).

191. HARRIS, P. L. and MASON, K. E.: *Am. J. Clin. Nutr.*, *4*:402 (1956).

192. HARVEY, A. M., LILIENTHAL, J. L. and TALBOT, S. A.: *Bull. Johns Hopkins Hosp.*, *69*:529 (1941).

193. HARVEY, A. M. and MASLAND, E. L.: *Bull. Johns Hopkins Hosp.*, *68:*81 (1941).
194. HASTINGS, A. B. and EICHELBERGER, L.: *J. Biol. Chem.*, *117:*73 (1937).
195. HAZZARD, W. R. and LEONARD, S. L.: *Proc. Soc. Exper. Biol. & Med.*, *102:*720 (1959).
196. HEATHFIELD, K. W. G. and WILLIAMS, J. R. B.: *Brain*, *77:*122 (1954).
197. HEBB, C. O.: *Internat. Rev. Neurobiol.*, *1:*169 (1959.
198. HED, R.: *Acta med. scandinav.*, suppl., 303 (1955).
199. HENSON, R. A.: *Tr. Am. Neurol. A.*, *84:*71 (1959).
200. HENSON, R. A., RUSSELL, D. S. and WILKINSON, M.: *Brain*, *77:*82 (1954).
201. HOBBIGER, F.: *Brit. J. Pharmacol.*, *6:*21 (1956).
202. HOBBIGER, F. and SADLER, P. W.: *Nature London*, *182:*1672 (1958).
203. HODES, R., LARRABEE, M. G. and GERMAN, W.: *Arch. Neurol. & Psychiat.*, *60:*340 (1948).
204. HODGKIN, A. L.: *Biol. Rev.*, *26:*339 (1951).
205. HODGKIN, A. L.: *Proc. Roy. Soc., B.*, *148:*1 (1957).
206. HODGKIN, A. L. and KEYNES, R. D.: *J. Physiol.*, *138:*253 (1957).
207. HOLLER, J. W.: *J.A.M.A.*, *131:*1186 (1946).
208. HOLMSTEDT, B.: *Acta physiol. scandinav.*, *25:*suppl. 90 (1951).
209. HOLMSTEDT, B.: *Pharmacol. Rev.*, *11:*567 (1959).
210. HOPKINS, T. R., CONNOR, T. B. and HOWARD, J. E.: *Bull. Johns Hopkins Hosp.*, *93:*249 (1953).
211. HORVATH, B.: *Neurology*, *8:*suppl. 1, 52 (1958).
212. HORVATH, B., BERG, L., CUMINGS, D. J. and SHY, M. G.: *J. Appl. Physiol.*, *8:*22 (1955).
213. HUMMEL, J. P. and MELVILLE, R. S.: *J. Biol. Chem.*, *191:*391 (1951).
214. HURLEY, K. E. and WILLIAMS, R. J.: *Arch. Biochem. & Biophys.* *54:*384 (1955).
215. HUXLEY, A. F.: *Progress in Biophysics and Biophysical Chemistry*, Vol. 7, p. 255 (1957).
216. HUXLEY, A. F.: *Ann. New York Acad. Sc.*, *81:*446 (1959).
217. HUXLEY, H. E. and HANSON, J.: *Ann. New York Acad. Sc.*, *81:*403 (1959).
218. HYDEN, H.: *Genetic Neurology*, p. 177, Weiss, Ed. Chichago, Univ. of Chicago Press (1950).
219. JACOB, W. and NEUHAUS, J.: *Klin. Wchschr.*, *32:*923 (1954).
220. JOHNS, R. J., GROB, D. and HARVEY, A. M.: *Bull. Johns Hopkins Hosp.*, *99:*125 (1956).
221. JOLLIFFE, N.: *J.A.M.A.*, *122:*299 (1943).
222. KANDUTSCH, A. A. and RUSSELL, A. R.: *Am. J. Physiol.*, *194:*553 (1958).
223. KAPLAN, M., STRAUS, P., GRUMBACH, R. and AYMARD, B.: *Presse méd.*, *65:*1305 (1957).
224. KATTUS, A. A. JR., WATANABE, R., SEMENSON, C. and DRELL, W.: *J.A.M.A.*, *160:*16 (1956).
225. KATZ, B.: *Bull. Johns Hopkins Hosp.*, *102:*275 (1958).
226. KATZ, B. and THESLEFF, S.: *J. Physiol.*, *138:*63 (1957).
227. KAUNITZ, H. and PAPPENHEIMER, A. M.: *Am. J. Physiol.*, *138:*328 (1943).
228. KETY, S. S.: *Am. Heart J.*, *38:*321 (1949).
229. KEWITZ, H., WILSON, I. B. and NACHMANSON, D.: *Arch. Biochem. & Biophys.*, *64:*456 (1956).
230. KEYNES, G.: *Brit. M. J.*, *2:*611 (1949).
231. KEYNES, G.: *Lancet*, *1:*1197 (1954).

232. KEYNES, R. D. and LEWIS, P. R.: In *Neurochemistry*, 1st Edition. Elliott, K. A. C,. Page I. H., and Quastel, J. H., eds. Springfield, Ill., Thomas (1955).
233. KILOH, L. G. and NEVIN, S.: *Brain, 74:*369 (1951).
234. KLEIN, R.: *Maandschr. kindergeneesk., 28:*60 (1960).
235. KLÜVER, H. and WEIL, A.: *J. Neuropath., 7:*144 (1948).
236. KOLB, L. C.: *Bull. Johns Hopkins Hosp., 63:*221 (1938).
237. KOREIN, J., CODDON, D. R., and MOWREY, F. H.: *Neurology, 9:*767 (1959).
238. KUGELBERG, E.: *Acta physiol. scandinav. 8:*suppl. 24 (1944).
239. KUGELBERG, E.: *Brain, 69:*310 (1946).
240. KUGELBERG, E.: *J. Neurol., Neurosurg. & Psychiat., 10:*122 (1947).
241. KUGELBERG, E.: *Arch. Neurol. & Psychiat., 60:*153 (1948).
242. KUGELBERG, E.: *J. Neurol., Neurosurg. & Psychiat., 10:*129 (1949).
243. KUHN, E.: *Klin. Wchschr., 37:*236 (1959).
244. KUHN, E. and WEICKER, H.: *Schweiz. med. Wchschr., 87:*460 (1957).
245. KUHN, E. and WÖRNER, W.: *Ztschr. klin. Med., 155:*544 (1959).
246. KURLAND, L. T. and ALTER, M.: In *Second Symposium on Myasthenia Gravis.* H. R. Viets, ed. Springfield, Ill., Thomas (1961).
247. LAGET, P.: *Arch. Sc. physiol., 3:*273 (1949).
248. LAMBERT, E. H.: *A. Res. Nerv. & Ment. Dis. Proc., 38:*247 (1960).
249. LAMBERT, E. H. and BECKETT, S.: *Am. J. Physiol., 163:*728 (1950).
250. LAMBERT, E. H., EATON, L. M. and ROOKE, E. D.: *Am. J. Physiol., 187:*612 (1956).
251. LAMBERT, E. H., ROOKE, E. D., EATON, L. M. and HODGSON, C. H.: In *Second Symposium on Myasthenia Gravis.* H. R. Viets, ed. Springfield, Ill., Thomas (1961).
252. LAMY, M. and DE GROUCHY, J.: *J. Génét. Hum., 3:*219 (1954).
253. LANARI, A.: *Medicina* (Buenos Aires), 7:21 (1947).
254. LANDAU, W. M.: *Neurology, 2:*369 (1952).
255. LANDOUZY, D. and DÉJÉRINE, J.: *Rev. méd. franc., 5:*81; *6:*977 (1885).
256. LANS, H. S., STEIN, I. F. and MEYER, K. A.: *Surg. Gynec. & Obst., 95:*321 (1952).
257. LARDY, H. A.: In *Phosphorous Metabolism*, Chap. 8, p. 447. McElroy, W. D. Glass, B., Eds. Baltimore, Johns Hopkins Press (1951).
258. LARNER, J. and VILLAR-PALASI, G.: *Proc. Nat. Acad. Sc., 45:*1234 (1959).
259. LEHMANN, J. E.: *Am. J. Physiol., 118:*600 (1937).
260. LENNOX, B. and PRITCHARD, S.: *Quart. J. Med., 19:*97 (1950).
261. LEVIN, M.: *Arch. Neurol. & Psychiat., 32:*1286 (1934).
262. LEVISON, H.: *Acta psychiat. et neurol.,* suppl. 76 (1951).
263. LEYBURN, P. and WALTON, J. N.: *Brain, 82:*81 (1959).
264. LILIENTHAL, J. L., and ZIERLER, K. L.: In *Biochemical Disorders in Human Disease.* Thompson, R. H. S., King, E. J., eds. London. J. A. Churchill (1957).
265. LILIENTHAL, J. L., ZIERLER, K. L., FOLK, B. P., BUKA, R. and RILEY, M. J.: *J. Biol. Chem., 182:*501 (1950).
266. LINDER, M. A.: *Ann. Int. Med., 43:*241 (1955).
267. LIVERSEDGE, L. A. and NEWMAN, M. J. D.: *Brain, 79:*395 (1956).
268. LORENTE DE NO, R.: *Stud. Rockefeller Inst. M. Res., 131* and *132:* (1947).
269. LÖWENTHAL, A. and VAN SANDE, M.: *Acta. neurol. et psychiat. belg., 54:*864 (1954).
270. LÖWENTHAL, A. and VAN SANDE, M.: *Rev. franç Études clin. et bol., 1:*765 (1956).
271. LUNDSGAARD, E.: *Biochem. Ztschr., 227:*162 (1930).
272. McARDLE, B.: *Clin. Sc., 10:*13 (1951).

273. MCARDLE, B.: *Brit. M. Bull., 12:*226 (1956).
274. MCARDLE, B. and MERTON, P. A.: *Physiol., 116:*51P (1952).
275. MCCALLUM, W. G. and VOEGTLIN, C.: *J. Exper. Med., 11:*118 (1909).
276. MACDERMOT, V.: *Brain, 83:*24 (1960).
277. MCEACHERN, D.: *Medicine, 22:*1 (1943).
278. MCEACHERN, D.: *Bull. New York Acad. Med., 27:*3 (1951).
279. MACGREGOR, G. A. and SHAPER, A. G.: *Brit. M. J., 1:*917 (1957).
280. MACH, R. S.: In *Physiopathologie du Potassium,* p. 153. Paris, C.N.R.S. (1954).
281. MACINTOSH, F. C.: *Canad. J. Biochem. & Physiol., 37:*345 (1959).
282. MACINTOSH, F. C., BIRKS, R. I. and SASTRY, P. B.: *Neurology, 8:*90 (1958).
283. MCINTYRE, A. R., BENNETT, A. L. and BRODKEY, J. S.: *Arch. Neurol. & Psychiat., 81:*678 (1959).
284. MACKENZIE, C. G. and MCCOLLUM, E. V.: *J. Nutrition, 19:*345 (1940).
285. MACKENZIE, J. B. and MACKENZIE, C. G.: *J. Nutrition, 67:*223 (1959).
286. MACKENZIE, J. B., ROSENKRANTZ, H., ULICK, S. and MILHORAT, A. T.: *J. Biol. Chem., 183:*655 (1950).
287. MCLEAN, F. C. and HASTINGS, A. B.: *Am. J. M. Sc., 189:*601 (1935).
288. MCQUARRIE, I. and ZIEGLER, M. R.: *Metabolism, 1:*129 (1952).
289. MANERY, J. F.: *Physiol. Rev., 34:*334 (1954).
290. MASLAND, R. L. and GAMMON, G. D.: *J. Pharmacol., 97:*499 (1949).
291. MASON, K R., DJU, M. Y. and CHAPIN, S. J.: *Proc. 1st and 2nd Med. Conf. Musc. Dystrophy A. America,* p. 94 (1952).
292. MATTHEWS, W. B. and SMITH, M. J. H.: *J. Neurol., Neurosurg. & Psychiat., 16:*184 (1953).
293. MERRILL, J. P., LEVINE, H. D., SOMERVILLE, W. and SMITH, S.: *Ann. Int. Med., 33:*797 (1950).
294. MERTON, P. A.: *J. Physiol., 123:*553 (1954).
295. MERTON, P. A.: *Brit. M. Bull., 12:*219 (1956).
296. MEYER-BETZ, F.: *Deutsch. Arch. Klin. Med., 85:*85 (1911).
297. MEYERHOF, O. and KIESSELING, W.: *Biochem. Ztschr., 264:*40 (1933).
298. MEYERHOF, O. and KIESSELING, W.: *Biochem. Ztschr., 267:*313 (1933).
299. MICHELSON, A. M., RUSSELL, E. S. and HARMAN, P. J.: *Proc. Nat. Acad. Sc., 41:*1079 (1955).
300. MILHORAT, A. T.: *A. Res. Nerv. & Ment. Dis., Proc., 32:*400 (1953).
301. MILHORAT, A. T. and WOLFF, H. G.: *Arch. Neurol. & Psychiat., 38:*992 (1937).
302. MILHORAT, A. T. and WOLFF, H. G.: *Arch. Neurol. & Psychiat., 39:*354 (1938).
303. MILHORAT, A. T. and WOLFF, H. G.: *Arch. Neurol. & Psychiat., 40:*663 (1938).
304. MILHORAT, A. T. and WOLFF, H. G.: *Arch. Neurol & Psychiat., 40:*680 (1938).
305. MILLIKAN, G. A.: *Physiol. Rev., 19:*503 (1939).
306. MILMAN, A. and MILHORAT, A. T.: *Proc. Soc. Exper. Biol. & Med., 84:*654 (1953).
307. MINOT, A. S.: *J. Lab. & Clin. Med., 29:*772 (1944).
308. MINOT, A. S., FRANK, H. and DZIEWIATKOWSKI, D.: *Arch. Biochem., 20:*394 (1949).
309. MOLLARET, P., GOULON, M. and TOURNILHAC, M.: *Rev. neurol., 99:*241 (1958).
310. MOLLARET, P., GOULON, M. and TOURNILHAC, M.: *Presse méd., 67:*2137 (1959).
311. MOMMAERTS, W. F. H. M., ILLINGWIRTH, B., PEARSON, C. M., GUILLORY, R. J. and SERAYDARIAN, K.: *Proc. Soc. Nat. Acad. Sc., 45:*791 (1959).
312. MONNIER, A. M.: *Arch. sc. physiol., 3:*371 (1949).
313. MONNIER, A. M.: *Cold Spring Harbor Symp. Quant. Biol., 17:*69 (1952).
314. MONOD, H., RHOR, D., SAINT-SAENS, M., SCHERRER, J. and SOULA, C. *J. Physiol. Paris, 51:*1011 (1959).

315. MURNAGHAN, M. F.: *Rev. canad. biol.*, *14*:273 (1955)
316. MURNAGHAN, M. F.: *Nature*, London, *181*:131 (1958).
317. MURNAGHAN, M. F.: *Canad. J. Biochem.*, *38*:287 (1960).
318. MURNAGHAN, M. F.: *Science*, *131*:418 (1960).
319. NAMBA, T. and HIRAKI, K.: *J.A.M.A.*, *166*:1834 (1958).
320. NASTUK, W. L.: *Ann. New York Acad. Sc.*, *81*:317 (1959).
320a. NASTUK, W. L., PLESCIA, O. J., and OSSERMAN, K. E.: *Proc. Soc. exp. Biol. & Med.*, *105*:177 (1960).
321. NASTUK, W. L., STRAUSS, A. J. L. and OSSERMAN, K. E.: *Am. J. Med.*, *26*:349 (1959).
322. NATTRASS, F. J.: *Brain*, *77*:549 (1954).
323. NEEDHAM, D. M.: *Brit. M. Bull.*, *12*:194 (1956).
324. NEVIN, S.: *Brain*, *57*:239 (1934).
325. NEVIN, S.: In *Modern Trends in Neurology*, p. 494. London, Butterworth (1951).
326. NICHOLSON, W. M. and BRANNING, W. S.: *J.A.M.A.*, *134*:1292 (1947).
327. NITOWSKI, H. M., GORDON, H. H. and TILDON, J. T.: *Johns Hopkins Hosp. Bull.*, *98*:361 (1956).
328. O'LEARY, P. A., LAMBERT, E. H. and SAYRE, G. P.: *J. Invest. Dermat.*, *24*:301 (1955).
329. OLIVER, C. P., McQUARRIE, I. and ZIERLER, M.: *Am. J. Dis. Child.*, *68*:308 (1944).
330. OPPENHEIMER, E. H.: *Bull. Johns Hopkins Hosp.*, *98*:353 (1956).
331. OPPENHEIMER, H., DE LUCA, A. and MILHORAT, A. T.: *Proc. Soc. Exper. Biol. & Med.*, *100*:568 (1959).
332. OPPENHEIMER, H., SHULMAN, S., ROBERTS, S. and MILHORAT, A. T.: *Proc. Soc. Exper. Biol. & Med.*, *100*:564 (1959).
333. ORENT, E. R., KRUSE, H. D. and McCOLLUM, E. V.: *Am. J. Physiol.*, *101*:454 (1932).
334. ORR, W. F. and MINOT, A. S.: *Arch. Neurol. & Psychiat.*, *67*:483 (1952).
335. OSSERMAN, K. E.: *Myasthenia Gravis*. New York, Grune & Stratton (1958).
336. OSSERMAN, K. E. and TENG, P.: *J.A.M.A.*, *150*:265 (1952).
337. OSWALD, B.: *Ann. Parasit.*, *16*:548 (1938).
338. PACHOMOV, N. and CAUGHEY, J. E.: *Neurology*, *10*:28 (1960).
339. PAPPENHEIMER, A. M.: *On Certain Aspects of Vitamin E Deficiency*. Springfield, Ill., Thomas (1948).
340. PAPST, W., MERTENS, H. G. and ESSLEN, E.: *Klin. Monatsbl. Augenh.*, *134*:374 (1959).
341. PEARSON, C. M.: *New England J. Med.*, *256*:1069 (1957).
342. PEARSON, C. M., BECK, W. S. and BLAHD, W. H.: *Arch. Int. Med.*, *99*:376 (1957).
343. PEARSON, C. M. and RIMER, D. G.: *Proc. Soc. Exper. Biol. & Med.*, *100*:671 (1959).
344. PEARSON, C. M., RIMER, D. G. and MOMMAERTS, W. F. N. M.: *Clin. Res.*, *7*:298 (1959).
345. PELIKAN, E. W., TETHER, J. E. and UNNA, K.: *Neurology*, *3*:284 (1953).
346. PERKOFF, G. T. and TYLER, F. H.: *Metabolism*, *5*:563 (1956).
347. PERRY, W. L. M.: *J. Physiol.*, *119*:439 (1953).
348. PINELLI, P. and BUCHTHAL, F.: *Neurology*, *3*:347 (1953).
349. PONCHER, H. and WADE, H. W.: *Am. J. Dis. Child.*, *55*:945 (1938).
350. PUDENZ, R. H., McINTOSH, J. F. and McEACHERN, D.: *J.A.M.A.*, *111*:2253 (1938).

351. RANDALL, R. E. JR., ROSSMEISL, E. C. and BLEIFER, K. H.: *Ann. Int. Med., 50:*257 (1959).
352. RAVIN, A.: *Medicine, 18:*443 (1939).
353. RAVIN, A. and WARING, J. J.: *Ann. J. M. Sc., 197:*593 (1939).
354. REGENDANZ, P. and REICHENOW, E.: *Arch. Schiffs. u. Trop. Hyg., 35:*255 (1931).
355. REINER, L., KONIKOFF, N., ALTSCHULE, M. D., DAMMIN, G. J. and MERRILL, J. M.: *Arch. Int. Med., 97:*537 (1956).
356. RICHARDSON, A. T.: *Proc. Roy. Soc. Med., 49:*111 (1956).
357. RONA, P. and TAKAHASHI, D.: *Biochem. Ztschr. 49:*370 (1913).
358. RONZONI, E., WALD, S. M., LAM, R. L. and GILDEA, E. F.: *Neurology, 5:*412 (1955).
359. ROOKE, E. D., LAMBERT, E. H., HODGSON, G. H. and EATON, L. M.: *Tr. Am. Neurol. A., 83:*24 (1958).
360. ROSCH, J. P.: *Lancet, 2:*389 (1954).
361. ROSE, I.: *Canad. M.A.J., 70:*175 (1954).
362. ROSE, I. and GREGSON, J. D.: *Nature, 178:*95 (1956).
363. ROSS, I. C.: *Parasitology, 18:*410 (1926).
364. ROWLAND, L. P.: *J. Chron. Dis., 8:*510 (1958).
365. ROWLAND, L. P. and ESKENASI, A. N.: *Neurology, 6:*667 (1956).
366. ROWLAND, L. P., HOEFER, P. F. A. and ARANOW, H.: In *Second Symposium on Myasthenia Gravis.* H. R. Viets, ed. Springfield, Ill., Thomas (1961).
367. RUBIN, I. L. and BUCHBERG, A. S.: *Am. Heart J., 43:*161 (1952).
368. SANDOW, A.: *Yale J. Biol. & Med., 25:*176 (1952).
369. SANDOW, A.: *Am. J. Phys. Med., 34:*145 (1955).
370. SANDOW, A. and BURST, M.: *Am. J. Physiol., 194:*557 (1958).
371. SCARZELLA, R.: *Psichiat. Neuropat., 85:*1001 (1957).
372. SCHAAR, F. E., LaBREE, J. W. and GLEASON, D. F.: *Proc. Central Soc. Clin. Res., 22:*71 (1949).
373. SCHAPIRA, G. and DREYFUS, J. C.: *Biochim. méd., 17:*251 (1955).
374. SCHAPIRA, G. and DREYFUS, J. C.: *Compt. rend. Soc. biol.,* Paris, *152:*1705 (1958).
375. SCHAPIRA, G. and DREYFUS, J. C.: *Am. J. Phys. Med., 38:*207 (1959).
376. SCHAPIRA, G., DREYFUS, J. C. and SCHAPIRA, F.: *Semainè hôp. Paris, 29:*1917 (1953).
377. SCHAPIRA, G., DREYFUS, J. C., SCHAPIRA, F. and KRUH, J.: *Am. J. Phys. Med., 34:*313 (1955).
378. SCHAPIRA, G., JOLLY, M. and DREYFUS, J. C.: *Compt. rend. Soc. biol.,* Paris, *148:*1056 (1954).
379. SCHAPIRA, F., SCHAPIRA, G. and DREYFUS, J. C.: *Compt. rend. Acad. sc.,* Paris, *245:*754 (1957).
380. SCHERRER, J. and MONOD, H.: *J. Physiol. Paris, 52:*419 (1960).
381. SCHMID, R. and MAHLER, R.: *J. Clin. Invest., 38:*2044 (1959).
382. SCHMID, R., ROBBINS, P. W. and TRAUT, R. R.: *Proc. Nat. Acad. Sc., 45:*1236 (1959).
383. SCHRADER, G.: *Die Entwicklung neuer Insektizide auf Grundlage von organischen Fluor- und Phosphorverbindungen.* Monogr. No. 62, Aufl. Verlag Chemie, Weinheim (1952).
384. SCHUELER, F. W.: *J. Pharmacol., 115:*127 (1955).
385. SCHWAB, R. S. and LELAND, C. C.: *J.A.M.A., 153:*1270 (1953).
386. *Second Symposium on Myasthenia Gravis.* H. R. Viets, ed. Springfield, Ill., Thomas (1961).
387. SHANES, A. M.: *Pharmacol. Rev., 10:*59 (1958).

388. SHANK, R. E., GILDER, H. and HOAGLAND, C. L.: *Arch. Neurol. & Psychiat.,* *52*:431 (1944).
389. SHINOSAKI, T.: *Ztschr. ges. Neurol., 100*:264 (1925).
390. SHY, G. M., BRENDLER, S., RABINOVITCH, R. and MCEACHERN, D.: *J.A.M.A., 144*:1353 (1950).
391. SHY, G. M., CUMMINGS, D. J., BERG, L. and HORVARTH, B.: *J. Appl. Physiol., 8*:33 (1955).
392. SHY, G. M., WANKO, T., ROWLEY, P. T. and ENGEL, A. G.: *Exp. Neurol., 3*:53 (1961).
393. SIBLEY, J. A. and FLEISHER, G. A.: *Proc. Staff. Meet., Mayo Clin., 29*:591 (1954).
394. SIEKERT, R. G. and FLEISHER, G. A.: *Proc. Staff. Meet., Mayo Clin., 31*:459 (1956).
395. SIMON, E. J., LESSELL, I., GROSS, C. S. and MILHORAT, A. T.: *Federation Proc., 17*:311 (1958).
396. SIMPSON, J. A.: *J. Neurol., Neurosurg. & Psychiat., 19*:275 (1956).
397. SIMPSON, J. A.: *Brain, 81*:112 (1958).
398. SIMPSON, J. A.: *Scottish Med. J., 5*:419 (1960).
399. SPAET, T. H., ROSENTHAL, M. C. and DAMESHEK, W.: *Blood, 9*:881 (1954).
400. STEINBERG, H. and WALDRON, B. R.: *Medicine, 31*:133 (1952).
401. STEINERT, H.: *Deutsch. Ztschr. Nervenh., 37*:58 (1909).
402. STEPHENS, F. E. and TYLER, F. H.: *Am. J. Human Genet., 3*:111 (1951).
403. STEVENSON, J. W.: *Amer. J. Med. Sci., 235*:317 (1958).
404. TALBOTT, J. H.: *Medicine, 20*:85 (1941).
405. THESLEFF, S.: *Physiol. Revs., 40*:734 (1960).
406. THIEBAUT, F., ISCH, F. and ISCH-TREUSSARD, C.: *L'Encéphale*, 1300 (1956).
407. THOMASEN, E.: *Myotonia. Thomsen's Disease. Paramyotonia. Dystrophia Myotonica.* Aarhus, Universitetsforlaget (1948).
408. THOMPSON, R. A. and VIGNOS, P. J. JR.: *Arch. Int. Med., 103*:551 (1959).
409. THOMSEN, J.: *Arch. Psychiat. Nervenk., 6*:706 (1876).
410. THOMSON, D. L. and COLLIP, J. B.: *Physiol. Rev., 12*:309 (1932).
411. THORN, G. W., DORANCE, S. S. and DAY, E.: *Ann. Int. Med., 16*:1053 (1942).
412. THORN, G. W., FORSHAM, P. H., FRAWLEY, T. F., HILL, S. R., ROCHE, M., STAEHELIN, D. and WILSON, D. L.: *New England Med. J., 242*:824 (1950).
413. TOMPKINS, V., LASCELLES, R. G. and MCKINNEY, B.: *J. Neurol., Neurosurg. & Psychiat., 22*:50 (1959).
414. TOURNILHAC, M.: *Paralysies avec dyskaliémie.* Paris, Maloine (1959).
415. TOWER, S. S.: *Physiol. Rev., 19*:1 (1939).
416. TOWER, D. B., PETERS, E. L. and POGORELSKIN, M. A.: *Neurology, 6*:37 (1956).
417. *Toxic Hazards of Pesticides to Man.* World Health Organisation tech. Rep. Serv. No. 114. Geneva (1956).
418. TUFTS, E. V. and GREENBERG, D. M.: *J. Biol. Chem., 122*:715 (1937).
419. TURPIN, R., LEFEBVRE, J. and LERIQUE, J.: *Compt. rend. Acad. sc.,* Paris, *216*:579 (1943).
420. TYLER, F. H. and PERKOFF, G. T.: *Arch. Int. Med., 88*:175 (1951).
421. TYLER, F. H. and STEPHENS, F. E.: *Ann. Int. Med., 32*:640 (1950).
422. TYLER, F. H., STEPHENS, F. E., GUNN, F. D. and PERKOFF, G. T.: *J. Clin. Invest., 30*:492 (1951).
423. TYLER, F. H. and WINTROBE, M. M.: *Ann. Int. Med., 32*:72 (1950).
424. VALLEE, B. L., WACKER, W. E. C. and ULMER, D. D.: *New England Med. J., 262*:155 (1960).
425. VAN HARREVELD, A.: *Am. J. Physiol., 150*:670 (1947).
426. VICTOR, J.: *Am. J. Physiol., 108*:229 (1934).

427. VIETS, H. R. and SCHWAB, R. S.: *J.A.M.A., 113:*559 (1939).

428. VIETS, H. R. and SCHWAB, R. S.: *Thymectomy for Myasthenia Gravis,* Springfield, Ill., Thomas (1960).

429. VIGNOS, P. J. and LEFKOWITZ, M.: *J. Clin. Invest., 38:*873 (1959).

430. VOLK, B. W., LOSNER, S., ARONSON, S. M. and LEW, H.: *Am. J. M. Sc., 232:*38 (1956).

431. WACKER, W. E. C. and ULMER, D. D.: *J. Clin. Invest., 39:*1038 (1960).

432. WACKER, W. E. C. and VALLEE, B. L.: *New England Med. J., 259:*431 (1958).

433. WALDER, D. N.: *Clin. Sc., 12:*153 (1955).

434. WALTON, J. N.: *Ann. Hum. Genet., 20:*1 (1955).

435. WALTON, J. N.: *Acta Genet. & Statist. Med., 7:*318 (1957).

436. WALTON, J. N. and ADAMS, R. D.: *J. Path. Bact., 72:*273 (1956).

437. WALTON, J. N. and ADAMS, R. D.: *Polymyositis.* Edinburgh, Livingston (1958).

438. WALTON, J. N. and LATNER, A. L.: *Arch. Neurol. & Psychiat., 72:*362 (1954).

439. WALTON, J. N. and NATTRASS, F. J.: *Brain, 77:*169 (1954).

440. WEINSTOCK, I. M., EPSTEIN, S. and MILHORAT, A. T.: *Proc. Soc. Exper. Biol. & Med., 99:*272 (1958).

441. WEISS, P. ED.: *Genetic Neurology: Problems of the Development, Growth and Regeneration of the Nervous System and Its Function.* Chicago, Univ. Chicago Press (1950).

442. WEISS, P. and EDDS, M. V.: *Am. J. Physiol., 145:*587 (1946).

443. WEISS, P. and HISCOE, H. N.: *J. Exper. Zool., 107:*315 (1948).

445. WELANDER, L.: *Acta med. scandinav., 141:*Suppl. 265 (1951).

446. WEST, R.: *Brain, 58:*1 (1935).

447. WEST, W. T. and MASON, K. E.: *Am. J. Phys. Med., 34:*223 (1955).

448. WEST, W. T. and MASON, K. E.: *Am. J. Anat., 102:*323 (1958).

449. WESTPHAL, C.: *Berl. Klin. Wchnschr., 22:*498 (1885).

450. WHITE, L. P.: *California Med., 90:*1 (1959).

451. WIDDOWSON, E. M., McCANCE, R. A. and SPRAY, C. M.: *Clin. Sc., 10:*113 (1951).

452. WIGTON, R. S. and BRINK, F. JR.: *J. Clin. Invest., 23:*898 (1944).

453. WILKINS, L.: In *The Diagnosis and Treatment of Endocrine Disorders in Childhood and Adolescence.* Springfield, Ill., Thomas (1953).

454. WILLIAMS, R. C.: *Ann. Int. Med., 50:*1174 (1959).

455. WILSON, A., OBRIST, A. R. and WILSON, H.: *Lancet, 2:*368 (1953).

456. WILSON, A. and STONER, H. B.: *Quart. J. Med., 64:*237 (1947).

457. WILSON, A. and WILSON, H.: *Am. J. Med., 19:*697 (1955).

458. WILSON, I. B.: *Biochem. et biophys. acta, 27:*196 (1958).

459. WOHLFART, G.: *J. Neuropath. & Exper. Neurol., 10:*109 (1951).

460. WOHLFART, G.: *Deutsch. Ztschr. Nervenh., 173:*426 (1955).

461. WOHLFART, G.: *Am. J. Phys. Med., 38:*223 (1959).

462. WOLF, A.: *Arch. Neurol. & Psychiat., 36:*328 (1936).

463. YOUNG, J. Z.: *Physiol. Rev., 22:*318 (1942).

464. YUILE, C. L. and CLARK, W. F.: *J. Exp. Med., 74:*187 (1941).

465. ZABRISKIE, E. G. and FRANTZ, A. M.: *Bull. Neurol. Inst. New York, 2:*57 (1932).

466. ZIERLER, K. L.: *Bull. Johns Hopkins Hosp., 102:*17 (1958).

467. ZIERLER, K. L.: *Ann. New York Acad. Sc., 75:*227 (1958).

468. ZIERLER, K. L. and ANDRES, R.: *J. Clin. Invest., 36:*730 (1957).

469. ZIERLER, K. L., ANDRES, R., LEVY, R. I., ANDERSON, H. M. and LILIENTHAL, J. L.: *Bull. Johns Hopkins Hosp., 92:*32 (1953).

470. ZIERLER, K. L., FOLK, B. P., MAGLADERY, J. W. and LILIENTHAL, J. L.: *Bull. Johns Hopkins Hosp., 85:*370 (1949).

471. ZIERLER, K. L. and LILIENTHAL, J. L.: *Aùer. J. Med., 15:*829 (1953).

XXXVIII

NUTRITIONAL DISORDERS OF THE NERVOUS SYSTEM

John D. Spillane and C. E. C. Wells

THE CHANGING CONCEPT

In the past 20 years certain currents of thought, in the laboratory and at the bedside, have contributed with varying emphasis to our present concept of nutritional disorders of the nervous system. The war of 1939-1945 with its constant threat of starvation to many countries and peoples stimulated an intensified study of nutritional problems; at the same time the mass imprisonment of captive combatants and non-combatants, often with their own doctors, led to a large-scale human experiment in starvation. With the end of hostilities a spate of observations was published by experienced workers who had recorded the effects of nutritional lack of all kinds either during the period of imprisonment or in the critical days immediately after release. Among Allied personnel an extraordinary contrast was seen between the clinical disorders of those captive in the Far East and of those who had been imprisoned in Europe. Starvation was common to both groups. Among the former who had existed largely on a rice diet, vitamin deficiencies particularly of the B complex were common;[1-3] a similar state of affairs was observed among Germans and Italians imprisoned in the Middle East.[4,5] Neurological disorders were frequent. In the prisoners from Europe, however, where the main deficiency had been of protein, neurological conditions were seldom encountered. The experience in the Ruhr in the next few years was identical.[6] It is of interest that in the "pure" form of kwashiorkor, the widespread tropical disorder of young children due to protein lack, the syndrome is characterised by the absence of any neural lesion.

Clinical thought, therefore, in the immediate post-war world was dominated by wartime experience. The definition of nutritional disorder had not changed for half a century: it implied a primary deficiency in the diet of a vitamin, or of an essential food factor, the lack of which caused a well defined clinical syndrome. In some instances, such as classical beri-beri, the vitamin had been identified and prepared synthetically; but in many more the deficiency was suspected without clear identification of a specific vitamin. The many reports of nutritional neuropathy in the tropics fell into this category, of which the Jamaican syndrome described by Cruickshank and his colleagues[7,8] is a recent example.

Within a few years, however, two outstanding biochemical discoveries, that of folic acid[9] in 1945 and of cyanocobalamin[10,11] in 1948, opened up a new era in nutritional thought. Although these two substances were at first investigated because of their relationship to megaloblastic anaemia, their true place on the wider background of nutritional and alimentary disorders rapidly became evident. With this shift of emphasis a whole group of conditions which had not previously been recognised as clinically related began to be considered under the title of the malabsorption syndrome. In these disorders inadequate intake of food, structural abnormality of the stomach and small intestine, alterations in the intestinal flora, and genetic factors were all found to play their part. Recognition of this syndrome has widened the scope of nutritional neurological disease: malabsorption may cause not only a shortage of vitamins, particularly those of the B group which play a vital rôle in the enzyme systems of the brain and nerves, but also of inorganic elements such as calcium and potassium. This may lead to an immediate disturbance of neural physiology or to a more remote effect by alteration in bone density and subsequent compression of nervous tissues.

The way to a revolution in neurological thinking had already been cleared by two major contributions in the years before the war. Peters[12] and his colleagues at Oxford had established the nature and site of the biochemical lesion in pigeons made opisthotonic by deprivation of thiamine: confirmation in the two syndromes of human thiamine deficiency, beri-beri[13] and Wernicke's encephalopathy,[14] soon followed. In the same decade Krebs[15] was working out his theory of the tricarboxylic acid cycle, now accepted as the final common pathway in the combustion of many foodstuffs. This cycle, almost too close to life to be a source of clinical syndromes,—its disruption quickly leads to death—has become a catalyst of neurochemical thought. Following his further analysis of the pyruvate oxidase system by a wartime study of arsenite poisoning and its reversal by dimercaprol, Peters[16] investigated the toxic action of fluoroacetate. This substance which occurs naturally in the South African plant Dichapetalum cymosum is characterised by an extremely stable C-F bond. Peters found that it was accepted, with the chemically similar two-carbon fragments of pyruvate breakdown, by the enzymes at the condensing stage of the Krebs cycle: fluorocitrate was formed which blocked the cycle at the citrate-alpha-ketoglutarate stage by inhibition of aconitase. To this pathological enzyme reaction he gave the name and the idea of the "lethal synthesis."[17]

From the clinical point of view a result of this experimental work has been the demonstration that syndromes superficially similar but aetiologically very different may in fact have a common basis in a closely related biochemical lesion. In 1950 Thompson and his colleagues[18] introduced a classification of polyneuropathy based on the response of the patient to a pyruvate tolerance test and, in those cases in which this was abnormal, on the result of thiamine therapy. Half of their cases showed normal pyruvate metabolism: in some of the others the abnormally high level of pyruvate in the blood after a loading dose of glucose was corrected by giving thiamine. But a third group of patients was found in whom the abnormality persisted despite prolonged treatment with large doses of thiamine. Some of these cases might be examples of a "lethal synthesis" which could be reversed by the action of dimercaprol or of chelating agents; others might be deficient in another factor needed at this stage of the metabolic chain such as magnesium ions or lipothiamide. On the other hand pyruvate accumulation might be a secondary phenomenon due to block at a more distant stage of the pathway, it being but one of several excess metabolites. An example of this has been shown in the raised levels of pyruvate and of alpha-ketoglutarate in the blood of patients in hepatic coma.[19]

When Woolley and his colleagues[20] tested the effect of nineteen derivatives of pyridine on canine black tongue, they left "open to some question" the apparent inactivity of two of these. In fact two dogs treated with pyridine-3-sulphonic acid and one with 3-acetylpyridine died, and others became more toxic. These chemical analogues of nicotinic acid are now included among the anti-vitamins, a class of compounds which has greatly simplified the production of deficiency states in experimental animals and in man. Analysis of their action has in some cases led to the recognition of the toxic effect of a drug. Soon after the introduction of the anti-tuberculous drugs, a series of neurological sequelae began to be reported in patients who had been treated with isoniazid. These included psychosis, epilepsy, neuropathy and, in rare cases, optic atrophy. Investigation showed that there was an interference with the metabolism of pyridoxine very similar to that caused by the anti-vitamin deoxypyridoxine.[21]

In man and in the higher animals vitamins of the B complex are obtained either directly from food or from biosynthesis by intestinal commensuals. The demonstration, therefore, by Krehl, Teply, Sarma and Elvehjem[22,23] in 1945 that nicotinic acid could be synthesised in rats from an amino-acid precursor, tryptophan, was an important discovery. This work was subsequently confirmed in man by Sarett and Goldsmith[24] four years later. Further study of this process revealed that other members of the B complex were required at various stages of the reaction and that deficiency of any one of them could block specific stages and liberate abnormal amounts of intermediate metabolites. The pattern of their excretion would depend on the stage at which blockade occurred.[25] Lack of tryptophan and of nicotinic acid are closely linked in man with the deficiency disease, pellagra; the signs of this condition, particularly the dermal lesions, are mimicked by several disorders in which no vitamin deficiency is known to occur. Some of these with neurological signs will be discussed below.

Commerce has had its effect on nutritional disease. The causation of canine hysteria by agenised flour is now well known as the result of the classical studies of Sir Edward Mellanby. Despite stringent precautions by many governments further nutritional disorders of this kind are to be expected. A dramatic example was the epidemic of convulsions induced by pyridoxine deficiency in infants who had been fed on a particular brand of cow's milk industrially prepared and stored.[26-29] Another aspect of the hazard of commercialised therapy is the blunderbuss haematinic pill: this may contain iron, folic acid and B_{12} in sufficient quantity to maintain a normoblastic marrow but in true addisonian anaemics the B_{12} will not be adequately absorbed and neuropathy may occur.[30,31] The abuse of vitamin therapy is very real. Already the dangers of excess vitamin D are widely recognised: in recent years Marie and Sée have described a syndrome of acute hydrocephalus in infants due to hypervitaminosis A.[32]

A sharp distinction between nutritional disorders, in the older sense, and metabolic diseases is no longer practicable. Now another current of research is under way which will increasingly modify our concept of nutritional disorders of the nervous system. This is the study of human genetics in their biochemical context. Galactosaemia, Hartnup-disease and hepato-lenticular degeneration will be discussed as examples of this new aspect of nutritional problems. A footnote to this would be mention of the precipitation of a malabsorption syndrome, with its neurological lesions, in previously healthy but genetically abnormal subjects after an acute gastro-enteritis and after operations.[33,34]

Although primary deficiency of a factor in the diet remains the standard clinical illustration of a biochemical lesion, the real importance of the deficiency in modern nosology is seen to be its localising value within the series of highly complex enzyme systems on which the function of the nerve cell and axon depends. Clinical neurology continues to lead the exploration of biochemical disorders of the nervous system.

THE MALABSORPTION SYNDROME

The discoveries of folic acid and of cyanocobalamin resulted in a new orientation towards the megaloblastic anaemias and the disorders of the alimentary system with which they are often associated. In this way a classification of alimentary diseases has arisen round the central symptom of "malabsorption."[35] Features of this syndrome are diarrhoea, steatorrhoea, abdominal pain and distension, weight loss and the whole gamut of signs of malnutrition. In any one case, any or all of these may be present; but not infrequently patients present with an obscure anaemia, or with symptoms of vitamin deficiency, without evident abdominal disease. It is with this "cryptic" group that the neurologist tends to be concerned.

Several factors may contribute to the development of the syndrome. Heredity plays its part and is seen in such disorders as addisonian anaemia, coeliac disease and idiopathic steatorrhoea and in the Peutz-Jegher syndrome. Avery Jones[36] has graphically described the "hopper mechanism" of the stomach which delivers measured quantities of food into the mixing mill of jejunum and intestine: disturbance of this mechanism by surgery or by disease can interfere seriously with digestion—each bolus is followed by its ration of digestive juices instead of being mixed intimately with them. Similarly, failure of the juices themselves, and resection of the absorptive area of the jejunum and ileum, or its destruction by disease, will seriously impair nutrition. An important aspect of malnutrition is the distribution and nature of the intestinal flora: the many varieties of the "blind loop" have in common stasis of intestinal contents and invasion by bacteria not usually found in such numbers in this part of the intestine.[37] The harmful effect of these bacteria is usually attributed to their competitive use of vitamins needed by the host, and by their suppression of the biosynthesis of vitamins by the normal intestinal cogeners.

The many causes of the malabsorption syndrome have often been reviewed.[38] Of more immediate interest to the neurologist is their expected frequency. In a series of 75 cases which she had investigated by intestinal biopsy Shiner published an instructive aetiological table.[39] Eliminating post-operative cases (18 cases) and cases of steatorrhoea due to pancreatic disease (9 cases), 24 of the remaining 48 cases are seen to be due to idiopathic steatorrhoea or coeliac disease. These two conditions, which are probably identical, are diagnosed by finding more than 6 gm. of fat daily in the stools when the patient is taking a normal diet and are confirmed by jejunal biopsy and by a good response to a gluten-free diet. Macrocytic anaemia with low serum B_{12} levels and impaired folic acid absorption may be expected together with impaired absorption of glucose and of D-xylose.[36] These observations suggest that idiopathic steatorrhoea may cause B_{12} neuropathy. Cooke[40] has suggested that steatorrhoea is a genetic disorder associated with an enzyme deficiency which disrupts folic acid metabolism.

The main site of absorption of B_{12} in man is thought to be in the lower ileum,[41,42] whereas folic acid is chiefly absorbed from the jejunum.[40,43-45] Calcium, defect of which in its neurological context is discussed below, is absorbed in the duodenum and jejunum.

Although the malabsorption of folic acid and of B_{12} and of the other members of the B complex is of primary interest to neurologists, deficient absorption of calcium and potassium, perhaps also of magnesium, and of vitamin D can give rise to important neurological conditions. The clinical manifestations of tetany—paraesthesiae, cramps, carpo-pedal and laryngeal spasms, epilepsy—are well recognized, but the underlying biochemical disorder remains obscure. In calcium deficiency, decreased ionisation of the various calcium complexes in the blood has long been accepted as a fundamental factor, but the problem is complicated by the tetany of alkalosis and by that described in patients with normal or near normal calcium levels who are deficient in potassium or in magnesium. Changes in hydrogen-ion and calcium-ion concentration may act independently of each other, but their total effect is algebraic. Local CO_2 tension may be another factor.[46] Fourman[47] induced tetany in healthy subjects by restricting potassium intake, but was unable to offer a satisfactory hypothesis. The rôle of magnesium in causing tetany has been in dispute. Vallee and his associates[48] have recently brought forward further evidence in favour of a primary deficiency: the validity of their results has been challenged by Fraser and his colleagues[49] who have described a syndrome of magnesium deficiency in man in which tetany was not found. One of their cases had steatorrhoea, another developed symptoms after parathyroidectomy. Loss of calcium and potassium are accepted complications of the malabsorption syndrome: Fraser's case increases the number already on record in which magnesium deficiency is believed to have been due to this.[34,48-50]

Although hypoparathyroidism is not strictly a nutritional disorder, reference must be made to the striking neurological signs in familial pseudo-hypoparathyroidism as it is possible that the clinical presentation of this genetic disorder depends in part on the ratio of calcium to phosphorus in the diet and on their relative absorption.[51,52] Features of this condition are dementia, epilepsy, ataxia and striatal signs together with short stature, lens opacities and stunted metacarpal bones.[53] Radiologically there may be calcification of the basal or cerebellar ganglia.[54] Biochemical formes frustes have been described as "pseudo-" and "pseudo-pseudo-" varieties.[55,56]

Tetany is not the only way in which calcium insufficiency may present to the neurologist. It is of historic interest that Milkman's original case of pseudo-fractures due to osteomalacia had such difficulty in walking that a diagnosis of myopathy was considered.[57] Similar cases are seen from time to time in which a differential diagnosis from motor neurone disease and from myopathy has to be made. These patients present with a waddling gait and a much greater disability than their neurological signs would suggest. This sometimes leads to confusion with hysteria.[58,59]

The severe osteomalacia which results in some patients from malabsorption, due to lack of both calcium and vitamin D, may cause spontaneous fracture of a vertebral body with compression of the cord. In other cases softening of bones at the base of the skull produces a secondary basilar impression which may be followed by a posterior fossa syndrome.

Gastro-intestinal disorders, including steatorrhoea, have long been recognised as the commonest cause of potassium deficiency. The muscular weakness and paralysis are related to the serum potassium level, but the correspondence may not be absolute.[60] Chronic hypokalaemia certainly contributes to the general lethargy and weakness of patients with the malabsorption syndrome; slowness to empty the bladder may be overlooked as a sign of this. We have recently seen a patient who had presented with this symptom and had undergone a full urological investigation before neurogenic atony of the bladder was suspected.

B$_{12}$ NEUROPATHY

The older term of subacute combined degeneration of the spinal cord has long been subject to criticism, not least for its clumsiness.[61] In their review of the neurological conditions arising in patients with megaloblastic anaemia not of addisonian type, Richmond and Davidson[62] suggested that "Vitamin B$_{12}$ neuropathy" was more suitable. It avoids undue emphasis on the cord lesions of a disorder which affects the nervous system at many levels, it does not inevitably link the condition with addisonian pernicious anaemia, and in a short title refers to the fundamental defect of B$_{12}$ deficiency.

There are three major causes of this deficiency. The most common in Britain and North America is failure to absorb adequate dietary B$_{12}$

due to absence of Castle's intrinsic factor. Although studies in children[63] have suggested that the gastric lesion of addisonian anaemia as originally described by Magnus and Ungley[64] may not be aetiologically important, the primary deficiency of intrinsic factor itself has not been disproved. There are grounds for thinking that this may be due to a genetic cause.[65-69] Premature greying of the hair in subjects who later develop anaemia is an established clinical sign: recent observations have shown a high incidence of deficient secretion of intrinsic factor in the families of these patients.[70,71]

The second major cause of the neuropathy is the malabsorption syndrome. As described elsewhere, recognition of this syndrome is only the first step in diagnosis. The frequency distribution of the possible underlying disorders is a lesson in geomedicine. In Scandinavia, for instance, cases will be found due to infestation with the fish tapeworm[72] whereas in Britain this is rarely seen. The commonest cause of the malabsorption syndrome has been stated to be idiopathic steatorrhoea:[39] but in the writers' experience B_{12} neuropathy is more often a consequence of gastric surgery for ulcer and ulcer-cancer.[73-76]

The third group is very small, but of particular interest, as it links these other causes of B_{12} neuropathy with a deficiency disease in the older sense. These are cases of deficiency due to absolute lack of B_{12} in the diet—occurring in the group of vegetarians whose food is virtually devoid of animal protein.[77-79] The majority of these persons become vegetarian in early adult life when the bodily stores of B_{12} have been built up and many years may elapse before symptoms of their deficiency appear. This may easily lead to a mistaken diagnosis.

Although it is now widely known that B_{12} neuropathy may occur without anaemia or glossitis, some of its modes of presentation are less obvious. Holmes[80] has drawn attention to the syndrome of organic dementia, where progressive clouding of the sensorium may obscure the clinical signs and make diagnosis very difficult. An estimation of the serum B_{12} content in every case of organic dementia of uncertain aetiology is sometimes rewarding. The EEG is often abnormal in these cases, normal rhythms returning quickly after administration of B_{12}.[81-83] In his review of the macrocytic anaemias Wilkinson[67] drew attention to the increased frequency of certain other disorders in patients with pernicious anaemia. One of these was diabetes mellitus. The differential diagnosis of diabetic and B_{12} neuropathy may seem obvious; but in a single six-month period the writers have seen two cases of longstanding diabetic neuropathy in whom routine B_{12} estimations have revealed a significant defect. Although B_{12} therapy has no place in the management of diabetic neuropathy,[84] the occurrence of coincident B_{12} deficiency in a few cases should not be overlooked.

Cyanocobalamin is the only vitamin which contains a metal.[85] An atom of cobalt, carrying a positive charge, lies at the heart of a ring of four partially reduced pyrrols thus resembling a porphyrin. This part of the molecule is linked by aminopropanol with its acidic "tail" which is built like a nucleotide but which contains dimethylbenzimin-azole instead of a purine or pyrimidine. The cobalt atom can be re-duced; *in vitro* the redox potential of the vitamin seems outside the physiological range but this may be modified by the apoenzyme with which it combines in a particular system. It may also be biologically active by dint of the propionamide groups of the porphyrin com-plex.[86,87]

For nearly 30 years cobalt deficiency had been recognized as the cause of a wasting disease of sheep in Western and Southern Australia. The identification of cobalt in the red crystals of B_{12}[88] was the clue to solv-ing this veterinary problem. Later it was shown that bacteria synthe-sised cyanocobalamin in the gut of ruminants provided that the pas-ture contained enough cobalt.

Radioactive B_{12} using ^{60}Co has been prepared but its use is limited by its low specific activity and long half-life of 5.3 years.[89,90] Prepara-tions using ^{56}Co and ^{57}Co with half-lives of 72 and 270 days have a very high specific activity. With these a total dose of 5 millicuries is permis-sible: in normal subjects an oral dose of only a fraction of a microgram is distributed sufficiently in the blood stream to be detected by a scintil-lation counter. Repeated experiments on the same subject can be car-ried out, the patient serving as his own control.[85,87]

Unlike most of the B vitamins, cyanocobalamin is poorly absorbed even under optimal conditions. Intrinsic factor is needed for absorp-tion from the gut and perhaps also for uptake of the vitamin by the tissues.[91] A transport mechanism within the intestinal mucosal cell has been postulated, analogous to the apoferritin of iron absorption, but proof of this has yet to come. With small doses of intrinsic factor B_{12} is absorbed stoichiometrically but with larger doses this relation no longer holds.[92] Intrinsic factor has been identified as a mucoprotein; several fractions with molecular weights varying from 5,000 to 20,000 having been obtained together with an inhibitory substance. The most active fraction has a molecular weight between 5,000 and 10,000. Only 0.33 mg. has an activity comparable to 50 mg. of a standard prepara-tion, using the Schilling test as the method of assay.[93,94] Absorption is increased when B_{12} is given in aqueous solution and when it is given in divided doses; and it is increased further by adsorption with resins.[95] Absorption is enhanced in normal individuals by D-sorbitol but not in patients with addisonian anaemia.[96]

The ileum has been shown to be the principal site of absorption both

in experimental animals and in patients who have had total gastrec-
tomy.[41,42] In the latter the size of the dose may be important, up to 3
mg. daily having been found necessary by some workers.[31] The fate
of oral B_{12} is not fully known. Finding most of the ingested dose in
the faeces does not necessarily mean that only the remaining fraction
has been absorbed: a much larger amount may be absorbed and excreted back into the gut in the bile.[97,98]

B_{12} absorption may depend on thyroid activity.[99] In experimental
rats thyroidectomy abolishes absorption which returns when thyroid
is given.[100] Chow found newborn cretins with an abnormally low
level of B_{12} in the serum. He quoted two cases of athyroid cretinism
in which the serum concentration both in maternal and in cord blood
was virtually nil. The infants were treated with thyroid, their clinical
recovery being matched by the return of the serum B_{12} levels to normal.
One of the mothers had no treatment, her serum level becoming normal within 6 weeks.[95]

Serum concentrations of B_{12}, and the glutathione content of red
cells which is dependent on this, are significantly lower than normal
at term, and are correspondingly higher in the foetus. Foetal requirements are high, but this obligatory withdrawal of vitamin from
the mother to the foetus is probably compensated by an increased
absorption during pregnancy.[101,102] Although this lowered maternal
level of B_{12} has not been shown as a primary cause of neuropathy,
clearly it may precipitate neurological symptoms in a predisposed patient. These might be found among those relatives of frank addisonian
anaemics who have a deficient output of intrinsic factor.[70,71] In elderly
patients also a significantly lower concentration of serum B_{12} and of
the glutathione content of red cells has been found.[103] The cause of
this is uncertain, but in these persons also marginal absorption may
precipitate frank disease in the predisposed.

The biological action of B_{12} is unknown.[87,104] Many hypotheses
exist, some of which like that of Johnson and his colleagues[105,106]
—that B_{12} is an important catalyst of protein synthesis—outstrip
the proven facts. Of particular interest to the neurologist is the
evidence that B_{12} is closely concerned with the synthesis of deoxyribonucleic acid (DNA) and ribonucleic acid (RNA). These acids contain pyrimidine and purine bases, sugar and phosphoric acid. A folic
acid derivative is needed for the introduction of one-carbon units in
purine and pyrimidine synthesis and B_{12} for the formation of ribose
from glucose. The pentose of RNA is D-ribose which may be the precursor of deoxyribose, the only pentose found in DNA.[107] In addisonian pernicious anaemia in relapse, the RNA/DNA and the uracil/thy-
mine ratios in bone marrow increase, being rapidly restored to normal

after B_{12} *or* folic acid has been given. The return to normal precedes
the reticulocyte crisis.[85] It has been suggested that folic acid and B_{12}
are both needed for the methylation of uracil to thymine, the former
taking part in the formation of an intermediate metabolite, hydroxy-
methyluracil, the latter continuing the final reduction to thymine.[108,109]
The response of megaloblastic marrow either to B_{12} or to folic acid is
paradoxical. Smith[85] has offered an ingenious hypothesis. Vitamin deficiencies, compatible with life, are only relative: there is a shortage,
not an absolute lack. A build-up of intermediate metabolites could,
under the law of mass action, effect conversion of enough substrate to
DNA to maintain normoblastic red cell formation even with a shortage of the essential vitamin-enzymes.

The hypothesis on which much of the present theory about genes and
chromosomes is built emphasises the importance of DNA in mitosis:
impaired synthesis of DNA might lead early to slowing down of mitosis, or to a qualitative change, and to changes in those tissues where
repair is carried out by cellular replacement. Such tissues in man are
the marrow, the gastric serosa and the epithelium of the tongue. A
characteristic of B_{12} deficiency states is the variable clinical picture:
most commonly the disorder presents with anaemia, but glossitis may
precede other symptoms by many months and neuropathy without
anaemia is not very unusual.[116-119] Where DNA synthesis is impaired,
anaemia or glossitis will occur: this presumes a functional deficiency
of folic acid as well as a shortage of B_{12} (Another postulated action of
B_{12} is the reduction of folic acid to its physiologically active form,
folinic acid or citrovorum factor). By contrast in those cases in which
folic acid is plentiful, a deficiency of B_{12} alone might lead to impaired
synthesis only of RNA: then those tissues in which repair is carried out
within the cell by RNA would be the first to suffer. Early involvement
of the neurone could be expected, and this is seen in cases of B_{12}
neuropathy where the cells with longest axons are most severely damaged.[87,109]

THIAMINE AND LIPOIC ACID

The physiologically active form of thiamine is its pyrophosphate.
This substance is concerned in the oxidative decarboxylation of pyruvate, the final stage in the breakdown of carbohydrate before the two-
carbon fragments enter the Krebs cycle by condensation with oxaloacetate. Following Peters'[16] demonstration of this enzyme system, other
factors have been shown to take part. One of these is lipoic acid which
can form a CO-NH linkage with the pyrimidine ring of thiamine to
give lipothiamide, a naturally occurring co-enzyme. Peters[17] has suggested that the lipothiamide pyrophosphate could be present in animal

tissues: inactivation of this complex in different ways by thiamine deficiency or by arsenite ring formation with the dithiol groups would account for the similarity of the biochemical lesion. Reed[120,121] has suggested that pyruvate first reacts with thiamine to form acetyl thiamine pyrophosphate; this substance then reacts with the oxidised form of lipoic acid which in turn passes on the acetyl radicle to conenzyme A. Lipoic acid is reoxidised by diphosphopyridine nucleotide. Sinclair[122] has postulated a lesion in this system due to "functional" deficiency of lipoic acid which could then give rise to a neuropathy similar to that occurring in thiamine deficiency—beri-beri and Wernicke's encephalopathy. This could be the biochemical lesion of the neuropathy of arsenic, alcohol and diabetes. He has suggested that in diabetes ketone bodies might form a ring compound with the dithiol groups analogous to Peters' suggestion of the mode of action of arsenite. An important objection to this theory has been Thompson's demonstration that the pyruvate levels of the blood are not raised in patients with diabetic neuropathy.[123]

Certain antagonists of thiamine, the thiaminases, occur naturally. One of these which causes Chastek paralysis of silver foxes—so-named after the Minnesota ranch-owner where the disorder was first reported—has been found in many kinds of freshwater and seagoing fish. Within days of a change of diet to a much higher proportion of raw fish, always more than a tenth of the total, the affected foxes become weak, lose their appetite and develop ataxia and progressive paraplegia. Severe cases die within 72 hours. Green and his colleagues described the rapid recovery of a moribund fox to which they had given a single injection of thiamine. Their description is akin to Peters' well known illustrations of the opisthotonic pigeon whose recovery is measured with a stop-watch.[124,125]

Another thiaminase has been described in bracken which causes paralysis in horses[126] and its anti-thiamine activity demonstrated in human subjects who had included young bracken fronds in their salad.[127,128] Cooking is probably an adequate safeguard against harmful effects as the important anti-thiamine factor is heat-labile. Pyrithiamine is an anti-vitamin which inhibits the phosphorylation of thiamine. In it the thiazole ring of thiamine is replaced by a pyridine ring: poisoning with this substance causes paralysis in animals. Another analogue, oxythiamine, which is toxic but does not cause paralysis has a hydroxyl group in place of the amino group on the pyrimidine ring. On the strength of these differing actions Albert[129] has sugggested that modification of the thiazole ring of thiamine may determine the neurotoxic action of the analogue.

Although in temperate climates thiamine deficiency is seen in alcoholics and, as something of a curiosity, in a few patients with mental and gastro-intestinal disease, it is a great public health problem in many areas of the world. Ortanez and Pallilo,[130] for example, quoted 25,000 deaths annually from beri-beri in the Philippines. Williams[131] has stated that in 1923 the death rate in Japan from this disorder was 44 per 100,000; during the next 20 years the incidence fell steadily to 6 per 100,000. He attributed this improvement to a national policy of limiting the bran extraction of rice to 5 per cent. Similarly in Manilla the death rate from this cause had fallen from 577 in 1910 to 14 per 100,000 in 1950, as a result of better nutrition. The war years brought many interesting observations about vitamin deficiency in previously healthy Europeans. From their study of 400 cases at Changi, Cruickshank and his colleagues[3,132] in captivity confirmed Spies' earlier observation that 0.3 mg thiamine per 1,000 non-fat calories was a critical level below which clinical beri-beri would develop. At a time of adequate calorie intake (March-October 1942) the estimated thiamine intake was below this level, probably less than 0.2 mg. per 1,000 calories, and the incidence of beri-beri rose above 5 per 1,000 camp inmates per month. It was also noticed that beri-beri was seen more frequently among those doing heavy manual work and those who had been heavy drinkers before captivity. Infection also played a part, 250 of the 400 cases of beri-beri occurring soon after dysentery and malaria.

NICOTINIC ACID AND TRYPTOPHAN

Although Goldberger suspected that in pellagra there was a deficiency both of a vitamin and of an amino-acid, the synthesis of nicotinic acid from tryptophan in mammals was not reported until 1945.[22,23] The tryptophan-nicotinic acid relationship has been closely investigated: one of the most interesting findings has been the dependence of this system on at least three other vitamins of the B complex, thiamine, riboflavin and pyridoxine. An abnormal pattern of metabolites is determined by the level of blockade and by deficiency of the vitamin on which this particular enzyme reaction depends.[25] Lack of tryptophan and nicotinic acid lead in man to pellagra. Skin lesions of pellagrous type and neurological signs have been described in patients without frank deficiency but in whom some disturbance of the metabolism of tryptophan and nicotinic acid has been suspected. In several of these abnormal metabolites have appeared in the urine.

In 1956 Baron and his colleagues[133] described an extraordinary condition affecting, with varying severity, a woman and three of her four brothers, three other sisters being normal. They were children of a marriage between first cousins, the parents being unaffected. The eldest sister came under medical care when she was 6 years old with a photo-sensitive dermatitis and an episode of mental confusion with nystag-mus, ataxia and incontinence. With nicotinic acid therapy she re-covered. Later relapses occurred when vitamin deficiency seemed im-probable. Investigation of this patient and of her siblings revealed an abnormal amino-aciduria and indicanuria together with an excess urinary excretion of indolylacetic acid and indolylacetyl glutamine. An interesting observation has been the abolition of the indicanuria by antibiotics, suggesting that the source of this metabolite was bac-terial activity in the gut. A similar disorder had previously been de-scribed by Hersov[134] in a 10 year old boy with psychosis and light-sensitive dermatitis. Like the patient just described, he improved with nicotinic acid therapy. The biochemical disturbance in this patient was studied by Rodnight and McIlwain[135] who suggested that the heavy indicanuria might be due to diversion of the normal pathway of tryptophan metabolism from nicotinic acid to indican formation. This could have caused the signs of pellagra.

This experience led to a search for similar cases at the Maudsley Hospital and another family was found in which two of three daugh-ters were affected.[136] The parents had noticed an abnormal reaction of the skin to sunlight in one of their daughters when she was eight. Ten years later she had a psychiatric illness with depression and feel-ings of depersonalisation. These became worse after exposure to sun-light and were accompanied by an erythema of the exposed areas of her skin. Dramatic response to 200 mg. daily of nicotinic acid was observed within 72 hours. In the following years she had frequent fainting attacks, not frankly epileptic, and another episode of derma-titis which responded to nicotinic acid. The aminoaciduria of all the cases described by Hersov was similar to that of the cases of Hartnup disease.[133]

A further disturbance of tryptophan metabolism leading to signs of nicotinic acid deficiency has been described in patients with carci-noid tumours.[137,138] Tryptophan is the precursor of 5-hydroxytrypta-mine (serotonin) which has been shown by isotope studies to be held in very large quantities in these tumours, one estimate being over 2 gm. Much of the dietary tryptophan is therefore used parasitically by the tumour which appears to have a priority "demand" on the cir-culating amino-acid as plasma levels have been found to be low even on a high intake.[137] Diarrhoea may complicate the clinical picture and this will further decrease the amount of tryptophan available for conversion to nicotinic acid. Pellagra may then result.

H. A. Peters et al.[139] have demonstrated an abnormal production of intermediate metabolites in cases of acute intermittent porphyria.

After a loading dose of 2 gm. of tryptophan the patients failed to metabolise this amino-acid in the normal manner, excess quantities of kynurenine, hydroxykynurenine, acetylkynurenine, and of kynurenic and xanthurenic acids subsequently appearing in the urine. These findings might indicate a block in the conversion of tryptophan to nicotinic acid, at the stage at which 3-hydroxykynurenine is converted to 3-hydroxyanthrilic acid. This abnormal metabolic pattern is analogous to that occurring in pyridoxine-deficient rats. Treatment of porphyria with pyridoxine is ineffective, but Peters and his colleagues claim good results with dimercaprol (British anti-lewisite) and with versenate.[139-142]

These workers have applied their tryptophan loading test to a further analysis of the toxic action of deoxypyridoxine on tryptophan metabolism and to the closely allied biochemical lesion of isoniazid neuropathy. Following isoniazid or deoxypyridoxine administration, the predominant urinary metabolite was hydroxykynurenine, which was consistent with a block at the stage of pyridoxine activity.[139]

For many years it has been suggested that pellagra, which is predominantly a disorder of maize eaters, is due not only to lack of tryptophan and nicotinic acid but, to the presence of an additional toxic factor in the diet. A recent paper by Gopalan and Srikantia[143] is an interesting commentary on this hypothesis. They have found a high incidence of pellagra in Hyderabad among the poorer populace, whose staple food is the millet, Sorghum vulgaris, or Jowar. Only one of their patients was a maize-eater. Millet and maize, in contrast to rice, have in common a high content of leucine. They produced experimental evidence that by feeding 5 gm. of L-leucine daily to human subjects the urinary output of N-methyl nicotinamide was increased, corresponding to the metabolism of 3.5 mg. nicotinic acid daily. This factor could be significant when the dietary intake of nicotinic acid and tryptophan was marginal.

PYRIDOXINE

As pyridoxal phosphate this vitamin takes part in many enzyme systems: these include at least three within the tricarboxylic acid cycle and others concerned with the metabolism of lipids and of amino-acids, particularly with the synthesis and breakdown of tryptophan.[144] Functional or absolute deficiency of it gives rise to neurological signs.

In 34 out of 50 human subjects Vilter and his colleagues[145] induced an illness characterised by listlessness, loss of appetite, nausea and lesions of the skin and mucous membranes when they were given a diet deficient in pyridoxine together with an antivitamin, the analogue

4-desoxypyridoxine in a daily dose of 50 to 500 mg. Symptoms of the deficiency state developed more quickly in those who had both analogue and vitamin-deficient diet than in those given only the analogue, with a normal diet. Three subjects among the 34 with symptoms attributed to pyridoxine deficieny showed signs of a peripheral neuropathy. The tryptophan loading test was abnormal; increased output of xanthurenic acid was probably due to a block in the conversion of hydroxykynurenine to hydroxyanthranilic acid which is thought to be catalysed by a pyridoxine-dependent enzyme. The symptoms quickly responded to pyridoxine therapy. From this study Vilter calculated that the daily requirement of pyridoxine (which occurs naturally as pyridoxine, pyridoxal or pyridoxamine) was between 1 and 2 mg.[146]

The similarity of the neuropathy induced by deoxypyridoxine to that occurring in tuberculous patients under treatment with isoniazid led to the successful prophylaxis of the latter condition by giving pyridoxine.[146,147] Isoniazid (isonicotinic acid hydrazide,) is believed to inactivate pyridoxine by combining with it to form a hydrazone.[146] Its side-effects include psychosis, convulsion, neuropathy and, least commonly, optic atrophy.[148] Their development is directly related to the dose of isoniazid: 14 out of 36 patients given this drug in a dose of 20 mg. per kg. of body weight developed neuropathy within 4 to 8 weeks. Twenty patients treated with the same dose but also having pyridoxine supplements had no signs of neuropathy at the end of 10 weeks' therapy. During isoniazid therapy the urinary excretion of pyridoxine (as pyridoxal and pyridoxamine) increased eightfold, returning to normal levels when the drug was stopped. Tryptophan loading was followed by increased xanthurenic aciduria, in proportion to the dose of isoniazid.[146]

During the second and third trimesters of pregnancy the output of xanthurenic acid is increased after tryptophan, this being restored rapidly to normal with pyridoxine. This probably reflects a mild deficiency due to increased demands by the foetus.[145,149] It became customary to treat the vomiting of pregnancy with pyridoxine. Following an epidemic of convulsions in infants fed on a milk preparation which was found to be accidentally deficient in pyridoxine, it became a routine to try the effect of pyridoxine on all cases of infantile convulsions. These two fashions in clinical practice merged in the description by Hunt and colleagues of a case of pyridoxine dependence.[150,151] The patient was the third child: during the second and third pregnancies the mother had been treated with pyridoxine for hyperemesis. Repeated convulsions in the child were stopped by parenteral administration of the vitamin. A similar example of response to pyridoxine was given by Coursin:[29] his two-year-old patient became comatose with convulsions 19 weeks after a Torkildsen operation for aqueductal stenosis. Within a minute of the intramuscular injection of 100 mg. pyridoxine, convulsions ceased and the grossly abnormal EEG returned to normal. The improvement was only temporary and subsequent relapse was resistant to vitamin therapy.

Hydrazides have been shown to inhibit enzyme systems in which pyridoxal phosphate is incorporated. This inhibition is accompanied by a fall in the concentration of gamma-aminobutyric acid in the brain.[152] This acid can be derived from glutamate by a pyridoxine-dependent decarboxylase. It has been identified as Florey's factor I, the substance present in mammalian brain extracts known to inhibit impulses generated in the stretch-receptor neurones of the crayfish. Reduction of the brain content of gamma-aminobutyric acid increases its irritability: the epileptic threshold is lowered. This may therefore be a consequence of pyridoxine deficiency.[153]

PANTOTHENIC ACID

This enzyme, as its name implies, is so widely distributed in nature that pure deficiency of it is unlikely to occur spontaneously. It is an essential part of coenzyme A, being joined to diphosphoadenosine through a pyrophosphate bridge and by a peptide link to beta-mercaptoethylamine. The sulphydryl group is stated to be the active part of the enzyme which accepts activated acyl groups, thus forming acyl-coenzyme A, in turn passing them to acceptor systems with the formation of such substances as acetylcholine, citrate and acetoacetate.[154] The vital role of this enzyme, and of its vitamin component, may be judged from its position at the threshold of the tricarboxylic acid cycle and also of the fatty acid cycle described by Lynen.[155]

A deficiency syndrome has been induced in volunteers by a diet lacking in pantothenic acid and supplemented with its antagonist omega-methylpantothenic acid.[156] Neuropathy with paraesthesiae and "burning feet" was only partially relieved by pantothenic acid alone; a liberal diet and mixed vitamins were needed. Bibile and his colleagues[157] found a placebo as effective as pantothenate in a series of 60 cases of "burning feet." A later study by Lubin, Daum and Bean[158] described a hypokalaemic hypochloraemic alkalosis in three subjects on a deficiency regime. Neuromuscular symptoms included paraesthesiae, weakness, cramps, tenderness and sluggish reflexes together with a positive Trousseau sign. No mention was made of magnesium metabolism. The possible therapeutic value of pantothenic acid in the "burning feet" syndrome, a symptom reported in many examples of tropical neuropathy, had earlier been indicated by Gopalan who treated his patients with 20 to 40 mg. parenterally.[159]

RIBOFLAVIN

Deficiency of riboflavin, is common in both temperate and tropical zones. Signs of deficiency which were classically described by Stannus[160,161] are found in the skin and in the outer coverings of the eye. It is doubtful if it causes a neurological disorder, but some reports from Japan on Shibi-Gattchaki disease, a malnutrition syndrome prevalent in Aomori Province, have described an optic neuropathy.[162,163] This may be due to concurrent deficiency of another member of the B complex.[163]

INTER-RELATIONSHIP OF METABOLIC ERRORS AND NUTRITION

Study of the inborn error of metabolism, galactosaemia, has shown how a specific biochemical lesion which is genetically determined—deficiency of the enzyme galactose-1-phosphate unidyl transferase—depends for its clinical manifestations on the inclusion in the diet of a specific substance, galactose.[164] When this sugar is rigidly excluded from the diet, the disorder regresses provided that the diagnosis has been established before permanent changes have occurred. The consequences of the untreated disease are mental and physical retardation, cataracts, hepatomegaly, proteinuria and aminoaciduria.[165]

The occurrence of an inherited metabolic disorder which depends on a factor in the diet for the development of clinical disease implies an unlimited widening of the boundaries of nutritional neurology. Phenylpyruvic oligophrenia is another example of this kind of disorder. The position of hepato-lenticular degeneration, Wilson's disease, remains uncertain: the clinical criteria have now given place to the biochemical which include an abnormality of copper metabolism, but cases very similar have been described in which this is normal.[166,167]

Although Kinnier Wilson's account[168] was preceded by many earlier descriptions, he is generally credited with the unifying concept of a familial disorder involving both the liver and the basal ganglia. The genetic aspects[169,170] have been fully studied in recent years: Bearn[160] has suggested that inheritance is by an autosomal recessive gene. It is, however, possible that there is more than one type of defect, giving rise to variations in the biochemical lesions. There is both genetic and biochemical evidence for thinking this.[171]

The disorder affects predominantly young people becoming manifest during the second and third decades. The full clinical presentation is unmistakable with drooling, fatuous grin, tremor which increases with action and is often of wing-beating type, dystonic and spasmodic movements of the axial muscles, and rigidity. The Kaiser-Fleischer ring is nearly always seen. Jaundice and signs of liver disease are less common, or there may be a history of this. Dementia, if not initially obvious, soon becomes detectable. There are two principal biochemical disorders: a decrease of the plasma caeruloplasmin and of the copper oxidase activity, and an aminoaciduria. Histologically the copper disorder is reflected in an increased content of this metal in the cirrhotic liver and in the lenticular and other regions of the brain.[172]

Although two main hypotheses about the cause of this disease are usually quoted, clinically identical disorders without the associated biochemical defects have been described and this casts doubt on the validity of both hypotheses. Uzman[173,174] has suggested that the primary disturbance is one of protein synthesis, the abnormal protein having an excessive affinity for copper and being associated with the peptiduria and aminoaciduria which are often but not invariably present. Scheinberg and his colleagues[175] proposed that defective synthesis of caeruloplasmin was the underlying abnormality which leads to a high turnover of copper. The lesions in liver and brain, as well as those in the kidney which cause a renal leak of aminoacids, are a consequence of copper poisoning. Bearn and Kunkel[176] have warned against too ready an acceptance of the view that deficiency of caeruloplasmin is the genetically determined lesion.

Most workers are agreed that the abnormal turnover of copper is an important aspect of Wilson's disease, and copper restriction is part of the standard treatment.[172] The use of B.A.L. (dimercaprol) as a decoppering agent was suggested in 1948 by Cumings;[177] versenate and penicillamine have also been used, although the final place of these drugs has yet to be decided.[178] Penicillamine is even more effective in removing copper than dimercaprol and has the immense advantage that it is given by mouth.[179]

REFERENCES

1. DENNY-BROWN, D.: *Medicine, 26:*41 (1947).
2. SMITH, D. A. and WOODRUFF, M. F. A.: *Report on Deficiency Diseases in Japanese Prison Camp.* M.R.C. sp. rep. series No. 274. London, H.M.S.O. (1951).
3. CRUICKSHANK, E. K.: *Vitamins and Hormones, 10:*1 (1952).
4. SPILLANE, J. D. and SCOTT, G. I.: *Lancet,* 2:261 (1945).
5. SPILLANE, J. D.: *Nutritional Disorders of the Nervous System.* Edinburgh, Livingstone (1947).
6. McCANCE, R. A. and others: *Studies of Undernutrition,* Wuppertal 1946-1949. M.R.C. sp. rep. series No. 275. London, H.M.S.O. (1951).
7. CRUICKSHANK, E. K.: *W. Indian Med. J.,* 5:147 (1956).

8. CRUICKSHANK, E. K., MONTGOMERY, R. D., and SPILLANE, J. D.: *World Neurology, 2:*199 (1961).

9. ANGIER, R. B. and others: *Science, 102:*228 (1945).

10. RICKES, E. L., BRINK, N. G., KONIUSZY, F. R., WOOD, T. R. and FOLKERS, K.: *Science, 107:*396 (1948).

11. SMITH, E. L.: *Nature,* London, *161:*638 (1948).

12. PETERS, R. A.: *Lancet, 1:*1161 (1936).

13. PLATT, B. S. and LU, G. D.: *Biochem J., 33:*1525 (1939).

14. JOLLIFFE, N., WORTIS, H. and FEIN, H. D.: *Arch. Neurol & Psychiat, 46:*569 (1941).

15. KREBS, H. A.: *Advances Enzymol., 3:*191 (1943).

16. PETERS, R. A.: *Brit. M. Bull., 9:*116 (1953).

17. PETERS, R. A.: *Bull. Johns Hopkins Hosp., 97:*1, 21 (1955).

18. JOINER, C. L., McCARDLE, B. and THOMPSON, R. H. S.: *Brain, 73:*431 (1950).

19. DAWSON, A. M., DE GROOTE, J., ROSENTHAL, W. S. and SHERLOCK, S.: *Lancet, 1:*392 (1957).

20. WOOLLEY, D. W., STRONG, F. M., MADDEN, R. J. and ELVEHJEM, C. A.: *J. Biol. Chem., 124:*715 (1938).

21. BIEHL, J. P. and VILTER, R. W.: *Proc. Soc. Exper. Biol. & Med., 85:*389 (1954).

22. KREHL, W. A., TEPLY, L. J. and ELVEHJEM, C. A.: *Science, 101:*283 (1945).

23. KREHL, W. A., TEPLY, L. J., SARMA, P. S. and ELVEHJEM, C. A.: *Science, 101:*489 (1945).

24. SARETT, H. P. and GOLDSMITH, G.: *J. Biol. Chem., 177:*461 (1949).

25. DALGLIESH, C. E.: *Brit. M. Bull., 12:*49 (1956).

26. MOLONEY, C. J. and PARMELEE, A. H.: *J.A.M.A., 154:*405 (1954).

27. COURSIN, D. B.: *Ibid., 154:*406 (1954).

28. COURSIN, D. B.: *Am. J. Dis. Child., 90:*344 (1955).

29. COURSIN, D. B.: *Am. J. Clin. Nutrition, 4:*354 (1956).

30. CONLEY, C. L. and KREVANS, J. R.: *New England J. Med., 245:*529 (1951).

31. CONLEY, C. L. and KREVANS, J. R.: *Ann. Int. Med., 43:*758 (1955).

32. MARIE, J. and SÉE, G.: *Am. J. Dis. Child., 87:*731 (1954).

33. PAULLEY, J. W., FAIRWEATHER, F. A. and LEEMING, A.: *Lancet, 1:*406 (1957).

34. KING, M. J. and JOSKE, R. A.: *Brit. M. J., 1:*1324 (1960).

35. MUDGE, G. H.: *Am. J. Med., 15:*790 (1953).

36. JONES, F. A.: *Proc. Roy. Soc. Med., 52:*38 (1959).

37. BADENOCH, J.: In *Modern Trends in Gastro-enterology,* Vol. II, p. 231. London, Butterworth (1958).

38. VOLWILER, W.: *Am. J. Med., 23:*250 (1957).

39. SHINER, M.: *Proc. Roy. Soc. Med., 52:*10 (1959).

40. COOKE, W. T.: *Brit. M. J., 2:*261 (1958).

41. McINTYRE, P. A., SACHS, M. V., KREVANS, J. R. and CONLEY, C. L.: *Arch. Int. Med., 98:*541 (1956).

42. MOLLIN, D. L., BOOTH, C. C. and BAKER, S. J.: *Brit. J. Haematol., 3:*412 (1957).

43. CLOAKE, P. C. P., COOKE, W. T. and HALL, G. S.: *Quart. J. Med., 23:*462 (1954).

44. COOKE, W. T., COX, E. V., MEYNELL, M. J. and GADDIE, R.: *Lancet, 2:*1231 (1957).

45. COX, E. V., MEYNELL, M. J., COOKE, W. T. and GADDIE, R.: *Gastroenterology, 35:*390 (1958).

46. BRINK, F.: *Pharmacol. Rev., 6:*243 (1954).

47. FOURMAN, P.: *Lancet, 2:*525 (1954).

48. VALLEE, B. L., WACKER, W. E. C. and ULMER, D. D.: *New England J. Med.,* 262:155 (1960).

49. HANNA, S., HARRISON, M., MacINTYRE, I. and FRASER, R.: *Lancet,* 2:172 (1960).

50. FLETCHER, R. F., HENLY, A. A., SAMMONS, H. G. and SQUIRE, J. R.: *Lancet,* 1:522 (1960).

51. ALBRIGHT, F., BURNETT, C. H., SMITH, P. H. and PARSON, W.: *Endocrinology,* 30:922 (1942).

52. ALBRIGHT, F., FORBES, A. P. and HENNEMAN, P. H.: *Tr. A. Am. Physicians,* 65:337 (1952).

53. ALBRIGHT, F. and REIFENSTEIN, E. C., JR.: *The Parathyroid Glands and Metabolic Bone Disease.* Baltimore, Williams & Wilkins (1948).

54. MASCHERPA, F. and VALENTINO, V.: *Intracranial Calcification.* Springfield, Thomas (1959).

55. TEN BOSCH, J. J. VAN DER W.: *Lancet,* 1:69 (1959).

56. DICKSON, L. G., MORITA, Y., COWSERT, E. J., GRAVES, J. and MEYER, J. S.: *J. Neurol., Neurosurg. & Psychiat.,* 23:33 (1960).

57. MILKMAN, L. A.: *Am. J. Roentgenol,* 24:29 (1930).

58. VICALE, C. T.: *Tr. Am. Neurol. A.,* 74:143 (1949).

59. WORTHINGTON, J. W. JNR., and MULDER, D. W.: *Neurology,* 9:475 (1959).

60. McCARDLE, B.: In *Clinical Effects of Electrolyte Disturbances,* p. 104. London, Pitman (1959).

61. RUSSELL, J. S. R., BATTEN, F. E. and COLLIER, J.: *Brain,* 23:39 (1900).

62. RICHMOND, J. and DAVIDSON, S.: *Quart. J. Med.,* 27:517 (1958).

63. STEVENSON, T. D., LITTLE, J. A. and LANGLEY, L.: *New England J. Med.,* 255:1219 (1956).

64. MAGNUS, H. A. and UNGLEY, C. C.: *Lancet,* 1:420 (1938).

65. MEULENGRACHT, E.: *Am. J. M. Sc.,* 169:177 (1925).

66. NEEL, J. V.: *Medicine,* 26:115 (1947).

67. WILKINSON, J. F.: *Lancet,* 1:249, 291, 336 (1949).

68. MOSBECH, J.: *Heredity in Pernicious Anaemia.* Copenhagen. Munksgaard (1953).

69. FOLLIS, R. H., JR.: *Deficiency Diseases,* Springfield, Ill., Thomas (1958).

70. CALLENDER, S. T. and DENBOROUGH, H. A.: *Brit. J. Haemat.,* 3:88 (1957).

71. McINTYRE, P. A., HAHN, R., CONLEY, C. L. and GLASS, B.: *Bull. Johns Hopkins Hosp.,* 104:309 (1959).

72. NYBERG, W. and ÖSTLING, G.: *Nature,* London 178:934 (1956).

73. BASTRUP-MADSEN, P.: *Acta med. scandinav.,* 147:399 (1953).

74. BADENOCH, J., EVANS, J. R., RICHARDS, W. C. D. and WITTS, L. J.: *Brit. J. Haemat.,* 1:339 (1955).

75. HARVEY, J. C.: *Surgery,* 40:977 (1956).

76. MacLEAN, L. D. and SUNDBERG, R. D.: *New England J. Med.,* 254:885 (1956).

77. WOKES, F., BADENOCH, J. and SINCLAIR, H. M.: *Am. J. Clin. Nutrition,* 3:375 (1955).

78. HARRISON, R. J., BOOTH, C. C. and MOLLIN, D. L.: *Lancet,* 1:727 (1956).

79. POLLYCOVE, M., APT, L. and COLBERT, M. J.: *New England J. Med.,* 255:1219 (1956).

80. HOLMES, J. M.: *Brit. M. J.,* 2:1394 (1956).

81. SAMSON, D. C., SWISHER, S. N., CHRISTIAN, R. M. and ENGEL, G. L.: *Arch. Int. Med.,* 90:4 (1952).

82. WALTON, J. N., KILOH, L. G., OSSELTON, J. W. and FARRALL, J.: *EEG & Clin. Neurophysiol,* 6:45 (1953).

83. SPILLANE, J. D.: In *Biochemical Aspects of Neurological Disorders*, p. 10. Oxford, Blackwell (1959).
84. SHUMAN, C. R. and GILPIN, S. F.: *Am. J. M. Sc., 227:*612 (1954).
85. SMITH, E. L.: *Brit. M. Bull., 12:*52 (1956).
86. SMITH, E. L.: *Nature*, London, *181:*305 (1958).
87. SMITH, E. L.: *Vitamin B 12.* London, Methuen (1960).
88. SMITH, E. L.: *Nature*, London, *162:*144 (1948).
89. HEINLE, R. W., WELCH, A. D., SCHARF, V., MEACHAM, G. C. and PRUSOFF, W. H.: *Tr. A. Am. Physicians, 65:*214 (1952).
90. GLASS, G. B. J., BOYD, L. J. and STEPHANSON, L.: *Science, 120:*74 (1954).
91. CASTLE, W. B.: *New England J. Med., 249:*603 (1953).
92. BAKER, S. J. and MOLLIN, D. L.: *Brit. J. Haemat., 1:*46 (1955).
93. LATNER, A. L., MERRILLS, R. J. and RAINE, L. C. D. P.: *Lancet, 1:*497 (1954).
94. LATNER, A. L. and RAINE, L. C. D. P.: *Biochem. J., 71:*344 (1959).
95. CHOW, B. F.: In *World Review of Nutrition and Dietetics*, Vol. I, p. 135. London, Pitman (1959).
96. CHOW, B. F., HSU, J. M., OKUDA, K., GRASBECK, R. and HORONICK, A.: *Nutr. symp. series*, No. 16. New York, The National Vitamin Foundation (1958).
97. OKUDA, K., GRASBECK, R. and CHOW, B. F.: *J. Lab. & Clin. Med., 51:*17 (1958).
98. GRASBECK, R., NYBERG, W. and REIZENSTEIN, P.: *Proc. Soc. Exper. Biol. & Med., 97:*780 (1958).
99. TUDHOPE, G. R.: *Quart. J. Med., 28:*591 (1959).
100. OKUDA, K., STEELMAN, S. and CHOW, B. F.: *Federation Proc., 15:*567 (1956).
101. BOGER, W. P., WRIGHT, L. D., BECK, G. D. and BAYNE, G. M.: *Proc. Soc. Exper. Biol. & Med., 92:*140 (1956).
102. OKUDA, K., HELLEGERS, A. and CHOW, B. F.: *Am. J. Clin. Nutrition, 4:*440 (1956).
103. BOGER, W. P., WRIGHT, L. D., STRICKLAND, S. C., GYLFE, J. S. and CIMINERA, J. L.: *Proc. Soc. Exper. Biol. & Med., 89:*375 (1955).
104. FOX, M. R. S.: In *World Review of Nutrition and Dietetics*, Vol. I, p. 129. London, Pitman (1959).
105. WAGLE, S. R. and JOHNSON, B. C.: *Arch. Biochem. & Biophys., 70:*619 (1957).
106. WAGLE, S. R., MEHTA, R. and JOHNSON, B. C.: *J. Biol. Chem., 230:*137 (1958).
107. DAVIDSON, J. N.: *The Biochemistry of the Nucleic Acids*, 4th Ed. London, Methuen (1960).
108. VILTER, R. W., HORRIGAN, D., MUELLER, J. F., JARROLD, T., VILTER, C. F., HAWKINS, V. and SEAMAN, A.: *Blood, 5:*695 (1950).
109. NIEWEG, H. O., FABER, J. G., DE VRIES, J. A. and KROESE, W. F. S.: *J. Lab. & Clin. Med., 44:*118 (1954).
110-115. [References deleted.]
116. GRAHAM, R. M. and RHEAULT, M. H.: *J. Lab. & Clin. Med., 43:*235 (1954).
117. FARRANT, P. C.: *Brit. M. J., 1:*1694 (1960).
118. UNGLEY, C. C.: *Brit. J. Nutrition, 6:*299 (1952).
119. ADAMS, J. F.: *Lancet, 1:*1120 (1957).
120. REED, L. J.: *Physiol. Rev., 33:*544 (1953).
121. REED, L. J.: *Advances Enzymol., 18:*319 (1957).
122. SINCLAIR, H. M.: *Brit. M. Bull., 12:*18 (1956).
123. THOMPSON, R. H. S., BUTTERWORTH, W. J. H. and FRY, I. K.: *Proc. Roy. Soc. Med., 53:*143 (1960).
124. GREEN, R. G. and EVANS, C. A.: *Science, 92:*154 (1940).
125. GREEN, R. G., CARLSON, W. E. and EVANS, C. A.: *J. Nutrition, 21:*243 (1941).

126. EVANS, E. T. R., EVANS, W. C. and ROBERTS, H. E.: *Brit. Vet. J. 107*:364, 399 (1951).
127. HOAR, W. S., BARBERIE, M. and DAVIDSON, D. W.: *J. Canad. Dietetic A., 10*:14 (1948).
128. SAMRUATRUAMPHOL, S. and PARSONS, H. T.: *J. Am. Dietetic A., 31*:790 (1955).
129. ALBERT, A.: *Brit. M. Bull., 12*:67 (1956).
130. ORTANEZ, J. and PALILLO, L.: *J. Philippine M. A., 31*:33 (1955); quoted in *Nutrition Abst. & Rev., 26*:198 (Abstract 1032) (1956).
131. WILLIAMS, R. R.: *J. Clin. Nutrition 1*:513 (1953).
132. BURGESS, R. C.: *Lancet, 2*:411 (1946).
133. BARON, D. N., DENT, C. E., HARRIS, H., HART, E. W. and JEPSON, J. B.: *Lancet, 2*:421 (1956).
134. HERSOV, L. A.: *J. Ment. Sc., 101*:878 (1955).
135. RODNIGHT, R. and McILWAIN, H.: *Ibid., 101*:884 (1955).
136. HERSOV, L. A. and RODNIGHT, R.: *J. Neurol., Neurosurg. & Psychiat., 23*:40 (1960).
137. SJOERDSMA, A., WEISSBACH, H., TERRY, L. L. and UDENFRIEND, S.: *Am. J. Med., 23*:5 (1957).
138. SMITH, A. N., NYHUS, L. M., DALGLIESH, C. E., DUTTON, R. W., LENNOX, B. and MACFARLANE, P. S.: *Scottish M. J., 2*:24 (1957).
139. PRICE, J. M., BROWN, R. R. and PETERS, H. A.: *Neurology, 9*:456 (1959).
140. PETERS, H. A.: *Ibid., 4*:477 (1954).
141. PETERS, H. A., WOODS, S., EICHMAN, P. L. and REESE, H. H.: *Ann. Int. Med., 47*:889 (1957).
142. PETERS, H. A., EICHMAN, P. L. and REESE, H. H.: *Neurology, 8*:621 (1958).
143. GOPALAN, C. and SRIKANTIA, S. G.: *Lancet, 1*:954 (1960).
144. TOWER, D. B.: *Am. J. Clin. Nutrition, 4*:329 (1956).
145. VILTER, R. W., MUELLER, J. F., GLAZER, H. S., JARROLD, T., ABRAHAM, J., THOMPSON, C. and HAWKINS, V. R.: *J. Lab. & Clin. Med., 42*:335 (1953).
146. VILTER, R. W.: *Am. J. Clin. Nutrition, 4*:378 (1956).
147. CARLSON, H. B., ANTHONY, E. M., RUSSELL, W. F. and MIDDLEBROOK, G.: *New England J. Med., 255*:118 (1956).
148. DIXON, G. J., ROBERTS, G. B. S. and TYWELL, W. F.: *Scottish M. J., 1*:350 (1956).
149. WACHSTEIN, H.: *Am. J. Clin. Nutrition, 4*:369 (1956).
150. HUNT, A. D., STOKES, J., JR., McCRORY, W. W. and STROUD, H. H.: *Pediatrics, 13*:140 (1954).
151. SOKOLOFF, L., LASSEN, N. A., McKHANN, G. M., TOWER, D. B. and ALBERS, W.: *Nature*, London, *183*:751 (1959).
152. ELLIOTT, K. A. C.: *Neurology, 8*:suppl. 1, 98 (1958).
153. ROBERTS, E. and BAXTER, C. F.: *Neurology, 8*:suppl. 1, 77 (1958).
154. NOVELLI, G. D.: *Physiol. Rev., 33*:525 (1953).
155. LYNEN, F.: *The Centennial Lectures.* New York, Putnam (1959).
156. BEAN, W. B. and HODGES, R. E.: *Proc. Soc. Exper. Biol. & Med., 86*:693 (1954).
157. BIBILE, S. W., LIONEL, N. D. W., DUNNWILLE, R. and PERERA, G.: *Brit. J. Nutrition, 11*:434 (1957).
158. LUBIN, R., DAUM, K. A. and BEAN, W. B.: *Am. J. Clin. Nutrition, 4*:420 (1956).
159. GOPALAN, C.: *Indian M. Gaz., 81*:22 (1946).
160. STANNUS, H. S.: *Tr. Roy. Soc. Trop. Med. & Hyg., 5*:112 (1912).
161. STANNUS, H. S.: *Ibid., 7*:32 (1913).

162. IRINODA, K. and SATO, S.: *Tohoku J. Exper. Med., 61:*93 (1954); quoted in *Nutrition Abst. & Rev., 25:*1065 (Abstract 5613) (1955).

163. IRINODA, K. and YAMADA, S.: *J. Vitaminol., Japan, 2:*83 (1956); quoted in *Nutrition Abst. & Rev., 27:*210 (Abstract 984) (1957).

164. ISSELBACHER, K. J., ANDERSON, E. P., KIRAHASHI, K. and KALCKAR, H. M.: *Science, 123:*635 (1956).

165. HOLZEL, A., KOMROWER, G. M. and SCHWARZ, V.: *Am. J. Med., 22:*703 (1957).

166. GREENFIELD, J. G.: *Proc. Roy. Soc. Med., 47:*150 (1954).

167. FIELD, E. J., WORT, A. J. and ELLIS, E.: *Lancet, 1:*625 (1960).

168. WILSON, S. A. K.: *Brain, 34:*295 (1912).

169. BEARN, A. G.: *Am. J. Med., 15:*442 (1953).

170. MATTHEWS, W. B., MILNE, M. D. and BELL, M.: *Quart. J. Med., 21:*425 (1952).

171. BEARN, A. G.: *Proc. Roy. Soc. Med., 52:*61 (1959).

172. CUMINGS, J. N.: *Heavy Metals and the Brain.* Oxford, Blackwell (1959).

173. UZMAN, L. L.: *Am. J. M. Sc., 226:*645 (1953).

174. UZMAN, L. L., IBER, F. L., CHALMERS, T. C. and KNOWLTON, M.: *Am. J. M. Sc., 231:*511 (1956).

175. SCHEINBERG, I. H. and GITLIN, D.: *Science, 116:*484 (1952).

176. BEARN, A. G. and KUNKEL, H. G.: *J. Clin. Invest., 33:*400 (1954).

177. CUMINGS, J. N.: *Brain, 71:*410 (1948).

178. BICKEL, H., NEALE, F. C. and HALL, G.: *Quart. J. Med., 26:*527 (1957).

179. WALSHE, J. M.: *Lancet, 1:*188 (1960).

XXXIX

STEROID HORMONES AND EVENTS IN THE NERVOUS SYSTEM

Hudson Hoagland

Despite striking progress in neurophysiology and in endocrinology understanding of the relation of endocrine substances to events in the nervous system is not far advanced.

It is not surprising that little is known about the detailed mechanisms of action of hormones on the nervous system since insight into these mechanisms is dependent upon a degree of knowledge of neurochemistry not yet available. The exquisite sensitivity of the electric recording of nerve action currents has no operational counterpart in biochemistry. The nerve impulse, for example, with its after potentials implies physiochemical processes occurring in terms of the order of milliseconds, but these potential changes have not as yet been interpreted satisfactorily in terms of specific chemical events. The following discussion will make no attempt to review the broad field of endocrinology in relation to nerve function but will, rather, be confined to a consideration of aspects of the action of steroid hormones on the nervous system.

The steroid hormones are a group of substances with far-reaching metabolic actions. These small molecules with molecular weights of about 300 are produced by the ovaries, testes and adrenal cortex and their production is controlled by protein or polypeptide hormones from the anterior pituitary. The steroid hormones are characterized by a four ring structure with short side chains. Small differences in the side chains profoundly affect their physiological action. Thus it has been established that certain steroids from the adrenal cortex in part regulate salt and water metabolism, protein, fat and carbohydrate metabolism. In addition, the sex hormones play important roles in regulating the development of secondary sexual characteristics, the oestrus cycle and sex drives.

In this review we shall consider some effects of steroids on the nervous system but shall not discuss the important studies of hypothalamic pituitary relationships involved in the control of gonado-trophic and corticotrophic hormone release. This latter subject has been covered by a number of reviews.[1-8] Fortier, and Fortier and DeGroot, have presented annual reviews of neuroendocrine relation-ships in Spiegel's *Progress in Neurology and Psychiatry*,[8a,b,c,d] and re-views by Fortier,[5] Harris[6] and de Jongh[7] are contained in a published symposium on the relations between pituitary and hypothalamus pre-sented at the 1956 International Physiological Congress. A discussion of some neuroendocrine problems by a group of investigators has ap-peared in a symposium edited by Hoagland, entitled Hormones, Brain Function and Behavior.[9] The papers are grouped under four headings: "Effects of Steroid Hormones on the Nervous System," "Sex Hormones and Behavior," "Serotonin, Epinephrine and Their Metabolites in Relation to Experimental Psychiatry," and "The Thyroid and Behavior."

STEROIDS AND BRAIN FUNCTION

Various unrelated observations indicate that steroid hormones di-rectly or indirectly affect events in the nervous system. Thus, Addi-sonian patients display a slowing of the frequency of the electro-encephalogram which is restored by cortisone[10,11] and according to Friedlander and Rottger[12] cortisone slightly but definitely increases the frequency of the alpha rhythm in patients undergoing cortisone therapy who are not hypoadrenal. Pine, Engel and Schwartz[13] studied EEG's in 40 patients with a wide variety of diagnoses undergoing treatments with ACTH and cortisone. Thirty-two per cent of the patients had abnormal pretreatment records and 59% of these showed definite improvement. No specific EEG correlation was found, how-ever, between either blood electrolytes or mental changes during the treatments.

Euphoria, mental elation, depression, irritability, restlessness and insomnia are found in patients undergoing cortisone and ACTH therapy and the occurrance of severe mental disturbances, including psychoses in some patients when taking large doses of cortisone or ACTH over extended periods of time, is not uncommon.[14-21] Glaser[22] has reported that 40% of spontaneous Cushing's syndrome cases and 36% of patients treated for an average of 14.6 months with ACTH or cortisone develope disturbances. The hypoadrenalism of some Ad-disonian cases may also be accompanied by psychosis.[23]

We have demonstrated that Δ5-pregnenolone, an intermediate in the syntheses of corticoids by the adrenal[24] has an action facilitating skilled psychomotor performance[25-27] and in contrast to this might be mentioned the anesthetizing action of some of the steroid hormones in very large doses.[28]

Gordan and his collaborators[29] have demonstrated effects on human cerebral metabolism of the water-soluble glucoside of desoxycorticosterone (DCG). This substance also transiently reduces EEG abnormalities in epileptic patients. In studies of the brain blood flow it was found that in man DCG liberates sugar from the brain, apparently primarily as galactose in about one-third of the subjects tested. Schieve and Wilson were, however, unable to confirm this.[30] Sections of gray and white matter of brain taken at lobotomy operations from psychotic patients were found[29] to show a decrease in white matter galactose content in a third of the samples removed immediately after the intravenous injection of 50 mg. of DCG.

Severe adrenal insufficiency in man is accompanied by a slowing of the electroencephalogram (EEG) which is restored by cortisone. Bergen[31] also found a significant decrease of about 10 per cent in the dominant EEG frequency in rats following adrenalectomy. When the rats were injected with Lipo-Adrenal extract (Upjohn), with physiological doses of cortisone or $\triangle 5$ pregnenolone, but not with desoxycorticosterone, the EEG frequency was restored to normal. Bergen, Hunt and Hoagland[32] found in rats that the changes in EEG frequencies following adrenalectomy and restoration with replacement therapy were correlated with rates of blood flow through the brain and with brain oxygen utilization. This was not an unexpected finding since the alpha frequency of the EEG in man has been shown, within limits, to depend upon the rate of the brain's oxygen utilization.[33,34] The mechanisms of the decline of brain blood flow, oxygen consumption and EEG frequencies and their restorations with steroids appeared to reflect primary changes in systemic blood pressure following adrenalectomy and replacement therapy.

Torda and Wolff[35] have found that the administration of ACTH modifies the convulsive thresholds of rats to pentamethylene tetrazol and that ACTH has a specific transient action on the brain independent of effects mediated by the adrenal cortex. Prolonged administration of ACTH produced a decrease in sensitivity to the convulsant which they attribute to shifts in electrolyte balance. However, single injections had an opposite effect. Following ACTH injection in rats the EEG showed transiently increased voltage and spiking discharge and paroxysmal bursts together with lowered convulsive threshold. These transient effects also occurred in hypophysectomized and adrenalectomized rats and in sodium-injected nonoperated animals.

The effects are manifest in one to three minutes post-injection and appeared not to be due to electrolyte shifts but to some other mechanism. In other studies Torda and Wolff[36] and Torda[37] report an average increase of 60% in the ammonia content of rat brain within five minutes after ACTH injection, followed by a return to normal some 30 minutes later. Accompanying the increase in ammonia, a peak titer of acetylcholine content of the brain was reached some 40% above normal[38] which also returned to normal 30 minutes later. "The results imply that the increase of the electrical activity of the brain induced by a single administration of ACTH is a manifestation of both the increase of the acetylcholine and the ammonium ion of the brain." These findings are of special interest because ACTH may precipitate seizures in patients with previous seizure histories and even in those without such history.[39,40] ACTH injections are also often followed by sleeplessness and restlessness.[41]

It has been well established that some of the steroids have marked effects on protein metabolism. Thus, methyltestosterone has been demonstrated to have specific protein anabolic action. In contrast to this the 11-oxysteroids of the adrenal cortex normally exert pronounced protein catabolic action. The lymphoid system appears to be especially susceptible to the action of this class of hormones showing, when they are released endogenously or injected, a rapid disappearance of lymphocytes and a shift in nitrogen balance with corresponding deposition of liver glycogen. These far-reaching repercussions of the steroids on protein metabolism include tissues other than the lymphatic system and since enzymes are proteins, one is led to consider the possible action of adrenal steroids on protein metabolism of the brain. Hyden[42] and Hyden and Hartelius[43] using ultraviolet microspectroscopy found an increase in protein catabolism in single cells of the central nervous system in connection with increased functional demands when the cells conduct nerve impulses over periods of time. In both motor activity and sensory stimulation a rapid breakdown of nucleoproteins is reported to take place in the cell bodies of central nervous units of the conducting apparatus, and the restitution of the nucleoprotein content of the cells can be demonstrated after the period of action. In a functional balance, restitution appears to compensate for the catabolism. Hyden's work indicates a surprisingly rapid turnover of nucleoprotein in cells of the central nervous system, and it is interesting to consider the possibility that this turn-over may be modified by steroid hormones which are important regulators of protein metabolism in other tissues.

Nurnberger[44] has investigated the concentrations of nucleic acids and proteins in the cytoplasm, nucleus, and nucleolus of cells of the liver and of the supraoptic neurones in the rat's hypothalamus by the ultra violet microabsorption technique of Caspersson. Changes of these cellular constituents following fasting and exposures to cold stress were found and correlated with changes in adrenal ascorbic acid. In subsequent studies,[45] he examined cytoplasmic protein and ribonucleic acid concentrations in liver and in the supraoptic nucleus cells of the hypothalamus from normal and from bilaterally adrenalectomized rats maintained on 0.9% NaCl in their drinking water. Adrenalectomy approximately doubles the protein concentration of both types of cells, i.e., liver cell protein increases from 26% to 51% and that of the supraoptic nucleus cells from 14% to 32%. Concentration changes in ribonucleic acid following adrenalectomy were not significant. When intact rats are stressed by short (1 hour) exposures to cold, cellular protein content was increased from 26% to 40% in the liver and ribonucleic acid concentration fell from 1.8% to 1%. Comparable changes were also seen in the supraoptic nucleus cells. The most extensive changes were, however, found in adrenalectomized rats exposed to cold, in that liver protein dropped from 51% to 17% and protein of the supraoptic nucleus cells fell from 32% to 11%. Insignificant changes in ribonucleic acid accompanied these marked changes in protein concentrations. These are concentration changes expressed as grams per 100 cc. of tissue, not per 100 gr. of tissue, and Nurnberger considers that some of these concentration changes may reflect changes in intracellular water and cell volume, but he believes that the marked changes in protein and ribonucleic acid are not primarily due to this factor. Nurnberger has pointed out that in acute experiments bilateral adrenalectomy produces alterations in the activity of cellular proteins and that these changes in protein represent substantial alterations in cellular gluconeogenesis. Small changes in the nucleic acids that may appear in the intact animal may have as their function the storage and liberation of labile phosphate. Certainly the cell protein changes seem to be very sensitive to the level of adrenal cortical function.

These findings indicate to us increased cellular protein concentration following adrenalectomy as a result of the withdrawal of catabolic effects of the 11-oxycorticoids. Cold stress in intact animals resulting in increased 11-oxycorticoids might be expected to lower cellular proteins but a marked increase was found due to unknown factors. One is tempted to speculate that perhaps adrenal androgens under these circumstances may, by their protein anabolic action, overcompensate for effects of the 11-oxysteroids. In adrenalectomized rats the high cellular protein titer is dropped to a third of its high resting value following the stress. Presumably proteins are rapidly broken down as a result of the lack of homeostatic action of an adrenal factor, perhaps of an androgenic nature. While these considerations are entirely speculative they may be tested by the administration of suitable steroids.

It is interesting to note that the effect of the adrenal on brain protein metabolism is typical of that on liver cells.

The anesthetizing actions of large doses of steroids first reported by Selye in 1941[46] have been traced to their direct effects on cerebral metabolism. He investigated 75 steroids[47] and found that absence of double bonds and oxygenations at opposite ends of the molecule made for potency of anesthetic activity. A steroid anesthetic useful in human surgery has recently been described.[48,49] This is pregnane-3, 20-dione-21-ol sodium hemisuccinate (sodium hydroxydione). It has been found in man to decrease cerebral blood flow, oxygen and glucose consumption to about the same degree as that of barbiturate-meperidine anesthesia.[50] Elliott, Krueckel and Sutherland[9] have studied the *in vitro* effects of this steroid on rat and guinea pig brain, using manometric technics and measurements of glucose uptake and/or lactic acid production. Their evidence indicates that sodium hydroxydione acts on oxidative reactions to inhibit the entrance of glucose into the tricarboxylic acid cycle. Inhibition of oxidation of tricarboxylic acid cycle substrates appears to be a secondary action.

A number of investigations have indicated direct effects of some steroid hormones on the *in vitro* oxygen consumption of brain. Thus, Gordan and Elliott[51] have demonstrated direct parallels between the anesthetic action of steroids and their ability to inhibit glucose oxidation of rat brain homogenates. It should be noted, however, that these studies have involved excessive amounts of steroids compared to those involved in normal physiological function. This parallelism between anesthetic action and inhibition of respiration of the homogenates was true of desoxycorticosterone, progresterone, testosterone, and α-estradiol. They also used stilbestrol, a synthetic compound of high estrogenic potency, which is less strongly anesthetic than the first three of the above steroids, but more so than the fourth. This substance inhibits brain respiration more strongly (91%) than any of the above steroids in comparable concentrations and is thus out of the order of expectancy based on anesthetic potency. Michaelis and Quastel[52] have suggested that the action of anesthetics is due to the inhibition of carbohydrate oxidation produced by interrupting the usual reactions of flavoprotein or some other component of the tissue respiratory system which plays an intermediate role between flavoprotein and cytochrome oxidase. In confirmation there is evidence that Amytal inhibits DPNH oxidase. The experiments of Gordan and Elliott indicate an action of the steroids on the dehydrogenases of the cellular respiratory system. In this same connection it is interesting that Hochster and Quastel[53] have found that stilbestrol competes as an intracellular hydrogen carrier with a dehydrogenase. It is a sluggish carrier but an effective competitor and inhibits the anaerobic oxidation of lactate by lactic dehydrogenase when this reaction is catalyzed by cytochrome-c. It does not inhibit lactic dehydrogenase itself since it actively catalyzes its activity with MnO_2. It thus follows that stilbestrol may exert its effect (possibly as a quinone) by competing with cytochrome-c as a hydrogen acceptor for the lactic dehydrogenase.

Eisenberg, Gordan and Elliott[54] studied the effect of castration on the *in vitro* glucose utilization of rat brain homogenates and concluded that testicular hormone acts as a metabolic "brake." They found a marked enhancement of glucose utilization (32%) in brains from castrated rats which could be prevented if the castrated rats were treated with testosterone before sacrifice. The addition of testosterone further suppresses the oxygen uptake of brains from all groups (normal, castrated and castrated testosterone treated) but the inhibition was less in the castrated untreated group. They suggest that this effect may be due to a decrease of the intracellular enzyme system by which testosterone exerts its inhibiting action and that this decrease can be prevented, for the most part, by the administration of testosterone. In a later paper these same workers[55] reported that testosterone suspensions inhibit the oxygen consumption of striated muscle and of rat brain and liver slices *in vitro*. Eisenberg *et al.*[56] have found that desoxycorticosterone inhibits the oxygen consumption of rat brain homogenates in a logarithmic relation as a function of dose. They have found that desoxycorticosterone inhibits the aerobic respiration of rat brain suspensions quantitatively in doses ranging from 0.06 to 4.0 mg. and that the inhibition can be used as a bioassay for this substance and for desoxycorticosterone glucoside. They conclude "that the relatively large amounts of steroid necessary to produce inhibition of aerobic respiration *in vitro* entirely penetrate and are absorbed by the affected system. These amounts exceeded the concentrations of steroid which will affect other systems *in vitro* or that occur in living organisms. This does not necessarily exclude the possibility that steroidal inhibition of aerobic respiration may be of significance in the intact organism." Gordan *et al.*[57] have published a paper on "The influence of steroids on cerebral metabolism" which summarizes and discusses various phases of their work.

Hayano, Schiller and Dorfman[58] found that desoxycorticosterone, dehydroisoandrosterone and testosterone in relatively large amounts beyond the physiological range depressed the oxygen consumption of rat brain slices but that progesterone, cholesterol and pregnanediol were inactive. These inhibiting substances acted in a similar fashion in depressing oxygen consumption of liver and kidney slices. Because desoxycorticosterone was the most potent of the inhibitors, they studied its action further on brain homogenate fractions separated by centrifugation. To quote from their paper "with the use of the washed residue fraction a preliminary investigation of the effect of desoxycorticosterone on a variety of oxidizable substrates was then carried out with the result that the oxidation of every substance thus treated was inhibited 30 to 90%. These results pointed to the possibility that the site of the steroid suppression was a reaction or reactions common to all oxidations, namely those involved in the transfer of hydrogen ions or electrons. The assay of cytochrome-c-cytochrome oxidase reaction with the use of p-phenylenediamine and brain homogenate residue as the source of the enzyme system showed that this reaction was not inhibited in the presence of desoxycorticosterone. . . It thus appears that the site of inhibition may be a flavoprotein entity of the electron transfer system."

Bergen, Hunt and Hoagland[59] have found that rat brain, liver and kidney slices from normal and adrenalectomized rats showed no differences in *in vitro* oxygen consumption. They also were unable to find differences in activities of succinic dehydrogenase and cytochrome oxidase in studies of rat brain homogenates by the Schneider and Potter method when whole brain homogenates from normal and adrenalectomized rats were compared. However, Bourne and Malatoy[60] using an *in situ* histochemical reaction for succinic dehydrogenase have found it to increase in liver, heart, kidney and cerebellum of intact rats following injection of cortisone. Adrenalectomy causes a marked reduction of succinic dehydrogenase in all four tissues which is restored nearly to normal by cortisone in kidney and fully to normal in other tissues. DCA also partially restores succinic dehydrogenase in these depleted tissues of adrenalectomized rats. Testosterone is without effect and progesterone has some restorative action on succinic dehydrogenase.

STEROIDS AND ELECTROLYTE BALANCE

Kendall[61] has pointed out the interdependence of protein, fat, carbohydrate and electrolyte metabolism. Adrenalectomized animals and Addisonian patients excrete excessive amounts of sodium and retain potassium. This abnormal balance of electrolytes is brought about primarily through changes in kidney thresholds resulting from the absence of adrenal hormones and can be corrected by replacement therapy. Evidence also indicates modifications of permeability of other tissue cells as well as those controlling kidney thresholds when the organism is deprived of its supply of adrenal cortical hormones. It is well-known that most adrenalectomized animals and many Addisonian patients can be kept in good condition by the administration of sodium chloride and that this administration corrects abnormalities not only of electrolyte balance but also of nitrogen balance and carbohydrate metabolism. Such organisms are, however, unable to resist stress effectively in the absence of adequate adrenal function or hormone replacement therapy. Anderson[62] has presented evidence indicating that the administration of sodium chloride to adrenalectomized rats not only replenishes the body with needed ions but also restores to the kidney the mechanism which is responsible for the normal excretion of sodium and potassium.

Shifts in sodium and potassium balance accompanying the ebb and flow of adrenal hormones may be important in regulating the excitability of nerve and in modifying synaptic conduction.

Hodgkin and Katz[63] have demonstrated that the resting membrane of nerve is more permeable to potassium than it is to sodium. However, the active membrane, in the process of conducting the nerve impulse, becomes more permeable to sodium than to potassium. They present cogent evidence for the view that this reversal of permeability is brought about by a large increase in sodium permeability while the potassium permeability remains unchanged. This view is in accord with the reversal of the action potential, with respect to the resting potential of nerve, when the nerve becomes active in conduction. Thus, while the resting potential and excitability are largely dependent upon potassium gradients the action potential is due, in the main, to movements of sodium. The nerve message itself is thus subject to modification both by sodium and potassium gradients across the nerve membrane suggesting the importance of homeostatic regulation of these cations for normal function of the nervous system including synaptic conduction.

Davenport[64] has demonstrated that following adrenalectomy the electroshock seizure threshold (EST) of non-salt-maintained rats decreases progressively for 4 days to a minimum of 23% below their preoperative control levels. Thus adrenalectomy increases overall brain excitability as inversely measured by EST. The threshold of rats maintained on 0.9% sodium chloride solution in their drinking water was the same as that of non-adrenalectomized controls. When the adrenalectomized rats received magnesium chloride and potassium chloride solutions their EST decreased more rapidly than that of the water controls whereas calcium chloride maintained the EST at control levels. A direct correlation was found between EST and the plasma Na concentration. Total brain Na, K and Cl were unchanged by the experimental procedures but Davenport found that adrenalectomy causes an increase of intracellular sodium and a decrease of the ratio of extracellular to intracellular sodium accompanying the enhanced excitability. This was calculated on the basis of chloride space as a measure of apparent extracellular fluid volume.

Woodbury and his collaborators have found that DCA increases plasma sodium and decreases intracellular brain sodium in the rat. The increased plasma to intracellular sodium ratio following DCA administration was accompanied by a decrease in excitability of the brain as measured by the EST. Opposite effects on the EST threshold and on the extracellular to intracellular sodium ratio followed the administration of cortisone and 17-hydroxycorticosterone. Thus a mechanism for the anticonvulsive action of DCA in epileptic seizures and the contra-indication of cortisone and cortisol is indicated.

Woodbury, Timiras and Vernadakis[9] have reported their extensive studies of brain excitability in rats and they summarize their major results as follows:

"Chronic administration of excessive amounts of adrenocortical steroids alters electroshock seizure threshold (EST); deoxycorticosterone acetate (DCA) increases EST (decreases excitability), whereas cortisone acetate and cortisol acetate decrease it (increase excitability); corticosterone has little effect. 11-Deoxy-17-hydroxycorticosterone acetate elevates EST slightly, whereas 11-dehydrocorticosterone acetate decreases it slightly.

"The increase in EST induced by a single dose of DCA was associated with a decrease in intracellular brain Na concentration, an increase in ratio of extracellular to intracellular brain Na, an increase in brain concentration of glutamic and aspartic acids and a decrease in brain concentrations of glutamine and asparagine; in contrast, the decrease in EST induced by a single dose of cortisol was associated with the opposite effects. On the basis of these facts, DCA and cortisol are postulated to affect, in opposite manner, the active transport of Na across brain cells and thereby to modify brain excitability. The glutamic acid-glutamine and the aspartic acid-asparagine systems are thought to be involved in the process of Na transport.

"Aldosterone, the natural electrolyte-regulating hormone of the adrenal cortex, was found to have less effect on EST than did an equivalent dose of DCA.

"The duration of the postictal depression which follows maximal electroshock seizures in rats was found to be correlated with the blood sugar level, but unrelated to brain excitability or brain electrolyte metabolism.

"On the basis of results derived from a study of the effects of certain central nervous system drugs on the pituitary-adrenal system, the conclusion has been reached that the adrenal cortex has a regulatory influence on the excitability of the brain. This regulatory function is operative only when changes in excitability occur, and the adrenocortical hormones then act so as to restore normal brain excitability, regardless of the direction of the original deviation. However, this normal regulatory activity may be modified if the drug being tested activates the pituitary-adrenal system and thereby changes the normal pattern of adrenocortical secretion. Examples of such drugs' effects are presented and it is suggested that these drugs stimulate the pituitary-adrenal system by virtue of an action directly on the central nervous system."

While adrenalectomy has thus been shown to increase excitability of the brain as measured by the EST and to be correlated with an increase of intracellular brain sodium, in peripheral nerve on the contrary, several groups of investigators[65-67] have found that adrenalectomy decreases excitability of peripheral nerve. Moreover, conduction of invoked responses from foot to sensory cortex of the rat were also shown by Slocombe and Hoagland[68,69] to be slowed by adrenalectomy and restored by physiological amounts of adrenocortical extract.

This last finding, together with the slowing of the EEG in adrenal insufficiency, suggests a decreased excitability in conducting fiber pathways. Slocombe *et al.* regarded a simple unitary conception of excitability inadequate to explain these divergent phenomena.

Slocombe, Tozian and Hoagland[69] measured Hill's excitation constant in sciatic nerves taken from normal and from adrenalectomized salt-maintained rats. They studied nerves both *in situ* and *in vitro*, i.e., in a chamber with a Ringer's solution and an O_2 and CO_2 atmosphere. The values for the excitability constant were the same for the *in vivo* and *in vitro* tests. All nerves from adrenalectomized rats showed decreased excitabilities which were not due to temperature differences or to oxygen. The decreased excitabilities also did not appear to be due to differences in salt concentration bathing the nerves, and these findings led the authors to suggest that some non-environmental factor intrinsic to the electrical properties of the tissue was modified by the lack of adrenocortical hormones.

More recently Wright and Lester[70] have reported a well controlled study of the effect of adrenalectomy and cortisone on peripheral nerve function. While fully confirming the earlier findings of decreased excitability of nerves taken from adrenalectomized rats, they also showed that this is sodium dependent. It results from decreased plasma sodium in the adrenalectomized animal and excitability is restored by adding sodium to the medium bathing the nerve.

Wright and Lester also point out that there need be no discrepancy between effects of adrenalectomy on excitability of the brain and that of peripheral nerve. They point out that the effect of a decrease in excitability and increase in chronaxie of peripheral nerve enhances its tendency to respond to stimulation by repetitive firing. Such tissue may be regarded as more excitable despite its lowered excitation constant and increased chronaxie. The brain seizure threshold is determined by the current necessary to bring into repetitive synchronized discharge numbers of neurones. Adrenalectomy both lowers this threshold and enhances that of peripheral nerve to repetitive discharge.

Because of the role of the adrenal cortex in the regulation of the metabolism of sodium and potassium and its possible effects on permeability of the blood-brain barrier to potassium, and because of the importance of potassium in relation to nerve function, Hoagland and Stone[71] determined the content of potassium in brains of normal and adrenalectomized rats before and after severe stress and after the administration of steroids. Thirty-six hours after injection of K^{42}, adrenalectomized rats had accumulated 24% more K^{42} in brain and 37.5% more in muscle than did control animals. However, the total content of potassium in the brain determined by flame photometry was the same for adrenalectomized and normal rats (see also ref. 64) although the total content of potassium in muscle was significantly increased by 6.2% in the adrenalectomized animals.

Leiderman and Katzman[72] confirmed these findings in rats fed *ad libitum* and presented evidence that the discrepancy is due to differences in rates of exchange of potassium, only 80% of the potassium of the brain of normal rats exchanging with K^{42}, while all of it appeared to be exchangeable after adrenalectomy.

In a study of the fate of injected K^{42}, Bergen, Stone and Hoagland found[73] specific radioactivities in plasma and muscle to be identical for intact and adrenalectomized rats. There was a slow uptake of K^{42} by brain in normal rats, reaching equilibrium with plasma and muscle in 70 hours. In the adrenalectomized rats the specific activity curve for brain had not equilibrated with that of muscle and plasma in 70 hours. However, the concentration of K^{42} in the brains of these animals was actually greater than that in control animals, as had been reported previously by Leiderman and Katzman.[72] But we noted that after adrenalectomy the appetites of these rats decreased, suggesting that they might not be taking sufficient potassium in their food to dilute the K^{42} to the same extent as occurred in the normal animals. When both groups of rats were fasted, K^{42} uptake curves for brain were identical. Thus, the observed differences in content of K^{42} in the brains of normal and adrenalectomized rats are ascribed to K intake differences resulting from anorexia in the operated rats. Adrenalectomy does not significantly affect the rate of exchange of brain potassium.

ADRENAL CORTEX FUNCTION IN SCHIZOPHRENIA*

1. Physiologic Studies.—The functioning of the adrenal cortex in schizophrenic patients has been the subject of numerous investigations since the publication in 1946 by Pincus and Elmadjian[74] and Pincus and Hoagland[75] of papers dealing with 17-ketosteroid and lymphocyte responses to stress in schizophrenics and normal controls. Pincus and Elmadjian reported that schizophrenic patients show a lesser fall in the lymphocyte count following a severe heat stress than do normal controls. Further investigations by the Worcester Foundation and Worcester State Hospital group[76-81] extended the indices of adrenocortical reactivity to the eosinophils, urinary 17-ketosteroids, corticoids (measured both as neutral reducing lipids and as formaldehydrogenic steroids), uric acid, sodium, potassium, and phosphates. Investigations using this group of measures were carried out on approximately 100 male chronic schizophrenic patients and 100 well and nonpsychotic male controls matched for age with the patients. The patients were selected by the psychiatric staff of the Worcester State Hospital from mixed categories of schizophrenia. The stress stimuli employed for this study were the injection of 25 mg. of adrenocorticotrophic hormone (ACTH), the ingestion of glucose, a pursuitmeter task and a target-ball frustration test. The various physical and psychological stresses could be compared with the final physiological pathway through which the stresses worked, namely by the injection of ACTH. The changes in most of these indices were not well correlated with one another so that to obtain a simple formulation of the result of the test procedures, an index was used which was a composite of the changes in the various factors studied. The general conclusion was reached that, in terms of this total response index, approximately two thirds of the patient group displayed a lesser degree of adrenocortical reactivity to ACTH and to the other stresses than was obtained in the normal group of corresponding age and size. This lesser reactivity appeared not only in the younger patients (age 20 to 39) but equally well in the middle-aged group (age 40 to 60)[82] and even in the aged schizophrenic patients (age 60 to 90).[83,84] It should be noted that in the pre-stress or basal period, the patients showed significant differences from the normal subjects in urinary 17-ketosteroids (somewhat higher), potassium (higher), sodium (much higher), corticoids (somewhat lower), phosphates (much lower), giving from these urinary measures a mixed picture of hyper- and hypoadrenalism. The average adrenal stress re-

---

*This section, with some changes, is from Hoagland, H., and Freeman, H. *Proceedings of the Association for Research in Nervous and Mental Disease, 37*:183 (1959). It is republished here with permission of the Association.

sponses of the patients to the battery of four tests determined from urinary samples collected for 3 hours from the beginning of a 1-hour stress test or after an injection of ACTH showed significant differences from the normal subjects. The per cent increase in potassium was lower as was that of sodium and uric acid. No differences between the two groups were found in per cent increases of urinary corticoids or in per cent drugs in lymphocytes or eosinophils in response to target-ball, pursuitmeter stress tests, to the oral glucose tolerance test, or to the injection of 25 mg. of ACTH. The deficient response under stress seems to lie in the mineral-controlling elements of the adrenal cortex. The high basal sodium excretion of the chronic schizophrenics is consistent with findings of Elmadjian and coworkers[85] of studies of aldosterone excretion. They found a mean value of excretion of 4.1 μg./24 hr. (range 2.4 to 4.8) for a group of nine normal subjects. Fourteen schizophrenic patients showed a wide range of values with a mean of 4.4 μg./24 hr. (range 1.0 to 10.0). It was noted that eight of the fourteen samples from the schizophrenics showed values of 2.4 μg./24 hr. or less. In general acutely ill patients tended to excrete more aldosterone than did the chronic patients. The excretion rate did not, however, appear to be related to this directly since, in general, for both controls and patients, it was best correlated with the emotional state of the subject when sampled. The most tense and anxious subjects excreted the most aldosterone. Thus the flat, indifferent affect of many chronic schizophrenic patients appears to be accompanied by low aldosterone production and a correspondingly high rate of sodium excretion.

In attempting to localize the abnormal adrenal responses, Hoagland and Pincus[77,79] demonstrated that the peripheral target organs of the patients react normally to administered adrenocortical extract (Upjohn's Lipo-Adrenal extract). Thus, since the target organs of steroids responded normally in the patients, the deficiency appeared to be at the level of the adrenal cortex itself. Responses to the injection of ACTH and to the stresses in the schizophrenics suggest that either the adrenal cortex is releasing an abnormal product or that normal corticoids are metabolized abnormally after release and before appearing in the urine. It was considered possible that normal secreted corticoids might be abnormally metabolized in the liver or other tissues or that different urinary 17-ketosteroid precursors might be involved. Such differences would not be reflected by determinations of blood 17-hydroxycorticoids belonging to the C-21 series of steroids. Whether such abnormalities are primary or secondary to the psychosis was undetermined.

Further evidence for steroid dysgenesis in the patients was furnished by a study of Mittelman, Romanoff, Pincus and Hoagland[86] in 19 schizophrenic and 13 normal men. They found that the 24-hour excretion of total adrenal steroid metabolites was quantitatively similar in both groups, but that the patients excreted a significantly greater amount of 3-β-hydroxy-17-ketosteroids than the normal subjects. After the injection of ACTH, the per cent increase in excretion of ketosteroids, though less in the patients, still showed a disproportionately higher output of β-ketosteroids than was seen in the normals. Thus, a qualitative as well as quantitative difference in steroid excretion patterns in schizophrenia was indicated. This finding of a higher β-ketosteroid output in schizophrenics has been confirmed by the findings of Reiss and Stitch[87] and by Werbin and others.[88]

The ever recurrent question of dietary insufficiency as a cause of the adrenal adnormality was studied by Pincus, Schenker, Elmadjian and Hoagland.[89] In 7 schizophrenic patients who showed adrenocortical response abnormalities, a dietary supplement of high protein and high vitamin potency was administered for 2 weeks. Subsequent tests showed no change in adrenocortical responsivity to ACTH.

A group of psychoneurotic patients hospitalized for some months were found by Pincus and Hoagland to show normal responsivity to ACTH[79] so that hospitalization did not account for the deficiency. The abnormal findings in chronic schizophrenics are not to be interpreted, according to the Worcester group, as being specific for the schizophrenias nor is it implied that the steroid dysgenesis is necessarily a causal factor in the disorder. If anything, the contrary is suggested in view of the lack of success in treating schizophrenia by steroid medication and the fact that adrenalectomy and cortisol maintenance does not relieve the disorder. Pincus[90] has reported further qualitative differences from chromatographic studies of urinary steroid fractions in normal persons and schizophrenic patients. When column chromatogram eluates are separated in terms of polarities of substances, there appear to be more highly hydroxylated *alpha* ketols and glycols in the patients' urines. Some evidence also exists from paper chromatography of 35 urinary steroids for differences in frequencies of occurrence of specific steroid metabolites in the normal and patient groups, but these results have not been carried far enough for satisfactory conclusions by identification of specific steroids. Pincus[90] has reviewed evidence for the following conclusions. The chronic schizophrenics excrete somewhat lesser amounts of corticosteroids and neutral nonketonic steroids; among the corticosteroids the schizophrenics exhibit a higher proportion of more polar compounds; among the neutral ketonic steroids the β-ketosteroids of schizophrenics are disproportionately high. The suggestion of steroid dysgenesis is therefore stressed.

It is as if the schizophrenic subject secretes corticosteroid which differs qualitatively as well as quantitatively from the secretory product of the normals' adrenals; the secretory product of the schizophrenics' adrenals is a poor precursor of non-ketonic steroid and of β-ketosteroid. The low output of aldosterone in the chronic schizophrenics is consistent with their high sodium excretion.

The Worcester group's findings of subnormal adrenocortical reactivity have met with a mixed response. Faurbye, Vestergaard, Kobbernagel and Neilson[91] found that the response to ACTH in 17-ketosteroid excretion, uric acid and potassium excretion and effect on lymphocytes and eosinophils was subnormal in about one half of the schizophrenic group studied (10 patients, 10 controls). Similarly, the effect of epinephrine on the eosinophils was less than normal in 6 of 11 patients (11 patients, 9 controls) and was equivocal on the excretion of 17-ketosteroids. Hemphill and Reiss[92] find, in general, a subnormal adrenocortical responsivity to stress, particularly in the catatonic type. Høyrup[93] reports a tendency to a low content of blood sodium in chronic schizophrenic patients, with no alteration in the blood potassium levels. Lingjaerde[94] found remarkably low excretion of 17-ketosteroids in patients. Grunebaum and Altschule[95] report sweat sodium concentrations above normal in most psychotic patients, including schizophrenics, a finding which suggests diminished production of adrenocortical hormones controlling electrolyte balance.

Stevenson, Metcalve and Hobbs[96] found subnormal responses to epinephrine and corticotrophin, particularly in paranoid patients, while catatonic patients showed relatively normal findings. Werbin, Forley and Seidlin[88] reported considerable differences between the 17-ketosteroid excretion patterns of psychotic and normal individuals on the basis of chromatographic studies.

Fry[97] using the epinephrine test on eosinophils, concluded that the pituitary adrenocortical system was not impaired in schizophrenia. But epinephrine itself has been shown to cause eosinopenia in adrenalectomized persons and is not a suitable test for such a general conclusion. The Worcester group also found eosinophil responses to stress and ACTH not to differentiate patients and controls. Hobbs, Goddard and Stevenson,[98] investigating the diurnal cycle of blood eosinophils and body temperature, found no difference between chronic schizophrenic patients and normal controls. Parsons, Gildea, Ronzoni and Hulbert[99] found no difference in the lymphocyte response to physical stresses (epinephrine, ECT and insulin) between schizophrenic and normal subjects, but did note that the patients showed a marked lack of response to psychologic stress. Stein, Ronzoni and Gildea[100] found no statistically significant differences in the physiologic responses of chronically ill schizophrenics to heat stress and ACTH in their effects on lymphocytes and eosinophils as compared with normal controls and non-schizophrenic patients. Gildea[101] states that the eosinophils vary only slightly more in psychotic than in normal individuals and that schizophrenics show a defective response in this regard only in their capacity to react to psychologic stress. Dickes, Flamm, Bowman, Hollander and Potter[102] studied the responses of the eosinophils and lymphocytes to ACTH in schizophrenic patients and concluded that they fell within the normal range. No significant difference between the decline in eosinophil counts after epinephrine injection in psychotic and normal individuals was observed by Werbin, Seidlin, Cohen and Miller[103] or Pechstein.[104]

Altschule and Parkhurst[105] found the daily excretion level of 17-ketosteroids to be in or slightly above the normal range in schizophrenic patients. Altschule[106,107] states further that 39% of the schizophrenic patients have eosinophil counts below 100 (as compared with 0% of the normal controls) and that the injections of ACTH in the patients cause marked (normal) drops in the eosinophil count. These findings agree with those of the Worcester group. Altschule reports that ACTH causes a normal fall in the sodium concentration of sweat, but unlike the Worcester group, he finds it causes normal increases in the excretion of uric acid. He found abnormality in the carbohydrate response since ACTH injections resulted in a lower sugar tolerance in psychotic patients compared with no change seen in normal individuals. Unlike the Worcester group, he[108] is of the opinion that the adrenal cortex is hyperactive in the schizophrenic psychosis as indicated by the impaired glucose tolerance, the insulin resistance, the eosinopenia, the increased tendency toward glycogen formation, the ketonemia, the relatively high 17-ketosteroid output and the phosphaturia, but he did not employ comparative stress tests with normal persons and schizophrenic patients and his number of patients was small.

Bliss, Migeon, Nelson, Samuels and Branch[109] have studied the blood levels of 17-hydroxycorticosteroids in 33 subjects, of whom 29 were acute and 4 were chronic schizophrenic patients. A total of 47 determinations was made, the average level being $16.5\gamma/100$ cc. of blood. The normal range of values by their techniques lies between 4 and 10γ. In the patients only two values fell within this range. On this basis, the adrenal cortex seems to be functioning at an overactive level. They also noted that electric and insulin shock therapy resulted in increases in the blood steroid level equivalent to that produced by the intravenous injection of 0.1 to 1.0 I.U. of corticotropin. They concluded, therefore, that in these cases (which were mostly in an acute phase) the adrenal cortex of the patients was quite reactive. Another study by the same authors[110] in 26 chronic schizophrenic patients and 20 normal controls showed that the mean levels of plasma 17-hydroxy-corticosteroids were the same in both groups and that the responses to varying stresses (ACTH, insulin and pyrogenic substances) resulted in equivalent effects in the normal and psychotic subjects. Hoagland and Pincus[111] have pointed out that these findings on blood steroids do not controvert their urinary findings. Thus, they found adreno-cortical responsivity to 25 mg. of ACTH and to their three stress tests (oral glucose tolerance, pursuitmeter and targetball frustration tests) the same in normals as in schizophrenics, and this also applied to changes in eosinophils and lymphocytes. It is the urinary 17-ketosteroids rather than either blood or urinary corticoids that indicate, according to them, subnormal responsivity to stress and to ACTH, and no meas-ures of blood C-19 steroids have been carried out. The beta-ketosteroids, of which dehydroepiandrosterone is the principal one, are relatively high in schizophrenics compared to controls and their precursor is probably adrenal cholesterol. The beta-ketosteroids of the C-19 series are not metabolites of the C-21 corticoids measured by Bliss et al.

Corticoids and 17-ketosteroids do not necessarily vary together. Thus, in fever, burns, and severe trauma, the corticoid output may increase three- to fivefold while the 17-ketosteroid output may fall. In the ad-renogenital syndrome, the 17-ketosteroids may increase ten-fold while the corticoid output remains normal or may be depressed. The Wor-cester group has confirmed Bliss and associates with respect to levels of blood corticoids in schizophrenics and normals, but the fact that basal blood corticoids are normal in schizophrenics while basal urinary corticoids are slightly but significantly reduced would suggest dif-ferences in metabolism of the steroids after secretion and before appear-ance in the urine.

Altschule[108] finds that while in the untreated cases the adrenal cor-tex is in a hyperactive phase, with recovery there tends to be a mild de-pression in activity. Friedlander, Perrault, Turner and Gottfried[112] hypothesize that initially in the psychosis there is a hyperactivity of the adrenal cortex, followed by an inability to respond because of ex-haustion, and that with recovery there is a return to a normal phase of activity. These phasic variations were noted in the changes in 17-keto-steroid excretion levels during hospitalization. Gottfried and Minsky[113] have studied several patients who had spontaneous remissions and who had marked increases in 17-ketosteroids during the period of improve-ment. Hoagland and others[41] noted that patients with higher adrenal response have a better prognosis for electroshock therapy. Rowntree and Kay[114] studied intensively the relationship between adrenocortical

activity and nitrogen balance in two patients with recurrent schizophrenia. They found in the early stages of an attack a preponderance
of androgenic substances, and during recovery and remission, a preponderance of sugar-active cortin. A relationship between the degree
of adrenocortical responsivity and the state of psychiatric illness was
also described by Reiss, Hemphill, Early, Maggs, Cook and Pelly.[115]
There was no response characteristic of individual disease groups,
but there were special features about the distribution of response types
in acute and chronic schizophrenic patients and in patients with anxiety. In this connection, Fisher[116] draws attention to a similarity of
pathophysiologic phenomena occurring during certain stages of the
schizophrenic process and certain phases of the general adaptation
syndrome of Selye.

With this diversity of opinions it is difficult to draw conclusions.
Investigators of adrenocortical physiology in schizophrenic patients
have seldom repeated the experimental procedures of others so that
confirmation or denial of results based on comparable operational procedures is not available, and patient populations are highly variable.
Eosinophil changes used in so many of the studies to assay overall
adrenocortical function are not an acceptable procedure, nor is the
use of epinephrine as an adequate stimulating agent of the pituitary
adrenal axis in man. Injected epinephrine does not significantly enhance the output of corticoids, and eosinopenia occurs in Addisonians
and in bilaterally adrenalectomized persons in response to injected
epinephrine. The adrenal cortex is, thus, not necessary for this response, though of course adrenal corticoids also will cause eosinopenia. There seems to be some consensus from the urinary studies for
a dysgenesis of steroid metabolism in schizophrenics but the significance
of this, if any, and its specificity and relation to the etiology of schizophrenia remain obscure.

The findings of a dysfunction of adrenocortical origin in schizophrenia are obviously not in the nature of a simple syndrome. Schizophrenia is not a common psychiatric reaction found in hypoadrenalism (Addison's disease) or hyperadrenalism (Cushing's disease). Schizophrenia is not provoked in nonpsychotic individuals to whom corticotropin or cortisone has been administered. Most workers have reported
that schizophrenia is not improved by the administration of these hormones,[117-123] although a few studies have reported some favorable
results with steroid medication.[124-126] Total bilateral adrenalectomy
followed by replacement therapy has also not resulted in remission
from schizophrenia.[127]

REFERENCES

1. PORTER, R. W.: *Recent Progr. Hormone Res., 10:*1 (1954).
2. SCHARRER, E. and SCHARRER, B.: *Recent Progr. Hormone Res., 10:*183 (1954).
3. HARRIS, G. W.: *Ciba Foundation Colloquia on Endocrinology, 8:*531 (1955).
4. LONG, C. N. H.: *Ann. Rev. Physiol., 18:*409 (1956).
5. FORTIER, C.: *20th International Physiological Congress,* Brussels, p. 490 (1956).
6. HARRIS, G. W.: *20th International Physiological Congress,* Brussels, p. 508 (1956).
7. DE JONGH, S. E.: *20th International Physiological Congress,* Brussels, p. 528 (1956).
8. Reviews by FORTIER, C., and by FORTIER and DEGROOT, J.: *Prog. Neurol. & Psychiat.,* (a) *11:*108 (1956); (b) *12:*252 (1957); (c) *13:*118 (1958); (d) *14:*256 (1959).
9. HOAGLAND, H. (ED.): *Hormones, Brain Function and Behavior.* New York, Acad. Press (1957).
10. THORN, G. W.: *Adrenal Cortex,* Tr. First Macy Conference, p. 189. New York Josiah Macy, Jr. Foundation, (1949).
11. THORN, G. W. and FORSHAM, P. H.: *Recent Prog. Hormone Res., 4:*243 (1949).
12. FRIEDLANDER, W. J. and ROTTGER, E.: *EEG & Clin. Neurophysiol., 3:*311 (1951).
13. PINE, I., ENGEL, F. L. and SCHWARTZ, T. B.: *EEG & Clin. Neurophysiol., 3:*301 (1951).
14. BROSTER, L. R.: *The Suprarenal Cortex,* p. 201. J. M. Yoffey, Ed., London, Butterworths (1953).
15. HENCH, P. S., KENDALL, E. C., SLOCUMB, C. H. and POLLEY, H. F.: *Proc. Staff Meet., Mayo Clin., 24:*181 (1949).
16. KLEIN, R. and LIVINGSTON, S.: *J. Pediat., 37:*733 (1950).
17. LEWIN, E. and WASSEN, E.: *Lancet, 2:*993 (1949).
18. McQUARRIE, I., ANDERSON, J. A. and ZIEGLER, M. R.: *J. Clin. Endocrinol., 2:*406 (1942).
19. SPRAGUE, R. G., POWER, M. H., MASON, H. L., ALBERT, A., MATHIESON, D. R., HENCH, P. S., KENDALL, E. C., SLOCUMB, C. H. and POLLEY, H. F.: *Arch. Int. Med., 85:*199 (1950).
20. CLARK, L. D., BAUER, W. and COBB, S.: *New England J. Med., 246:*205 (1952).
21. GLASER, G. H.: *Psychosom. Med., 15:*280 (1953).
22. GLASER, G. H.: *A Res. Nerv. & Ment. Dis., Proc., 32:*21 (1953).
23. CLEGHORN, R. A.: *Ciba Foundation Colloquia on Endocrinology, 3:*187 (1952).
24. HECHTER, O., ZAFFARONI, A., JACOBSEN, R. P., LEVY, H., JEANLOZ, R. W., SCHENKER, V. and PINCUS, G.: *Recent Progr. Hormone Res., 6:*215 (1951).
25. PINCUS, G. and HOAGLAND, H.: *J. Aviation Med., 15:*98 (1944).
26. PINCUS, G., HOAGLAND, H.: *Psychosom. Med., 7:*342 (1945).
27. PINCUS, G., HOAGLAND, H., WILSON, C. H. and FAY, N. J.: *Psychosom. Med., 7:*347 (1945).
28. SELYE, H.: *J. Immunol., 41:*259 (1941).
29. GORDAN, G. S., ADAMS, J. E., BENTINCK, R. C., EISENBERG, E., HARPER, H. and HOBSON, Q. J. G.: *California Med., 78:*87 (1953).
30. SCHIEVE, J. R. and WILSON, W. P.: *J. Clin. Invest., 31:*984 (1952).
31. BERGEN, J. R.: *Am. J. Physiol., 164:*16 (1951).
32. BERGEN, J. R., HUNT, C. A. and HOAGLAND, H.: *Am. J. Physiol., 175:*327 (1953).
33. HOAGLAND, H.: *Am. J. Physiol., 116:*604 (1936).
34. HOAGLAND, H.: In *Colloid Chemistry,* Vol. V, p. 762. J. Alexander, Ed. New York, Reinhold (1944).

35. TORDA, C. and WOLFF, H. G.: *Am. J. Physiol., 168:*406 (1952).
36. TORDA, C. and WOLFF, H. G.: *Federation Proc., 11:*163 (1952).
37. TORDA, C.: *Am. J. Physiol., 173:*176 (1953).
38. TORDA, C.: *Am. J. Physiol., 173:*179 (1953).
39. DORFMAN, A., APTER, N. S., SMULL, K., BERGENSTALL, D. M. and RICHTER, R. B.: *J.A.M.A., 146:*25 (1951).
40. SOFFER, L. J., LEVOTT, M. F. and BOEHR, G.: *Arch. Int. Med., 86:*558 (1950).
41. TORDA, C. and WOLFF, H. G.: *J. Clin. Invest., 28:*1228 (1949).
42. HYDÉN, H.: *Symp. Soc. Exper. Biol.,* 1 (1947).
43. HYDÉN, H. and HARTELIUS, H.: *Acta psychiat. et neurol., Suppl., 48:*110 (1947).
44. NURNBERGER, J. I.: *A. Res. Nerv. & Ment. Dis., Proc., 32:*132 (1953).
45. NURNBERGER, J. I.: Neurology Symposium, 25th Anniversary Program, Columbia Presbyterian Medical Center, October 12, (1953).
46. SELYE, H.: *Proc. Soc. Exper. Biol. & Med., 46:*116 (1941).
47. SELYE, H.: *Endocrinology, 30:*437 (1942).
48. LAUBACH, G. D., P'AN, S. Y. and RUDEL, H. W.: *Science, 122:*78 (1955).
49. P'AN, S. Y., GARDOCKI, J. F., HUTCHEON, D. E., RUDEL, H., KODET, M. J. and LAUBACH, G. D.: *J. Pharmacol. & Exper. Therap., 115:*432 (1955).
50. GORDAN, G. S., GAUDAGNI, N., PICCHI, J. and ADAMS, J. E.: *J. Internat. Coll. Surgeons, 25:*9 (1956).
51. GORDAN, G. S. and ELLIOTT, H. W.: *Endocrinology, 41:*517 (1947).
52. MICHAELIS, M. and QUASTEL, J. H.: *Biochem. J., 35:*518 (1941).
53. HOCHSTER, R. M. and QUASTEL, J. H.: *Nature,* London, *164:*865 (1949).
54. EISENBERG, E., GORDAN, G. S. and ELLIOTT, H. W.: *Science, 109:*337 (1949).
55. EISENBERG, E., GORDAN, G. S. and ELLIOTT, H. W.: *Endocrinology, 45:*113 (1949).
56. EISENBERG, E., GORDAN, G. S., ELLIOTT, H. W. and TALBOT, J.: *Proc. Soc. Exper. Biol. & Med., 73:*140 (1950).
57. GORDAN, G. S., BENTINCK, R. C. and EISENBERG, E.: *Ann. New York Acad. Sc., 54:*575 (1951).
58. HAYANO, M., SCHILLER, S. and DORFMAN, R. I.: *Endocrinology, 46:*387 (1950).
59. BERGEN, J. R., HUNT, C. and HOAGLAND, H.: Unpublished data.
60. BOURNE, G. H. and MALATY, H. A.: *J. Physiol., 122:*178 (1953).
61. KENDALL, E. C.: *Vitamins & Hormones, 6:*277 (1948).
62. ANDERSON, E.: *Essays in Biology in Honor of Herbert M. Evans,* pp. 35-49. Berkeley, Univ. California Press (1943).
63. HODGKIN, A. L. and KATZ, B. T.: *J. Physiol., 108:*37 (1949).
64. DAVENPORT, V. D.: *Am. J. Physiol., 156:*322 (1949).
65. CHAUCHARD, P.: *Ann. endocrinol.,* Paris, *4:*257 (1943).
66. SLOCOMBE, A., HOAGLAND, H. and PRAGLIN, J.: *Federation Proc., 11:*149 (1952).
67. HARTMAN, F. A. and LOCKWOOD, J. E.: *Proc. Soc. Exper. Biol. & Med., 29:*141 (1931).
68. HOAGLAND, H., BERGEN, J. R., SLOCOMBE, A. G. and HUNT, C. A.: In *Metabolic and Toxic Diseases of the Nervous System,* p. 40. Baltimore, Williams & Wilkins (1953).
69. SLOCOMBE, A. G., TOZIAN, L. S. and HOAGLAND, H.: *Am. J. Physiol., 179:*89 (1954).
70. WRIGHT, E. B. and LESTER, E. J.: *Am. J. Physiol., 196:*1057 (1959).
71. HOAGLAND, H. and STONE, D.: *Am. J. Physiol., 152:*423 (1948).
72. LEIDERMAN, P. H. and KATZMAN, R.: *Am. J. Physiol., 175:*271 (1953).
73. BERGEN, J. R., STONE, D. and HOAGLAND, H.: *Proc. Internat. Conf. Peaceful Uses Atomic Energy* (1955).

74. PINCUS, G. and ELMADJIAN, F.: *J. Clin. Endocrinol., 6:*295 (1946).

75. PINCUS, G. and HOAGLAND, H.: *Arch. Neurol. & Psychiat., 56:*717 (1946).

76. HOAGLAND, H.: *Psychosom. Med., 12:*142 (1950).

77. HOAGLAND, H.: In *The Biology of Mental Health and Disease*, p. 434. New York, Hoeber (1952).

78. PINCUS, G.: *Recent Progr. Hormone Res., 1:*123 (1947).

79. PINCUS, G. and HOAGLAND, H.: *Am. J. Psychiat., 106:*641 (1950).

80. PINCUS, G., HOAGLAND, H., FREEMAN, H., ELMADJIAN, F. and ROMANOFF, L. P.: *Psychosom. Med., 11:*74 (1949).

81. PINCUS, G., HOAGLAND, H., FREEMAN, H. and ELMADJIAN, F.: *Recent Progr. Hormone Res., 4:*291 (1949).

82. HOAGLAND, H., PINCUS, G., ELMADJIAN, F., ROMANOFF, L., FREEMAN, H., HOPE, J., BALLAN, J., BERKELEY, A. and CARLO, J.: *A.M.A. Arch. Neurol. & Psychiat., 69:*470 (1953).

83. FREEMAN, H., PINCUS, G., ELMADJIAN, F. and ROMANOFF, L. P.: *Geriatrics, 10:*72 (1955).

84. FREEMAN, H., PINCUS, G., ELMADJIAN, F. and ROMANOFF, L. P.: *Ciba Foundation Colloquia on Aging, 1:*219 (1955).

85. ELMADJIAN, F.: *First International Endocrinology Congress*, Copenhagen (1960).

86. MITTELMAN, A., ROMANOFF, L. P., PINCUS, G. and HOAGLAND, H.: *J. Clin. Endocrinol., 12:*831 (1952).

87. REISS, M. and STITCH, S. R.: *J. Ment. Sc., 100:*704 (1954).

88. WERBIN, H., FORLEY, R. and SEIDLIN, S. M.: *J. Hillside Hosp., 3:*204 (1954).

89. PINCUS, G., SCHENKER, V., ELMADJIAN, F. and HOAGLAND, H.: *Psychosom. Med., 11:*146 (1949).

90. PINCUS, G.: *Ciba Foundation Colloquia on Endocrinology, 3:*154 (1952).

91. FAURBYE, A., VESTERGAARD, P., KOBBERNAGEL, F. and NEILSEN, A.: *Acta endocrinol., 8:*215 (1951).

92. HEMPHILL, R. E. and REISS, M.: *Proc. Roy. Soc. Med., 41:*533 (1948).

93. HØYRUP, E.: *Acta Psychiat. Neurol., 25:*179 (1950).

94. LINGJAERDE, O.: *Acta Psychiat. Neurol. Scand., 80:*Suppl. 202 (1953).

95. GRUNEBAUM, H. and ALTSCHULE, M. D.: *Arch Neurol. & Psychiat., 53:*444 (1950).

96. STEVENSON, J. A. F., METCALFE, E. V. and HOBBS, G. E.: *A.M.A. Arch. Neurol. & Psychiat., 70:*802 (1953).

97. FRY, W. F., JR.: *A.M.A. Arch. Neurol. & Psychiat., 70:*598 (1953).

98. HOBBS, G. E., GODDARD, E. S. and STEVENSON, J. A. F.: *Canad. M. A. J., 70:*533 (1954).

99. PARSONS, E. H., GILDEA, E. F., RONZONI, E. and HULBERT, S. Z.: *Am. J. Psychiat., 105:*573 (1949).

100. STEIN, M., RONZONI, E. and GILDEA, E. F.: *Am. J. Psychiat., 108:*450 (1951).

101. GILDEA, E. F.: In *The Biology of Mental Health and Disease*, p. 454. New York, Hoeber (1952).

102. DICKLES, R., FLAMM, G. H., BOWMAN, W., HOLLANDER, E. E. and POTTER, H. W.: *Am. J. Psychiat., 110:*124 (1953).

103. WERBIN, H., SEIDLIN, S. M., COHEN, L. and MILLER, J. S. A.: *Psychosom. Med., 14:*469 (1952).

104. PECHSTEIN, J.: *Psychiat. Quart., 26:*425 (1952).

105. ALTSCHULE, M. D. and PARKHURST, B. H.: *Arch. Neurol. & Psychiat., 64:*516 (1950).

106. ALTSCHULE, M.: In *The Biology of Mental Health and Disease,* p. 449. New York, Hoeber (1952).
107. ALTSCHULE, M. D., SIEGEL, E. P., RESTAINO, R. M. and PARKHURST, B. H.: *A.M.A. Arch. Neurol. & Psychiat., 67*:228 (1952).
108. ALTSCHULE, M. D.: *Internat. Rec. Med. & Gen. Pract. Clin., 166*:190 (1953).
109. BLISS, E. L., MIGEON, C. J., NELSON, D. H., SAMUELS, L. T. and BRANCH, C. H. H.: *A.M.A. Arch. Neurol. & Psychiat., 72*:352 (1954).
110. BLISS, E. L., MIGEON, C. J., BRANCH, C. H. H. and SAMUELS, L. T.: *Am. J. Psychiat., 112*:358 (1955).
111. HOAGLAND, H. and PINCUS, G.: *Am. J. Psychiat., 112*:748 (1956).
112. FRIEDLANDER, J. H., PERRAULT, R., TURNER, W. J. and GOTTFRIED, S. P.: *Psychosom. Med., 12*:86 (1950).
113. GOTTFRIED, S. P. and MINSKY, I.: *A.M.A. Arch. Neurol. & Psychiat., 66*:708 (1951).
114. ROWNTREE, D. W. and KAY, W. W.: *J. Ment. Sc., 98*:100 (1952).
115. REISS, M., HEMPHILL, R. E., EARLY, D. F., MAGGS, R., COOK, E. R. and PELLY, J. E.: *J. Clin. & Exper. Psychopath., 12*:171 (1951).
116. FISCHER, R.: *J. Nerv. & Ment. Dis., 119*:492 (1954).
117. COHN, J. B., STECKLER, G. A. and RUBINSTEIN, J.: *J. Clin. & Exper. Psychopath., 14*:161 (1953).
118. GILDEA, E. F., RONZONI, E. and TRUFANT, S. A.: In *The Biology of Mental Health and Disease,* p. 600. New York, Hoeber (1952).
119. GLASER, G. H. and HOCH, P. H.: *A.M.A. Arch. Neurol. & Psychiat., 66*:697 (1951).
120. HOPE, J. M., ELMADJIAN, F. and MALAMUD, W.: *J. Clin. & Exper. Psychopath., 12*:267 (1951).
121. POLATIN, P., LESSE, S. and HARRIS, M. M.: *A.M.A. Arch. Neurol. & Psychiat., 73*:485 (1955).
122. REES, L. and KING, G. M.: *J. Ment. Sc., 98*:401 (1952).
123. REES, L. and KING, G. M.: *J. Ment. Sc., 97*:376 (1951).
124. COHN, J. B., KARNOSH, L. J. and STECKLER, R. M.: *Dis. Nerv. System, 12*:291 (1951).
125. CRANSWICK, E. H. and HALL, T. C.: *Lancet, 1*:540 (1950).
126. JENS, R.: *A.M.A. Arch. Neurol. & Psychiat., 68*:372 (1952).
127. APTER, N. S.: *Am. J. Psychiat., 115*:55 (1958).

XL

HEREDITARY NERVOUS AND MENTAL DISEASES

L. S. Penrose

INTRODUCTION

Intoxications by alcohol, drugs, or poisonous alkaloids alter emotional and intellectual balance. These states must be distinguished from those in which a permanent inborn metabolic disturbance is responsible. The study of inborn biochemical constitution perhaps may be said to have begun when A. B. Garrod[1] measured the uric acid content of the blood in cases of gout and other chronic diseases. The first fully characteristic contribution, however, was made by A. E. Garrod,[2] who observed that alkaptonuria was an inborn peculiarity recessively inherited and the effect of a single abnormal gene. Though usually harmless there were associated disabilities, such as arthritis. This and other inborn errors have been brought into relation to one another by the assumption that the disabilities are all due to lack of specific enzymes. It is convenient, when the prominent peculiarity is excretion in the urine of an abnormal metabolite, to express this in the nomenclature, e.g., cystinuria, fructosuria or phenylketonuria.

None of the inborn errors of metabolism described by Garrod[3] was known to be associated with nervous or mental disease. Since that time many conditions have come to light which are undoubtedly inborn biochemical specificities and which, to different degrees and in different ways, produce mental abnormality as a by-product. Phenylketonuria, for instance, is almost invariably associated with some degree of mental impairment, porphyria causes acute attacks of confusional insanity and methaemoglobinaemia causes severe mental deficiency in a small proportion of cases. Many other abnormal nervous or mental conditions are associated with inborn biochemical peculiarities though the precise chemical abnormality cannot yet be specified. End results of metabolic errors can be seen in the amaurotic idiocies, Wilson's disease and gargoylism, as well as in some more slowly degenerative conditions such as Huntington's chorea and Alzheimer's disease, which have not yet been reduced to chemically pathological conditions. A warning, however, is needed for sometimes an inborn metabolic error is identified in a mentally ill subject which may not be of causal significance. For example, the enzyme anomaly which Kalow and Gunn[4] described in certain psychotic patients was afterwards also found in a comparable proportion of subjects in the general population.

It is difficult to make a systematic classification of the inborn mental and nervous diseases which have been studied biochemically. They form a mixed group and they will be considered, now, starting with those conditions about which there is the greatest amount of relevant information.

PHENYLKETONURIA

Fölling[5] observed the presence of phenylpyruvic acid in the urines of some imbeciles in Oslo. He pointed out that the spontaneous excretion of phenylpyruvic acid in man had not been observed previously and that all affected subjects were mentally subnormal. The chemical anomaly appears in the first few weeks after birth and is constant throughout life. Excretors show a limitation of mental powers in early life which becomes more obvious as they grow older. The sexes are equally affected. Most commonly the phenylketonuric child is an imbecile but, occasionally, subjects can pass for normal. Cowie[6] has recorded a case whose intelligence level, judged by standardized tests, was very close to the average.

The disease is a recessive trait caused by a rare gene in homozygous form. This explanation depends upon observations on the perfect segregation of affected and unaffected members in families, the extreme rarity of transmission from parent to child (Jervis[7]), the high incidence of consanguinity among parents of cases (Penrose,[8] Fölling, Mohr and Ruud[9]) and the ratio of one quarter affected in sibships with unaffected parents (Jervis,[10] Munro[11]). The frequencies of the condition in the general populations of North America, England and Norway are of the order of one in 40,000. This implies a gene frequency of one in 200 so that one person in every hundred of the population is a heterozygous carrier of the gene. Some evidence has been produced suggesting that carriers of the gene are especially liable to develop presenile psychosis (Penrose,[8] Thompson[12]) but this is considered doubtful by Fölling, Mohr and Ruud.[9] Phenylketonurics have been found also in many families of Dutch, French, German, Irish, Italian and Slavonic origin but, so far, only very occasionally among negroes, Jews or Asiatic peoples.

Besides causing mental defect, the gene produces numerous physical and temperamental characteristics and these, again, are variable from one subject to another. Patients are often blondes and the degree of dilution of hair colour has been measured (Cowie and Penrose[13]). The mean stature and mean head measurements are reduced. Deep and superficial reflexes are always extremely brisk but it is rare to find any evidence of neurological lesions. Severely affected subjects make peculiar manneristic and hyperkinetic movements, especially with their hands. Many suffer from epileptic seizures in infancy and childhood. In temperament, all grades are uniformly docile. Many cases have an abnormal tendency to sweat; the secretion itself, which imparts an aromatic odour to the skin, contains phenylpyruvic acid, phenylacetic acid and phenyllactic acid (Jervis[14]).

The subjects are, on the whole, surprisingly healthy and few cases have been examined post mortem. Neither the nerve tumours found by Penrose[15] nor the degenerative changes in the brain and liver, noticed by Coquet, Myle, Nyssen and van Bogaert,[16] are characteristic of phenylketonuria. Crome and Pare[17] considered that micrencephaly and fibrous gliosis of the white matter, together with slight pallor of the myelin staining, may be significant. The suggestion that impaired liver function might be demonstrated during life was made by Delay, Pichot, Desgrez and Delbarre[18] on the basis of some abnormal results of the galactose tolerance test in one patient. However, since then, Cowie[19] has found normal galactose tolerance in 12 cases.

In affected homozygotes about one gram of phenylpyruvic acid is excreted each day in the urine. The quantity can be artificially increased by feeding subjects on phenylalanine, phenyllactic acid or phenylpyruvic acid but not by giving tyrosine or alanine. Normal subjects have only been observed to excrete noticeable quantities of phenylpyruvic acid after ingestion of 15 gm. doses of L-phenylalanine (Penrose and Quastel[20]). An interesting point is that 0.5 gm. D-phenylalanine is sufficient to produce the same effect. On the basis of the experimental work of Krebs[21] this phenomenon is explained because D-phenylalanine is very rapidly excreted, after deaminization in the liver and kidney by a D-amino acid deaminase, as phenylpyruvic acid (Fölling, Mohr and Ruud[9]).

The spontaneous presence of L-phenylalanine in the urine of affected subjects was first detected by Fölling and Closs.[22] Jervis[10] has shown that phenyllactic acid is also present in the urine. The exact quantities of these substances depend upon the diet and they vary also from one subject to another. The output has been shown to have no statistical relationship to the subject's degree of mental impairment and appears to be dependent ultimately upon the reabsorptive power of the renal tubules.

The abnormal contents of body fluids show a quite different picture. Phenylpyruvic acid is not found in the tissues at post mortem examination. During life, the body fluids, cerebrospinal fluid and the blood contain only very small traces or none at all (Jervis[23]). On the other hand, normal protein-free plasma contains slightly less than 1 mg./100 cc. (Prescott, Borek, Brecker and Waelsch[24]) whereas that of affected subjects, in fasting condition, contains nearly 30 mg./100 cc. The level of phenyllactic acid is also raised to an equivalent degree. The cerebrospinal fluid of abnormals contains L-phenylalanine in quantities of 0.6 to 0.8 mg./100 cc. whereas normally there is none present.

From these findings, the inference can be drawn that the inborn error is concerned with a failure to metabolize phenylalanine. It is assumed that, normally, phenylalanine in the body is changed into tyrosine (Embden and Baldes[25]). In phenylketonuria it accumulates in the blood and is disposed of by direct excretion and by being broken down into phenylpyruvic acid and phenyllactic acid. The process involved is explained by assuming that the missing enzyme is one which is required for the conversion of phenylalanine to tyrosine (Jervis[26]), not, as at first supposed, one which is concerned with the immediate breakdown of phenylpyruvic acid. It is now known that the basic abnormality is the lack of an enzyme in the liver, the hydroxylase which normally converts phenylalanine into tyrosine (Mitoma, Auld and Udenfriend[27]). There is consequently an excess of phenylalanine in the blood in these patients and it is thought that the mental weakness is, at least in part, caused by this. There is indeed good ground for supposing that the hair colour dilution is due to the blocking effect of too much phenylalanine in the system. The excretion of tryptophane derivatives, such as indolylacetic acid and indolyllactic acid in increased quantities has been frequently described. This is generally supposed to be caused by secondary effects connected with the increased quantities of phenylalanine in the body. These substances tend to disappear when phenylalanine is removed from the diet (Armstrong and Tyler[28]).

Search for evidence of mild enzymic defect among parents who are heterozygous carriers of the abnormal gene (Hsia, Driscoll, Troll and Knox,[29] Hsia[30]) resulted in the development of a phenylalanine tolerance test. The average levels in the blood plasma, at intervals after a dose of 0.1 gm./kg. of body weight, shown in Figure 1, demonstrate clear distinctions between the three genotypes. It is claimed that about nine out of ten carriers could be confidently diagnosed by this method. Tests of this kind have been used for genetical linkage studies by Renwick, Lawler and Cowie.[31]

Attempts at rational therapy centre round the restriction of phenylalanine in the diet. Good results have been reported by several investigators. It is believed that the natural mental deterioration which occurs

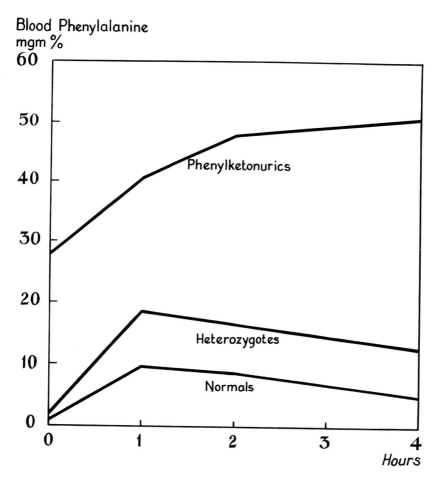

Fig. 1. Phenylalanine Tolerance Tests (*after* Hsia[30]) Mean blood plasma
levels of phenylalanine, at hourly intervals, following a dose of 0.1 gm./kg.

in most cases can be prevented if a low phenylalanine diet can be given
from a very early age. It is thought that the myelination of the central
nervous system may be interfered with by the high levels during the
first year of life (Woolf, Griffiths, Moncrieff, Coates and Dillistone[32]).

OTHER SPECIFIC AMINOACIDURIAS

There are several diseases associated with loss of mental functioning and the occurrence of specific aminoacids in the urine which are not yet so well understood as phenylketonuria. In no instance has the enzyme defect yet been identified.

Allan, Cusworth, Dent and Wilson[33] described two sibs who were mentally retarded and who were found by chromatography to be excreting large amounts of a substance which has been isolated and identified by Westall[34] as argininosuccinic acid. The quantities excreted were of the order of 1 to 2 gm. per day. Two other sibs, both parents and a number of other relatives were examined and found to be apparently quite normal. In the affected children the unusual substance was also found in appreciable amounts in the blood plasma and the cerebrospinal fluid. Its concentration in the cerebrospinal fluid was, however, two and a half to three times that in the plasma and this led to the suggestion that the substance was being formed in the brain, possibly as a result of a block in cerebral metabolism. The blood urea was within normal limits in the affected children. The disease is not incompatible with good general health. It is most probably inherited recessively.

Another rare anomaly, the excretion of cystathionine in the urine was found in an adult imbecile by Harris, Penrose and Thomas.[35] Cystathionine is believed to be an intermediate in the formation of cysteine from methionine. Feeding of methionine increased the quantity of cystathionine in the urine. A metabolic block was thought to be situated at the point where cystathionine is normally cleaved to give cysteine and homoserine. A mild degree of cystathioninuria was found in two normal relatives. It was considered probable that the disease was caused by a gene in homozygous state and that there were slight manifestations in heterozygous carriers.

A very severe disease affecting the nervous system within the first few days of life was described first by Menkes, Hurst and Craig.[36] Signs of spasticity and of cerebellar lesions develop rapidly and the infants only survive a few weeks. The biochemically characteristic feature is the occurrence in the urine of a substance, with the odour of maple sugar, which has not been identified. Three branched chain aminoacids, valine, leucine and isoleucine, are found in greatly increased concentrations in the urine and also in the blood (Westall, Dancis and Miller[37]). Though the mode of inheritance has not yet been fully studied it appears to be that of a single gene recessive character.

GALACTOSAEMIA

Galactosaemia is diagnosed by the presence of galactose in the urine. Infants who suffer from it appear normal at birth but, after a few days of milk-feeding, they begin to vomit, they become lethargic and fail to gain weight. The liver becomes enlarged and there is often jaundice. Those infants who survive may show mental retardation and aminoaciduria.

The inheritance is that of an autosomal recessive trait. The incidence in the population is not known but it is evidently a very rare condition, judging from the relatively few cases which have been reported from all over the world.

There are characteristic lesions, cataract, fatty degeneration in the liver, and there is retardation of brain function. As shown by Schwarz, Goldberg, Komrower and Holzel,[38] there is an accumulation of a galactose-1-phosphate in the red blood cells. These aberrations occur only if the affected individuals are fed on galactose. If a strictly galactose-free diet is imposed from birth, the subjects are practically insured against the development of specific galactosaemic lesions. The defective enzyme in galactosaemia is gal-1-P uridyl transferase; this was first demonstrated by Isselbacher, Anderson, Kurahashi and Kalckar who used lysates of erythrocytes.[39]

One might expect to find partial enzyme defects in parents of galactosaemic children. The first approach to this problem was made by Holzel and Komrower.[40] They used the galactose tolerance test as a criterion and found that either one or both parents of galactosaemic children showed abnormal values in the tolerance test. Kirkman[41] used manometric determination of oxygen consumption in haemolysates for the purpose of comparing transferase activities from normals and suspected carriers. This method gives nearly an 80% efficiency in carrier identification.

HEPATOLENTICULAR DEGENERATION

The conditions so far described have effects on the nervous system mainly expressed in impairment of cerebral function. In the disease first observed by Wilson,[42] there is a progressive development of neurological symptoms. These include rigidity, spasticity and tremor of the limbs; there are also mental changes, particularly in the direction of emotional deterioration which may end in dementia. The cause was shown to be degeneration of the lenticular nucleus in the brain which was accompanied, for no obvious reason, by cirrhosis of the liver. In recent years, Schienberg and Gitlin[43] discovered that patients with Wilson's disease had substantially lower concentrations than normal subjects of a protein called caeruloplasmin, previously isolated by Holmberg and Laurell.[44] Caeruloplasmin, which normally is present in the blood serum in the concentration of 30 mg./100 cc., contains eight atoms of copper per molecule. Its function is not known but some failure in its synthesis, which occurs in Wilson's disease, leads to the deposition of grossly abnormal excess of copper in the brain, liver and other tissues including, probably, the iris where it produces a visible greenish brown ring. Generalized aminoaciduria present in later stages of the illness is caused by defective reabsorption in the kidney tubules.

Analysis of family data has shown conclusively that the disease is recessively inherited (Bearn[45]). The measurement of caeruloplasmin level in the serum of normal heterozygotes has not yet been shown to be consistently abnormal. This may be a reflection of the variations in caeruloplasmin formation which are found between different patients. The level has little relationship to the duration or the severity of symptoms. It has sometimes been suggested that there may be more than one genetical type classed under the same category. This view receives support from the results of therapy which can be very beneficial in some cases but less so in others. The most successful method has been to increase the urinary excretion of copper by the prolonged administration to the patient of penicillamine.

CONDITIONS ASSOCIATED WITH ACUTE NERVOUS DISEASE

In contrast to the chronic or slowly progressive nervous symptoms produced by metabolic errors already mentioned there are certain acute states which can arise in other heritable metabolic diseases. An example of this is the severe crisis which can occur in acute intermittent porphyria. The characteristic biochemical feature is the excretion of large quantities of porphobilinogen accompanied by delta aminolaevulic acid. This is not found in children before puberty though it persists in a lesser degree in adults between acute attacks. It is thought that abnormal amounts of porphobilinogen accumulate in the liver and are periodically discharged. The metabolic block which produces this accumulation is unknown. In the course of an acute attack the patient suffers from severe intestinal colic, widespread muscular paralyses and mental confusion.

The genetics of acute porphyria has been studied by Waldenström.[46] It seems clear that the inheritance is dominant. Affected subjects are heterozygous for a gene which is not always fully manifested. The frequency of the disease in Sweden is of the order of 1 in 60,000 though in some northern districts it is much commoner than this. Females are more often affected than males.

Another condition in which neurological signs are only temporary is Hartnup disease, described by Baron, Dent, Harris, Hart and Jepson.[47] The chief manifestation is multiple aminoaciduria, which is renal in origin since there are no detectable abnormalities in the blood aminoacid concentrations. Large quantities of indolylacetic acid and indolylacetyl glutamine are excreted in the urine. No consistent hypothesis has been found to explain all the peculiarities but there are some similarities to pellagra. Neurological symptoms appear in the form of ataxia together with mental confusion if a patient is exposed to sunlight and, at the same time, the exposed skin surfaces, face, neck, arms and legs, develop an extensive scaly rash. Some improvement has been obtained by administering nicotinamide.

The hereditary basis of the condition is almost certainly recessive. No relevant abnormalities have been found in heterozygous normal carriers.

MISCELLANEOUS CONDITIONS

Among the less well understood examples of hereditary metabolic error are the conditions in which there is disturbance of lipoid metabolism. When the anomaly affects the brain cells there is serious interference with mental function. In the infantile form of amaurotic idiocy the child appears normal at birth but, in a few months, becomes blind through optic atrophy; paralysis and idiocy develop and the disease is fatal within two years. This condition, first described by Tay[48] and Sachs,[49] is recessively inherited (Slome[50]). Abnormal accumulation of pre-lipoid substances (Schaffer[51]) is found in the nerve cells of the brain. Substances resembling neutral fat in their staining reactions are found within and also between the cells. No biochemical abnormalities have been noticed in the urine, blood or cerebrospinal fluid.

The infantile form of the disease is exceedingly rare; it is not confined to Jewish populations, as was formerly believed, but occasionally occurs among other Europeans and among Asiatics (Komai[52]). The juvenile type is not so rare and is less confined to local populations. Sjögren[53] analysed the Swedish cases which had a population incidence of one in 40,000, and demonstrated that the cause was a recessive trait. The progress of this form of the disease, beginning at about 6 years, is parallel to but slower than that in the infantile type, lasting from five to ten years. Retinal degeneration with pigmentation is a notable additional feature. Congenital, late infantile and adult forms of amaurotic idiocy have also been described, though it is doubtful whether they are all separate diseases.

Gargoylism is the name given to a dystrophic condition first described by Hunter[54] and Hurler.[55] In consequence of an inborn metabolic error, the skeleton gradually becomes deformed, especially the skull, spine and digits. Stature is dwarfed and the face is coarsened. The liver and spleen enlarge. There is usually severe mental retardation which may progress. Genetically there are two types, one with autosomal recessive inheritance and the other sex-linked and confined to males. In the recessive type, the eyes show corneal opacities (Lamy, Maroteaux and Bader[56]). As in the amaurotic idiocies, cerebral nerve cells are found to contain lipoid substances and Jervis[57] found their staining reactions indistinguishable. Thannhauser[58] suggests that the fault is in enzymes which normally convert one high lipoid into another. However, in gargoylism there is a distinguishing feature, namely the urinary excretion of mucopolysaccharides (Muir[59]). Vacuoles seen in lymphocytes and in the cells of enlarged organs, such as liver and spleen, are believed to contain polysaccharides also.

A remarkable disease, studied by Lowe, Terrey and MacLachlan,[60] is known as the oculo-cerebro-renal syndrome. Here the critical phenomenon is proteinuria which can be present very soon after birth. The infant does not thrive and remains dwarfed, physically feeble and mentally retarded. Cataract with glaucoma is an accompanying symptom. The primary lesion, as in Hartnup disease, is thought to be situated in the kidney tubules. The disease is sex-linked and confined to males. Females who carry the gene can be detected by ophthalmological examination (Donnell[61]).

Another inherited disease deserving notice in the present context is congenital methaemoglobinaemia. Examination of the pedigrees suggests recessive inheritance. The missing factor is an accessory co-enzyme necessary for methaemoglobin reduction in the red blood cells, as shown by Gibson.[62] Sufferers are noticeable on account of their blue complexions. Sometimes, but by no means always, they may be imbeciles (Hitzenberger[63]). Good therapeutic results have been reported, in so far as the methaemoglobinaemia is concerned, by administering excess of ascorbic acid. Unfortunately this treatment appears to have no effect on the mental functioning.

Yet another relevant finding, by Richards and Rundle,[64] was of a family in which severe mental deficiency was associated with excretion of abnormal ketosteroids in four sibs. Other symptoms were sexual infantilism, ataxia and deafness. The inheritance was probably recessive.

COMMON MENTAL DISEASES

The contribution of inborn metabolic errors to mental illness, if judged by the examples of the known rare diseases, may appear, at first glance, relatively insignificant. There are, however, some important hereditary diseases which cause mental illness and which may eventually be shown to be due to metabolic errors. The most striking example is Huntington's chorea, which is due to a heterozygous dominant gene. Degenerative changes in the cerebral cortex and basal ganglia begin gradually at about the age of 35 years and psychotic mental deterioration is a usual accompaniment. Another example is the presenile psychosis, described first by Alzheimer, in which there is progressive cortical atrophy: the disposition appears to be due to a dominant factor (Schottky[65]) but, since the onset is late in life, familial incidence often escapes notice. Although the bulk of cases of mental illness is not attributable to inborn metabolic error, the study of rare disease can sometimes point the way towards the elucidation of commoner problems.

Sometimes an inborn error only gives rise to symptoms under special conditions or stresses. Any inherited dispositions likely to be causal factors in the commoner psychoses, such as schizophrenia and manic depressive disease, probably must be of this type. In these common conditions, irregularities in the functional aspects of biochemistry are found but not, as yet, any constant peculiarities of metabolism. Typical of such findings are, for example, the abnormal blood sugar levels (McCowan and Quastel[66]), which have been sometimes attributed to the presence of anti-insulin substances (Meduna[67]). Abnormal proportions of androgens and estrogens in the urine have been demonstrated by Hoskins and Pincus[68] and peculiarities in serum concentration of choline esterase (Richter and Lee[69]). It is to be expected that eventually some of these abnormalities may be traced back to more constant biochemical dispositions, which, though not necessarily harmful in themselves, at times may give rise to severe disturbances.

REFERENCES

1. GARROD, A. B.: Med.-chir. Tr. London, 31:83 (1848).
2. GARROD, A. E.: Lancet, 2:1616 (1902).
3. GARROD, A. E.: Inborn Errors of Metabolism, 2nd Ed. London, Hodder & Stoughton (1923).
4. KALOW, W. and GUNN, D. R.: Ann. Hum. Genet., London, 23:239 (1958).
5. FÖLLING, A.: Hoppe-Seyler's Ztschr. physiol. Chem., 227:169 (1934).
6. COWIE, V. A.: Lancet, 1:272 (1951).
7. JERVIS, G. A.: Arch. Neurol. & Psychiat., 38:944 (1937).
8. PENROSE, L. S.: Lancet, 1:23; 2:192 (1935).
9. FÖLLING, A., MOHR, O. and RUUD, L.: Norsk. Videnskaps-Akad. i Oslo, Mat.-Naturv. Klasse, 13: (1945).
10. JERVIS, G. A.: J. Ment. Sc., 85:719 (1939).
11. MUNRO, T. A.: Ann. Eugenics, London, 14:60 (1947).

12. THOMPSON, J. H.: *J. Ment. Defic. Res., 1*:67 (1957).
13. COWIE, V. A. and PENROSE, L. S.: *Ann. Eugenics, 15*:297 (1951).
14. JERVIS, G. A.: *Proc. Soc. Exper. Biol. & Med., 75*:83 (1950).
15. PENROSE, L. S.: *Lancet, 1*:572 (1939).
16. COQUET, M., MYLE, G., NYSSEN, R. and VAN BOGAERT, L.: *Monatsschr. Psychiat. u. Neurol., 109*:133 (1944).
17. CROME, L. and PARE, C. M. B.: *J. Ment. Sc., 106*:862 (1960).
18. DELAY, J., PICHOT, P., DESGREZ, P. and DELBARRE, F.: *Semaine hôp., Paris, 23*:1749 (1947).
19. COWIE, V. A.: *J. Ment. Sc., 96*:799 (1950).
20. PENROSE, L. S. and QUASTEL, J. H.: *Biochem. J., 31*:266 (1937).
21. KREBS, H. A.: *Ztschr. physiol. Chem., 217*:191; *218*:157 (1933).
22. FÖLLING, A. and CLOSS, K.: *Hoppe-Seyler's Ztschr. physiol. Chem., 254*:115 (1938).
23. JERVIS, G. A.: *J. Biol. Chem., 126*:305 (1938).
24. PRESCOTT, B. A., BOREK, E., BRECHER, A. and WAELSCH, H.: *J. Biol. Chem., 181*:273 (1949).
25. EMBDEN, G. and BALDES, K.: *Biochem. Ztschr., 55*:301 (1913).
26. JERVIS, G. A.: *J. Biol. Chem., 169*:651 (1947).
27. MITOMA, C., AULD, R. M. and UDENFRIEND, S.: *Proc. Soc. Exper. Biol. & Med., 94*:634 (1957).
28. ARMSTRONG, M. D. and TYLER, F. H.: *J. Clin. Invest., 34*:565 (1955).
29. HSIA, D. Y.-Y., DRISCOLL, K., TROLL, W. and KNOX, W. E.: *Nature,* London, *178*:1239 (1956).
30. HSIA, D. Y.-Y.: *Postgraduate Med., 22*:203 (1957).
31. RENWICK, J. H., LAWLER, S. D. and COWIE, V. A.: *Am. J. Hum. Genet., 12*:287 (1960).
32. WOOLF, L. I., GRIFFITHS, R., MONCRIEFF, A., COATES, S. and DILLISTONE, F.: *Arch. Dis. Childhood, 33*:31 (1958).
33. ALLAN, J. D., CUSWORTH, D. C., DENT, C. E. and WILSON, V. K.: *Lancet, 1*:182 (1958).
34. WESTALL, R. G.: *Biochem. J., 77*:135 (1960).
35. HARRIS, H., PENROSE, L. S. and THOMAS, D. H. H.: *Ann. Hum. Genet.,* London, *23*:442 (1959).
36. MENKES, J. H., HURST, P. L. and CRAIG, J. M.: *Pediatrics, 14*:462 (1954).
37. WESTALL, R. G., DANCIS, J. and MILLER, S.: *A.M.A. J. Dis. Child., 94*:571 (1957).
38. SCHWARZ, V., GOLDBERG, L., KOMROWER, G. M. and HOLZEL, A.: *Biochem. J., 62*:34 (1956).
39. ISSELBACHER, K. J., ANDERSON, E. P., KURAHASHI, K. and KALCKAR, H. M.: *Science, 123*:635 (1956).
40. HOLZEL, A. and KOMROWER, G. M.: *Arch. Dis. Childhood, 30*:155 (1955).
41. KIRKMAN, H. N.: *Ann. Hum. Genet.,* London, *23*:117 (1959).
42. WILSON, S. A. K.: *Brain, 34*:295 (1912).
43. SCHIENBERG, I. H. and GITLIN, D.: *Science, 116*:484 (1952).
44. HOLMBERG, C. G. and LAURELL, C. B.: *Acta chem. scandinav., 2*:550 (1948).
45. BEARN, A. G.: *Ann. Hum. Genet.,* London, *24*:33 (1960).
46. WALDENSTRÖM, J.: *Acta genet., 6*:122 (1956).
47. BARON, D. N., DENT, C. E., HARRIS, H., HART, E. W. and JEPSON, J. B.: *Lancet, 2*:421 (1956).
48. TAY, W.: *Tr. Ophth. Soc. U. Kingdom, 1*:55 (1881).
49. SACHS, B.: *J. Nerv. & Ment. Dis., 14*:541 (1887).
50. SLOME, D.: *J. Genet., 27*:363 (1933).

51. SCHAFFER, C.: *Arch. Neurol. & Psychiat., 14:*731 (1925).
52. KOMAI, T.: *Pedigrees of Hereditary Diseases.* Kyoto, Japan (1934).
53. SJÖGREN, T.: *Die juvenile amaurotische Idiotie.* Lund, Berlingska Boktryckeriet (1931).
54. HUNTER, C.: *Proc. Roy. Soc. Med., 10:*104 (1917).
55. HURLER, G.: *Ztschr. Kinderh., 24:*220 (1920).
56. LAMY, M., MAROTEAUX, P. and BADER, J. P.: *J. génét. hum., 6:*156 (1957).
57. JERVIS, G. A.: *Arch. Neurol. & Psychiat., 47:*943 (1942).
58. THANNHAUSER, S. J.: *Lipidoses.* Oxford Med. Pub. (1950).
59. MUIR, H.: Personal communication (1960).
60. LOWE, C. U., TERREY, M. and MACLACHLAN, E. A.: *Am. J. Dis. Child., 83:*164 (1952).
61. DONNELL, G. N.: *Proc. Roy. Soc. Med., 54:* (April 1861).
62. GIBSON, Q. H.: *Biochem. J., 42:*13 (1948).
63. HITZENBERGER, K.: *Wien. Arch. inn. Med., 50:*574 (1933).
64. RICHARDS, B. W. and RUNDLE, A. T.: *J. Ment. Defic. Res. 3:*33 (1959).
65. SCHOTTKY, J.: *Ztschr. Ges. Neurol. u. Psychiat., 140:*333 (1932).
66. McCOWAN, P. K. and QUASTEL, J. H.: *J. Ment. Sc., 77:*525 (1931).
67. MEDUNA, L.: *Actualités scientifiques et industrielles, 1099:*135 (1950).
68. HOSKINS, R. G. and PINCUS, G.: *Psychosom. Med., 9:*102 (1949).
69. RICHTER, D. and LEE, M. H.: *J. Ment. Sc., 88:*1 (1942).

XLI

BIOCHEMICAL ABNORMALITIES IN MENTAL DISEASES

T. L. SOURKES

INTRODUCTION

PROGRESS IN the treatment of mental diseases has been much more rapid than the growth of understanding of their etiology. The last 25 years have witnessed the introduction of useful physical and drug therapies for the psychoses, but there is no clearer picture today than many decades ago of the factors at the root of these distressing illnesses. Organically oriented schools have advanced the working hypothesis that in mental diseases abnormal biochemical processes are at work leading to the formation of a cerebrotoxic principle, by a defectively functioning liver or other organ, and ultimately upsetting the metabolic machinery of the brain. However, anyone looking into the pertinent literature on this subject will be struck by the conflicting results obtained with apparently similar groups of patients. McIlwain[1] has described how disagreements between investigators may arise through inadequate sampling of the population and through insufficient dietary and drug controls. Horwitt[2] has listed emotional stress, dietary condition, state of hepatic function, training and diurnal variation as factors which are most frequently uncontrolled, although they are among those known to affect biochemical and physiological results. Infections with Endamoeba histolytica may be added to this list.[3] One of the important sources of disagreement can probably be attributed to differences in the patient material studied, i.e., in the diagnostic labels employed.

In the past (and still not infrequently) it has been the practice to sample generously from the population of the mental hospital by carrying out the standard tests available in the clinical laboratory. Lately, many specialized tests have been introduced into psychiatric research. The voluminous literature which has resulted from all this effort has been compiled on many occasions since Rudolf Allers[4] dis-

990

cussed the subject in 1910 (see refs. 5-11). In spite of the many data which have accumulated and the enthusiasm occasionally expressed about their significance for psychiatry, it is not possible to write a chemical description of any of the major endogenous psychoses which will assist in differential diagnosis. Nor has any biochemical defect been found the correction of which initiates the return to a state of clinical normality. Nevertheless, there are abnormalities of a biochemical nature found among certain groups of mental patients, and these presage important contributions by biochemistry to psychiatry. Among these abnormalities are alterations in chromosomal structure which constitute the basis of some hereditary diseases carrying the stigma of mental or neurological defect. Their study is currently being pursued very actively and represents a flowering of the work begun by Garrod concerning the "inborn errors of metabolism". Phenylketonuria is an outstanding example of this group, and one whose clinical management has profited from advancing knowledge of intermediary metabolic processes. With improved methods of examining chromosomes some diseases have been recognized as stemming from an increase or decrease in the chromosomal count. In the present context the extra chromosome (47 as against a normal 46) in mongolian idiocy is of great interest for it certifies that mental deficiency may arise not only with a single molecular change in the chromosome, as in phenylketonuria, but also with a gross change in the number of chromosomes.

Other biochemical abnormalities are represented by changes in function of an endocrine gland. Dietary factors are usually considered as being environmental and as acting upon an equilibrated internal environment, but the capacity of the body for adaptive changes goes well beyond this static concept. For example, the dietary history of an individual affects his response in the glucose absorption test and his sensitivity to insulin. Vitamin deficiency (external influence of a negative character) may also lead to mental and neurological disturbance as in the encephalopathies of nicotinic acid and of vitamin B_{12} deficiencies. It is therefore important to keep in mind that in a clinical context over- or underconcentration of a metabolite is a resultant of many influences: hormonal, dietary, metabolic, genetic, and others.

A characteristic of mental patients, especially of schizophrenics, is their great variability in many biochemical measurements as compared with the control population. According to some the variability reflects a "failure" in homeostatic control; but this merely states that under- or overactivity in a given function occurs more frequently in a psychotic population than in a normal one. To other investigators the overlapping of clinical subcategories, whose differential diagnosis within the "schizophrenias" has not yet been elaborated, gives rise to the broad, flat distribution curve. When the guide-lines have been developed and it is possible to define the subcategories, then—on this view—several groups will crystallize representing normal, decreased, and increased biochemical function.

CARBOHYDRATE METABOLISM

A. Sugar Tolerance Tests

Tests of carbohydrate tolerance havs been extensively used in the study of mental patients for a half-century; unfortunately, their application in psychiatry has been repetitive beyond the requirements of scientific confirmation. Low tolerance has been observed in catatonia,[12] in the depressive phase of manic-depressive psychosis,[12-15] In endogenous depression,[16,17] and in schizophrenia.[12,14,16] In manic cases glucose tolerance is high;[12,13,16] in the psychoneuroses it is normal.[12] A broad correlation exists between test results and clinical state in longitudinal studies: as health improves the tolerance curve returns toward normal.[13,15,18,19]

The above statement paraphrases the summary presented by S. A. Mann as long ago as 1925; the numerous later investigations have not affected his conclusions. He wrote that the blood-sugar curves "may be just one expression of a general causative disordered metabolism," investigation of which might lead to the discovery of other important metabolic defects.[18] Some of the metabolic factors affecting sugar tolerance have been analyzed since then. For example, the rate of intestinal absorption of the sugar, which is difficult to investigate *in vivo,* can be eliminated from consideration by administering the glucose intravenously. The conflicting results obtained in such studies indicate that changes in the intestinal epithelium resulting in delayed absorption of sugar into the portal circulation remain a possibility, but that their occurrence is not sufficiently consistent to explain the abnormality in carbohydrate metabolism. Hormonal imbalances have also been investigated in this connection. Freeman[20] and others[21,22] have observed a smaller response to insulin than normal in mental patients, but the degree of hypoglycemia bears no relation to the diagnosis. It is noteworthy that the insulin resistance may disappear after the patients have been placed on a high-carbohydrate diet.[22] Glucose tolerance is also reduced in patients consuming low-carbohydrate diets, and improves when the carbohydrate content of the diet is increased. The dietary history of the patient is so influential that mere repetition of the oral glucose tolerance curve may improve the results. There is also the possibility that insulin resistance in some mental patients arises from the presence of a contra-insulin factor in the serum in greater than normal amounts. Many of these contra-insulins have now been described, including one in the blood serum[23] and another in the urine[24] of some psychotic patients.

Disturbances in sugar metabolism may reflect more fundamental changes in the autonomic nervous system, as suggested by Diethelm[25] and Gellhorn.[26] Freeman and Elmadjian[27] have pointed out the influence of psychological tension in lowering tolerance.

Some investigators have suggested that a defect exists at an intermediary stage of the metabolism of glucose, causing a delay in its removal from the blood or defective breakdown in the tissues. Reports that blood lactic acid tends to be elevated in psychotic patients[28,29] fit in with this hypothesis. As the elevation is particularly marked after physical exercise the "defect" may be merely a function of (lack of) training. α-Ketoglutaric acid has also been measured in the plasma of fasting subjects,[28,30] but great individual variation precludes detecting any difference associated with mental illness. Acetoin is said to be elevated in the blood of manic-depressive patients, but normal in psychoneurotics.[31] Finally, there is a report that phosphoglycollic acid occurs in the erythrocytes of schizophrenic subjects in supranormal amounts.[32] These findings require confirmation.

B. Neuraminic Acid

Neuraminic acid occurs in the acylated form in serum and cerebrospinal fluid (C.S.F.). In the brain (and other organs) it occurs as a component of the high-molecular weight gangliosides. The gangliosides may help in exchange of nutrients across the blood-brain barrier.[33] Bogoch claims that schizophrenic subjects have a lower content of neuraminic acid in C.S.F. than non-schizophrenic adults; he thinks this may represent a lack of maturation in the development of the blood-brain barrier. Others have not stressed this abnormality in the neuraminic acid level.[34]

LIPID METABOLISM

A. Non-esterified Fatty Acids

Psychophysiological studies have shown that the non-esterified fatty acids of the plasma, now considered to be the pre-eminent transport form of fat, respond rapidly during emotional stress. The concentration of the non-esterified fatty acids (but not of triglycerides) in the serum rises during interviews directed at arousing anxiety, hostility, or fear.[35]

B. Cholesterol

Serum cholesterol was one of the first lipids to be studied in patients with mental disease. As an index of thyroid function it was expected to reveal metabolic deviations from normal. However, there is no characteristic change in schizophrenia,[5,36] although the cholesterol level may undergo rapid diurnal variations.[37] Nevertheless, a number of investigators are convinced that cholesterol tends to the low side in schizophrenia.[38] Manic-depressive cases often show hypercholesterol-emia.[38]

There has been great interest in the relationship between serum cholesterol levels and coronary artery disease, and also between both of these and personality types. In this respect the mean serum cholesterol is much higher in men exhibiting "a behavior pattern primarily characterized by intense ambition, competitive 'drive,' constant preoccupation with occupational 'deadlines,' and a sense of time urgency" than in a group showing the converse pattern.[39] The "stress" of university examinations also serves to elevate cholesterol.[40]

C. Serum Lipoproteins

Ultracentrifugal studies of the serum obtained from schizophrenic patients have revealed some small abnormalities in the high-density lipoproteins. Those with a mean density of 1.075 gm./ml. are present in significantly higher concentration in schizophrenic males of the 30 to 49 year age group than in a normal group. Serum lipoproteins of density 1.145 gm./ml. are somewhat lower in the schizophrenics.[41]

METABOLISM OF NITROGENOUS CONSTITUENTS

Serum non-protein nitrogen, uric acid and urea, and urinary urea, creatinine, and ammonia all appear to be normal in mental diseases. L. Gjessing and his colleagues have reported changes in the concentration of certain amino acids in serum during the catatonic phase of periodic catatonia.[42] Some quantitative abnormalities have been observed in the amino acids of C.S.F. of patients with psychoses, but these changes are non-specific to the diseases mentioned.[43]

A. Aromatic Amino Acids

The quest for constituents of the body fluids characteristic of schizophrenic patients has frequently turned to the metabolism of phenylalanine, tyrosine, tryptophan and histidine. This work has been reviewed by McGeer et al.,[44] who have remarked upon the frequent reports of high titers of aromatic metabolites in the urine and blood of schizophrenic subjects. Unfortunately, the literature abounds in "differences" between normals and schizophrenics—differences which are later dissipated when a larger series is studied or when ulterior factors actually responsible are discovered. For example, in one study, a high proportion of urines of schizophrenic patients gave a positive "cold" Millon's test, in contrast to normal urines. Later the chromogen proved to be indoxyl sulfate, and the reason for its frequent presence in the urine of schizophrenics was attributable to the reduced intestinal mobility common in the schizophrenic group and, therefore, to prolonged bacterial action upon dietary tryptophan.[45] Similarly, the material giving a positive Hopkins-Cole glyoxylic acid reaction in the urines of schizophrenics[46] (and thought to be associated with the disease) has now been shown to be present in these urines inconstantly.[47] Furthermore, its presence there is quite unrelated to schizophrenia, for the examination of a larger series of patients has revealed that positive results are obtained in other psychoses, in epilepsy, and in various non-mental illnesses.[48,49] The need for the utmost caution in drawing conclusions from these tests is illustrated by the finding that patients receiving chlorpromazine excrete a chromogen giving the Hopkins-Cole reation.[48]

The suggestion that schizophrenics are defective in their metabolism of tryptophan has been tested in several laboratories, but the results have been contradictory. Lauer et al.[50] observed an increase in the excretion of 5-hydroxyindoleacetic acid in their normal, but not in their schizophrenic, group of subjects after giving tryptophan. Banerjee and Agarwal got precisely the opposite results.[51] Others have found no difference between the two groups.[52] There is agreement, however, that schizophrenics excrete normal amounts of endogenous 5-hydroxyindoleacetic acid in the urine. Price et al. have observed an abnormal pattern of urinary metabolites of the kynurenine pathway in some schizophrenics given the tryptophan load test.[53] Brown et al. did not find this, but noted that their patients excreted less of a nicotinamide metabolite than the controls did.[54] The difference was abolished by a tryptophan supplement. This may signify that the schizophrenic subjects examined had a relative dietary deficiency of nicotinic acid, tryptophan, or both.

Many investigations of aromatic metabolites in mental diseases have been prompted by the report of Young et al.[55] that the urines of schizophrenics contain increased amounts of diazo coupling substances, as estimated from paper chromatograms. This has been confirmed,[56] and has also been claimed for other body fluids.[57] Results of this nature, suggestive as they are, have proven to be of limited value, for they are poorly quantitated and give no indication of what or how many substances are involved. With more refined fractionation and chromatographic procedures some authors have found the differences between the urines of normal persons and schizophrenic patients to disappear.[58] In one study the "abnormalities" detected by paper chromatographic comparisons were attributable to the excretion of coffee metabolites by the patient group which, unlike the controls, happened to include some coffee drinkers.[59]

Felix introduced a liver function test based upon the ability to metabolize *p*-hydroxyphenylpyruvic acid. Defective metabolism, attributed to hepatic dysfunction, was found to occur in manic-depressive psychosis, reactive depression, and maniacal states;[60] as clinical improvement occurred the test results approach normal.[61]

B. Glutamic Acid and Glutathione

Because of the central role of glutamic acid in amino acid metabolism of the brain and because of its reputed efficacy in some neurological conditions there has been an interest in its metabolism in mental diseases. Foss found normal amounts of glutamic acid and glutamine in the urine of schizophrenic patients.[62] In schizophrenia and in some other mental disorders the level of glutamic acid in the plasma is reported to be below normal, with a somewhat elevated plasma glutamine concentration.[63]

In 1934 Looney and Childs reported that the glutathione concentration in venous blood is slightly lower (about 10%) in schizophrenics than in normals.[64] A significant difference of this type could signify a defect in some oxidative system associated with schizophrenia. Since then many studies have dealt with this important catalyst. They show that the difference is small and not statistically significant,[29,65,66] or non-existent.[67] Persky states that after severe psychological stress the reduced glutathione of the blood is decreased.[68]

C. Glycine

Quick's hippuric acid test of liver function measures several metabolic activities, among them the ability of the body to mobilize or to synthesize glycine (or both), to form coenzyme A, and to conjugate glycine with the proffered benzoic acid. The test assumes that the only important metabolite of benzoic acid in the doses used is the glycine conjugate. However, it is known that the glucuronide is formed also under some conditions. Abnormal results are found not only in patients with impaired liver function but also in some anemias and malignancies.[69]

The test was introduced into psychiatric research in 1938 by Quastel and Wales, who found that catatonic schizophrenics excrete subnormal amounts of hippuric acid[70] (cf. also ref. 71). The most severe impairment is in chronic schizophrenic patients. In hebephrenic and paranoid cases hippuric acid excretion is higher, but still subnormal. Manic patients have normal values. Persky et al.[72] have noted a parallelism between the rate of hippuric acid excretion and the degree of "free anxiety."

Hippuric acid excretion is poorly correlated with body weight and with physical activity, but may be related to liver weight. If so, the reputedly lower liver weights in schizophrenics would bias the result in favor of reduced hippuric acid excretion. Some authors have denied the reported relation between the Quick test and mental diseases.[73]

Abnormal test results have been corrected by giving the patient a supplement of glycine.[74] Hence, the impairment, when observed, may lie in a deficient mobilization of glycine by the liver for the "detoxication" of benzoic acid.

D. Serum Protein Flocculation Tests

Changes in serum proteins, as revealed by flocculation and turbidity tests, may reveal underlying hepatic dysfunction. In the exploration of liver-brain relationships many of these tests have been performed, e.g., cephalin-cholesterol flocculation, erythrocyte sedimentation, Takata-Ara, Wunderly-Wuhrmann, thymol turbidity, and others. Each test indicates somewhat different changes, and therefore a given serum does not prove to be uniformly positive with all tests. Buscaino[9] has reviewed much of the work done with these tests in mental diseases; he concludes that the frequently positive test results point to the role of hepatic dysfunction in the etiology of schizophrenia. Serum protein tests are highly empirical and have often been performed in psychiatric research without the necessary controls. Electrophoretic methods yield more precise information about these proteins, and may yet lead to description of specific changes in mental disease.

ENDOCRINE FUNCTION

A. Thyroid Gland

There have been extensive studies on thyroid function in mental disease. Some authors suggest that metabolism is sluggish in schizophrenic patients. Extensive metabolic and endocrine investigations of mental patients led Hoskins[6] to describe a low-grade hypothyroidism in many schizophrenic patients; a course of thyroid therapy was frequently of value in this condition. In addition he noted an unusually high tolerance to thyroid hormone in schizophrenia. This resistance has not been explained; it is conceivable that such patients have a partial metabolic block in the deiodination of thyroid hormone to the iodo-organic derivative which acts at the subcellular level.

Actually, there is rather little evidence for defective thyroid function in the major psychoses. Bowman *et al.* found normal levels of serum protein-bound iodine in mental patients.[75] Within the schizophrenic group the paranoid cases were above the mean value and the catatonics below, but all were within the normal range. Manic depressives and psychoneurotics, too, showed normal values. In this study other tests also indicated normal thyroid function in 71 mental patients: B.M.R., rate of uptake of radioactive iodine, and plasma cholesterol concentration. Reiss *et al.* have determined the radio-iodine uptake rate in mental patients.[76] About one-fifth of their cases fell outside the normal limits, but many of these were judged to be euthyroid upon clinical examination. Thyroidal and psychiatric states were not correlated.

There is a small number of mental patients in whom thyroid function is clearly deficient, as judged from therapeutic tests. Among these are myxedematous cases, whose psychosis as well as physical manifestations of hypothyroidism can be treated successfully with thyroid preparations.[77] Another condition which responds to thyroid therapy is the periodic catatonia so intensively studied by R. Gjessing.[78] He has observed phasic changes in the nitrogen balance of certain schizophrenics which are correlated with periods of catatonic excitement (sometimes stupor) and of remission. The mode of therapeutic action of thyroid has not been satisfactorily explained. Cases of this type prove to be valuable "models" for metabolic study of mental disease.[79]

B. Sympatho-adrenal System

Within the last decade adequate chemical methods for the determination of the catecholamines have become available. It is of interest that one of these was developed by Weil-Malherbe and Bone in connection with psychiatric research. These procedures permit an unusually close approach to the functioning nervous system in humans, through assessment of a specific chemical activity of the sympathetic nervous system.

The concentrations of epinephrine and norepinephrine in the plasma have been measured in many different mental diseases. These levels are within the normal range for the psychoses and neuroses.[80,81] The concentration of epinephrine, however, is subnormal in the oligophrenias.[80] Because of the very small amount of catecholamines in plasma and the difficulties attending their estimation, many investigators have turned to urinary determinations.

Urinary catecholamine studies show that notable deviations from normal occur in manic and depressed states but that the values found in schizophrenics are generally in the normal range. The excretion of epinephrine and norepinephrine is higher during the manic phase of manic-depressive psychosis than during the depressive phase; the rate of excretion of dopamine is more variable and does not show a consistent difference between the two phases.[82] Similarly, manic patients show a higher rate of excretion of epinephrine and norepinephrine than those suffering from endogenous depression.[82,83] In the insulin-response test the manic group excrete large amounts of epinephrine above the normal; the depressed patients give very weak responses, significantly lower than those found in healthy persons.[83] Not all depressives excrete low or normal quantities of the catecholamines; the minority who excrete large amounts tend to be further differentiated by their poor therapeutic response to electroshock therapy.[84]

Epinephrine excretion is normal in chronic schizophrenics but elevated in the acute cases; the latter show a poor response (epinephrine output) to insulin administration.[83] Very low rates of excretion of epinephrine are found in patients with senile dementia and with mongolism, but the urinary catecholamines are normal in the phenylketonuric group.[83]

Despite the differential secretion of epinephrine and norepinephrine the amounts of these excreted in the urine over the 24-hour period are correlated significantly (coefficient of correlation, about 0.5) in mental patients and in patients under special stress, just as in normal persons.[85]

Following upon Cannon's description of the role of the sympathetic nervous system in emotional expression some investigators have sought to achieve chemical characterization of the emotions by determining catecholamine levels, taken as a rough function of the amounts secreted at nerve endings and from the adrenal medullary cells. A study by Regan and Reilly[86] shows the difficulties in trying, at present, to establish relationships between changes in concentration of plasma catecholamines and emotional change, for the amine levels are relatively constant, with some tendency to increase in states of greater "emotional rating." Elmadjian *et al.* have concluded from studies of players in competitive sports and of normal persons and psychiatric patients that aggressive emotional displays are associated with the excretion of increased amounts of norepinephrine, whereas the passive type of display is associated with release of epinephrine.[87] These studies are a current development of the past attempts to describe emotional stress in physiological terms. One of the more recent and better known examples of this effort is the "Funkenstein test," in which pressor responses to intravenously injected methacholine and to epine-phrine are observed.[88] Indeed, evidence from studies of urinary cate-cholamines has been offered in partial substantiation of the physiologi-cal basis claimed for the Funkenstein test,[89] but conflicting reports about this test leave its status in clinical evaluation indefinite.[90] In this connection it may be necessary to heed Gellhorn's warning[26] that physiological investigation has already demonstrated "how much more complex the 'downward discharge' (from hypothalamus to viscera and skeletal muscle) is than Cannon assumed it to be. Indeed, there are few physiological—i.e., reversible—reactions of the organism which in-volve as many organs and systems and as profound changes as are seen in emotion."

Another kind of study of the catecholamines in mental patients has to do with the action of plasma upon epinephrine. According to some authors[66,91] the plasma of schizophrenic patients oxidizes added epine-phrine more rapidly than does normal plasma; high concentrations of epinephrine relative to the native antioxidants of the plasma are re-quired to demonstrate this effect. But under physiological conditions epinephrine and norepinephrine are stable in the plasma, and the plasma of schizophrenic persons does not differ in this respect from normal.[92]

C. Adrenal Cortex

Because of the role of the adrenal cortex in the body's response to stress this gland has received a great deal of attention from those interested in psychiatric research. Does a stress operating in the pre-psychotic state initiate endogenous changes in the same way as they are evoked by some physical agent? The evidence required to answer this question is not decisive. Hoagland and his collaborators found that schizophrenics excrete a smaller amount of cortical hormone under resting conditions in the morning hours than do normal per-sons.[93] The difference may be simply a diurnal one for the output of 17-hydroxycorticosteroids in the 24-hour urine is normal.[94] Plasma levels of cortisol are the same in the two groups.[95] Urinary 17-keto-steroids tend to be elevated in schizophrenic patients.[93,96]

Tests of responsiveness of the anterior pituitary-adrenal cortical axis in schizophrenics (through the injection of corticotropin, pyrogen, or insulin) yield normal increases in the concentration of cortisol in plasma. Psychoneurotics over-react to corticotropin in contrast to nor-mals, schizophrenics, and depressive patients;[97] this is true also in anxiety states.[98]

There is much evidence for involvement of the adrenal cortex in the physiological concomitants of emotional experience. In situations eliciting strong emotional expression, as in competive sports and surgery and in emotional disturbances, glandular activity is stimulated as judged by an increased level of adrenal cortical hormone in the plasma, and of the hormone and its metabolites in the urine.[99] Anxiety arising from life situations[100] or induced experimentally[101] also causes an increase in adrenal cortical activity. Plasma cortisol levels are above normal in maniacal patients and in those anticipating electroshock therapy.[101] Persky claims that anxious persons metabolize exogenous cortisol significantly faster than do normals, and excrete less of it.[102]

Aldosterone secretion is also increased in anxiety.[103]

INORGANIC CONSTITUENTS
A. Bulk Cations

Several studies attest to the presence of normal concentrations of sodium, potassium, and chloride in the blood serum and cerebral tissue of schizophrenic patients. Harris and Sonnenblick claim that the calcium: magnesium ratio of the C.S.F. is upset in the psychoses.[104]

Crammer[105] has drawn attention to the rapid shifts in body weight which occur in certain mental patients; he attributes these swings to alterations in salt and water metabolism.

B. Copper

The concentration of serum copper rises during pregnancy, infections, some blood dyscrasias, hemochromatosis, and cirrhosis. Some have reported it to be elevated also in schizophrenia.[106] Scheinberg *et al.* found a mean elevation of 17% in the concentration of ceruloplasmin, the predominant form of plasma copper, in a group of schizophrenics; but some of the individual values fell within the normal range.[107] Studies on the ceruloplasmin content of the serum have been carried out in many centers as a result of the renewed claim in 1957 that this cuproprotein, as estimated by the rate of oxidation of N,N-dimethyl-*p*-phenylenediamine by serum in vitro, is elevated above normal in serum drawn from schizophrenics.[108] Through carefully controlled investigations[109] the observed differences have for the most part been attributed to the low ascorbic acid content of institutional diets. Holmberg, one of the discoverers of ceruloplasmin and of its oxidase properties, states that he is "still far from convinced that quantitative or qualitative alterations in ceruloplasmin have anything to do with the development of schizophrenia."[110]

C. Magnesium

Serum magnesium is within normal limits in many diseases of the

nervous system,[111] but together with erythrocyte magnesium, it tends
to be low in delirium tremens.[112] This appears to be due to coexisting
magnesium deficiency syndrome as a result of severe alcoholism.[113]

D. Phosphate

According to Hoagland *et al.*[114] schizophrenic patients excrete inorganic phosphate at a subnormal rate. The output of phosphate following the injection of corticotropin is much greater than in normal
subjects although other urinary constituents such as 17-ketosteroids,
sodium, potassium, and uric acid do not increase as much in the schizophrenics as in the controls. Two laboratories[115] have reported reduced
turnover of phosphorylated intermediates in the erythrocytes of schizophrenics under certain conditions. On the other hand, Laity[116] has
found no abnormalities in the (whole) blood of patients in two psychiatric categories, with respect to incorporation of radioactive phosphate into the inorganic and into three organic phosphate fractions,
or in the concentration of the various phosphate fractions.

CRITIQUE OF BIOCHEMICAL RESEARCH IN PSYCHIATRY

A. The "Toxic Agent" Hypothesis

Thus far the reported positive differences between schizophrenics
and normal individuals have been presented and evaluated. It is now
necessary to look into some recently proposed general hypotheses,
which ascribe the symptomatology of mental diseases to the action of
a toxic chemical factor in the blood or C.S.F. Such views have circu-
lated for many years, but current consideration of them is undoubtedly
influenced and fortified by the new studies on hallucinogenic agents.
Many of these hypotheses have an implicit genetic orientation; the
toxic substance claimed to exist in the body fluids of psychotic patients
is presumed to arise through the action of genetically transmitted
factors and to be so determined. The hypotheses are based upon various grounds, some experimental, others obviously speculative. The
role they play in present-day psychiatric research can be gauged from
the extensive list of publications on the subject;[117] in general, these
papers describe the toxic action of some body fluid of mental patients.
Examples of the toxicity assays are: failure of growth of plant seed-
lings; death of amphibian larvae; failure of proliferation of tissues
in culture; abnormal web patterns created by spiders; abnormal behavior of rats; electrocorticographic changes in cats; death of rabbits.
These studies still await unchallenged confirmation. The criticisms
directed against them indicate that whatever in the body fluid is responsible for the reported biological activity must exert its action

under conditions which are as yet poorly comprehended and controlled.

Among the attempts to purify the presumed toxic agents is the search for an abnormal aromatic metabolite (see above) and the preparation of taraxein. Taraxein is a protein obtained by fractionation of plasma of schizophrenic patients, and said to be capable of evoking electroencephalographic changes in monkeys and (reversible) disturbances of thought and behavior in normal volunteers.[118] The animal investigative work has been repeated in another laboratory successfully[119] but the studies in man have produced inconsistent results.[120] Whether taraxein is ceruloplasmin or an altered form of this cuproprotein is not known; Heath and his colleages did not find it in normal plasma.

The cerebrotoxicity which some authors assume to be the starting-point of the pathological process in schizophrenia and other psychoses has most often been attributed to a nitrogenous constitutent. Investigators have beeen impressed with the potent pharmacological actions which many biogenic amines exert, including influences on central processes. The example of mescaline has long been available to point this up, and the discovery about twenty years ago of the hallucinogenic action of the diethylamide of lysergic acid, an alkaloid containing (among other structures) the indole ring, has been a fillip in this field. Two amines in particular have been postulated to play a role in the etiology of psychoses. These are epinephrine and 5-hydroxytryptamine (serotonin). In the case of the former the argument has run that a disordered metabolism of epinephrine leads to the accumulation of a hallucinogenic product of its oxidation: adrenochrome, adrenolutin, or some related material. The hypothesis has undergone some changes in the course of its promulgation,[121] partly because of increasing knowledge of the metabolism of epinephrine, but also because of the exigencies of negative and contrary evidence. Smythies, one of the originators of the "adrenochrome hypothesis," has lately reviewed the studies in man using the heterocyclic derivatives of epinephrine and has not been able to find satisfactory evidence for their hallucinogenic action.[122] One of the early alternatives envisaged in the hypothesis of deviant epinephrine metabolism was methylation of norepinephrine on the phenolic groups instead of the amino group. The importance of O-methylation in the metabolism of the catecholamines is now well established and some of the O-methylated derivatives have been studied pharmacologically. As yet it is not known if any of them has central action of the types already known for epinephrine, norepinephrine, and mescaline. Another metabolite, 2,4,5-trihydroxyphenylethylamine, has been identified as a minor product of the oxidation of dopamine; its resemblance to 3,4,5-trihydroxyphenylethylamine, the non-methylated progenitor of mescaline, re-commends it and its O-methylated derivatives for investigation of possi-ble central pharmacological activity.

B. Hypotheses of "Amine Imbalance"

Hypotheses centering on the cerebral metabolism of serotonin were first put forward by Woolley and Shaw[123] and by Amin et al.;[123a] they envisaged some process at work which interferes with the function of this amine in the brain or with its metabolism, so that schizophrenia, for example, may ultimately be due to a cerebral deficiency of sero-tonin. The serotonin content of the brain can be increased by admin-istration of the precursor amino acid 5-hydroxytryptophan. This has been tried clinically in cases of schizophrenia but has thus far not been found to cause any significant changes in behavior of the patients tested.[124]

Much of the evidence favoring a role for serotonin in processes of mental activity has come from studies with "psychopharmacological agents." As the action of many of these is only partially or not at all specific, one cannot decide on the strength of such experiments alone whether serotonin or another amine is involved in the etiology or the maintenance of the disturbed mental state. Nevertheless, this type of research has established the importance of cerebral amines in central processes. The depletion of tissue amines accompanying the sedative action of reserpine is now well known. Brodie has adduced evidence for the view that the sedation is more closely related to the decrease in brain serotonin than norepinephrine[125] (other amines were not measured). It can be surmised that an opposite state (excitation) may stem from a supranormal concentration of one or another amine. In-deed, excitation can be induced by the administration of dihydroxy-phenylalanine to experimental animals[126,127] and man,[128] as well as by m-tyrosine.[129] The amino acids are decarboxylated in vivo after passing into the parenchymal cells of various organs, including the brain.

The discovery of the cerebral-stimulating action of iproniazid and of its inhibitory action on monoamine oxidase (among other enzymes) has further contributed to the development of the hypothesis of amine imbalance in mental diseases. The effectiveness of iproniazid and of some other chemically related inhibitors of monoamine oxidase in the treatment of depressive illness appears to be associated with the in-creased cerebral content of amines which are ordinarily substrates for the enzyme. Use of these metabolic inhibitors may simply cause the accumulation of sufficient endogenous amine to elicit central stimulatory effects, in the same way as obtained by injection of an appropriate amino acid. Possibly the inverse situation obtains in clinical states which respond to monoamine oxidase inhibitors: (a) deficiency of amines because of a local excess of monoamine oxidase, or (b) defective binding of amines stored within the brain cells. Exceedingly little information is available on this score.

It is interesting that a-methyldihydroxyphenylalanine, an inhibitor of amino acid decarboxylation *in vitro* and *in vivo* (cf. Chp. 23), has a slight sedative action in man[130] and animals.[127] Its anti-decarboxylase action would be expected to favor a reduction in amine levels.

To summarize, there is growing evidence from studies in biochemical pharmacology of the importance of amine metabolism in cerebral activity. It is likely that catecholamines and indolylethylamines play some type of regulatory function in that respect, and, if this be the case, then their over- or underproduction would bring about changes with reverberating effects within the central nervous system, ultimately recognizable in a clinical syndrome. There are many possibilities for such imbalances in amine concentration in the brain, for even a small increase in the relative concentration of one enzyme concerned in the metabolism of an amine could lead sooner or later to significant changes. Much needed is the cooperation of neuro-anatomist and biochemist to map the distribution and relative activities of these enzymes in specific functional parts of the normal brain and of the brains of persons whose history included nervous and mental diseases. At the same time it should be kept in mind that some aromatic amines, formed in minor alternative metabolic routes and other than the well-known ones already discussed, may be important in cerebral function.

C. Conclusion

Biochemical research in psychiatry proceeds in many directions. Foremost historically has been the investigation of body fluids of mentally ill persons for some abnormality in the constituents there, after the fashion of research in other diseases. The indifferent results obtained with the major components have led to studies of organ function through biochemical tests and to studies of some of the minor constituents of the body fluids. New and specialized techniques developed for the latter are being gradually applied in psychiatric research. Thus far, no distinctive chemistry of the major psychoses has been revealed, but even the non-specific chemical and metabolic abnormalities which have been described possess an important positive aspect in indicating the organic relationship of psychiatric illness to other bodily disorders. The elaboration of some biochemical concomitants of affective experience also holds out promise for the future. Research on metabolic changes in mental illness cannot avoid recognizing the complexity of diseases of the cerebrum, in which life-experiences of the individual, developing upon the basis of his physical and genetic constitution, give rise in some as yet unknown manner to physiological disturbances and adaptations; unassuaged, these ultimately appear as mental pathology. The dramatic results with chemical agents which cause hallucinations, catatonic behavior, and disorders of thinking, and with others which allay the manifestations of mental disease have at once directed attention to the probable operation of outstanding chemical factors in mental diseases and at the same time have diverted attention from the neurophysiological investigation of these diseases. The alternative to finding a specific chemical cause or change in mental diseases is by no means simply psychological causation. What is required is physiological research, based upon neurochemical and pharmacological investigations, in alliance with clinical psychiatry.

REFERENCES

1. McILWAIN, H. M.: *Chemical Physiology and Pathology of the Mind.* London, H. K. Lewis (1955).
2. HORWITT, M. K.: *Science, 124:*429 (1956).
3. VESTERGAARD, P., ABBOTT, M. T., KLINE, N. S. and STANLEY, A. M.: *J. Clin. Exper. Psychopath., 19:*44 (1958).
4. ALLERS, R.: *J. Psychol. u. Neurol., 16:*157, 240 (1910).
5. McFARLANE, R. A. and GOLDSTEIN, H.: *Am. J. Psychiat., 93:*1073 (1937); *95:*509 (1938); *96:*21 (1939).
6. HOSKINS, R. G.: *The Biology of Schizophrenia.* New York, W. W. Norton (1946).
7. ALTSCHULE, M. D.: *Bodily Physiology in Mental and Emotional Disorders.* New York, Grune & Stratton (1953).
8. BUSCAINO, G. A.: *Acta neurol.* (Naples), *8:*475 (1953).
9. RIEBELING, C.: *Fortschr. Neurol. u. Psychiat., 22:*181 (1954); HUSZAK, I.: *Arch. Psychiat., 197:*32 (1958); KETY, S.: *Science, 129:*1528, 1590 (1959).
10. RICHTER, D. (ED.): *Schizophrenia: Somatic Aspects.* London, Pergamon (1957).
11. GEORGE, F. and MALL, G. (EDS.): *Pathophysiological Aspects of Psychoses.* Basel, Karger (1958).
12. LORENZ, W. F.: *Arch. Neurol. & Psychiat., 8:*184 (1922).
13. McCOWAN, P. K. and QUASTEL, J. H.: *Lancet, ii:*731 (1931); *J. Ment. Sc., 77:*525 (1931).
14. RAPHAEL, T. and PARSONS, J. P.: *Arch. Neurol. & Psychiat., 13:*742 (1925).
15. RAPHAEL, T., FERGUSON, W. and SEARLE, O.: *Arch. Neurol. & Psychiat., 19:*120 (1928).
16. HENRY, G. W. and MANGUM, E.: *Arch. Neurol. & Psychiat., 13:*743 (1925).
17. DRURY, K. K. and FARRAN-RIDGE, C.: *J. Ment. Sc., 71:*8 (1925).
18. MANN, S. A.: *J. Ment. Sc., 71:*443 (1925).
19. FREEMAN, H. and ZABORENKO, R. N.: *Arch. Neurol. & Psychiat., 61:*569 (1949).

20. FREEMAN, H.: *Arch. Neurol. & Psychiat.*, *56*:74 (1946).
21. LANGFELDT, G.: *Acta psychiat. et neurol. scandinav.*, Suppl. 80, 189 (1953); LINGJAERDE, P. and SKAUG, E. K.: *Ibid.*, Suppl. 136, *34*:370 (1959).
22. LINGJAERDE, O.: *Acta psychiat. et neurol. scandinav.*, Suppl. 80, 202 (1953); Suppl. 106, 302 (1956).
23. WALAAS, O., LINGJAERDE, O., LÖKEN, F. and HUNDEVADT, E.: *Scandinav. J. Clin. & Lab. Invest.*, *6*:245 (1954); HAAVALDSEN, R., LINGJAERDE, O. and WALAAS, O.: *Confinia neurol.*, *18*:270 (1958).
24. MOYA, F., DEWAR, J., MACINTOSH, M., HIRSCH, S. and TOWNSEND, R.: *Canad. J. Biochem. & Physiol.*, *36*:505 (1958).
25. DIETHELM, O.: *Arch. Neurol. & Psychiat.*, *36*:342 (1936); DIETHELM, O., DOTY, E. J. and MILHORAT, A. T.: *Ibid.*, *54*:110 (1945).
26. GELLHORN, E.: *Physiological Foundations of Neurology and Psychiatry*. Univ. Minnesota Press (1953).
27. FREEMAN, H. and ELMADJIAN, F.: *Am. J. Psychiat.*, *106*:660 (1950).
28. HENNEMAN, D. H., ALTSCHULE, M. D. and GONCZ, R. M.: *A. M. A. Arch. Int. Med.*, *94*:402 (1954).
29. EASTERDAY, O. D., FEATHERSTONE, R. M., GOTTLIEB, J. S., NUSSER, M. L. and HOGG, R. V.: *A. M. A. Arch. Neurol. & Psychiat.*, *68*:48 (1952).
30. BUSCAINO, G. A. and RAPISARDA, A.: *Acta neurol.* (Naples), *3*:251 (1948).
31. DAWSON, J., HULLIN, R. P. and POOL, A.: *J. Ment. Sc.*, *100*:536 (1954).
32. ÖRSTRÖM, A.: *Arch. Biochem. & Biophys.*, *33*:484 (1957).
33. BOGOCH, S.: *A. M. A. Arch. Neurol. & Psychiat.*, *80*:221 (1958).
34. PAPADOPOULOS, N. M., McLANE, J. E., O'DOHERTY, D. and HESS, W. C.: *J. Nerv. & Ment. Dis.*, *128*:450 (1959).
35. BOGDONOFF, M. D.: *A. M. A. Arch. Int. Med.*, *105*:505 (1960); CARDON, P. V. and GORDON, R. S.: *J. Psychosom. Res.*, *4*:5 (1959).
36. PETERS, J. P. and VAN SLYKE, D. D.: *Quantitative Clinical Chemistry: Interpretations*, 2nd Ed., Vol. I, p. 517. Baltimore, Williams & Wilkins (1946).
37. LaRUE, G. H., PAINCHAUD, C. A. and NADEAU, G.: *Canad. M. A. J.*, *82*:581 (1950); NADEAU, G. and LaRUE, G. H.: *Ibid.*, *66*:320 (1952).
38. EATON, M. T., JR., and MUNTZ, H. M.: *Am. J. Psychiat.*, *104*:315 (1947).
39. FRIEDMAN, M. and ROSENMAN, R. H.: *J.A.M.A.*, *169*:1286 (1959).
40. WERTLAKE, P. T., WILCOX, A. A., HALEY, M. I. and PETERSON, J. E.: *Proc. Soc. Exper. Biol. & Med.*, *97*:163 (1958).
41. STRISOWER, E. H., DELALLA, O., GOFMAN, J. W. and STRISOWER, B.: *Am. J. Psychiat.*, *114*:263 (1957).
42. GJESSING, L., BERNARDSON, A. and FRÖSHAUG, H.: *J. Ment. Sc.*, *104*:188 (1958).
43. REITMAN, F., HULME, W. and THOMAS, B.: *J. Ment. Sc.*, *100*:149 (1954); KEMALI, D., PASTORE, E. J. and PORCELLATI, G.: *Acta neurol.* (Naples), *12*:419 (1957); RIEBELING, C.: *Confinia neurol.*, *18*:205 (1958).
44. McGEER, P. L., McNAIR, F. E., McGEER, E. G. and GIBSON, W. C.: *J. Nerv. & Ment. Dis.*, *125*:166 (1957).
45. DECKER, P. and SANO, I.: *Ztschr. physiol. Chem.*, *300*:252 (1955); SANO, I. and DECKER, P.: *Klin. Wchnschr.*, *33*:614 (1955).
46. RIEGELHAUPT, L. M.: *J. Nerv. & Ment. Dis.*, *123*:383 (1956); VELEK, M. and VALENTOVA, M.: *Ibid.*, *128*:184 (1959); HOBSON, J. A.: *Proc. Soc. Exper. Biol. & Med.*, *101*:780 (1959).
47. RIEGELHAUPT, L. M.: *J. Nerv. & Ment. Dis.*, *127*:228 (1958).
48. HELLINGER, B. S. and PACHTER, M. R.: *J. Nerv. & Ment. Dis.*, *128*:456 (1959).

49. EDELSTEIN, E. L. and KRASSILOWSKY, D.: *J. Nerv. & Ment. Dis.*, *128*:459 (1959); FLEISCHHACKER, H. H. and LANCASTER, J. B.: *J. Ment. Sc.*, *105*:777 (1959).

50. LAUER, J. W., INSKIP, W. M., BERNSOHN, J. and ZELLER, E. A.: *A. M. A. Arch. Neurol. & Psychiat.*, *80*:122 (1958).

51. BANERJEE, S. and AGARWAL, P. S.: *Proc. Soc. Exper. Biol. & Med.*, *97*:657 (1958).

52. KOPIN, I. J.: *Science*, *129*:835 (1959); SHAW, C. R., LUCAS, J. and RABINOVITCH, R. D.: *A. M. A. Arch. Gen. Psychiat*, *1*:366 (1959).

53. PRICE, J. M., BROWN, R. R. and PETERS, H. A.: *Neurology*, *9*:456 (1959).

54. BROWN, F. C., WHITE, J. B., JR., and KENNEDY, J. J.: *Am. J. Psychiat.*, *117*:63 (1960).

55. YOUNG, M. K., JR., BERRY, H. K., BEERSTECHER, E., JR., and BERRY, J. S.: *Biochem. Inst. Studies*, *IV*:189 (1951). (Univ. Texas Publ. 5109.)

56. DOTSENKO, N. P.: *Voprosy Fiziol.*, 229 (1953); in *Chem. Abst.*, *50*:5895f (1956); MCGEER, E. G., BROWN, W. T. and MCGEER, P. L.: *J. Nerv. & Ment. Dis.* *125*:176 (1957); MASUDA, M., SLONECKER, J. S. and DORPAT, T. L.: *Ibid.*, *130*:125 (1960).

57. GORODKOVA, T. M.: *Voprosy Fiziol.*, 211 (1953); in *Chem. Abst.*, *50*:6652i (1956); POROSHINA, A. A.: *Zhur. Nevropatol. Psikhiat. Korsakova*, *55*:266 (1955): in *Chem. Abst.*, *51*:1435f (1957).

58. ACHESON, R. M., PAUL, R. M. and TOMLINSON, R. V.: *Canad. J. Biochem. & Physiol.*, *36*:295 (1958); SMITH, D. M., PAUL, R. M., MCGEER, E. G. and MCGEER, P. L.: *Ibid.*, *37*:1493 (1959); ACHESON, R. M. and DEARNALEY, D. P.: *Ibid.*, *38*:503 (1960).

59. MANN, J. D. and LABROSSE, E. H.: *A. M. A. Arch. Gen. Psychiat.*, *1*:547 (1959).

60. FELIX, K.: *Schweiz. med. Wchnschr.*, *78*:1165 (1948); ALBERT, E.: *Nervenarzt*, *12*:542 (1949).

61. CHEMNITZ, H. J.: *Nervenarzt*, *23*:31 (1952).

62. FOSS, O. P.: *Scandinav. J. Clin. & Lab. Invest.*, *6*:107 (1954).

63. MUNKVAD, I.: *Acta psychiat. et neurol.*, *25*:269 (1950).

64. LOONEY, J. M. and CHILDS, H. M.: *J. Clin. Invest.*, *13*:963 (1934).

65. ALTSCHULE, M. D., SIEGEL, E. P. and HENNEMAN, D.: *A. M. A. Arch. Neurol. & Psychiat.*, *67*:64 (1952); MARTENS, S., LEACH, B. E., HEATH, R. G. and COHEN, M.: *A. M. A. Arch. Neurol. & Psychiat.*, *76*:630 (1956).

66. ANGEL, C., LEACH, B. E., MARTENS, S., COHEN, M. and HEATH, R. G.: *A. M. A. Arch. Neurol. & Psychiat.*, *78*:500 (1957).

67. BARAK, A. J., HUMOLLER, F. L., STEVENS, J. D. and LLUNBERG, E.: *Acta psychiat. et neurol.*, *11*:369 (1937).

68. PERSKY, H.: *Psychosom. Med.*, *16*:489 (1954).

69. SHERLOCK, S.: *Lancet*, *i*:159 (1946).

70. QUASTEL, J. H. and WALES, W. T.: *Lancet*, *ii*:301 (1938); *Ibid.*, *i*:402 (1940).

71. DAVIES, D. R. and HUGHES, T. P. E.: *Lancet*, *i*:403 (1940); BERKENAU, P.: *J. Ment. Sc.*, *86*:514 (1940); WONG, Y. T.: *J. Nerv. & Ment. Dis.*, *102*:183 (1945).

72. PERSKY, H., GAMM, S. R. and GRINKER, R. R.: *Psychosom. Med.*, *14*:34 (1952).

73. STRÖM-OLSEN, R., GREVILLE, G. D. and LENNON, R. W.: *Lancet*, *ii*:995 (1938); FINKELMAN, I., HORA, J., SHERMAN, I. C. and HORWITT, M. K.: *Am. J. Psychiat.*, *96*:951 (1940); MICHAEL, S. T., LOONEY, J. M. and BORKOVIC, E. J.: *Arch. Neurol. & Psychiat.*, *52*:57 (1944).

74. GEORGI, F., FISCHER, R., WEBER, R. and WEISS, P.: *Schweiz. med. Wchnschr.*, *78*:1194 (1948).

75. BOWMAN, K. M., MILLER, E. R., DAILEY, M. E., SIMON, A. and MAYER, B. F.: *J. Nerv. & Ment. Dis.*, *112*:404 (1950).

76. REISS, M., HEMPHILL, R. E., MAGGS, R., HAIGH, C. P. and REISS, J. M.: *Brit. M. J.*, *i*:1181 (1951); *Ibid.*, *i*:906 (1953).

77. ASHER, R.: *Brit. M. J.*, *ii*:555 (1949); CALVERT, R. J., SMITH, E. and ANDREWS, L. G.: *Brit. M. J.*, *ii*:891 (1954).

78. GJESSING, R.: *J. Ment. Sc.*, *84*:608 (1938); REY, J. H.: in ref. 10.

79. HARDWICK, S. W. and STOKES, A. B.: *Proc. Roy. Soc. Med.*, *34*:733 (1941); GORNALL, A. G., EGLITIS, B., MILLER, A., STOKES, A. B. and DEWAN, J. G.: *Am. J. Psychiat.*, *109*:584 (1953).

80. WEIL-MALHERBE, H.: *J. Ment. Sc.*, *101*:733 (1955).

81. REILLY, J. and REGAN, P. F.: *Proc. Soc. Exper. Biol. & Med.*, *95*:377 (1957).

82. STRÖM-OLSEN, R. and WEIL-MALHERBE, H.: *J. Ment. Sc.*, *104*:696 (1958).

83. BERGSMAN, A.: *Acta psychiat. et neurol. scandinav.*, *34*:Suppl. 133 (1959).

84. SOURKES, T. L., SLOANE, R. B. and DRUJAN, B. D.: *Confinia neurol.*, *18*:299 (1958).

85. CURTIS, G. C., CLEGHORN, R. A. and SOURKES, T. L.: *J. Psychosom. Res.*, *4*:176 (1960).

86. REGAN, P. F. and REILLY, J.: *J. Nerv. & Ment. Dis.*, *127*:12 (1958).

87. ELMADJIAN, F., HOPE, J. M. and LAMSON, E. T.: *Recent Progr. Hormone Res.*, *14*:513 (1958).

88. FUNKENSTEIN, D. H., GREENBLATT, M. and SOLOMON, H. C.: *Psychosom. Med.*, *14*:347 (1952); *Idem.*, *Am. J. Psychiat.*, *108*:652 (1952).

89. ELMADJIAN, F., HOPE, J. M. and FREEMAN, H.: *A. M. A. Arch. Neurol. & Psychiat.*, *77*:399 (1957).

90. FEINBERG, I.: *A. M. A. Arch. Neurol. & Psychiat.*, *80*:489 (1958).

91. HOFFER, A. and KENYON, M.: *A. M. A. Arch. Neurol. & Psychiat.*, *77*:437 (1957).

92. COHEN, G., HOLLAND, B. and GOLDENBERG, M.: *A. M. A. Arch. Neurol. & Psychiat.*, *80*:484 (1958); BERTHIAUME, M., LEDUC, J. and D'IORIO, A.: *A. M. A. Arch. Gen. Psychiat.*, *2*:468 (1960).

93. HOAGLAND, H.: *Internat. Rec. Med.*, *156*:183 (1953).

94. ROMANOFF, L. P., RODRIGUEZ, R. M., SEELYE, J. M. and PINCUS, G.: *J. Clin. Endocrinol. & Metab.*, *17*:777 (1957).

95. BLISS, E. L. and MIGEON, C. J.: *Am. J. Psychiat.*, *112*:358 (1955).

96. STEVENSON, J. A. F., DERRICK, J. B., HOBBS, G. E. and METCALFE, E. V.: *A. M. A. Arch. Neurol. & Psychiat.*, *78*:312 (1957).

97. SLOANE, R. B., SAFFRAN, M. and CLEGHORN, R. A.: *A. M. A. Arch. Neurol. & Psychiat.*, *79*:549 (1958).

98. PERSKY, H.: *A. M. A. Arch. Neurol. & Psychiat.*, *78*:95 (1957).

99. Editor: *Brit. M. J.*, *ii*:496 (1958).

100. BOARD, F., PERSKY, H. and HAMBURG, D. A.: *Psychosom. Med.*, *18*:324 (1956); PERSKY, H., GRINKER, R. R., HAMBURG, D. A., SABSHIN, M. A., KORCHIN, S. J., BASOWITZ, H. and CHEVALIER, J. A.: *A. M. A. Arch. Neurol. & Psychiat.* *76*:549 (1956).

101. HETZEL, B. S., SCHOTTSTAEDT, W. W., GRACE, W. J. and WOLFF, H. G.: *J. Clin. Endocrinol. & Metab.*, *15*:1057 (1955).

102. PERSKY, H.: *J. Clin. Endocrinol. & Metab.*, *17*:760 (1957).

103. VENNING, E. H., DYRENFURTH, I. and BECK, J. C.: *J. Clin. Endocrinol. & Metab.*, *17*:1005 (1957).

104. HARRIS, W. H. and SONNENBLICK, E. H.: *Yale J. Biol. & Med.*, *27*:297 (1955); *Ibid.*, *29*:117 (1956).

105. CRAMMER, J. L.: *Lancet, ii:*259 (1957); *Brit. M. J., i:*545 (1959).
106. HEILMEIER, L., KEIDERLING, W. and STRUVE, G.: *Kupfer und Eisen als körperei-gene Wirkstoffe and ihre Bedeutung beim Krankheitsgeschehen.* Jena, Fisher (1941); BRENNER, W. and BREIER, A.: *Ztschr. Kinderh., 66:*620 (1949); ELSTE, R.: *Multipel-Sklerose und Schizophrenie als Syndrom bei Spurenelement-mangelkrankheiten.* Stuttgart, Hippokrates-Marquardt (1951); BISCHOFF, A.: *Monatsschr. Psychiat. u. Neurol., 124:*211 (1952); OZEK, M.: *Arch. Psychiat., 195:*408 (1957).
107. SCHEINBERG, I. H., MORELL, A. G., HARRIS, R. S. and BERGER, A.: *Science, 126:*925 (1957).
108. AKERFELDT, S.: *Science, 125:*117 (1957).
109. HORWITT, M. K., MEYER, B. J., MEYER, A. C., HARVEY, C. C. and HAFFRON, D.: *A. M. A. Arch. Neurol. & Psychiat., 78:*275 (1957); MCDONALD, R. K.: In *Chemical Concepts of Psychosis,* M. Rinkel and H. C. B. Denber, Eds. New York, McDowell, Obolensky (1958).
110. HOLMBERG, C. G. and BLOMSTRAND, R.: *Ann. Rev. Biochem., 28:*321 (1959).
111. HAURY, V. G.: *J. Lab. & Clin. Med., 27:*1361 (1942).
112. KRYSTAL, H.: *Am. J. Psychiat., 116:*137 (1959); SMITH, W. O. and HAMMARSTEN, J. F.: *Am. J. M. Sc., 237:*413 (1959).
113. FLINK, E. B.: *J.A.M.A., 160:*1406 (1956); VALLEE, B. L., WACKER, W. E. C. and ULMER, D. D.: *New England J. Med., 262:*155 (1960).
114. PINCUS, G. and HOAGLAND, H.: *Am. J. Psychiat., 106:*641 (1950); HOAGLAND, H., RINKEL, M. and HYDE, R. W.: *A. M. A. Arch. Neurol. & Psychiat., 73:*100 (1955).
115. BOSZORMENYI-NAGY, I. and GERTY, F. J.: *Am. J. Psychiat., 112:*11 (1955); GOTTLIEB, J. S., FROHMAN, C. E., TOURNEY, G. and BECKETT, P. G. S.: *A. M. A. Arch. Neurol. & Psychiat., 81:*504 (1959).
116. LAITY, J. L. H.: *Lancet, ii:*422 (1958).
117. MCGEER, E. G. and MCGEER, P. L.: *J. Ment. Sc., 105:*1 (1959).
118. HEATH, R. G., MARTENS, S., LEACH, B. E., COHEN, M. and ANGEL, C.: *Am. J. Psychiat., 114:*14 (1957).
119. MELANDER, B. and MARTENS, S.: *Dis. Nerv. System, 19:*478 (1958).
120. ROBINS, E., SMITH, K. and LOWE, I. P.: *Tr. 4th Conf. Neuropharmacology.* Josiah Macy Jr. Foundation (1957); HEATH, R. G., COHEN, S. B., SILVA, F., LEACH, B. and COHEN, M.: *Dis. Nerv. System, 20:*206 (1959).
121. OSMOND, H. and SMYTHIES, J.: *J. Ment. Sc., 98:*309 (1952); HOFFER, A., OS-MOND, H. and SMYTHIES, J.: *Ibid., 100:*29 (1954); OSMOND, H. and HOFFER, A.: *Ibid., 105:*653 (1959).
122. SMYTHIES, J. R.: *Lancet, ii:*308 (1958); Cf. *ibid., i:*1287 (1960).
123. WOOLLEY, D. W. and SHAW, E.: *Brit. M. J., ii:*122 (1954); *Idem.: Ann. New York Acad. Sc., 66:*649 (1957).
123a. AMIN, A. H., CRAWFORD, T. B. B. and GADDUM, J. H.: *J. Physiol., 126:*596 (1954).
124. HOAGLAND, H.: *J. Nerv. & Ment. Dis., 126:*211 (1958); BRENGELMANN, J. C., PARE, C. M. B. and SANDLER, M.: *J. Ment. Sc., 105:*770 (1959); KLEE, G. D., BERTINO, J., GOODMANN, A. and ARONSON, H.: *J. Ment. Sc., 106:*309 (1960).
125. BRODIE, B. B.: *Dis. Nerv. System, 21:*Section 2, 107 (1960); SULSER, F. and BRODIE, B. B.: *Science, 131:*1440 (1960).
126. CARLSSON, A., LINDQVIST, M. and MAGNUSSON, T.: *Nature, 180:*1200 (1957).
127. SOURKES, T. L.: *Rev. Canad. de Biol., 20:*187 (1961).

128. DEGKWITZ, R., FROWEIN, R., KULENKAMPFF, C. and MOHS, U.: *Klin. Wchnschr.,* *38:*120 (1960).

129. MITOMA, C., POSNER, H. S., BOGDANSKI, D. F. and UDENFRIEND, S.: *J. Pharmacol.* *& Exper. Therap., 120:*188 (1957).

130. OATES, J. A., GILLESPIE, L., UDENFRIEND, S. and SJOERDSMA, A.: *Science, 131:*1890 (1960); AZIMA, H. and TAN, B. K.: Personal communication.

INDEX